Chemistry in Context

Applying Chemistry to Society

ACS
Chemistry for Life®

A Project of the American Chemical Society

Eighth Edition

Chemistry in Context

Applying Chemistry to Society

Catherine H. Middlecamp
University of Wisconsin—Madison

Michael T. Mury
American Chemical Society

Karen L. Anderson
Madison College

Anne K. Bentley
Lewis & Clark College

Michael C. Cann
University of Scranton

Jamie P. Ellis
The Scripps Research Institute

Kathleen L. Purvis-Roberts
Claremont McKenna,
Pitzer, and Scripps Colleges

ACS
Chemistry for Life®

Mc
Graw
Hill
Education

A Project of the American Chemical Society

CHEMISTRY IN CONTEXT: APPLYING CHEMISTRY TO SOCIETY, EIGHTH EDITION

Published by McGraw-Hill Education, 2 Penn Plaza, New York, NY 10121. Copyright © 2015 by McGraw-Hill Education. All rights reserved. Printed in the United States of America. Previous editions © 2012, 2009, and 2006. No part of this publication may be reproduced or distributed in any form or by any means, or stored in a database or retrieval system, without the prior written consent of McGraw-Hill Education, including, but not limited to, in any network or other electronic storage or transmission, or broadcast for distance learning.

Some ancillaries, including electronic and print components, may not be available to customers outside the United States.

This book is printed on acid-free paper.

1 2 3 4 5 6 7 8 9 0 DOW/DOW 1 0 9 8 7 6 5 4

ISBN 978–1–259–25423–9

MHID 1–259–25423–2

All credits appearing on page or at the end of the book are considered to be an extension of the copyright page.

The Internet addresses listed in the text were accurate at the time of publication. The inclusion of a website does not indicate an endorsement by the authors or McGraw-Hill Education, and McGraw-Hill Education does not guarantee the accuracy of the information presented at these sites.

Brief Contents

Appendices

Contents

Chapter 4

Chapter 5

Chapter 6

Chapter 7

Dear Readers,

The word *context* appears in the title of this book. And context has multiple meanings.

Context! Did you know that the word derives from the Latin word meaning "to weave"? The spiderweb image on the cover conveys the connections that this book weaves between chemistry and society. In the absence of societal issues, there could be no *Chemistry in Context*. Similarly, without teachers and students who were willing (and brave enough) to engage in these issues, there could be no *Chemistry in Context*. Chemistry is woven into the fabric of practically every issue that our society faces today.

Context! Do you enjoy good stories about the world in which you live? If so, look inside this book for stories that intrigue, challenge, and possibly even motivate you to act in new or different ways. In almost all contexts—local, regional, and global—parts of these stories are still unfolding. The ways in which you and others make choices today will determine the nature of the stories told in the future.

Context! Are you aware that using a real-world context to engage people is a high-impact practice backed by the research on how people learn? *Chemistry in Context* offers real-world contexts through which to engage learners on multiple levels: personal, societal, and global. Given the rapidly changing nature of these contexts, *Chemistry in Context* also offers teachers the opportunity to become learners right along with their students.

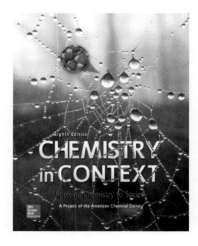

Sustainability—The Ultimate Context

Global sustainability is not just a challenge. Rather, it is *the* defining challenge of our century. Accordingly, the eighth edition of *Chemistry in Context* is designed to help students meet this challenge. The opening chapter, "Chemistry for a Sustainable Future," sets the stage for the 12 chapters that follow. By placing sustainability first, sustainability is established as a core, normative part of the chemistry curriculum.

Sustainability adds a new degree of complexity to *Chemistry in Context*. This complexity arises in part because sustainability can be conceptualized in two ways: as a topic worth studying and as a problem worth solving. As a topic, sustainability provides a new body of content for students to master. For example, the tragedy of the commons, the Triple Bottom Line, and the concept of cradle-to-cradle all are part of this new body of content. As a problem worth solving, sustainability generates new questions for students to ask—ones that help them to imagine and achieve a sustainable future. For example, students will find questions about the risks and benefits of acting (or not acting) to reduce emissions of greenhouse gases.

Incorporating sustainability requires more than a casual rethinking of the curriculum. Which approach do the authors take? Unlike most general chemistry texts, this one is context rich. Thus, the writers already had the necessary vehicle through which to convey the concepts of sustainability—rich real-world scenarios about energy, food, and water. However, the connections to sustainability were not always readily apparent. In essence, the dots needed to be connected for the reader. Here are some examples of how this was done:

Chapter 1, "The Air We Breathe," now more strongly reminds the reader that the air is a resource held in common. We all must breathe it, and nobody owns it. Air pollution is thus a perfect means by which to introduce the concept of the tragedy of the commons.

Chapter 2, "Protecting the Ozone Layer," now more clearly points out that the older replacements for chlorofluorocarbons (CFCs), although not harmful to the ozone layer, are potent greenhouse gases. The chapter ends with a decisive call to action: "We all,

The tragedy of the commons is the situation in which a resource is common to all and used by many, but has no one in particular responsible for it. As a result, the resource may be destroyed by overuse to the detriment of all that use it.

breathing on this planet today and having the potential, must guarantee its future, rapidly and decisively. We have no right to delay; we have no luxury of losing time."

Chapter 3, "The Chemistry of Global Climate Change," now presents more data on the chemistry of global climate change, and challenges students to evaluate the changes occurring on Earth from greenhouse gases and the consequences of these changes.

Chapter 5, "Water for Life," now better connects the scarcity of fresh water, sustainable management of water resources, and water contamination. These themes are echoed in discussing food production in Chapter 11.

Chapter 7, "The Fires of Nuclear Fission," while introducing students to the nuclear crisis that occurred in Japan, also challenges students to evaluate nuclear power as a sustainable resource.

Chapter 8, "Energy from Electron Transfer," was recast to better show the match between our energy needs and the available technologies. The sustainability concept of cradle-to-cradle, introduced in Chapter 0, is connected to battery design.

Chapter 11, "Nutrition: Food for Thought," still describes how what you eat affects your health. Now, however, it more strongly connects what you eat to the health of the planet and has students track food production and consumption.

Green chemistry, a means to sustainability, continues to be an important theme in *Chemistry in Context*. As in previous editions, examples of green chemistry are highlighted in each chapter. In this new edition, look for more examples. This expanded coverage offers the reader an even better sense of the need for and the importance of greening our chemical processes. For easier access, key ideas in green chemistry are listed on the inside front cover of the text.

Updates to Existing Content

People sometimes ask us, "Why do you release new editions so often?" Indeed, we are on a fast publishing cycle, turning out a new version every three years. We do this because the content in *Chemistry in Context* is time sensitive.

With each new edition, the author team reworks the content of practically every chapter, updating it to reflect new scientific developments, changes in policies, energy trends, and current world events. These updates are nontrivial to implement. Some involve writing new content; others involve producing new graphs and data tables. For example, since the publication of the 7th edition, the tragedy in Fukushima, Japan, has influenced nuclear power industries and policies. The atmospheric concentration of CO_2 increased to over 400 ppm. A final example is the release of new dietary guidelines from the USDA.

In addition, the issues that we select to "hook" the reader at the start of the chapter are recast from edition to edition. Chapter 9, "The World of Polymers and Plastics," is one example. The new version now opens with a quote from the book coauthored by a chemist who greatly influenced our thinking in revising this chapter: "Nature doesn't have a design problem. People do." (William McDonough and Michael Braungart, *Cradle-to-Cradle*, 2002)

The story of polymers unfolds using a spiderweb as an example, noting that orb spiders may build new webs each day. So how does an orb spider manage to spin so much silk and still survive? Most simply, it recycles. Orb spiders have the ability to ingest old spider silk and recover the raw materials from which they are constructed. The theme of recycling is then carried throughout the chapter.

Teaching and Learning in Context

This new edition of *Chemistry in Context* continues with the organizational scheme used in previous editions, one that has stood the test of time. The first six chapters, all with real-world themes such as air, water, and energy, provide a foundation of chemistry concepts on which to build in subsequent chapters. For example, early chapters introduce elements, compounds, and the periodic table. In later chapters, we build upon these chemistry concepts to consider other contexts and chemistry content. Chapters 7 and 8 consider additional energy sources—nuclear power, batteries, fuel cells, and hydrogen. Chapters 9–12 are all carbon based, focusing on polymers, drugs, food production, and genetic engineering. They provide students with the opportunity to explore interests, as time permits, beyond the core topics.

The New Edition—A Team Effort

Once again, we have the pleasure of offering our readers a new edition of *Chemistry in Context.* But the work is not done by just one individual; rather, it is the work of many talented individuals. The eighth edition builds on the legacy of prior author teams led by A. Truman Schwartz, Conrad L. Stanitski, and Lucy Pryde Eubanks, all now retired from long and successful careers of teaching chemistry.

This new edition was prepared by a team of writers: Cathy Middlecamp, Michael Mury, Karen Anderson, Anne Bentley, Michael Cann, Jamie Ellis, and Katie Purvis-Roberts. The laboratory manual to accompany it was revised by Jennifer Tripp and Lallie McKenzie and reviewed by Teresa Larson. Each person brought different expertise to the project. In common, though, each brought goodwill, hopes, dreams, and seemingly boundless enthusiasm to bring real-world chemistry into the classroom and into the lives of our readers.

At the American Chemical Society, leadership was provided by Mary Kirchhoff, Director of the Education Division. She supported the writing team, cheering on its efforts to "connect the dots" between chemistry and sustainability, even to the point of writing parts of Chapter 0. Furthermore, she and Terri Taylor, Assistant Director for K–12 Science at the American Chemical Society, made it possible for Michael Mury to expand his role in the project, taking the reins as a production manager. His abilities to bring together all of the parties involved—the author team, the publisher, and the American Chemical Society—were unparalleled.

The McGraw-Hill team was superb in all aspects of this project, with special thanks to Jodi Rhomberg for shepherding the project to the finish line. Marty Lange (Vice President and General Manager), Thomas Timp (Managing Director), David Spurgeon, PhD (Brand Manager), Rose Koos (Director of Development), Shirley Hino, PhD (Director of Digital Content Development), and Jodi Rhomberg (Developmental Editor) led this outstanding team. Heather Wagner served as the Executive Marketing Manager. Sandra Schnee (Content Project Manager) coordinated the production team of Carrie Burger (Content Licensing Specialist), Tara McDermott (Designer), and Nichole Birkenholz (Buyer). The team also benefited from the careful editing of Carol Kromminga and proofreading by Kim Koetz and Patti Evers.

The author team truly benefited from the expertise of a wider community. We would like to thank the following individuals who wrote and/or reviewed learning-goal-oriented content for **LearnSmart.**

Peter de Lijser, *California State University—Fullerton*
David G. Jones, *University of North Carolina at Chapel Hill*
Adam I. Keller, *Columbus State Community College*

We also extend our thanks to David McNelis, *University of North Carolina,* for the technical expertise he provided in preparing the manuscript.

Input from instructors teaching this course is invaluable to the development of each new edition. Our thanks and gratitude go out to the following instructors who participated in *Chemistry in Context* workshops:

Sana Ahmed	*Boca Raton Community High School*
Nikki Burnett	*Baldwin High School*
Donghai Chen	*Malone University*
Tammy Crosby	*Hillsborough High School*
Mohammed Daoudi	*University of Central Florida*
Sidnee-Marie Dunn	*Saint Martins University*
Kimberly Fields	*Florida Southern College*

Tam'ra Kay Francis	*University of Tennessee*
Andrew Frazer	*University of Central Florida*
Song Gao	*Nova Southeastern University*
Carmen Gauthier	*Florida Southern College*
Myung Han	*Columbus State Community College*
Al Hazari	*University of Tennessee*
Sandra Helquist	*Loyola University Chicago*
Martha Kellner	*Westminster College*
Todd Knippenberg	*High Point University*
Candace Kristensson	*University of Denver*
Shamsher-Patrick Lambda	*Young Men's Preparatory Academy (M-DCPS)*
Laura Lanni	*Newberry College*
Devin Latimer	*University of Winnipeg*
Toby Long	*Rollins College*
Sara Marchlewicz	*University of Illinois at Chicago*
Jessica Menke	*University of Wisconsin—Whitewater*
Mark Mitton-Fry	*Ohio Wesleyan University*
Mark Morris	*University of Tampa*
Jung Oh	*Kansas State University at Salina*
Tatyana Pinayayev	*Miami University*
Kresimir Rupnik	*Lousiana State University*
Indrani Sindhuvalli	*Florida State College at Jacksonville*
Jose Vites	*Eastern Michigan University*

Wishing Our Readers Well

When first published in 1993, *Chemistry in Context* was "the book that broke the mold." Unlike the books of its time, it did not teach chemistry in isolation from people and the real-world issues they were facing. Similarly, it did not introduce a fact or concept for the sake of "covering it" as part of the curriculum. Rather, *Chemistry in Context* carefully matched each chemical principle to a real-world issue such as air quality, energy, or water use.

We are very excited by the features of this new edition that continue to break the mold in bringing chemistry to you, our reader. We have selected engaging and timely topics that we hope will serve you not only today but also in the years to come.

We wish you well as you read, explore the issues, respectfully argue with each other (and with the authors), and, most important, as you use what you learn to bring your dreams to reality.

Sincerely, and with all good wishes from the author team,

Cathy Middlecamp

Cathy Middlecamp
Senior Author and Editor–in–Chief
June 2013

Digital Resources

McGraw-Hill offers various tools and technology products to support *Chemistry in Context,* 8th edition.

McGraw-Hill's ConnectPlus™

McGraw-Hill's Connect Plus (www.mcgrawhillconnect.com/Chemistry) is a web-based assignment and assessment platform that gives students the means to better connect with their coursework, with their instructors, and with the important concepts that they will need to know for success now and in the future. The following resources are available in Connect:

- Autograded assessments
- LearnSmart, an adaptive diagnostic tool
- Powerful reporting against learning outcomes and level of difficulty
- McGraw-Hill Tegrity Campus, which digitally records and distributes your lectures with a click of a button
- The full textbook as an integrated, dynamic eBook that you can also assign
- Instructor resources, such as Instructor's Manual
- PowerPoints and Test Banks
- Image Bank, which includes all images available for presentation tools.

With ConnectPlus, instructors can deliver assignments, quizzes, and tests online. Instructors can edit existing questions and author entirely new problems; track individual student performance—by question and assignment or in relation to the class overall—with detailed grade reports; integrate grade reports easily with Learning Management Systems (LMS), such as WebCT and Blackboard; and much more.

By choosing Connect, instructors are providing their students with a powerful tool for improving academic performance and truly mastering course material. Connect allows students to practice important skills at their own pace and on their own schedule. Importantly, students' assessment results and instructors' feedback are all saved online, so students can continually review their progress and plot their course to success.

McGraw-Hill LearnSmart™

McGraw-Hill LearnSmart™ is available as a stand-alone product as well as an integrated feature of McGraw-Hill Connect® Chemistry. It is an adaptive learning system designed to help students learn faster, study more efficiently, and retain more knowledge for greater success. LearnSmart assesses a student's knowledge of course content through a series of adaptive questions. It pinpoints concepts the student does not understand and maps out a personalized study plan for success. This innovative study tool also has features that allow instructors to see exactly what students have accomplished and a built-in assessment tool for graded assignments. Visit the following site for a demonstration: www.mhlearnsmart.com.

McGraw-Hill SmartBook™

Powered by the intelligent and adaptive LearnSmart engine, SmartBook is the first and only continuously adaptive reading experience available today. Distinguishing what students know from what they don't, and honing in on concepts they are most likely to forget, SmartBook personalizes content for each student. Reading is no longer a passive and linear experience but an engaging and dynamic one, where students are more likely to master and retain important concepts, coming to class better prepared.

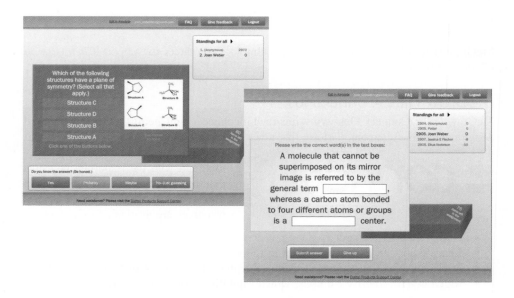

SmartBook includes powerful reports that identify specific topics and learning objectives students need to study. These valuable reports also provide instructors insight into how students are progressing through textbook content and are useful for identifying class trends, focusing precious class time, providing personalized feedback to students, and tailoring assessment.

How does SmartBook work?

Each SmartBook contains four components: Preview, Read, Practice, and Recharge. Starting with an initial preview of each chapter and key learning objectives, students read the material and are guided to topics over which they need the most practice based on their responses to a continuously adapting diagnostic. Read and Practice continue until SmartBook directs students to recharge important material they are most likely to forget to ensure concept mastery and retention.

Customizable Textbooks: Create™

Create what you've only imagined. Introducing McGraw-Hill Create—a new, self-service website that allows you to create custom course materials—print and eBooks—by drawing upon McGraw-Hill's comprehensive, cross-disciplinary content. Add your own content quickly and easily. Tap into other rights-secured third party sources as well. Then, arrange the content in a way that makes the most sense for your course. Even personalize your book with your course name and information. Choose the best format for your course: color print, black and white print, or eBook. The eBook is now viewable on an iPad! And when you are finished customizing, you will receive a free PDF review copy in just minutes! Visit McGraw-Hill Create at www.mcgrawhillcreate.com today and begin building your perfect book.

My Lectures—Tegrity®

McGraw-Hill Tegrity® records and distributes your class lecture with just a click of a button. Students can view anytime/anywhere via computer, iPod, or mobile device. It indexes as it records your PowerPoint® presentations and anything shown on your computer so students can use keywords to find exactly what they want to study. Tegrity is available as an integrated feature of McGraw-Hill Connect® Chemistry and as a stand-alone product.

Chemistry in Context

Applying Chemistry to Society

ACS
Chemistry for Life®

A Project of the American Chemical Society

0 Chemistry for a Sustainable Future

The "blue marble," our Earth, as seen from outer space.

"The first day or so, we all pointed to our countries. The third or fourth day, we were pointing to our continents. By the fifth day, we were aware of only one Earth."

Prince Sultan bin Salman Al Sa'ud, Astronaut, Saudi Arabia, 1985.

Only one Earth. From the vantage point of outer space, the planet we call home is truly magnificent—a "blue marble" of water, land, and clouds. In 1972, the crew of the Apollo 17 spacecraft photographed the Earth at a distance of about 28,000 miles (45,000 kilometers). In the words of Soviet cosmonaut Aleksei Leonov, "The Earth was small, light blue, and so touchingly alone."

Are we alone in the universe? Possibly. Clearly, though, we are not alone on our planet. We share it with other creatures large and small. Biologists estimate that upwards of 1.5 million species exist in addition to our own. Some help to feed and sustain us. Others contribute to our well-being. Still others (like mosquitoes) annoy and perhaps even sicken us.

We also share the planet with more than 7 billion other people. Over the past century, the human population on Earth has more than tripled, an unprecedented growth spurt in the history of our planet. By 2050, the population may grow by another 2 to 3 billion.

Large and small, all of the species on our planet somehow connect. Exactly how this happens, however, may not be so obvious to us. For example, unseen microorganisms shuttle nitrogen from one chemical form to another, providing nutrients for green plants to grow. These plants harness the light energy of the Sun during the process of photosynthesis. Using this energy, they convert the compounds carbon dioxide and water to that of glucose. At the same time, they release the element oxygen into the air that we breathe. And we humans are host to countless microorganisms that have taken up residence in our skin and internal organs.

Large and small, these connections are breaking at an alarming rate.

Chapter 6 describes the nitrogen cycle. Chapter 4 describes photosynthesis.

A change has occurred in our perspective. Today, we are accustomed to reading reports of declining fish populations and of endangered species. Have you run across the term **shifting baselines?** This refers to the idea that what people expect as "normal" on our planet has changed over time, especially with regard to ecosystems. The abundance of fish and wildlife that once was normal is no longer carried in the memories of those living today. Similarly, many of us no longer carry memories of cities unclogged by vehicles. Fewer people remember clear summer days when it really did seem that you could see forever.

Clearly we humans are industrious creatures. We grow crops, dam rivers, burn fuels, build structures, and jet across time zones. When we carry out such activities by the million, we change the quality of the air we breathe, the water we drink, and the land on which we live. Over time, our actions have changed the face of our planet. What was it once like? See what you can find out by doing the next activity.

Consider This 0.1   Shifting Baselines

Seek out one of the elders in your community. This person may be a friend, relative, or possibly even a community historian.

a. Think about the current price of a loaf of bread, a gallon of gas, or a candy bar. Then inquire about what things used to cost. How has what people expect as "normal" shifted?
b. Now a more difficult task. Think about the local rivers, air quality, vegetation, and/or wildlife. In talking with an elder, see if you can identify at least one case in which the perception of what is "normal" has shifted. It may be that nobody remembers.

Consider This activities appear in all chapters. These activities give you a chance to use what you are learning to make informed decisions. For example, they may require you to consider opposing viewpoints or to make and defend a personal decision. They may require additional research.

The bottom line? The things we perceive today as "normal" were not normal in the past. Although we cannot turn back the clock, we still can make choices that promote our health and the health of our planet today and in the future. A knowledge of chemistry can help. The global problems that we face—and their solutions—are intimately linked with chemical expertise and good old human ingenuity.

0.1 | The Choices We Make Today

Individually, it may seem that our actions have little effect on a system as large as our planet. After all, in comparison to a hurricane, a drought, or an earthquake, what we do on a daily basis can seem pretty inconsequential. What difference could it possibly make if we biked to work instead of driving, used a reusable cloth bag instead of discarding a plastic one, or ate foods grown locally instead of consuming those shipped from hundreds or even thousands of miles away?

Look for more about crude oil and how it is refined in Chapter 4.

Look for more about what comes out a tailpipe in Chapter 1.

Most human activities—including biking, driving, using bags of whatever sort, and eating—have two things in common: *They require the consumption of natural resources, and they result in the creation of waste.* Driving a car requires gasoline (refined from crude oil), and burning gasoline sends waste products out the exhaust pipe. Although riding a bike is a more ecological choice, all bicycles, just like automobiles, still require the manufacture and disposal of metals, plastics, synthetic rubbers, fabrics, and paints. Shopping bags, whether paper or plastic, require the materials to produce them. Later down the line, these bags become a waste product. And growing food requires water and energy to harvest and transport to market. In addition, food production may require fertilizer and involve the use of insecticides and herbicides.

You can see where this is going. Any time we manufacture and transport things, we consume resources and produce waste. Clearly, though, some activities consume fewer resources and produce less waste than others. Biking produces less waste than driving; reusing cloth bags produces less waste than continually throwing plastic ones away. Although what you do may be negligible in the grand scheme of things, what 7 billion people do clearly is not. Our collective actions not only cause local changes to our air, water, and soil but also hurt regional and global ecosystems.

Chapters 1, 3, 4, and 6 all explore the connections between fuels and the waste products they release when burned.

We need to think by the billion. A single cooking fire? No problem; well, unless it accidentally burns down a dwelling. But imagine a few billion people across the planet each tending an individual cooking fire. Add in fires from those who cook using stoves, brick ovens, and outdoor grills. Now you have a lot of fuel being burned! Each fuel releases waste products into the atmosphere as it is burned. Some of these waste products—better known as air pollutants—are *highly* unfriendly to our lungs, our eyes, and of course to our ecosystems.

Today, the waste products we release are unprecedented in their scale and in their potential to lower our quality of life and even shorten it. For example, in a large city such as New York, New Delhi, Mexico City, or Beijing, you will find that hospital admissions and death rates correlate with air pollution levels. Although the health risks are smaller than those caused by obesity or smoking, the issues of public health loom large because people are exposed to air pollutants both indoors and out over a lifetime.

Also worrisome is that our actions (by the billion) release waste products that destroy the habitats of other species on the planet. Extinction, of course, is a natural phenomenon. But today the rate is many times faster than would be expected from natural causes. Our destruction of local specialized habitats, particularly those of plants, has led to these extinctions.

Underpinning much of our waste production is *energy*. The need to find energy sources that are both clean and sustainable arguably is the major challenge of our century. Currently we are both consuming renewable and nonrenewable resources and adding waste to our air, land, and water at a rate that cannot be sustained. This should come as no surprise. Time is the key factor in determining if a resource is renewable or nonrenewable. **Renewable resources** are those that are replenished more quickly over time than they are being consumed. Examples of renewable resources include solar energy and biomass, such as trees and agricultural crops. **Nonrenewable resources** are those that have a limited supply or are consumed more quickly than they are produced. Metal ores and fossil fuels (coal, oil, and natural gas) are examples of nonrenewable resources.

With any problem comes the opportunity to find creative solutions. We hope you are asking yourself "What can I do?" and "How can I make a difference in my community?" As you ask questions such as these, remember to include chemistry in your deliberations. Indeed, chemistry is well named the "Central Science." Today, chemists are at the center of the action when it comes to the sustainable use of resources. Chemists are challenged to use their knowledge responsibly to protect human health and the environment. The same, of course, is true for you. In this book, we will support you as you learn and encourage you to use what you learn to act responsibly in preserving our one Earth.

0.2 | The Sustainable Practices We Need for Tomorrow

What does it mean to use the resources of our planet in a sustainable manner? We hope that you can answer this question—at least in part—from what you already have learned in other classes. People from many disciplines, including those from economics, political science, engineering, history, nursing, and agriculture, have a stake in developing sustainable practices. And, as you will learn in this text, those of us in chemistry play a major role in creating a sustainable world.

Because the term **sustainability** is used by so many groups of people, it has taken on different meanings. We have selected one that is frequently quoted: "Meeting the needs of the present without compromising the ability of future generations to meet their own needs." This definition is drawn from a statement written in a 1987 report, *Our Common Future*, by the World Commission on Environment and Development of the United Nations. In Table 0.1, we reprint excerpts from the foreword to *Our Common Future* so that you can read its challenging words in their original context.

Our Common Future is also called the *Brundtland Report*. It was named after Gro Harlem Brundtland, the woman who chaired the commission.

Table 0.1	Our Common Future (excerpts from the Foreword)

"A global agenda for change"—this was what the World Commission on Environment and Development was asked to formulate. It was an urgent call by the General Assembly of the United Nations.

In the final analysis, I decided to accept the challenge. The challenge of facing the future, and of safeguarding the interests of coming generations.

After a decade and a half of a standstill or even deterioration in global co–operation, I believe the time has come for higher expectations, for common goals pursued together, for an increased political will to address our common future.

The present decade has been marked by a retreat from social concerns. Scientists bring to our attention urgent but complex problems bearing on our very survival: a warming globe, threats to the Earth's ozone layer, deserts consuming agricultural land.

The question of population—of population pressure, of population and human rights—and the links between these related issues and poverty, environment, and development proved to be one of the more difficult concerns with which we had to struggle.

But first and foremost our message is directed towards people, whose well being is the ultimate goal of all environment and development policies. In particular, the Commission is addressing the young. The world's teachers will have a crucial role to play in bringing this report to them.

If we do not succeed in putting our message of urgency through to today's parents and decision makers, we risk undermining our children's fundamental right to a healthy, life–enhancing environment.

In the final analysis, this is what it amounts to: furthering the common understanding and common spirit of responsibility so clearly needed in a divided world.

Gro Harlem Brundtland, Oslo, 1987.

Brundtland's words carry a message to those who teach and learn. She writes: "In particular, the Commission is addressing the young. The world's teachers will have a crucial role to play in bringing this report to them." We agree. To this end, we hope that your chemistry course will stimulate conversations both inside and outside of the classroom. One such conversation is about practices that are *not* sustainable. For example, you will study fossil fuels and learn why their use is not sustainable (Chapter 4). But don't stop there. You also need to discuss what you can do to *solve* the problems we face today. Use what you learn about air quality to act to improve local air quality *and* to make informed decisions as a citizen to improve it more widely (Chapter 1). Similarly, use what you learn about aqueous solubility and waste water to evaluate public policies that relate to water quality (Chapter 5).

In 2000, the United Nations adopted the Millennium Development Goals, which are targeted toward helping the world's poor through such efforts as improving maternal and child health care and ending poverty and hunger. One of these eight goals focuses on environmental sustainability. The four targets identified to ensure environmental sustainability are:

1. Integrate the principles of sustainable development into country policies and programmes and reverse the loss of environmental resources.
2. Reverse biodiversity loss, achieving, by 2010, a significant reduction in the rate of loss.
3. Halve, by 2015, the proportion of the population without sustainable access to safe drinking water and basic sanitation.
4. Achieve, by 2020, a significant improvement in the lives of at least 100 million slum dwellers.

Significant progress has been made in achieving these targets, and Target 3, with respect to drinking water, and Target 4 are on track. The biodiversity target has been missed, however. Science and technology continue to be essential in meeting the Millennium Development Goals and other sustainability efforts.

Scientific societies across the globe recognize the importance of mobilizing their members in applying their knowledge and expertise to the challenges of sustainability. The American Chemical Society's "Sustainability and the Chemical Enterprise" policy statement notes:

> Preserving the habitability of the Earth and its ability to provide the resources required for future generations to thrive is a basic human obligation. It is now necessary for society to address the challenges of limited resources, an expanding population, and the unintended impacts of technological achievements on human health and ecosystem viability. The best way to handle these challenges is by redirecting human development towards a path of sustainability, which would allow humanity "to meet current environmental and human health, economic, and societal needs without compromising the progress and success of future generations" (WCED, 1987; NRC, 1999; NRC, 2005).
>
> The chemical enterprise—consisting of the chemical and allied industries, their trade associations, and the educational and professional organizations (schools, colleges, universities, research institutions, government laboratories, professional societies) that produce both the enabling scientific knowledge and the necessary scientific and engineering workforce—has a crucial role to play in advancing sustainable development.

In this text, we will explore the contributions of science and technology, especially chemistry, to a sustainable world. The next section describes the Triple Bottom Line, a paradigm that looks beyond profit in assessing business success.

WCED, 1987, *Our Common Future* (the "Brundtland" Report), World Commission on Environment and Development, Oxford University Press, Oxford, UK.

NRC, 1999, *Our Common Journey: A Transition Toward Sustainability*, National Research Council, National Academy Press, Washington, D.C.

NRC, 2005, *Sustainability in the Chemical Industry*, National Research Council, National Academy Press, Washington, D.C.

0.3 | The Triple Bottom Line

Scientists aren't the only ones responsible for a sustainable planet. If you are a business or economics major, you may be well aware that people in the business sector have put sustainability on the corporate agenda. In fact, sustainable practices can offer a competitive advantage in the marketplace.

In the world of business, the bottom line always has included turning a profit, preferably a large one. Today, however, the bottom line includes more than this. For example, corporations are judged to be successful when they are fair and beneficial to workers and to the larger society. Another measure of their success is how well they protect the health of the environment, including the quality of the air, water, and land.

Taken together, this three-way measure of the success of a business based on its benefits to the economy, to society, and to the environment has become known as the **Triple Bottom Line.** One way to represent the Triple Bottom Line is with the overlapping circles shown in Figure 0.1. The economy must be healthy, that is, the annual reports need to show a profit. But no economy exists in isolation; rather, it connects to a community whose members also need to be healthy. In turn, communities connect to ecosystems that need to be healthy. Hence the figure includes not one, but three connecting circles. At the intersection of these circles lies the "Green Zone." This represents the conditions under which the Triple Bottom Line is met.

The Triple Bottom Line sometimes is shortened to the 3Ps: Profits, People, and the Planet.

Harm that occurs in any of the circles of Figure 0.1 will ultimately translate into harm for the business. Conversely, achieving success can provide a competitive advantage, both immediately and in the years to come. Businesses can turn a profit; at the same time, they can get good publicity (and minimize any harm) by using less energy, consuming fewer resources, and creating less waste. A triple win!

Recent news articles document the changes that are occurring. For example, read this excerpt from a news article that explains how the use of compostable plastics is diverting organic waste from landfills to compost piles. The source is *Chemical & Engineering News (C&EN)*, the weekly publication of the American Chemical Society.

> Houston had a problem. The city's composting program called for residents to put their lawn clippings and leaves in polyethylene bags and leave them curbside. The sanitation workers who collected the bags had to cut them open and dump the contents into the backs of their trucks. It was laborious and time-consuming. Overtime was piling up.
>
> The city decided to end the program and stop composting yard waste, recalls Gary Readore, chief of staff and recycling manager for Houston's Solid Waste Management Department. "Everything was going to the landfill." That system wasn't cheap either. Houston was collecting 60,000 tons of clippings per year. With a $25-per-ton "tipping fee," the

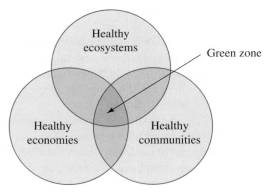

Figure 0.1

A representation of the Triple Bottom Line. The "Green Zone" (where the Triple Bottom Line is achieved) lies at the intersection of these three circles.

C&EN
CHEMICAL & ENGINEERING NEWS

NEUROSCIENCE R&D
Big pharma rethinks how to
find CNS drugs P.22
AMYLOID STRUCTURES
Surprising possible
intermediates found P.38

COMPOSTABLE PLASTICS
Keeping organic waste out of the landfill P.12

charge for sending it to the landfill, yard waste cost the city $1.5 million per year.

In 2010, Houston resumed collecting yard waste for composting, but now residents leave it out in compostable plastic bags. The bags are translucent, allowing workers to peer inside to see if residents are cheating by commingling regular trash with the leaves. In addition to saving the tipping fee, the city gets $5.00 per ton for the material from its composting contractor, Living Earth Technology. The firm composts the bags right along with the rest of the waste; no special handling is required.

Houston's experience illustrates the value of compostable plastics. Such materials aren't meant to make the problem of plastic waste magically disappear. But they are intended to help municipalities and institutions divert organic waste away from the landfill and to the compost pile by making participation in composting programs convenient for consumers (*C&EN*, Mar. 19, 2012).

Consider This 0.2   Compostable vs. Recyclable

Plastics are often referred to as compostable or recyclable. But is there a difference? Explain, in your own words, the difference between a plastic that is compostable versus one that is recyclable. What are the benefits of composting and recycling with respect to the fate of plastics?

The point? The debates over how to be "green" are likely to continue over your lifetime. The issues are not new; they are not likely to be resolved anytime soon. *Chemistry in Context* will encourage you to explore these issues, arming you with the knowledge you need to formulate more creatively your own response.

"A sustainable society is one that is far-seeing enough, flexible enough, and wise enough not to undermine either its physical or its social systems."

Donella Meadows, 1992

Donella Meadows (1941–2001) was a scientist and writer. Her books include *The Limits to Growth* and *The Global Citizen*.

0.4 | Cradle-to-Where?

You may have heard the expression **cradle-to-grave,** that is, an approach to analyzing the life cycle of an item, starting with the raw materials from which it came and ending with its ultimate disposal someplace, presumably on Earth. This catchy phrase offers a frame of reference from which to ask questions about consumer items. Where did the item come from? And what will happen to the item when you are finished with it? More than ever, individuals, communities, and corporations are recognizing the importance of asking these types of questions. Cradle-to-grave means thinking about *every* step in the process.

Companies should take responsibility—as should you—for items from the moment the natural resources used to make them were taken out of the ground, air, or water to the point at which they were ultimately "disposed of." Think of items such as batteries, plastic water bottles, T-shirts, cleaning supplies, running shoes, cell phones—anything that you buy and eventually discard.

Look for more about batteries in Chapter 8 and more about plastics in Chapter 9.

Cradle-to-grave thinking clearly has its limitations. As an illustration, let us follow one of the plastic bags that supermarkets provide for your groceries. The raw material for these bags is petroleum. Accordingly, the "cradle" of this plastic bag most likely was crude oil somewhere on our planet, for example, the oil fields of Canada. Let's assume that the oil was pumped from a well in Alberta and then transported to a refinery in the United States. At the refinery, the crude oil was separated into fractions. One of the fractions was then cracked into ethylene, the starting material for a polymer. Ethylene next was polymerized and formed into polyethylene bags. These bags were packaged and then trucked (burning diesel fuel, another refinery product) to your

Chapter 4 explains how and why crude oil is separated into fractions.

Chapter 9 explains how polyethylene is made from ethylene (and why).

grocery store. Ultimately, you purchased groceries and used one of the bags to carry them home.

As stated, this is not a cradle-to-grave scenario. Rather, it was cradle-to-your-kitchen, definitely several steps short of any graveyard. So what happened to this plastic bag after you used it? Did it go into the trash? The term *grave* describes wherever an item eventually ends up. One trillion plastic bags, give or take, are used each year in supermarkets. Only about 5% are recycled. The rest end up either in our cupboards, our landfills, or littered across the planet. As litter, these bags begin a 1000-year cycle, again give or take, of slow decomposition into carbon dioxide and water.

Cradle-to-a-grave-somewhere-on-the-planet is a poorly planned scenario for a supermarket bag. If each of the trillion plastic bags instead were to serve as the starting material for a new product, we then would have a more sustainable situation. **Cradle-to-cradle,** a term that emerged in the 1970s, refers to a regenerative approach to the use of things in which the end of the life cycle of one item dovetails with the beginning of the life cycle of another, so that everything is reused rather than disposed of as waste. In Chapter 9, we will examine different recycle-and-reuse scenarios for plastic bottles. But right now, you can do your own cradle-to-cradle thinking in the next activity.

The term *cradle-to-cradle* caught on with the publication in 2002 of a book of this same title.

Your Turn 0.3   The Can That Holds Your Beverage

People tend to think of an aluminum can as starting on a supermarket shelf and ending in a recycling bin. There is more to the story!

a. Where on the planet is aluminum ore (bauxite) found?

b. Once removed from the ground, the ore usually is refined to alumina (aluminum oxide) near the mining site. The alumina is then transported to a production facility. What happens next to produce aluminum metal?

c. What happens to the can after you recycle it?

Answers

a. Bauxite is mined in several places, including Australia, China, Brazil, and India.

b. The ore must be refined electrolytically to produce aluminum metal. This process is energy-intensive and carried out in many locations worldwide.

Your Turn activities appear in all chapters. They provide an opportunity for you to practice a new skill or calculation that was just introduced in the text. Answers are given either following the *Your Turn* activity or in Appendix 4.

As you can tell from these examples, it is not just the decisions of manufacturers that matter. Your decisions do as well. What you buy, what you discard, and how you discard it all warrant attention. The choices that we make—individually and collectively—matter.

At the risk of repeating ourselves, we remind you that the current state of affairs in which we consume the nonrenewable resources of our planet and add waste to our air, land, and water is *not* sustainable. In the next section, we explain why, setting the stage for the topics in chemistry that you will explore in this text.

0.5 | Your Ecological Footprint

You already may know how to estimate the gas mileage for a vehicle. Likewise, you can estimate how many calories you consume. How might you estimate how much of the Earth's natural capital it takes to support the way in which you live? Clearly, this is far more difficult. Fortunately, other scientists already have grappled with how to do the math. They base the calculations on the way in which a person lives coupled with the available renewable resources needed to sustain this lifestyle.

Consider the metaphor of a footprint. You can see the footprints that you leave in sand or snow. You also can see the muddy tracks that your boots leave on the kitchen

Although you may not know how much air you breathe in a day, Chapter 1 will help you to estimate this.

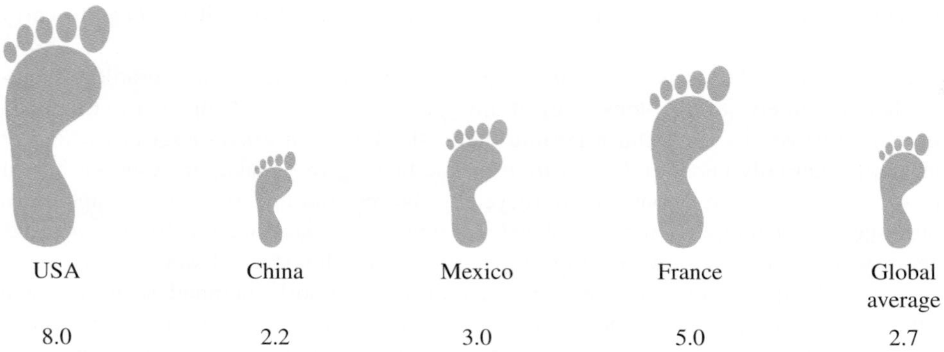

USA	China	Mexico	France	Global average
8.0	2.2	3.0	5.0	2.7

Figure 0.2

A comparison of ecological footprints, in global hectares per person.

Source: The Ecological Footprint Atlas, 2010.

floor. Similarly, one might argue that your life leaves a footprint on planet Earth. To understand this footprint, you need to think in units of hectares or acres. A hectare is a bit more than twice the area of an acre. The **ecological footprint** is a means of estimating the amount of biologically productive space (land and water) necessary to support a particular standard of living or lifestyle.

For the average U.S. citizen, the ecological footprint was estimated in 2007 to be about 8.0 hectares (20 acres). In other words, if you live in the United States, on average it requires 8.0 hectares of land to provide the resources to feed you, clothe you, transport you, and give you a dwelling with the creature comforts to which you are accustomed. The people of the United States have relatively big feet, as you can see in Figure 0.2. The world average in 2007 was estimated to be 2.7 hectares per person.

How much biologically productive land and water is available on our planet? We can estimate this by including regions such as croplands and fishing zones, and omitting regions such as deserts and ice caps. Currently, the value is estimated at about 12 billion hectares (roughly 30 billion acres) of land, water, and sea surface. This turns out to be about a quarter of the Earth's surface. Is this enough to sustain everybody on the planet with the lifestyle that people in the United States have? The next activity allows you to see for yourself.

Ecological footprints consider resource consumption based on land and water use; carbon footprints are based upon the release of greenhouse gases associated with the combustion of fossil fuels. Look for more about carbon footprints in Section 3.9.

A hectare is 10,000 square meters, or 2.471 acres.

Your Turn 0.4   Your Personal Share of the Planet

As stated earlier, an estimated 12 billion hectares (~30 billion acres) of biologically productive land, water, and sea are available on our planet.

a. Find the current estimate for the world population. Cite your source.
b. Use this estimate together with the one for biologically productive land to calculate the amount of land theoretically available for each person in the world.

Answers
a. In 2012, the population of the Earth was between 7.0 and 7.1 billion.
b. About 1.7 hectares or ~4 acres per person.

Why is this important? We have been exceeding the Earth's ability to meet our demands since the 1970s. A nation whose people have an average footprint greater than about 1.7 hectares is exceeding the "carrying capacity" of the Earth. Using the United States as an example, let's do one more calculation to see by how much.

Your Turn 0.5   How Many Earths?

In 2007, the United States had an ecological footprint of about 8.0 hectares (~20 acres) per person.

a. Find an estimate of the current population of the United States. Cite your source.
b. Calculate the amount of biologically productive land that the United States currently requires for this population.
c. What percentage is this amount of the biologically productive space (about 12 billion hectares or ~30 billion acres) available on our planet?

Answer

b. Estimating the U.S. population at 315 million and using the estimate of 8.0 hectares per person, the United States required about 2.5 billion hectares (6.2 billion acres).

Let's now say that *everyone* on the planet lived like the average citizen in the United States. Here is the calculation based on the world population in 2012.

$$\frac{7.0 \text{ billion people} \times 8.0 \text{ hectares/person} \times 1 \text{ planet}}{12 \text{ billion hectares}} = 4.7 \text{ planets}$$

Thus, to sustain this same standard of living for everybody on the planet we would need nearly 4 more Earths in addition to the one we currently have!

"*Only One Earth.*" On this Earth, the number of people has risen dramatically in the last few hundred years. So has economic development. As a result, the estimated global ecological footprint is rising, as shown in Figure 0.3. In 2003, we estimate that humanity used the equivalent of 1.25 Earths. By the 2030s, the projection is that we will be using 2 Earths. Clearly this rate of consumption cannot be sustained.

Through your study of chemistry, we hope you will learn ways either to reduce your ecological footprint or to keep it low, if it already is. The next section describes how chemists can help make this process work in some ways you might not expect.

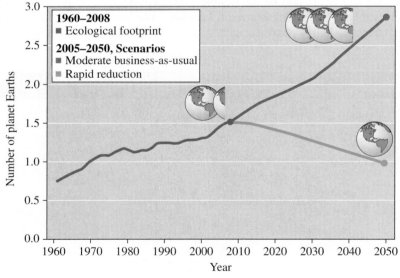

Figure 0.3

The current and projected ecological footprint of humans. Current estimates place the footprint above 1.0 Earths, that is, above what the Earth can sustain. *Note:* The upper projection assumes "moderate business as usual." The lower projection assumes a change to sustainable practices.

Source: Adapted from data provided by the Global Footprint Network.

ACS Green Chemistry Institute

Look for green chemistry examples throughout this book, designated with this icon.

0.6 | Our Responsibilities as Citizens and Chemists

We humans have a special responsibility to take care of our planet. Living out this responsibility, however, has proven to be no easy task. Each chapter in *Chemistry in Context* highlights an issue of interest such as air quality, water quality, or nutrition. These issues not only affect you personally, they also affect the health and well-being of the wider communities of which you are a part. For each issue, you will work on two related tasks: (1) learning about the issue and (2) finding ways to act constructively.

How do chemists meet the challenges of sustainability? The answer lies in part with "green chemistry," a set of principles originally articulated by people at the Environmental Protection Agency (EPA) and now actively pursued by the American Chemical Society (ACS). **Green chemistry** is the design of chemical products and processes that reduce or eliminate the use and generation of hazardous substances. The desired outcome is to produce less waste, especially toxic waste, and to use fewer resources.

Recognize that green chemistry is a tool in achieving sustainability, not an end in itself. As stated in the article "Color Me Green" from an issue of *Chemical & Engineering News* published in 2000: "Green chemistry represents the pillars that hold up our sustainable future. It is imperative to teach the value of green chemistry to tomorrow's chemists." Actually, we believe that it is imperative to teach the value of green chemistry to citizens as well. This is why so many applications of green chemistry are woven throughout *Chemistry in Context*.

To get you started, we list six key ideas about green chemistry (Table 0.2). They also are printed on the inside cover of this book.

Initiated under the EPA's *Design for the Environment Program*, green chemistry leads to cleaner air, water, and land, and the consumption of fewer resources. Chemists are now designing new processes (or retooling older ones) to make them more environmentally friendly. We call this "benign by design." Every green innovation does not necessarily have to be successful in achieving all six of these key ideas. But achieving several of them is an excellent step on the road to sustainability.

For example, an obvious way to reduce waste is to design chemical processes that don't produce it in the first place. One way is to have most or all of the atoms in the reactants end up as part of the desired product molecules. This "atom economy" approach, although not applicable to all reactions, has been used for the synthesis of many products, including pharmaceuticals, plastics, and pesticides. The approach saves

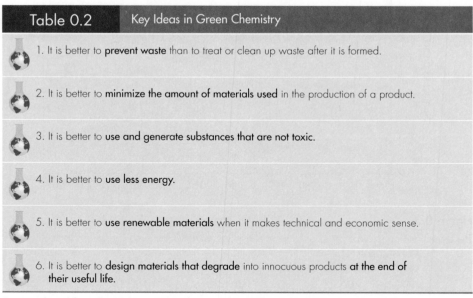

Table 0.2	Key Ideas in Green Chemistry
	1. It is better to **prevent waste** than to treat or clean up waste after it is formed.
	2. It is better to **minimize the amount of materials used** in the production of a product.
	3. It is better to **use and generate substances that are not toxic.**
	4. It is better to **use less energy.**
	5. It is better to **use renewable materials** when it makes technical and economic sense.
	6. It is better to **design materials that degrade** into innocuous products **at the end of their useful life.**

Source: Adapted from *The Twelve Principles of Green Chemistry* by Paul Anastas and John Warner.

money, uses fewer starting materials, and minimizes waste. The connection between green chemistry and the Triple Bottom Line should be apparent!

VOC stands for volatile organic compound. Look for more about VOCs in connection with air pollution in Chapter 1, "The Air We Breathe."

Many chemical manufacturing processes now use innovative green chemical methods. For example, you will see applications of green chemistry that have led to cheaper, less wasteful, and less toxic production of low VOC paint (Chapter 1). You also will see the key ideas in green chemistry applied to processing raw cotton, dry-cleaning methods (Chapter 5), and economical and healthier ways to process vegetable oils (Chapter 11).

Green chemistry efforts have been rewarded! A select group of research chemists, chemical engineers, small businesses, large corporations, and government labs has received the Presidential Green Chemistry Challenge Award. Initiated in 1995, this presidential-level award recognizes chemists and the chemical industry for their innovations aimed at reducing pollution. These awards recognize innovations in "cleaner, cheaper, and smarter chemistry."

0.7 | Back to the Blue Marble

Before we send you off to Chapter 1, we revisit the 1987 United Nations document *Our Common Future*. Earlier, we drew from this document our definition of sustainability: "Meeting the needs of the present without compromising the ability of future generations to meet their own needs." The foreword to this report was written by the chair, Gro Harlem Brundtland. She also wrote these words, ones that call us back to the image of Earth that opened this chapter:

> In the middle of the 20th century, we saw our planet from space for the first time. Historians may eventually find that this vision had a greater impact on thought than did the Copernican revolution of the 16th century, which upset the human self-image by revealing that the Earth is not the centre of the universe. From space, we see a small and fragile ball dominated not by human activity and edifice but by a pattern of clouds, oceans, greenery, and soils. Humanity's inability to fit its activities into that pattern is changing planetary systems, fundamentally. Many such changes are accompanied by life-threatening hazards. This new reality, from which there is no escape, must be recognized—and managed.

We agree. The new reality must be recognized. There is no escape. And all of us—students and teachers alike—have important roles to play. With *Chemistry in Context*, we will strive to provide you with the chemical information that can make a difference in your life and in the lives of others. We hope that you will use it to meet the challenges of today and tomorrow, equipped with a deeper understanding of chemistry.

Questions

1. This chapter opened with a famous quote from a Saudi astronaut, Prince Sultan. Later, in a 2005 interview, he remarked: "Being an astronaut has had an enormous impact on me. Looking at the planet from the perspective of the blackness of space, it makes you wonder, . . ." Prince Sultan went on to describe what he wondered about. We did not reprint his words. Rather, we hoped that you would write your own.

   a. Write a three-paragraph essay. In the first, introduce yourself briefly. In the second, describe what is important to you as you begin your study of chemistry. And in the third, describe what you most wonder about that relates to planet Earth.

   b. Share your self-introduction with others in your class, as indicated by your instructor.

2. When you look at a picture of Earth, "the blue marble," what are your first impressions?

3. Classify the following resources as renewable or nonrenewable: wind power, minerals, water, biofuel, and natural gas.

4. Read the full text of the Foreword to the *Brundtland Report*, easily found by a web search. It is only a few pages in length and contains some of the most compelling language ever written. Pick a small section and write a short piece that connects it to something you care about. You may choose a stance of agreement or disagreement.

5. This chapter introduces the idea that the species on our planet are all connected, sometimes in ways that are not obvious. From your studies in other fields, give three examples of how organisms are linked or in some way depend on one another.

6. Energy is the focus of one of the key ideas in green chemistry, and this chapter notes that finding "energy sources that are both clean and sustainable arguably is the major challenge of our century."

   a. Why are our current sources of energy – fossil fuels – neither clean nor sustainable?

   b. Why is it so important to replace our current sources of energy with ones that are clean and sustainable?

7. This chapter introduces the concept of "cradle-to-grave," one that you will encounter in subsequent chapters as well.

   a. Explain what is meant by a "cradle."

   b. For each of these items, name the cradle: plastic bag, paper cup, cotton T-shirt.

   c. Explain what is meant by a "grave."

   d. For the items listed in part **b**, suggest possible "graves" for each.

8. Choose an item that you use at school and describe the cradle-to-grave approach for its resources. Describe how you could change the cycle of the resources to "cradle-to-cradle."

9. Figure 0.1 shows one possible representation of the Triple Bottom Line. Here is another. Comment on the similarities and differences between these two figures.

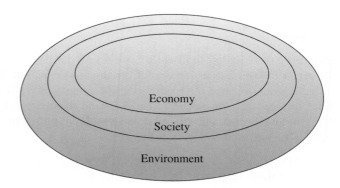

10. Propose a business practice that could follow the Triple Bottom Line.

11. This chapter also introduces the concept of "shifting baselines."

    a. In your own words, explain what "shifting baselines" means.

    b. Name an example of shifting baselines that has occurred in the past 20 years.

12. Calculate your ecological footprint. Feel free to use any of the websites available.

13. A bus serving a university campus had this sign painted on its side: "Reduce your footprints. Take the bus." Explain the double meaning.

14. Based on your experiences, why do you think that chemistry is called "the central science"?

15. Consider the waste produced as a result of an activity that you enjoy.

    a. Describe the activity and the waste that accompanies it.

    b. As more and more people participate in this activity, does the waste produced become a concern? Explain why or why not.

16. Define sustainability in your own words and describe two of your current activities that you can make more sustainable.

17. Describe the progress that has been made with regard to Target 4 in the Millennium Development Goals, "Achieve, by 2020, a significant improvement in the lives of at least 100 million slum dwellers."

18. Propose some ways that you can personally lower your ecological footprint.

19. Which key idea in green chemistry do you think is most important? Why?

20. Select a corporation of your choice, visit its website, and look for the pages that describe its efforts in regards to sustainability and/or corporate responsibility. Possibilities include Coca-Cola, WalMart, ExxonMobil, and Burger King. Report on what you find.

21. Mel George, a retired mathematics professor and one of the architects of *Shaping the Future: New Expectations for Education in Undergraduate Science, Technology, Engineering, and Mathematics* (National Science Foundation), remarked: "Putting a man on the moon did not require me to do anything. In contrast, we all must do something to save the planet." Describe five things that you could do, given who you are and your field of study.

22. Although the key ideas in green chemistry were written to guide chemists, you may find that these concepts are relevant to you as well. Perhaps you are an economics major. Or you are planning to become a nurse or a teacher. Perhaps you spend time gardening or you like to commute by bike. Pick two of the key ideas in green chemistry and describe ways in which they connect to your life and/or intended profession.

23. Newspaper and magazine advertisements often proclaim how "green" a business or corporation is. Find one and read it closely. What do you think—is it a case of "greenwashing," in which a corporation is trying to use as a selling point one tiny green drop in an otherwise wasteful bucket? Or is it a case of a real improvement that significantly reduces the waste stream? *Note:* It may be difficult to tell. For example, eliminating 7 tons of waste may sound large unless you know that the actual waste stream is in the billions of tons.

24. The mission statement of the American Chemical Society, the world's largest scientific society, is "Advance the broader chemistry enterprise and its practitioners for the benefit of Earth and its people." Explain how the final six words of this statement connect to the definition of sustainability used in this chapter.

25. Thomas Berry, theologian and cultural historian (1914–2009), described in his book *The Great Works* (1999) how humanity is faced with the job of moving from the present geological age, the Cenozoic, to the coming age. He names this age as "Ecozoic," reflecting the tremendous power of humans to shape the face of the world. "The universities must decide whether they will continue training persons for temporary survival in the declining Cenozoic Era or whether they will begin educating students for the emerging Ecozoic. . . . While this is not the time for continued denial by the universities or for attributing blame to the universities, it is the time for universities to rethink themselves and what they are doing."

   a. What do you see as the coming age? Describe it. If you don't prefer the term *Ecozoic Age,* suggest one of your own.

   b. How have your studies to date been preparing you for the future world in which you will live?

   c. In what ways do you think your study of chemistry might prepare you?

26. Select an idea in this chapter that caught your attention.

   a. Which idea did you select? Expand upon it in a few sentences.

   b. What was it about this idea that caught your attention? Explain.

The Air We Breathe

California blue skies, Lake Tahoe region.

"Ancient Greeks saw air as one of nature's basic elements, along with earth, fire, and water. Californians see it . . . Ah, perhaps those words offer clarification: Californians see too much of something that ought to be less visible. They also feel effects from breathing that air, which too often brings the routine act of respiration to their attention."

David Carle, *Introduction to Air in California*, 2006, page xiii

People have always noticed—and been curious about—the air they breathe. Together with earth, fire, and water, the ancient Greeks named air as a basic element of nature. Hundreds of years later, chemists experimented to learn more about the composition of air. Today, we can view the Earth's atmosphere from outer space. And daily, just like the ancients, we can peer up through the night air to catch a glimpse of the twinkling stars.

Our atmosphere is the thin veil between us and outer space. This chapter describes the atmospheric gases that support the life on Earth. The next chapter describes the ozone in the stratosphere that protects us from harmful ultraviolet radiation emitted by the Sun. The third chapter describes the greenhouse gases in our atmosphere that protect us from the bitter cold of outer space. Truly, our atmosphere is a resource beyond price. Our goal is to convey its beauty, its magnitude, and its frailty.

As you will learn in this chapter, we humans have altered the composition of the atmosphere. This is not surprising, because over 7 billion humans currently live on the planet. In a few decades, the population may reach 9 or 10 billion. The next activity invites you to think about how our actions, both individually and collectively, can change the air we breathe.

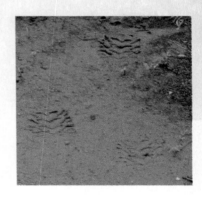

Consider This 1.1   Footprints in the Air

Hiking boot treads, asphalt pavement, corn fields. Each of these is an example of a "ground print" left by humans because each one alters the lay of the land. Similarly, our activities leave "air prints" that alter the composition of our atmosphere.

a. Name three things that leave an *indoor* air print.
b. Does each (1) hurt the air quality, (2) improve the air quality, or (3) have some effect, but you don't know what it is? Explain.
c. Repeat parts **a** and **b** for an *outdoor* air print.

Answers
a. Indoor air prints are left by growing house plants, burning candles, and applying paint.
b. Green plants remove carbon dioxide from the air and add oxygen, both a plus. Some plants emit pollen. For some people, this reduces the air quality. Burning candles emit carbon dioxide and soot into the air, and certain kinds of paint emit volatile organic compounds into the room. Both of these processes hurt the air quality.

As *Homo sapiens*, we have a special responsibility to guard the quality of the air on our planet. Living out this responsibility has proven to be no easy task. In fact, we have made some tragic errors that have killed people, animals, and vegetation. Ultimately, as we pointed out in Chapter 0, our responsibility is to live in ways today that will not compromise either our own health or the health of future generations. Keeping the air clean is part of this responsibility.

In this chapter, you will learn more about the air you breathe and its importance to your well-being. We hope you will also learn how important it is to make choices about air quality—both as an individual and as a member of a larger society—that demonstrate wisdom now and in the years to come.

In 1948, smog killed 20 people and sickened upwards of 5000 residents in or near Donora, Pennsylvania. In 1952, the Great London Smog killed thousands.

1.1 | What's in a Breath?

Take a breath! Automatically and unconsciously, you do this thousands of times each day. Certainly you do not need us to tell you to breathe! Although a doctor or nurse may have encouraged your first breath, from then on nature took over. Even if you were to hold your breath in a moment of fear or suspense, you soon would involuntarily gasp a lungful of that invisible stuff we call air. Indeed, you could survive only minutes without a fresh supply.

Consider This 1.2   Take a Breath

What total volume of air do you inhale (and exhale) in a typical day? Figure this out. First determine how much air you exhale in a single "normal" breath. Then determine how many breaths you take per minute. Finally, calculate how much air you exhale per day. Describe how you made your estimate, provide your data, and list any factors you believe may have affected the accuracy of your answer.

Were you surprised at how much you breathe? For an adult, the value typically is more than 11,000 liters (about 3000 gallons) of air per day. The value would be even higher had you spent the day on a bike trail or paddling a kayak.

Although you cannot tell by looking, the air you are breathing is not a single pure substance. Rather, it is a **mixture,** that is, a physical combination of two or more pure substances present in variable amounts. Mixtures are one of the two forms of matter that we encounter on our planet (Figure 1.1). The other form is pure substances. In this section, we focus on the pure substances that are the major components of air: nitrogen, oxygen, argon, carbon dioxide, and water vapor. All are colorless gases, invisible to the eye.

> Some mixtures are composed of gases. But gasoline is a mixture of liquids (Section 1.10), and soil is a mixture of solids and liquids.

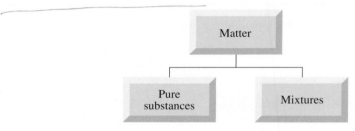

Figure 1.1
Matter can be classified either as a single pure substance or as a mixture.

The composition of the mixture that we call "air" depends on where you are. There's less oxygen in a stuffy room and more pollutants in an urban area. Exhaled air is a slightly different mixture than inhaled air. Trace amounts of substances may vary in the air as well. For example, the scent of lilacs may permeate the air outside. Indoors, the aroma of freshly brewed coffee may beckon you to the kitchen. In fact, the human nose is an extremely sensitive odor detector. In some cases, only a minute trace of a substance is needed to trigger the olfactory receptors responsible for detecting odors. Thus, tiny amounts of substances can have a powerful effect on our noses, as well as on our emotions.

Consider This 1.3   Your Nose Knows

The air is different in a pine forest, a bakery, an Italian restaurant, and a dairy barn. Blind-folded, you could smell the difference. Our noses alert us to the fact that air contains trace quantities of many substances.

a. Name three indoor and three outdoor smells that indicate small quantities of chemicals in the air.
b. Our noses warn us to avoid certain things. Give three examples of when a smell indicates a hazard.

> The composition of our atmosphere has not been constant over the millennia. For example, the concentration of oxygen has varied.

Using a pie chart and a bar graph, Figure 1.2 represents the composition of air. The pie chart emphasizes the fractions of the whole, whereas the bar graph emphasizes the relative amounts of each substance. Regardless of how we present the data, the air you breathe is primarily nitrogen and oxygen. More specifically, the composition of air by volume is about 78% nitrogen, 21% oxygen, and 1% other gases. **Percent (%)** means "parts per hundred." In this case, the parts are either molecules or atoms.

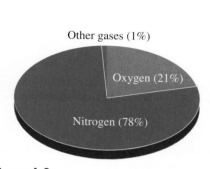

Other gases (1%)

Oxygen (21%)

Nitrogen (78%)

Figure 1.2

The composition of dry air, by volume.

 Figures Alive! Visit Connect™ to access Figures Alive! when you see this icon. Watch for the Figures Alive! icon throughout this text.

The percents shown in Figure 1.2 are for *dry* air. Water vapor is not included, as its concentration varies by location. In dry desert air, the concentration of water vapor can be close to 0%. In contrast, it can reach 5% by volume in a warm tropical rain forest. Whether at high or low concentration, water vapor is a colorless gas that is invisible to the eye. Since you can see fog banks and clouds, they are not composed of water vapor. Rather, these consist of tiny droplets of liquid water or crystals of ice (Figure 1.3).

Nitrogen is the most abundant substance in the air and constitutes about 78% of what we breathe. This gas is colorless, odorless, and relatively unreactive, passing in and out of our lungs unchanged (Table 1.1). Although nitrogen is essential for life and part of all living things, most plants and animals obtain it from sources other than the nitrogen in our atmosphere.

Water vapor is the gas that we think of as "humidity."

Section 6.9 describes the cycle by which atmospheric nitrogen becomes part of living plants and animals.

Figure 1.3

Clouds consist of minuscule droplets of water that remain suspended because of upward air currents. Clouds can weigh millions of pounds.

Table 1.1	Typical Composition of Inhaled and Exhaled Air	
Substance	Inhaled Air (%)*	Exhaled Air (%)*
nitrogen	78.0	78.0
oxygen	21.0	16.0
argon	0.9	0.9
carbon dioxide	0.04	4.0
water vapor	variable	variable

*Percents are by volume

Even though oxygen is less abundant than nitrogen in our atmosphere, it still plays a key role on our planet. Oxygen is absorbed into our blood via the lungs and reacts with the foods we eat to release the energy to power the chemical processes within our bodies. It is necessary for many other chemical reactions as well, including burning and rusting. As the "O" in H_2O (water), oxygen is the most abundant element in the human body by mass. Present in many rocks and minerals, it is also the most abundant element in the Earth's crust. Given this broad distribution, it is somewhat surprising that oxygen was not isolated as a pure substance until 1774. But once isolated, oxygen proved to be of great significance in establishing the young science of chemistry.

Chapter 11 provides more information about the energy content of foods.

We explain the term *element* in Section 1.6.

Consider This 1.4   More Oxygen. . . ?

We live in an atmosphere of 21% oxygen. A match burns in less than a minute, a fireplace consumes a small pine log in about 20 minutes, and we exhale about 15 times a minute. Life on Earth would be *very* different if the oxygen concentration were twice as high. List at least four differences.

Every time we exhale, we add carbon dioxide to the atmosphere. Table 1.1 indicates the difference between inhaled dry air and exhaled air. Clearly some changes have taken place that use up some of the oxygen and give off carbon dioxide and water. In the process of **respiration,** the foods we eat are metabolized to produce carbon dioxide and water. With each breath, some of the water in our bodies evaporates from the moist tissue in our lungs.

Respiration also provides the energy to power chemical reactions in our bodies. Look for more about breathing and respiration in Chapter 4.

Other gases are found in our atmosphere as well (see Figure 1.2). Argon, for example, is about 0.9% of the air. The name *argon,* meaning "lazy" in Greek, reflects the fact that argon is chemically inert. As you can see from Table 1.1, any argon that you inhale you simply exhale.

The percentages we have been using to describe the composition of the atmosphere are based on volume, that is, the amount of space that each gas occupies. If we wanted to, we could closely approximate 100 liters (L) of dry air by mixing 78 L of nitrogen, 21 L oxygen, and 1 L argon (78% nitrogen, 21% oxygen, and 1% argon).

1 liter = 1.06 quart Appendix 1 contains this and many other conversion factors.

The composition of air also can be represented in terms of the numbers of molecules and atoms present. This works because equal volumes of gases contain equal numbers of molecules, provided the gases are at the same temperature and pressure. Thus, if you took a sample of 100 of the molecules and atoms in air (an unrealistically small amount), 78 would be nitrogen molecules, 21 would be oxygen molecules, and 1 would be an argon atom. In other words, when we say that air is 21% oxygen, we mean that there are 21 molecules of oxygen per 100 of the molecules and atoms in the air. A bit later we'll explain why nitrogen and oxygen are found as molecules. In contrast, argon is found as an atom.

Look for more about atoms and molecules in Section 1.7.

You now know that air contains nitrogen, oxygen, argon, carbon dioxide, and usually some water vapor. As you might imagine, there is more to the story.

1.2 | What Else Is in a Breath?

No matter where you live, each lungful of air you inhale contains tiny amounts of substances other than nitrogen and oxygen. Many are present at concentrations of less than 1%, or one part per hundred. Such is the case with carbon dioxide, a gas you both inhale and exhale. In our atmosphere, the concentration of carbon dioxide reached 0.0393% in 2012. This value is slowly but steadily rising as we humans burn fossil fuels.

Although we could express 0.0393% as 0.0393 molecules of carbon dioxide per 100 molecules and atoms in the air, it sounds strange to refer to 0.0393 of a molecule. For low concentrations, it is more convenient to use **parts per million (ppm).** One ppm is a unit of concentration 10,000 times smaller than 1% (one part per hundred). Here are the relationships.

0.0393%	means	0.0393 parts per hundred
	means	0.393 parts per thousand
	means	3.93 parts per ten thousand
	means	39.3 parts per hundred thousand
	means	393 parts per million

Out of a sample of air containing 1,000,000 molecules (and some atoms), we now can say that 393 of them will be carbon dioxide molecules. The carbon dioxide concentration is 393 ppm, or 0.0393%.

Chapter 3 provides information about CO_2 concentrations in the atmosphere.

To convert between % and ppm move the decimal point four places to the right. The activities in Figures Alive! provide practice for you.

Skeptical Chemist 1.5   Really One Part per Million?

Some say that a part per million is the same as one second in nearly 12 days. Is this a correct analogy? How about one step in a 568–mile journey? Check the validity of these analogies, explaining your reasoning. Then come up with an analogy of your own.

Your Turn 1.6   Practice with Parts per Million

a. In some countries, the limit for the average concentration of carbon monoxide in an 8–hour period is set at 9 ppm. Express this as a percentage.
b. Exhaled air typically contains about 78% nitrogen. Express this concentration in parts per million.

Answers
a. 0.0009%   b. 780,000 ppm

Some of the substances found in low concentrations are air pollutants. Although these are found everywhere on the globe, you are most likely to encounter them in large metropolitan areas. For example, Figure 1.4 shows smog against the mountains near Santiago, Chile, a city of over 6 million inhabitants. Other large cities such as Los Angeles, Mexico City, Mumbai, and Beijing often have dirty air. Earlier, we noted how human activities leave "air prints," both indoors and out. When large numbers of people cook meals and drive vehicles, they tend to dirty the air.

In this chapter, we focus on four gases that contribute to air pollution at the surface of the Earth. One of these gases, carbon monoxide, is odorless; the other three—ozone, sulfur dioxide, and nitrogen dioxide—have characteristic odors. With sufficient exposure, all are hazardous to your health, even at concentrations well below 1 ppm. Together with particulate matter (PM), they represent the most serious air pollutants. Here is more information about each.

Today, over half of the people on the planet live in cities. In contrast, in 1' only 10–15% did.

Figure 1.4

Sunny November spring day in Santiago, Chile.

Figure 1.5

A propane camping stove.

In the stratosphere, ozone absorbs some wavelengths of UV radiation. Look for more about this in Chapter 2.

Figure 1.6

White pine needles damaged by ozone.

(Courtesy of Missouri Botanical Garden PlantFinder)

SO_2 and NO_2 dissolve in moist lung tissue to form sulfurous acid and nitric acid, respectively. Look for more about these acids and about acid rain in Chapter 6.

- **Carbon monoxide (CO)** has earned the nickname "silent killer" because it has no color, taste, or smell. When you inhale carbon monoxide, it passes into your bloodstream and then interferes with the ability of your hemoglobin to carry oxygen. If you breathe carbon monoxide, at first you may feel dizzy and nauseous, or get a headache, symptoms that easily could be mistaken for another illness. Continued exposure, however, can make you extremely ill or kill you. Both automobiles and charcoal grills are sources of carbon monoxide. Propane camping stoves (Figure 1.5) are another and, if used indoors, they require proper venting.
- **Ozone (O_3)** has a sharp odor that you may have detected around electric motors or welding equipment. Even at very low concentrations, ozone can reduce your lung function. The symptoms you experience may include chest pain, coughing, sneezing, or lung congestion. Ozone also mottles the leaves of crops and yellows pine needles (Figure 1.6). Here on the surface of the Earth, ozone is definitely a bad actor. At high altitudes, however, it plays an essential role in screening out ultraviolet radiation.
- **Sulfur dioxide (SO_2)** has a sharp, unpleasant odor. If you inhale sulfur dioxide, it dissolves in the moist tissue of your lungs to form an acid. The elderly, the young, and individuals with emphysema or asthma are most susceptible to sulfur dioxide poisoning. At present, sulfur dioxide in the air comes primarily from the burning of coal. For example, the 1952 London smog that eventually killed over 10,000 people was in part caused by the emissions of coal-fired stoves. The causes of death included acute respiratory distress, heart failure (from preexisting conditions), and asphyxiation. Some who survived had permanent lung damage.
- **Nitrogen dioxide (NO_2)** has a characteristic brown color. Like sulfur dioxide, it can combine with the moist tissue in your lungs to produce an acid. In our atmosphere, nitrogen dioxide is produced from nitrogen monoxide, another pollutant that is a colorless gas. Nitrogen monoxide is formed in the air from anything that is hot, including vehicle engines and coal-fired power plants. Nitrogen oxides, NO and NO_2, also can form naturally in grain silos, and can injure or kill farmers who may inadvertently inhale the gases.
- **Particulate matter (PM)** is a complex mixture of tiny solid particles and microscopic liquid droplets and is the least understood of the air pollutants that

Figure 1.7
A 2004 wildfire near San Jose, California. This fire is releasing particulate matter, some of which is visible as soot.

we have listed. Particulate matter is classified by size rather than composition, because the size determines the health consequences. **PM₁₀** includes particles with an average diameter of 10 μm or less, a length on the order of 0.0004 inches. **PM₂.₅** is a subset of PM₁₀ and includes particles with an average diameter of less than 2.5 μm. These tinier and more deadly particles are sometimes called *fine particles*. Particulate matter originates from many sources, including vehicle engines, coal-burning power plants, wildfires, and blowing dust. Sometimes particulate matter is visible as soot or smoke (Figure 1.7). However, of more concern are the particles too tiny to see: PM₁₀ and PM₂.₅. These particles, when inhaled, go deep into your lungs, irritating them. The smallest particles pass from your lungs into your bloodstream and can cause heart disease.

A **micrometer** (μm) is a millionth of a meter (m). A micrometer is also sometimes referred to as a micron.

We end this section with a fact that may surprise you. All of the air pollutants that we just listed can occur naturally! For example, a wildfire (see Figure 1.7) produces particulate matter and carbon monoxide, lightning produces ozone and nitrogen oxides, and volcanoes release sulfur dioxide. The pollutants have the same hazards, whether released from natural or human sources. What are the risks to your health? We now turn to this topic.

1.3 | Air Pollutants and Risk Assessment

Risk is part of living. Although we cannot avoid risk, we still try to minimize it. For example, certain practices are illegal because they carry risks that are judged to be unacceptable. Other activities carry high risks and we label them as such. For example, cigarette packages carry a warning about lung cancer. Wine bottles carry warnings about birth defects and about operating machinery under the influence of alcohol. The absence of a warning, however, does not guarantee safety. The risk may be too low to label, it may be obvious or unavoidable, or it may be far outweighed by other benefits.

Warnings are just that. They do not mean that somebody *will* be affected. Rather, they report the likelihood of an adverse outcome. Let's say that the odds of dying from a vehicle accident are one in a million for each 30,000 miles traveled. On average, this means that one person out of every million traveling 30,000 miles would die in an accident. Such a prediction is not simply a guess, but the result of **risk assessment,** the process of evaluating scientific data and making predictions in an organized manner about the probabilities of an outcome.

When is it risky to breathe the air? Fortunately, existing air quality standards can offer you guidance. We say *guidance,* because standards are set through a complex interaction of scientists, medical experts, governmental agencies, and politicians. People may not necessarily agree on which standards are reasonable and safe. Standards also change over time, as new scientific knowledge is generated.

In the United States, national air quality standards were established in 1970 as a result of the Clean Air Act. If pollutant levels fall below these standards, presumably the air is healthy to breathe. We say "presumably" because air quality standards change over time, usually becoming stricter. If you look worldwide, you will find that air quality regulations vary both in their strictness and in the degree to which they are enforced.

The risks presented by an air pollutant are a function of both **toxicity,** the intrinsic health hazard of a substance, and **exposure,** the amount of the substance encountered. Toxicities are difficult to accurately assess for many reasons, including that it is unethical to run experiments on people. Even if data were available, we still would have to determine the levels of risk that are acceptable for different groups of people. In spite of the complexities, government agencies have succeeded in establishing limits of exposure for the major air pollutants. Table 1.2 shows the National Ambient Air Quality Standards established by the U.S. Environmental Protection Agency (EPA). Here, **ambient air** refers to the air surrounding us, usually meaning the outside air. As our knowledge grows, we modify these standards. For example, in 2006 these standards were made more stringent for $PM_{2.5}$. Similarly, in 2008 they were lowered for ozone, and in 2010 a new standard for nitrogen dioxide was added.

The U.S. EPA was formed in 1970 by President Richard Nixon. Senators from earlier years also played key roles in the legislation.

Table 1.2	U.S. National Ambient Air Quality Standards	
Pollutant	Standard (ppm)	Approximate Equivalent Concentration (µg/m³)
carbon monoxide		
8–hr average	9	10,000
1–hr average	35	40,000
nitrogen dioxide		
1–hr average	0.100	200
Annual average	0.053	100
ozone		
8–hr average	0.075	147
*particulates**		
PM_{10}, 24–hr average	—	150
$PM_{2.5}$, annual average	—	15
$PM_{2.5}$, 24–hr average**	—	35
sulfur dioxide		
1–hr average	0.075	210
3–hr average	0.50	1,300

Source: U.S. Environmental Protection Agency.
Note: Standards also exist for lead but are not included here.

*PM_{10} refers to all airborne particles 10 µm in diameter or less.
$PM_{2.5}$ refers to particles 2.5 µm in diameter or less.

**The unit of ppm is not applicable to particulates.

Exposure is far more straightforward to assess than toxicity, because exposure depends on factors that we more easily can measure. These include:

- **Concentration in the air**
  The more toxic the pollutant, the lower its concentration must be set. Concentrations are expressed either as parts per million or as micrograms per cubic meter ($\mu g/m^3$), as shown in Table 1.2. Earlier, we used the prefix *micro-* with micrometers (μm), meaning a millionth of a meter (10^{-6} m). Similarly, one **microgram** (μg) is a millionth of a gram (g), or 10^{-6} g.

- **Length of time**
  Higher concentrations of a pollutant can be tolerated only briefly. A pollutant may have several standards, each for a different length of time.

- **Rate of breathing**
  Physically active people, such as athletes or laborers, breathe at a higher rate. If the air quality is poor, reducing activity is one way to reduce exposure.

> 1 μg is approximately the mass of a period printed on a page.

Suppose you collect an air sample on a city street. An analysis shows that it contains 5000 μg of carbon monoxide (CO) per cubic meter of air. Is this concentration of CO harmful to breathe? We can use Table 1.2 to answer this question. Two standards are reported for carbon monoxide, one for a 1-hour exposure and another for an 8-hour exposure. The 1-hour exposure is set at a higher level (4×10^4 μg CO/m^3) because a higher concentration can be tolerated for a short time.

Both concentrations are expressed in **scientific notation,** a system for writing numbers as the product of a number and 10 raised to the appropriate power. Scientific notation enables us to avoid writing strings of zeros either before or after the decimal point. For example, the value 1×10^4 is equivalent to 10,000. To understand this conversion, simply count the number of zeros to the right of the 1 in 10,000. There are four of them. The number 1 is then multiplied by 10^4 to obtain 1×10^4 μg CO/m^3. Similarly, 4×10^4 μg CO/m^3 is equivalent to 40,000 μg CO/m^3. Scientific notation is even more useful for very large numbers, such as the 20,000,000,000,000,000,000,000 molecules in a typical breath. In scientific notation, this value is written as 2×10^{22} molecules.

> If you need help with scientific notation, consult Appendix 2.

Using scientific notation, we now can express the value of 5000 μg CO/m^3 as 5×10^3 μg CO/m^3. Clearly, this value is *less* than either standard. In the case of an 8-hour exposure, 5×10^3 is less than 1×10^4. Similarly, for a 1-hour period, 5×10^3 is less than 4×10^4. For all values, the units are μg CO/m^3.

Table 1.2 also allows us to assess the relative toxicities of pollutants. For example, we can compare the 8-hour average exposure standards for carbon monoxide and ozone: 9 ppm vs. 0.075 ppm. Doing the math, ozone is about 130 times more hazardous to breathe than carbon monoxide! Nonetheless, carbon monoxide still can be exceedingly dangerous. As the "silent killer," it may impair your judgment before you recognize the danger.

Your Turn 1.7   Estimating Toxicities

a. Which pollutant in Table 1.2 is likely to be the most toxic? Exclude particulate matter.
b. Examine the particulate matter standards. Earlier, we stated that "fine particles," $PM_{2.5}$, are more deadly than the coarser ones, PM_{10}. Do the values in Table 1.2 support this claim?

Answer

a. O_3. This is a hard call, as no common exposure period exists on which to base the comparison. Clearly CO is not the most toxic, as all its standards are higher. It is not NO_2, because SO_2 has a lower 1–hr average standard. Between SO_2 and O_3, ozone has the tighter standard because of the lower 8–hr average in comparison to the 3–hr average standard for sulfur dioxide.

Although the standards for air pollutants are expressed in parts per million, the concentrations of sulfur dioxide and nitrogen dioxide could conveniently be reported in **parts per billion (ppb),** meaning one part out of one billion, or 1000 times less concentrated than one part per million.

$$\text{sulfur dioxide } 0.075 \text{ ppm} = 75 \text{ ppb}$$
$$\text{nitrogen dioxide } 0.100 \text{ ppm} = 100 \text{ ppb}$$

As these values reveal, converting from parts per million to parts per billion involves moving the decimal point three places to the right.

Your Turn 1.8   Living Downwind

Copper metal can be recovered from copper ore by smelting, a process that releases sulfur dioxide (SO_2). Let's assume that a woman living downwind of a smelter inhaled 44 μg of SO_2 in an hour.

a. If she inhaled 625 liters (0.625 m^3) of air per hour, would she exceed the 1–hr average for the U.S. National Ambient Air Quality Standards for SO_2? Support your answer with a calculation.

b. If she were exposed at this rate for three hours, would she exceed the 3–hr average?

To end this section, we note that our *perception* of a risk also plays an important role. For example, the risks of traveling by car far exceed those of flying. Each day in the United States, more than 100 people die in automobile accidents. Yet some people avoid taking a flight because of their fear of a plane crash. Similarly, some people fear living near a dormant volcano. Yet as some notorious hurricanes have demonstrated, living in a coastal area can be a far riskier proposition. Whether perceived as a risk or not, *air pollution presents real hazards,* both to present and future generations. In the next section, we offer you the tools to assess these hazards.

1.4 | Air Quality and You

Depending on where you live, you will breathe air of different quality. Some locations always have good air; others have air of moderate quality, and still others have unhealthy air much of the time. As we will see, the differences arise because of the number of people living in a region, their activities, the geographical features, the prevailing weather patterns, and the activities of people in neighboring regions.

To improve air quality, many nations have enacted legislation. For example, we already have cited the U.S. Clean Air Act (1970) that led to the establishment of air quality standards. Like many environmental laws, this one focused on limiting our exposure to hazardous substances. It has been named as a "command and control law" or an "end of the pipe solution" because it tries to limit the spread of hazardous substances or clean them up after the fact.

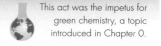

This act was the impetus for green chemistry, a topic introduced in Chapter 0.

The Pollution Prevention Act (1990) was a significant piece of legislation that followed the Clean Air Act. It focused on *preventing* the formation of hazardous substances, stating that "pollution should be prevented or reduced at the source whenever feasible." The language shift is significant. Rather than attempting to regulate existing pollutants, people should not produce them in the first place! With the Pollution Prevention Act, it became national policy to employ practices that reduce or ideally eliminate pollutants at their source.

Your Turn 1.9   The Logic of Prevention

Take off your muddy shoes at the door rather than cleaning up the carpet later! List three "common sense" examples that prevent air pollution rather than cleaning it up after the fact. *Hint:* Revisit Consider This 1.1 on "air prints."

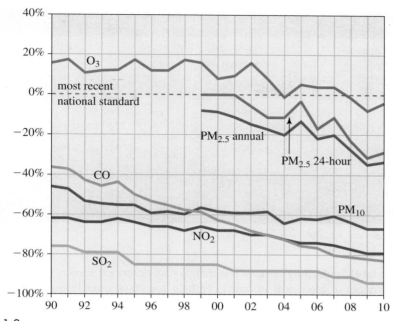

Figure 1.8

U.S. average levels of air pollutants (at selected sites) compared with national ambient air quality standards, *1990–2010.*

Source: EPA

    The decrease in the concentration of air pollutants in the United States has been dramatic (Figure 1.8). Some improvements occurred through a combination of laws and regulations, such as the ones we just mentioned. Others stemmed from local decisions. For example, a community may have built a new public transportation system or an industry may have installed more modern equipment. Still others occurred because of the ingenuity of chemists, most notably via a set of practices called "green chemistry." Look for green chemistry examples throughout this book that are designated with the green chemistry icon.

However, aggregate data such as those in Figure 1.8 hide the fact that people in some places still breathe dirty air. Although air quality may have improved on average, people in some metropolitan areas breathe air that contains unhealthy levels of pollutants. Check the data for the United States presented in Table 1.3.

The green chemistry examples in this text include some of the winners of the prestigious Presidential Green Chemistry Challenge Awards.

Table 1.3	Air Quality Data for Selected U.S. Metropolitan Areas	
	# of Unhealthy Days/Year*	
Metropolitan Area	O_3	$PM_{2.5}$
Boston	0	8
Chicago	10	0
Cleveland	10	1
Houston	21	0
Los Angeles	43	0
Phoenix	11	4
Pittsburgh	14	1
Sacramento	35	13
Seattle	2	0
Washington, DC	21	2

Seattle has few bad air days because of its rainy climate. Section 1.12 describes the connections between climate and smog formation.

Source: EPA, Air Trends: Air Quality Index Information.
*Days for which the AQI for the pollutant exceeds 100; five-year average (2006–2010)

Table 1.4	Levels for the Air Quality Index (AQI)	
When the AQI is in this range:	...air quality conditions are:	...as symbolized by this color.
0–50	Good	Green
51–100	Moderate	Yellow
101–150	Unhealthy for sensitive groups	Orange
151–200	Unhealthy	Red
201–300	Very unhealthy	Purple
301–500	Hazardous	Maroon

Source: Environmental Protection Agency.

The label "unhealthy" means just that. As we described earlier, air pollutants are the perpetrators of biological mischief. To help you more quickly assess the hazards, the U.S. EPA developed the color-coded Air Quality Index (AQI) shown in Table 1.4. This Index is scaled from 1–500, with the value of 100 pegged to the national standard for the pollutant. Green or yellow ($\leq$100) indicates air of good or moderate quality. Orange indicates that the air has become unhealthy for some groups. Red, purple, or maroon ($>$150) indicates that the air is unhealthy for *everybody* to breathe.

Some newspapers provide only a general air quality report. For example, the air quality may be listed as "moderate" for a city. This means that at least one pollutant was moderate, but possibly others were as well. Sometimes the report is given in numerical terms rather than general terms. For example, if two pollutants were present, one with a value of 85 and the other with a value of 91, the daily value would be reported as 91.

More and more, though, metropolitan areas are beginning to report each pollutant separately. This is helpful, because how you act depends on which pollutants are present. For example, Figure 1.9 shows the air quality forecast for carbon monoxide,

FORECAST DATE AIR POLLUTANT	YESTERDAY SAT 12/24/2011 Highest AQI Reading/SITE	TODAY SUN 12/25/2011	TOMORROW MON 12/26/2011	EXTENDED TUES 12/27/2011
O_3	30 BLUE POINT	32 GOOD	30 GOOD	32 GOOD
CO	22 SOUTH PHOENIX & WEST PHOENIX	32 GOOD	20 GOOD	15 GOOD
PM_{10}	60 WEST PHOENIX	52 MODERATE	46 GOOD	35 GOOD
$PM_{2.5}$	141 SOUTH PHOENIX	156 UNHEALTHY	85 MODERATE	42 GOOD

Figure 1.9

Air quality forecast for Phoenix on December 25, 2011. See Table 1.4 for the color code legend.

Source: Arizona Department of Environmental Quality.

ozone, and particulates on a sunny spring day in Phoenix, Arizona. The pollutant of concern was PM$_{2.5}$ from wood smoke. People were advised to "limit or even avoid outdoor exertion such as jogging or riding bicycles."

1.5 | Where We Live: The Troposphere

As we pointed out earlier, our atmosphere is a mixture that varies slightly in composition at different locations. About 75% of our air, by mass, is in the **troposphere,** the lower region of the atmosphere in which we live that lies directly above the surface of the Earth. *Tropos* is Greek for "turning" or "changing." The troposphere contains the air currents and turbulent storms that turn and mix our air.

The warmest air in the troposphere usually lies at ground level because the Sun primarily heats the ground, which in turn warms the air above it. Cooler air is found higher up, a phenomenon you may have observed as you hike or drive to higher elevations. However, air inversions occur when cooler air gets trapped beneath warmer air. Air pollutants can accumulate in an inversion layer, especially if the layer remains stationary for an extended period. This often occurs in cities ringed by mountains, such as Salt Lake City (Figure 1.10).

Air pollutants might better be termed "people fumes." One hundred years ago, our Earth was home to fewer than 2 billion people. We are now over the 7-billion mark, with the majority of people living in urban regions. This growth in population has been accompanied by a massive growth in both the consumption of resources and the production of waste. The waste that we stash in our atmosphere is called air pollution.

Air pollution provides the first context in which we can discuss **sustainability,** the topic that set the stage for this book. As we pointed out in Chapter 0, we need to make decisions with an eye not only for today's outcomes but also for the needs of generations to come. It makes sense to avoid actions that produce pollutants that can compromise our health and well-being. Does this sound familiar? Again, this is the logic behind the Pollution Prevention Act of 1990, legislation that calls for preventing pollution rather than controlling our exposure to it.

The Pollution Prevention Act provided the impetus for **green chemistry,** a set of key ideas to guide all in the chemical community, including teachers and students. Green chemistry is "benign by design." It calls for designing chemical products and processes that reduce or eliminate the use or generation of hazardous substances. Begun under the EPA Design for the Environment Program, green chemistry reduces pollution through the design or redesign of chemical processes. The goal is to use less energy, create less waste, use fewer resources, and use renewable resources. Green chemistry is a tool for achieving sustainability, rather than an end in itself.

Innovative "green" chemical methods already have decreased or eliminated toxic substances used or created in chemical manufacturing processes. For example,

The depth of the troposphere varies with season and location. Its depth ranges from about 12 miles (20 km) at the equator to about 4 miles (6 km) at the poles.

Hurricanes in the troposphere clearly illustrate the meaning of the Greek word *tropos* (= turning or changing).

Key ideas in green chemistry are listed on the inside cover of this book.

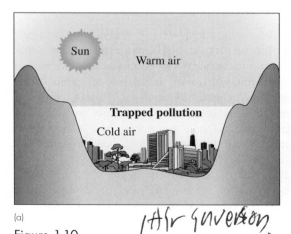

(a) Air inversion

Figure 1.10

(a) An air inversion can trap pollution. (b) An air inversion, trapping a smoggy layer of air over Salt Lake City, Utah.

The green chemistry awards are given in five areas: greener synthetic pathways, greener reaction conditions, designing greener chemicals, small business, and academia.

we now have cheaper and less wasteful ways to produce ibuprofen, pesticides, disposable diapers, and contact lenses. We have new dry cleaning methods and recyclable silicon wafers for integrated circuits. Some of the research chemists and chemical engineers who developed these methods have received Presidential Green Chemistry Challenge Awards. Begun in 1995, these presidential-level awards recognize chemists for their innovations on behalf of a less polluted world. Each year since 1996, five awards have been given with the theme "Chemistry is not the problem, it's the solution."

Consider This 1.10   Green Chemistry

Recall these two key ideas in green chemistry:

It is better to *use less energy.*
It is better to *prevent waste* than to treat or clean up waste after it is formed.

a. Why is it better to use less energy? Give two examples that demonstrate the connection between using energy and putting waste in the air.
b. Now choose an air pollutant. Give two examples that demonstrate why it makes more sense to prevent its formation rather than to try to clean it up once in the air.

Bottom line: Nobody wants dirty air. It makes you sick, reduces the quality of your life, and may hasten your death. However, the problem is that many people have become so accustomed to breathing dirty air that they don't notice it. Recall the concept of **shifting baselines** mentioned in Chapter 0. Haze is now so common that we have forgotten the clear days when it seemed we really could see forever. Burning eyes and breathing disorders have become so common that we have forgotten that they once were not. We have become accustomed to living in **megacities,** urban areas with 10 million people or more. Tokyo, New York City, Mexico City, and Mumbai are examples. Pollutants such as wood smoke, car exhaust, and industrial emissions often are generated in populated areas, and thus they are concentrated in the troposphere around megacities.

Clearly, we have some problems! As promised, your knowledge of chemistry can lead you to making better choices to deal with these problems, both as an individual and in your local community. The next two sections give you a better grasp of the language of chemistry. We then use this language to approach the issues of air pollution in more detail.

1.6 | Classifying Matter: Pure Substances, Elements, and Compounds

In describing air and its quality, we already have employed several chemical names. For example, in Section 1.1 we listed nitrogen, oxygen, argon, and usually water vapor as four of the pure substances that make up the majority of our atmosphere. We named some pollutants found at very low concentrations: ozone, sulfur dioxide, carbon monoxide, and nitrogen dioxide. We included their chemical formulas as well: O_3, SO_2, CO, and NO_2. We also mentioned the terms *atom* and *molecule*. For example, we noted that air is a mixture that contains different molecules (and a few atoms). In this section, we explain more about elements and compounds. In the next, we will focus on atoms and molecules that these elements and compounds contain.

Matter consists of elements and compounds, as shown in Figure 1.11. An **element** is one of the 100 or so pure substances in our world from which compounds are formed. As we will see shortly, they contain only one type of atom. Nitrogen (N_2), oxygen (O_2), and argon (Ar) are examples of elements. So is ozone (O_3), another form of oxygen. Over 100 elements are known. In contrast, a **compound** is a pure substance made up of two or more different elements in a fixed, characteristic chemical combination. Compounds

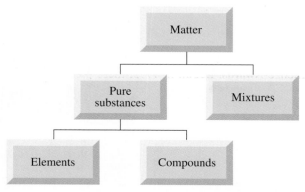

Figure 1.11

One way to classify matter.

contain two or more different types of atoms. For example, water (H_2O) is a compound of the elements oxygen and hydrogen. Similarly, carbon dioxide (CO_2) is a compound of the elements oxygen and carbon. In CO_2, the two elements are chemically combined and are no longer in their elemental forms. Sulfur dioxide (SO_2) and methane (CH_4) are other examples of compounds.

About 90 elements occur naturally on Earth and, as far as we know, elsewhere in the universe. The others have been created from existing elements through nuclear reactions. Plutonium is probably the best known of the human-made elements, although it does occur in trace amounts in nature. The vast majority of elements are solids. Nitrogen, oxygen, argon, and eight other elements are gases; and only bromine and mercury are liquids at room temperature.

Chemical symbols are one- or two-letter abbreviations for the elements. These symbols, established by international agreement, are used throughout the world. Some of them make immediate sense to those who speak English or related languages. For example, oxygen is O, nitrogen is N, sulfur is S, and nickel is Ni. Other symbols have their origin in other languages. For example, Fe is iron, Pb is lead, Au is gold, and Hg is mercury. These metals were known to the ancients and given Latin names long ago. For example, *ferrum* is iron, *plumbum* is lead, *aurum* is gold, and *hydrargyrum* is mercury.

Elements have been named for properties, planets, places, and people. Hydrogen (H) means "water former," because hydrogen gas (H_2) burns in oxygen (O_2) to form the compound water (H_2O). Neptunium (Np) and plutonium (Pu) were named after two planets in our solar system. Berkelium (Bk) and californium (Cf) honor the Berkeley lab in which a team of researchers first produced them. Flerovium (Fl) and Livermorium (Lv) were the most recently named elements. Both were named after the laboratories in which the elements were discovered. Only a few atoms of each have been produced.

> Plutonium can fuel both nuclear reactors and nuclear bombs. See Chapter 7 for the details.

> Chemical symbols sometimes also are referred to as atomic symbols.

> In 2006, Pluto lost its status as a planet.

Your Turn 1.11   Pure Substances in Air

a. Hydrogen (0.54 ppm), helium (5 ppm), and methane (17 ppm) are found in our atmosphere. Two of these are elements. Which ones?

b. List five other substances found in the air and classify them as elements or compounds.

c. Express each concentration in part **a** as a percent.

It is fitting that the 19th-century Russian chemist Dmitri Mendeleev has his own element (Md), because the most common way of arranging the elements—the **periodic table**—reflects the system he developed. This is an orderly arrangement of all the elements based on similarities in their properties. The inside back cover has a copy for handy reference, and we will explain more about it in Chapter 2.

> Lothar Meyer, a German chemist, also developed a periodic table at the same time as Mendeleev.

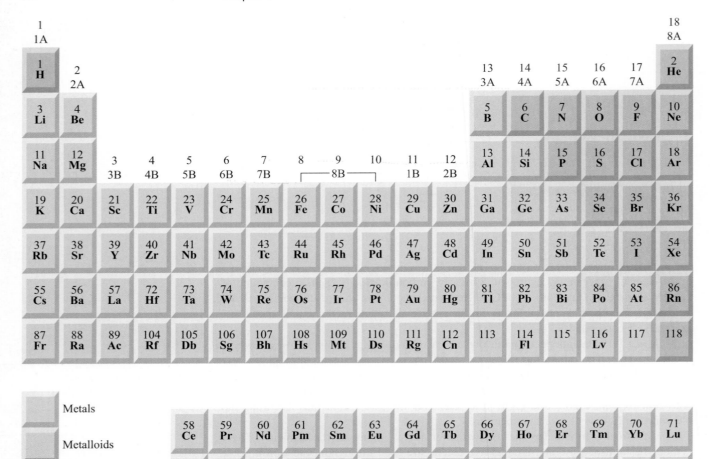

Figure 1.12

A simplified period table that shows the locations of metals, metalloids, and nonmetals.

Source: Raymond Chang, General Chemistry: The Essential Concepts, Third Edition. Copyright 2003 McGraw-Hill Education, New York, NY.

Note: The 1–18 group designation has been recommended by the International Union of Pure and Applied Chemistry (IUPAC) but is not yet in wide use. This text uses the standard U.S. notation for group numbers (1A–8A and 1B–8B).

Metals, nonmetals, and the ions they form are discussed in Section 5.6.

Semiconductors are explained in Section 8.7.

Figure 1.12 shows a simplified version of the periodic table that lists the elements by number but does not include their masses. The *light green* shading indicates the **metals,** elements that are shiny and conduct electricity and heat well. These include familiar substances such as iron, gold, and copper. Far fewer are the **nonmetals,** elements that do not conduct heat or electricity well and have no one characteristic appearance. These elements are indicated by the *light blue* shading and include sulfur, chlorine, and oxygen. A mere eight elements fall into a category known as **metalloids,** elements that lie between metals and nonmetals on the periodic table and do not fall cleanly into either category. Metalloids also are called semimetals and are indicated in *light gray* shading. The semiconductors silicon and germanium are examples of metalloids.

The elements fall into vertical columns called **groups.** These organize elements according to important properties that they have in common and are numbered from left to right. Some groups are given names as well. For example, a **halogen** is one of the reactive nonmetals in Group 7A, such as fluorine (F), chlorine (Cl), bromine (Br), or iodine (I). Similarly, a **noble gas** is one of the inert elements in Group 8A that undergoes few, if any, chemical reactions. We already mentioned argon, a noble gas that is a constituent of our atmosphere. You may recognize helium as the noble gas used to make balloons float, as it is less dense than air. Radon is the one noble gas that is radioactive, a characteristic that distinguishes it from the other elements in Group 8A.

Although only 100 or so elements exist, over 20 million compounds have been isolated, identified, and characterized. Some are very familiar naturally occurring substances such as water, table salt, and sucrose (table sugar). Many known compounds were chemically synthesized by men and women across our planet. You might be wondering how 20 million compounds could possibly be formed from so few elements. In short, elements have the ability to combine in many different ways.

For example, carbon dioxide is a chemical combination of the elements carbon and oxygen. All pure samples of carbon dioxide contain 27% carbon and 73% oxygen by mass. Thus, a 100-g sample of carbon dioxide always consists of 27 g of carbon and 73 g of oxygen, chemically combined to form this particular compound. These values never vary, no matter the source of the carbon dioxide. This illustrates the fact that every compound exhibits a constant characteristic chemical composition.

Carbon monoxide (CO) is a different compound of carbon and oxygen. Pure samples of carbon monoxide contain 43% carbon and 57% oxygen by mass. Thus, 100 g of carbon monoxide contain 43 g of carbon and 57 g of oxygen, a composition different from that of carbon dioxide. This is not surprising, because carbon monoxide and carbon dioxide are two different compounds.

As we will see, each compound has its own set of properties. For example, water (H_2O) is a compound that is 11% hydrogen and 89% oxygen by mass. At room temperature, water is a colorless, tasteless liquid. At sea level, it boils at 100 °C and freezes at 0 °C. All samples of pure water have these same properties. Water is composed of molecules, a term that we now have used several times. The next section will help you to use the terms atom and molecule with more confidence.

1.7 | Atoms and Molecules

The definitions we just gave for elements and compounds made no assumptions about the nature of matter. We now know that elements are made up of **atoms,** the smallest unit of an element that can exist as a stable, independent entity. The word *atom* comes from the Greek for "uncuttable." Although today it is possible to "cut" atoms using specialized processes, atoms remain indivisible by ordinary chemical or mechanical means.

Atoms are extremely small. Because they are so tiny, we need huge numbers of atoms in order to see, touch, or weigh them. For example, the molecules in a single drop of water contain about 5×10^{21} atoms. This is roughly a trillion times greater than the 7 billion people on Earth, almost enough to give each person a trillion atoms.

As Figure 1.13 reveals, atoms now can be photographed. Using a scanning tunneling microscope, scientists at the IBM Almaden Research Center lined up iron atoms on a copper surface to create the kanji (Japanese character) for "atom." **Nanotechnology** refers to the creation of materials at the atomic and molecular (nanometer) scale: 1 nanometer (nm) = 1×10^{-9} m. This kanji is a few nanometers high and wide. At this size, about 250 million nanoletters could fit on a cross section of a human hair, equivalent to about 90,000 pages of text!

Using the concept of atoms, we can better explain the terms *element* and *compound*. Elements are made up of only one kind of atom. For example, the element carbon is made up only of carbon atoms. By contrast, compounds are made up of two or more different kinds of atoms. For example, the compound carbon dioxide contains carbon and oxygen atoms. Similarly, water is made up of hydrogen and oxygen atoms.

But we need to be careful with our language. The carbon and oxygen atoms in carbon dioxide are *not* present as such. Rather, the carbon and oxygen atoms are chemically combined to form a carbon dioxide **molecule,** two or more atoms held together by chemical bonds in a certain spatial arrangement. More specifically, two oxygen atoms (*red*) are combined with one carbon atom (*black*) to form a carbon dioxide

Radon affects the quality of indoor air, as we will see in Section 1.13. Chapter 7 tells more about other radioactive substances.

A small paper clip weighs about a gram.

Water is not tasteless if it contains dissolved gases or minerals. Look for more about water as a solvent in Chapter 5. As we will see, water is rarely "pure."

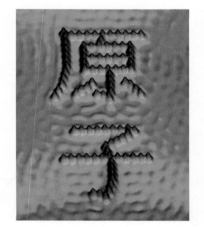

Figure 1.13

Iron atoms arranged on a copper surface, as imaged with a scanning tunneling microscope. This is the Japanese kanji for the word *genshi* (atom).

Section 3.3 explains why these two
molecules have different shapes.

Atoms are color-coded:

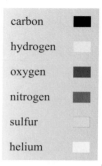

carbon	■
hydrogen	□
oxygen	■
nitrogen	■
sulfur	□
helium	□

molecule. Similarly, the water molecule contains two hydrogen atoms (*white*) combined with one oxygen atom (*red*).

water molecule   carbon dioxide molecule

A chemical formula is a symbolic way to represent the elementary composition of a substance. It reveals both the elements present (by chemical symbols) and the atom ratio of those elements (by the subscripts). For example, in the compound CO_2, the elements C and O are present in a ratio of one carbon atom for every two oxygen atoms. Similarly, H_2O indicates two hydrogen atoms for each oxygen atom. Note that when an atom occurs only once, such as the O in H_2O or the C in CO_2, the subscript of "1" is omitted.

Some elements exist as single atoms, such as helium or radon. We represent these as He and Rn, respectively. Other elements exist as molecules. For example, nitrogen and oxygen are found in our atmosphere as N_2 and O_2 molecules. Each is a **diatomic molecule,** meaning that it is a molecule consisting of two atoms. These representations clearly show the difference.

oxygen molecule   nitrogen molecule   helium atom

Table 1.5 summarizes our discussion of elements, compounds, and mixtures, listing both what we can observe experimentally and what exists at the atomic level that we cannot see.

We now apply these concepts to the mixture we call air. Some of its components, such as nitrogen, oxygen, and argon, are elements. Others, most notably water vapor and carbon dioxide, are compounds. All of the compounds discussed so far consist of molecules (e.g., CO_2 and H_2O). But with the elements, it is not so simple. In the troposphere, the elements nitrogen and oxygen exist primarily as diatomic molecules (N_2 and O_2). In contrast, elements such as argon and helium exist as uncombined atoms.

Dry air is composed mainly of nitrogen and oxygen, that is, *molecules* of N_2 and O_2. If the air is humid, add in some water vapor in the form of H_2O *molecules*. Dry air contains just under 1% of Ar (argon) *atoms*, as well as tiny amounts of He (helium) *atoms*, Xe (xenon) *atoms*, and extremely small amounts of Rn (radon) *atoms*. Remember also to include the concentration of carbon dioxide, that is, 400 ppm or 400 CO_2 *molecules* per 1×10^6 of the *molecules and atoms* in the air as of 2013.

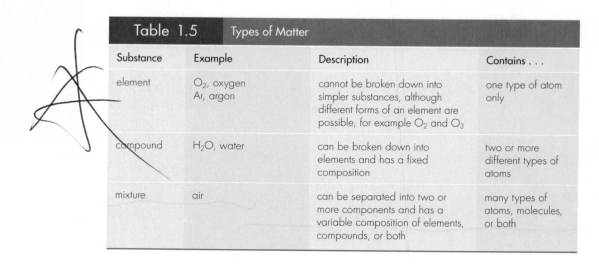

Table 1.5	Types of Matter		
Substance	Example	Description	Contains . . .
element	O_2, oxygen Ar, argon	cannot be broken down into simpler substances, although different forms of an element are possible, for example O_2 and O_3	one type of atom only
compound	H_2O, water	can be broken down into elements and has a fixed composition	two or more different types of atoms
mixture	air	can be separated into two or more components and has a variable composition of elements, compounds, or both	many types of atoms, molecules, or both

---

Skeptical Chemist 1.12   The Chemistry of Lawn Care

News reports and advertisements should be viewed with a critical eye for their accuracy. For example, a lawn care service ad reports its fertilizers as "a balanced blend of nitrogen, phosphorus, and potassium. They have an organic nature, made up of carbon molecules. These fertilizers are biodegradable and turn into water." Edit the text of this ad to fix the chemical glitches.

1.8 | Names and Formulas: The Vocabulary of Chemistry

If chemical symbols are the alphabet of chemistry, then chemical formulas are the words. The language of chemistry, like any other language, has rules of spelling and syntax. In this section we help you to "speak chemistry" using chemical formulas and names. As you'll see, each name corresponds uniquely to one chemical formula. However, chemical formulas are *not* unique and may correspond to more than one name. In addition, some compounds are known by several names.

In this section, we follow a need-to-know philosophy. We help you learn what you *need to know* to understand the topic at hand and omit other naming rules until the need arises. Right now, you need to know the chemical names and formulas of compounds that relate to the air you breathe. So, for now, we work on these.

We already named some of the pure substances found in air, including carbon monoxide, carbon dioxide, sulfur dioxide, ozone, water vapor, and nitrogen dioxide. Although it may not be apparent, this list includes two types of names: systematic and common.

Systematic names for compounds follow a reasonably straightforward set of rules. Here are the rules for compounds composed of two nonmetals, such as carbon dioxide (CO_2) and carbon monoxide (CO):

- Name each element in the chemical formula, modifying the name of the second element to end in *-ide*. For example, oxygen becomes oxide, and sulfur becomes sulfide.
- Use prefixes to indicate the numbers of atoms in the chemical formula (Table 1.6). For example, *di-* means 2, and thus the name carbon *di*oxide means two oxygen atoms for each one carbon atom.
- Omit the prefix *mono-* if there is only one atom for the first element in the chemical formula. For example, CO is carbon monoxide, not monocarbon monoxide.

If instead you are writing a chemical formula from a name, keep in mind that the subscript of 1 is not used in chemical formulas. Thus the chemical formula for carbon dioxide is CO_2 and *not* C_1O_2. Similarly, carbon monoxide is CO and *not* C_1O_1. The next activity gives you a chance to practice.

Section 5.7 explains another set of naming rules, those for ionic compounds.

Remember that ozone, O_3, is an element, not a compound.

Table 1.6	Prefixes Used in Naming Compounds		
Prefix	Meaning	Prefix	Meaning
mono-	1	hexa-	6
di- or bi-	2	hepta-	7
tri-	3	octa-	8
tetra-	4	nona-	9
penta-	5	deca-	10

Your Turn 1.13   Oxides of Sulfur and Nitrogen

a. Write chemical formulas for nitrogen monoxide, nitrogen dioxide, dinitrogen monoxide, and dinitrogen tetraoxide.
b. Give chemical names for SO_2 and SO_3.

Answer

a. NO, NO_2, N_2O, and N_2O_4. *Note:* NO and N_2O also are called nitric oxide and nitrous oxide.

Some names ("common names") do not follow a set of rules. Water is one example. You might have expected H_2O to be called dihydrogen monoxide. This makes sense! But water was given its name long before anybody knew anything about hydrogen and oxygen. Chemists, being reasonable folks, did not rename water. Rather, they call the stuff they swim in and drink by the common name water, just like everybody else. Ozone (O_3) is another common name, as is ammonia (NH_3). Common names cannot be figured out; you have to know them or look them up.

In the next two sections, we explore the connection between air quality and the fuels we burn. Following our need-to-know philosophy, we need to introduce the names of several **hydrocarbons,** that is, compounds made up only of the elements hydrogen and carbon. Hydrocarbons follow a very different set of naming rules from the ones just presented.

Methane (CH_4) is the smallest hydrocarbon. Other small hydrocarbons include ethane, propane, and butane. Although methane may not appear to be a systematic name, it indeed is one if you are willing to accept that *meth-* means 1 carbon atom. Similarly, *eth-* means 2 carbon atoms, and C_2H_6 is ethane. *Prop-* means 3 carbon atoms, and *but-* means 4. So propane is C_3H_8, and butane is C_4H_{10}. Just as *mono-, di-, tri-,* and *tetra-* are used to count, so are *meth-, eth-, prop-,* and *but-*. In Chapter 4, we will explain the suffix *-ane* as well as explain the different numbers of C atoms and H atoms in the chemical formulas.

These new prefixes are very versatile. They can be used not only at the beginning of chemical names, but also within them.

Prefixes in hydrocarbon names

meth-	1 C atom
eth-	2 C atoms
prop-	3 C atoms
but-	4 C atoms

Look for more about hydrocarbons in Section 4.4.

Your Turn 1.14   Mother Eats Peanut Butter

Many generations of students have used the memory aid "<u>m</u>other <u>e</u>ats <u>p</u>eanut <u>b</u>utter" for *meth-, eth-, prop-, but-*. Use this or another memory aid of your choice to tell how many carbon atoms are in each of these compounds.

a. ethanol (a gasoline additive)
b. methylene chloride (a component of paint strippers and sometimes an indoor air pollutant)
c. propane (the major component in LPG, liquid petroleum gas)

Answer

b. The *meth-* in methylene indicates 1 C atom in the chemical formula.

As we'll see, hydrocarbon molecules can contain over 50 carbon atoms! For the smaller molecules, use the prefixes shown in Table 1.6 or in the above margin note. For example, the octane molecule contains 8 carbon atoms.

That's it for names and chemical formulas, at least for now. In the next section, we put this chemical vocabulary to work.

1.9 | Chemical Change: The Role of Oxygen in Burning

Life on Earth bears the stamp of oxygen. Compounds containing oxygen occur in the atmosphere, in your body, and in the rocks and soils of the planet. Why? The answer is that many different elements combine chemically with oxygen. One such element is carbon. You were already introduced to the compound carbon monoxide, CO, a pollutant listed in Table 1.2. Fortunately, CO is relatively rare in our atmosphere. In contrast, carbon dioxide, CO_2, is far more abundant, but still only about 400 ppm. Even so, at this concentration CO_2 plays an important role as a greenhouse gas. In this section, we explain how both CO_2 and CO are emitted into our atmosphere.

As you know, humans exhale CO_2 with each breath. Breathing is one natural source of CO_2 in our atmosphere. Carbon dioxide also is produced when humans burn fuels. **Combustion** is the chemical process of burning, that is, the rapid reaction of fuel with oxygen to release energy in the form of heat and light. When carbon-containing compounds burn, the carbon combines with oxygen to produce carbon dioxide (CO_2). When the oxygen supply is limited, carbon monoxide (CO) is likely to form as well.

Combustion is a major type of **chemical reaction,** a process whereby substances described as reactants are transformed into different substances called products. A **chemical equation** is a representation of a chemical reaction using chemical formulas. To students, a chemical equation is probably better known as "the thing with an arrow in it." Chemical equations are the sentences in the language of chemistry. They are made up of chemical symbols (corresponding to letters) that often are combined in the formulas of compounds (the words of chemistry). Like a sentence, a chemical equation conveys information, in this case about the chemical change taking place. A chemical equation also must obey some of the same constraints that apply to a mathematical equation.

At the most fundamental level, a chemical equation is a qualitative description of this process:

$$\text{reactant(s)} \longrightarrow \text{product(s)}$$

By convention, the reactants are always written on the left and the products on the right. The arrow represents a chemical transformation and can be read as "is converted to."

The combustion of carbon (charcoal) to produce carbon dioxide as shown in Figure 1.14 can be represented in several ways. One is with chemical names.

$$\text{carbon} + \text{oxygen} \longrightarrow \text{carbon dioxide}$$

Another more common way is to use chemical formulas.

$$C + O_2 \longrightarrow CO_2 \qquad \text{[1.1]}$$

This compact symbolic statement conveys a good deal of information. It might sound something like this: "One atom of the element carbon reacts with one molecule of the element oxygen to yield one molecule of the compound carbon dioxide." Using black for carbon and red for oxygen, we also can represent the molecules and atoms involved.

These equations are similar to a mathematical expression in that the number and kind of atom on the left side of the arrow *must* equal the number and kind of each atom on the right:

$$\text{Left side: 1 C and 2 O} \longrightarrow \text{Right side: 1 C and 2 O}$$

Atoms are neither created nor destroyed in a chemical reaction. The elements present do not change their identities when converted from reactants to products, although they may be bonded in different ways. This relationship is known as the **law of conservation of matter and mass:** In a chemical reaction, matter and mass are conserved. The mass of the reactants consumed equals the mass of the products formed.

The concentration of CO_2 in the atmosphere is increasing, as we will explain in Chapter 3.

See Section 4.1 for more about combustion.

Figure 1.14
Charcoal burns in air.

The colors displayed here for atoms reflect the standard used in molecular modeling software and many model kits.

Here is an analogy. The building materials used to construct a warehouse (reactants) can be disassembled and rearranged to build three houses and a garage (products).

Let's look at another example. Using yellow for sulfur, we can represent how sulfur burns in oxygen to produce the air pollutant sulfur dioxide.

$$S + O_2 \longrightarrow SO_2 \qquad \text{[1.2]}$$

This equation is balanced: the same number and types of atoms are present on each side of the arrow. These atoms, however, were rearranged. This is what a chemical reaction is all about!

It is possible to pack even more information into a chemical equation by specifying the physical states of the reactants and products. A solid is designated by *(s)*, a liquid by *(l)*, and a gas by *(g)*. Because carbon and sulfur are solids, and oxygen, carbon dioxide, and sulfur dioxide are gases at ordinary temperatures and pressures, equations 1.1 and 1.2 become

$$C(s) + O_2(g) \longrightarrow CO_2(g)$$

$$S(s) + O_2(g) \longrightarrow SO_2(g)$$

We designate the physical states when this information is particularly important, but otherwise for simplicity we will omit them.

In a correctly balanced chemical equation, some things must be equal, others need not be. Table 1.7 summarizes our discussion so far.

Equation 1.1 describes the combustion of pure carbon in an ample supply of oxygen. But this is not always the case. If the oxygen supply is limited, CO may be one of the products. Let's take the extreme case in which carbon monoxide is the sole product.

$$C + O_2 \longrightarrow CO \text{ (unbalanced equation)}$$

This equation is not balanced because there are 2 oxygen atoms on the left but only 1 on the right. You might be tempted to balance the equation by simply adding an additional oxygen atom to the right side. But once we write the *correct* chemical formulas for the reactants and products, we cannot change them. We use whole-number coefficients (or occasionally fractional ones) in front of the given chemical formulas. In simple cases like this, the coefficients can be found by trial and error. If we place a 2 in front of CO, it signifies two molecules of carbon monoxide. This balances the oxygen atoms.

A subscript follows a chemical symbol, as in O_2 or CO_2. A coefficient precedes a symbol or a formula, as in 2 C or 2 CO.

$$C + O_2 \longrightarrow 2\,CO \text{ (still not balanced)}$$

But now the carbon atoms do not balance. Fortunately, this is easily corrected by placing a 2 in front of the C on the left side of the equation.

$$2\,C + O_2 \longrightarrow 2\,CO \text{ (balanced equation)} \qquad \text{[1.3]}$$

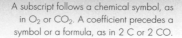

Table 1.7	Characteristics of Chemical Equations

Always Conserved

identity of atoms in reactants = identity of atoms in products

number of atoms of each element in reactants = number of atoms of each element in products

mass of all reactants = mass of all products

May Change

number of molecules in reactants may differ from the number in products

physical states (s, l, or g) of reactants may differ from those of products

By comparing equations 1.1 and 1.3, you can see that more O_2 is required to produce CO_2 from carbon than is needed to produce CO. This matches the conditions we stated for the formation of carbon monoxide; namely, that the supply of oxygen was limited.

You may be surprised to learn the origin of the air pollutant nitrogen monoxide (also called nitric oxide). It comes from the nitrogen and oxygen found in the air! These two gases chemically combine in the presence of something very hot, such as an automobile engine or a forest fire.

$$N_2 + O_2 \xrightarrow{\text{high temperature}} NO \text{ (unbalanced equation)}$$

The equation is not balanced, as 2 oxygen atoms are on the left side, but only 1 is on the right. The same is true for nitrogen atoms. Placing a 2 in front of NO supplies 2 N and 2 O atoms on the right. The equation is now balanced.

$$N_2 + O_2 \xrightarrow{\text{high temperature}} 2\,NO \qquad \textbf{[1.4]}$$

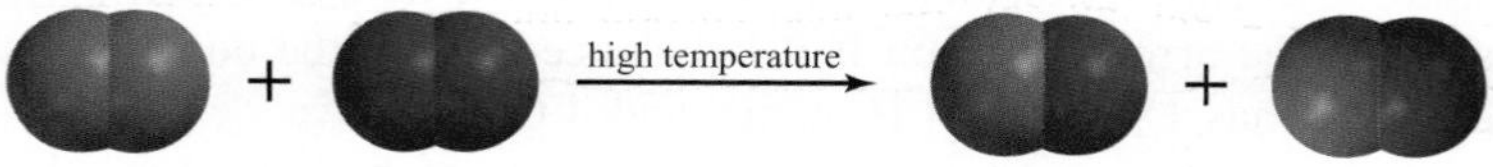

Nitrogen and oxygen both are diatomic molecules.

Your Turn 1.15　Chemical Equations

Balance these chemical equations and draw representations of all reactants and products, analogous to equation 1.4. In H_2O and NO_2, O and N are the central atoms, respectively.

a. $H_2 + O_2 \longrightarrow H_2O$
b. $N_2 + O_2 \longrightarrow NO_2$

Note: Both H_2O and NO_2 are bent molecules. We will explain why in Chapter 3.

Answer

a. $2\,H_2 + O_2 \longrightarrow 2\,H_2O$

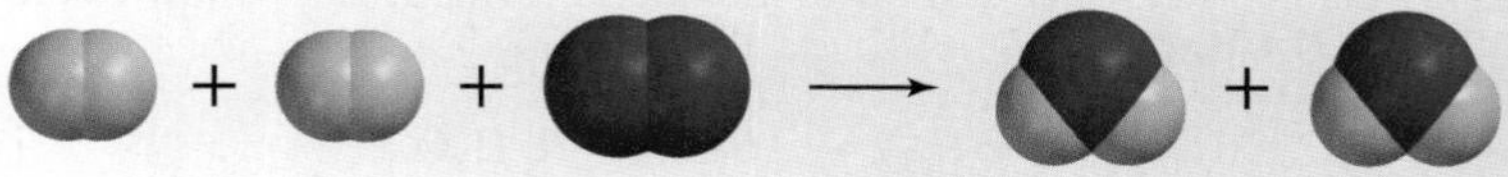

Consider This 1.16　Advice from Grandma

A grandmother offered this advice to rid the garden of pesky caterpillars. "Hammer some iron nails about a foot up from the base of your trees, spacing them every 3 to 5 inches." According to this grandmother, the iron nails convert the sugary tree sap (a compound containing the elements carbon, hydrogen, and oxygen) into ammonia (NH_3), a substance the caterpillars cannot stand. Comment on the accuracy of grandma's chemistry (allowing for the possibility that the nails may still work, regardless of her explanation).

1.10 | Fire and Fuel: Air Quality and Burning Hydrocarbons

As we mentioned earlier, hydrocarbons are compounds of hydrogen and carbon. The hydrocarbons that we use today are primarily obtained from crude oil. Methane (CH_4), the simplest hydrocarbon, is the primary component of natural gas. Both gasoline and kerosene are mixtures of many hydrocarbons.

Given an ample supply of oxygen, hydrocarbon fuels burn completely. You may hear this called "complete combustion." In essence, all of the carbon atoms in the hydrocarbon molecule combine with O_2 molecules from the air to form CO_2. Similarly, all the hydrogen atoms combine with O_2 to form H_2O. For example, here is the chemical

Look for other examples of burning fuels throughout Chapter 4.

equation for the complete combustion of methane. This equation is your first peek at why burning carbon-based fuels releases carbon dioxide into the atmosphere.

$$CH_4 + O_2 \longrightarrow CO_2 + H_2O \text{ (unbalanced equation)}$$

Note that O appears in *both* products: CO_2 and H_2O. To balance it, start with an element that appears in *only one substance* on each side of the arrow. In this case, both H and C qualify. No coefficients need to be changed for carbon, because both sides contain one C atom. Balance the H atoms by placing a 2 in front of the H_2O.

$$CH_4 + O_2 \longrightarrow CO_2 + 2\,H_2O \text{ (still not balanced)}$$

Balance the oxygen atoms last. Four O atoms are on the right side and two O atoms are on the left, so we need $2\,O_2$ to balance the equation.

$$CH_4 + 2\,O_2 \longrightarrow CO_2 + 2\,H_2O \text{ (balanced equation)} \qquad \textbf{[1.5]}$$

A nice feature of chemical equations is that counting the number of each type of atom on both sides of the arrow tells you if it is balanced. Here, the equation is balanced because each side has 1 C atom, 4 H atoms, and 4 O atoms.

Most automobiles run on the complex mixture of hydrocarbons that we call gasoline. Octane, C_8H_{18}, is one of the pure substances in this mixture. With sufficient oxygen, octane burns to form carbon dioxide and water.

$$2\,C_8H_{18} + 25\,O_2 \longrightarrow 16\,CO_2 + 18\,H_2O \qquad \textbf{[1.6]}$$

Both products travel from the engine out the exhaust pipe and into the air. Are these combustion products visible? Usually not. Water, in the form of water vapor, and carbon dioxide are both colorless gases. But if you happen to be outside on a winter day, the water vapor condenses to form clouds of steam or tiny ice crystals that you can see. Occasionally, the frozen vapor gets trapped in an inversion layer and forms an ice fog (Figure 1.15).

With less oxygen, the hydrocarbon mixture we call gasoline burns incompletely ("incomplete combustion"). Water is still produced together with both CO_2 and CO. The extreme case occurs when only carbon monoxide is formed, as is shown here for the incomplete combustion of octane.

$$2\,C_8H_{18} + 17\,O_2 \longrightarrow 16\,CO + 18\,H_2O \qquad \textbf{[1.7]}$$

Figure 1.15

A winter ice fog in Fairbanks, Alaska.

Compare the coefficient of 17 for O_2 in equation 1.7 with that of 25 for O_2 in equation 1.6. Less oxygen is needed for incomplete combustion, as CO contains less oxygen than CO_2.

Your Turn 1.17   Balancing Equations

Demonstrate that equations 1.6 and 1.7 are balanced by counting the number of atoms of each element on both sides of the arrow.

Answer

Equation 1.6 contains 16 C, 36 H, and 50 O on each side.

What is the actual mixture of products formed when gasoline is burned in your car? This is not a simple question, as the products vary with the fuel, the engine, and its operating conditions. It is safe to say that gasoline burns primarily to form H_2O and CO_2. However, some CO and soot also are produced. The amounts of soot, CO, and CO_2 that go out the tailpipe indicate how efficiently the car burns the fuel, which in turn indicates how well the engine is tuned. Some regions of the United States monitor auto emissions with a probe that detects CO (Figure 1.16). The CO concentrations

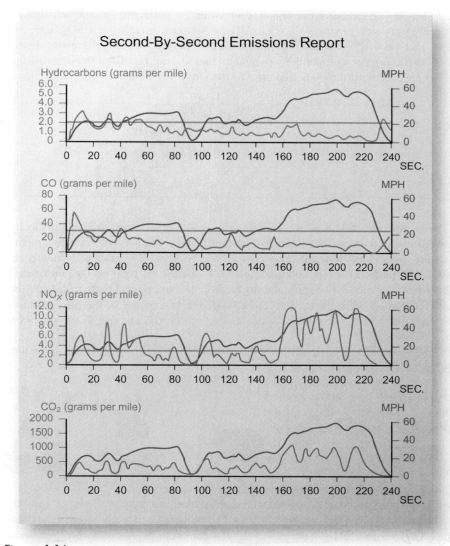

CO_2 emissions are measured but not yet regulated. Look for more about CO_2 emissions in Chapter 3.

Figure 1.16

A U.S. auto emissions report. The blue line shows the change in engine speed; the red line shows the change in emissions. Any emissions below the green line are in the acceptable range.

in the exhaust are compared with established standards, for example, 1.20% in the state of Minnesota. If the vehicle fails the emissions test, it must be serviced.

Consider This 1.18   Auto Emissions Report

a. Figure 1.16 reports NO_x emissions in grams per mile. NO_x is a way to collectively represent the oxides of nitrogen. If $x = 1$ and $x = 2$, write the corresponding chemical formulas. Also give the chemical names.
b. NO is the primary oxide of nitrogen emitted. What is the source of this compound? *Hint:* Revisit equation 1.4.
c. The green line is missing on the CO_2 graph, but present on the others. Explain.

Answers

a. NO, nitrogen monoxide and NO_2, nitrogen dioxide
c. In the year that this graph was produced, CO_2 was not classified as an air pollutant in the United States. Accordingly, it has no green line indicating an acceptable range.

1.11 | Air Pollutants: Direct Sources

In this section, we examine two major sources of air pollutants: motor vehicles and coal-fired plants that generate electricity. These sources directly emit SO_2, CO, NO, and PM, and we will revisit each of these pollutants in turn. We also digress to discuss VOCs (volatile organic compounds), pollutants that are not regulated but are still intimately connected with the ones that are. We tackle ozone in the section that follows.

Your Turn 1.19   Tailpipe Gases

What comes out of the tailpipe of an automobile? Start your list now and build it as you work through this section.
Hint: Some of the air that enters the engine also comes out the tailpipe.

See Section 4.3 for more about coal and its chemical composition.

Sulfur dioxide emissions are linked to the coal that is burned to generate electric power. Although coal consists mostly of carbon, it may contain 1–3% sulfur together with small amounts of minerals. The sulfur burns to form SO_2, and the minerals end up as fine ash particles. If not contained, the SO_2 and ash go right up the smokestack. The hundreds of millions of tons of coal burned in the United States translates into millions of tons of waste in the air. As we will see in Chapter 6, the SO_2 produced by burning coal can dissolve in the water droplets of clouds and fall to the ground as acid rain.

The story does not end with SO_2. Once in the air, sulfur dioxide can react with oxygen to form sulfur trioxide, SO_3.

$$2\,SO_2 + O_2 \longrightarrow 2\,SO_3 \qquad\qquad [1.8]$$

Although normally quite slow, this reaction is faster in the presence of small ash particles. The particles also aid another process. If the humidity is high enough, they help condense water vapor into an aerosol of tiny water droplets. **Aerosols** are liquid and solid particles that remain suspended in the air rather than settling out. Smoke, such as from a campfire or a cigarette, is a familiar aerosol made up of tiny particles of solids and liquids.

The aerosol of concern here is made up of tiny droplets of sulfuric acid, H_2SO_4. It forms because sulfur trioxide dissolves readily in water droplets to produce sulfuric acid.

Section 6.12 describes how sulfuric acid aerosols contribute to haze.

$$H_2O + SO_3 \longrightarrow H_2SO_4 \qquad \qquad \textbf{[1.9]}$$

If inhaled, the droplets of the sulfuric acid aerosol are small enough to become trapped in the lung tissue and cause severe damage.

The good news? Sulfur dioxide emissions in the United States are declining (see Figure 1.8). For example, in 1985, approximately 20 million tons of SO_2 was emitted from the burning of coal. Today the value is closer to 9 million tons. This impressive decrease can be credited to the Clean Air Act of 1970 that mandated many reductions, including those from coal-fired electric power plants. More stringent regulations were established in the Clean Air Act Amendments and the Pollution Prevention Act of 1990. For example, gasoline and diesel fuel both once contained small amounts of sulfur, but the allowable amounts were drastically lowered in 1993 and in 2006, respectively. But continued progress has a price tag. Cleaning up the smaller older and dirty power plants will not come cheaply. Then again, allowing emissions to continue is costly in terms of human and environmental health.

Look for more about the economic and societal costs of atmospheric SO_2 in Chapter 6.

Your Turn 1.20 SO_2 from the Mining Industry

Burning coal is not the only source of sulfur dioxide. As you saw in Your Turn 1.8, smelting is another. For example, silver and copper metal can be produced from their sulfide ores. Write the balanced chemical equations.

a. Silver sulfide (Ag_2S) is heated in air to produce silver and sulfur dioxide.
b. Copper sulfide (CuS) is heated in air to produce copper and sulfur dioxide.

Answer
a. $Ag_2S + O_2 \longrightarrow 2\,Ag + SO_2$

With more than 250 million vehicles (and over 300 million people), the United States has more vehicles per capita than any other nation. Do these vehicles emit sulfur dioxide? Fortunately, the answer is no, because cars have internal combustion engines primarily fueled by gasoline. We already mentioned that the combustion of hydrocarbons in gasoline produces—at best—carbon dioxide and water vapor (see equation 1.6). Because gasoline contains little or no sulfur, burning it produces little or no sulfur dioxide. Nonetheless, each tailpipe puffs out its share of air pollutants. The ubiquitous automobile adds to the atmospheric concentrations of carbon monoxide, volatile organic compounds, nitrogen oxides, and particulate matter. We discuss each of these in turn.

Carbon monoxide pollution comes primarily from automobiles. But think in terms of *all* the tailpipes out there, not just those attached to cars. Some are attached to heavy trucks, SUVs, and the three m's: motorcycles, minibikes, and mopeds. Others are on equipment such as farm tractors, bulldozers, and motor boats. The tailpipes attached to *all* gasoline and diesel engines emit carbon monoxide.

Your Turn 1.21   Other Tailpipes

Visit "Nonroad Engines, Equipment, and Vehicles" on the EPA's website to answer the following:

a. The text mentioned tractors, bulldozers, and boats. Name five other engine–powered machines or vehicles that do not run on roads.
b. Select a machine or vehicle of interest to you. How are emissions from its engine being reduced? What is the time scale for the reduction?

Even though the number of cars has risen, a dramatic reduction in CO emissions has occurred. Based on measurements by the EPA at over 250 sites in the United States, since 1980 the average CO concentration has decreased almost 60% (see Figure 1.8).

Wildfires contribute additional CO, increasing emissions as much as 10% each year.

If wildfires are excluded, today's levels are the lowest reported in three decades. The decrease is due to several factors, including improved engine design, computerized sensors that better adjust the fuel–oxygen mixture, and most importantly, the requirement that all cars manufactured since the mid-1970s have catalytic converters (Figure 1.17). Catalytic converters reduce the amount of carbon monoxide in the exhaust stream by catalyzing the combustion of CO to CO_2. They also lower NO_x emissions by catalyzing the conversion of nitrogen oxides back to N_2 and O_2, the two atmospheric gases that formed them. In general, a **catalyst** is a chemical substance that participates in a chemical reaction and influences its rate without itself undergoing permanent change. Catalytic converters typically use metals such as platinum and rhodium as catalysts.

Look for more about organic compounds in Chapter 4.

Cars not only emit carbon in the form of carbon monoxide but also in the form of unburned and partially burned hydrocarbons. This leads us to the topic of VOCs, volatile organic compounds. A **volatile** substance readily passes into the vapor phase, that is, it evaporates easily. Gasoline and nail polish remover are both volatile. If you were to spill either of these, the puddle would soon evaporate. When you apply varnish to a surface, you can smell the volatile compounds that evaporate with each brush stroke. An **organic compound** always contains carbon, almost always contains hydrogen, and may contain other elements such as oxygen and nitrogen. Organic compounds include methane and octane, hydrocarbons mentioned earlier. They also include alcohol and sugar, compounds that contain oxygen in addition to carbon and hydrogen.

Accordingly, **volatile organic compounds (VOCs)** are carbon-containing compounds that pass easily into the vapor phase. They originate from a variety of sources. For example, you can smell naturally occurring VOCs in a spruce or pine forest. VOCs from tailpipes are not so pleasant, as they are vapors of incompletely burned gasoline molecules or fragments of these molecules. The exhaust gas still contains oxygen, as not all of it is consumed in the engine. Catalytic converters utilize this oxygen to burn VOCs to form carbon dioxide and water. Section 1.12 describes the connection between VOCs and ozone formation. But right now, we want to connect VOCs with the formation of NO_2.

Nitrogen monoxide and nitrogen dioxide are collectively known as NO_x, as mentioned in Consider This 1.18. NO_2 is brown in color, giving smog its characteristic brownish tinge. Recall that N_2 and O_2 combine to produce NO which is a colorless gas (see equation 1.4). But what is the origin of NO_2? Here is a balanced equation that appears to be a likely candidate.

$$2\,NO + O_2 \longrightarrow 2\,NO_2 \qquad\qquad \textbf{[1.10]}$$

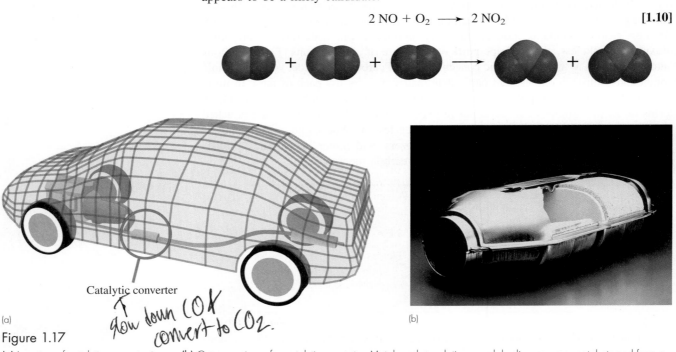

Catalytic converter

slow down CO & convert to CO_2.

(a)

(b)

Figure 1.17

(a) Location of catalytic converter in car. (b) Cutaway view of a catalytic converter. Metals such as platinum and rhodium serve as catalysts and form a coating on the surface of ceramic beads.

However, this is not what actually occurs. Instead, NO_2 is formed by other pathways that are more complex. Here is the one that predominates in urban settings where you are likely to find NO. In some cities, this actually lowers the ozone concentrations along highways congested with vehicles emitting NO.

$$NO + O_3 \longrightarrow NO_2 + O_2 \qquad\qquad \text{[1.11]}$$

To further complicate things, on a sunny day, some of the NO_2 converts back into NO, as we will see in the next section. Again, this is why people refer to NO_x, rather than to either NO or NO_2.

The conversion of NO to NO_2 connects to the breakdown of VOCs in the air. A new player is involved, the reactive hydroxyl radical ·OH. This reactive species is present in tiny amounts in air, polluted or otherwise.

$$VOC + \cdot OH \longrightarrow A$$
$$A + O_2 \longrightarrow A'$$
$$A' + NO \longrightarrow A'' + NO_2 \qquad\qquad \text{[1.12]}$$

Here, A, A′, and A″ represent reactive molecules that can form in the air from ·OH and VOCs. The bottom line? Atmospheric chemistry is complex and involves many players. You have met some of them, including NO, NO_2, O_2, O_3, VOCs, and ·OH.

The United States has had limited success in curbing NO_x emissions. In turn, as we'll see in the next section, this means limited success in curbing ozone. Nonetheless, given the increasing number of vehicles, *any* decrease in NO_x is impressive. Despite early claims from the auto industry that it would be impossible (or too costly) to meet new emissions standards, the industry is curbing emissions by improving catalytic converters, engine designs, and gasoline formulations.

> ## Consider This 1.22   Forget Road Rage
>
> Burning less gasoline equates to fewer tailpipe emissions. Which driving practices conserve fuel? Which practices expend it more than necessary? Think about the behavior of motorists on highways, city streets, and in parking lots. For each of these venues, list at least three ways that drivers could burn less gasoline.
>
> *Hint:* Consider how you accelerate, coast, idle, brake, and park.
>
> *Answer*
> Some possibilities relate to parking. For example, if you are able–bodied, take a spot farther away and walk, rather than cruising around to find a closer spot. Find a parking space that you can pull through. This way, when you exit you don't need to back and turn, thus conserving fuel.

Particulate matter comes in a range of sizes, but only the tiny particles (PM_{10} and $PM_{2.5}$) are regulated as pollutants. Particles of this size can penetrate deeply into your lungs, pass into your bloodstream, and inflame your cardiovascular system. In terms of regulation, particles are the new pollutant on the block. Data collection in the United States for PM_{10} and $PM_{2.5}$ started in 1990 and 1999, respectively (see Figure 1.8). In 2006, the daily air quality standard for $PM_{2.5}$ was lowered from 65 to 35 µg/m^3 because these particles proved to be more hazardous than originally thought.

Particulate matter has many different sources. In the summer, wildfires may raise the concentration of particulate matter to a hazardous level. In the winter, wood stoves may produce exactly the same effect. At any time of the year in almost any urban environment, older diesel engines on trucks and buses emit clouds of black smoke. Diesel engines on tractors similarly can pollute. Construction sites, mining operations, and the unpaved roads that serve them also loft tiny particles of dust and dirt into the atmosphere. Particulate matter can even form right in the atmosphere. For example, the compound ammonia, used in agriculture, is a major player in forming ammonium sulfate and ammonium nitrate in the air, both $PM_{2.5}$.

The dot in ·OH indicates an unpaired electron. In Chapter 2, you will encounter other reactive species with unpaired electrons.

Chapter 8 discusses alternatives to gasoline-powered vehicles.

A 2012 study of the National Cancer Institute showed that underground miners exposed to diesel fumes have an increased risk of developing lung cancer.

Ammonia (NH_3) is a colorless gas with a pungent odor. It is condensed to the liquid phase and applied to soil as a fertilizer. Look for more about ammonia in Chapter 6.

Given all these sources, particulate matter has proven a tough pollutant to control. Even so, in 2010 the EPA reported a decrease of 27% in the annual $PM_{2.5}$ concentrations from 2000 to 2010. However, 10% of the sites monitored still showed an increase in particle pollution. Again, what you breathe very much depends on where you live.

Consider This 1.23   Particles Where You Live

Here is a map of the continental U.S. that shows $PM_{2.5}$ data for December 8, 2011.

a. In terms of air quality, what do the green, yellow, and orange colors indicate?
b. Which groups of people are most sensitive to particulate matter?
c. Visit *State of the Air,* a website posted by the American Lung Association. How many days a year does your state have "orange days" and "red days" for particle pollution? What is the difference?

Source: AIRNow.gov

1.12 | Ozone: A Secondary Pollutant

Ozone definitely is a bad actor in the troposphere. Even at very low concentrations, it reduces lung function in healthy people who are exercising outdoors. Ozone also damages crops and the leaves of trees. But ozone does *not* come out of a tailpipe and is *not* produced when coal is burned. How is it produced? Before we fill you in on the details, do this activity.

> Today, background tropospheric levels for ozone are about 40 parts per billion (ppb). In pre-industrial times, the level was about 10 ppb.

Consider This 1.24   Ozone Around the Clock

Ozone concentrations vary during the day, as shown in Figure 1.18.
a. Near which cities is the air hazardous to one or more groups?
   Hint: Refer back to the color-coded AQI (see Table 1.4).
b. At about what time does the ozone level peak?
c. Can moderate levels (shown in yellow) of ozone exist in the absence of sunlight? Assume sunrise occurs around 6 AM and sunset at about 8 PM.

Answer
c. In the absence of sunlight, ozone does not persist for long. After sundown, the ozone levels drop.

The previous activity raises several related questions. Why is ozone more prevalent in some areas than others? What role does sunlight play in ozone production? We now address these.

Unlike the pollutants described in Section 1.11, ozone is a **secondary pollutant.** It is produced from chemical reactions involving one or more other pollutants. For ozone, these other pollutants are VOCs and NO_2. Recall from Section 1.11 that NO, rather than NO_2, comes directly out of a tailpipe (or a smokestack). But over time and in the presence of VOCs and ·OH, NO in the atmosphere is converted to NO_2.

> Recall from Section 1.11 that ·OH is the hydroxyl radical.

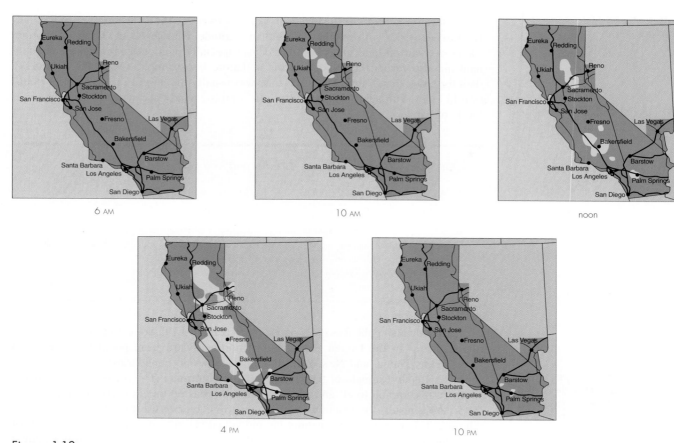

Figure 1.18

Air Quality Index (AQI) maps for ozone pollution on a summer day in July 2006 in California. See Table 1.4 for the AQI color code.

Nitrogen dioxide meets several fates in the atmosphere. The one of most interest to us occurs when the Sun is high in the sky. The energy provided by sunlight splits one of the bonds in the NO_2 molecule:

$$NO_2 \xrightarrow{\text{sunlight}} NO + O \qquad \textbf{[1.13]}$$

The oxygen atoms produced then can react with oxygen molecules to produce ozone.

$$O + O_2 \longrightarrow O_3 \qquad \textbf{[1.14]}$$

This explains why ozone formation requires sunlight. Sunlight splits NO_2 to release O atoms. These in turn react with O_2 to form O_3. Thus once the Sun goes down, the ozone concentrations drop off sharply, as you can see in Figure 1.18. What happened to the ozone? In just a matter of hours, the ozone molecules react with many things, including animal and plant tissue.

Note that equation 1.14 contains three different forms of elemental oxygen: O, O_2, and O_3. All three are found in nature, but O_2 is the least reactive and by far the most abundant, constituting about one fifth of the air we breathe. Our atmosphere naturally contains tiny amounts of protective ozone up in the stratosphere. Oxygen atoms also exist in our upper atmosphere and are even more reactive than ozone.

"Good" ozone is in the stratosphere.
"Bad" ozone is in the troposphere.

Consider This 1.25 O_3 Summary

Summarize what you have learned about ozone formation by developing your own way to arrange these chemicals sequentially and in relation to one another: O, O_2, O_3, VOCs, NO, NO_2. Chemicals may appear as many times as you like. You also may wish to include sunlight.

Because sunlight is involved in ozone formation, the concentration of ground-level ozone varies with weather, season, and latitude. High levels of O_3 are much more likely to occur on long sunny summer days, especially in congested urban areas. Stagnant air also favors the buildup of air pollution. For example, revisit the air quality data for cities shown in Table 1.3. Ozone was usually the culprit responsible for pollution in cities with sunny summer days. In contrast, windy and rainy cities have lower levels of ozone.

Consider This 1.26   Ozone and You

The AIRNow website, courtesy of the EPA, provides a wealth of information about ground–level ozone levels in the United States.

a. Let's say that the ozone level is "orange," actually a common occurrence in many U.S. cities during the summer months. Does air of this quality affect you if you have no health concerns, but are actively exercising out of doors?
b. Again assume you are active out of doors. How does the air quality in your state compare with others?

Canada also publishes daily ozone maps (Figure 1.19). Some of Canada's polluted air originates in the United States, blown northeastward from population centers in Ohio, Pennsylvania, and New York. Pollution knows no boundaries!

This is an example of the **tragedy of the commons.** The tragedy arises when a resource is common to all and used by many, but has no one in particular responsible for it. As a result, the resource may be destroyed by overuse to the detriment of all who use it. For example, we cannot lay individual claim to the air; it belongs to all of us. If the air we breathe has waste dumped into it, this leads to an unhealthy situation for everyone. Individuals whose activities have little or no effect on the air still suffer the same consequences as those who pollute. The costs are shared by all. In later chapters, we will see other examples of the tragedy of the commons that relate to water, energy, and food.

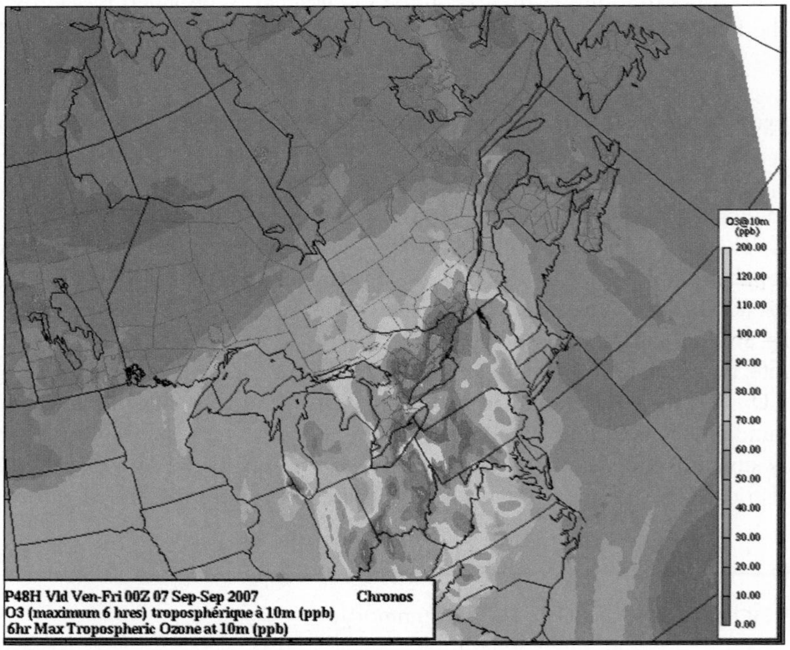

Garrett Hardin is credited with coining the term "tragedy of the commons." In an article published in 1968, he pointed out how individuals using a common resource may destroy it such that ultimately nobody can use it.

Figure 1.19
Tropospheric ozone map for September 7, 2007.

Source: Environment Canada.

Air pollution, once primarily a local concern, is now a serious international issue. Many cities worldwide have high ozone levels. Couple motor vehicles with a sunny location anywhere on the planet, and you are likely to find unacceptable levels of ozone. Some places, however, are worse than others. London with its cool foggy days has low ozone levels. In contrast, ozone is a serious problem in Mexico City.

Ozone attacks rubber and so it damages the tires of the vehicles that led to its production in the first place. Should you park your car indoors in the garage to minimize possible rubber damage? In fact, should you park *yourself* indoors if the levels of ozone outside are unhealthy? The next section speaks to the quality of indoor air.

1.13 | The Inside Story of Air Quality

In *The Wizard of Oz,* Dorothy hugged her dog Toto and exclaimed, "There's no place like home!" Of course she was right, but when it comes to air quality, your home may not always be the best place to be. Indoors, the levels of air pollution may far exceed those outside. Given that most of us sleep, work, study, and play indoors, we should learn about the air in the place we call home.

Indoor air may contain up to a thousand substances at low levels. If you are in a room where somebody is smoking, add another thousand or so. Indoor air contains some familiar culprits: VOCs, NO, NO_2, SO_2, CO, ozone, and PM. These pollutants are present either because they came in with the outside air or because they were generated right inside your dwelling.

Let's begin our discussion with the question posed in the previous section. Should you move indoors to escape the ozone present outside? In general, if a pollutant is highly reactive, it does not persist long enough to be transported indoors. Thus, for highly reactive molecules such as O_3, NO_2, and SO_2, you expect lower levels indoors. Indeed, this is the case, as indoor air is typically 10–30% lower in ozone concentration than outdoor air. Similarly, sulfur dioxide and nitrogen dioxide levels are lower indoors, although the decrease is not as dramatic as that for ozone.

Carbon monoxide is a different story. As a relatively unreactive pollutant, CO has a long enough atmospheric lifetime to move freely in and out of buildings through doors, windows, or a ventilation system. The same is true for some VOCs, but not for the more reactive ones such as those that give pine forests their scent. If you want to inhale the delicious volatile compounds emitted from the bark of Ponderosa pines, it is best to remain outside near the trees.

Some pollutants are trapped by the filters in the heating or cooling system of the building. For example, many air-handling systems contain filters that remove larger-sized particulate matter and pollen. As a result, people who suffer from seasonal allergies can find relief indoors. Similarly, those near a wildfire can go inside to escape some of the irritating smoke particles. However, gas molecules such as O_3, CO, NO_2, and SO_2 are *not* trapped by the filters used in most ventilation systems.

These days, many buildings are constructed with an eye to increasing their energy efficiency. This is a win–win, lowering your heating bills and lowering the amounts of pollutants generated in producing the heat. But there can be a down side. A building that is air-tight with a limited intake of fresh air may have unhealthy levels of indoor air pollutants. Therefore what appeared initially to be a benefit (better energy efficiency) can turn into a higher risk (increased pollutant levels). In some cases, poor ventilation can cause indoor pollutants to reach hazardous levels, creating a condition known as "sick building syndrome." Clearly this is an undesirable outcome. Today, architects and builders are finding ways to make buildings more energy efficient while maintaining a good air exchange.

Even with good ventilation, indoor activities can compromise air quality. For example, tobacco smoke is a serious indoor air pollutant, containing over a thousand chemical substances. Nicotine is one that you may recognize; others include benzene and formaldehyde. Taken as a whole, tobacco smoke is **carcinogenic,** meaning capable of causing cancer.

Some copy machines and air cleaners generate ozone, which may increase indoor ozone levels.

Ponderosa pine bark emits compounds with a scent reminiscent of butterscotch.

Sick building syndrome has many causes. One way or another, most relate to air quality. The source of the bad air may come both from inside the building, outside the building, or both.

Combustion of carbon-containing fuels also can generate carbon monoxide and nitrogen oxides. For example, carbon monoxide from cigarette smoking in bars can reach 50 ppm, a value well within the unhealthy range. In cigarette smoke, NO_2 levels can exceed 50 ppb. Fortunately, smokers take puffs rather than constantly breathing cigarette smoke.

Your Turn 1.27   Indoor Cigar Party

In 2007, student researchers attended a cigar party and trade show in Times Square, New York. They carried concealed detectors and found levels of 1193 μg of particulate matter per cubic meter of air inside the ballroom.

  a. The news article did not report whether the particulate matter was $PM_{2.5}$ or PM_{10}. For either, does the value they measured exceed the air quality standards in the United States? *Hint:* See Table 1.2.
  b. Assume that the students were measuring $PM_{2.5}$. What are the health implications?

People also burn candles, perhaps to soften the lighting or set a mood. However, candles deplete the oxygen in a room. They also can produce soot, carbon monoxide, and VOCs. Similarly, people may burn incense in their homes for one reason or another. Atmospheric scientist Stephen Weber, a researcher who studied incense burning in churches in Europe, found that "the pollutants in smoke from incense and candles may be more toxic than fine-particle pollution from sources such as vehicle engines."

Burning candles or incense can generate fumes more rapidly than these can be removed by your ventilation system or by the breezes that pass through open windows. The next activity gives you the opportunity to further investigate sources of indoor pollutants.

Your Turn 1.28   Indoor Activities

Name 10 activities that add pollutants or VOCs to indoor air. To get you started, two are pictured in Figure 1.20. Remember that some pollutants have no detectable odors.

As Figure 1.20 suggests, paints and varnishes are a source of VOCs. Your nose alerts you to these while you paint; so does your head if it starts aching. Although the amount of VOCs released per volume of paint applied varies widely, all oil-based paints

Figure 1.20
Activities that can pollute indoor air.

Figure 1.21
All ingredients in YOLO paints are selected as "zero VOC."

and varnishes rank higher than water-based ones. Check out the VOC emission values printed right on the paint can. These range from zero for low-VOC paints to more than 600 grams VOCs per liter for some outdoor oil paints. You would be fortunate to find an oil paint with less than 350 grams VOCs per liter.

Consumers today can purchase high-quality paints that are nontoxic and odor-free. For example, check out the label on the paint can shown in Figure 1.21. This "zero-VOC" water-based paint emits less than 5 grams of VOCs per liter applied. This paint has earned a "Green Seal" certification, meaning that not only does it emit less than 50 grams of VOCs per liter, but also that it contains no toxic metals such as lead, mercury, or cadmium. Low- or zero-VOC paints are equally important to use outside. The paint applied to buildings, bridges, and railings in the United States once added up to over 7 million pounds of VOCs per year. In 2005, the value was reported at less than 4 million pounds, thanks to changes in the formulation of paints.

Before we can explain how volatile compounds have been removed from paint, we first need to address why paints contain them in the first place. Some VOCs are additives that evaporate as the paint dries. For example, you may recognize the two antifreeze additives listed in Table 1.8. Antifreeze ("glycols") allows the folks who live

Table 1.8	VOCs Emitted by Some Paints
Glycols (antifreeze)	
ethylene glycol	
propylene glycol	
Coalescents (used in latex paints)	
2,2,4-trimethyl-1,3-pentanediol monoisobutyrate (trade name: Texanol)	
Hazardous Air Pollutants (solvents and preservatives)	
benzene	
formaldehyde	
ethylbenzene	
methylene chloride	
vinyl chloride	

in colder climates to store paint in their basements without worrying that it will be damaged by repeated freezing and thawing. Antifreeze also allows paint to be applied in colder weather and provides longer "open time," so that the paint does not dry out too quickly.

Coalescents are another additive used in latex paints. **Coalescents** are chemicals added to soften the latex particles in paint so that these particles spread to form a continuous film of uniform thickness. After all, you want your paint to brush on evenly! As the paint dries and hardens, the coalescents evaporate into the air. Between 2 and 3 gallons of volatile coalescents are used for every 100 gallons of paint. But do the math. In the United States this additive translates to over 100 million pounds of coalescents emitted each year, and approximately 3 times this amount worldwide.

Oil-based paints contain just that, oils. Most are oils derived from plants, such as linseed oil. These oils slowly react with the oxygen in the air and over time release a host of volatile compounds to the air. Oil paints also may contain solvents (thinners) that evaporate as the paint dries.

Look for more about the oils found in plants in Chapter 11.

Skeptical Chemist 1.29   Varnish Fumes

A can of clear satin floor varnish claims a maximum of 450 grams/liter of VOCs. A consumer group computes this to just under 4 pounds of VOCs emitted per gallon as the varnish is applied. Did this group do the math correctly?

Stricter government regulations on VOC emissions have prompted paint manufacturers to devise new formulations for latex paints. In 2005, the Archer Daniels Midland Company won a Presidential Green Chemistry Challenge award for developing nonvolatile coalescents. The coalescents developed by the company react with the oxygen in the air, enabling them to chemically bond to the latex. Thus, the coalescents become part of the paint film rather than evaporating into the atmosphere.

Another advantage of these new coalescents is that they are produced from vegetable oils (a renewable resource) as opposed to crude oil (nonrenewable). Their production also creates less waste and requires less energy, a plus for both environmental and cost savings. There is no loss in quality, as the paints formulated with vegetable oil-based coalescents meet or exceed the performance of traditional paints. They have lower odors, better scrub resistance, and better opacity. Do these environmental, economic, and societal benefits sound reminiscent of the Triple Bottom Line? Again, this is the heart of sustainability.

If you have ever been to an auto body shop, you most likely have smelled the odors from the VOCs in the paints. More stringent laws and regulations in many countries have forced manufacturers to reformulate automotive primers (undercoats) and finishes. Most traditional primers are made by mixing two components that have a limited shelf life. The primer is then applied and cured in an oven that requires large amounts of energy to heat. BASF Corporation won a 2005 Presidential Green Chemistry Challenge award for the development of a one-component primer that reduces VOCs by 50% and that is rapidly cured in sunlight or with a UV-A lamp. This greatly reduces the time required to make and cure the primer. Here again, the reduced costs associated with less waste, reduced energy consumption, and greater throughput equate to an improved Triple Bottom Line.

UV-A lamps emit longer-wave ultraviolet light, similar to tanning lamps. Look for more about UV light in Chapter 2.

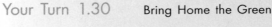

Your Turn 1.30   Bring Home the Green

Revisit the key ideas in green chemistry listed on the inside front cover of this book. Which of the key ideas are met by the new coalescents developed by the Archer Daniels Midland Company? By the new undercoat developed by BASF? Prepare a list for each company.

We end our discussion of indoor air quality by turning to radon, a noble gas (Group 8A) that we mentioned earlier. Radon is a special case of indoor air pollution. It occurs naturally in tiny amounts and usually is no problem. But it may reach hazardous levels in basements, mines, and caves. Like all noble gases, radon is colorless, odorless, tasteless, and chemically unreactive. But unlike the others, it is radioactive. Radon is generated in the decay series of uranium, another naturally occurring radioactive element. Because uranium occurs at a concentration of about 4 ppm in the rocks of our planet, radon is ubiquitous. Depending on how your apartment or dorm is constructed, the radon produced from uranium-containing rocks may find entry into the basement. Radon causes lung cancer and is the second leading cause behind tobacco smoke. As is the case for other pollutants, the threshold for danger can be estimated but is not precisely known. Radon test kits, such as the one shown in Figure 1.22, are used to measure the radon concentration in living spaces.

Indoors or out, we need to breathe healthy air. And with each breath, we inhale a truly prodigious number of molecules and atoms. We end this chapter by revisiting these molecules and atoms.

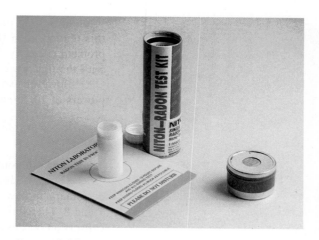

Figure 1.22
A home radon test kit.

Look for more about uranium and its natural decay series in Chapter 7.

1.14 | Back to the Breath—at the Molecular Level

The maximum concentrations of pollutants allowed by the air quality standards seem very small (see Table 1.2). Indeed, an exposure to 9 ppm CO is a tiny amount! But even this low concentration of CO contains a staggering number of carbon monoxide molecules. This seeming contradiction is a consequence of the minuscule mass of molecules. Recall Consider This 1.2: Take a Breath. If you are an average-sized adult, the capacity of your lungs is between 5 and 6 L. You do not empty your lungs each time you take a breath. Rather, as you are at rest reading this, you are inhaling about 500 milliliters of air or approximately half a quart with each breath.

Accurately measuring the volume of air you inhale and exhale can be done with the help of a spirometer (Figure 1.23). Determining the number of molecules and atoms in this volume of air is a harder task, but it can be done. From experiments, we know that a typical breath of 500 mL contains about 2×10^{22} molecules and atoms. Remember that air is primarily N_2 and O_2 molecules together with a small amount of Ar atoms and a varying amount of H_2O molecules (humidity).

Using this number of molecules and atoms in the air (2×10^{22}), we now can calculate the number of CO molecules in the breath you just inhaled. We assume the breath contained 2×10^{22} molecules and atoms, and that the CO concentration in the air was at the air quality standard of 9 ppm. Thus, out of every million (1×10^6) molecules and atoms in the air, nine will be CO molecules. To compute the number of CO molecules in a breath, multiply the total number of molecules and atoms in the air by the fraction that are CO molecules.

Check Figures Alive! for more about your breathing and lung capacity.

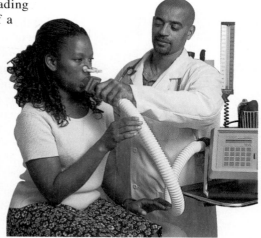

Figure 1.23
A spirometer is used for measuring an individual's breathing capacity.

$$\frac{\text{\# of CO molecules}}{1 \text{ breath of air}} = \frac{2 \times 10^{22} \text{ molecules and atoms in air}}{1 \text{ breath of air}} \times \frac{9 \text{ CO molecules}}{1 \times 10^6 \text{ molecules and atoms in air}}$$

$$= \frac{2 \times 9 \times 10^{22}}{1 \times 10^6} \frac{\text{CO molecules}}{1 \text{ breath of air}}$$

$$= \frac{18 \times 10^{22}}{1 \times 10^6} \frac{\text{CO molecules}}{1 \text{ breath of air}}$$

In writing this out, we carefully retain the units on the numbers. Not only does this remind us of the physical entities involved, but also it guides us in setting up the problem correctly. The units "molecules and atoms in the air" cancel, and we are left with the unit we want: CO molecules per breath of air.

However, we need to divide 10^{22} by 10^6 to determine a final answer. To *divide* powers of 10, simply *subtract* the exponents. In this case,

$$\frac{10^{22}}{10^6} = 10^{(22-6)} = 10^{16}$$

Thus, a breath contains 18×10^{16} CO molecules.

The preceding answer is mathematically correct, but in scientific notation it is customary to have only one digit to the left of the decimal point. Here we have two: 1 and 8. Therefore, our last step is to rewrite 18×10^{16} as 1.8×10^{17}. We can make this conversion because $18 = 1.8 \times 10$, which is the same as 1.8×10^1. We *add* exponents to *multiply* powers of 10. Thus, 18×10^{16} CO molecules equals $(1.8 \times 10^1) \times 10^{16}$ CO molecules, which equals 1.8×10^{17} CO molecules in that last breath you inhaled. If this use of exponents is coming at you a little too fast, consult Appendix 2.

It may sound surprising, but it is more accurate to round off the answer and report it as 2×10^{17} CO molecules. Certainly 1.8×10^{17} looks more accurate, but the data that went into our calculation were not very exact. The breath contains *about* 2×10^{22} molecules, but it might be 1.6×10^{22}, 2.3×10^{22}, or some other number. We say that 2×10^{22} expresses a physically based property to "one significant figure." A **significant figure** is a digit that is included (or excluded) to correctly represent the accuracy with which an experimental quantity is known. Only one digit, the 2 from the value 2.3 is used, and so 2×10^{22} has only one significant figure. Accordingly, the number of molecules in the breath is closer to 2×10^{22} than to 1×10^{22} or to 3×10^{22}, but anything beyond this we cannot say with certainty.

Similarly, the concentration of carbon monoxide is known to only one significant figure, 9 ppm. That 2×9 equals 18 is certainly correct mathematically, but our question about CO is based on physical data. The answer, 1.8×10^{17} CO molecules, includes two significant figures: the 1 and the 8. Two significant figures imply a level of knowledge that is not justified. The accuracy of a calculation is limited by the *least accurate* piece of data that goes into it. In this case, both the concentration of CO and the number of molecules and atoms in the breath were known only to one significant figure (9 and 2, respectively). Thus two significant figures in the answer are unjustified. The common-sense rule is that you cannot improve the accuracy of experimental measurements by manipulations like multiplying and dividing. Therefore, the answer must also contain only one significant figure and is 2×10^{17}.

Your Turn 1.31   Ozone Molecules

The local news reports that today's ground–level ozone readings are at the unacceptable level, 0.12 ppm. How many ozone molecules do you inhale in each breath? Assume that one breath contains 2×10^{22} molecules and atoms.

Answer

Start with the number of molecules and atoms in a breath. If the ozone concentration is 0.12 ppm, this gives the ratio 0.12 O_3 molecules per 10^6 molecules and atoms in air.

$$\frac{2 \times 10^{22} \text{ molecules and atoms in air}}{1 \text{ breath of air}} \times \frac{0.12 \, O_3 \text{ molecules}}{1 \times 10^6 \text{ molecules and atoms in air}}$$

$$= 2.4 \times 10^{15} \, O_3 \text{ molecules / breath}$$

$$= 2 \times 10^{15} \, O_3 \text{ molecules / breath (to one significant figure)}$$

You may well question the significance of all of this talk about significant figures. It has been observed that "figures don't lie, but liars can figure." Numbers often lend an air of authenticity to newspaper or television stories, so popular press accounts are full of numbers. Some are meaningful; others are not. Informed citizens can discriminate one from the other. For example, the assertion that the concentration of carbon dioxide in the atmosphere is 400.6537 ppm should be taken with a rather large grain of sodium chloride (salt). Values such as 401 ppm or 400.7 ppm (three or four significant figures) better represent what we actually can measure; any assertion with seven significant figures simply is not valid.

Figure 1.24
Carbon monoxide meter showing 35 ppm.

Your Turn 1.32   CO Monitors

Carbon monoxide monitors are available for homes and businesses. Figure 1.24 shows a convenient handheld CO detector that reads 35 ppm.

a. Would it be more helpful to have a meter that read 35.0388217 ppm? Explain.
b. Would 35.0388217 ppm be more valid? Explain.

Answer

a. No, it wouldn't be more helpful. The issue is whether the concentration of CO exceeds a certain value, such as 9 ppm over an 8-hour period or 35 ppm over a 1-hour period. The extra decimal places are of no use.

Recall that we started with the concentration of CO in an air sample of 9 ppm. Even so, the number of CO molecules in a breath is enormous, about 2×10^{17}. From these numbers, you can see that it is *impossible* to completely remove all the CO molecules from the air. "Zero pollutants" is an unattainable goal. At present, our most sensitive methods of chemical analysis are capable of detecting one target molecule out of a trillion. One part per trillion is analogous to moving 6 inches in the 93 million-mile trip to the Sun, a single second in 320 centuries, or a pinch of salt in 10,000 tons of potato chips.

Again, air always has trace levels of contaminants, ones that we cannot detect. A breath of air contains molecules of hundreds, perhaps thousands of different compounds, most in minuscule concentrations. Their origin could be either natural or related to human activity. As with all chemicals, "natural" is not necessarily good, and "human-made" is not necessarily bad. As you learned earlier, exposure and toxicity are what matter.

> Absence of evidence is not the same as evidence of absence. The substance may be present but in undetectable amounts.

Your Turn 1.33   CO Molecules in Perspective

To help you comprehend the magnitude of the 2×10^{17} CO molecules in one breath, assume that they were equally distributed among the 7.0 billion (7.0×10^9) inhabitants of the Earth. Calculate each person's share of the 2×10^{17} CO molecules you just inhaled.

Answer

You are trying to distribute the huge number of molecules in a breath among all the human inhabitants of the Earth. This can be found by dividing the total number of CO molecules by the total number of humans:

$$\text{Each person's share is } \frac{2 \times 10^{17} \text{ CO molecules}}{7.0 \times 10^9 \text{ people}}$$

Thus, to one significant figure, each person's share is 3×10^7 (or 30,000,000) molecules of CO.

In addition to being extremely small, the molecules and atoms you breathe possess other remarkable characteristics. They are in constant motion. At room temperature and pressure, a nitrogen molecule travels at about 1000 feet per second and experiences approximately 400 billion collisions with other molecules in that time interval. Nevertheless, relatively speaking, the molecules are quite far apart. The actual volume of the extremely tiny molecules making up the air is only about 1/1000 of the total volume of the gas. If the particles in your half-liter breath were squeezed together, their volume would be about 0.5 mL, less than a quarter teaspoon. Sometimes people mistakenly think that air is empty space. It is 99.9% empty space, but the matter it contains is literally a matter of life and death!

Moreover, it is matter that we continuously exchange with other living things. The carbon dioxide we exhale is used by plants to make the food we eat. The oxygen that plants release is essential for our existence. Our lives are linked by the elusive medium of air. With every breath, we exchange millions of molecules with one another. As you read this, your lungs contain 4×10^{19} molecules that have been previously breathed by other human beings, and 6×10^8 molecules that have been breathed by some *particular* person, say Julius Caesar, Mahatma Gandhi, or Joan of Arc. In fact, the odds are very good that right now your lungs contain one molecule that was in Caesar's *last* breath. The consequences are breathtaking!

Skeptical Chemist 1.34   Caesar's Last Breath

We just claimed that your lungs currently contain one molecule that was in Caesar's last breath. That assertion is based on some assumptions and a calculation. Are these assumptions reasonable? We are not asking you to reproduce the calculation, but rather to identify some of the assumptions and arguments we might have used.

Hint: The calculation assumes that all of the molecules in Caesar's last breath have been uniformly distributed throughout the atmosphere.

Consider This 1.35   Air Quality Today

The addition of waste to our atmosphere has not occurred overnight. Rather, air pollution has been a growing concern since at least the time of the Industrial Revolution. Why have nations and the larger world community become more concerned about air quality? Identify at least four factors that have brought air quality to the attention of citizens and voters.

Conclusion

The air we breathe affects both our health and the health of the planet. Our atmosphere contains the essentials for life, including two elements (oxygen and nitrogen) and two compounds (water and carbon dioxide). Our very existence on this planet depends on having a large supply of relatively clean, unpolluted air.

But the air you breathe may be polluted with carbon monoxide, ozone, sulfur dioxide, and the oxides of nitrogen. Polluted air is more common in large cities, the very places where most people now live. Emergency room visits correlate with bad air quality. So do shortness of breath, scratchy throats, and stinging eyes. The pollutants that cause us harm are, for the most part, relatively simple chemical substances. They largely are produced as consequences of our dependence on coal for electricity production in power plants, gasoline in internal combustion engines, and the fuels we burn to heat and cook.

Over the past 30 years, governmental regulations, industry initiatives, and modern technology have reduced pollutant levels. Both catalytic converters on cars and emissions controls on smokestacks have been important players. But it makes more sense not to generate "people fumes" in the first place. Here is where green chemistry plays an important role. By designing new processes that do not produce air pollutants, we do not later have to clean them up.

Indoors or out, the oxygen-laden air we breathe is very close to the surface of the Earth. However, the Earth's atmosphere extends upward for considerable distance and contains other gases that also are essential for life on this planet. Chapters 2 and 3 will describe two of these: stratospheric ozone and carbon dioxide. We will see that our human footprints and "air prints" on planet Earth connect in surprising ways to both of these gases.

Chapter Summary

The numbers in parentheses indicate the sections in which the topics are introduced. Having studied this chapter, you should be able to:

- Explain the connection between your health and what you breathe (entire chapter)
- Describe air in terms of its major components, their relative amounts, and the local and regional variations in the composition of air (1.1, 1.5)
- List the major air pollutants and describe the health effects of each (entire chapter)
- Compare and contrast indoor and outdoor air in terms of which pollutants are likely to be present and their sources (1.3, 1.13)
- Interpret local air quality data, including why air quality standards are set separately for each pollutant (1.3)
- Evaluate the risks and benefits of a particular activity (1.3)
- Discuss the green chemistry initiative and why it makes sense to prevent pollution rather than to clean it up afterward (1.5)
- Relate these terms: matter, pure substances, mixtures, elements, compounds, metals, nonmetals (1.6)

- Discuss the features of the periodic table, including the groups it contains (1.6)
- Explain the difference between atoms and molecules, giving examples of each (1.7)
- Name chemical elements and compounds that relate to air quality (1.7)
- Write and interpret chemical formulas that relate to air quality (1.8)
- Balance and interpret chemical equations that relate to air quality (1.9–1.10)
- Understand oxygen's role in combustion, including how hydrocarbons burn to form carbon dioxide, carbon monoxide, and soot (1.9–1.10)
- Describe how ozone forms, including how sunlight, NO, NO_2, and VOCs are involved (1.12)
- Identify the sources and nature of indoor air pollution (1.13)
- Explain the unreasonableness of "pollution-free" air (1.14)
- Use scientific notation and significant figures in performing basic calculations (1.4, 1.14)
- Apply what you know about air pollution to ways of living that result in cleaner air (entire chapter)

Questions

The end-of-chapter questions are grouped in three ways:

- **Emphasizing Essentials** questions give you the opportunity to practice fundamental skills. They are similar to the *Your Turn* exercises in the chapter.
- **Concentrating on Concepts** questions are more difficult and may relate to societal issues. They are similar to the *Consider This* activities in the chapter.
- **Exploring Extensions** questions challenge you to go beyond the information presented in the text.

Appendix 5 contains the answers to questions with numbers in **blue**.

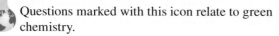 Questions marked with this icon relate to green chemistry.

Emphasizing Essentials

1. a. Calculate the volume of air in liters that you might inhale (and exhale) in an 8-hour working day. Assume that each breath has a volume of about 0.5 L, and that you are breathing 15 times a minute.

   b. From this calculation, you can see that breathing exposes you to large volumes of air. Name five things that you can do to improve the quality of the air that you and others breathe.

2. Our atmosphere can be characterized both as a thin veil that supports life and as a few vertical miles of chemicals. Explain what makes each description accurate. Also state which feature(s) of our atmosphere each description emphasizes and which one(s) it omits.

3. These gases are found in the troposphere: Rn, CO_2, CO, O_2, Ar, and N_2.

   a. Rank them in order of their abundance in the troposphere.

   b. For which of these gases is it convenient to express its concentration in parts per million?

   c. Which of these gases is/are currently regulated as an air pollutant where you live?

   d. Which of these gases is/are found in Group 8A of the periodic table, the noble gases?

4. Give three examples of particulate matter found in air. Explain the difference between $PM_{2.5}$ and PM_{10} in terms of size and health effects.

5. Radon is one of the noble gases found in Group 8A on the periodic table. Which properties does it share with the other inert gases? In which way is it distinctly different?

6. a. The concentration of argon in air is approximately 0.9%. Express this value in ppm.

  b. The air exhaled from the lungs of a smoker has a concentration of 20–50 ppm CO. In contrast, air exhaled by nonsmokers is 0–2 ppm CO. Express each concentration as a percent.

  c. In a tropical rain forest, the water vapor concentration may reach 50,000 ppm. Express this as a percent.

  d. In the dry polar regions, water vapor may be a mere 10 ppm. Express this as a percent.

7. In these diagrams, two different types of atoms are represented by color and size. Characterize each sample as an element, a compound, or a mixture. Explain your reasoning.

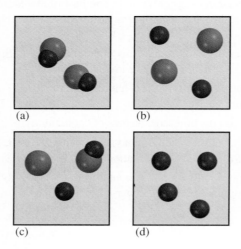

(a)   (b)

(c)   (d)

8. Consider this representation of the reaction between nitrogen and hydrogen to form ammonia (NH_3).

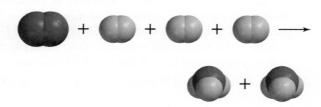

  a. Are the masses of reactants and products the same? Explain.

  b. Are the numbers of molecules of reactants and of products the same? Explain.

  c. Are the total number of atoms in the reactants and the total number of atoms in the products the same? Explain.

9. Express each of these numbers in scientific notation.

  a. 1500 m, the distance of a foot race

  b. 0.0000000000958 m, the distance between O and H atoms in a water molecule

  c. 0.0000075 m, the diameter of a red blood cell

  d. 150,000 mg of CO, the approximate amount breathed daily

10. Write each of these values as a "regular" number.

  a. 8.5×10^4 g, the mass of air in an average room

  b. 2.1×10^8 gallons, the volume of crude oil spilled into the Gulf of Mexico in 2010

  c. 5.0×10^{-3}%, the concentration of CO in the air on a city street

  d. 1×10^{-5} g, the recommended daily allowance of vitamin D

11. The threshold for detecting NO_2 by smell is 0.00022 g/m^3 of air.

  a. Express this value in scientific notation.

  b. Would you expect a similar value for the odor threshold of CO?

  c. Name another pollutant that has a sharp, easily detected odor.

12. Wildfires occur all across our planet. The one shown here was photographed from a commercial flight north of Phoenix, AZ.

  a. What combustion products would you expect from the burning of wood?

  b. This fire is emitting at least three pollutants. Which are visible and which are not?

13. Consider this portion of the periodic table and the groups shaded on it.

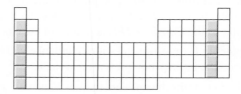

  a. What is the group number for each shaded region?

  b. Name the elements that make up each group.

  c. Give a general characteristic of the elements in each of these groups.

14. Consider the following blank periodic table.

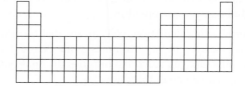

a. Shade the region of the periodic table in which metals are found.

b. Common metals include iron, magnesium, aluminum, sodium, potassium, and silver. Give the chemical symbol for each.

c. Give the name and chemical symbol for five nonmetals (elements that are not in your shaded region).

15. Classify each of these substances as an element, a compound, or a mixture.

a. a sample of "laughing gas" (dinitrogen monoxide, also called nitrous oxide)

b. steam coming from a pan of boiling water

c. a bar of deodorant soap

d. a sample of copper

e. a cup of mayonnaise

f. the helium filling a balloon

16. These gases are found in the atmosphere in small amounts: CH_4, SO_2, and O_3.

a. What information does each chemical formula convey about the number and types of atoms present?

b. Give the names of these gases.

17. Hydrocarbons are important fuels that we burn for many different reasons.

a. What is a hydrocarbon?

b. Rank these hydrocarbons by the number of carbons they contain: propane, methane, butane, octane, ethane.

c. We suggested "mother eats peanut butter" as a memory aid for the names of the first four hydrocarbons. Propose a new one that includes *pent-*, the prefix that indicates five carbon atoms.

18. Write balanced chemical equations to represent these reactions. *Hint:* Nitrogen and oxygen are both diatomic molecules.

a. Nitrogen reacts with oxygen to form nitrogen monoxide.

b. Ozone decomposes into oxygen and atomic oxygen (O).

c. Sulfur reacts with oxygen to form sulfur trioxide.

19. Analogous to equation 1.8, draw models to represent the chemical equations from the question 18.

20. These questions relate to combustion of hydrocarbons.

a. LPG (liquid petroleum gas) is mostly propane, C_3H_8. Balance this equation.

$$C_3H_8(g) + O_2(g) \longrightarrow CO_2(g) + H_2O(g)$$

b. Cigarette lighters burn butane, C_4H_{10}. Write a balanced equation, assuming complete combustion, that is, plenty of oxygen.

c. With a limited supply of oxygen, both propane and butane can burn incompletely to form carbon monoxide. Write balanced equations for both reactions.

21. Balance these equations in which ethane (C_2H_4) burns in oxygen.

a. $C_2H_4(g) + O_2(g) \longrightarrow C(s) + H_2O(g)$

b. $C_2H_4(g) + O_2(g) \longrightarrow CO(g) + H_2O(g)$

c. $C_2H_4(g) + O_2(g) \longrightarrow CO_2(g) + H_2O(g)$

22. Examine the coefficients for oxygen in the balanced equations from question 21. Explain why they vary, depending on whether C, CO, or CO_2 is formed.

23. Count the atoms on both sides of the arrow to demonstrate that these equations are balanced.

a. $2 C_3H_8(g) + 7 O_2(g) \longrightarrow 6 CO(g) + 8 H_2O(l)$

b. $2 C_8H_{18}(g) + 25 O_2(g) \longrightarrow 16 CO_2(g) + 18 H_2O(l)$

24. Platinum, palladium, and rhodium are used in the catalytic converters of cars.

a. Give the chemical symbol for each metal.

b. Locate each metal on the periodic table.

c. What can you infer about the properties of these metals, given that they are useful in this application?

25. Nail polish remover containing acetone was spilled in a room 6 m × 5 m × 3 m. Measurements indicated that 3600 mg of acetone evaporated. Calculate the acetone concentration in micrograms per cubic meter.

Concentrating on Concepts

26. "Air prints" were mentioned in the opening activity of this chapter. Examine these two photographs. The first is a beautiful view from a lodging on the Hilo coast of the island Hawaii. The second shows the tarmac on a hazy summer day at the Narita International Airport in Tokyo. List three ways in which each photo shows the air print of humans. *Hint:* Some may not be visible but rather implied by the photograph.

27. The AIRNow website (EPA) states that "Quality of air means quality of life." Demonstrate the wisdom of this statement for two air pollutants of your choice.

28. In Consider This 1.2, you calculated the volume of air exhaled in a day. How does this volume compare with the volume of air in your chemistry classroom? Show your calculations. *Hint:* Think ahead about the most convenient unit to use for measuring or estimating the dimensions of your classroom.

29. According to Table 1.1, the percentage of carbon dioxide in inhaled air is *lower* than it is in exhaled air, but the percentage of oxygen in inhaled air is *higher* than in exhaled air. How can you account for these relationships?

30. Cars don't inhale and exhale like humans do. Nonetheless, the air that goes into a car is different from what comes out. In Your Turn 1.19 you listed what comes out of a tailpipe. Now comment on the *differences* between the air that goes into the car engine and what comes out the tailpipe. For which chemicals have the concentrations noticeably increased or decreased?

31. A headline from the *Anchorage Daily News* in Alaska (January 17, 2008): "Family in car overcome by carbon monoxide. Fire department saves five after slide into snow bank."

    a. If your car is in a snow bank and the engine is running, CO may accumulate inside the car. Normally, however, CO does not accumulate in the car. Explain.

    b. Why didn't the occupants detect the CO?

32. A headline from the *Pioneer Press* in St. Paul, Minnesota (January 8, 2008): "Man dies after exposure to gas; carbon monoxide sickens five others."

    a. Name two possible sources of CO inside a home.

    b. The level measured was 4700 ppm. Express this value as a percent.

    c. How does this level compare with the U.S. ambient air quality standards set by the EPA?

    d. Name three symptoms that the survivors most likely experienced.

    e. Where in a home should you install CO detectors? *Note:* Adjacent to a furnace is *not* usually recommended.

33. In Consider This 1.4, you considered how life on Earth would change if the concentration of oxygen were twice as high. Now consider how life would change if the concentration of O_2 were cut in half. Give two examples of things that would be affected.

34. Explain why CO is named the "silent killer." Select two other pollutants for which this name would not apply and explain why not.

35. Undiluted cigarette smoke may contain 2–3% carbon monoxide.

    a. How many parts per million is this?

    b. How does this value compare with the National Ambient Air Quality Standards for CO in both a 1-hour and an 8-hour period?

    c. Propose a reason why smokers do not die from carbon monoxide poisoning.

36. In the Northern Hemisphere, the ozone season runs from about May 1 to October 1. Why are ozone levels typically not reported in the winter months?

37. The EPA characterizes ozone as "good up high, bad nearby." Explain.

38. Here are ozone air quality data for Atlanta, Georgia, from July 4 to 13, 2011. The primary pollutant was ozone.

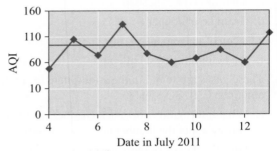

Source: www.AIRNow.gov.

    a. In general, which groups of people are the most sensitive to ozone?

    b. The U.S. Environmental Protection Agency determined that air rated above 100 is hazardous for some or all groups. For the data shown, how many days was the air hazardous?

    c. Ozone levels drop off sharply at night. Explain why.

    d. During the daytime, the ozone dropped off sharply after July 7. Propose two different reasons that could account for this observation.

    e. Data for the month of December is not shown. Would you expect the ozone levels to be higher or lower than those in July? Explain.

39. Here are air quality data for December 21–31, 2011, in Modesto, California. The primary pollutant was PM_{10}.

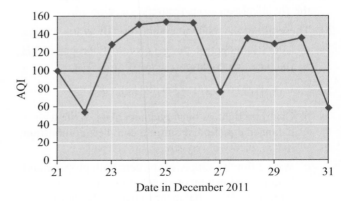

Source: www.AIRNow.gov.

a. In general, which groups of people are the most sensitive to particulate matter?

b. The U.S. Environmental Protection Agency determined that air rated above 100 is hazardous for some or all groups. For the data shown, how many days was the air hazardous?

c. The levels of PM do not necessarily drop off at night the way they do for ozone. Explain.

d. The levels of particulate matter increased sharply on December 23. Propose two different reasons that could account for this observation.

40. Prior to 1990, diesel fuel in the United States could contain as much as 2% sulfur. New regulations have changed this, and today most diesel fuel is ultra-low sulfur diesel (ULSD) containing a maximum of 15 ppm sulfur.

> **ULTRA-LOW SULFUR HIGHWAY DIESEL FUEL**
> (15 ppm Sulfur Maximum)
>
> **Required** for use in all model year 2007 and later highway diesel vehicles and engines.
>
> Recommended for use in all diesel vehicles and engines.

a. Express 15 ppm as a percent. Likewise, express 2% in terms of ppm. How many times lower is the ULSD than the older formulation of diesel fuel?

b. Write a chemical equation that shows how burning diesel fuel containing sulfur contributes to air pollution.

c. Diesel fuel contains the hydrocarbon $C_{12}H_{26}$. Write a chemical equation that shows how burning diesel adds carbon dioxide to the atmosphere.

d. Comment on burning diesel fuel as a sustainable practice, both in terms of how things have improved and in terms of where they still need to go.

41. A certain city has an ozone reading of 0.13 ppm for 1 hour, and the permissible limit is 0.12 for that time. You have the choice of reporting that the city has exceeded the ozone limit by 0.01 ppm or saying that it has exceeded the limit by 8%. Compare these two methods of reporting.

42. Here is a U.S. map with the peak ozone data for July 1, 2011.

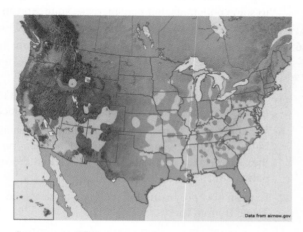

Source: www.AIRNow.gov.

a. These data are typical in that most of the ozone pollution is expected in California, Denver, Texas, the Midwest, and the East Coast. Why is ozone pollution so high in these regions of the country?

b. Eastern Texas typically has high ozone levels in the summer, but not on this particular day. Offer a possible explanation.

c. Why are inland areas in California, such as the Sacramento Valley, likely to have worse air quality than the California coast?

43. Look up the air quality data for ozone in two different cities, one hot and dry, and the other cooler and more rainy. Account for any difference you find. *Hint:* Use *State of the Air*, a website posted by the American Lung Association.

44. At certain times of the year, inhabitants of the beautiful city of Santiago, Chile, breathe some of the worst air on the planet.

a. Driving private cars has been severely restricted in Santiago. How specifically does this improve air quality?

b. Although the population of Santiago is comparable to that in other cities, its air quality is much worse. Suggest geographical features that might be responsible.

45. a. Explain why jogging outdoors (as opposed to sitting outdoors) increases your exposure to pollutants.

    b. Jogging indoors at home can decrease your exposure to some pollutants, but may increase your exposure to others. Explain.

46. Consumers now can purchase paints that emit only low amounts of VOCs. However, these consumers may not know why it matters to purchase this paint.

    a. What would you print on the label of a paint can to make the point that a low-VOC paint is a good idea?

    b. We apply paint to many outdoor surfaces, such as buildings, bridges, and fence posts. Comment on the environmental effects of the VOCs that these paints emit.

    c. Explain how producing low-VOC paint meets the Triple Bottom Line.

47. One can purchase a carbon monoxide monitor that immediately sounds an alarm if the concentration of CO reaches a threshold. In contrast, most radon detection systems sample the air over a period of time before an alarm sounds. Why the difference?

48. Select a profession of your choice, possibly the one you intend to pursue. Name at least one way that a person in this profession could have a positive effect on air quality.

Exploring Extensions

49. "Air pollution is a diffuse problem, the shared fault of many emitters. It is a classic example of the tragedy of the commons." (*Source: Introduction to Air in California* by David Carle, 2006.) Explain the phrase "tragedy of the commons," and how air pollution is a classic example.

50. Mercury, another serious air pollutant, is not described in this chapter. If you were a textbook author, what would you include about mercury emissions? How would you connect mercury emissions to the sustainable use of resources? Write several paragraphs in a style that would match that of this textbook.

51. The EPA oversees the Presidential Green Chemistry Challenge Awards. Use the EPA website to find when the program started and to find the list of the most recent winners of the award. Pick one winner and summarize in your own words the green chemistry advance that merited the award.

52. Recreational scuba divers usually use compressed air that has the same composition as normal air. A mixture being used is called Nitrox. What is its composition and why is it being used?

53. Here are two scanning electron micrograph images of particulate matter, courtesy of the National Science Foundation and researchers at Arizona State University. The first is of a soil particle and the second of a rubber particle, and each is about 10 μm in diameter.

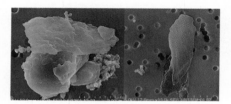

    a. Suggest a likely source of the rubber particle. Name two other substances that might contribute PM to the air.

    b. The soil particle is composed mainly of silicon and oxygen. What other elements are commonly present in the rocks and minerals in Earth's crust?

    c. What about these photographs suggests that these particles would inflame your blood vessels?

54. Ultrafine particles have diameters less than 0.1 μm. In terms of their sources and health effects, how do these particles compare with $PM_{2.5}$ and PM_{10}? Use the Internet to locate the most up-to-date information.

55. Most lawnmowers do not have catalytic converters (at least as this book went to press). What comes out of the tailpipe of a gasoline-powered lawn mower? Why has adding a catalytic converter been so controversial? What are the immediate benefits to curbing these emissions, as well as the longer term ones?

56. Consider this graph that shows the effects of carbon monoxide inhalation on humans.

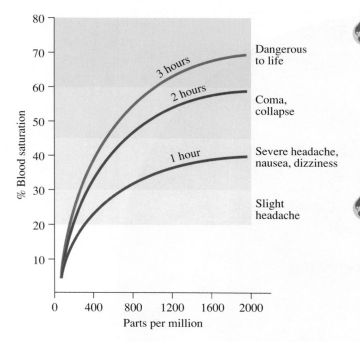

a. Both the amount of exposure and the duration of exposure have an effect on CO toxicity in humans. Use the graph to explain why.

b. Use the information in this graph to prepare a statement to include with a home carbon monoxide detection kit about the health hazards of carbon monoxide gas.

57. Consider This 1.4 asks you to consider how our world would be different if the oxygen content of the atmosphere were doubled. Develop your answer into an essay. Title your essay "An Hour in the Life of . . ." and describe how life would be different for a person of your choice. If an hour is too short to make your point, substitute "A Morning . . ." or "A Day...."

58. You may have admired the beauty of hardwood floors. Polyurethane is the finish of choice for floors because it is more durable than varnishes and shellacs. Until recently, polyurethane was always an oil-based paint. But recently, the Bayer Corporation developed a water-based polyurethane that reduces the amount of VOCs by 50–90%. In 2000, Bayer was awarded a Presidential Green Chemistry Challenge award for this development. Prepare a summary of this work. Also check stores to see if any water-based polyurethanes are available in your area.

59. Composite wood is made by gluing smaller pieces of wood (often waste scraps of wood) together. Examples include plywood, particle board, and fiber board.

a. Many glues release formaldehyde, a volatile compound. What are its hazards?

b. Professor Kaichang Li of Oregon State University and Columbia Forest Products developed a new soy-based adhesive glue, winning a Presidential Green Chemistry Challenge Award in 2007. Prepare a summary of his accomplishments.

CHAPTER 2

Protecting the Ozone Layer

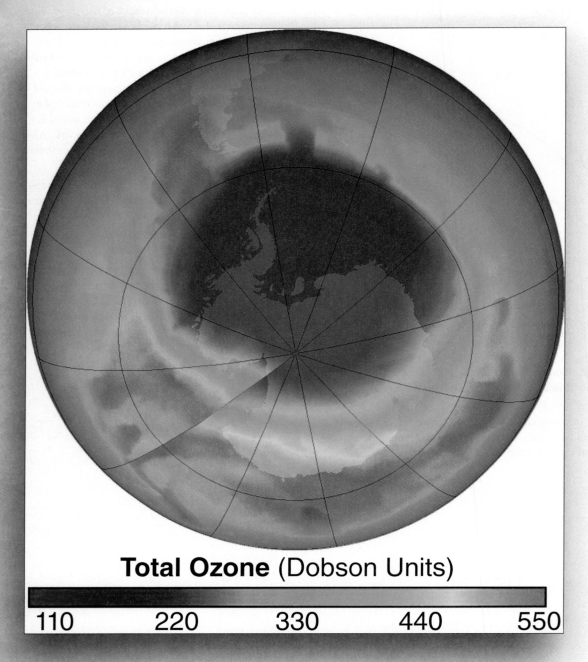

Total Ozone (Dobson Units)

110   220   330   440   550

The 2012 stratospheric ozone "hole" over Antarctica. The purple and blue areas show where the ozone is at a minimum. On September 22, the hole reached a maximum area of 21.2 million km². The record high for the hole was 29.9 million km² in 2000.

Source: NASA Ozone Watch.

"Good up high; bad nearby." To understand ozone, think *location*. Down here in the troposphere, where we live, ozone is a pollutant that forms in the presence of sunlight from other pollutants in our atmosphere. Once the Sun goes down, the generation of ozone ceases. Any ozone that is present quickly reacts with something else, and the concentrations drop in the twilight hours. Were the Sun not to rise again, we wouldn't have to worry about breathing ozone (but we'd face a few other problems).

But up in the stratosphere, the story of ozone is altogether different. All of the ozone up high is formed naturally. Also unlike ground-level ozone, stratospheric ozone plays a vital role in protecting us from damaging solar radiation. One might say it acts like the Earth's sunglasses.

In the 1970s, chemists discovered that certain chemicals could make their way into the upper atmosphere and partially destroy the protective ozone found there. Ever since, scientists, policy makers, and concerned citizens worldwide have participated in efforts to control and reverse ozone destruction. Somewhat surprisingly, the most severe depletion has been over Antarctica, and the yearly images of the ozone hole have become some of the most widely recognized scientific graphics. Later in this chapter, you will have the opportunity to examine past trends and update the Antarctic ozone-hole story.

You may be wondering what this story has to do with you, because the last time we checked, not many college students were living in Antarctica. Even though ozone depletion was first documented in that faraway region, it also has been observed to a lesser extent in many other locations on Earth. Where you live and the season of the year both influence the amount of stratospheric ozone overhead and how well it provides its protective effects. Take a look at some of the important data for yourself.

Consider This 2.1   Ozone Levels Above You

As you read this, an instrument onboard a satellite is measuring ozone levels in the stratosphere. Visit the NASA website, www.nasa.gov, to complete these questions.

a. What is the current total column ozone (in Dobson units) at your location? Request data for three different years and compute an average.

b. Now retrieve data for Antarctica for the same dates. How does the ozone measurement where you live compare? *Note:* If you are making the comparison in September or October, you are likely to see the biggest difference.

One DU (Dobson unit) corresponds to about one ozone molecule for every billion molecules and atoms present in air.

What caused this stratospheric ozone depletion? Why is this depletion so serious? Look for the answers to these questions and more in the sections that follow.

As we explore the topic of ozone depletion, we also highlight the **precautionary principle.** This principle stresses the wisdom of acting, even in the absence of complete scientific data, before the adverse effects on human health or the environment become significant or irrevocable. As you will learn, the world community did act. The wisdom of the collective actions is evident, as the measures taken to protect the ozone layer appear to be working. Even so, another warning bell will sound in the final section of this chapter. Listen for it in regards to global climate change—the topic of Chapter 3.

2.1 | Ozone: What and Where Is It?

If you have ever been near a sparking electric motor or in a severe lightning storm, most likely you have smelled ozone. Its odor is unmistakable but difficult to describe. Some compare it to that of chlorine gas; others think the odor reminds them of newly

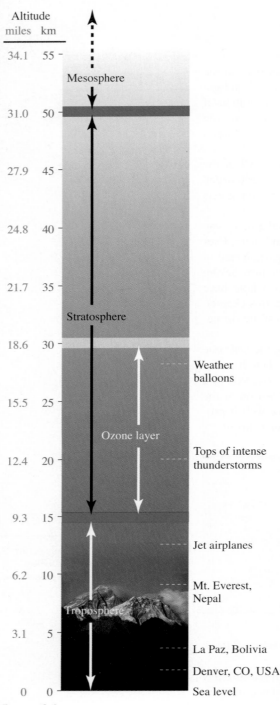

Figure 2.1

The regions of the atmosphere. Altitudes
are approximate and vary with latitude.

Source: Environmental Protection Agency.

mown grass. It is possible for humans to detect concentrations as low
as 10 parts per billion (ppb), that is, 10 molecules out of 1 billion.
Appropriately enough, the name *ozone* comes from a Greek word
meaning "to smell."

The ozone and oxygen molecules differ by only one atom.

oxygen molecule O_2 ozone molecule O_3

As we will see, this difference in molecular structure translates to
significant differences in chemical properties. One difference is that
ozone is far more chemically reactive than O_2. As you will learn in
Chapter 5, ozone can be used to kill microorganisms in water. Ozone
is also used to bleach paper pulp and fabrics. At one time, ozone was
even advocated as a deodorizer for air. This use only makes sense,
however, if nobody breathes the air during the deodorizing process.
In contrast, you safely can (and must) breathe oxygen day in and day
out. Although oxygen is still quite chemically reactive, it is not reactive enough to bleach paper or purify water.

Ozone forms both naturally and as a result of human activities. Given the high reactivity of ozone, it does not usually persist
very long. If it were not for the fact that ozone is formed anew on
our planet, you would not find it except as a curiosity in the chemistry lab.

Ozone can be formed from oxygen, but the process requires
energy. A simple chemical equation summarizes the process:

$$\text{energy} + 3\,O_2 \longrightarrow 2\,O_3 \qquad \textbf{[2.1]}$$

This chemical equation helps to explain why ozone is formed from
oxygen in the presence of an electrical discharge, whether from an
electric spark or lightning.

Ozone is reasonably rare in the troposphere, the region of the
atmosphere closest to the Earth's surface (Figure 2.1). Only somewhere between 20 and 100 ozone molecules typically occur for each
billion molecules and atoms that make up the air. Unhealthy concentrations are sometimes found near Earth's surface, the result of chemical reactions that produce it as a component of photochemical smog.
But these concentrations are very low. As was noted in the previous
chapter, the air quality standard in the United States for ground-level
ozone was set at 0.075 ppm for an 8-hr average as of 2012. This
standard is equivalent to 75 ozone molecules for every billion molecules and atoms found in air.

But what is detrimental in one region of the atmosphere, even at very low
concentrations, can be essential in another. The stratosphere is where ozone does
most of its filtering of some types of ultraviolet light from the Sun. The concentration of ozone in this region is several orders of magnitude greater than in the
troposphere, but still very low. As an upper limit, about 12,000 ozone molecules
are present for every billion molecules and atoms of gases that make up the atmosphere at this level.

Most of the ozone on our planet, about 90% of the total, is found in the stratosphere. The term **ozone layer** refers to a designated region in the stratosphere of maximum ozone concentration. Figure 2.2 shows the ozone concentrations in the troposphere
and stratosphere.

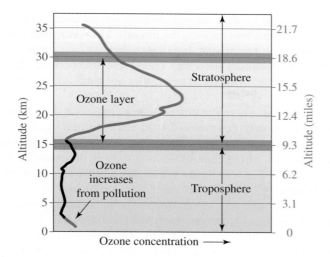

Figure 2.2

The ozone layer is a region of maximum ozone concentration in the stratosphere. Altitudes are approximate and vary with latitude.

Source: Global Ozone Research and Monitoring Project Report No. 44, 1998. *Reprinted with permission of World Meteorological Organization.*

Your Turn 2.2   **The Ozone Layer**

Use Figure 2.2 and values given in the text to answer these questions.

a. What is the approximate altitude of maximum ozone concentration?
b. What is the maximum number of ozone molecules per billion molecules and atoms of all types found in the stratosphere?
c. What is the maximum number of ozone molecules per billion molecules and atoms of all types found in ambient air just meeting the EPA limit for an 8–hr average?

Answer
a. About 23 km (14 miles).

Because the range of altitudes is so broad, the concept of an "ozone layer" can be a little misleading. No thick, fluffy blanket of ozone exists in the stratosphere. At the altitudes of the maximum ozone concentration, the atmosphere is very thin, so the total amount of ozone is surprisingly small. If all the O_3 in the atmosphere could be isolated and brought to the average pressure and temperature at Earth's surface (1.0 atm and 15 °C), the resulting layer of gas would have a thickness of less than 0.5 cm, or about 0.20 inch. On a global scale, this is a minute amount of matter. Yet, this ozone shield protects the surface of the Earth and its inhabitants from the harmful effects of ultraviolet radiation.

The total amount of ozone in a vertical column of air of known volume can be determined fairly easily. The determination can be done from Earth's surface by measuring the amount of UV radiation reaching a detector; the lower the intensity of the radiation, the greater the amount of ozone in the column. G. M. B. Dobson, a scientist at Oxford University, pioneered this measurement method. In 1920, he invented the first instrument to quantitatively measure the concentration of ozone in a column of the Earth's atmosphere. Therefore, it is fitting that the unit of such measurements is named for him.

Consider This 2.3   **Interpreting Ozone Values**

A classmate used the National Aeronautics and Space Administration (NASA) website to check the atmospheric ozone above her hometown in Ohio. She found the readings to be 417 DU (Dobson units) on April 10 and 386 DU on May 10. The student, reassured by these findings, concluded there had been an improvement in protection from damaging UV radiation. Do you agree? Explain.

One Dobson unit (DU) is equivalent to about 3×10^{16} O_3 molecules in a vertical column of air with a cross section of 1 cm^2.

Scientists continue to measure and evaluate ozone levels using ground observations, weather balloons, and high-flying aircraft. However, since the 1970s, measurements of total column ozone have also been made from the top of the atmosphere. Satellite-mounted detectors record the intensity of the UV radiation scattered by the upper atmosphere. The results are then related to the amount of O_3 present.

The Space Shuttle *Columbia* tested a new approach for monitoring ozone. Rather than looking directly downward toward Earth from a satellite, the equipment aboard the Shuttle looked sideways through the thin blue haze (see photo) that rises above the denser regions of the troposphere and follows the curve of the Earth. This region is known as the Earth's "limb" and is responsible for the name of this new technique, "limb viewing." Reliable information can be gathered at each level of the atmosphere, particularly allowing scientists to better understand chemistry taking place in the lower regions of the stratosphere. In January 2004, NASA launched a new mission called Earth Observing System (EOS) *Aura* that also uses a variety of viewing geometries, including limb viewing, to gather additional data about changes in Earth's stratospheric ozone layer.

The process by which ozone protects us from damaging solar radiation involves the interaction of matter and energy from the Sun. To help you to understand this, we turn first to a submicroscopic view of matter.

2.2 | Atomic Structure and Periodicity

Both the O_2 and O_3 molecules are composed of oxygen atoms. What do we know about these atoms? During the 20th century, scientists probed the inner workings of the atom. The physicists were almost too successful in their endeavors, finding more than 200 subatomic particles. Fortunately, most chemical behavior can be explained with only three.

Every atom has a **nucleus,** a minuscule and highly dense center of an atom composed of protons and neutrons. **Protons** are positively charged particles, and **neutrons** are electrically neutral particles. Both have almost exactly the same mass. Indeed, the protons and neutrons in the nucleus account for almost all the mass of an atom. Outside the nucleus are the electrons that define the boundary of the atom. An **electron** has a mass much smaller than that of a proton or neutron and a negative electric charge equal in magnitude to that of a proton, but opposite in sign. Therefore, in any electrically neutral atom, the number of electrons equals the number of protons. The properties of these particles are summarized in Table 2.1.

The number of protons in the nucleus determines the identity of the atom. The term **atomic number** refers to the number of protons in the nucleus of an atom. For example, all hydrogen (H) nuclei contain 1 proton; hydrogen has an atomic number of 1. Similarly, all helium (He) nuclei contain 2 protons and have an atomic number of 2. With each successive element in the periodic table, the atomic number increases. For example, the nucleus of element #92 (U, uranium) contains 92 protons.

Table 2.1	Properties of Subatomic Particles		
Particle	Relative Charge	Relative Mass	Actual Mass, kg
proton	+1	1	1.67×10^{-27}
neutron	0	1	1.67×10^{-27}
electron	−1	0*	9.11×10^{-31}

* This value is zero when rounded to the nearest whole number. The electron does indeed have mass, though very small.

Your Turn 2.4   Atomic Bookkeeping

Using the periodic table as a guide, specify the number of protons and electrons in a neutral atom of each of these elements.

a. carbon (C)   b. calcium (Ca)   c. chlorine (Cl)   d. chromium (Cr)

Answers

a. 6 protons, 6 electrons
b. 20 protons, 20 electrons

We wish we could show you a picture of a typical atom. However, atoms defy easy representation, and depictions in textbooks are at best oversimplifications. For one thing, the relative size of the nucleus and the atom creates serious problems for the illustrator. Electrons are sometimes pictured as moving in "orbits" about the nucleus, but the modern view of electrons is a good deal more complicated and abstract. If the nucleus of a hydrogen atom were the size of a period on this page, the atom's single electron would most likely be found at a distance of about 10 feet from that period. Moreover, electrons do not follow specific circular orbits. In spite of what you may have learned early in your education, an atom is really not very much like a miniature solar system. Rather, the distribution of electrons in an atom is described best using concepts of probability and statistics.

If this sounds rather vague to you, you are not alone. Common sense and our experience of ordinary things are not particularly helpful in our efforts to visualize the interior of an atom. Instead, we are forced to resort to mathematics and metaphors. The mathematics required (a field called quantum mechanics) can be formidable. Chemistry majors do not normally encounter this field until rather late in their undergraduate study. Although we cannot fully share with you the strange beauties of the peculiar quantum world of the atom, we can provide some useful generalizations.

The periodic table lists elements in order of increasing atomic number. The table also has elements arranged so that those with similar chemical properties fall in the same column (group). For example, lithium (Li, atomic number 3), sodium (Na, 11), potassium (K, 19), rubidium (Rb, 37), and cesium (Cs, 55) all fall in the same column and all are highly reactive metals. What fundamental feature accounts for this?

Today we know that the chemical properties of elements are the consequence of the distribution of electrons in the atoms of these elements. When chemical properties repeat themselves, this signals a repeat in electronic arrangement. As we will see, the electrons farthest from the nucleus are the main determinant of chemical properties.

Both experiment and calculation demonstrate that the electrons are arranged in certain energy levels about the nucleus. The electrons in the innermost level are the most strongly attracted by the positively charged protons in the nucleus. The greater the distance between an electron and the nucleus, the weaker the attraction between them. We say that the more distant electron is in a higher energy level, which means that the electron itself possesses more potential energy.

Each energy level has a maximum number of electrons that can be accommodated and is particularly stable when fully occupied. The innermost level, corresponding to the lowest energy, can hold only two electrons. The second level has a maximum capacity of eight, and the higher levels are also particularly stable when they contain eight electrons.

Table 2.2 shows some important information about electrons in neutral atoms of the first 18 elements. The total number of electrons in each atom is printed in blue and the number of outer electrons is printed in maroon. **Outer (valence) electrons** are found in the highest energy level and help to account for many of the observed trends in chemical properties. Observe that the group designation (1A, 2A, etc.) corresponds to the number of *outer* electrons for the A group elements, one of the most useful organizing features of the periodic table.

What we call "levels" used to be referred to as "shells," using the earlier solar system model of atomic structure.

Look for more about potential energy in Chapter 4.

The periodic table also contains B group elements. Table 2.2 does not show these, as these elements start with the fourth row.

Lithium (stored in oil)

Sodium (removed from oil, being cut)

Potassium (in a sealed glass tube)

Rubidium (in a sealed glass tube)

Figure 2.3

Selected Group 1A elements.

The smallest noble gas, helium, has 2 valence electrons rather than 8.

Table 2.2		Atoms of the First 18 Elements (Total and Outer Electrons)					
Group 1A	2A	3A	4A	5A	6A	7A	8A
1							2
H							He
1							2
3	4	5	6	7	8	9	10
Li	Be	B	C	N	O	F	Ne
1	2	3	4	5	6	7	8
11	12	13	14	15	16	17	18
Na	Mg	Al	Si	P	S	Cl	Ar
1	2	3	4	5	6	7	8

- *Above* the atomic symbol is the atomic number, the number of protons in the nucleus. For a neutral atom, this also is the number of electrons.
- *Below* the atomic symbol is the number of **outer** electrons in a neutral atom.

Take another look at the first column in Table 2.2. Lithium and sodium atoms both have one *outer* electron per atom, despite having different *total* numbers of electrons. This fact explains much of the chemistry that these two alkali metals have in common. It places them in Group 1A of the periodic table (the 1 indicates one outer electron). Moreover, we would be correct in assuming that potassium, rubidium, and the other elements in column 1A of the periodic table also have a single outer electron in each of their atoms. They are all metals that react readily with oxygen, water, and a wide range of other chemicals. Figure 2.3 shows photographs of some Group 1A elements.

The periodic table is a useful guide to electron arrangement. In the families (another name for groups) of elements marked "A," the number that heads the column indicates the number of outer electrons in each atom. We introduced the terms *alkali metal, alkaline earth metal, halogen,* and *noble gas* in Chapter 1. We now connect these terms with their group number.

- Alkali metals (Group 1A)—highly reactive metals with one outer electron
- Alkaline earth metals (Group 2A)—reactive metals with two outer electrons
- Halogens (Group 7A)—reactive nonmetals with 7 outer electrons
- Noble gases (Group 8A)—unreactive nonmetals with 8 outer electrons

Your Turn 2.5   Outer Electrons

Using the periodic table as a guide, specify the group number and number of outer electrons in a neutral atom of each element.

a. sulfur (S)   b. silicon (Si)   c. nitrogen (N)   d. krypton (Kr)

Answers

a. Group 6A; 6 outer electrons   b. Group 4A; 4 outer electrons

Your Turn 2.6   Family Features

a. In terms of their outer electrons, what do fluorine (F), chlorine (Cl), bromine (Br), and iodine (I) have in common?

b. The element beryllium (Be), like the other elements in Group 2A, has two outer electrons. Give the names and symbols for the other Group 2A elements.

Answer

a. All have seven outer electrons. They belong to Group 7A, the halogens.

Table 2.3	Isotopes of Hydrogen			
Name	Isotope	# of Protons (atomic number)	# of Neutrons	#n + #p (mass number)
hydrogen	H–1 or $_1^1$H	1	0	1
deuterium	H–2 or $_1^2$H	1	1	2
tritium	H–3 or $_1^3$H	1	2	3

Elements can have both stable and radioactive isotopes. For example, H-3 (tritium) is radioactive, but H-1 and H-2 are not. Look for more about radioisotopes in Chapter 7.

In addition to electrons and protons, atoms also contain neutrons. The one (and only) exception is an atom of the most common form of hydrogen, which consists of only one proton in its nucleus. But the nucleus of 1 out of every 6700 hydrogen atoms also contains a neutron. This naturally occurring form of hydrogen is called deuterium. Tritium, a radioactive form of hydrogen that is quite rare in nature, has two neutrons in its nucleus. Hydrogen, deuterium, and tritium are examples of **isotopes,** two or more forms of the same element (same number of protons) whose atoms differ in number of neutrons, and hence in mass.

An isotope is identified by its **mass number,** the sum of the number of protons and neutrons in the nucleus of an atom. The mass number can vary for the same element. In contrast, the atomic number cannot vary for the same element. For example, the full atomic symbol $_1^1$H represents the most common isotope of hydrogen. Because the atomic number of 1 for hydrogen is invariant, the subscript is sometimes omitted. Thus you also may see ^{1}H, hydrogen-1, or H-1. Table 2.3 summarizes information about the isotopes of hydrogen.

Your Turn 2.7   Protons and Neutrons

Specify the number of protons and neutrons in the nucleus of each of these.

a. carbon–14 ($_6^{14}$C)   b. uranium–235 ($_{92}^{235}$U)   c. iodine–131 ($_{53}^{131}$I)

Answers

a. 6 protons, 8 neutrons
b. 92 protons, 143 neutrons

All elements have more than one isotope, but the number of stable ones varies considerably. Each element's atomic mass, the number you see on every periodic table, takes the relative natural abundance of isotopes, as well as their masses, into account. Following our general rule of introducing information on a need-to-know basis, we will return to a discussion of atomic masses in Chapter 3.

Mass number is the total number of protons and neutrons in a specific isotope. Atomic mass refers to a weighted average of all naturally occurring isotopes of an element.

2.3 | Molecules and Models

Having taken a short excursion into the atomic realm, we now move to the topic of bonding in molecules so that in turn, we can understand the ozone hole.

Let's begin with the simplest molecule, H_2. Each hydrogen atom has one electron. If two hydrogen atoms bond, the two electrons become common property. If we represent each electron by a dot, the two hydrogen atoms might look something like this:

H· and ·H

Bringing the two atoms together yields a molecule that can be represented this way.

H**:**H

Each atom effectively has a share in both electrons. The resulting H_2 molecule has a lower energy than the sum of the energy in the two individual H atoms, and consequently the molecule with its bonded atoms is more stable than the separate atoms. The two electrons that are shared constitute a **covalent bond.** Appropriately, the name *covalent* implies "shared strength."

A **Lewis structure** is a representation of an atom or molecule that shows its outer electrons. The name honors Gilbert Newton Lewis (1875–1946), an American chemist who pioneered its use. Lewis structures, also called dot structures, can be predicted for many simple molecules by following a set of straightforward steps. We first illustrate the procedure with hydrogen fluoride, HF, another simple molecule.

You are unlikely to use HF in your chemistry laboratory. It is a highly reactive compound, and in aqueous solution it is used to etch glass.

1. Note the number of outer electrons contributed by each of the atoms.
   Hint: The periodic table is a useful guide for Group A elements.

   $$1 \text{ H atom (H·)} \times 1 \text{ outer electron per atom} = 1 \text{ outer electron}$$
   $$1 \text{ F atom (:\ddot{F}·)} \times 7 \text{ outer electrons per atom} = 7 \text{ outer electrons}$$

2. Add the outer electrons contributed by the individual atoms to obtain the total number of outer electrons available.

   $$1 + 7 = 8 \text{ outer electrons}$$

3. Arrange the outer electrons in pairs. Then distribute them so as to maximize stability by giving each atom a share in enough electrons to fully fill its outer level: 2 electrons in the case of hydrogen, 8 electrons for most other atoms.

   $$H : \ddot{\underset{..}{F}} :$$

We surrounded the F atom with 8 dots, organized into 4 pairs. The pair of dots between the H and the F represents the electron pair that forms the bond uniting the hydrogen and fluorine atoms. The other 3 pairs of electrons are not shared with other atoms. As such, they are called nonbonding electrons, or "lone pairs."

A **single covalent bond** is formed when two electrons (one pair) are shared between two atoms. A line may be used to represent the two electrons in the bond.

$$H — \ddot{\underset{..}{F}} :$$

Sometimes the nonbonding electrons are removed from a Lewis structure, simplifying it still more. The result is called a **structural formula,** a representation of how the atoms in a molecule are connected.

$$H — F$$

Remember that the single line represents one pair of shared electrons. These 2 electrons plus the 6 electrons in the 3 nonbonding pairs mean that the fluorine atom is associated with 8 outer electrons, whether or not the electrons are specifically shown. Remember that the hydrogen atom has no additional electrons other than the single pair shared with fluorine. It is at maximum capacity with two electrons.

The fact that electrons in many molecules are arranged so that every atom (except hydrogen) shares in eight electrons is called the **octet rule.** This generalization is useful for predicting Lewis structures and the formulas of compounds. Consider the Cl_2 molecule, the diatomic form of elemental chlorine. From the periodic table, we can see that chlorine, like fluorine, is in Group 7A, which means that its atoms each have 7 outer electrons. Using the scheme given for HF earlier, we first count and add up the outer electrons for Cl_2.

$$2 \text{ Cl atoms (:\ddot{Cl}·)} \times 7 \text{ outer electrons per atom} = 14 \text{ outer electrons}$$

For the Cl_2 molecule to exist, a bond must connect the two atoms. The remaining 12 electrons constitute 6 nonbonding pairs, distributed in such a way as to give each chlorine atom a share in 8 electrons (2 bonding and 6 nonbonding). Here is the Lewis structure.

$$:\ddot{\underset{..}{Cl}} — \ddot{\underset{..}{Cl}} :$$

Your Turn 2.8   Lewis Structures for Diatomic Molecules

Draw the Lewis structure for each molecule.

a. HBr   **b.** Br_2

Answer

a.   1 H atom (H·) × 1 outer electron per atom = 1 outer electron

1 Br atom (·B̈r:) × 7 outer electrons per atom = 7 outer electrons

Total = 8 outer electrons

Here is the Lewis structure: H:B̈r: or H—B̈r:

So far we have dealt only with molecules having just two atoms. But the octet rule applies to larger molecules as well. Let's use a water molecule, H_2O, as an example. Just as with two-atom molecules, first tally the outer electrons.

2 H atoms (H·) × 1 outer electron per atom = 2 outer electrons

1 O atom (·Ö·) × 6 outer electrons per atom = 6 outer electrons

Total = 8 outer electrons

In molecules like water that have a single atom bonded to two or more atoms of a different element (or elements), *the single atom is the central one.* You'll encounter exceptions, but this is a useful rule. Since oxygen is the "single atom" in H_2O, we place it in the center of the Lewis structure. Each of the H atoms bonds to the O atom, using 4 electrons. The remaining 4 electrons go on the O atom as 2 nonbonding pairs.

H:Ö:H

A quick count confirms that the O atom is surrounded by 8 electrons, as predicted by the octet rule. Alternatively, we could use lines for the single bonds.

H—Ö—H

Chemical formulas show the types and ratio of atoms present. In contrast, Lewis structures also indicate how the atoms are connected and show the nonbonding pairs of electrons, if present. Note that Lewis structures do *not* directly reveal the shape of a molecule. For example, from the Lewis structure we drew it might appear that the water molecule is linear. In fact, the molecule is bent.

H—O—H   or   (space-filling model)

Another molecule to consider is methane, CH_4. Again, we begin by tallying the valence electrons.

4 H atoms (H·) × 1 outer electron per atom = 4 outer electrons

1 C atom (·Ċ·) × 4 outer electrons per atom = 4 outer electrons

Total = 8 outer electrons

The central carbon atom is surrounded by the 8 electrons, giving carbon an octet of electrons. In the Lewis structure, each H atom uses 2 of the electrons to bond with the C atom, for a total of 4 single covalent bonds.

```
                        H
      H                 |
 H:C:H    or      H — C — H
      H                 |
                        H
```

Remember that H can only accommodate a pair of electrons. The next activity gives you the opportunity to practice with other molecules.

Each hydrogen atom forms only one bond (two shared electrons). Oxygen can form two bonds and is the central atom in H_2O.

The space-filling model of water was shown in Section 1.7. We will explain why the water molecule is bent in Chapter 3.

The combustion of methane was discussed in Section 1.10. Look in Chapter 3 for an explanation of the shape of the methane molecule.

Your Turn 2.9   More Lewis Structures

Draw the Lewis structure for each of these molecules. Both obey the octet rule.

a. hydrogen sulfide (H_2S)
b. dichlorodifluoromethane (CCl_2F_2)

Answer

a.   2 H atoms (H·) × 1 outer electron per atom = 2 outer electrons
      1 S atom (·S̈·) × 6 outer electrons per atom = 6 outer electrons
                                              Total = 8 outer electrons

The Lewis structure is H:S̈:H or H—S̈—H.
The Lewis structures for H_2S and H_2O differ only in the central atom.

In some structures, single covalent bonds do not allow the atoms to follow the octet rule. Consider, for example, the O_2 molecule. Here we have 12 outer electrons to distribute, 6 from each of the oxygen atoms. There are not enough electrons to give each of the atoms a share in eight electrons if only one pair is held in common. However, the octet rule can be satisfied if the two atoms share four electrons (two pairs). A covalent bond consisting of two pairs of shared electrons is called a **double bond.** This bond is represented by four dots or by two lines.

$$\ddot{O}::\ddot{O} \quad \text{or} \quad \ddot{O}=\ddot{O}$$

Double bonds are shorter, stronger, and require more energy to break than single bonds involving the same atoms. The experimentally measured length and strength of the bond in the O_2 molecule correspond to a double bond. However, oxygen has a property that is not fully consistent with the Lewis structure just drawn. When liquid oxygen is poured between the poles of a strong magnet, it sticks there like iron filings. Such magnetic behavior implies the presence of unpaired electrons rather than the paired arrangement shown in the preceding Lewis structures. But this is hardly a reason to discard the useful generalizations of the octet rule. After all, simple scientific models seldom if ever explain all phenomena, but they can be helpful approximations. There are other common examples in which the straightforward application of the octet rule leads to discrepancies in interpreting experimental evidence. Coming across data that do not seem to fit has led to the development of more sophisticated models.

A **triple bond** is a covalent linkage made up of three pairs of shared electrons. For the same atoms, triple bonds are even shorter, stronger, and harder to break than double bonds. For example, the nitrogen molecule, N_2, contains a triple bond. Each Group 5A nitrogen atom contributes 5 outer electrons for a total of 10. These 10 electrons can be distributed in accordance with the octet rule if 6 of them (three pairs) are shared between the two atoms, leaving 4 of them to form two nonbonding pairs, one on each nitrogen atom.

$$:N{::}N: \quad \text{or} \quad :N{\equiv}N:$$

The stability of the triple bond linking N atoms in N_2 gas helps explain nitrogen's relative inertness in the troposphere.

The ozone molecule introduces another structural feature. We again start with the octet rule. Each of the three oxygen atoms contributes 6 outer electrons for a total of 18. These 18 electrons can be arranged in two ways; each way gives a share in 8 outer electrons to each atom.

$$\ddot{O}::\ddot{O}:\ddot{O}: \qquad :\ddot{O}:\ddot{O}::\ddot{O}$$
$$\textbf{a} \qquad\qquad\qquad \textbf{b}$$

Structures **a** and **b** predict that the molecule should contain one single bond and one double bond. In structure **a,** the double bond is shown to the left of the central atom; in **b** it is shown to the right. But experiments reveal that the two bonds in the O_3 molecule are identical, being intermediate between the length and strength of a single and double bond. Structures **a** and **b** are called **resonance forms,** Lewis structures that represent hypothetical extremes of electron arrangements in a molecule. For example, no single resonance form represents the electron arrangement in the ozone molecule. Rather, the actual structure is something like a hybrid of the two resonance forms. A double-headed arrow linking the different forms is used to represent the resonance phenomenon.

$$\ddot{O}=\ddot{O}-\ddot{\underset{..}{O}}: \longleftrightarrow :\ddot{\underset{..}{O}}-\ddot{O}=\ddot{O}$$

Resonance is just another modeling concept invented by chemists to represent the complex microworld of molecules. It is not intended to be "the truth," but rather just a way to describe the structures of molecules that do not exactly fit the octet rule model. Figure 2.4 compares the Lewis structures of several different oxygen-containing species relevant to the chemistry in this and other chapters.

$\cdot\ddot{O}\cdot$	$\ddot{O}=\ddot{O}$	$:\ddot{O}-\ddot{O}=\ddot{O}$	$\cdot\ddot{O}-H$
oxygen atom	oxygen molecule	ozone molecule	hydroxyl free radical

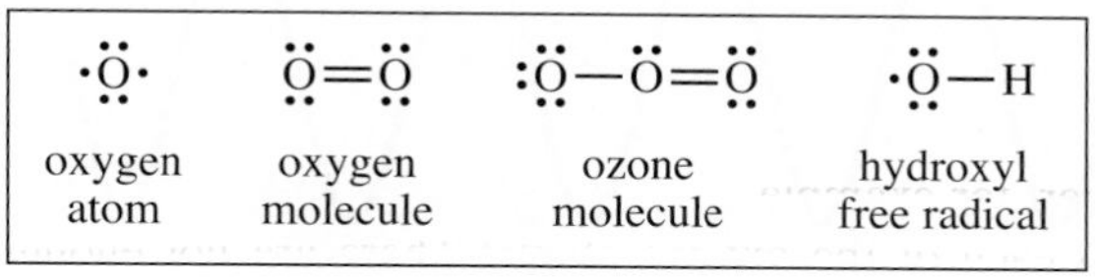

Figure 2.4

Lewis structures for several oxygen-containing species. Only one resonance form of ozone is shown.

A closer experimental inspection of that microworld reveals that the O_3 molecule is not linear as the simple Lewis structures just drawn seems to indicate. Remember that Lewis structures tell us only what is connected to what and do not necessarily show the shape of the molecule. The O_3 molecule is actually bent, as in this representation.

$$\ddot{O}=\overset{\ddot{O}}{\diagdown}\ddot{\underset{..}{O}}: \longleftrightarrow :\ddot{\underset{..}{O}}\diagup\overset{\ddot{O}}{\diagdown}=\ddot{O}$$

An explanation of why the O_3 molecule is bent must wait until Chapter 3. At this point, we only need to know how the bonding in the O_2 and O_3 molecules relates to their interaction with sunlight.

The hydroxyl radical was mentioned in Chapter 1 in connection with smog formation.

Observe that both H_2O and O_3 are bent molecules, with O as the central atom.

Your Turn 2.10   **Lewis Structures with Multiple Bonds**

Draw the Lewis structure for each compound. Both follow the octet rule.

  a. carbon monoxide (CO)   **b.** sulfur dioxide (SO_2)

Answer

  a. 1 C atom ($\cdot\dot{C}\cdot$) × 4 outer electrons per atom = 4 outer electrons

    1 O atom ($\cdot\ddot{O}\cdot$) × 6 outer electrons per atom = 6 outer electrons

                              Total = 10 outer electrons

The Lewis structure is $:C::O:$ or $:C\equiv O:$ and has 10 outer electrons. The N_2 molecule also has 10 outer electrons and similarly forms a triple bond.

2.4 | Waves of Light

Every second, light is emitted by the Sun and, after some time, reaches our planet. Some of this light we can see; some we cannot. Prisms and raindrops break the light we see into a spectrum of colors. Sometimes we name these colors simply as violet, indigo, blue, green, yellow, orange, and red. Other times, we distinguish between the hues with more descriptive names such as cherry red or forest green.

Another way to describe a color is with a numerical value that corresponds to its wavelength. The word *wavelength* correctly suggests that light behaves something like a wave in a body of water. **Wavelength** is the distance between successive peaks. It is

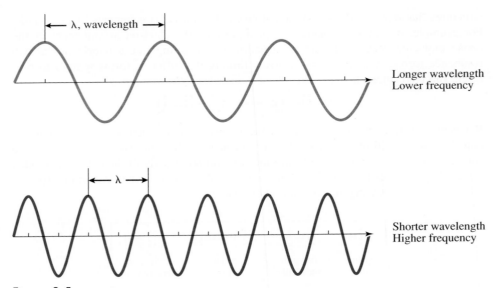

Longer wavelength
Lower frequency

Shorter wavelength
Higher frequency

Figure 2.5
Comparison of two different waves.

As wavelength ↑, frequency ↓.

expressed in units of length and symbolized by the Greek letter lambda (λ). Waves are also characterized by a certain **frequency,** the number of waves passing a fixed point in 1 second. Frequency is symbolized by the Greek letter nu (v). Figure 2.5 shows two waves of different wavelength and frequency.

The relationship between frequency and wavelength can be summarized in a simple equation in which v is the frequency and c is the constant speed at which visible light and other forms of electromagnetic radiation travel, 3.00×10^8 m·s^{-1}.

$$\text{frequency } (v) = \frac{\text{speed of light } (c)}{\text{wavelength } (\lambda)} \qquad \textbf{[2.2]}$$

Equation 2.2 indicates that wavelength and frequency are *inversely* related. As λ decreases, v increases, and vice versa.

It is both interesting and humbling to realize that out of the vast array of radiant energies, our eyes are sensitive only to the tiny portion between roughly 700×10^{-9} meters (red light) and 400×10^{-9} meters (violet light). These wavelengths are very short, so we typically express them in nanometers. One **nanometer (nm)** is defined as one billionth of a meter (m).

$$1 \text{ nm} = \frac{1}{1,000,000,000} \text{ m} = \frac{1}{1 \times 10^9} \text{ m} = 1 \times 10^{-9} \text{ m}$$

We can use this equivalence to convert meters to nanometers. For example, this calculation shows how many nanometers are in 700×10^{-9} m.

$$\text{wavelength } (\lambda) = 700 \times 10^{-9} \text{ m} \times \frac{1 \text{ nm}}{1 \times 10^{-9} \text{ m}} = 700 \text{ nm}$$

The units of meters cancel, leaving nanometers.

Consider This 2.11   Analyzing a Rainbow

Water droplets in a rainbow act as prisms to separate visible light into its colors.

a. In Figure 2.6, which color has the longest wavelength? The highest frequency?
b. Green light has a wavelength of 500 nm. Express this value in meters.

Answer
b. 500×10^{-9} m. In scientific notation, this is 5×10^{-7} m.

Figure 2.6
A rainbow of color.

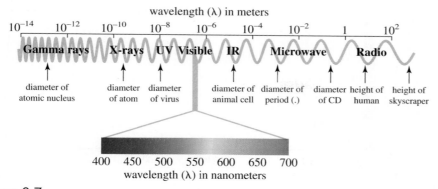

Figure 2.7

The electromagnetic spectrum. The wavelength variation from gamma rays to radio waves is not drawn to scale.

 Figures Alive!

The **electromagnetic spectrum** is a continuum of waves that ranges from short, high-energy X-rays and gamma rays to long, low-energy radio waves. Visible light is only a narrow band in this spectrum. The term **radiant energy** refers to the entire collection of different wavelengths, each with its own energy. Figure 2.7 shows the electromagnetic spectrum, the relative wavelengths (not drawn to scale), and some examples to help you develop perspective on the range of wavelengths represented.

In this chapter, we consider the **ultraviolet (UV)** region that lies adjacent to the violet end of the visible region of the electromagnetic spectrum, but at shorter wavelengths. At still shorter wavelengths are the X-rays used in medical diagnosis and the determination of crystal structures, and gamma rays that are given off in processes of nuclear decay. At wavelengths longer than those of red visible light lies the **infrared (IR)** region. We cannot see these wavelengths, but can feel their heating effect. The microwaves used in radar and to cook food quickly have wavelengths on the order of centimeters. At still longer wavelengths are the regions of the spectrum used to transmit your favorite AM and FM radio and television programs.

> We will consider the IR region of the spectrum in Chapter 3.

Your Turn 2.12   Relative Wavelengths

Consider these four types of radiant energy from the electromagnetic spectrum: infrared, microwave, ultraviolet, visible. *Hint:* See Figure 2.7.

a. Arrange them in order of *increasing* wavelength.
b. Approximately how many times longer is a wavelength associated with a radio wave than one associated with an X–ray?

Answer
a. ultraviolet < visible < infrared < microwave

Our local star, the Sun, emits many types of radiant energy but not with equal intensity. This is evident from Figure 2.8, a plot of the relative intensity of solar radiation as a function of wavelength. The curve represents the spectrum as measured *above* the atmosphere, before there has been opportunity for interaction of radiation with the molecules found in air. The peak indicating the greatest intensity is in the visible region. However, 53% of the total energy emitted by the Sun is radiated to Earth as infrared radiation. This is the major source of heat for the planet.

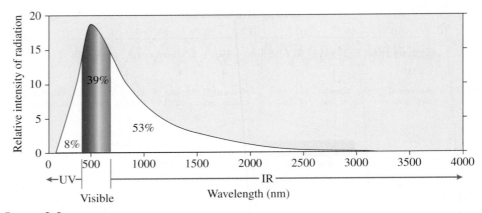

Figure 2.8
Wavelength distribution of solar radiation above Earth's atmosphere.

Source: From An Introduction to Solar Radiation by Muhammad Iqbal, Academic Press, 1983. Copyright Elsevier 1983.

Approximately 39% of the energy comes to us as visible light and only about 8% as ultraviolet. (The areas under the curve give an indication of these percentages.) But in spite of its small percentage, the Sun's UV radiation can be the most damaging to living things. To understand why, we need to look at electromagnetic radiation in terms of its energy.

2.5 | Radiation and Matter

The idea that radiation can be described in terms of wave-like character is well established and very useful. However, around the beginning of the 20th century, scientists found several phenomena that seemed to contradict this model. In 1909, a German physicist named Max Planck (1858–1947) argued that the shape of the energy distribution curve pictured in Figure 2.8 could only be explained if the energy of the radiating body were the sum of many energy levels of minute but discrete size. In other words, the energy distribution is not really continuous, but consists of many individual steps. Such an energy distribution is called **quantized.** An often-used analogy is that the quantized energy of a radiating body is like steps on a staircase, which are also quantized (no partial steps allowed), not like a ramp that allows any size stride. Albert Einstein (1879–1955), in the work that won him the 1921 Nobel Prize in physics, suggested that radiation itself should be viewed as constituted of individual bundles of energy called **photons.** One can regard these photons as "particles of light," but they are definitely not particles in the usual sense. For example, they have no mass. These ideas form the basis of modern quantum theory.

The wave model remains useful, even with the development of the quantum theory. Both are valid descriptions of radiation. The dual nature of radiant energy seems to defy common sense. How can light be described in two different ways at the same time, both waves and particles? There is no obvious answer to that very reasonable question—that's just the way nature is. The two views are linked in a simple relationship that is one of the most important equations in modern science. It is also an equation relevant to the role of ozone in the atmosphere.

$$\text{energy } (E) = \frac{hc}{\lambda} \qquad \textbf{[2.3]}$$

Here E represents the energy of a single photon. Both symbols h and c represent constants. The symbol h is called Planck's constant and c is the speed of light. This equation therefore shows that energy, E, is *inversely* proportional to the wavelength, λ. Consequently, as the wavelength of radiation gets shorter, its energy increases. This qualitative relationship is important in the story of ozone depletion.

Planck and Einstein were both amateur violinists who played duets together.

As wavelength ↓, energy ↑.

Your Turn 2.13   Color and Energy Relationships

Arrange these colors of the visible spectrum in order of *increasing* energy per photon:

green, red, yellow, violet.

Answer

red < yellow < green < violet

Using equation 2.3, one can calculate that the energy associated with a photon of UV radiation is approximately 10 million times larger than the energy of a photon emitted by your favorite radio station. A consequence of this large difference in energy is that you can damage your skin with exposure to UV radiation, but not with exposure to radio waves. Whether or not your radio is turned on, you are continuously bombarded by radio waves. Your body cannot detect them, but your radio can. The energy associated with each of the radio photons is very low and not sufficient to produce a local increase in the concentration of the skin pigment, melanin, as happens with exposure to UV. Producing melanin involves a quantum jump, an electronic transition between energy levels that requires far more energy than radio wave photons can supply.

The Sun bombards Earth with countless photons—indivisible packages of energy. The atmosphere, the planet's surface, and Earth's living things all absorb these photons. Radiation in the infrared region of the spectrum warms Earth and its oceans. The cells of our retinas are tuned to the wavelengths of visible light. Photons associated with different wavelengths are absorbed, and the energy is used to "excite" electrons in biological molecules. Some electrons jump to higher energy levels, triggering a series of complex chemical reactions that ultimately lead to sight. Compared with animals, green plants capture most of their photons in an even narrower region of the visible spectrum (corresponding to red light). **Photosynthesis** is the process through which green plants (including algae) and some bacteria capture the energy of sunlight to produce glucose and oxygen from carbon dioxide and water.

Remember that as the wavelength of light *decreases*, the energy carried by each photon *increases*. Photons in the UV region of the spectrum are sufficiently energetic to displace electrons from neutral molecules, converting them into positively charged species. Even shorter UV wavelength photons break bonds, causing molecules to come apart. In living things, such changes disrupt cells and create the potential for genetic defects and cancer. The interaction of UV radiation with chemical bonds is shown schematically in Figure 2.9.

It is part of the fascinating symmetry of nature that this interaction of radiation with matter explains both the damage ultraviolet radiation can cause and the atmospheric mechanism that protects us from it. We turn next to understanding the ultraviolet shield provided by oxygen and ozone in our stratosphere.

See Sections 3.2 and 3.5 for more about the role of photosynthesis in climate change and in the carbon cycle.

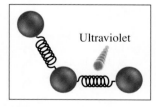 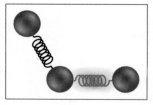 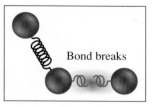

Figure 2.9

Ultraviolet radiation is able to break some, but not all, chemical bonds. Bonds are represented as springs that hold the atoms together but allow the atoms to move relative to each other.

2.6 | The Oxygen–Ozone Screen

We know the colors of visible light by their names, red, blue, yellow, and so on. Similarly, we call ultraviolet light by different names. Admittedly, however, these names are not as colorful: UV-A, UV-B, and UV-C. UV-A lies closest to the violet region of visible light and is the lowest in energy; you may know it as "black light." In contrast, UV-C has the highest energy and lies next to the X-ray region of the electromagnetic spectrum. Table 2.4 shows the characteristics of the different types of UV light.

Your Turn 2.14   The ABCs of Solar UV

a. Arrange UV–A, UV–B, and UV–C in order of increasing wavelength.
b. Is the order for increasing energy the same as for wavelength? Explain.
c. Should you use a sunscreen that claims to protect against UV–C? Explain.

Answer

c. No, you should not. No protection is needed for UV–C, because this set of UV wavelengths is absorbed up in the stratosphere.

As you saw from the previous activity, UV-C radiation from the Sun is absorbed in the upper atmosphere before it ever reaches the ground. Both oxygen and ozone absorb light of these wavelengths. As we noted in Chapter 1, about 21% of the atmosphere consists of oxygen, O_2. Photons with energy corresponding to 242 nm or less have sufficient energy to break the bond in an O_2 molecule. These wavelengths are found in the UV-C region.

$$O_2 \xrightarrow[\lambda \leq 242 \text{ nm}]{\text{UV photon}} 2\,O \qquad\qquad \textbf{[2.4]}$$

If O_2 were the only molecule absorbing UV light from the Sun, Earth's surface and the creatures that live on it would still be subjected to damaging radiation in the range of 242–320 nm. It is here that O_3 plays its important protective role. The O_3 molecule is more easily broken apart than O_2. Recall that the atoms in the O_2 molecule are connected with a double bond, but each of the bonds in O_3 is somewhere between a single and double bond in length and in strength. Accordingly, the bonds in O_3 are weaker than the double bonds in O_2. Therefore, photons of a lower energy (longer wavelength) are sufficient to separate the atoms in O_3. Indeed, photons of wavelength 320 nm or less break the O-to-O bond in ozone.

$$O_3 \xrightarrow[\lambda \leq 320 \text{ nm}]{\text{UV photon}} O_2 + O \qquad\qquad \textbf{[2.5]}$$

Table 2.4	Types of UV Radiation		
Type	Wavelength	Relative Energy	Comments
UV–A	320–400 nm	Lowest energy	Least damaging and reaches the Earth's surface in greatest amount
UV–B	280–320 nm	Higher energy than UV–A but less energetic than UV–C	More damaging than UV–A but less damaging than UV–C. Most UV–B is absorbed by O_3 in the stratosphere.
UV–C	200–280 nm	Highest energy	Most damaging but not a problem because it is completely absorbed by O_2 and O_3 in the stratosphere

Consider This 2.15   Energy and Wavelength

We just stated that it takes photons in the UV–C range ($\leq$ 242 nm) to break the double bond in O_2. The bonds in O_3 are somewhat weaker than those in O_2, so lower energy photons ($\leq$ 320 nm) can break those bonds. Just how much greater is the energy of a 242–nm photon than that of a 320–nm photon?

Hint: One approach could be to calculate the ratio of the energies for a 242–nm photon and that of a 320–nm photon and then to compare that with the ratio of their wavelengths. Look for values of Planck's constant and the speed of light in Appendix 1.

Equations 2.4 and 2.5, together with earlier equation 2.1 (that showed the formation of O_3 from O_2), are part of a set of chemical reactions in the stratosphere. Every day, 300,000,000 (3×10^8) tons of stratospheric O_3 forms, and an equal mass decomposes. New matter is neither created nor destroyed but merely changes its chemical form. So the overall concentration of ozone remains constant in this natural cycle. The process is an example of a **steady state,** a condition in which a dynamic system is in balance so that there is no net change in concentration of the major species involved. A steady state arises when a number of chemical reactions, typically competing reactions, balance each other. The **Chapman cycle,** as shown in Figure 2.10, represents the first set of natural steady-state reactions proposed for stratospheric ozone. This natural cycle includes chemical reactions for both ozone formation and decomposition.

This set of reactions is named after Sydney Chapman, a physicist who first proposed it in 1929.

Your Turn 2.16   The Ozone Layer

a. Ozone is formed by the reaction of oxygen atoms with oxygen molecules. Write the chemical reaction.
b. Up in the stratosphere, what is the source of the oxygen atoms?
c. Up in the stratosphere, the lifetime of a given ozone molecule ranges from days to years. For example, in the ozone layer, an O_3 molecule can persist for several months. What does stratospheric ozone break down into?
d. In contrast, at ground level, ozone molecules react in a matter of minutes rather than months. Why the difference?

Answer
d. Down in the troposphere, the air is much denser ("thicker"). Ozone molecules quickly bump into other molecules and react with them. For example, if you happen to breathe air containing ozone pollution, the O_3 quickly reacts with your lung tissue, potentially damaging it.

In a later section, we consider what happens when something disturbs the steady state of the Chapman cycle, leading to destruction of the protective stratospheric ozone.

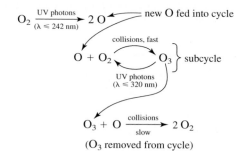

Figure 2.10

The Chapman cycle.

Because of the presence of O_2 and O_3 in the stratosphere, only certain UV wavelengths reach the surface of the Earth. However, these wavelengths still can cause harm, which is the topic of the next section.

2.7 | Biological Effects of Ultraviolet Radiation

NASA, the National Aeronautical and Space Administration (U.S.)

Look for more about the Montreal Protocol in Section 2.11.

The following scenario is from an unexpected source.

> *The year is 2065. Nearly two-thirds of Earth's ozone is gone—not just over the poles, but everywhere. The infamous ozone hole over Antarctica, first discovered in the 1980s, is a year-round fixture, with a twin over the North Pole. The ultraviolet (UV) radiation falling on mid-latitude cities like Washington, D.C., is strong enough to cause sunburn in just five minutes. DNA-mutating UV radiation is up 650 percent, with likely harmful effects on plants, animals, and human skin cancer rates.*

Is this a grim portrayal of the future from some sci-fi novel? Not at all! Rather, these words are quoted from a U.S. federal administration, NASA. They are based on the findings of a 2009 scientific journal article in which scientists described the world in which we would have lived had the nations of the world not acted to repair the ozone hole.

Thanks to the Montreal Protocol on Substances that Deplete the Ozone Layer—an amazing piece of world history—we are not and will not be living in a world with dangerous levels of ultraviolet (UV) radiation. But in order to understand why in the 1980s a hole in the ozone layer set off such planetary alarm bells, you need to know how the UV radiation affects the cells of animals and plants. Accordingly, we now turn to this topic.

As you learned in the previous section, the sunlight that reaches Earth's surface contains different types of light, including UV-A and UV-B. When this radiation falls on your skin and is absorbed, it sets off a chain of events. First, the energy of the UV photons is deposited in the cell. In turn, if the energy is high enough, it may cause some of the chemical bonds in nearby molecules to break. Earlier, in Figure 2.9, you saw a representation of the bond-breaking process. In most cases, your body repairs the damage or the cell dies. Depending on your skin color, your skin may tan or burn and you may never develop skin cancer.

DNA stands for deoxyribonucleic acid. Look for more about the chemistry of DNA in Chapter 12.

Another outcome is possible, however. Although bonds can break in many different molecules, those broken in the DNA molecule of a skin cell are of the most concern because the DNA may be mutated in a way that leads to cancer. Important points about skin cancer include:

- Most skin cancers are linked to the exposure to sunlight.
- Although skin cancer can appear at any age, it is more common in older people. Skin cancers can develop many years after repeated, excessive exposure has stopped.
- The UV-B in sunlight at the Earth's surface is the culprit. UV-A may also play a role.
- Cancer can arise in different types of skin cells. Those in the basal and squamous cells are common but seldom fatal. In contrast, cancers in the melanocytes (melanomas) are more deadly.

Consider This 2.17   Biological Sensitivity

The sensitivity of DNA in a skin cell to UV light from the Sun increases with decreasing wavelength.

a. Propose an explanation for this fact.
b. Once the wavelength becomes short enough to fall in the UV–C region, the UV light is no longer of concern for skin cancer. Explain why.

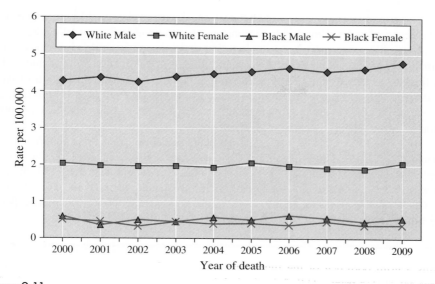

Figure 2.11

Melanoma mortality rates for people (all ages) in the United States, 2000–2009.
Note: All groups include Hispanics.

Source: National Cancer Institute, SEER Fast Stats, 2012.

Skin cancer rates are slowly rising in all countries, despite increased awareness of the dangers of exposure to UV radiation. Figure 2.11 presents the trends in skin cancer in the United States. Although everybody is susceptible to skin cancer, from the graphs you can see that it is more common for whites, with the highest rates for white males. You also can see that the rate of skin cancer is either constant or very slowly increasing. Not shown, the rates for lung and colorectal cancer have been slowly dropping in the United States.

The yearly mortality rates for lung and colorectal cancers are approximately 170 and 50 deaths per 100,000 each year, respectively.

Your Turn 2.18   Skin Cancer Trends

Trends in melanoma mortality, such as those in Figure 2.11, don't reveal the actual number of deaths.

a. Estimate the number of deaths from melanoma skin cancer in the United States in 2000 and in 2009. In 2000 and 2009, the overall death rates were 2.7 and 2.8 people per 100,000, respectively. By how many people has the number increased or decreased?
   Hint: Assume the population of the United States to be 281 million in 2000 and 307 million in 2009.
b. Why don't the values that you obtain correlate to the overall skin cancer death rate in the United States of about 12,000 people per year?

Answers

a. From Figure 2.11, there were approximately 7.5 deaths per 100,000 people in both 2000 and 2009. If you retrieve the actual values from SEER, it was 7.4 and 7.7 deaths, respectively. Using the population estimates, this translates to about 7600 deaths in 2000 and 8600 deaths in 2009, showing an increase of about 1000 deaths.
b. These data are for melanoma only. Basal and squamous cell skin cancers also contribute to the total.

Skeptical Chemist 2.19   Skin Cancer in White Men and Women

Depending on its source (and who funded the research), data do not always stand the test of time. Consider the possibility that Figure 2.11 is in error, that is, skin cancer rates actually are higher for white women than for white men. Why might this be the case? Research the data yourself, from multiple sources if possible, to check this possibility. Comment on why you either trust or distrust the data sources.

Again, as noted in the opening of this section, we avoided a world with higher rates of skin cancer (and sunburns) via the concerted actions of nations worldwide.

Currently, your risk of developing skin cancer connects to a complex blend of chemistry, physics, biology, geography, and human psychology. Factors include where you live, how well you protect yourself from the Sun when its rays are the most harsh, whether or not you do indoor tanning, and how well you respond to public health campaigns for early detection of skin cancer. Our genetic makeup is another important factor that we are unable to change.

The U.S. Centers for Disease Control and Prevention (CDC) warns that the use of tanning booths, tanning beds, and sun lamps is dangerous, particularly for younger people. The reason is straightforward: these booths use both UV-A and UV-B, the same dangerous wavelengths that are emitted by the Sun. Tanning is a response to skin injury. The CDC points out that the concept of "getting a base tan" is not as smart as people may think. Rather, it is wise to protect your skin from the Sun.

According to the Australian Department of Health and Aging (2007), Australia has the highest skin cancer rates in the world.

Consider This 2.20   Tanning Spas

The indoor tanning industry runs a public relations campaign that highlights positive findings about indoor tanning, promoting it as part of a healthy lifestyle. Countering these claims are the public health campaigns that there is no such thing as a "safe tan" for any skin type. Investigate at least two sources that present different points of view and list the arguments on both sides. State the course of action that you recommend.

Wearing protective sunscreen is one way to reduce the risk of skin cancer. Such products contain compounds that absorb UV-B to some extent together with others that absorb UV-A. The American Academy of Dermatology recommends a sunscreen with a skin protection factor (SPF) of 15 to 30. But wearing a sunscreen does not mean that you are without risk from UV rays. Because you may expose yourself for a longer time without burning, sunscreens ultimately may cause greater skin damage.

Wearing protective sunblock is another. These products physically block the light from reaching your skin, as does tightly woven clothing. Sunblock creams reflect the light; some absorb UV as well. A familiar example may be the white opaque cream used by lifeguards ("lifeguard nose") at a pool or beach. This sunblock contains small white particles of ZnO (zinc oxide) and/or TiO_2 (titanium dioxide) and has a long-term track record of safety.

However, the "see-through" formulations of ZnO and TiO_2 that contain these compounds in nanoparticle form are more controversial. Because the particles of ZnO and TiO_2 are so microscopically tiny, they do not scatter light. As a result, the sunblock is transparent rather than opaque, definitely a plus to those who wear it. The nanoparticle products spread more evenly, are cost-effective, and are extremely effective at both absorbing and reflecting UV radiation. However, nanoparticles may present a risk if they penetrate the skin. Both consumers and government agencies continue to call for further studies to better quantify the risks. Controversial or not, sunblocks play an important role in protecting us from UV radiation.

Nanotechnology was defined in Section 1.7. Look for more on nanoparticles in Chapter 8.

Should you put on protective sunblock or sunscreen and/or cover up? The Ultraviolet Index Forecast, issued by the U.S. National Weather Service, provides a convenient way to assess the harshness of the Sun's rays. Ranging from 0 to 15, the UV Index values are based on how long it takes skin damage to occur. Notice the inverse relationship: the higher the number, the less time it takes skin damage to occur. They are color coded for ease of interpretation.

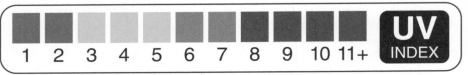

1   2   3   4   5   6   7   8   9   10   11+   **UV INDEX**

Source: U.S. EPA.

Table 2.5	The UV Index Scale	
Exposure Category	**Index**	**Tips to Avoid Harmful Exposure to UV**
LOW	< 2	If you burn easily, cover up and use sunscreen.
MODERATE	3–5	Stay in shade when the rays of the Sun are the strongest.
HIGH	6–7	Reduce exposure between 10 AM and 4 PM. Cover up, wear a hat and sunglasses, and use sunscreen.
VERY HIGH	8–10	White sand and bright surfaces reflect UV, increasing your exposure. Minimize exposure between 10 AM and 4 PM.
EXTREME	11+	Take full precaution against sunburn. Unprotected skin can burn in minutes. Avoid the Sun between 10 AM and 4 PM.

Source: U.S. EPA, 2009.

The UV Index values also are accompanied by suggestions to help you protect eyes and skin from sun damage, as shown in Table 2.5.

Although the UV Index focuses on skin damage, this is not the only biological effect of UV radiation. Your eyes can be damaged as well. For example, all people, no matter what the pigmentation level of their skin, are susceptible to retinal damage caused by UV exposure. Another effect is cataracts, a clouding of the lens of the eye caused by excessive exposure to UV-B radiation. It has been estimated that a 10% decrease in the ozone layer could create up to 2 million new cataract cases globally. However, just as proper clothing and sunscreen can cut down on skin damage, wearing optical-quality sunglasses capable of blocking at least 99% of UV-A and UV-B can protect your eyes. Learn more about sunglasses in this next activity.

Consider This 2.21   Protecting Your Eyes

Sunglasses do more than offer a fashion statement. They also protect your eyes from UV rays. Check out several manufacturers to learn the virtues of their products. What activities especially require good UV eye protection? Report on your findings.

As you might suspect, the UV light that hits the surface of our planet affects more than the skin and eyes of humans. Plants, animals, and microorganisms also are susceptible to damage. The extent depends on the particular animal or plant, again with the shorter wavelength being the most highly damaging. Viruses and bacteria are particularly sensitive; in fact, UV-C can be used to sterilize surfaces and medical instruments. UV radiation also can harm young marine life near the surface of the water, such as floating fish eggs, fish and shrimp larvae, and young fish.

Given the harmful effects of too much UV radiation, you now can see why the decreasing stratospheric ozone concentrations observed in the 1980s set off planetary alarm bells. The next two sections tell the tale of the ozone hole and how it unexpectedly appeared on our planet.

The shorter the wavelength of UV light, the higher the energy.

2.8 | Stratospheric Ozone Destruction: Global Observations and Causes

Switzerland holds the record for the longest continuous set of ozone level measurements. Since 1926, stratospheric O_3 concentrations have been measured at the Swiss Meteorological Institute. More recently, starting in 1979, satellite-mounted detectors have been beaming down data on ozone levels at many points. These measurements show both that the natural concentration of stratospheric O_3 is not uniform across the globe and that the levels have changed over time.

On average, the total O_3 concentration is higher the closer one gets to either pole, with the exception of the seasonal ozone "hole" over the Antarctic. The formation of ozone in the Chapman cycle is triggered when an O_2 molecule absorbs a photon of UV-C light, splitting into two O atoms. These in turn react with O_2 to form O_3.

$$O_2 \xrightarrow[(\lambda \leq 242 \text{ nm})]{\text{UV-C}} 2\,O \qquad \text{[2.6a]}$$

$$O + O_2 \longrightarrow O_3 \qquad \text{[2.6b]}$$

Therefore, ozone production increases with the intensity of the radiation striking the stratosphere, which in turn depends primarily on the angle of the Earth with respect to the Sun and the distance between the Sun and the Earth. At the equator, the period of highest intensity occurs at the equinox (March and October) when the Sun is directly overhead. Outside the tropics, the Sun is never directly overhead, so the maximum intensity occurs at the summer solstice (June in the Northern Hemisphere, December in the Southern). The angle of Earth with respect to the Sun dominates both ozone production and the seasons. There is a slight (~7%) increase, however, in solar power reaching Earth in early January, when the Earth is nearest the Sun, compared with July, when the Earth is farthest away. In addition, the amount of radiation emitted by the Sun changes over an 11- to 12-year cycle related to sunspot activity. This variation also influences O_3 concentrations, but only by a percent or two. The wind patterns in the stratosphere cause other variations in ozone concentrations, some on a seasonal basis and others over a longer cycle. To further complicate matters, seemingly random fluctuations often occur.

Extraordinary images of the Earth, such as the one that opens this chapter, are color-coded to show stratospheric ozone concentrations. The dark blue and purple regions indicate where the lowest concentrations of O_3 are observed. Total ozone levels above Earth's surface are expressed in Dobson units (DU). A value of 250–270 DU is typical at the equator. As one moves away from the equator, values range between 300 and 350 DU, with seasonal variations. At the highest northern latitudes, values can be as high as 400 DU.

Of special interest is the thinning of ozone (the "ozone hole") that occurs seasonally over the South Pole. Indeed, these changes were so pronounced that, when the British monitoring team at Halley Bay in Antarctica first observed it in 1985, they thought their instruments were malfunctioning! The area over which ozone levels are reported to be less than 220 DU is usually considered to be the "hole." From the mid-1990s on, the annual size of the ozone hole has nearly equaled the total area of the North American continent, and in some cases exceeded it.

Check out the dramatic decline in stratospheric ozone levels observed near the South Pole shown in Figure 2.12. In recent years, the minimum has been around 100 DU. Keep in mind that seasonal variation has always occurred in ozone concentration over the South Pole, with a minimum in late September or early October—the Antarctic spring. Unprecedented, however, is the striking decrease in this minimum that has been observed in recent decades.

In conjunction with the Earth's energy balance and global warming, look for information about solar irradiance in Section 3.9.

Recall that a Dobson unit corresponds to about one ozone molecule for every billion molecules and atoms of air.

Consider This 2.22   This Year's Ozone Hole

Starting in September, citizens and scientists alike examine the data for the ozone hole over Antarctica. What is happening this year? NASA posts the data on its website. For the most recent year:

a. What is the area of the hole? How does this compare with recent years?
b. What is the lowest reading observed for ozone? Again, how does this compare?

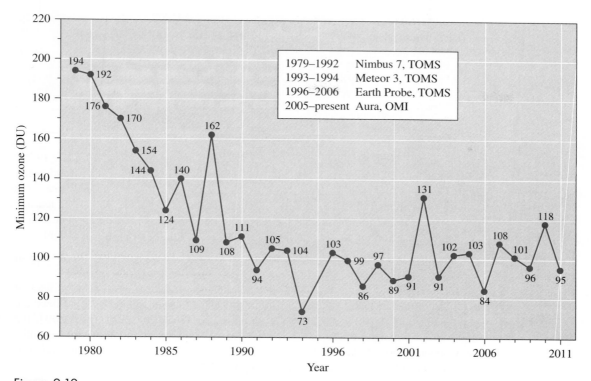

Figure 2.12

The lowest values, in Dobson units, recorded each spring (1979–2011) for stratospheric ozone in Antarctica. TOMS (Total Ozone-Measuring Spectrometer) and OMI (Ozone Monitoring Instrument) are analytical instruments.

Note: The high value in 2002 was due to an early breakdown of the vortex that isolates polar from mid-latitude air. No data were acquired in 1995.

Source: NASA Ozone Watch.

The major natural cause of ozone destruction, wherever it takes place around the globe, is a series of reactions involving water vapor and its breakdown products. The great majority of the H_2O molecules that evaporate from the oceans and lakes fall back to Earth's surface as rain or snow. But a few molecules reach the stratosphere, where the H_2O concentration is about 5 ppm. At this altitude, photons of UV radiation trigger the dissociation of water molecules into hydrogen (H·) and hydroxyl (·OH) free radicals. A **free radical** is a highly reactive chemical species with one or more unpaired electrons. An unpaired electron is often indicated with a dot:

$$H_2O \xrightarrow{\text{photon}} H\cdot + \cdot OH \qquad \textbf{[2.7]}$$

Because of the unpaired electron, free radicals are highly reactive. Thus, the H· and ·OH radicals participate in many reactions, including some that ultimately convert O_3 to O_2. This is the most efficient mechanism for destroying ozone at altitudes above 50 km.

Water molecules and their breakdown products are not the only agents responsible for natural ozone destruction. Another is the free radical ·NO, also called nitrogen monoxide. Most of the ·NO in the stratosphere is of natural origin. It is formed from nitrous oxide, N_2O, a naturally occurring compound of nitrogen that is produced in the soil and oceans by microorganisms and gradually drifts up to the stratosphere. Although N_2O is quite stable in the troposphere, up in the stratosphere it can react with O atoms to produce ·NO. Little can or should be done to control this process. It is part of a natural cycle involving compounds of nitrogen, as we will see in Chapter 6.

Free radicals appear in several other contexts.

Chapter 1: ·OH, formation of NO_2 and then tropospheric ozone

Chapter 6: ·OH, formation of SO_3 in acid rain

Chapter 7: ·OH and $H_2O\cdot^+$, damage to cells by nuclear radiation

Chapter 9: R·, polymerization of ethylene

The air pollutant NO (nitrogen monoxide or nitric oxide) is highly reactive, which is one of the reasons it causes harm to your lungs. In contrast, N_2O (nitrous oxide or "laughing gas") is a very stable molecule that persists for decades.

Your Turn 2.23   Free Radicals

a. Draw the Lewis structure for the ·OH free radical. The unpaired electron goes on the O atom.
b. Draw the Lewis structure for the ·NO free radical. The unpaired electron goes on the N atom. *Note:* In Chapter 1, in the context of air pollution, we wrote simply NO.
c. In contrast, N_2O has no unpaired electrons. Draw its Lewis structure. *Hint:* Place one of the N atoms in the middle.

Human activities also can alter steady-state concentrations of NO. In the 1970s, people became concerned about the increase in NO concentration that would result from building a fleet of Concorde SSTs (supersonic transports). These planes were designed to fly at an altitude of 15–20 km, the region of the ozone layer. As you learned in Chapter 1, hot engines produce NO as part of the exhaust gas stream. The NO is produced by the hot engines of a jet plane on takeoff, landing, and during flight.

$$N_2 + O_2 \xrightarrow{\text{high temperature}} 2\,NO \qquad\qquad \textbf{[2.8]}$$

Scientists carried out experiments and calculations to predict the effects of a fleet of SSTs. They concluded that the risks would outweigh the benefits. So people decided, partly on scientific grounds, not to build an American fleet of SSTs. Until 2003, the Anglo–French Concorde was the only commercial plane that operated at this altitude. The Concorde took its last flight on October 24, 2003. Both safety concerns and economic factors played roles in ending the flights of these remarkable jets.

Even when the effects of water, nitrogen oxides, and other naturally occurring compounds are included in stratospheric models, the measured ozone concentration is still lower than predicted. Measurements worldwide indicate that the ozone concentration has been decreasing over the past 20 years. There is a good deal of fluctuation in the data, but the trend is clear. The stratospheric ozone concentration at midlatitudes (60° south to 60° north) has decreased by more than 8% in some cases. These changes cannot be correlated with changes in the intensity of solar radiation, so we must look elsewhere for an explanation. Thus it is time to turn our attention to chlorofluorocarbons.

2.9 | Chlorofluorocarbons: Properties, Uses, and Interactions with Ozone

A major cause of stratospheric ozone depletion was uncovered through the masterful scientific sleuthing of F. Sherwood Rowland, Mario Molina, and Paul Crutzen. For their work, the trio jointly won the 1995 Nobel Prize in chemistry. They analyzed vast quantities of atmospheric data and studied hundreds of chemical reactions. As with most scientific investigations, some uncertainties remained. Nonetheless, their evidence all pointed to an unlikely group of compounds: the chlorofluorocarbons.

As the name implies, **chlorofluorocarbons (CFCs)** are compounds composed of the elements chlorine, fluorine, and carbon (but do not contain the element hydrogen). Fluorine and chlorine are members of the same chemical group, the halogens (Figure 2.13). In their elemental state, all of the halogens are diatomic molecules, but only fluorine and chlorine are gases. Fluorine is not shown in the figure because it is so reactive that it would react with the glass vessel. In contrast, CFC molecules are highly unreactive.

To get started with CFCs, let's examine two examples.

Chlorine

Bromine

Iodine

Figure 2.13

Selected elements from Group 7A, the halogen family.

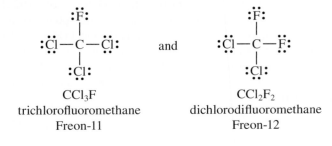

CCl₃F
trichlorofluoromethane
Freon-11

and

CCl₂F₂
dichlorodifluoromethane
Freon-12

Note how the names show the connection of CFCs to methane, CH_4. The prefixes *di-* and *tri-* specify the number of chlorine and fluorine atoms that substitute for hydrogen atoms of methane. These two CFCs also are known by their trade names, Freon-11 and Freon-12. You may also hear them called CFC-11 and CFC-12, respectively, following a naming scheme developed in the 1930s by chemists at DuPont.

Methane, the smallest hydrocarbon, was described in Chapter 1.

CFCs do not occur in nature; we humans synthesized them for a variety of uses. This is an important verification point in the debate over the role of CFCs in stratospheric ozone depletion. As we saw in the previous section, other contributors to the destruction of ozone, such as the ·OH and ·NO free radicals, are formed in the atmosphere both from natural sources and human activities.

For more about naming Freons see end-of-chapter question #53.

Rightly, the introduction of CCl_2F_2 as a refrigerant gas in the 1930s was hailed as a great triumph of chemistry and an important advance in consumer safety. It replaced ammonia or sulfur dioxide, two toxic and corrosive refrigerant gases. In many respects, CCl_2F_2 was (and still is) an ideal substitute. It is nontoxic, odorless, colorless, and does not burn. In fact, the CCl_2F_2 molecule is so stable that it does not react with much of anything!

Given the desirable nontoxic properties of CFCs, they soon were put to other uses. For example, CCl_3F was often blown into polymer mixtures to make foams for cushions and foamed insulation. Other CFCs served as propellants in aerosol spray cans and as nontoxic solvents for oil and grease.

Polymers and plastics are the topic of Chapter 9. Gases that "puff up" the plastic, making it into a foam, are called blowing agents.

Halons are close cousins of CFCs. Like them, halons are inert, nontoxic compounds that contain chlorine or fluorine (or both, but no hydrogen). But in addition, they contain bromine. For example, here is the Lewis structure for bromotrifluoromethane, $CBrF_3$, also known as Halon-1301.

$$\ddot{:}\!\overset{\displaystyle ..}{\underset{\displaystyle ..}{Br}}\!\ddot{:}$$
$$\ddot{:}\!F\!-\!C\!-\!F\!\ddot{:}$$
$$\ddot{:}\!\underset{..}{F}\!\ddot{:}$$

You will find different definitions for the chemical composition of halons, depending on where you look. Sometimes halons are defined by their use (in suppressing fires) rather than by their chemical composition.

Halons are used as fire suppressants. They are especially helpful when a fire hose or sprinkler system would be inappropriate, for instance in libraries (especially rare book rooms), grease fires (where water might spread the fire), chemical stockrooms (where some chemicals react with water), and aircraft (where hosing down the cockpit would definitely be a bad idea).

For better or worse, the synthesis of CFCs has had a major effect on our lives. Because CFCs are nontoxic, nonflammable, cheap, and widely available, they revolutionized air conditioning, making it readily accessible for homes, office buildings, shops, schools, and automobiles. Beginning in the 1960s and 1970s, CFCs helped to spur the growth of cities in hot and humid parts of the world. In effect, a major demographic shift occurred because of CFC-based technology that transformed the economy and business potential of entire regions of the globe.

In the United States, CFCs helped spur the growth of cities with hot, humid weather, including Atlanta, Houston, Tampa, and Memphis.

Ironically, the very property that makes CFCs ideal for so many applications—their chemical inertness—ended up doing harm to our atmosphere. The C−Cl and C−F bonds in the CFCs are so strong that the molecules are virtually indestructible. For example, it has been estimated that an average CCl_2F_2 molecule can persist in the atmosphere for 120 years before it meets some fate that decomposes it. In contrast, it only takes about five years for atmospheric wind currents to bring molecules up to the stratosphere, which is exactly where some of the CFC molecules ended up.

In 1973, Rowland and Molina, motivated largely by intellectual curiosity, set out to study the fate of stratospheric CFC molecules. They understood that with increasing altitude, the concentrations of oxygen and ozone decrease, but the intensity of UV radiation increases. They reasoned photons of high-energy UV-C light (< 220 nm) would break C−Cl bonds. Here is the chemical reaction that releases chlorine atoms from dichlorodifluoromethane.

$$F\!-\!\overset{\displaystyle Cl}{\underset{\displaystyle F}{\overset{|}{\underset{|}{C}}}}\!-\!Cl \xrightarrow[\lambda\,\leq\,220\text{ nm}]{\text{UV photon}} F\!-\!\overset{\displaystyle Cl}{\underset{\displaystyle F}{\overset{|}{\underset{|}{C}}}}\!\cdot\; +\; \cdot Cl \qquad \textbf{[2.9]}$$

A chlorine atom has seven outer electrons, one of them unpaired. We depict it as Cl· or ·Cl to emphasize this unpaired electron. The chlorine atom exhibits a strong tendency to achieve a stable octet by combining and sharing electrons with another atom. Rowland and Molina and subsequent researchers hypothesized that this reactivity would result in a series of reactions. Although CFCs are known to destroy stratospheric ozone via several pathways, we illustrate with a typical one known to take place in polar regions.

First, the Cl· free radical pulls an oxygen atom away from an O_3 molecule to form ClO·, chlorine monoxide and an O_2 molecule. The coefficient 2 is not canceled because we anticipate using it the next step.

$$2\,Cl\cdot + 2\,O_3 \longrightarrow 2\,ClO\cdot + 2\,O_2 \qquad \textbf{[2.10]}$$

The ClO· species is another free radical; it has 13 outer electrons (7 + 6). Recent experimental evidence indicates that 75–80% of stratospheric ozone depletion involves joining two ClO· radicals to form ClOOCl.

$$2\,ClO\cdot \longrightarrow ClOOCl \qquad \textbf{[2.11]}$$

In turn, ClOOCl decomposes in a two-step sequence.

$$ClOOCl \xrightarrow{\text{UV photon}} ClOO\cdot + \cdot Cl \qquad \textbf{[2.12a]}$$

$$ClOO\cdot \longrightarrow Cl\cdot + O_2 \qquad \textbf{[2.12b]}$$

We can treat this set of chemical equations as if they were mathematical equations. If we add them together, here is the result.

$$2\,\cancel{Cl\cdot} + 2\,O_3 + 2\,\cancel{ClO\cdot} + \cancel{ClOOCl} + \cancel{ClOO\cdot} \longrightarrow$$
$$2\,\cancel{ClO\cdot} + 2\,O_2 + \cancel{ClOOCl} + \cancel{ClOO\cdot} + \cancel{Cl\cdot} + \cancel{Cl\cdot} + O_2 \quad \textbf{[2.13]}$$

Just as is done with mathematical equations, we can eliminate the duplicate Cl·, ClO·, and ClOOCl species from both sides of the chemical equation. The terms for O_2 on the right side of the equation, 2 O_2 and O_2, can be combined into 3 O_2. What remains is the net equation showing the conversion of ozone into oxygen gas.

$$2\,O_3 \longrightarrow 3\,O_2 \qquad \textbf{[2.14]}$$

Thus, the complex interaction of ozone with atomic chlorine provides a pathway for the destruction of ozone.

Notice that Cl· appears both as a reactant in equation 2.13 and as a product in equations 2.12a and 2.12b. This means that Cl· is both consumed *and* regenerated in the cycle, with no net change in its concentration. Such behavior is characteristic of a catalyst, a chemical substance that participates in a chemical reaction and influences its speed without undergoing permanent change. Atomic chlorine acts catalytically by being regenerated and recycled to remove more ozone molecules. On average, a single atom can catalyze the destruction of as many as 1×10^5 ozone molecules before it is carried back to the lower atmosphere by winds.

Interestingly, the mechanism just described for ozone destruction by CFCs in the stratosphere was not the one first proposed by Rowland and Molina. Their initial hypothesis was that Cl· reacted with O_3 to form ClO· and O_2. The second step proposed was that ClO· reacted with oxygen atoms to form O_2 and regenerate radicals.

$$Cl\cdot + O_3 \longrightarrow ClO\cdot + O_2 \qquad \textbf{[2.15]}$$

$$ClO\cdot + O \longrightarrow Cl\cdot + O_2 \qquad \textbf{[2.16]}$$

Although this mechanism did not prove to be the major one in the formation of the ozone hole, it did provide a reasonable explanation for why recycling a limited number of chlorine atoms could be responsible for the destruction of a large number of ozone molecules. But it is the cycle that primarily accounts for the destruction of ozone in the tropical and midlatitudes, regions in which the incident sunlight is more intense. As is often true in science, hypotheses need to be recast in light of experimental evidence.

Thankfully, almost all of the chlorine in the stratosphere is not in the active form of Cl· or ClO·. Rather, chlorine is incorporated into stable compounds that do not

The Br· free radical undergoes a comparable reaction, starting another cycle of ozone destruction. Br· is up to 10 times more effective than Cl· in destroying O_3.

Catalyst was defined in Section 1.11 in connection with catalytic converters.

destroy ozone. Hydrogen chloride (HCl) and chlorine nitrate (ClONO$_2$) are two such compounds. These form quite readily at altitudes below 30 km. Thus, chlorine atoms are fairly effectively removed from the region of highest ozone concentration (about 20–25 km). These gases, as we will see in Chapter 5, are water-soluble. So in the troposphere, they are removed from the air when they wash out in the rain.

Although HCl and ClONO$_2$ do not destroy ozone, they still are potential sources of Cl·. For example, HCl can react with the hydroxyl radical (·OH) to produce Cl·.

Your Turn 2.24   Bromine, Too!

Although we have been casting the discussion in terms of chlorine atoms, bromine atoms also play a role.

  a. Write chemical reactions involving bromine analogous to equations 2.10 and 2.15.
  b. Bromine concentrations are much lower than those of chlorine. Propose a reason why.

Answer

  b. Fewer of the substances that deplete ozone contain the element bromine. These compounds, such as CBrF$_3$ (Halon–1301) have been manufactured in smaller amounts.

Rowland, a professor at the University of California at Irvine, and Molina, then a postdoctoral fellow in Rowland's laboratory, published their first paper on CFCs and ozone depletion in 1974 in the scientific journal *Nature*. At about the same time, other scientists were obtaining the first experimental evidence of stratospheric ozone depletion and CFCs in the stratosphere. The conclusions were troublesome; the implications were that the use of CFCs should be discontinued. These initial reports were met with skepticism, as might be expected when much was at stake economically. But the precautionary principle ultimately prevailed. Action was taken to mitigate the loss of ozone before even worse ozone destruction took place.

Over the years, the Rowland–Molina hypothesis has been experimentally confirmed. Perhaps the most compelling evidence for the involvement of chlorine and chlorine monoxide is presented in Figure 2.14. It shows two sets of data from the Antarctic, one for O$_3$ concentration and the other for ClO·. Both are plotted versus the latitude at which samples were measured. As stratospheric O$_3$ concentration decreases, the concentration of stratospheric chlorine increases; the two curves mirror each other almost perfectly. The major effect is a decrease in ozone and an increase in chlorine monoxide as the South Pole is approached. Because equation 2.10 links ClO·, Cl·, and

Dr. Susan Solomon, a chemist, headed the team that first gathered stratospheric ClO· and ozone data over Antarctica. The data solidified the connection between CFCs and the ozone hole. She was just 30 years old at the time.

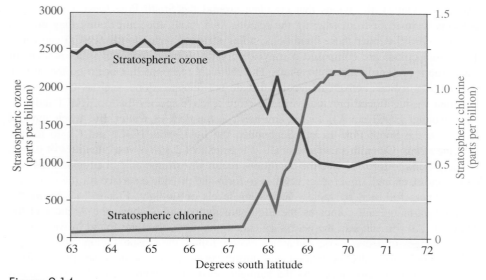

Figure 2.14

Antarctic stratospheric concentrations of ozone and reactive chlorine (from a flight into the Antarctic ozone hole, 1987).

Source: United Nations Environment Programme.

O_3, the conclusion is compelling. Figure 2.14 is sometimes described as the "smoking gun" for stratospheric ozone depletion.

Not all of the chlorine implicated in stratospheric ozone destruction comes from CFCs. Other chlorinated carbon compounds come from natural sources, such as sea water and volcanoes. However, most chlorine from natural sources is in water-soluble forms. Therefore, any natural chlorine-containing substances are washed out of the atmosphere by rainfall long before they can reach the stratosphere. Of particular significance are the data gathered by NASA and by international researchers that establish that high concentrations of HCl (hydrogen chloride) and HF (hydrogen fluoride) always occur together. Although some of the HCl might conceivably arise from a variety of natural sources, the only reasonable origin of stratospheric concentrations of HF is CFCs.

Consider This 2.25   Radio Talk Show Opinions

"And if prehistoric man merely got a sunburn, how is it that we are going to destroy the ozone layer with our air conditioners and underarm deodorants and cause everybody to get cancer? Obviously we're not . . . and we can't . . . and it's a hoax. Evidence is mounting all the time that ozone depletion, if occurring at all, is not doing so at an alarming rate."

Consider the first thing you would ask this talk-show host about these statements. Remember that you need to formulate a short and focused question to get any airtime!

Source: Limbaugh, R. 1993. *See, I Told You So.* New York: Pocket Books.

2.10 | The Antarctic Ozone Hole: A Closer Look

Ozone-depleting gases are present throughout the stratosphere. Furthermore, as a result of global wind patterns, CFCs are present in comparable abundance in lower parts of the atmosphere over *both* hemispheres. Why, then, have the greatest losses of stratospheric ozone occurred over Antarctica? And given that more ozone-depleting gases are emitted in the Northern Hemisphere, why are their effects felt most strongly in the Southern Hemisphere?

A special set of conditions exist in Antarctica, ones that relate to the fact that the lower stratosphere over the South Pole is the coldest spot on Earth. From June to September (Antarctic winter), the winds that circulate around the South Pole form a vortex that prevents warmer air from entering the region. As a result, the temperature may drop as low as -90 °C. Under these conditions, **polar stratospheric clouds (PSCs)** can form. These thin clouds are composed of tiny ice crystals formed from the small amount of water vapor present in the stratosphere. The chemical reactions that occur on the surface of these ice crystals convert molecules that do not deplete ozone, such as $ClONO_2$ and HCl that we mentioned previously, to the more reactive species that do: HOCl and Cl_2.

Neither HOCl nor Cl_2 causes any harm in the dark of winter. But when sunlight returns to the South Pole in late September, the light splits HOCl and Cl_2 to release chlorine atoms. Given this increase in Cl·, a species that destroys vast quantities of ozone, the hole starts to form. Notice the conditions required: extreme cold, a circular wind pattern (vortex), enough time for ice crystals to form and provide a surface for the reactions, and darkness followed by rapidly increasing levels of sunlight. Figure 2.15 shows the seasonal variation and compares the minimum temperatures above the Arctic and the Antarctic. As you can see, the necessary conditions more often are found in Antarctica.

Changes in ozone above Antarctica closely follow the seasonal temperatures. Typically a rapid ozone decline takes place during spring at the South Pole, that is, from September to early November. As the sunlight warms the stratosphere, the polar stratospheric clouds dissipate, halting the chemistry that occurs on the surfaces of their ice crystals. Then air from lower latitudes flows into the polar region, replenishing the depleted ozone levels. By the end of November, the hole is largely refilled. Although the deepest decrease in the ozone layer over Antarctica occurs during the spring, recent discoveries by

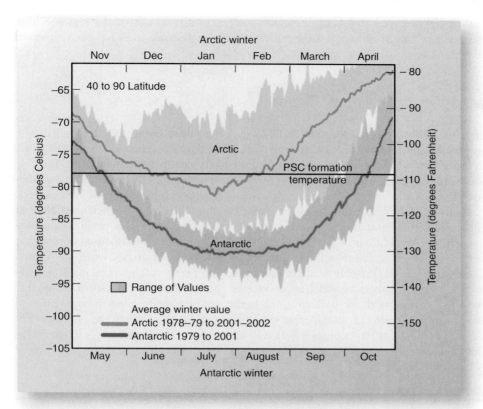

Figure 2.15

Minimum air temperatures in the polar lower stratosphere. Polar stratospheric clouds (PSCs) are thin clouds of ice crystals that form at very low temperatures.

Source: Scientific Assessment of Ozone Depletion: 2002, *World Meteorological Organization, United Nations Environment Programme.*

In the context of air quality, the tragedy of the commons was defined in Chapter 1.

British Antarctic Survey researchers indicate that the ozone depletion may begin earlier, as early as midwinter at the edges of the Antarctic, including over populated southern areas of South America.

This situation presents us with another example of the tragedy of the commons—a resource that is common to all and used by many, but has no one in particular responsible for it. As a result, the resource may be harmed to the detriment of all. Here, the resource is our protective ozone layer. Decreased stratospheric ozone over the South Pole leads to increased UV-B levels reaching the Earth. In turn, skin cancer rates increase in Australia and southern Chile. Australian scientists believe that wheat, sorghum, and pea crop yields have decreased as a result of increased UV radiation. Similar effects are also being felt in southern Chile in the area around Punta Arenas, and on the island of Tierra del Fuego at the southernmost tip of South America. Chile's health minister has warned the 120,000 residents of Punta Arenas not to be out in the Sun during the noon hours in the spring, when ozone depletion is greatest.

It turns out that the depletion in the Northern Hemisphere is not nearly as severe as it is in the Southern. The difference stems mainly from the fact that the air above the North Pole is not as cold. Even so, polar stratospheric clouds have been repeatedly observed in the Arctic. For example, the "mother-of-pearl" polar stratospheric clouds shown in Figure 2.16 were photographed above Porjus, a village in Swedish Lapland. However, these clouds do not lead to the formation of an ozone hole, as

Figure 2.16

Arctic polar stratospheric clouds in the northern part of Sweden.

Photo credit: Ross J. Salawitch, University of Maryland.

the air trapped over the Arctic generally begins to diffuse out of the region before the Sun gets bright enough to trigger as much ozone destruction as has been observed in Antarctica.

2.11 | Responses to a Global Concern

Once people understood the role of CFCs in ozone destruction, they responded with surprising speed. Individual countries took the first steps. For example, the use of CFCs in spray cans was banned in the United States and Canada in 1978; their use as foaming agents for plastics was discontinued in 1990. The problem of CFC production and subsequent release, however, spanned the globe and required global cooperation to address.

In 1977, in response to growing experimental evidence, UNEP (United Nations Environment Programme) brought together national leaders. Those in attendance adopted the World Plan of Action on the Ozone Layer and established a coordinating committee to guide future actions. The next step took place in 1985 with the Vienna Convention on the Protection of the Ozone Layer. Those nations present, eventually joined by all members of the United Nations, signed and later ratified a treaty that provided a framework for protecting the ozone layer. A major breakthrough came in 1987 with the signing of a treaty that set a timetable for phasing out the production of CFCs: the Montreal Protocol on Substances That Deplete the Ozone Layer. Each nation that signed the treaty then needed to ratify it. By 2009, all members of the United Nations had ratified it.

Consider This 2.26   Graffiti with a Message

a. This cartoon dates from the mid–1970s. Explain the basis of its humor.
b. Is this cartoon still relevant to the problem of ozone depletion today? Explain.
c. Create a cartoon of your own that deals with ozone depletion. Be sure that the chemistry is correct!

As shown in Figure 2.17 the decline in global CFC production was dramatic. The use of CFCs was gradually phased out by developed nations with a complete phase out in 2010. Halons, the bromine-containing cousins of CFCs, also were phased out.

Halting the production of CFCs and halons did not immediately cause the stratospheric concentration of chlorine to drop. Most Earth systems, including those in the atmosphere, are complex and slow to respond. In fact, the atmospheric concentrations of ozone-depleting gases continued to rise steadily through the 1990s, despite the restrictions of the Montreal Protocol and its subsequent amendments. One reason for this rise is the long atmospheric lifetime of CFCs, with many well over 100 years.

Even so, the signs are encouraging that the Montreal Protocol has had a beneficial effect. Decreases are now being observed in the amount of **effective stratospheric chlorine,** a measurement reflecting both chlorine- and bromine-containing gases in the stratosphere. The values take into account the greater effectiveness but lower concentration of bromine relative to chlorine in depleting stratospheric ozone. Figure 2.18 shows past levels of effective stratospheric chlorine together with a projection of those in the future.

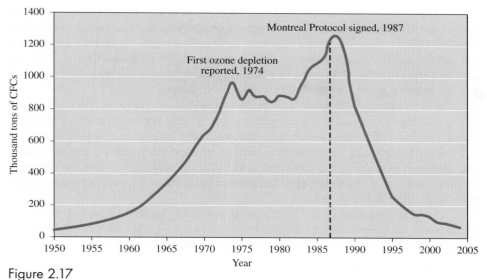

Figure 2.17

Global production of CFCs, 1950–2004.

Source: UNEP (United Nations Environment Programme).

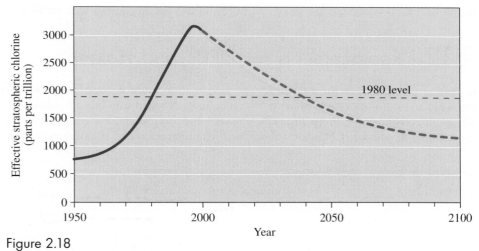

Figure 2.18

Concentrations of effective chlorine, 1950–2100. The yellow band shows an estimate of the uncertainty in the prediction.

Source: Scientific Assessment of Ozone Depletion: 2002, World Meteorological Organization, United Nations Environment Programme.

Stratospheric chlorine levels peaked in the late 1990s. Scientists estimate that even with the most stringent international controls of ozone-depleting chemicals, the stratospheric chlorine concentration will not drop to 2000 parts per trillion for many years. This concentration is significant because the Antarctic ozone hole first was documented when effective stratospheric chlorine reached that level.

Consider This 2.27   Past and Future Effective Chlorine Levels

Use Figures 2.17 and 2.18 to answer these questions.

a. In approximately what year did effective chlorine concentration peak? What was the reading in that year?

b. Is the peak year for effective chlorine concentration the same as the peak year for CFC production? Why or why not?

Although the Montreal Protocol and its subsequent adjustments set dates for the halt of all CFC production, the sale of existing stockpiles and recycled materials remains for now. This is necessary because appliances designed to operate using CFCs are still in use. For example, air conditioning units produced in the United States for cars and homes before 1996 use CFCs. But as you might surmise, both the paperwork and the price of legally obtained CFCs have risen sharply.

In large measure, the success of the Montreal Protocol lay in its provision to hold future meetings to set new goals and revise existing ones. For example, the 23rd Meeting of Parties in 2011 was held in Bali, Indonesia; the 24th meeting was held in 2012 in Geneva, Switzerland. At the early meetings, atmospheric scientists, environmentalists, chemical manufacturers, and government officials soon agreed that the Montreal Protocol was not stringent enough. Each subsequent meeting produced amendments that the parties ratified to increase the restrictions.

The year 2012 marked the 25th anniversary of the Montreal Protocol. By avoiding a world with increased levels of ultraviolet radiation, this anniversary was the occasion of much celebration. Even so, several challenges lie ahead:

MONTREAL PROTOCOL
1987-2012

Source: UNEP

- Securing funds to assist developing nations in phasing out substances that deplete the ozone layer
- Policing the illegal trade of substances that have been banned
- Phasing out the chemicals that replaced CFCs because they are potent greenhouse gases

In the next section, we tell the story of CFC replacements, beginning with HCFCs.

2.12 | Replacements for CFCs and Halons

In finding a replacement for a CFC, no one advocated a return to toxic gases such as ammonia and sulfur dioxide in home refrigeration units. Similarly, no one advocated giving up air-conditioning entirely. Instead, chemists sought to prepare new compounds that were similar to nontoxic CFCs but without their long-term effects on stratospheric ozone.

Your Turn 2.28   Home Refrigerators

Both ammonia and sulfur dioxide have excellent properties as refrigerant gases. However, they are dangerous for use in home refrigerators and air-conditioning units.

a. Sulfur dioxide (SO_2) is one of the air pollutants mentioned in Chapter 1. What are its health effects, even at very low concentrations?
b. Although not an outside air pollutant, ammonia (NH_3) may be present as one indoors. If you have ever cleaned with household ammonia (Figure 2.19), you perhaps have choked on the smell of ammonia. Why is ammonia dangerous as a refrigerant gas?

Answer
b. If accidentally released, ammonia rapidly dissolves in water, including the moist tissues of your lungs. The alkaline solution of ammonium hydroxide that is produced damages lung tissue and in severe cases can cause death. Household ammonia, although much less potent than pure ammonia, nonetheless carries the warning to use in a well-ventilated area and to avoid contact with skin and eyes.

Figure 2.19

Household ammonia is not a refrigerant gas. Rather, it is a dilute solution of ammonia (NH_3) in water.

Any substitute for a CFC should minimize three undesirable properties—toxicity, flammability, and a long atmospheric lifetime. At the same time, it should preserve a boiling point that is compatible with those of existing refrigerant gases, typically in the range of −10 to −40 °C. Obtaining a substitute is a delicate balancing act!

One strategy for reducing the atmospheric lifetime of a CFC is to replace one of its C–Cl bonds with a C–H bond. Unlike C–Cl bonds, the C–H bond is susceptible to attack by the hydroxyl radical (·OH) and therefore breaks down more quickly in the lower atmosphere. However, the substitution of a hydrogen atom increases the flammability of the molecule, an undesirable outcome. The introduction of a lighter atom such as hydrogen also decreases the boiling point and thus necessitated re-engineering some of the equipment. Even so, this strategy produced some very useful substitutes.

When a hydrogen atom is substituted for one of the chlorine atoms of a CFC, the result is a **hydrochlorofluorocarbon (HCFC),** a compound of hydrogen, chlorine, fluorine, and carbon (and no other elements). For example, the substitution of a chlorine atom in CCl_2F_2 produces $CHClF_2$.

The hydroxyl radical, introduced in Section 1.11, has been called nature's tropospheric "vacuum cleaner."

CCl_2F_2
CFC-12 or R-12

$CHClF_2$
HCFC-22 or R-22

This compound has an atmospheric lifetime of about 12 years, compared with 110 years (or so) for the CFC-12, also called R-12 or Freon-12. Because $CHClF_2$ is largely broken down in the lower atmosphere, it does not accumulate in the stratosphere. As a result, its ozone-depleting potential is about 5% that of CCl_2F_2, definitely a step in the right direction. But hydrochlorofluorocarbons still contain chlorine and deplete the ozone layer. Thus, they are not the best solution, as we will see in the next section.

Another HCFC used to produce foamed containers and foam insulation.

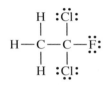

Even so, HCFCs offered considerable improvements over CFCs. At one point, $CHClF_2$ (also called R-22) was the most widely used HCFC. It is suitable for many applications, including air conditioners and as a blowing agent to produce lightweight fast-food containers from plastic "foam." Starting with the 1996 model year, automobiles in the United States used HCFCs in their air-conditioning units rather than CFCs.

Look for more about foam containers for fast food and blowing agents in Section 9.5.

Also phased out under the Montreal Protocol were halons, the bromine-containing cousins of CFCs mentioned earlier in Section 2.9. Used in fighting fires, halons have an even higher potential to deplete ozone than do CFCs.

 In 1998, Pyrocool Technologies of Monroe, Virginia, won a Presidential Green Chemistry Challenge Award for developing Pyrocool Fire-Extinguishing Foam (FEF). More effective than the halon it replaced, it is a water-based environmentally benign foam. For example, Pyrocool FEF was used to control the spread of fires in the sublevels beneath the collapsed towers of the World Trade Center following the terrorist attack of September 11, 2001 (Figure 2.20). The foam also is used to protect the huge refrigerant gas storage tanks necessary for large-scale air-conditioning systems. Pyrocool FEF foam has a cooling effect that helps firefighters, a useful feature when fighting fires either outdoors or in.

Figure 2.20

An aqueous foam of Pyrocool FEF is being applied to subterranean fires at the Ground Zero north tower of the World Trade Center, September 30, 2001.

Your Turn 2.29   Another Replacement for Halon–1301

Fluoroform (CHF_3), also called HFC–23, can be used as a replacement for Halon–1301 ($CBrF_3$).

a. Examine the chemical formulas of Halon–1301 and HFC–23. From this information, what can you conclude about the ability of these two fire suppressants to deplete stratospheric ozone?
b. What is the current status of Halon–1301?
c. Why is fluoroform (HFC–23) unlikely to be used long term?

Answer

b. All halons, including Halon–1301, were phased out in 2010.

The phaseout of CFCs and the continuing development of alternative materials were accompanied by major economic concerns. At its peak, the annual worldwide market for CFCs reached $2 billion, the tip of a very large financial iceberg. In the United States alone, CFCs were used in or used to produce goods valued at about $28 billion per year. Although the conversion to CFC replacements has been accompanied by some additional costs in retooling equipment, the overall effect on the U.S. economy was minimal. Furthermore, the conversions provided a market opportunity for innovative syntheses based on the key ideas in green chemistry to produce environmentally benign substances, a win for both current and future generations.

CFCs played an important role in improving the quality of life in the developed nations. Few of their citizens would be willing to give up the convenience and health benefits of refrigeration or the comfort of air-conditioning. Developing countries faced—and continue to face—a different set of economic issues and priorities. Understandably, millions of people worldwide aspire to a similar lifestyle. But, if the developing nations are banned from using the relatively inexpensive CFC-based technology, they may not be able to afford alternatives. "Our development strategies cannot be sacrificed for the destruction of the environment caused by the West," asserted Ashish Kothari, a member of an Indian environmental group. Both India and China originally refused to sign the Montreal Protocol because they felt that it discriminated against developing countries. To gain the participation of these highly populated nations, the industrially developed nations created a fund administered through the World Bank. The goal of the fund is to help countries phase out their use of ozone-depleting materials without hurting their economic development.

As we saw in this section, phasing out CFCs was not simple, but nonetheless it was accomplished in a straightforward manner. Furthermore, not only did CFCs need to be replaced, but HCFCs had to be replaced as well. In part this was necessary because HCFCs still contained chlorine. But a second reason for replacement also was discovered, namely, that the replacements were all greenhouse gases. The next section provides the details.

2.13 | Replacements for the Replacements

Humanity's need for refrigeration and desire to cool indoor environments have been fraught with unintended consequences.

Chemical & Engineering News
December 5, 2011, page 31

When first utilized, CFCs appeared to be ideal refrigerant gases. But unexpectedly, they turned out to be the party responsible for destroying Earth's protective ozone layer. When HCFCs replaced CFCs, these were only an interim solution because they also affected the ozone layer though to a lesser extent.

Through the Montreal Protocol and its later amendments, most HCFCs are scheduled to be phased out by 2030. Currently, HCFCs are no longer being manufactured in developed nations. Although this should lower the concentrations of HCFCs in the atmosphere, as of 2010 the concentration of $CHClF_2$ (R-22) was still increasing. Given the high demand for R-22 worldwide, including home air-conditioning units, this is not surprising. Higher demand also has brought higher prices. For example, during the

For older appliances, the R–22 must be recovered and either recycled or destroyed. Venting it to the atmosphere is prohibited.

exceptionally hot summer months of 2012, R-22 was reportedly in short supply in the United States and selling for several times its usual price.

With HCFCs on their way out, what is replacing them? **Hydrofluorocarbons (HFCs)**, compounds of hydrogen, fluorine, and carbon (and no other elements), seemed to be the likely candidates because they are similar compounds but without any chlorine. Here are two examples.

C₂HF₅ — pentafluoroethane — HFC-125   CH₂F₂ — difluoromethane — HFC-32

Neither of these depletes stratospheric ozone and neither has an excessively long atmospheric lifetime.

The switch from HCFCs to HFCs is currently underway. In some cases, a blend of HFCs is substituted for $CHClF_2$ (R-22), rather than dropping in a single HFC. Among the most widely used is R-410a, a blend of C_2HF_5 and CH_2F_2. Even so, using the blend requires retooling the equipment so that it can run smoothly with it. Newer designs for air conditioners are engineered from the start to use R-410a rather than its HCFC predecessor, R-22. Another compound, HFC-134a, also known as R-134a, is widely used in home refrigerators and in the air conditioners of automobiles.

Consider This 2.30   HFC Blends

R–407c is a blend of three compounds: HFC–125, HFC–32, and HFC–134a. The chemical formula, name, and Lewis structure for the first two were provided earlier. The chemical formula for the third is $C_2H_2F_4$.

a. How do these three compounds differ from CFCs? From HFCs? Prepare a table that highlights the differences.
b. Draw the Lewis structure for HFC–134a, placing two F atoms on each C atom.

But with HFCs, another unintended consequence emerges. HFCs are greenhouse gases! Actually, so were the HCFCs and CFCs that they replaced, as can be seen from Figure 2.21. Like carbon dioxide, HFCs absorb infrared radiation, trap heat in the atmosphere, and contribute to global warming. In particular, HFC-23 is of interest because it is a by-product in the synthesis of HCFC-22 (also called R-22), currently one of the world's most widely used coolants, as pointed out in the previous section. Thus both in the short haul and over the long one, HFCs are problematic as replacements. What is the current thinking on replacing HFCs?

> Greenhouse gases are explained in Chapter 3.

If you got bogged down with CFCs, HCFCs, and HFCs, prepare yourself for more alphabet soup. One of the newest classes of refrigerant gases is HFOs, that is, hydrofluoroolefins. First, let's take a moment to focus on the name.

- **hydro** means that these compounds contain C–H bonds, just as do *hydro*fluorocarbons and *hydro*chlorofluorocarbons.
- **fluoro** means that these compounds contain C–F bonds, just as do hydro*fluoro*carbons and hydrochloro*fluoro*carbons.
- **olefin** means that these compounds contain C=C bonds.

> The x–axis of Figure 2.21 is global warming potential. Look for an explanation of the term in Section 3.8.

Putting these three pieces together, here is the structural formula for HFO-1234yf, an example of an HFO.

> In the name HFO–1234yf, the 1 is for 1 double bond, the 2 is for 2 H atoms, the 3 is for 3 C atoms, and the 4 is for 4 F atoms.

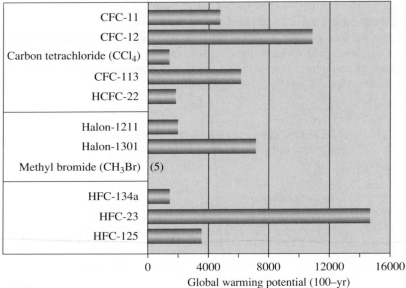

Figure 2.21

Relative importance of equal amounts (by mass) of selected CFCs, HCFCs, HFCs and halons in terms of their global warming potential. The values are for a 100-year time interval after emission.

Source: Taken from D.W. Fahey, 2006, Twenty Questions and Answers About the Ozone Layer—2006 Update, *a supplement to Scientific Assessment of Ozone Depletion: 2006, the World Meteorological Organization Global Ozone Research and Monitoring Project—Report No. 50, released 2007, and reproduced here with the kind permission of the United Nations Environment Programme.*

Although it absorbs infrared radiation, the presence of the reactive C=C bond shortens its atmospheric lifetime. Therefore, it does not persist long in the atmosphere, and its global warming potential is so low that it barely would register on the scale used in Figure 2.21. The compound is somewhat flammable, not unexpected given the C–H bonds that it contains.

In 2007, HFO-1234yf was announced jointly by Honeywell and DuPont. Three years later, commercial production began. As of 2012, the gas was approved for use in Europe, the United States, and Japan. In 2013, HFO-1234yf was introduced by General Motors for use in the air conditioners of cars in the United States. Conveniently, it is practically a drop-in replacement for HFC-134a.

Consider This 2.31   Unintended Consequences

Do hydrofluoroolefins cause environmental harm in ways that we have missed? As this book went to print, some expressed concern about the increased concentration in our waterways of one of the environmental degradation products, trifluoroacetic acid (TFA). Another concern is the possible production of hydrofluoric acid (HF) were a fire to occur.

a. The use of HFO–1234yf initially was opposed by those in some nations, including Germany. Is this still the case? Why or why not?

b. Other than TFA and HF, are there other issues raised with the use of HFO–1234yf?

Two other refrigerant gases deserve notice. One is R-744, better known as carbon dioxide. This gas was used in refrigeration systems in the 1800s, but suffered from the disadvantage that high pressures are needed to compress it, sometimes over 100 times atmospheric pressure. It was largely replaced, first by ammonia and then by CFCs. Although today there is renewed interest in using CO_2 as a refrigerant gas, no revival has yet occurred.

The second is another naturally occurring compound, propane, a small hydrocarbon (C_3H_8) mentioned earlier in Chapter 1. Although it is inexpensive and nontoxic, like all hydrocarbons, it is flammable. As a refrigerant gas, propane has properties similar to R-22. With the advent of the HFOs, also more flammable than their earlier counterparts, propane is poised to make a comeback.

As we end this chapter, an analogy comes to mind, one that Nobel laureate Mario Molina employed at a 2011 symposium on ozone depletion and global climate change. He commented that some perceive science as a house of cards: if one part is disturbed, the whole house crumbles. He suggested that a better metaphor is a jigsaw puzzle of a kitten, noting that even if pieces are missing, you still can see the kitten.

With stratospheric ozone depletion, this was the case. Even with a few key pieces missing, the picture was still discernible. Although with the help of chemistry one can see the picture, clearly this is not sufficient. Ultimately, the debate among governments and their citizens about how best to protect the stratospheric ozone layer determines the outcome in the global political arena.

Consider This 2.32   History Still Being Written

Each year, nations gather to continue conversations about the Montreal Protocol and its amendments. Where was this year's gathering held? Summarize the accomplishments and the controversies.

Conclusion

Chemistry is intimately entwined with the story of ozone depletion. Chemists created the chlorofluorocarbons whose near-perfect properties only later revealed their dark side as predators of stratospheric ozone. Chemists worked internationally to discover the mechanism by which CFCs destroy stratospheric ozone and warned of the dangers of increased ultraviolet radiation reaching the Earth. And chemists will continue to synthesize the substances necessary to replace CFCs and other related compounds.

Although chemistry is a necessary part of the solution, it was only part of the solution. At the 2005 meeting of parties to the Montreal Protocol on Substances That Deplete the Ozone Layer held in Dakar, Senegal, Executive Secretary Marco González reminded delegates that the final 20% of any global cooperative effort can be the hardest. Fundamental differences in domestic regulatory approaches have the potential to deplete the stockpiles of goodwill, placing long-term goals in jeopardy. In their complexity, the economic, social, and political issues rival that of the scientific and technological ones.

Thus the problem of ozone depletion brought together an array of different participants in pursuit of a common end. Chemists provided the information on the causes and effects of ozone depletion. People in industry, responding to the stimulus provided by the control measures, developed alternatives far more rapidly and more cheaply than anyone initially thought possible, participating fully in the debates over further reductions. NGOs (nongovernmental organizations) and the media served as essential channels of communication with the peoples of the world in whose name the measures had been taken. Governments worked well together in patiently negotiating agreements acceptable to a range of countries with widely varying circumstances, aims, and resources—and showed courage and foresight in applying the **precautionary principle** before the scientific evidence was entirely clear.

In 2007 a symposium was held on the 20th anniversary of the Montreal Protocol. Georgios Souflias from Greece gave the opening address, pointing out that we cannot remain indifferent toward the environment, as the environment is our home. *"The environment does not only provide people a better quality of life, but life itself."*

Souflias also pointed out the connection between CFCs and their replacements and global climate change. His call to action was unequivocal: *"We all, breathing on this planet today and having the potential, must guarantee its future, rapidly and decisively. We have no right to delay; we have no luxury of losing time."*

We urge you to carry these words with you as we turn to our next topic, the chemistry of global climate change.

Chapter Summary

Having studied this chapter, you should be able to:

- Differentiate between harmful ground-level ozone and beneficial stratospheric ozone layer (2.1)

- Describe the chemistry of ozone, including how it is formed in our atmosphere (2.1, 2.6, 2.8–2.10)

- Describe the ozone layer, characterizing it in several different ways (2.1, 2.6, 2.8–2.10)

- Apply the basics of atomic structure to atoms of certain elements (2.2)

- Understand what it means when elements fall into the same group of the periodic table (2.2)

- Differentiate atomic number from mass number and apply the latter to isotopes (2.2)

- Write Lewis structures for small molecules with single, double, and triple covalent bonds (2.3)

- Describe the electromagnetic spectrum in terms of frequency, wavelength, and energy (2.4, 2.5)

- Interpret graphs related to wavelength and energy, radiation and biological damage, and ozone depletion (2.4–2.8)
- Understand the natural Chapman cycle of stratospheric ozone depletion (2.6)
- Understand how the stratospheric ozone layer protects against harmful ultraviolet radiation (2.6, 2.7)
- Compare and contrast UV-A, UV-B, and UV-C radiation along several different lines (2.6, 2.7)
- Discuss the interaction of radiation with matter and changes caused by such interactions, including biological sensitivity (2.6, 2.7)
- Relate the meaning and the use of the UV Index (2.7)
- Write Lewis structures for chlorine and bromine atoms, as well as for some other free radicals. Be able to explain why these free radicals are so reactive (2.8)
- Recognize the complexities of collecting accurate data for stratospheric ozone depletion and interpreting them correctly (2.8, 2.9)

- Understand the chemical nature and role of CFCs in stratospheric ozone depletion (2.9, 2.10)
- Explain the unique circumstances responsible for seasonal ozone depletion in the Antarctic (2.10)
- Summarize the outcomes of the Montreal Protocol and its amendments (2.11, 2.12)
- Evaluate articles on green chemistry alternatives to stratospheric ozone-depleting compounds (2.12)
- Discuss factors that will help lead to the recovery of the ozone layer (2.11, 2.12)
- Explain why HCFCs, the replacements for CFCs, needed replacements. Then explain why HFCs, the replacements for HCFCs, also needed replacements. (2.13)
- As the opening to this section points out, our desire to cool our homes and workplaces has been "fraught with unintended consequences." Provide evidence to back up this statement. (2.13)

Questions

Emphasizing Essentials

1. How does ozone differ from oxygen in its chemical formula? In its properties?

2. Explain why it is possible to detect the pungent odor of ozone after a lightning storm or around electrical transformers.

3. The text states that the odor of ozone can be detected in concentrations as low as 10 ppb. Would you be able to smell ozone in either of these air samples?

   a. 0.118 ppm of ozone, a concentration reached in an urban area

   b. 25 ppm of ozone, a concentration measured in the stratosphere

4. A journalist wrote "Hovering 10 miles above the South Pole is a sprawling patch of stratosphere with disturbingly low levels of radiation-absorbing ozone."

   a. How big is this sprawling patch?

   b. Is the figure of 10 miles correct? Express this value in kilometers.

   c. What type of radiation does ozone absorb?

5. It has been suggested that the term *ozone screen* would be a better descriptor than *ozone layer* to describe ozone in the stratosphere. What are the advantages and disadvantages to each term?

6. Describe three differences between air in the troposphere and the stratosphere. In your answer, consider material from both Chapter 1 and Chapter 2.

7. a. What is a Dobson unit?

   b. Does a reading of 320 DU or 275 DU indicate more total column ozone overhead?

8. Using the periodic table as a guide, specify the number of protons and electrons in a neutral atom of each of these elements.

   a. oxygen (O)   **b.** nitrogen (N)

   c. magnesium (Mg)   **d.** sulfur (S)

9. Consider this representation of a periodic table.

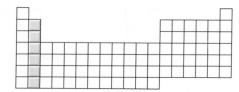

   a. What is the group number of the shaded column?

   b. Which elements make up this group?

   c. What is the number of electrons for a neutral atom of each element in this group?

   d. What is the number of outer electrons for a neutral atom of each element of this group?

10. Give the name and symbol for the element with this number of protons.

    a. 2   b. 19   c. 29

11. Give the number of protons, neutrons, and electrons in each of these neutral atoms.

    a. oxygen-18 ($^{18}_{8}O$)   b. sulfur-35 ($^{35}_{16}S$)

    c. uranium-238 ($^{238}_{92}U$)   d. bromine-82 ($^{82}_{35}Br$)

    e. neon-19 ($^{19}_{10}Ne$)   f. radium-226 ($^{226}_{88}Ra$)

12. Give the symbol showing the atomic number and the mass number for the isotope that has:

a. 9 protons and 10 neutrons (used in nuclear medicine).

b. 26 protons and 30 neutrons (the most stable isotope of this element).

c. 86 protons and 136 neutrons (the radioactive gas found in some homes).

13. Draw the Lewis structure for each of these atoms.

   a. calcium   b. nitrogen

   c. chlorine   d. helium

14. Assuming that the octet rule applies, draw the Lewis structure for each of these molecules.

   a. CCl_4 (carbon tetrachloride, a substance formerly used as a cleaning agent)

   b. H_2O_2 (hydrogen peroxide, a mild disinfectant; the atoms are bonded in this order: H–O–O–H)

   c. H_2S (hydrogen sulfide, a gas with the unpleasant odor of rotten eggs)

   d. N_2 (nitrogen gas, the major component of the atmosphere)

   e. HCN (hydrogen cyanide, a molecule found in space and a poisonous gas)

   f. N_2O (nitrous oxide, "laughing gas"; the atoms are bonded N–N–O)

   g. CS_2 (carbon disulfide, used to kill rodents; the atoms are bonded S–C–S)

15. Several oxygen species play important chemical roles in the stratosphere, including oxygen atoms, oxygen molecules, ozone molecules, and hydroxyl radicals. Draw Lewis structures for each.

16. Consider these two waves representing different parts of the electromagnetic spectrum. How do they compare in terms of:

   Wave 1   Wave 2

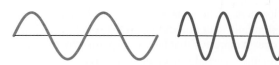

   a. wavelength   b. frequency   c. speed of travel

17. Use Figure 2.7 to specify the region of the electromagnetic spectrum where radiation of each wavelength is found. *Hint:* Change each wavelength to meters before making the comparison.

   a. 2.0 cm   b. 400 nm

   c. 50 μm   d. 150 mm

18. Arrange the wavelengths in question 17 in order of *increasing* energy. Which wavelength possesses the most energetic photons?

19. Arrange these types of radiation in order of *increasing* energy per photon: gamma rays, infrared radiation, radio waves, visible light.

20. The microwaves in home microwave ovens have a frequency of 2.45×10^9 s^{-1}. Is this radiation more or less energetic than radio waves? Than X-rays?

21. Ultraviolet radiation is categorized as UV-A, UV-B, or UV-C. Arrange these types in order of increasing:

   a. wavelength

   b. energy

   c. potential for biological damage

22. Draw Lewis structures for any three different CFCs.

23. CFCs were used in hair sprays, refrigerators, air conditioners, and plastic foams. Which properties of CFCs made them desirable for these uses?

24. a. Can a molecule that contains hydrogen be classified as a CFC?

   b. What is the difference between an HCFC and an HFC?

25. a. Most CFCs are based either on methane, CH_4, or ethane, C_2H_6. Use structural formulas to represent these two compounds.

   b. Substituting both chlorine atoms and fluorine atoms, for all of the hydrogen atoms on a methane molecule, you obtain CFCs. How many possibilities exist?

   c. Which of the substituted CFC compounds in part **b** has been the most successful?

   d. Why weren't all of these compounds equally successful?

26. These free radicals all play a role in catalyzing ozone depletion reactions: Cl·, ·NO_2, ClO·, and ·OH.

   a. Count the number of outer electrons available and then draw a Lewis structure for each free radical.

   b. What characteristic is shared by these species that makes them so reactive?

27. a. How were the original measurements of increases in chlorine monoxide and the stratospheric ozone depletion over the Antarctic obtained?

   b. How are these measurements made today?

28. Which graph shows how measured increases in UV-B radiation correlate with percent reduction in the concentration of ozone in the stratosphere over the South Pole?

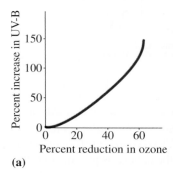

(a)

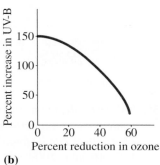

(b)

Concentrating on Concepts

29. The EPA has used the slogan "*Ozone: Good Up High, Bad Nearby*" in some of its publications for the general public. Explain the message.

30. Nobel laureate F. Sherwood Rowland referred to the ozone layer as the Achilles heel of our atmosphere. Explain the metaphor.

31. In the abstract of a talk he gave in 2007, Nobel laureate F. Sherwood Rowland wrote "Solar UV radiation creates an ozone layer in the atmosphere which in turn completely absorbs the most energetic fraction of this radiation."

    a. What is the most energetic UV fraction?
       Hint: See Table 2.4.

    b. How does solar UV radiation "create an ozone layer"?

32. In the conclusion of this chapter, we reported the words that Georgios Souflias spoke at the Symposium for the 20th Anniversary of the Montreal Protocol: *"We all, breathing on this planet today and having the potential, must guarantee its future, rapidly and decisively. We have no right to delay; we have no luxury of losing time."*

    a. What danger in delaying was he referring to?

    b. Look back at the definitions of sustainability in the prologue. How do his words connect to these definitions?

33. Consider the Chapman cycle in Figure 2.10.

    a. Explain the source of the oxygen atoms.

    b. Can this cycle take place in the troposphere as well? Explain.

34. What are some of the reasons that the solution to ozone depletion proposed in this Sydney Harris cartoon will not work?

"OH, FOR PETE'S SAKE, LET'S JUST GET SOME OZONE AND SEND IT BACK UP THERE!"

Source: ScienceCartoonsPlus.com. Reprinted with permission.

35. *"We risk solving one global environmental problem while possibly exacerbating another unless other alternatives can be found."* The date of this quote by a U.S. official is 2009, and the context is phasing out the use of HCFCs.

    a. What compounds were HCFCs being replaced with in 2009?

    b. What is the risk of this replacement?

36. It is possible to write three resonance structures for ozone, not just the two shown in the text. Verify that all three structures satisfy the octet rule and offer an explanation of why the triangular structure is not reasonable.

37. The average length of an O–O single bond is 132 pm. The average length of an O–O double bond is 121 pm. What do you predict the O–O bond lengths will be in ozone? Will they all be the same? Explain your predictions.

38. Consider the Lewis structures for SO_2. How do they compare with the Lewis structures for ozone?

39. Even if you have skin with little pigment, you cannot get a tan from standing in front of a radio. Why?

40. The morning newspaper reports a UV Index Forecast of 6.5. Given the amount of pigment in your skin, how might this affect how you plan your daily activities?

41. All the reports of the damage caused by UV radiation focus on UV-A and UV-B radiation. Why is there no attention on the damaging effects of UV-C radiation?

42. If all 3×10^8 tons of stratospheric ozone that are formed every day are also destroyed every day, how is it possible for stratospheric ozone to offer any protection from UV radiation?

43. How does the chemical inertness of CCl_2F_2 (Freon-12) relate both the usefulness and the problems associated with this compound?

44. Explain how the small changes in Cl· concentrations (measured in parts per billion) can cause the much larger changes in O_3 concentrations (measured in parts per million).

45. Development of the stratospheric ozone hole has been most dramatic over Antarctica. What set of conditions exist over Antarctica that help to explain why this area is well-suited to studying changes in stratospheric ozone concentration? Are these same conditions not operating in the Arctic? Explain.

46. The free radical CF$_3$O· is produced during the decomposition of HFC-134a.

    a. Propose a Lewis structure for this free radical.

    b. Offer a possible reason why CF$_3$O· does not cause ozone depletion.

47. One mechanism that helps break down ozone in the Antarctic region involves the BrO· free radical. Once formed, it reacts with ClO· to form BrCl and O_2. BrCl, in turn, reacts with sunlight to break into Cl· and Br·, both of which react with O_3 and form O_2.

    a. Represent this information with a set of equations similar to those shown for the Chapman cycle.

    b. What is the net equation for this cycle?

48. Polar stratospheric clouds (PSCs) play an important role in stratospheric ozone depletion.

    a. Why do PSCs form more often over Antarctica than in the Arctic?

    b. Reactions occur more quickly on the surface of PSCs than in the atmosphere. One such reaction is the reaction of hydrogen chloride and chlorine nitrate ($ClONO_2$), two species that do not deplete ozone, to produce a chlorine molecule and nitric acid (HNO_3). Write the chemical equation.

    c. The chlorine molecule produced does not deplete ozone either. However, when the Sun returns to the Antarctic in the springtime, it is converted to a species that does. Show how with a chemical equation.

49. Consider this graph that shows the atmospheric abundance of bromine-containing gases from 1950 to 2100.

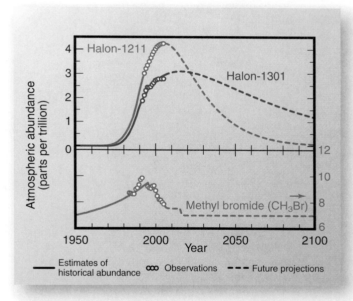

Source: Taken from D.W. Fahey, 2006, Twenty Questions and Answers About the Ozone Layer—2006 Update, a supplement to Scientific Assessment of Ozone Depletion: 2006, the World Meteorological Organization Global Ozone Research and Monitoring Project—Report No. 50, released 2007, and reproduced here with the kind permission of the United Nations Environment Programme.

    a. Halon-1301 is $CBrF_3$ and Halon-1211 is $CClBrF_2$. Why were these compounds once manufactured?

    b. Compare the patterns for Halon-1211 and Halon-1301. Why doesn't Halon-1301 drop off as quickly?

    c. In 2005, methyl bromide was phased out in the United States except for critical uses. Why is its future use predicted as a straight line, rather than tailing off?

Exploring Extensions

50. Chapter 1 discussed the role of nitrogen monoxide (NO) in forming photochemical smog. What role, if any, does NO play in stratospheric ozone depletion? Are NO sources the same in the stratosphere as in the troposphere?

51. Resonance structures can be used to explain the bonding in charged groups of atoms as well as in neutral molecules, such as ozone. The nitrate ion, NO_3^-, has one additional electron plus the outer electrons contributed by nitrogen and oxygen atoms. That extra electron gives the ion its charge. Draw the resonance structures, verifying that each obeys the octet rule.

52. Although oxygen exists as O_2 and O_3, nitrogen exists only as N_2. Propose an explanation for these facts. *Hint:* Try drawing a Lewis structure for N_3.

53. The chemical formulas for a CFC, such as CFC-11 (CCl_3F), can be figured out from its code number by adding 90 to it to get a three-digit number. For example, with CFC-11 you get $90 + 11 = 101$. The first digit is the # of C atoms, the second is the # of H atoms, and the third is the # of F atoms. Accordingly, CCl_3F has 1 C atom, no H atoms, and 1 F atom. All remaining bonds are assumed to be chlorine.

    a. What is the chemical formula for CFC-12?

    b. What is the code number for CCl_4?

    c. Does this "90" method work for HCFCs? Use HCFC-22 ($CHClF_2$) in explaining your answer.

    d. Does this method work for halons? Use Halon-1301 (CF_3Br) in explaining your answer.

54. Many different types of ozone generators ("ozonators") are on the market for sanitizing air, water, and even food. They are often sold with a slogan such as this one from a pool store. "Ozone, the world's most powerful sanitizer!"

    a. What claims are made for ozonators intended to purify air?

    b. What risks are associated with these devices?

55. The effect a chemical substance has on the ozone layer is measured by a value called its *ozone-depleting potential*, ODP. This is a numerical scale that estimates the lifetime potential stratospheric ozone that could be destroyed by a given mass of the substance. All values are relative to CFC-11, which has an ODP defined as equal to 1.0. Use those facts to answer these questions.

    a. Name two factors that affect the ODP value of a compound, and explain the reason for each one.

    b. Most CFCs have ODP values ranging from 0.6 to 1.0. What range do you expect for HCFCs? Explain your reasoning.

    c. What ODP values do you expect for HFCs? Explain your reasoning.

56. Recent experimental evidence indicates that $ClO\cdot$ initially reacts to form Cl_2O_2.

    a. Predict a reasonable Lewis structure for this molecule. Assume the order of atom linkage is $Cl-O-O-Cl$.

    b. What effect does this evidence have on understanding the mechanism for the catalytic destruction of ozone by $ClO\cdot$?

3 The Chemistry of Global Climate Change

This group of chimpanzees contributed minimally, or not at all, to global climate change and are not likely discussing the issue. However, they must adapt to the changes that will occur.

Unlike humans, chimpanzees, along with plants and other animals, don't argue with each other about whether climate is changing. They just attempt to adapt to the ever-changing world, which can affect their way of life including their access to food, water, and habitat. For example, as the climate changes, food availability shifts, thus forcing animals such as the chimpanzee to adapt in order to obtain enough calories to survive. The changes also affect their habitat, with variations due to differing weather patterns.

Like much of the planet, the salt water in the oceans has no voice, but it still responds to climate change and has a story to tell. In colder climates, it quietly freezes to form sea ice when temperatures drop. And perhaps more noisily, this ice breaks up with the return of warmer temperatures in the spring. This freeze–thaw cycle has been occurring for thousands of years, gradually shifting to form more or less ice as the temperatures on earth have shifted. In recent years, however, the freeze–thaw cycle has been more pronounced, and the waters in the Arctic have been free of ice for longer periods of time.

Might carbon dioxide be the culprit of changes witnessed in the Arctic? What about the shifts in plant and animal populations and habitats? No doubt you have heard about CO_2 in the news. As a greenhouse gas, carbon dioxide plays a role in keeping our planet comfortably warm and able to support life, but there can be too much of a good thing. Carbon dioxide isn't the only player, as we will see in this chapter. We also will talk about other gases, such as methane and water vapor, and how they contribute to the greenhouse effect.

What do you already know about CO_2? This next activity gives you an opportunity to assess your current knowledge.

The terms climate change and global warming are not the same but are closely related. We will use both in this chapter.

Consider This 3.1   Carbon Dioxide in the News

a. What facts do you already know about carbon dioxide? Make a list and save it for future reference.

b. As the cartoon points out, cars add CO_2 to our atmosphere. What else besides vehicles adds CO_2 to the atmosphere? Again, make a list and save it.

c. Vehicles emit other gases from their tailpipes as well, including air pollutants. When you reduce CO_2 emissions, you also reduce the emissions of other air pollutants. Name two of the air pollutants.

Hint: Revisit Your Turn 1.19.

My car adds only a little CO_2 to the air!

As Consider This 3.1 pointed out, carbon dioxide is emitted by vehicles. As you'll see in this chapter and in the next, when hydrocarbons and other carbon-containing fuels burn, carbon dioxide is a product along with other air pollutants. No one argues about whether or not these gases are being emitted. Rather, they disagree about how much can be released without significant negative consequences to the Earth's climate or even if we should be concerned with these emissions.

In order to make an informed decision about emissions, we first need to examine the Earth's energy balance. We will do this by exploring how this balance can be altered, for example by investigating greenhouse gases and interpreting data collected from ice cores taken from the Earth's glaciers. We will also explain key chemistry concepts throughout this chapter such as energy balance, greenhouse gases and the greenhouse effect, molecular shape, molecular vibrations, the carbon cycle, atomic mass, moles, atmospheric gases, and aerosols to help you evaluate the effect of emissions on climate.

Figure 3.1

Venus, as photographed by the Galileo spacecraft.

These and other types of electromagnetic radiation were introduced in Section 2.4.

In order to evaluate the effect of emissions on climate we cannot get ahead of ourselves. Ever wonder why Earth does not get too hot or too cold to sustain life? Let's find out as we begin thinking about climate change with a discussion of the energy balance of the Earth's atmosphere.

3.1 | In the Greenhouse: Earth's Energy Balance

As we begin our journey into understanding **global climate change,** we need to understand first how the Earth is heated and cooled. The energy to heat the Earth comes mainly from the Sun. However, this is not the entire story. Based on the Earth's distance from the Sun and the amount of solar radiation the Sun emits, the average temperature on Earth should be -18 °C (0 °F), and the oceans should be frozen year round. Thankfully this is not true as Earth's average temperature is currently around 15 °C (59 °F).

Venus (Figure 3.1) is another planet whose temperature is inconsistent with its distance from the Sun. Considered by many to be the brightest and most beautiful body in the night sky, after our own moon, Venus has an average temperature of about 450 °C (840 °F). Based simply on its distance from the Sun, however, the average temperature on Venus would be 100 °C, the boiling point of water. What do Earth and Venus have in common that would explain these discrepancies? They both have an atmosphere. To see the role that our atmosphere plays, we now examine what happens when solar radiation reaches the Earth.

The energy processes that contribute to the Earth's energy balance appear in Figure 3.2. The Earth receives nearly all of its energy from the Sun (orange arrows), primarily in the form of ultraviolet, visible, and infrared radiation. Some of this incoming radiation is reflected back into space (blue arrows) by the dust and aerosol particles that are suspended in our atmosphere (25%). Other parts of this incoming radiation are reflected by the surface of the Earth itself, especially those regions white with snow or sea ice (6%). Thus, 31% of the radiation received from the Sun is reflected.

The remaining 69% of the radiation from the Sun is absorbed, either by the atmosphere (23%) or by the land masses and oceans (46%). We can account for all of the Sun's radiation by adding the reflected and absorbed radiation: 31% + 69% = 100%.

Your Turn 3.2   Light From the Sun

Consider these three types of radiant energy, all emitted by the Sun: infrared (IR), ultraviolet (UV), and visible.

a. Arrange them in order of *increasing* wavelength.
b. Arrange them in order of *increasing* energy.

Answer
a. ultraviolet, visible, infrared

In order to maintain Earth's energy balance, all of the radiation that is absorbed from the Sun must eventually go back into space. Figure 3.2 shows us that:

- 46% of the Sun's radiation is absorbed by the Earth
- the Earth reemits all of the radiation it absorbs but at a longer wavelength (IR)
  - part of what the Earth emits escapes into space (9%)
  - the remainder is absorbed by the atmosphere (37%)
- 54% of the Sun's radiation is absorbed by the atmosphere (23%), reflected from the atmosphere (25%), or reflected from the Earth's surface (6%)

The 60% of the radiation that is absorbed by the atmosphere, either directly from the Sun (23%) or from the Earth's surface (37%), eventually is emitted into space to complete the energy balance.

Again, the 46% of the Sun's radiation that is absorbed and eventually emitted by the Earth, 37% is absorbed in the atmosphere prior to its emission into space. This

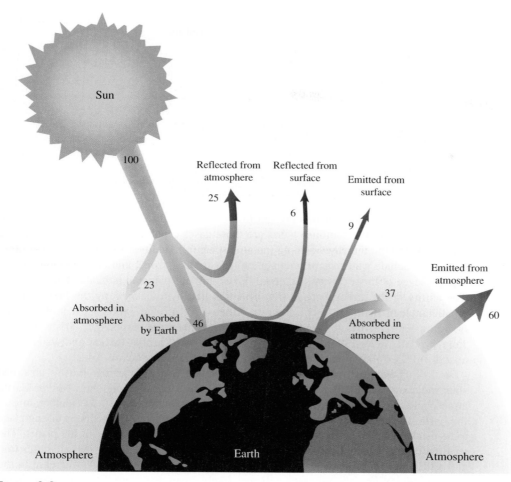

Figure 3.2

The Earth's energy balance. Orange represents a mixture of wavelengths. Shorter wavelengths of radiation are shown in blue, longer ones in red. The values are given in percentages of the total incoming solar radiation.

Figures Alive! Visit Figures Alive! to learn more about the electromagnetic spectrum, Earth's energy balance, and the greenhouse effect.

process of absorption adds heat to the Earth's atmosphere because the radiation causes collisions between neighboring molecules, warming up the atmosphere. At any one time, 80% (or $37 \div 46 \times 100\%$) of Earth's emitted radiation will be absorbed in the atmosphere. As we hope you can see, the gases in Earth's atmosphere act like a greenhouse!

If you have ever parked a car with its windows closed on a sunny day, you probably have experienced firsthand how a greenhouse can trap heat. The car, with its glass windows, operates much the same way as does a greenhouse for growing plants. The glass windows transmit visible and a small amount of UV light from the Sun. This energy is absorbed by the car's interior, particularly by any dark surfaces. Some of this radiant energy is then reemitted as longer wavelength IR radiation (heat). Unlike visible light, infrared light is not easily transmitted through the glass windows and so becomes "trapped" inside the car. When you reenter the vehicle, a blast of hot air greets you. The temperature inside of a car can exceed 49 °C (120 °F) in the summer in certain climates! Although the physical barrier of the windows is not an exact analogy to the Earth's atmosphere, the effect of warming the car's interior is similar to the warming of the Earth.

The **greenhouse effect** is the natural process by which atmospheric gases trap a major portion (about 80%) of the infrared radiation radiated by the Earth. Again, Earth's average annual temperature of 15 °C (59 °F) is a result of the heat trapping gases in our atmosphere. The atmosphere of Venus acts in a similar manner, however it traps even more heat. This is because it is made up of nearly 96% carbon dioxide, which, as we will see, is a far greater concentration than in the Earth's atmosphere.

Your Turn 3.3   Earth's Energy Balance

Refer to Figure 3.2 to answer these questions.

a. Incoming solar radiation (100%) is either absorbed or reflected. Outgoing radiation from the Earth into space also can be accounted for (100%), as required for energy balance. Show how.
b. What percent of the outgoing radiation is absorbed in the Earth's atmosphere? Calculate this by adding the percentage of incoming solar radiation absorbed in the atmosphere to that absorbed in the atmosphere after being radiated from Earth's surface. How does this value compare with the percentage emitted from the atmosphere?
c. Suggest reasons why the different colors were used for incoming and outgoing radiation.

Carbon dioxide, which is present in the atmospheres of both Earth and Venus, is a greenhouse gas. **Greenhouse gases** are those gases capable of absorbing and emitting infrared radiation, thereby warming the atmosphere. In addition to carbon dioxide, other examples include water vapor, methane, nitrous oxide, ozone, and chlorofluorocarbons. The presence of those gases is essential in keeping our planet at habitable temperatures. The ability of the atmosphere to trap heat was first hypothesized by the French mathematician Jean-Baptiste Joseph Fourier (1768–1830) around 1800, but it took another 60 years for scientists to identify the molecules that were responsible. Irish physicist John Tyndall (1820–1893) first demonstrated that both carbon dioxide and water vapor absorb infrared radiation. We will explain this process in Section 3.4.

> Water vapor is the most abundant greenhouse gas in our atmosphere. However, contributions of water vapor from human activity are negligible compared with those from natural sources.

In our energy balance discussion, we showed that 80% of the Earth's absorbed solar radiation is emitted into the atmosphere. The exchange of energy between the Earth, atmosphere, and space results in a steady state and a continuous average temperature of the Earth. However, the increase in concentration of greenhouse gases that is taking place today is changing the energy balance and causing increased warming of the planet. The term **enhanced greenhouse effect** refers to the process in which atmospheric gases trap and return *more than* 80% of the heat energy radiated by the Earth. An increase in the concentration of greenhouse gases will very likely mean that more than 80% of the radiated energy will be returned to Earth's surface, with an accompanying increase in average global temperature. The popular term **global warming** often is used to describe the increase in average global temperatures that results from an enhanced greenhouse effect.

> Another steady-state process, the Chapman cycle, was discussed in Section 2.6.

Why is the amount of greenhouse gases in the atmosphere increasing? One explanation considers **anthropogenic** influences on the environment, which stem from human activities such as industry, transportation, mining, and agriculture. These activities require carbon-based fuels, which produce carbon dioxide when burned. In the late 19th century, Swedish scientist Svante Arrhenius (1859–1927) considered the problems that increased industrialization might cause by building up CO_2 in the atmosphere. He calculated that doubling the concentration of CO_2 would result in an increase of 5–6 °C in the average temperature of the planet's surface. How are we adding CO_2 to the atmosphere?

> Section 1.9 described the chemistry of combustion. Look for more about coal (a fossil fuel) in Chapter 4.

Consider This 3.4   Evaporating Coal Mines

Writing in the *London, Edinburgh, and Dublin Philosophical Magazine*, Arrhenius described the phenomenon: "We are evaporating our coal mines into the air." Although the statement was effective in grabbing attention in 1898, what process do you think he really was referring to in discussing the amount of CO_2 being added to the air? Explain your reasoning.

To further investigate global climate change, we need answers to several important questions. For example, how have the atmospheric concentrations of greenhouse gases changed over time? Similarly, how has the average global temperature changed and how did we measure the changes? Can we determine if the changes in greenhouse gases and temperature are correlated? Can we distinguish natural climate variability from human influences? In the following section, we provide some data to help answer these questions.

3.2 | Gathering Evidence: The Testimony of Time

Over the past 4.5 billion years, the approximate age of the Earth, both Earth's climate and its atmosphere have varied widely. Earth's climate has been directly affected by periodic changes in the shape of Earth's orbit and the tilt of Earth's axis. Such changes are thought to be responsible for the ice ages that have occurred regularly during the past million years. Even the Sun itself has changed. Its energy output half a billion years ago was 25–30% less than it is today. In addition, changes in atmospheric greenhouse gas concentrations affect the Earth's energy balance, and hence its climate. Carbon dioxide was once 20 times more prevalent in the atmosphere than it is today. Chemical processes lowered that level by dissolving much of the CO_2 in the oceans, or incorporating it in rocks such as limestone. The biological process of photosynthesis also radically altered the composition of our atmosphere by removing CO_2 and producing oxygen. Certain geological events like volcanic eruptions add millions of tons of CO_2 and other gases to the atmosphere.

> Found in limestone, ionic compounds calcium carbonate ($CaCO_3$) and magnesium carbonate ($MgCO_3$) are both insoluble in water. Look for more about solubility in Chapter 5.

Although these natural phenomena will continue to influence Earth's atmosphere and its climate in the coming years, we must also assess the role that human activities are playing. With the development of modern industry and transportation, humans have moved huge quantities of carbon from terrestrial sources like coal, oil, and natural gas into the atmosphere in the form of CO_2. To evaluate the influence humans are having on the atmosphere, and hence on any enhanced greenhouse effect, it is important to investigate the fate of this large unnatural influx of carbon dioxide. Indeed, CO_2 concentrations in the atmosphere have increased significantly in the past half century. The best direct measurements are taken from the Mauna Loa Observatory in Hawaii (Figure 3.3). The red zigzag line shows the average monthly concentrations, with a small increase each April followed by a small decrease in October. The black line is a 12-month moving average. Notice the steady increase in average annual values from 315 ppm in 1960 to over 395 ppm in 2012. Later in this chapter, we will examine the evidence linking much of the added carbon dioxide to the burning of **fossil fuels,** combustible substances, of which coal, petroleum, and natural gas are the most common.

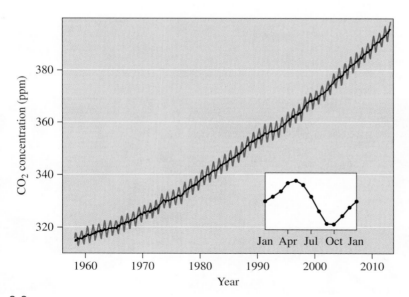

Figure 3.3

Carbon dioxide concentrations from 1958 to 2012, as measured at Mauna Loa, Hawaii.
Inset: One year of the monthly variations.

Source: Scripps Institution of Oceanography, NOAA Earth System Research Laboratory, 2012.

Your Turn 3.5   The Cycles of Mauna Loa

a. Calculate the percent increase in CO_2 concentration during the last 50 years.
b. Estimate the variation in parts per million (ppm) CO_2 within any given year.
c. On average, the CO_2 concentrations are higher each April than each October. Explain.

Answer

c. Photosynthesis removes CO_2 from the atmosphere. Spring begins in the northern latitudes in April; October is the start of spring in the southern latitudes. But the landmasses (and number of green plants) are greater in the northern hemisphere so the seasons in the northern hemisphere control the fluctuations.

How can we obtain data about the composition of our atmosphere farther back in time? Much relevant information comes from the analysis of ice core samples. Regions on the planet that have permanent snow cover contain preserved histories of the atmosphere, buried in layers of ice. Figure 3.4a shows a dramatic example of annual ice layers from the Peruvian Andes. The oldest ice on the planet is located in Antarctica, and scientists have been drilling and collecting ice core samples there for over 50 years (Figure 3.4b). Air bubbles trapped in the ice (Figure 3.4c) provide a vertical timeline of the history of the atmosphere; the deeper you drill, the farther back in time you go.

Relatively shallow ice core data show that for the first 800 years of the last millennium the CO_2 concentration was relatively constant at about 280 ppm. Figure 3.5 combines the Mauna Loa data (*red dots*) with data from a 200-meter ice core from the Siple station in Antarctica (*green triangles*), and a deeper core from the Law Dome, also in Antarctica (*blue squares*). Beginning about 1750, CO_2 began accumulating in the atmosphere at an ever-increasing rate, corresponding to the beginning of the Industrial Revolution and the accompanying combustion of fossil fuels that powered that transformation.

Skeptical Chemist 3.6   Checking the Facts on CO_2 Increases

a. A recent government report states that the atmospheric level of CO_2 has increased 30% since 1860. Use the data in Figure 3.5 to evaluate this statement.
b. A global warming skeptic states that the percent increase in the atmospheric level of CO_2 since 1957 has been only about half as great as the percent increase from 1860 to the present. Comment on the accuracy of that statement and how it could affect potential greenhouse gas emissions policy.

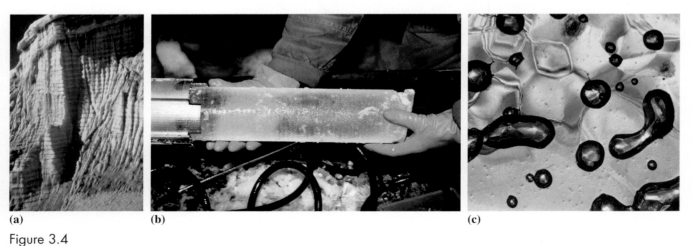

(a)   (b)   (c)

Figure 3.4

(a) Quelccaya ice cap (Peruvian Andes) showing the annual layers. (b) Ice core that can be used to determine changes in concentrations of greenhouse gases over time. (c) Microscopic air bubbles in ice.

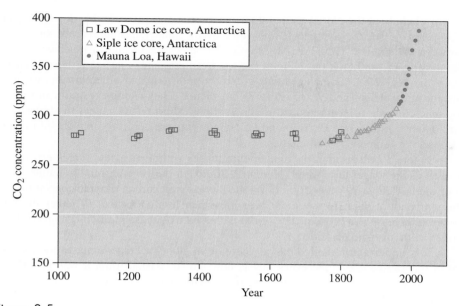

Figure 3.5

Carbon dioxide concentrations over the last millennium as measured from Antarctic ice cores (*blue squares and green triangles*) and the Mauna Loa observatory (*red dots*).

Source: "Climatic Feedbacks on the Global Carbon Cycle," in The Science of Global Change: The Impact of Human Activities on the Environment, *American Chemical Society Symposium Series, 1992.*

What about further back in time? Drilling by a team of Russian, French, and U.S. scientists at the Vostok Station in Antarctica yielded over a mile of ice cores taken from the snows of 400 millennia. The atmospheric carbon dioxide concentrations going back over 400,000 years are shown in Figure 3.6, with the data from Figure 3.5 in the inset.

Most obvious from the graph are the periodic cycles of high and low carbon dioxide concentrations, which occur roughly in 100,000-year intervals. Although not shown on the graph, analysis of other ice cores indicate these regular cycles go back at least 1 million years. Two important conclusions can be drawn from these data. First, the current atmospheric CO_2 concentration is about 100 ppm *higher* than any time in the last million years. Also during that time, never has the CO_2 concentration risen as rapidly as it is rising today.

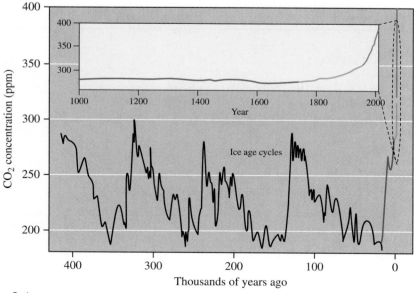

Figure 3.6

Carbon dioxide concentrations for the last 400,000 years. *Inset: Data from Figure 3.5 for comparison.*

What about the global temperature? Measurements indicate that during the past 120 years or so, the average temperature of the planet has increased somewhere between 0.4 and 0.8 °C (0.7–1.1 °F). Figure 3.7 shows the changes in surface air temperature from 1880 to 2006. Nine of the ten warmest years since 1880 have occurred since the year 2000. Some scientists correctly point out that a century or two is an instant in the 4.5-billion-year history of our planet. They caution restraint in reading too much into short-term temperature fluctuations. Short-term changes in atmospheric circulation patterns like El Niño and La Niña events are certainly implicated in some of observed temperature anomalies.

Figure 3.7 also shows the temperature ranges within each year (*black error bars*) as well as the longer term trend (*blue line*). Although the general trend in temperatures over the last 50 years generally follows the increases in carbon dioxide concentrations, the temperature data from year to year are much less consistent. Whether the temperature increase is a consequence of the increased CO_2 concentration cannot be determined with absolute certainty.

It is important to realize that an increase in global average temperature does not mean that across the globe every day is now 0.6 °C warmer than it was in 1970. A map of the temperatures for 2011 compared with the average temperature between 1951 and 1980 is displayed in Figure 3.8. Many regions have experienced just a little warming, and some others have even cooled (*blue areas*). Yet there are other regions (*dark red areas*), particularly in the higher latitudes, that have experienced much more than the average warming. The increases are most drastic in the Arctic, where not surprisingly, much of the tangible effects of climate change have already been observed.

Ice cores also can provide data for estimating temperatures farther back in time because of the hydrogen isotopes found in the frozen water. Water molecules containing the most abundant form of hydrogen atoms, ^1H, are lighter than those that contain deuterium, ^2H. The lighter H_2O molecules evaporate just a bit more readily than the heavier ones. As a result, there is more ^1H than ^2H in the water vapor of the atmosphere than in the oceans. Likewise, the heavier H_2O molecules in the atmosphere condense just a bit more readily than the lighter ones. Therefore, snow that condenses from atmospheric water vapor is enriched in ^2H. The degree of enrichment depends on temperature. The ratio of ^2H to ^1H in the ice core can be measured and used to estimate the temperature at the time the snow fell.

When we look back into the past, we see that the global temperature has undergone fairly regular cycles, matching the highs and lows in CO_2 concentration quite remarkably (Figure 3.9). Other data show that periods of high temperature also have been characterized by high atmospheric concentrations of methane, another significant

El Niño and La Niña are names given to natural cyclical changes in the ocean–atmosphere system in the tropical Pacific. El Niño events lead to warmer ocean temperatures in the middle latitudes, and La Niña cycles produce cooler ocean temperatures.

Isotopes of hydrogen (and other elements) were discussed in Section 2.2.

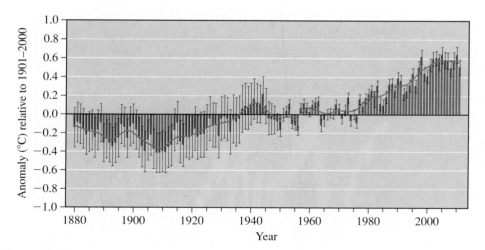

Figure 3.7

Global surface temperatures (1880–2011). The red bars indicate the average temperature for each year, and the ranges for each year are shown as the black error bars. The blue line shows the 5-year moving average.

Source: National Oceanic and Atmospheric Administration National Climatic Data Center.

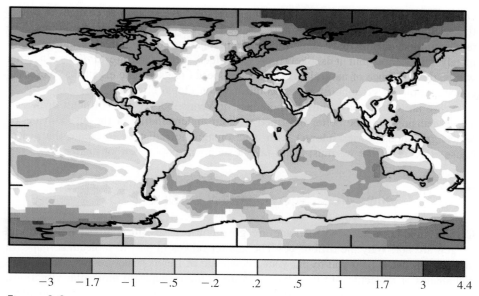

Figure 3.8

Change in global temperatures for 2011 (in °C) relative to the 1951–1980 average.

Source: NASA.

greenhouse gas. The precision of these data do not allow an assignment of cause and effect. It is difficult to conclude whether increasing greenhouse gases caused the temperature increases, or vice versa. What is clear, however, is that the current CO_2 and methane levels are much higher than any time in the last million years. Notice that the variation from hottest to coldest is only about 20 °F, yet that is the difference between the moderate climate we have today, and ice covering much of northern North America and Eurasia, as was the case during the last glacial maximum 20,000 years ago.

Over the past million years, Earth has experienced 10 major periods of glacier activity and 40 minor ones. Without question, mechanisms other than greenhouse gas concentrations are involved in the periodic fluctuations of global climate. Some of this temperature variation is caused by minor changes in Earth's orbit that affect the distance from Earth to the Sun and the angle at which sunlight strikes the planet. However, this hypothesis cannot fully explain the observed temperature fluctuations.

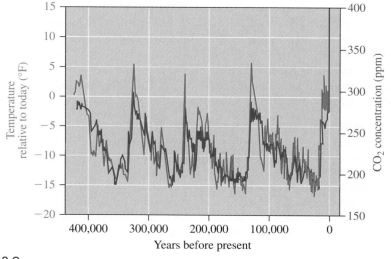

Figure 3.9

Carbon dioxide concentration (*blue*) and global temperatures (*red*) over the last 400,000 years from ice core data.

Source: Environmental Defense Fund.

Orbital effects most likely are coupled with terrestrial events such as changes in reflectivity, cloud cover, and airborne dust, as well as CO_2 and CH_4 concentrations. The feedback mechanisms that couple these effects together are complicated and not completely understood, but it is likely that the effects from each are *additive*. In other words, the existence of natural climate cycles doesn't preclude the effect that increased concentrations of greenhouse gases would have on global climate.

We are a long way from the hothouse of Venus, but we face difficult decisions. These decisions will be better informed with an understanding of the mechanisms by which greenhouse gases interact with electromagnetic radiation to create the greenhouse effect. For that we must again take a submicroscopic view of matter.

3.3 | Molecules: How They Shape Up

Carbon dioxide, water, and methane are greenhouse gases; in contrast, nitrogen and oxygen are not. Why the difference? The answer relates in part to molecular shape. In this section, we'll help you to put your knowledge of Lewis structures to work to predict shapes of molecules. In the next, we connect these shapes to molecular vibrations, which can help us to explain the difference between greenhouse gases and nongreenhouse gases.

In Chapter 2 you used Lewis structures to predict how electrons are arranged in atoms and molecules. Shape was not the primary consideration. Even so, in a few cases the Lewis structure did dictate the shape of the molecule. One example is for diatomic molecules such as O_2 and N_2. Here, the shape is unambiguous because the molecule must be linear.

$$:N::N:\quad \text{or}\quad :N\equiv N:\quad \text{or}\quad N\equiv N$$

$$\ddot{O}::\ddot{O}\quad \text{or}\quad \ddot{O}=\ddot{O}\quad \text{or}\quad O=O$$

Even though different geometries are possible with larger molecules, Lewis structures still can help us with the process of predicting the shape. Therefore, the first step in predicting the shape of a molecule is to draw its Lewis structure. If the octet rule is obeyed throughout the molecule, each atom (except hydrogen) will be associated with four pairs of electrons. Some molecules include nonbonding lone-pair electrons, but all molecules must contain some bonding electrons or they would not be molecules!

Opposite charges attract and like charges repel. Negatively charged electrons are attracted to a positively charged nucleus. However, the electrons all have the same charge and therefore are found as far from each other in space as possible while still maintaining their attraction to the positively charged nucleus. Groups of negatively charged electrons repel one another. *The most stable arrangement is the one in which the mutually repelling electron groups are as far apart as possible.* In turn, this determines the atomic arrangement and the shape of the molecule.

We illustrate the procedure for predicting the shape of a molecule with methane, a greenhouse gas.

1. **Determine the number of outer electrons associated with each atom in the molecule.** The carbon atom (Group 4A) has four outer electrons; each of the four hydrogen atoms contributes one electron. This gives $4 + (4 \times 1)$, or 8 outer electrons.

2. **Arrange the outer electrons in pairs to satisfy the octet rule.** This may require single, double, or triple bonds. For the methane molecule, use the eight outer electrons to form four single bonds (four electron pairs) around the central carbon atom. This is the Lewis structure.

$$\begin{array}{ccc} & & H \\ H & & | \\ H\!:\!\ddot{C}\!:\!H & \text{or} & H-C-H \\ \ddot{H} & & | \\ & & H \end{array}$$

Remember, the atmosphere is composed of 78% nitrogen and 21% oxygen.

Recall that Lewis structures and the octet rule were discussed in Section 2.3.

The octet rule applies for most atoms. Exceptions include hydrogen and helium.

Although this structure seems to imply that the CH_4 molecule is flat, it is not. In fact, the methane molecule is tetrahedral, as we will see in the next step.

3. **Assume that the most stable molecular shape has the bonding electron pairs as far apart as possible.** (*Note:* In other molecules we need to consider nonbonding electrons as well, but CH_4 has none.) The four bonding electron pairs around the carbon atom in CH_4 repel one another, and in their most stable arrangement they are as far from one another as possible. As a result, the four hydrogen atoms also are as far from one another as possible. This shape is *tetrahedral,* because the hydrogen atoms correspond to the corners of a **tetrahedron,** a four-cornered geometric shape with four equal triangular sides, sometimes called a triangular pyramid.

One way to describe the shape of a CH_4 molecule is by analogy to the base of a folding music stand. The four C–H bonds correspond to the three evenly spaced legs and the vertical shaft of the stand (Figure 3.10). The angle between each pair of bonds is 109.5°. The tetrahedral shape of a CH_4 molecule has been experimentally confirmed. Indeed, it is one of the most common atomic arrangements in nature, particularly in carbon-containing molecules.

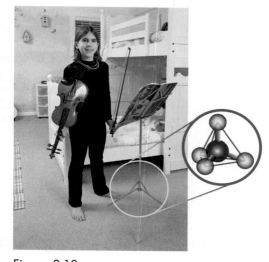

Figure 3.10

The legs and the shaft of a music stand approximate the geometry of the bonds in a tetrahedral molecule such as methane.

Consider This 3.7   Methane: Flat or Tetrahedral?

a. If the methane molecule really were flat, as the two–dimensional Lewis structure seems to indicate, what would the H–C–H bond angle be?

b. Offer a reason why the tetrahedral shape, not the two–dimensional flat shape, is more advantageous for this molecule.

c. Consider the music stand shown in Figure 3.10. In the analogy of shape using a music stand, where would the carbon atom be located? Where would each of the hydrogen atoms lie?

Answer

a. 90° (at right angles). The two H atoms across from each other would be at 180°.

Chemists represent molecules in several different ways. The simplest, of course, is the chemical formula itself. In the case of methane, this is simply CH_4. Another is the Lewis structure, but again this is only a two-dimensional representation that gives information about the outer electrons. Figure 3.11 shows these two representations as well as two others that are three-dimensional in appearance. One has a wedge-shaped line that represents a bond coming out of the paper in a direction generally toward the reader. The dashed wedge in the same structural formula represents a bond pointing away from the reader. The two solid lines lie in the plane of the paper. The other, a space-filling model, was drawn with a

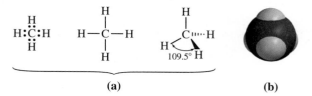

(a)   (b)

Figure 3.11

Representations of CH_4.

(a) Lewis structures and structural formula; (b) Space-filling model.

molecular modeling program. Space-filling models enclose the volume occupied by electrons in an atom or molecule. Seeing and manipulating physical models, either in the classroom or laboratory, can also help you visualize the structure of molecules.

Not all outer electrons reside in bonding pairs. In some molecules, the central atom has nonbonding electron pairs, also called lone pairs. For example, Figure 3.12 shows the ammonia molecule in which nitrogen completes its octet with three bonding pairs and one nonbonding pair.

Section 2.9 discussed replacement of NH_3 as a refrigerant gas by CFCs. The role of ammonia in the nitrogen cycle is the subject of Section 6.9 and Section 11.12 describes the importance of NH_3 in agriculture.

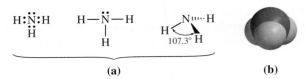

(a)   (b)

Figure 3.12

Representations of NH_3.
(a) Lewis structures and structural formula; (b) Space-filling model.

A nonbonding electron pair effectively occupies greater space than a bonding pair of electrons. Consequently, the nonbonding pair repels the bonding pairs somewhat more strongly than the bonding pairs repel one another. This stronger repulsion forces the bonding pairs closer to one another, creating an H–N–H angle slightly less than the predicted 109.5° associated with a regular tetrahedron. The experimental value of 107.3° is close to the tetrahedral angle, again indicating that our model is reasonably reliable.

The shape of a molecule is described in terms of its arrangement of atoms, not electrons (Table 3.1). The hydrogen atoms of NH_3 form a triangle with the nitrogen atom above them at the top of the pyramid. Thus, ammonia is said to have a *trigonal pyramidal* shape. Going back to the analogy of the folding music stand

Table 3.1	Common Molecular Geometries		
# of Bonded Atoms to the Central Atom	# of Nonbonded Electron Pairs on Central Atom	Geometry	Illustration
2	0	linear	CO_2 
2	2	bent	H_2O 
3	1	trigonal pyramid	NH_3 
4	0	tetrahedral	CH_4 

(see Figure 3.10), you could expect to find hydrogen atoms at the tip of each leg of the music stand. This places the nitrogen atom at the intersection of the legs with the shaft, with the nonbonded electron pair corresponding to the shaft of the stand.

The water molecule is *bent*, illustrating yet another shape. There are eight outer electrons on the central oxygen atom: one from each of the two hydrogen atoms plus six from the oxygen atom (Group 6A). These eight electrons are distributed in two bonding and two lone pairs of electrons (Figure 3.13a).

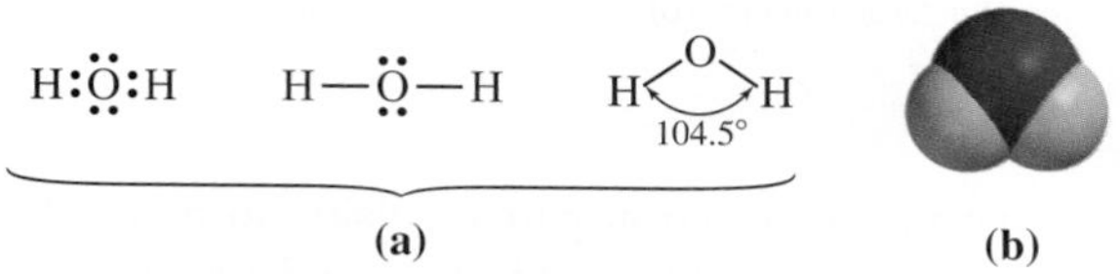

(a)   (b)

Figure 3.13

Representations of H_2O.
(a) Lewis structures and structural formula; (b) Space-filling model.

If these four pairs of electrons were arranged as far apart as possible, we might predict the H—O—H bond angle to be 109.5°, the same as the H—C—H bond angle in methane. However, unlike methane, water has two nonbonding pairs of electrons. The repulsion between the two nonbonding pairs causes the bond angle to be less than 109.5°. Experiments indicate a value of approximately 104.5°.

Your Turn 3.8   Predicting Molecular Shapes, Part 1

Using the strategies just described, sketch the shape for each of these molecules.

a. CCl_4 (carbon tetrachloride)
b. CCl_2F_2 (Freon–12; dichlorodifluoromethane)
c. H_2S (hydrogen sulfide)

Answer

a. Total outer electrons: $4 + 4(7) = 32$. Eight of these electrons form 4 single bonds around the central C atom, one to each Cl atom. The other 24 are in 12 nonbonding pairs on the 4 Cl atoms. The bonding electron pairs on C arrange themselves to maximize the separation, and the molecule is tetrahedral.

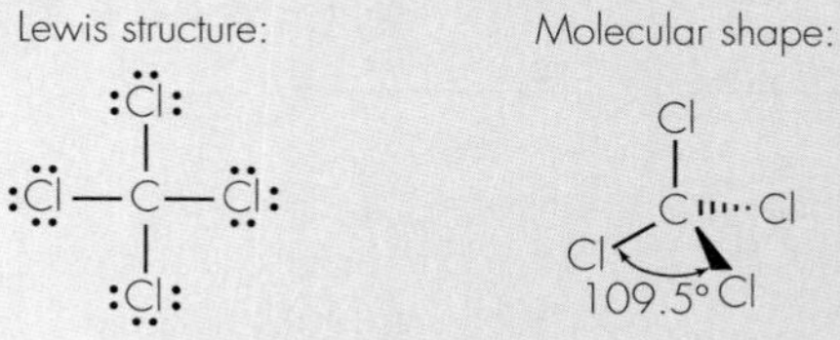

Lewis structure: Molecular shape:

We already looked at the structures of several molecules important for understanding the chemistry of climate change. What about the structure of the carbon dioxide molecule? With 16 outer electrons, the C atom contributes 4 electrons and 6 come from each of the 2 oxygen atoms. If only single bonds were involved, each atom would not have an octet. But the octet rule still can be obeyed if the central carbon atom forms a double bond with each of the 2 oxygen atoms, thus sharing 4 electrons.

What is the shape of the CO_2 molecule? Again, groups of electrons repel one another, and the most stable configuration provides the furthest separation of the negative charges. In this case, the groups of electrons are the double bonds, and these are furthest apart with an O=C=O bond angle of 180°. The model predicts that all three atoms in a CO_2 molecule will be in a straight line and that the molecule will be *linear*. This is, in fact, the case as shown in Figure 3.14.

Revisit Section 2.3 for more about drawing Lewis structures for molecules with double bonds.

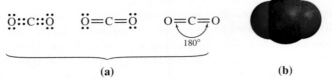

Figure 3.14

Representations of CO_2.

(a) Lewis structures and structural formula; (b) Space-filling model.

We applied the idea of electron pair repulsion to molecules in which there are four groups of electrons (CH_4, NH_3, and H_2O) and two groups of electrons (CO_2). Electron pair repulsion also applies reasonably well to molecules that include three, five, or six groups of electrons. In most molecules, the electrons and atoms are still arranged to maximize the separation of the electrons. This logic accounts for the bent shape we associated with the ozone molecule.

The Lewis structure for the ozone (O_3) molecule with its 18 outer electrons contains a single bond and a double bond, and the central oxygen atom carries a nonbonding lone pair of electrons. Thus, the central O atom has three groups of electrons: the pair that makes up the single bond, the two pairs that constitute the double bond, and the lone pair. These three groups of electrons repel one another, and the minimum energy of the molecule corresponds to their farthest separation. This occurs when the electron groups are all in the same plane and at an angle of about 120° from one another. We predict, therefore, that the O_3 molecule should be bent, and the angle made by the three atoms should be approximately 120°. Experiments show the bond angle to be 117°, just slightly smaller than the prediction (Figure 3.15). The nonbonding electron pair on the central oxygen atom occupies an effectively greater volume than bonding pairs of electrons, causing a greater repulsion force responsible for the slightly smaller bond angle. Table 3.1 shows the molecular geometry for several molecules.

> The O_3 molecule is best represented by two equivalent resonance structures. Again see Section 2.3.

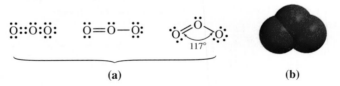

Figure 3.15

Representations of O_3.

(a) Lewis structures and structural formula for one resonance form; (b) Space-filling model.

Your Turn 3.9   Predicting Molecular Shapes, Part 2

Using the strategies just described, predict and sketch the shape of SO_2 (sulfur dioxide).
Hint: Because S and O are in the same group on the periodic table, the structures for SO_2 and O_3 will be closely related.

As promised, in this section we helped you see that molecules have different shapes, ones that can be predicted. In the next, we return to our story of greenhouse gases, putting your knowledge of shapes to work to help you understand why not all gases are greenhouse gases.

3.4 | Vibrating Molecules and the Greenhouse Effect

How do greenhouse gases trap heat, keeping our planet at more or less comfortable temperatures? In part, the answer lies in how molecules respond to photons of energy. This topic is complex, but even so, we can give you enough basics so you can understand how the greenhouse gases in our atmosphere function. At the same time, we'll reveal why some gases do *not* trap heat.

We begin this topic by revisiting the interaction of ultraviolet (UV) light with molecules, as discussed in Chapter 2 in relation to the ozone layer. You saw that high energy photons (UV-C) could break the covalent bonds in O_2 and that photons of lower energy (UV-B) could break the bonds in O_3. Put another way, both the ozone and the oxygen molecule can absorb UV radiation. When this absorption occurs, an oxygen-to-oxygen bond is broken.

Fortunately, infrared (IR) photons do not contain enough energy to cause chemical bonds to break. Instead, a photon of IR radiation can add energy to the vibrations in a molecule. Depending on the molecular structure, only certain vibrations are possible. The energy of the incoming photon must correspond exactly to the vibrational energy of the molecule for the photon to be absorbed. This means that different molecules absorb IR radiation at different wavelengths and thus vibrate at different energies.

We illustrate these ideas with the CO_2 molecule, representing the atoms as balls and the covalent bonds as springs. Every CO_2 molecule is constantly vibrating in the four ways pictured in Figure 3.16. The arrows indicate the direction of motion of each atom during each vibration. The atoms move forward and backward along the arrows. Vibrations **a** and **b** are stretching vibrations. In vibration **a,** the central carbon atom is stationary and the oxygen atoms move back and forth (stretch) in opposite directions away from the central atom. Alternatively, the oxygen atoms can move in the same direction and the carbon atom in the opposite direction (vibration **b**). Vibrations **c** and **d** look very much alike. In both cases, the molecule bends from its normal linear shape. The bending counts as two vibrations because it occurs in either of two possible planes. In vibration **c** the molecule is shown bending up and down in the plane of the paper on which the diagram is printed, whereas in vibration **d** the molecule is shown bending out of the plane of the paper.

If you ever examined a spring, you probably noticed that more energy is required to stretch it than to bend it. Similarly, more energy is required to stretch a CO_2 molecule than to bend it. This means that more energetic photons, those with shorter wavelengths, are needed to add energy to stretching vibrations **a** or **b** than to add energy to bending vibrations **c** or **d.** For example, absorption of IR radiation with a wavelength of 15.0 micrometers (μm) adds energy to the bending vibrations (**c** and **d**). When that occurs, the atoms move farther from their equilibrium positions and move faster (on average) than they do normally. For the same thing to happen with vibration **b,** higher energy radiation having a wavelength of 4.3 μm is required. Together, vibrations **b, c,** and **d** account for the greenhouse properties of carbon dioxide.

A micrometer is equal to one-millionth of a meter.
$1 \ \mu m = 1 \times 10^{-6} \ m = 1000 \ nm$

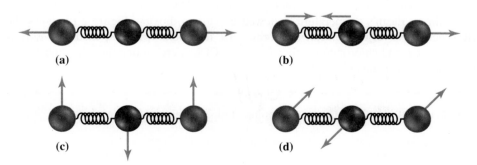

Figure 3.16

Molecular vibrations in CO_2. Each spring represents a C=O double bond. Vibrations (a) and (b) are stretching vibrations; (c) and (d) are bending vibrations.

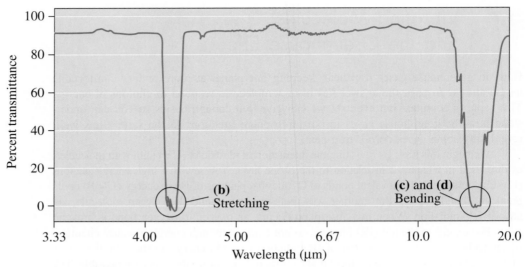

Figure 3.17

Infrared spectrum of carbon dioxide. The letters (b), (c), and (d) refer to the molecular vibrations shown in Figure 3.16.

In contrast, direct absorption of IR radiation does not add energy to vibration **a.** In a CO_2 molecule, the average concentration of electrons is greater on the oxygen atoms than on the carbon atom. This means that the oxygen atoms carry a partial negative charge relative to the carbon atom. As the bonds stretch, the positions of the electrons change, thereby changing the charge distribution in the molecule. Because of the linear shape and symmetry of CO_2, the changes in charge distribution during vibration **a** cancel and no infrared absorption occurs.

The infrared (heat) energy that molecules absorb can be measured with an instrument called an infrared spectrometer. Infrared radiation from a glowing filament is passed through a sample of the compound to be studied, in this case gaseous CO_2. A detector measures the amount of radiation, at various wavelengths, transmitted by the sample. High transmission means low absorbance, and vice versa. This information is displayed graphically, where the relative intensity of the transmitted radiation is plotted versus wavelength. The result is the *infrared spectrum* of the compound. Figure 3.17 shows the infrared spectrum of CO_2.

The infrared spectrum shown in Figure 3.17 was acquired using a laboratory sample of CO_2, but the same absorption takes place in the atmosphere. Molecules of CO_2 that absorb specific wavelengths of infrared energy experience different fates. Some hold that extra energy for a brief time, and then reemit it in all directions as heat. Others collide with atmospheric molecules like N_2 and O_2 and can transfer some of the absorbed energy to those molecules, also as heat. Through both of these processes, CO_2 "traps" some of the infrared radiation emitted by the Earth, keeping our planet comfortably warm. This is what makes CO_2 a greenhouse gas.

Any molecule that can absorb photons of IR radiation can behave as a greenhouse gas. There are many such molecules. Water is by far the most important gas in maintaining Earth's temperature, followed by carbon dioxide. Figure 3.18 shows the IR spectrum of H_2O molecules absorbing IR radiation. However, methane, nitrous oxide, ozone, and chlorofluorocarbons (such as CCl_3F) are among the other substances that help retain planetary heat.

Consider This 3.10   Bending and Stretching Water Molecules

a. Use Figure 3.18 to estimate the wavelengths corresponding to the strongest IR absorbance for water vapor.

b. Which wavelength do you predict represents bending vibrations and which represents stretching? Explain the basis of your predictions.
Hint: Compare the IR spectrum of H_2O with that of CO_2.

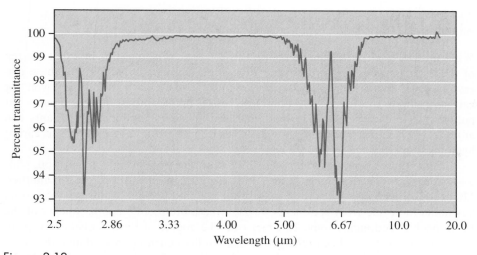

Figure 3.18

Infrared spectrum of water vapor.

Diatomic gases, such as N_2 and O_2, are not greenhouse gases. Although molecules consisting of two identical atoms do vibrate, the overall electric charge distribution does not change during these vibrations. Hence, these molecules cannot be greenhouse gases. Earlier we discussed this lack of change in the overall electric charge distribution as the reason why stretching vibration **a** in Figure 3.17 was not responsible for the greenhouse gas behavior of CO_2.

So far, you have encountered two ways that molecules respond to radiation. Highly energetic photons with high frequencies and short wavelengths (such as UV radiation) can break bonds within molecules. The less energetic photons (such as IR radiation) cause an increase in molecular vibrations. Both processes are depicted in Figure 3.19, but the figure also includes another response of molecules to radiant energy that is probably a good deal more familiar to you. Longer wavelengths than those in the IR range have only enough energy to cause molecules to rotate faster.

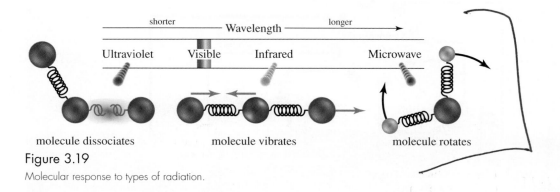

Figure 3.19

Molecular response to types of radiation.

For example, microwave ovens generate electromagnetic radiation that causes water molecules to spin faster. The radiation generated in such a device is of relatively long wavelength, about a centimeter. Thus the energy per photon is quite low. As the H_2O molecules absorb the photons and spin more rapidly, the resulting friction cooks your food, warms up the leftovers, or heats your coffee. The same region of the spectrum is used for radar. Beams of microwave radiation are sent out from a generator. When the beams strike an object such as an airplane, the microwaves bounce back and are detected by a sensor.

3.5 | The Carbon Cycle

What might be handy to know about the carbon cycle? Three things are at the top of the list. First, *carbon is found in many places on our planet*. We call these reservoirs, as shown in Figure 3.20. For example, our atmosphere is a reservoir for carbon in the form of CO_2 (~400 ppm), CH_4 (~17 ppm), and CO (trace amounts, air pollutant). Another reservoir for carbon is carbonate-containing rocks. Plants and animals are a third place that you will find carbon, this time in the form of carbohydrates, proteins, and lipids.

Second, *carbon is on the move!* Through processes such as combustion, photosynthesis, and sedimentation, carbon moves from one reservoir to another. Michael B. McElroy of Harvard University estimated, "The average carbon atom has made the cycle from sediments through the more mobile compartments of the Earth back to sediments some 20 times over the course of Earth's history." CO_2 in the air today may have been released from campfires burning more than a thousand years ago. All of the processes illustrated in Figure 3.20 happen simultaneously, but at different rates.

Third, *where carbon ends up matters*. For example, the slow transformation of carbon from living organisms into fossil fuels millions of years ago is of great importance to us. Today's transfer of carbon back into the atmosphere by burning fossil fuel matters not only to us but also to those in future generations who must deal with the consequences of climate change. The next activity gives you a closer look at carbon reservoirs and the processes that move carbon between these reservoirs.

> Look for more about carbonate-containing rocks in Chapter 5 and more about the carbon basis of food in Chapter 11.

> A gigatonne (Gt) is a billion metric tons, or about 2200 billion pounds. For comparison, a fully loaded 747 jet weighs about 800,000 lb. It would take nearly 3 million 747s to have a total mass of 1 Gt.

Your Turn 3.11   Understanding the Carbon Cycle

a. Which processes add carbon (in the form of CO_2) to the atmosphere?
b. Which processes remove carbon from the atmosphere?
c. What are the two largest reservoirs of carbon?
d. Which parts of the carbon cycle are most influenced by human activities?

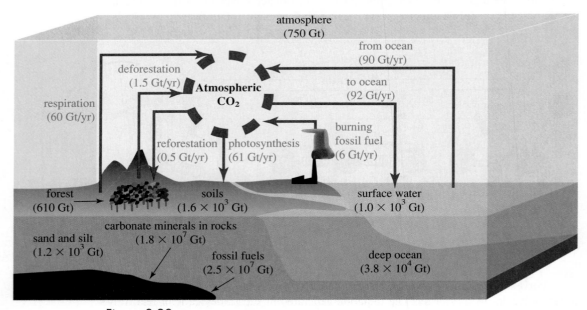

Figure 3.20

The global carbon cycle. The numbers show the quantity of carbon, expressed in gigatonnes (Gt), that is stored in various carbon reservoirs (*black numbers*) or moving through the system per year (*red numbers*).

From Purves, Orians, Heller and Sadava, *Life, The Science of Biology*, 5th edition, 1998, page 1186. Reprinted with permission of Sinauer Associates, Inc.

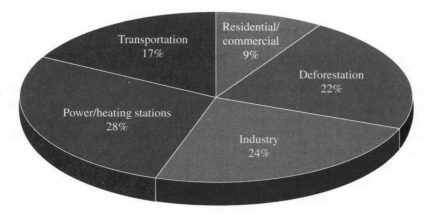

Figure 3.21

Global carbon dioxide emissions by end use.

Source: IPCC Fourth Assessment Report, Working Group III, 2007.

We hope that Your Turn 3.11 helped you to notice that the carbon cycle is a dynamic system. Notice the presence of both natural emission and removal mechanisms. Respiration adds carbon dioxide to the atmosphere, and photosynthesis removes it. Similarly, the oceans both absorb and emit carbon dioxide. As members of the animal kingdom, we *Homo sapiens* participate in the carbon cycle along with our fellow creatures. As is true for any animal, we inhale and exhale, ingest and excrete, live and die. In addition though, human civilization relies on processes that put much more carbon into the atmosphere than they remove (Figure 3.21). Widespread burning of coal for electricity production, of petroleum products for transportation, and of natural gas for home heating all transfer carbon from the largest underground carbon reservoir into the atmosphere.

Another human influence on CO_2 emissions is deforestation by burning, a practice that releases about 1.5 Gt of carbon to the atmosphere each year. It is estimated that forested land the size of two football fields is lost every second of every day from the rain forests of the world. Although firm numbers are rather elusive, Brazil continues as the country with the greatest annual loss of rain forest acreage; over 5.4 million acres of Amazon rain forest is vanishing each year. Trees, very efficient absorbers of carbon dioxide, are removed from the cycle through deforestation. If the wood is burned, vast quantities of CO_2 are generated; if it is left to decay, that process also releases carbon dioxide, but more slowly. Even if the lumber is harvested for construction purposes and the land is replanted in cultivated crops, the loss in CO_2-absorbing capacity may approach 80%.

The total quantity of carbon released by the human activities of deforestation and burning fossil fuels is about 7.5 Gt per year. About half of this is eventually recycled into the oceans and the biosphere, however carbon dioxide is not always removed with the speed required by its rate of increase in the atmosphere. Much of the CO_2 emitted stays in the atmosphere, adding between 3.1 and 3.5 Gt of carbon per year to the existing base of 750 Gt noted in Figure 3.20. We are concerned primarily with the relatively rapid *increase* in atmospheric carbon dioxide, because *excess* CO_2 from this increase is implicated in global warming. Therefore, it would be useful to know the mass (Gt) of CO_2 added to the atmosphere each year. In other words, what mass of CO_2 contains 3.3 Gt of carbon, the midpoint between 3.1 Gt and 3.5 Gt? Answering this question requires that we return to some more quantitative aspects of chemistry.

Remember that the natural "greenhouse effect" makes life on Earth possible. Problems occur when the amount of greenhouse gases *increases* faster than it can be removed. The result is the *enhanced* greenhouse effect.

3.6 | Quantitative Concepts: Mass

To solve the problem just posed, we need to know how the mass of C is related to the mass of CO_2. Regardless of the source of CO_2, its chemical formula is stubbornly the same. The mass percent of C in CO_2 is also unwavering, and therefore we must calculate the mass percent of C in CO_2, based on the formula of the compound. As you work through this and the next section, keep in mind that we are seeking a value for that percentage.

The approach requires the use of the masses of the elements involved. But this raises an important question: How much does an individual atom weigh? The mass of an atom is mainly attributable to the neutrons and protons in the nucleus. Thus, elements differ in mass because their atoms differ in composition. Rather than using absolute masses of individual atoms, chemists have found it convenient to employ relative masses—in other words, to relate the masses of all atoms to some convenient standard. The internationally accepted mass standard is carbon-12, the isotope that makes up 98.90% of all carbon atoms. C-12 has a mass number of 12 because each atom has a nucleus consisting of 6 protons and 6 neutrons plus 6 electrons outside the nucleus.

The periodic table in the text shows that the atomic mass of carbon is 12.01, not 12.00. This is not an error; it reflects the fact that carbon exists naturally as three isotopes. Although C-12 predominates, 1.10% of carbon is C-13, the isotope with six protons and *seven* neutrons. In addition, natural carbon contains a trace of C-14, the isotope with six protons and *eight* neutrons. The tabulated mass value of 12.01 is often called by the name atomic mass, an average that takes into consideration the masses and percent natural abundance of all naturally occurring isotopes of carbon. This isotopic distribution and average mass of 12.01 characterize carbon obtained from any chemical source—a graphite ("lead") pencil, a tank of gasoline, a loaf of bread, a lump of limestone, or your body.

The radioactive isotope carbon-14, although present only in trace amounts, provides direct evidence that the combustion of fossil fuels is the *predominant* cause of the rise in atmospheric CO_2 concentrations over the past 150 years. In all living things, only 1 out of 10^{12} carbon atoms is a C-14 atom. A plant or animal constantly exchanges CO_2 with the environment, and this maintains a constant C-14 concentration in the organism. However, when the organism dies, the biochemical processes that exchange carbon stop functioning and the C-14 is no longer replenished. This means that after the death of the organism, the concentration of C-14 decreases with time because it undergoes radioactive decay to form N-14. Coal, oil, and natural gas are remnants of plant life that died hundreds of millions of years ago. Hence, in fossil fuels, and in the carbon dioxide released when fossil fuels burn, the level of C-14 is essentially zero. Careful measurements show that the concentration of C-14 in atmospheric CO_2 has recently decreased. This strongly suggests that the origin of the added CO_2 is indeed the burning of fossil fuels, a decidedly human activity.

Isotopes and the relative masses of subatomic particles were discussed in Section 2.2.

You may notice that no units are used with the atomic masses. These are in atomic mass units (amu), which equals 1.66×10^{-17} kg.

You will learn to write equations for nuclear reactions in Section 7.2.

Your Turn 3.12   Isotopes of Nitrogen

Nitrogen (N) is an important element in the atmosphere and in biological systems. It has two naturally occurring isotopes: N–14 and N–15.

a. Use the periodic table to find the atomic number and atomic mass of nitrogen.
b. What is the number of protons, neutrons, and electrons in a neutral atom of N–14?
c. Compare your answers for part **b** with those for a neutral atom of N–15.
d. Given the atomic mass of nitrogen, which isotope has the greatest natural abundance?

Having reviewed the meaning of isotopes, we return to the matter at hand—the masses of atoms and particularly the atoms in CO_2. Not surprisingly, it is impossible to weigh a single atom because of its extremely small mass. A typical laboratory balance can detect a minimum mass of 0.1 mg; this corresponds to 5×10^{18} carbon atoms, or 5,000,000,000,000,000,000 carbon atoms. An atomic mass unit is far too small to measure in a conventional chemistry laboratory. Rather, the gram is the chemist's mass unit of choice. Therefore, scientists use exactly 12 g of carbon-12 as the reference for the atomic masses of all the elements. We define **atomic mass** as the mass (in grams) of the same number of atoms that are found in exactly 12 g of carbon-12. This number of atoms is, of course, *very* large. This important chemical number is named after an Italian scientist with the impressive name of Count Lorenzo Romano Amadeo Carlo Avogadro di Quaregna e di Ceretto (1776–1856). (His friends called him Amadeo.) **Avogadro's number** is the number of atoms in exactly 12 g of C-12. Avogadro's number, if written out, is 602,000,000,000,000,000,000,000. It is more compactly written in scientific notation as 6.02×10^{23}. This is the incredible number of atoms in 12 g of carbon, no more than a tablespoonful of soot!

Avogadro's number counts a large collection of atoms, much like the term *dozen* counts a collection of eggs. It does not matter if the eggs are large or small, brown or white, "organic" or not. No matter, for if there are 12 eggs, they are still counted as a dozen. A dozen ostrich eggs has a greater mass than a dozen quail eggs. Figure 3.22 illustrates this point with a half-dozen tennis and a half-dozen golf balls. Like atoms of different elements, the masses of a tennis ball and a golf ball differ. The number of balls is the same—six in each bag, a half dozen.

Figure 3.22
Six tennis balls have a greater mass than six golf balls.

Skeptical Chemist 3.13   Marshmallows and Pennies

Avogadro's number is so large that about the only way to hope to comprehend it is through analogies. For example, one Avogadro's number of regular-sized marshmallows, 6.02×10^{23} of them, would cover the surface of the United States to a depth of 650 miles. Or, if you are more impressed by money than marshmallows, assume 6.02×10^{23} pennies were distributed evenly among the approximately 7 billion inhabitants of the Earth. Every man, woman, and child could spend $1 million every hour, day and night, and half of the pennies would still be left unspent at death.

Can these fantastic claims be correct? Check one or both, showing your reasoning. Come up with an analogy of your own.

Knowledge of Avogadro's number and the atomic mass of any element permit us to calculate the average mass of an individual atom of that element. Thus, the mass of 6.02×10^{23} oxygen atoms is 16.00 g, the atomic mass from the periodic table. To find the average mass of just one oxygen atom, we must divide the mass of the large collection of atoms by the size of the collection. In chemist's terms, this means dividing the atomic mass by Avogadro's number. Fortunately, calculators help make this job quick and easy.

$$\frac{16.00 \text{ g oxygen}}{6.02 \times 10^{23} \text{ oxygen atoms}} = 2.66 \times 10^{-23} \text{ g oxygen/oxygen atom}$$

This very small mass confirms once again why chemists do not generally work with small numbers of atoms. We manipulate trillions at a time. Therefore, practitioners of this art need to measure matter with a sort of chemist's dozen—a very large one, indeed. To learn about it, read on . . . but only after stopping to practice your new skill.

Your Turn 3.14   Calculating Mass of Atoms

  a. Calculate the average mass in grams of an individual atom of nitrogen.
  b. Calculate the mass in grams of 5 trillion nitrogen atoms.
  c. Calculate the mass in grams of 6×10^{15} nitrogen atoms.

Answer

  a. $\dfrac{14.01 \text{ g nitrogen}}{6.02 \times 10^{23} \text{ nitrogen atoms}} = 2.34 \times 10^{-23} \text{ g nitrogen/nitrogen atom}$

Calculation Tip
Predict:
Will the answer be a large or a small number?

Check:
Does your answer match your prediction, and is it reasonable?

3.7 | Quantitative Concepts: Molecules and Moles

Chemists have another way of communicating the number of atoms, molecules, or other small particles present. This is to use the term **mole (mol),** defined as containing an Avogadro's number of objects. The term is derived from the Latin word to "heap," or "pile up." Thus, 1 mol of carbon atoms consists of 6.02×10^{23} C atoms, 1 mol of oxygen gas is made up of 6.02×10^{23} oxygen molecules, and 1 mol of carbon dioxide molecules corresponds to 6.02×10^{23} carbon dioxide molecules.

As you already know from previous chapters, chemical formulas and equations are written in terms of atoms and molecules. For example, reconsider the equation for the complete combustion of carbon in oxygen.

$$C + O_2 \longrightarrow CO_2 \qquad \text{[3.1]}$$

This equation tells us that one atom of carbon combines with one molecule of oxygen to yield one molecule of carbon dioxide. Thus it reflects the *ratio* in which the particles interact. It is equally correct to say that 10 C atoms react with 10 O_2 molecules (20 O atoms) to form 10 CO_2 molecules. Or, putting the reaction on a grander scale, we can say 6.02×10^{23} C atoms combine with 6.02×10^{23} O_2 molecules (12.0×10^{23} O atoms) to yield 6.02×10^{23} CO_2 molecules. The last statement is equivalent to saying: "one *mole* of carbon plus one *mole* of oxygen yields one *mole* of carbon dioxide." Thus the numbers of *atoms and molecules* taking part in a reaction are proportional to the numbers of *moles* of the same substances. The ratio of two oxygen atoms to one carbon atom remains the same regardless of the number of carbon dioxide molecules, as summarized in Table 3.2.

In the laboratory and the factory, the quantity of matter required for a reaction is often measured by mass. The mole is a practical way to relate number of particles to the more easily measured mass. The **molar mass** is the mass of Avogadro's number, or one *mole*, of whatever particles are specified. For example, from the periodic table we can see that the mass of one mole of carbon atoms, rounded to the nearest tenth of a gram, is 12.0 g. A mole of oxygen atoms has a mass of 16.0 g. But we can also speak of a mole of O_2 molecules. Because there are two oxygen atoms in each oxygen molecule, there are two moles of oxygen atoms in each mole of molecular oxygen, O_2. Consequently, the molar mass of O_2 is 32.0 g, twice the molar mass of O. Some refer to this as the molecular mass or molecular weight of O_2, emphasizing its similarity to atomic mass or atomic weight.

The same logic for the molar mass of the element O_2 applies to compounds, such as carbon dioxide. The formula, CO_2, reveals that each molecule contains one carbon atom and two oxygen atoms. Scaling up by 6.02×10^{23}, we can say that each mole of CO_2 consists of 1 mol of C and 2 mol of O atoms (see Table 3.2). But remember that we are interested in the molar mass of carbon dioxide, which we obtain by adding the molar mass of carbon to twice the molar mass of oxygen:

$$1 \text{ mol } CO_2 = 1 \text{ mol C} + 2 \text{ mol O}$$

$$= \left(1 \text{ mol C} \times \frac{12.0 \text{ g C}}{1 \text{ mol C}} \right) + \left(2 \text{ mol O} \times \frac{16.0 \text{ g O}}{1 \text{ mol O}} \right)$$

$$= 12.0 \text{ g C} + 32.0 \text{ g O}$$

$$1 \text{ mol } CO_2 = 44.0 \text{ g } CO_2$$

Table 3.2	Ways to Interpret a Chemical Equation		
C	+	O_2 $\longrightarrow$	CO_2
1 atom		1 molecule	1 molecule
6.02×10^{23} atoms		6.02×10^{23} molecules	6.02×10^{23} molecules
1 mol		1 mol	1 mol

This procedure is routinely used in chemical calculations, where molar mass is an important property. Some examples are included in Your Turn 3.15. In every case, you multiply the number of moles of each element by the corresponding atomic mass in grams and add the result.

Your Turn 3.15   Molecular Molar Mass

Calculate the molar mass of each of these greenhouse gases.

a. O_3 (ozone)
b. N_2O (dinitrogen monoxide or nitrous oxide)
c. CCl_3F (Freon–11; trichlorofluoromethane)

Answer

a. 1 mol O_3 = 3 mol O

$$= 3 \text{ mol O} \times \frac{16.0 \text{ g O}}{1 \text{ mol O}}$$

$$= 48.0 \text{ g } O_3$$

We started out on this mathematical excursion so that we could calculate the mass of CO_2 produced from burning 3.3 Gt of carbon. We now have all the pieces assembled. Out of every 44.0 g of CO_2, 12.0 g is C. This mass ratio holds for all samples of CO_2, and we can use it to calculate the mass of C in any known mass of CO_2. More to the point, we can use it to calculate the mass of CO_2 released by any known mass of carbon. It only depends on how we arrange the ratio. The C-to-CO_2 ratio is $\frac{12.0 \text{ g C}}{44.0 \text{ g } CO_2}$, but it is equally true that the CO_2-to-C ratio is $\frac{44.0 \text{ g } CO_2}{12.0 \text{ g O}}$.

For example, we could compute the number of grams of C in 100.0 g CO_2 by setting up the relationship in this manner.

$$100.0 \text{ g } CO_2 \times \frac{12.0 \text{ g C}}{44.0 \text{ g } CO_2} = 27.3 \text{ g C}$$

The fact that there is 27.3 g of carbon in 100.0 g of carbon dioxide is equivalent to saying that the mass percent of C in CO_2 is 27.3%. Note that carrying along the units "g CO_2" and "g C" helps you do the calculation correctly. The unit "g CO_2" can be canceled, and you are left with "g C." Keeping track of the units and canceling where appropriate are useful strategies in solving many problems. This method is sometimes called unit or dimensional analysis.

Your Turn 3.16   Mass Ratios and Percents

a. Calculate the mass ratio of S in SO_2.
b. Find the mass percent of S in SO_2.
c. Calculate the mass ratio and the mass percent of N in N_2O.

Answers

a. The mass ratio is found by comparing the molar mass of S with the molar mass of SO_2.

$$\frac{32.1 \text{ g S}}{64.1 \text{ g } SO_2} = \frac{0.501 \text{ g S}}{1.00 \text{ g } SO_2}$$

b. To find the mass percent of S in SO_2, multiply the mass ratio by 100.

$$\frac{0.501 \text{ g S}}{1.00 \text{ g } SO_2} \times 100 = 50.1\% \text{ S in } SO_2$$

To find the mass of CO_2 that contains 3.3 gigatonnes (Gt) of C, we use a similar approach. We could convert 3.3 Gt to grams, but it is not necessary. As long as we use the same mass unit for C and CO_2, the same numerical ratio holds. Compared with our

Calculation Tip

Predict:
Will the answer be larger or smaller than the given value? What are the units?

Check:
Does the answer match your prediction? Have units canceled, leaving the one needed for the answer?

last calculation, this problem has one important difference in how we use the ratio. We are solving for the mass of CO_2, not the mass of C. Look carefully at the units this time.

$$3.3 \ \cancel{Gt\ C} \times \frac{44.0 \ Gt \ CO_2}{12.0 \ \cancel{Gt\ C}} = 12 \ Gt \ CO_2$$

Once again the units cancel, and we are left with Gt of CO_2.

Our burning question, "What is the mass of CO_2 added to the atmosphere each year from the combustion of fossil fuels?" has finally been answered: 12 gigatonnes. Of course, we also managed to demonstrate the problem-solving power of chemistry and to introduce five of its most important ideas: atomic mass, molecular mass, Avogadro's number, mole, and molar mass. The next few activities provide opportunities to practice your skill with these concepts.

Your Turn 3.17   SO$_2$ from Volcanoes

a. It is estimated that volcanoes globally release about 19×10^6 t (19 million metric tons) of SO_2 per year. Calculate the mass of sulfur in this amount of SO_2.
b. If 142×10^6 t of SO_2 is released per year by fossil–fuel combustion, calculate the mass of sulfur in this amount of SO_2.

Answer
a. The mass ratio of S to SO_2 is known from Your Turn 3.16.

$$19 \times 10^6 \ \cancel{t\ SO_2} \times \frac{32.1 \times 10^6 \ t \ S}{64.1 \times 10^6 \ \cancel{t\ SO_2}} = 9.5 \times 10^6 \ t \ S$$

If you know how to apply these ideas, you have gained the ability to critically evaluate media reports about releases of C or CO_2 (and other substances as well) and judge their accuracy. One can either take such statements on faith or check their accuracy by applying mathematics to the relevant chemical concepts. Obviously, there is insufficient time to check every assertion, but we hope that you develop questioning and critical attitudes toward all statements about chemistry and society, including those found in this book.

Skeptical Chemist 3.18   Checking Carbon from Cars

A clean–burning automobile engine emits about 5 pounds of C in the form of CO_2 for every gallon of gasoline it consumes. The average American car is driven about 12,000 miles per year. Using this information, check the statement that the average American car releases its own weight in carbon into the atmosphere each year. List the assumptions you make in solving this problem. Compare your list and your answer with those of your classmates.

3.8 | Methane and Other Greenhouse Gases

Concerns about an enhanced greenhouse effect are based primarily on increases in concentrations of atmospheric CO_2. However, other gases also play a role. Methane, nitrous oxide, chlorofluorocarbons, and even ozone all take part in trapping heat in the atmosphere.

Our level of concern regarding each of these gases is related to their concentration in the atmosphere but also to other important characteristics. The **global atmospheric lifetime** characterizes the time required for a gas added to the atmosphere to be removed. It is also referred to as the "turnover time." Greenhouse gases also vary in their effectiveness in absorbing infrared radiation. This is quantified by the **global warming potential (GWP),** a number that represents the relative contribution of a molecule of the atmospheric gas to global warming. The GWP of carbon dioxide is assigned the reference value of 1; all other greenhouse gases are indexed with respect to it. Gases with relatively short lifetimes, such as water vapor, tropospheric ozone,

Global atmospheric lifetime values, although useful for comparison, are best thought of as approximations.

Table 3.3	Examples of Greenhouse Gases					
Name (Chemical Formula)	Preindustrial Concentration (1750)	Concentration in 2011	Atmospheric Lifetime (years)	Anthropogenic Sources		Global Warming Potential
carbon dioxide CO_2	270 ppm	396 ppm**	50-200*	Fossil fuel combustion, deforestation, cement production		1
methane CH_4	700 ppb	1816 ppb	12	Rice paddies, waste dumps, livestock		21
nitrous oxide N_2O	275 ppb	324 ppb	120	Fertilizers, industrial production, combustion		310
CFC-12 CCl_2F_2	0	0.53 ppb	102	Liquid coolants, foams		8100

*A single value for the atmospheric lifetime of CO_2 is not possible. Removal mechanisms take place at different rates. The range given is an estimate based on several removal mechanisms.

**The carbon dioxide value is from 2012 and the value has surpassed 400 ppm at several points during 2013.

tropospheric aerosols, and other ambient air pollutants, are distributed unevenly around the world. It is difficult to quantify their effect, and therefore GWP values are not usually assigned. Table 3.3 lists four greenhouse gases, their main sources, and their important properties in the climate change conversation.

Your Turn 3.19   Greenhouse Gases on the Rise

Using the data in Table 3.3, calculate the percentage increases for CO_2, CH_4, and N_2O since 1750. Rank the three in order of their percentage increase.

The current atmospheric concentration of CH_4 is about 50 times lower than that of CO_2, but as an infrared absorber, methane is about 20 times more efficient than carbon dioxide. Fortunately, CH_4 is quite readily converted to other chemical species by interaction with tropospheric free radicals, and therefore has a relatively short lifetime. By comparison, carbon dioxide is much less reactive. The primary removal mechanisms for CO_2 are dissolution in oceans, photosynthesis by plants, and the much longer process of mineralization into carbonate rocks.

Methane emissions arise from both natural and human sources. About 40% of total CH_4 emissions come from natural sources, of which emanations from wetlands are by far the largest contributor. These marshy habitats are perfectly suited for **anaerobic bacteria,** those that can function without the use of molecular oxygen. As they decompose organic matter, many types of anaerobic bacteria produce methane, which then escapes into the atmosphere. In Alaska, Canada, and Siberia, however, much of the methane produced from thousands of years of decomposition has remained trapped underground by the permafrost. There is concern that melting of the surface in the northern latitudes might trigger a massive release of methane into the atmosphere. There is geological evidence that such a release has occurred in the past and led to higher global temperatures.

Methane is also released from the oceans, where a substantial amount of it appears to be trapped in "cages" made of water molecules. Such deposits are referred to as methane hydrates. Australia's Commonwealth Scientific and Industrial Research Organization (CSIRO) has taken a series of ocean core drillings to gather evidence about methane hydrates and their role in global warming (Figure 3.23). There is concern that if some of these hydrates become unstable then large amounts of methane might rapidly be released to the atmosphere.

Termites are another natural source of methane. These ubiquitous insects have special bacteria in their guts that allow them to metabolize cellulose, the main component of wood. But instead of making water and CO_2, termites produce methane and CO_2. Not only can they inflict direct damage to homes, but they also add to greenhouse gas concentrations. The sheer number of termites is staggering, estimated to be more than half a metric ton for every man, woman, and child on the planet!

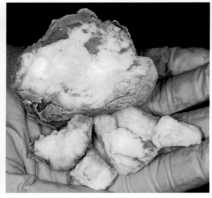

(a)   (b)

Figure 3.23

(a) A floating drilling platform used by the CSIRO.
(b) A sample of methane hydrate from the continental shelf off the coast of Florida.

The major human source of CH_4 is agriculture, with the biggest culprits being rice cultivation and the raising of livestock. Rice is grown with its roots under water, where, again, anaerobic bacteria produce methane. Most of the methane is released to the atmosphere. Additional agricultural CH_4 comes from an increasing number of cattle and sheep. The digestive systems of these ruminants (animals that chew their cud) contain bacteria that break down cellulose. In the process, methane is formed and released through belching and flatulence—about 500 liters of CH_4 per cow per day! The ruminants of the Earth release a staggering 73 million metric tons of CH_4 each year.

Landfills add another large quantity of methane to the atmosphere. The chemistry occurring within our buried garbage is controlled by the same anaerobic bacteria found in wetlands and produces the same result. Some of this methane is captured (biogas) and burned as a fuel, but the vast majority is released into the atmosphere.

For more information on using methane as a fuel, check Section 4.10.

The other main anthropogenic source of methane originates from our extraction of fossil fuels. Methane is often found with oil and coal deposits, and drilling and mining procedures release most of that methane to the atmosphere while recovering the liquid or solid products. There are also significant losses from transporting, purifying, and using natural gas.

Consider This 3.20   Methane Concentrations Stabilizing?

In recent years, scientists observed methane concentrations leveled off. Is this the case currently? Use the resources of the Internet to support your answer.

The role of N_2O in destroying stratospheric ozone was discussed in Section 2.8.

Another gas that contributes to global warming is nitrous oxide, also known as "laughing gas." It has been used as an inhaled anesthetic for dental and medical purposes. Its sources and sinks are not as well established as are those for carbon dioxide and methane. The majority of N_2O molecules in the atmosphere come from the bacterial removal of nitrate ion (NO_3^-) from soils, followed by removal of oxygen. Agricultural practices, again linked to population pressures, can speed up the removal of reactive compounds of nitrogen from soils. Other sources include ocean upwelling and stratospheric interactions of nitrogen compounds with high-energy oxygen atoms. Major anthropogenic sources of N_2O are automobile catalytic converters, ammonia fertilizers, biomass burning, and certain industrial processes (nylon and nitric acid production). In the atmosphere, a typical N_2O molecule persists for about 120 years,

Table 3.4	Climate Change and Ozone Depletion: A Comparison	
	Climate Change	Ozone Depletion
Region of atmosphere	primarily the troposphere	the stratosphere
Major players	H_2O, CO_2, CH_4, and N_2O	O_3, CFCs, HCFCs, and halons
Interaction with radiation	Molecules absorb IR radiation. This causes them to vibrate and return heat energy to the Earth.	Molecules absorb UV radiation. This causes one or more bonds in the molecule to break.
Nature of problem	Greenhouse gases are increasing in concentration. In turn this is trapping more heat, causing an increase in the average global temperatures.	CFCs are causing a decrease in concentrations of O_3 in the stratosphere. In turn, this is causing an increase in the UV radiation that reaches the surface of the Earth.

absorbing and emitting infrared radiation. Over the past decade, global atmospheric concentrations of N_2O have shown a slow but steady rise.

A few comments need to be made about ozone, a gas we encountered in Chapter 2. Often there is confusion between the phenomena of climate change and ozone depletion. Both are often in the news, both involve complex atmospheric processes, and both have anthropogenic as well as natural sources. In fact, ozone itself can act like a greenhouse gas, but its efficiency depends very much on its altitude. It appears to have its maximum warming effect in the upper troposphere. Therefore, depletion of ozone has a *slight cooling effect* in the stratosphere, and it may also promote slight cooling at Earth's surface. Other differences are summarized in Table 3.4.

Depletion of the stratospheric ozone layer is *not* a principal cause of climate change. However, stratospheric ozone depletion and climate change are linked in an important way, through ozone-depleting substances. CFCs, HCFCs, and halons, all implicated in the depletion of stratospheric ozone, also absorb infrared radiation and are all greenhouse gases. Emissions of these synthetic gases rose by 58% from 1990–2005, although their concentrations are still very low.

HCFCs were discussed in Section 2.12.

Consider This 3.21   Global Warming Potential As the Clock Ticks

Although Table 3.3 reports a single value of Global Warming Potential (GWP) for each greenhouse listed, in actuality different values are possible, depending on the time frame. For example:

	20 years	100 years	500 years
CH_4	72	21	7.6
N_2O	289	310	156

The reason for the differences is a function of the estimated atmospheric lifetime of the gas.

a. Compare the GWPs for methane for 20 and 100 years. Explain why these values are consistent with an estimated atmospheric lifetime of about 12 years for methane.
b. For both methane and nitrous oxide, the GWP values are lower for 500 years than for 100 years. Propose an explanation.

3.9 | How Warm Will the Planet Get?

"Prediction is very difficult, especially about the future." Niels Bohr, one of the foremost contributors to our modern view of the atom, spoke these words years ago. His words still hold true today!

Some people have stated that changes in the Sun are causing global climate change. What are your thoughts?

The IPCC received the 2007 Nobel Peace Prize (shared with former U.S. Vice President Al Gore) for its work in understanding global warming.

The unique properties of water, including its unusually large specific heat, will be described in Chapter 5.

Figure 3.24

Climate scientists use computer simulations to understand future climate change.

Periodic orbital eccentricities are a possible cause of the ice age oscillations shown in Figure 3.9.

Although admittedly a difficult task, we still need to make predictions. To this end, in 1988, the United Nations Environment Programme and the World Meteorological Organization teamed up to establish the UN Intergovernmental Panel on Climate Change (IPCC). The IPCC was charged with assembling and assessing the climate change data, including socioeconomic data. Thousands of international scientists were involved in this review. In their fourth and most recent report published in 2007, the vast majority of scientists agreed on several key points:

- The Earth is getting warmer.
- Human activities (primarily the combustion of fossil fuels and deforestation) are responsible for much of the recent warming.
- If the rate of greenhouse gas emissions is not curtailed, our water resources, food supply, and even our health will suffer.

A fifth report was scheduled for release in 2014.

The challenge, however, is to understand current climate change well enough to *predict* future changes and by doing so, to determine the decrease in emissions required to minimize harmful changes. To make predictions, scientists work with models. They design computer models of the oceans and the atmosphere that take into account the ability of each to absorb heat as well as to circulate and transport matter (Figure 3.24). If that weren't difficult enough, the models must also include astronomical, meteorological, geological, and biological factors, ones that are often incompletely understood. Human influences, such as population, industrialization levels, and pollution emissions must also be included. Dr. Michael Schlesinger, who directs climate research at the University of Illinois, remarked: "If you were going to pick a planet to model, this is the *last* planet you would choose."

Climate scientists call the factors (both natural and anthropogenic) that influence the balance of Earth's incoming and outgoing radiation by the term **radiative forcings.** Negative forcings have a cooling effect; positive forcings a warming effect. The primary forcings used in climate models are solar irradiance, greenhouse gas concentrations, land use, and aerosols. The effects of these forcings on the Earth's energy balance are summarized in Figure 3.25. Red, orange, and yellow bars represent positive forcings, and blue bars indicate negative ones. Each forcing has an error bar associated with it; the larger the error bar, the more uncertain the value.

Solar Irradiance ("solar brightness")

We can directly observe the natural seasonal variations in sunlight intensity. In the higher latitudes, temperatures are warmer in the summer. Compared to winter months, the Sun is higher in the sky and stays up longer. Across the globe, these variations essentially cancel, because when it is winter in the Northern Hemisphere it is summer in the Southern Hemisphere.

Subtle periodic changes occur in the brightness of the Sun. The Earth's orbit oscillates slightly over a 100,000-year period, changing its shape. In addition, the magnitude of the tilt of the Earth's axis and the direction of that tilt both change over the course of several tens of thousands of years, affecting the amount of solar radiation hitting the Earth. Neither of these occurs on a time scale short enough to explain the recent warming, however.

Additionally, sunspots occur in large numbers about every 11 years. You might think that dark spots on the Sun would mean a smaller amount of radiation hitting the Earth, but exactly the opposite is true. Sunspots occur when there is increased magnetic activity in the outer layers of the Sun, and the stronger magnetic fields stir up a larger amount of charged particles that emit radiation. Notably, the 17th and 18th centuries,

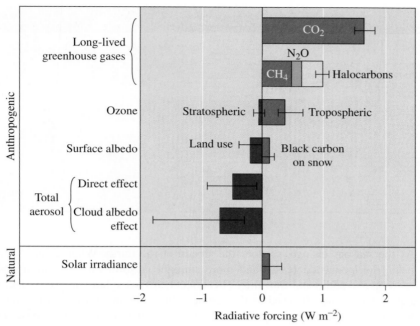

Figure 3.25

Selected radiative forcings of climate from 1750 to 2005. The units are in watts per square meter (W m^{-2}), the light energy hitting a square meter of the Earth's surface every second.

Source: Adapted from Climate Change 2007: The Physical Science Basis. *Contribution of Working Group I to the Fourth Assessment Report of the Intergovernmental Panel on Climate Change.*

sometimes called the "Little Ice Age" because of the below average temperatures in Europe, were preceded by a period of almost no sunspot activity. However, the solar brightness over those 11-year cycles varies only by about 0.1%. As you can see from Figure 3.25, this natural variability is the *smallest* of any positive forcing listed.

> During periods of high sunspot activity, the aurora borealis ("northern lights") is more spectacular because of the greater number of charged particles striking the Earth's atmosphere.

Your Turn 3.23   Radiation from the Sun

Sunlight strikes the Earth continually. Which types of light are emitted by the Sun? Which one makes up the largest percentage of sunlight? *Hint:* Refer back to Figure 2.8.

Greenhouse Gases

These are the dominant anthropogenic forcings. Largest among these is CO_2, constituting about two thirds of the warming from all greenhouse gases. However, as we explained in the previous section, methane, nitrous oxide, and other gases do contribute. Notice the relatively small contribution from "halocarbons" (CFCs and HCFCs) as shown in Figure 3.25. It has been estimated that without the ban on CFC production imposed by the Montreal Protocol, by 1990 the forcings from CFCs would have outweighed those from CO_2. In sum, the positive forcings from greenhouse gases are more than 30 times greater than the natural changes in solar irradiance.

> The Montreal Protocol was discussed in Section 2.11.

Land Use

Changes in land use drive climate change because these changes alter the amount of incoming solar radiation that is absorbed by the surface of the Earth. The ratio of electromagnetic radiation *reflected* from a surface relative to the amount of radiation *incident* on it is called the **albedo.** In short, albedo is a measure of the reflectivity of a surface. The albedo of the Earth's surface varies between about 0.1 and 0.9, as you can see from the values listed in Table 3.5. The higher the number, the more reflective the surface.

> Earth has an average albedo of 0.39. In contrast, that of the Moon is about 0.12.

Table 3.5	Albedo Values for Different Ground Covers
Surface	**Range of Albedo**
fresh snow	0.80–0.90
old/melting snow	0.40–0.80
desert sand	0.40
grassland	0.25
deciduous trees	0.15–0.18
coniferous forest	0.08–0.15
tundra	0.20
ocean	0.07–0.10

As the seasons change, so does the albedo of the Earth. When a snow-covered area melts, the albedo decreases and more sunlight is absorbed, creating a positive feedback loop and additional warming. This effect helps to explain the greater increases in average temperature observed in the Arctic, where the amount of sea ice and permanent snow cover is decreasing. Similarly, when glaciers retreat and expose darker rock, the albedo decreases, causing further warming.

Human activity also can change the Earth's albedo, most notably through deforestation in the tropics. The crops we plant reflect more incoming light than does the dark green foliage of the rain forests, causing an increase in the albedo and hence resulting in *cooling*. In addition, sunlight is more consistent in the tropics, so changes in land use at low latitudes produce greater effects than changes in the polar regions. The conversion of tropical rain forest to crop and pastureland has more than offset the decrease in the amount of sea ice and snow cover near the poles. Therefore, the changes in the Earth's albedo have caused a net *cooling* effect.

Consider This 3.24   White Roofs, Green Roofs

a. In 2009, U.S. Energy Secretary Steven Chu suggested that painting roofs white would be one way to combat global warming. Explain the reasoning behind this course of action.

b. The idea of "green roofs" is also attracting attention. Planting gardens on rooftops has benefits in addition to those of white roofs. But such gardens also have limitations. Explain.

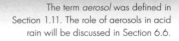

The term *aerosol* was defined in Section 1.11. The role of aerosols in acid rain will be discussed in Section 6.6.

Aerosols

A complex class of materials, aerosols have a correspondingly complex effect on climate. Many natural sources of aerosols exist, including dust storms, ocean spray, forest fires, and volcanic eruptions. Human activity also can release aerosols into the environment in the form of smoke, soot, and sulfate aerosols from coal combustion.

The effect of aerosols on climate is probably the least well understood of the forcings listed in Figure 3.25. Tiny aerosol particles (<4 μm) are efficient at scattering incoming solar radiation. Other aerosols absorb incoming radiation, and still other particles both scatter and absorb. Both processes decrease the amount of radiation available for absorption by greenhouse gases and therefore have a cooling effect (negative forcing). In a dramatic example, the 1991 eruption of Mt. Pinatubo in the Philippines spewed over 20 million tons of SO_2 into the atmosphere. In addition to providing spectacular sunsets for several months, the sulfur dioxide caused temperatures around the world to drop slightly. The results provided the climate modelers a mini-control experiment. The most reliable models were able to reproduce the cooling effect caused by the eruption.

In addition to that direct cooling effect, aerosol particles can serve as nuclei for the condensation of water droplets and hence promote cloud formation. Clouds reflect

Mt. Pinatubo eruption, 1991.

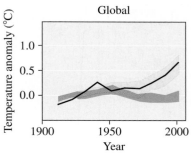
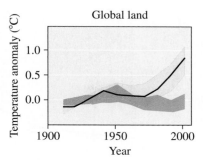
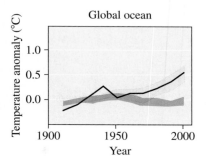

Figure 3.26

Climate model predictions of annual global mean surface temperatures for the 20th century. Black lines display temperature data relative to the average temperature for the years 1901–1950. The blue bands indicate the predicted temperature range using natural forcings only. The pink bands indicate the predicted temperature range using *both* natural and anthropogenic forcings.

Source: Adapted from Climate Change 2007: The Physical Science Basis. *Contribution of Working Group I to the Fourth Assessment Report of the Intergovernmental Panel on Climate Change.*

incoming solar radiation, although the effects of increased cloud cover are more complex than this. Therefore, in both direct and indirect ways, aerosols *counter* the warming effects of greenhouse gases.

Given the complexity inherent in all the forcings that we have just described, you can appreciate that assembling these forcings into a climate model is no easy task. Furthermore, once a model has been built, scientists have difficulty assessing its validity. However, scientists do have one trick in their back pockets. They can test climate models with known data sets as a means to tease apart the contributions of different forcings. For example, we know the temperature data of the 20th century. In Figure 3.26, the black lines represent the known data. Next examine the blue bands. These represent temperature ranges that were predicted by the climate model using *only* natural forcings. As you can see, the natural forcings do not map well onto the actual temperatures. Finally, examine the pink bands to see that when anthropogenic forcings are included, the temperature increases of the 20th century can be accurately reproduced. So although the last 30 years of warming were *influenced* by natural factors, the actual temperatures cannot be accounted for without including the effects of human activities.

Your Turn 3.25   Assessing Climate Models

Between 1950 and 2000, the climate models that used natural forcings only (blue bands in Figure 3.26) showed an overall cooling effect and thus did not match the observed temperatures.

a. Name the forcings included in the models that only included natural forcings.
b. List two additional forcings included in the models that more accurately recreate the temperatures of the 20th century (pink bands in Figure 3.26).

Answer
a. Aerosols (such as those from volcanic eruptions), solar irradiance.

The magnitude of future emissions, and hence the magnitude of future warming, depends on many factors. As you might expect, one is population. As of 2012, the global population stood at about 7 billion. Assuming that there will be more feet on the planet in the future, we humans are likely to have a larger **carbon footprint,** an estimate of the amount of CO_2 and other greenhouse gas emissions in a given time frame, usually a year. Having more people to feed, clothe, house, and transport will require the consumption of more energy. In turn, this translates to more CO_2 emissions, at least if using current fuels. In addition, scientists who create climate models have to include values for two factors: (1) the rate of economic growth, and (2) the rate of development of "green" (less carbon-intensive) energy sources. Again, as you might expect, both are difficult to predict.

Chapter 0 introduced the concept of an ecological footprint. Carbon footprints are a subset of the more general term.

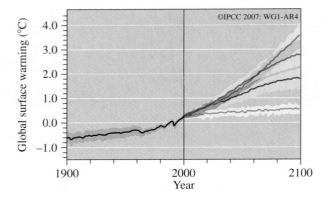

Figure 3.27

Four model projections for temperature scenarios in the 21st century based on different socioeconomic assumptions. The black line is the data for the 20th century with the gray regions indicating the uncertainty in those values. The four dark lines represent projected 21st-century temperatures, with the wider lighter colored bands representing the uncertainty range for each scenario.

Source: Adapted from Climate Change 2007: The Physical Science Basis. *Contribution of Working Group I to the Fourth Assessment Report of the Intergovernmental Panel on Climate Change.*

So what, if anything, can computer models tell us about the Earth's future climate? Given the uncertainties that we have listed, hundreds of different projected temperature scenarios for the 21st century are possible. Figure 3.27 shows four of these, together with the actual temperature data for the 20th century.

The four scenarios for 21st-century temperatures are based on different assumptions. The orange line assumes that emissions levels are kept at 2000 levels, admittedly an unrealistic target given the increases that already have occurred since 2000. Even with this most optimistic scenario, some additional warming will take place due to the persistence of CO_2 in the atmosphere for years to come. Both the blue and green lines assume that the global population will increase to 9 billion by 2050 but then gradually decrease. However, the blue line includes the more rapid development of energy-efficient technologies, leading to lower CO_2 emissions. The red line assumes a continually increasing population combined with a slower and less globally integrated transition to new, cleaner technologies.

All of the lines point in the same direction—up. With some amount of future warming virtually ensured, we now turn our discussion to the consequences of climate change.

3.10 | The Consequences of Climate Change

Considering even the most extreme predictions of warming described in the last section, you may be thinking, "So what?" After all, the temperature changes predicted in Figure 3.27 are only a few degrees. At any single spot on the planet, the temperature fluctuates several times that amount daily.

An important distinction needs to be made between the terms *climate* and *weather*. **Weather** includes the daily high and low temperatures, the drizzles and downpours, the blizzards and heat waves, and the fall breezes and hot summer winds, all of which have relatively short durations. In contrast, **climate** describes regional temperatures, humidity, winds, rain, and snowfall over decades, not days. And while the weather varies on a daily basis, our climate has stayed relatively uniform over the last 10,000 years. The values quoted for the "average global temperature" are but one measure of climate phenomena. The key point is that relatively small changes in average global temperature can have huge effects on many aspects of our climate.

In addition to modeling various future temperature scenarios (see Figure 3.27), the 2007 IPCC report estimated the likelihood of various consequences. The report employed descriptive terms ("judgmental estimates of confidence") to help both policy makers and the general public better understand the inherent uncertainty of the data.

Table 3.6	Judgmental Estimates of Confidence
Term	**Probability That a Result Is True (%)**
virtually certain	>99
very likely	90–99
likely	66–90
medium likelihood	33–66
unlikely	10–33
very unlikely	1–10

Source: Adapted from Climate Change 2007: The Physical Science Basis. *Contribution of Working Group I to the Fourth Assessment Report of the Intergovernmental Panel on Climate Change.*

Subsequent updates to the IPCC reports will use these terms, along with their assigned probabilities, which are found in Table 3.6.

Conclusions from the 2007 IPCC report are listed in Table 3.7. For example, it was judged *very unlikely* that all of the observed global warming was due to natural climate variability. Rather, the scientific evidence strongly supports the position that human activity factors significantly in the increase in average global temperature observed over the last century. Furthermore, from the scientific evidence for global warming, it was judged *virtually certain* that human activities were the main drivers of recent warming. Check Table 3.7 for other conclusions relevant to any discussion of global climate change.

Many scientific organizations, including the American Association for the Advancement of Science and the American Chemical Society, also have recognized the threats posed by climate change. In an open letter to United States senators, the organizations cited sea level rise, more extreme weather events, increased water scarcity, and disturbances of local ecosystems as likely eventualities of a warmer planet. To conclude this section, we describe these and other outcomes we might expect, including sea ice disappearance, more extreme weather, changes in ocean chemistry, loss of biodiversity, and harm to human health.

Each of the potential consequences can be considered in the context of the tragedy of the commons, which we encountered in Chapters 1 and 2.

Table 3.7	IPCC Conclusions, 2007

Virtually Certain

- Main drivers of recent warming are human activities.

Very Likely

- Human–caused emissions are the main factor causing warming since 1950.
- Higher maximum temperatures are observed over nearly all land areas.
- Snow cover decreased about 10% since the 1960s (satellite data); lake and river ice cover in the middle and high latitudes of the Northern Hemisphere was reduced by 2 weeks per year in the 20th century (independent ground–based observations).
- In most of the areas in the Northern Hemisphere, precipitation has increased.

Likely

- Temperatures in the Northern Hemisphere during the 20th century have been the highest of any century during the past 1000 years.
- Arctic sea ice thickness declined about 40% during late summer to early autumn in recent decades.
- An increase in rainfall, similar to that in the Northern Hemisphere, has been observed in tropical land areas falling between 108° North and 108° South.
- Summer droughts have increased.

Very Unlikely

- The observed warming over the past 100 years is due to climate variability alone, providing new and even stronger evidence that changes must be made to stem the influence of human activities.

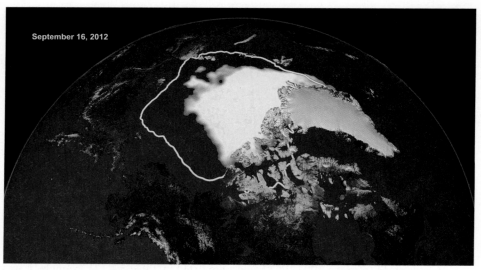

Figure 3.28

The extent of Arctic ice in September 2012 in comparison to the 30–year average sea ice minimum (yellow line).

Source: Earth Observatory, NASA.

Sea Ice Disappearance

As shown in Figure 3.8, the temperatures in the Arctic are rising faster than anywhere else on Earth. One result is that sea ice is shrinking (Figure 3.28). A record low for ice cover was set in September 2012. Summer sea ice has declined about 40% from when satellites started tracking ice coverage in the late 1970s. A new analysis that uses both computer models and data from actual conditions in the Arctic region forecasts that most of the Arctic sea ice will be gone in 30 years. Not only would significant populations of wildlife be endangered, but the accompanying decrease in albedo would lead to even more warming.

Albedo and positive feedback were discussed in Section 3.9.

Sea-Level Rise

Warmer temperatures result in an increase in sea level. This increase occurs primarily because as water warms, it expands. A smaller effect is caused by the influx of fresh-water into the ocean from glacier runoff. According to a 2008 study published in the journal *Nature*, the increase was about 1.5 millimeters each year (about 7.5 cm during the past 50 years) between 1961 and 2003. However, the increases are not seen uniformly across the globe. In addition, they are influenced by regional weather patterns. Even so, these small increases in sea levels can cause erosion in coastal areas and the stronger storm surges associated with hurricanes and cyclones.

Consider This 3.26   External Costs

The consequences described earlier and later on are examples of what are known as external costs. These costs are not reflected in the price of a commodity, such as the price of a gallon of gasoline or a ton of coal, but nevertheless take a toll on the environment. The external costs of burning fossil fuels often are shared by those who emit very little carbon dioxide, such as the people of the island nation of Maldives. Although a rise of sea level of just a few millimeters may not seem like much, the effects could be catastrophic for nations that lie close to sea level. Use the resources of the Internet to investigate how the people of Maldives are preparing for rising sea levels. Also comment on how this is an example of the tragedy of the commons.

More Extreme Weather

An increase in the average global temperature could cause more extreme weather, including storms, floods, and droughts. In the Northern Hemisphere, the summers are predicted to be drier and the winters wetter. Over the past several decades, more frequent wildfires and floods have occurred on every continent. The severity (although not the frequency) of cyclones and hurricanes also may be increasing. These tropical storms extract their energy from the oceans; a warmer ocean provides more energy to feed the storms.

Changes in Ocean Chemistry

"Over the past 200 years, the oceans have absorbed approximately 550 billion tons of CO_2 from the atmosphere, or about a third of the total amount of anthropogenic emissions over that period," reports Richard A. Feely, a senior scientist with the National Pacific Marine Environmental Laboratory in Seattle. Scientists estimate that a million tons of CO_2 is absorbed into the oceans every hour of every day! In their role as carbon sinks, the world's oceans have mitigated some of the warming that carbon dioxide would have caused had it remained in the atmosphere. However, this absorption has come with a cost. Critical changes are already occurring in the oceans, as we will further explore in Chapter 6. For example, carbon dioxide is slightly soluble in water and dissolves to form carbonic acid. In turn, this is affecting marine organisms that rely on a constant level of acidity in the ocean to maintain the integrity of their shells and skeletons. The increase in carbon dioxide concentrations in the atmosphere (and also in the corresponding concentration of carbonic acid in the oceans) is putting entire marine ecosystems at risk.

Coral bleaching caused by El Nino, a consequence of global warming, Maldives, Indian Ocean, Asia.

Consider This 3.27   Plankton and You

Plankton are microscopic plant- and animal-like creatures found in both salt and freshwater systems. Many plankton species have shells made of calcium carbonate that could be weakened by more acidic environments. Although humans do not eat plankton, many other marine organisms do. Construct a food chain to show the link between plankton and humans.

Look for more about carbon dioxide and ocean acidification in Chapter 6.

Loss of Biodiversity

Climate change already is affecting plant, insect, and animal species around the world. Species as diverse as the California starfish, Alpine herbs, and checkerspot butterflies all have exhibited changes in either their ranges or their habits. Dr. Richard P. Alley, a Pennsylvania State University expert on past climate shifts, sees particular significance in the fact that animals and plants that rely on each other will not necessarily change ranges or habits at the same rate. Referring to affected species, he said, "You'll have to change what you eat, or rely on fewer things to eat, or travel farther to eat, all of which have costs." In extreme cases, those costs can cause the extinction of species. Currently, the rate of extinction worldwide is nearly 1000 times greater than at any time during the last 65 million years! A 2004 report in the journal *Nature* projects that about 20% of the plants and animals considered will face extinction by 2050, even under the most optimistic climate forecasts.

Many different species of checkerspot butterflies exist. This one is found in parts of Wisconsin.

Vulnerability of Freshwater Resources

Like polar and sea ice, glaciers in many parts of the world are shrinking due to increased average temperatures (Figure 3.29). Billions of people rely on glacier runoff for both drinking water and crop irrigation. The 2007 report of the IPCC predicts that a 1 °C increase in global temperature corresponds to more than half a billion people experiencing water shortages that they have not known before. The redistribution of freshwater also has implications in food production. Drought and high temperatures could reduce crop yields in the American Midwest, but the growing range might extend farther into Canada. It is also possible that some desert regions could get sufficient rain to become arable. One region's loss may well become another locale's gain, but it is too early to tell.

For more on the chemistry of water availability and use, see Section 5.3.

Figure 3.29

A view of the Exit Glacier in Kenji Fjords National Park, Alaska, in 2008. The sign in the foreground marks the extent of the ice flow in 1978.

Figure 3.29

A view of the Exit Glacier in Kenji Fjords National Park, Alaska, in 2008. The sign in the foreground marks the extent of the ice flow in 1978.

Human Health

We may all be losers in a warmer world. In 2000, the WHO attributed over 150,000 premature deaths worldwide to the effects of climate change. Those effects included more frequent and severe heat waves, increased droughts in already water-stressed regions, and infectious diseases in regions where they had not occurred before. Further increases in average temperatures are expected to expand the geographical range of mosquitoes, tsetse flies, and other disease-carrying insects. The result could be a significant upturn in illnesses such as malaria, yellow and dengue fevers, and sleeping sickness in new areas, including Asia, Europe, and the United States.

3.11 | What Can (or Should) We Do About Climate Change?

The debate over climate change has shifted in the last 20 years. Today's scientific data leave little room for doubt about whether it is occurring. For example, measurements of higher surface and ocean temperatures, retreating glaciers and sea ice, and rising sea levels are unequivocal. In addition, the carbon isotopic ratio found in atmospheric CO_2 (discussed in Section 3.6) leaves little doubt that human activity is responsible for much of the observed warming. However, at issue is what we *can* do and what we *should* do about the changes that are occurring.

Consider This 3.28   Carbon Footprint Calculations

Investigate three websites that calculate your carbon footprint.

a. For each site, list the name, the sponsor, and the information requested in order to calculate the carbon footprint.
b. Does the information requested differ from site to site? If so, report the differences.
c. List two advantages and two disadvantages of doing a carbon footprint calculation.

For more on food metabolism as a source of energy, see Section 11.9.

Energy is essential for every human endeavor. Personally, you obtain the energy you need by eating and then metabolizing food. As a community or nation, we meet our energy needs in a variety of ways, including by burning coal, petroleum, and natural gas. The combustion of these carbon-based fuels produces several waste products, including carbon dioxide. The countries with large populations and those that are highly industrialized tend to burn the largest quantities of fuels and as a result emit the most CO_2. According to the Carbon Dioxide Information Analysis Center (CDIAC) of Oak Ridge National Laboratory, in 2008, the top CO_2 emitters were China, the United States, the Russian Federation, India, and Japan. Which other nations rank high on the list? The next activity shows you how to find out.

Consider This 3.29   Carbon Emissions by Nation

CDIAC publishes a list of the top 20 nations for CO_2 emissions.

   a. From what you already know, predict any five of the nations (in addition to those listed in the previous paragraph) that are on this list. Check how accurate your predictions were by using the Internet.
   b. How would these rankings change if they were listed per capita?

In a 2008 address, John Holdren summarized our options in dealing with climate change with three words: mitigation, adaptation, and suffering. "Basically, if we do less mitigation and adaptation, we're going to do a lot more suffering," he concluded. But who will be responsible for the mitigation? Who will be forced to adapt? Who will bear the brunt of the suffering? It is likely that significant disagreements will arise regarding answers to these questions. But we can agree that any practical solution must be global in nature and include a complicated mix of risk perception, societal values, politics, and economics.

Climate mitigation is any action taken to permanently eliminate or reduce the long-term risk and hazards of climate change to human life, property, or the environment. The most obvious strategy for minimizing anthropogenic climate change is to reduce the amount of CO_2 emitted into the atmosphere in the first place. Take a look back at Figure 3.21. It is difficult to imagine curtailing any of these "necessities" to any great extent. Therefore decreasing our energy consumption will not be easy, at least in the short term. The simplest and least expensive approach is to improve energy efficiency. Due to the inefficiencies associated with energy production, saving energy on the consumer end multiplies its effect on the production end three to five times. However, relying on the individual consumers worldwide to buy the right goods and do the right things will not be sufficient to hold CO_2 emissions below dangerous levels.

A developing technology aimed at slowing the rate of carbon dioxide emissions is to capture and isolate the gas after combustion. **Carbon capture and storage (CCS)** involves separating CO_2 from other combustion products and storing (sequestration) it in a variety of geologic locations. If the CO_2 is properly immobilized, it cannot reach the atmosphere and contribute to global warming. In addition to the large technological challenges posed by CCS, high start-up costs, usually in excess of $1 billion per power plant, so far are limiting this approach as a mitigation strategy.

Although at least two dozen projects are in development worldwide, as of 2009, only four industrial-scale CCS projects were in operation. Three remove CO_2 from natural gas reservoirs and store it in various underground geologic formations (Figure 3.30). The fourth and largest project, located in Saskatchewan, Canada, takes CO_2 captured from a coal-fired power plant in North Dakota and injects it into a depleted oil field. By doing so, additional oil is forced up through the existing wells for recovery. The benefits of enhancing oil recovery combined with CO_2 sequestration could become a model for other types of projects. Combined, these CCS efforts store about 5 million metric tons of carbon dioxide annually.

We will present more thoughts from John Holdren in the conclusion.

Chapter 4 focuses on energy from fossil fuels, Chapter 7 on nuclear energy, and Chapter 8 on some alternative energy sources such as wind and solar power.

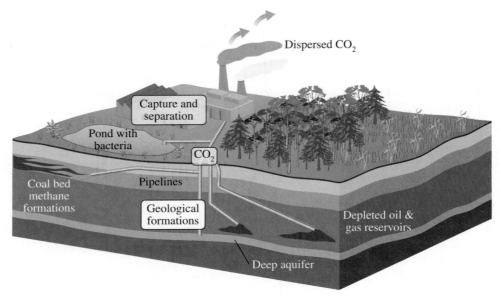

Figure 3.30
Methods for carbon dioxide sequestration.

Your Turn 3.30   Carbon Capture Limitations

Refer back to the global carbon cycle in Figure 3.20. What percent of global carbon dioxide emissions from fossil fuel burning is captured by current CCS technology?

Critics of CCS technology dispute its ultimate efficacy for slowing atmospheric CO_2 buildup, citing high costs as well as the long time frame for commercial implementation. Others contend that pursuing CCS simply delays and distracts attention from developing carbon-free energy sources. Finally, there is the sheer magnitude of the problem. According to the International Energy Agency, in order for CCS to make a meaningful contribution to mitigation efforts by 2050, it would require nearly 6000 installations *each* injecting a million metric tons of CO_2 per year into the ground.

A low-tech sequestration strategy is to reverse the extensive deforestation activities that are occurring predominantly in the world's tropical rainforests. Started in 2006 by the United Nations Development Programme and the World Agroforestry Center, the "Billion Trees Campaign" seeks to slow climate change by planting trees in depleted forests. During the first 18 months of the program, over 2 billion trees were planted, mostly in Africa. By 2012, over 12 billion trees were planted. If this number of trees seems like a lot, remember the scale of deforestation; in 2005, forest area equal to about 35,000 football fields was cleared *every day*!

Your Turn 3.31   Trees as Carbon Sinks

An average–sized tree absorbs 25 to 50 pounds of carbon dioxide each year. In the United States, the average annual per capita CO_2 emission is 19 tons.

a. How many trees would be required to absorb the annual CO_2 emissions for an average U.S. citizen?

b. What percentage of annual global emissions from burning fossil fuels could be absorbed by 12 billion trees?

Hint: Refer back to Figure 3.20.

Regardless of any potential decreases in future emissions, some effects of climate change are unavoidable. As mentioned previously, many of the CO_2 molecules emitted today will remain in the atmosphere for centuries. **Climate adaptation** refers to the ability of a system to adjust to climate change (including climate variability and extremes) to moderate potential damage, to take advantage of opportunities, or to cope with the consequences. Some adaptive methods include developing new crop varieties and shoring up or constructing new coastline defense systems for low-lying countries and islands. The further spread of infectious diseases could be minimized by enhanced public health systems. Many of these strategies are win–win situations that would benefit societies even in the absence of climate change challenges.

Compared with the scientific consensus on understanding the role greenhouse gases play in the Earth's climate, there is much less agreement among governments regarding what actions should be taken to limit greenhouse gas emissions. One outcome from the Earth Summit held in 1992 in Rio de Janeiro was the Framework Convention on Climate Change. The goal of this international treaty was "to achieve stabilization of greenhouse gas concentrations in the atmosphere at a low enough level to prevent dangerous anthropogenic interference with the climate system." Not only was this treaty nonbinding, but also there was no agreement about what "dangerous anthropogenic interference" meant, or what level of greenhouse gas emissions would be necessary to avoid it.

In 1997, the first international treaty imposing legally binding limits on greenhouse gas emissions was written by nearly 10,000 participants from 161 countries gathered in Kyoto, Japan. The result has come to be known as the Kyoto Protocol. Binding emission targets based on 1990 levels were set for 38 developed nations to reduce their emissions of six greenhouse gases. The gases regulated include carbon dioxide, methane, nitrous oxide, hydrofluorocarbons (HFCs), perfluorocarbons (PFCs), and sulfur hexafluoride. The United States was expected to reduce emissions to 7% below its 1990 levels, the European Union (EU) nations 8%, and Canada and Japan 6% by 2012.

Consider This 3.32   The British Experience

The British Labour Party in 1997, under the leadership of Tony Blair, committed to cut British greenhouse gas emissions 20% by 2010. This is significantly more than the 12.5% required by the Kyoto treaty. Did Britain meet its goal? Research this question and write a short report on the British experience in reducing greenhouse gases. Have other countries been able to reduce their emissions significantly since 1997?

Although the treaty went into effect in 2005 (when ratified by the Russian Federation), the United States never opted to participate. One reason was the belief that meeting the reduction requirements set by the protocol would cause serious harm to the U.S. economy. Another reason for not ratifying the protocol was concern about the lack of emissions limitations on developing nations, mainly China and India; those countries are expected to show the most dramatic increases in carbon dioxide emissions in the coming years. The administration of President George W. Bush argued that such unequal burdens between developed and developing countries would be economically disastrous to the United States.

The United States has also resisted domestic legislation to restrict CO_2 emissions on similar economic grounds. Voluntary reduction programs implemented during the early 2000s proved insufficient to reduce emissions for a variety of reasons. One "problem" is that fossil fuels are too cheap. A second problem is that any mitigation measures entail significant up-front costs, and just as importantly, the cost of mitigation is not known with certainty, making it difficult for corporations to plan effectively. The world's current energy infrastructure cost $15 trillion to develop and distribute, and reducing carbon dioxide emissions will mean replacing much of that infrastructure. A final problem lies in the fact that the benefits of emissions reductions will not be felt for decades because of the long residence time of CO_2 molecules in the atmosphere.

Now, 20 years after the Earth Summit, scientific consensus is beginning to focus on determining what levels of CO_2 are considered "dangerous." At the United Nations Climate Conference in 2007, participating scientists concluded that greenhouse gas emissions need to peak by about 2020, and then be reduced to well below half of current levels by 2050. In absolute terms, that means that annual global emissions must be decreased by about 9 billion tons. To give you a scale of the magnitude of this goal, reducing emissions by 1 billion tons requires one of the following changes.

- Cutting energy usage in the world's buildings by 20–25% below business-as-usual.
- Having *all* cars get 60 mpg instead of 30 mpg.
- Capturing and sequestering carbon dioxide at 800 coal-burning power plants.
- Replacing 700 large coal-burning power plants with nuclear, wind, or solar power.

Clearly, implementation of any one of those (and the projected goal is 9 billion tons) will not be accomplished on a purely voluntary basis. In the United States and elsewhere, there is a burgeoning realization that laws and regulations are needed to reduce greenhouse gas emissions. One example is a "cap-and-trade" system, such as the one that has been successful in reducing the emission of oxides of both sulfur and nitrogen in the United States. The "trade" part of the cap-and-trade system works through a system of allowances. Companies are assigned allowances that authorize the emission of a certain quantity of CO_2, either during the current year or any year thereafter. At the end of a year, each company must have sufficient allowances to cover its actual emissions. If it has extra allowances, it can trade or sell them to another company that might have exceeded their emissions limit. If a company has insufficient allowances, it must purchase them. The "cap" is enforced by creating only a certain number of allowances each year.

Here's an example of how cap-and-trade works. Without emission restrictions, Plant A emits 600 tons of CO_2 and Plant B emits 400 tons. To get under the imposed cap, they are required to reduce their combined emissions by 300 tons (30%). One way to accomplish this is for each to reduce their own emissions by 30%, each accruing the associated costs. It is likely, however, that one of the plants (Plant B in Figure 3.31) would be more efficient in their emissions reductions, and lower their emissions below the prescribed 30%. In that case, Plant A can purchase some unused emissions permits from Plant B, at a cost less than that required for Plant A to comply with the 30% emissions reduction. The *overall* emissions reductions are then arrived at in the most financially beneficial way for both plants.

Section 6.11 describes in detail the damage caused by the oxides of nitrogen and sulfur.

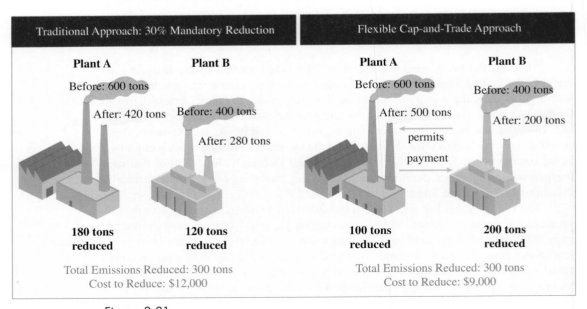

Figure 3.31

The emissions cap-and-trade concept.

Source: EPA, Clearing the Air, The Facts About Capping and Trading Emissions, *2002, page 3.*

The cap-and-trade system has some possible disadvantages, including a potentially volatile market for the emissions permits. Energy providers might experience wide, often unpredictable swings in their energy costs. Those swings would result in large fluctuations in consumer costs. As an alternative to cap-and-trade, some advocate a carbon tax instead of a cap-and-trade program. Instead of limiting emissions and letting the market decide how "best" to comply, a carbon tax simply increases the cost of burning fossil fuels. Placing an additional cost based on the amount of carbon contained in a certain quality of fuel is intended to make alternative energy sources more competitive in the near term. Of course, levying a tax on carbon fuels or emissions will mean higher prices for consumers as well.

Consider This 3.33   Climate Change Insurance?

Mitigation of climate change can be seen as a risk–benefit scenario. As such, uncertainty about future effects may discourage governments from taking financially costly actions. Another way of tackling climate change is to view it as a risk–management problem, analogous to the reasons we buy insurance. Having car insurance doesn't reduce the likelihood of being involved in an accident, but it can limit the costs if an accident should occur. How might the insurance analogy fit in with climate change actions and policies?

Although the U.S. federal government has been slow to produce binding climate change legislation, individual states have taken matters into their own hands. The 10 northeastern states that make up the Regional Greenhouse Gas Initiative (RGGI) signed the first U.S. cap-and-trade program for carbon dioxide. The program began by capping emissions at current levels in 2009 and then reducing emissions 10% by 2019. The Midwestern Regional Greenhouse Gas Reduction Accord states developed a multi-sector cap-and-trade system to help meet a long-term target of 60–80% below current emissions levels. Western Climate Initiative states, as well as British Columbia and Manitoba (the first participating jurisdictions outside of the United States), agreed to mandatory emissions reporting, as well as regional efforts to accelerate development of renewable energy technologies.

More locally, the U.S. Mayors Climate Protection Agreement included 227 cities committed to cutting emissions to meet the targets of the Kyoto Protocol. The cities represented include some of the largest in the Northeast, the Great Lakes region, and West Coast, and their mayors represent some 44 million people.

Skeptical Chemist 3.34   Drop in the Bucket?

Critics suggest that actions made by individual states or countries, even if successful, cannot possibly have a significant effect on global emissions of greenhouse gases. Proponents for immediate action, such as NASA climate scientist James Hansen, take a different approach. "China and India have the most to lose from uncontrolled climate change because they have huge populations living near sea level. Conversely then, they also have the most to gain from reduced local air pollution. They must be a part of the solution to global warming, and I believe they will be if developed nations such as the United States take the appropriate first steps." After studying this chapter, which side do you fall on? Explain.

Consider This 3.35   Carbon Dioxide Revisited

After reading this chapter, what facts do you now know about carbon dioxide? List them. Also list the sources of carbon dioxide in the atmosphere. Compare these lists to those from Consider This 3.1. Have they changed? Explain.

Conclusion

We began our journey into global climate change by stating that chimpanzees attempt to adapt to changes in climate without arguing whether change is happening. How are humans noticing and adapting to climate change? Let's look at the following assertion.

John Holdren, director of the White House Office of Science and Technology Policy, has said several times, "Global warming is a misnomer, because it implies something that is gradual, something that is uniform, something that is quite possibly benign. What we are experiencing with climate change is none of those things."

The first assertion is that global warming isn't gradual. By this he means that in comparison with the past, the climate changes we are seeing today are occurring much more rapidly. Natural climate changes are part of our planet's history. Glaciers, for example, have advanced and retreated numerous times, and global temperatures have been both much higher and much lower than the temperatures we currently experience. But the geologic evidence indicates these past changes occurred over millennia, not decades as they are today. So Holdren is correct. Global warming is not gradual, at least not in comparison with the geologic time frames of the past.

Second, he asserts that global warming does not occur uniformly across the globe. Holdren is right again. To date, the most dramatic effects have been observed at the poles. These include quickly receding glaciers, shrinking sea ice, and melting permafrost. So far, the more densely populated lower latitudes have experienced far smaller effects from climate change.

His third assertion, that global warming might not be benign, is the most difficult to assess. The issue is complicated in part because we cannot predict with certainty which aspects of our planet global warming will affect and to what degree. It is further complicated because we cannot easily understand why only a few degrees of warming might be catastrophic.

As evidenced by Holdren's points, global climate change is an extremely complicated phenomenon. Like it or not, we are in the midst of conducting a planetwide experiment, one that will test our ability to sustain both our economic development and our environment.

Chapter Summary

Having completed this chapter you should be able to:

- Understand the different processes that take part in Earth's energy balance (3.1)
- Compare and contrast the Earth's natural greenhouse effect and the enhanced greenhouse effect (3.1)
- Understand the major role that certain atmospheric gases play in the greenhouse effect (3.1–3.2)
- Explain the methods used to gather past evidence of greenhouse gas concentrations and global temperatures (3.2)
- Use Lewis structures to determine molecular geometry and bond angles of molecules (3.3)
- Relate molecular geometry to absorption of infrared radiation (3.4)
- List the major greenhouse gases and explain why each has the appropriate molecular geometry to be a greenhouse gas (3.4)
- Explain the roles that natural processes play in the carbon cycle and climate change (3.5)
- Evaluate how human activities contribute to the carbon cycle and climate change (3.5)
- Understand how molar mass is defined and used (3.6)

- Calculate the average mass of an atom using Avogadro's number (3.6)
- Demonstrate the usefulness of the chemical mole (3.7)
- Assess the sources, relative emission quantities, and effectiveness of greenhouse gases other than CO_2 (3.8)
- Evaluate the roles of natural and anthropogenic climate forcings (3.9)
- Recognize the successes and limitations of computer-based models in predicting climate change (3.9)
- Correlate some of the major consequences of climate change with their likelihood (3.10)
- Evaluate the advantages and disadvantages of proposed greenhouse gas regulations (3.11)
- Provide examples of climate mitigation and climate adaptation strategies (3.11)
- Analyze, interpret, evaluate, and critique news stories on climate change (3.1–3.12)
- Take an informed position with respect to issues surrounding climate change (3.1–3.12)

Questions

Emphasizing Essentials

1. The chapter concluded with a quote from John Holdren: "Global warming is a misnomer, because it implies something that is gradual, something that is uniform, something that is quite possibly benign. What we are experiencing with climate change is none of those things." Use examples to:

   a. explain why climate change is not uniform.

   b. explain why it is not gradual, at least in comparison to how quickly social and environmental systems can adjust.

   c. explain why it probably will not be benign.

2. The surface temperatures of both Venus and Earth are warmer than would be expected on the basis of their respective distances from the Sun. Explain.

3. Using the analogy of a greenhouse to understand the energy radiated by Earth, of what are the "windows" of Earth's greenhouse made? In what ways is the analogy not precisely correct?

4. Consider the photosynthetic conversion of CO_2 and H_2O to form glucose, $C_6H_{12}O_6$, and O_2.

   a. Write the balanced equation.

   b. Is the number of each type of atom on either side of the equation the same?

   c. Is the number of molecules on either side of the equation the same? Explain.

5. Describe the difference between climate and weather.

6. a. It is estimated that 29 megajoules per square meter (MJ/m^2) of energy comes to the top of our atmosphere from the Sun each day, but only 17 MJ/m^2 reaches the surface. What happens to the rest?

   b. Under steady-state conditions, how much energy would leave the top of the atmosphere?

7. Consider Figure 3.9.

   a. How does the present concentration of CO_2 in the atmosphere compare with its concentration 20,000 years ago? With its concentration 120,000 years ago?

   b. How does the present temperature of the atmosphere compare with the 1950–1980 mean temperature? With the temperature 20,000 years ago? How does each of these values compare with the average temperature 120,000 years ago?

   c. Do your answers to parts **a** and **b** indicate causation, correlation, or no relation? Explain.

8. Understanding Earth's energy balance is essential to understanding the issue of global warming. For example, the solar energy striking the Earth's surface averages 168 watts per square meter (W/m^2), but the energy leaving Earth's surface averages 390 W/m^2. Why isn't the Earth cooling rapidly?

9. Explain each of these observations.

   a. A car parked in a sunny location may become hot enough to endanger the lives of pets or small children left in it.

   b. Clear winter nights tend to be colder than cloudy ones.

   c. A desert shows much wider daily temperature variation than a moist environment.

   d. People wearing dark clothing in the summertime put themselves at a greater risk of heatstroke than those wearing white clothing.

10. Construct a methane molecule (CH_4) from a molecular model kit (or use Styrofoam balls or gumdrops to represent the atoms and toothpicks to represent the bonds). Demonstrate that the hydrogen atoms would be farther from one another in a tetrahedral arrangement than if they all were in the same plane (square planar arrangement).

11. Draw the Lewis structure and name the molecular geometry for each molecule.

    a. H_2S

    b. OCl_2 (oxygen is the central atom)

    c. N_2O (nitrogen is the central atom)

12. Draw the Lewis structure and name the molecular geometry for these molecules.

    a. PF_3

    b. HCN (carbon is the central atom)

    c. CF_2Cl_2 (carbon is the central atom)

13. a. Draw the Lewis structure for methanol (wood alcohol), H_3COH.

    b. Based on this structure, predict the H−C−H bond angle. Explain your reasoning.

    c. Based on this structure, predict the H−O−C bond angle. Explain your reasoning.

14. a. Draw the Lewis structure for ethene (ethylene), H_2CCH_2, a small hydrocarbon with a C=C double bond.

    b. Based on this structure, predict the H−C−H bond angle. Explain your reasoning.

    c. Sketch the molecule showing the predicted bond angles.

15. Three different modes of vibration of a water molecule are shown. Which of these modes of vibration contributes to the greenhouse effect? Explain.

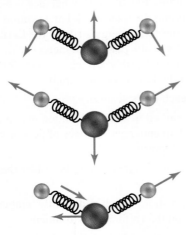

16. If a carbon dioxide molecule interacts with certain photons in the IR region, the vibrational motions of the atoms are increased. For CO_2, the major wavelengths of absorption occur at 4.26 μm and 15.00 μm.

    a. What is the energy corresponding to each of these IR photons?

    b. What happens to the energy in the vibrating CO_2 species?

17. Water vapor and carbon dioxide are greenhouse gases, but N_2 and O_2 are not. Explain.

18. Explain how each of these relates to global climate change.

    a. volcanic eruptions

    b. CFCs in the stratosphere

19. Termites possess enzymes that allow them to break down cellulose into glucose, $C_6H_{12}O_6$, and then metabolize the glucose into CO_2 and CH_4.

    a. Write a balanced equation for the metabolism of glucose into CO_2 and CH_4.

    b. What mass of CO_2, in grams, could one termite produce in one year if it metabolized 1.0 mg glucose in one day?

20. Consider Figure 3.21.

    a. Which sector has the highest CO_2 emission from fossil-fuel combustion?

    b. What alternatives exist for each of the major sectors of CO_2 emissions?

21. Silver has an atomic number of 47.

    a. Give the number of protons, neutrons, and electrons in a neutral atom of the most common isotope, Ag-107.

    b. How do the numbers of protons, neutrons, and electrons in a neutral atom of Ag-109 compare with those of Ag-107?

22. Silver only has two naturally occurring isotopes: Ag-107 and Ag-109. Why isn't the average atomic mass of silver given on the periodic table simply 108?

23. a. Calculate the average mass in grams of an individual atom of silver.

    b. Calculate the mass in grams of 10 trillion silver atoms.

    c. Calculate the mass in grams of 5.00×10^{45} silver atoms.

24. Calculate the molar mass of these compounds. Each plays a role in atmospheric chemistry.

    a. H_2O

    b. CCl_2F_2 (Freon-12)

    c. N_2O

25. a. Calculate the mass percent of chlorine in CCl_3F (Freon-11).

    b. Calculate the mass percent of chlorine in CCl_2F_2 (Freon-12).

    c. What is the maximum mass of chlorine that could be released in the stratosphere by 100 g of each compound?

    d. How many atoms of chlorine correspond to the masses calculated in part c?

26. The total mass of carbon in living systems is estimated to be 7.5×10^{17} g. Given that the total mass of carbon on Earth is estimated to be 7.5×10^{22} g, what is the ratio of carbon atoms in living systems to the total carbon atoms on Earth? Report your answer in percent and in ppm.

27. Consider the information presented in Table 3.3.

    a. Calculate the percent increase in CO_2 when comparing 2012 concentrations with preindustrial concentrations.

    b. Considering CO_2, CH_4, and N_2O, which has shown the greatest percentage increase when comparing 2011 concentrations with preindustrial concentrations?

28. Other than atmospheric concentration, what two other properties are included in the calculation of the global warming potential for a substance?

29. Total greenhouse gas emissions in the United States rose 16% from 1990 to 2005, growing at a rate of 1.3% a year since 2000. How is this possible when CO_2 emissions grew by 20% in the same time period? *Hint:* See Table 3.3.

Concentrating on Concepts

30. John Holdren, quoted in the conclusion of the chapter, suggests that we use the term *global climatic disruption* rather than *global warming*. After studying this chapter, do you agree with his suggestion? Explain.

31. The Arctic has been called "our canary in the coal mine for climate impacts that will affect us all."

    a. What does the phrase "canary in the coal mine" mean?

    b. Explain why the Arctic serves as a canary in a coal mine.

    c. The melting of the tundra accelerates changes elsewhere. Give one reason.

32. Do you think the comment made in the cartoon is justified? Explain.

Pepper . . . and Salt

"This winter has lowered my concerns about global warming . . . ."

Source: From The Wall Street Journal. *Permission by Cartoon Features Syndicate.*

33. Given that direct measurements of Earth's atmospheric temperature over the last several thousands of years are not available, how can scientists estimate past fluctuations in the temperature?

34. A friend tells you about a newspaper story that stated, "The greenhouse effect poses a serious threat to humanity." What is your reaction to that statement? What would you tell your friend?

35. Over the last 20 years, about 120 billion tons of CO_2 has been emitted from the burning of fossil fuels, yet the amount of CO_2 in the atmosphere has risen only by about 80 billion tons. Explain.

36. Carbon dioxide gas and water vapor both absorb IR radiation. Do they also absorb visible radiation? Offer some evidence based on your everyday experiences to help explain your answer.

37. How would the energy required to cause IR-absorbing vibrations in CO_2 change if the carbon and oxygen atoms were connected by single rather than double bonds?

38. Explain why water in a glass cup is quickly warmed in a microwave oven, but the glass cup itself warms much more slowly, if at all.

39. Ethanol, C_2H_5OH, can be produced from sugars and starches in crops such as corn or sugarcane. The ethanol is used as a gasoline additive and when burned, it combines with O_2 to form H_2O and CO_2.

    a. Write a balanced equation for the complete combustion of C_2H_5OH.

    b. How many moles of CO_2 are produced from each mole of C_2H_5OH completely burned?

    c. How many moles of O_2 are required to burn 10 mol of C_2H_5OH?

40. Explain whether each of the radiative forcings described in Section 3.9 is positive or negative and rank them in terms of importance to overall climate change predictions.

41. Why is the atmospheric lifetime of a greenhouse gas important?

42. Compare and contrast stratospheric ozone depletion and climate change in terms of the chemical species involved, the type of radiation involved, and the predicted environmental consequences.

43. Explain the term *radiative forcings* to someone unfamiliar with climate modeling.

44. It is estimated that Earth's ruminants, such as cattle and sheep, produce 73 million metric tons of CH_4 each year. How many metric tons of carbon are present in this mass of CH_4?

45. Nine of the ten warmest years since 1880 have occurred since the year 2000. Does this *prove* that the enhanced greenhouse effect (global warming) is taking place? Explain.

46. A possible replacement for CFCs is HFC-152a, with a lifetime of 1.4 years and a GWP of 120. Another is HFC-23, with a lifetime of 260 years and a GWP of 12,000. Both of these possible replacements have a significant effect as greenhouse gases and are regulated under the Kyoto Protocol.

    a. Based on the given information, which appears to be the better replacement? Consider only the potential for global warming.

    b. What other considerations are there in choosing a replacement?

47. The emissions of CO_2 from fossil fuel burning can be reported in different ways. For example, the Carbon Dioxide Information Analysis Center (CDIAC) reported in 2009 that China, the United States, and India ranked highest among world nations:

Ranking	Nation	Metric tons of CO_2
#1	China (mainland)	2,096,295
#2	United States	1,445,204
#3	India	539,794

   a. Would the rankings change if expressed on a per capita basis? If so, which nation would rank first?

   b. CDIAC reports the per capita rankings on the basis of metric tons carbon emitted, rather than metric tons CO_2. Qatar leads the world in per capita emissions at 12.01 metric tons carbon. Would this value be higher or lower if expressed on the basis of metric tons of CO_2 emitted? Explain.

48. Compare and contrast a cap-and-trade system with a carbon tax.

49. When Arrhenius first theorized the role of atmospheric greenhouses, he calculated that doubling the concentration of CO_2 would result in an increase of 5–6 °C in the average global temperature. How far off was he from the current IPCC modeling?

50. Now that you have studied air quality (Chapter 1), stratospheric ozone depletion (Chapter 2), and global warming (Chapter 3), which do you believe poses the most serious problem for you in the short run? In the long run? Discuss your reasons with others and draft a short report on this question.

Exploring Extensions

51. Former vice president Al Gore writes in his 2006 book and film, *An Inconvenient Truth*: "We can no longer afford to view global warming as a political issue—rather, it is the biggest moral challenge facing our global civilization."

   a. Do you believe that global warming is a moral issue? If so, why?

   b. Do you believe that global warming is a political issue? If so, why?

52. China's growing economy is fueled largely by its dependence on coal, described as China's "double-edged sword." Coal is both the new economy's "black gold" and the "fragile environment's dark cloud."

   a. What are some of the consequences of dependence on high-sulfur coal?

   b. Sulfur pollution from China may slow global warming, but only temporarily. Explain.

   c. What other country is rapidly stepping up its construction of coal-fired power plants and is expected to have a larger population than China by the year 2030?

53. The quino checkerspot butterfly is an endangered species with a small range in northern Mexico and southern California. Evidence reported in 2003 indicates that the range of this species is even smaller than previously thought.

   a. Propose an explanation why this species is being pushed north, out of Mexico.

   b. Propose an explanation why this species is being pushed south, out of southern California.

   c. Propose a plan to prevent further harm to this endangered species.

54. Data taken over time reveal an increase in CO_2 in the atmosphere. The large increase in the combustion of hydrocarbons since the Industrial Revolution is often cited as a reason for the increasing levels of CO_2. However, an increase in water vapor has *not* been observed during the same period. Remembering the general equation for the combustion of a hydrocarbon, does the difference in these two trends *disprove* any connection between human activities and global warming? Explain your reasoning.

55. In the energy industry, 1 standard cubic foot (SCF) of natural gas contains 1196 mol of methane (CH_4) at 15.6 °C (60 °F). *Hint:* See Appendix 1 for conversion factors.

   a. How many moles of CO_2 could be produced by the complete combustion of 1 SCF of natural gas?

   b. How many kilograms of CO_2 could be produced?

   c. How many metric tons of CO_2 could be produced?

56. An international conference on climate change was held in Copenhagen in December 2009. Write a brief summary of the outcomes of this conference.

57. A solar oven is a low-tech, low-cost device for focusing sunlight to cook food. How might solar ovens help mitigate global warming? Which regions of the world would benefit most from using this technology?

58. In 2005, the European Union adopted a cap-and-trade policy for carbon dioxide. Write a short report on the outcomes of this policy, both in terms of the economic result and the effect it has had on European greenhouse gas emissions.

59. The world community responded differently to the atmospheric problems described in Chapters 2 and 3. The evidence of ozone depletion was met with the Montreal Protocol, a schedule for decreasing the production of ozone-depleting chemicals. The evidence of global warming was met with the Kyoto Protocol, a plan calling for targeted reduction of greenhouse gases.

a. Suggest reasons why the world community dealt with the issue of ozone depletion *before* that of global warming.

b. Compare the current status of the two responses. When was the latest amendment to the Montreal Protocol? How many nations have ratified it? Has the level of chlorine in the stratosphere dropped as a result of the Montreal Protocol? How many nations have ratified the Kyoto Protocol? What has happened since it went into effect? Have any other initiatives been proposed? Have levels of greenhouse gases dropped as a result of the Kyoto Protocol?

Energy from Combustion

Since the beginning of recorded history, fire has been a source of heat, light, and security.

Ever since fire was harnessed by our early ancestors, combustion has been central to society. Our modern fuels—the substances we burn—come in many different forms. We use coal in power plants to generate electricity. We use gasoline to run our cars. We use natural gas or heating oil to warm our homes. We use propane, charcoal, or wood to cook our food at a summer barbeque. We might even use wax to provide light for a romantic candlelight dinner. In each of these cases, *using* fuels means *burning* them. The process of combustion releases the energy stored in the molecules that these substances contain.

However, the rate at which we are burning fuels is not sustainable. Perhaps you are somewhat skeptical of this claim. The supply of coal, petroleum, and natural gas may appear to be adequate, because new deposits are always being found and extraction technologies are continually improving. But even if the supply of fossil fuels were infinite (it is not), sustainability involves more than just availability. In Chapter 0, we mentioned the need to consider how our actions today will affect those who live tomorrow. In the final section of this chapter, we will connect our actions to our values, including that of **intergenerational justice.** A Lakota Sioux proverb emphasizes the same idea: *"We don't inherit this land from our ancestors, we borrow it from our children."* The effects of our current fossil fuel use will be felt for many decades to come.

Intergenerational justice is the obligation of each generation, in turn, to act in ways that are fair and just to those that will follow.

Consider This 4.1   Fuels in the News!

a. Locate two recent news articles concerning a fuel of your choice. Cite the title, author, date, and source. According to what you read, what is the intended use of the fuel?

b. Interpret each article in terms of the Lakota Sioux proverb. What, if anything, are we borrowing from our children?

Burning fossil fuels for energy fails to meet the criteria of sustainability in two ways. First, the fuels themselves—taking hundreds of millions of years to produce—are nonrenewable. Once gone, they cannot be replaced. Second, the waste products of combustion have adverse effects on our environment, both today and in the future. Chapter 3 described how atmospheric CO_2 concentrations have risen dramatically since the beginning of the Industrial Revolution. These increases will continue to affect our climate for generations to come. Burning coal also releases pollutants such as soot, carbon monoxide, mercury, and the oxides of sulfur and nitrogen. These emissions affect us right now because they lower the quality of our air, acidify our rain, aggravate existing health conditions, and generally lower our quality of life.

In this chapter, we will describe fuels and their characteristics. We begin with what happens inside a power plant. In the context of energy transformation, we introduce a law that tells us that energy is never created or destroyed; rather, it just changes forms. We also consider the efficiency (actually the inefficiency) of energy transformations, a factor in our ability to harness energy in convenient forms. But fuels differ, and so we need to describe how all fuels are not created equal; that is, how they have different heat contents and release different amounts of carbon dioxide. To do this, we take a closer look at coal and petroleum, describing their chemical composition, physical properties, the structures of the molecules they contain, and the ways we manipulate them for use. We learn how these molecules store energy and how to write the chemical reactions that describe energy release. We then move to biofuels, exploring the advantages and disadvantages of these renewable resources. This chapter closes with a discussion of the ethical principles that apply to producing biofuels, revisiting the challenges of meeting our future energy needs.

Chapter 1 described the connection between combustion and poor air quality.
Chapter 3 dealt with carbon dioxide as a greenhouse gas.
Chapter 6 focuses on acid rain.

4.1 | Fossil Fuels and Electricity

About 70% of the electricity generated in the United States comes from burning fossil fuels—primarily coal. How do electrical power plants "produce" electricity and what really goes on inside them? Our task in this section is to take a closer look at the energy transformations in a power plant. In Section 4.3, we discuss the chemistry of coal.

The first step in producing electricity from coal is to burn it. Examine the photographs in Figure 4.1. You can almost feel the heat from the burning coal! In the coal beds of the boilers, the temperature can reach 650 °C. To generate this heat, this small power plant burns a train car load of coal every few hours. As we pointed out in Chapter 1, **combustion** is the chemical process of burning, that is, the reaction of fuel with oxygen to release energy in the form of heat and light. Note that the two most common combustion products, CO_2 and H_2O, both contain oxygen.

The second step in producing electricity is to use the heat released from combustion to boil water, usually in a closed, high-pressure system (Figure 4.2). The elevated pressure serves two purposes: it raises the boiling point of the water and it compresses the resulting water vapor. The hot high-pressure steam is then directed at a steam turbine.

The third and final step generates electricity. As the steam expands and cools, it rushes past the turbine, causing it to spin. The shaft of the turbine is connected to a large coil of wire that rotates within a magnetic field. The turning of this coil generates an electric current. Meanwhile, the water vapor leaves the turbine and continues to cycle through the system. It passes through a condenser where a stream of cooling water carries away the remainder of the heat energy originally acquired from the fuel. The condensed water then reenters the boiler, ready to resume the energy transfer cycle.

To help you better understand these different steps, we define two types of energy. **Potential energy,** as the name suggests, is stored energy or the energy of position. For example, energy can be stored in the position of a book lifted against the force of gravity. The heavier the book and the higher you lift it, the more potential energy it has.

> Operating at full capacity, a large power plant can burn up to 10,000 tons of coal a day!

(a)   **(b)**

(c)   **(d)**

Figure 4.1

Photos from a small coal–fired electric power plant.
(a) Piles of coal outside the plant.
(b) A row of boilers into which the coal is fed.
(c) Behind the blue door in photograph (b).
(d) A close-up of coal burning on the boiler bed.

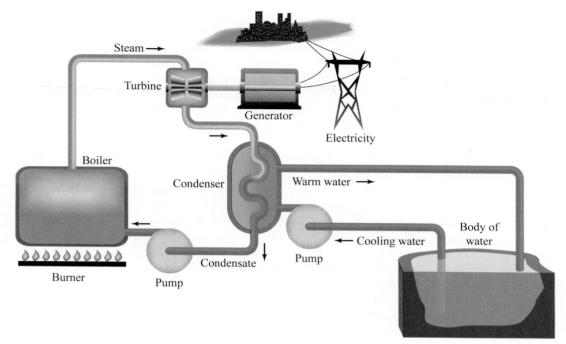

Figure 4.2

Diagram of an electric power plant illustrating the conversion of energy from the combustion of fuels to electricity.

The potential energy of a reactant or product is often referred to as its "chemical energy." We discuss the chemical energy stored in fuel molecules in Section 4.5. In contrast, **kinetic energy** is the energy of motion. The heavier an object is and the faster it is moving, the more kinetic energy it possesses. Would you rather be hit by a baseball traveling at 90 mph or a Ping-Pong ball traveling at 90 mph? The baseball has considerably more kinetic energy because of its larger mass.

Molecules that have high potential energy make good fuels. The process of combustion converts some of the potential energy of the fuel molecules into heat, which in turn is absorbed by the water in the boiler. As the water molecules absorb the heat, they move faster and faster in all directions; their kinetic energy increases. The temperature we observe is simply a measure of the average speed of that molecular motion. Hence, the temperature increases as the amount of kinetic energy of the molecules increases. When the water is vaporized to steam, the water molecules acquire a tremendous amount of kinetic energy. That energy is transformed into the *mechanical energy* of the spinning turbine that then turns the generator converting the mechanical energy into *electrical energy*. These energy transformation steps are summarized in Figure 4.3.

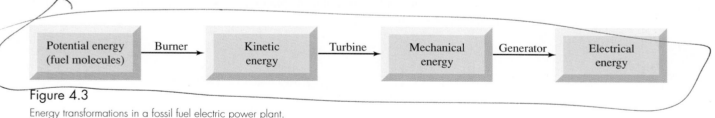

Figure 4.3

Energy transformations in a fossil fuel electric power plant.

Consider This 4.2   Energy Conversion

Although power plants require several steps to transform potential energy into electrical energy, other devices do this more simply. For example, a battery converts chemical energy to electrical energy in one step. List three other devices that convert energy from one form to another. For each one, name the types of energy involved.

Batteries are described in Section 8.1.

Section 3.2 introduced three fossil fuels: coal, petroleum, and natural gas.

Although coal is usable as a fuel, its combustion products are not. We stated that good fuels have high potential energy, but from what source does this energy come? A clue lies in the name "fossil fuel" itself. The creation of fossil fuels began when sunlight was captured by green plants that flourished on our primeval planet. Also, as mentioned earlier, **photosynthesis** is the process by which green plants (including algae) and some bacteria capture the energy of sunlight to produce glucose and oxygen from carbon dioxide and water. In essence, the energy from sunlight is converted into the potential energy of glucose and oxygen.

$$6\,CO_2 + 6\,H_2O \xrightarrow{\text{chlorophyll}} \underset{\text{glucose}}{C_6H_{12}O_6} + 6\,O_2 \qquad \text{[4.1]}$$

Plants contain nitrogen as well. Section 6.9 tells more about the nitrogen cycle.

When living organisms die and decay, they release energy and reverse this process, producing CO_2 and H_2O. Under certain conditions, however, the carbon-containing compounds that make up the organism only *partially* decompose. This happened in the prehistoric past when vast quantities of plant and animal life became buried beneath layers of sediment in swamps or at the bottom of the oceans. Oxygen failed to reach the decaying material, thus retarding the decomposition process. The temperature and pressure increased as additional layers of mud and rock covered the buried remnants, causing additional chemical reactions to occur. Over time, the plants that once captured the Sun's rays were transformed into the substances we call coal, petroleum, and natural gas. In a very real sense, these fossils are ancient solar energy (sunshine) stored in the solid, liquid, and gaseous states.

Yes, today's plants will become tomorrow's fossil fuels. But this will not occur in a time frame useful to humans. It is staggering to realize that we will consume in a few centuries what it took nature hundreds of millions of years to produce. We discuss the details of fuels at the molecular level in Section 4.6.

Your Turn 4.3   Steamy Compost

Want to recycle and reuse plant and animal material? Start a compost pile. Under the right weather conditions, steam can be seen rising from a pile of compost. Explain this observation.

Revisit the processes of combustion and photosynthesis. Energy is released in combustion but is required for photosynthesis. The relationship between the two hints at a cycle, as shown in Figure 4.4. The **first law of thermodynamics,** also called the law of conservation of energy, states that energy is neither created nor destroyed. It implies that although the *forms* of energy change, the total amount of energy before and after any transformation remains the same. The solar energy that is stored as potential energy during photosynthesis is released as heat and light during combustion.

The law of conservation of matter and mass was introduced in Section 1.9.

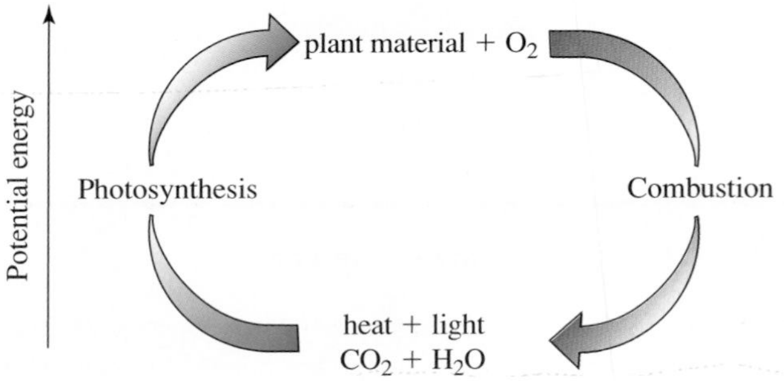

Figure 4.4

The energy relationship between photosynthesis and combustion.

4.2 | Efficiency of Energy Transformation

By the first law of thermodynamics, we are assured that the total energy of the universe is conserved. If this is true, how can we ever experience an energy crisis? To be sure, no new energy is created during combustion, but none is destroyed, either. Although we may not be able to win, can we at least break even? The question is not as facetious as it might sound. In fact, we *cannot* break even. In burning coal, natural gas, and petroleum, we always convert at least some of the energy in the fuels into forms that we cannot easily use.

You may have seen the desktop toy known as a Newton's cradle (Figure 4.5). This device transforms energy but is much simpler than a power plant! Here's how it works.

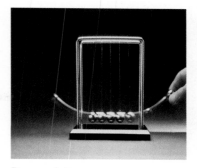

Figure 4.5
A Newton's cradle.

- A ball is lifted at one end. This gives potential energy to this ball.
- The ball is released and falls back toward its starting point. The potential energy (energy of position) is converted into kinetic energy (energy of motion).
- The ball hits the row of stationary balls. Kinetic energy is transferred along the row to the ball at the other end.
- The ball at the other end swings up. Kinetic energy is gradually converted into potential energy as the ball rises and slows.
- The second ball begins to fall and the process repeats.

With each successive cycle, however, each ball does not rise quite as high as the previous one. Eventually, the balls all come to rest at their original positions.

Why do they stop moving? Where did their energy go? Is this a violation of the first law of thermodynamics? Fortunately, it isn't. In each collision, some of the energy is used to make sound and some is used to generate heat. If we could measure precisely enough, we would observe the balls heating up slightly. This heat is then transferred to the surrounding atoms and molecules in the air, thus increasing their kinetic energy. In keeping with the law of conservation of energy, neither kinetic energy nor potential energy is conserved independently, but the sum of the two is. Therefore, when all the balls finally come to rest, the energy of the universe has been conserved. All the energy that you initially put into the system has been dissipated as random motion of the atoms and molecules in the surrounding air. In essence, the device is a fun way of dissipating a little bit of potential energy into heat (the kinetic energy of the atoms and molecules in the air).

These same principles can be used to explain why no electric power plant, no matter how well designed, can completely convert one type of energy into another. In spite of the best engineers and the most competent green chemists, inefficiency is inevitable. It is caused by the transformation of energy into useless heat. Overall, the % net efficiency is given by the ratio of the electrical energy produced to the energy supplied by the fuel.

$$\% \text{ net efficiency} = \frac{\text{electrical energy produced}}{\text{heat from fuel}} \times 100 \qquad \textbf{[4.2]}$$

Newer boiler systems and advanced turbine technologies have pushed the efficiencies of each step in Figure 4.3 to 90% or better. Efficiencies are multiplicative, so you might be surprised to learn that the net efficiencies of most fossil fuel power plants are between 35 and 50%. Why so low?

The problem is that not all of the heat energy from the fuel combustion in the boilers can be converted into electricity. Consider, for example, the high-temperature steam that initially spins the turbines. As the steam transfers energy to the turbines, the kinetic energy of the steam decreases, it cools, and its pressure drops. It isn't long before the steam does not have enough energy to spin the turbines anymore. Yet, the production of this "unused" steam still required a significant amount of energy; energy that is not converted into electricity.

Power plants using very high temperature steam (600 °C) have efficiencies at the high end of the range. In fact, the efficiency goes up as the difference between the steam temperature and the temperature outside the plant increases. Of course there is a limit. Higher temperature steam means higher pressures and improved construction materials that need to be able to withstand such extreme conditions.

One small potato (~150 g) has about
100 Calories (100 kilocalories).

Before we discuss a specific example, we need to say a word or two about energy units. The **calorie (cal)** was introduced with the metric system in the late 18th century and was defined as the amount of heat necessary to raise the temperature of one gram of water by one degree Celsius. When Calorie is capitalized, it generally means kilocalorie. The values tabulated on package labels and in cookbooks are, in fact, kilocalories.

1 kilocalorie (kcal) = 1000 calories (cal) = 1 Calorie (Cal)

The modern system of units uses the **joule (J)**, a unit of energy equal to 0.239 cal. One joule (1 J) is approximately equal to the energy required to raise a 1-kg book 10 cm against the force of gravity. On a more personal basis, each beat of the human heart requires about 1 J of energy.

1 joule (J) = 0.239 calories (cal)
1 calorie (cal) = 4.184 joules (J)

Now consider the case of electrical home heating, sometimes advertised as being clean and efficient. Assume that electricity from a coal-burning power plant (efficiency of 37%) is used to heat a house. If the house requires 3.5×10^7 kJ of energy for heat annually, a typical value for a city in a cooler climate, how much coal would be burned?

To answer this question, we need a value for the energy content of the coal. Let's assume that the combustion of 1 gram of this particular coal releases about 29 kJ. Remember that only 37% of the energy released by burning the coal is available to heat the house. We now can calculate the total yearly quantity of heat that we need to generate by burning coal at the power plant.

energy generated at plant $\times$ efficiency = energy required to heat house

energy generated at plant $\times$ 0.37 = 3.5×10^7 kJ

$$\text{energy generated at plant} = \frac{3.5 \times 10^7 \text{ kJ}}{0.37} = 9.5 \times 10^7 \text{ kJ}$$

In these calculations, note that we expressed the percent efficiency in decimal form. We now take into account that each gram of coal burned yields 29 kJ.

$$9.5 \times 10^7 \text{ kJ} \times \frac{1 \text{ g coal}}{29 \text{ kJ}} = 3.3 \times 10^6 \text{ g coal}$$

Heating this home annually requires
3.3 metric tons of coal. Railcars carry
about 100 metric tons of coal each.

This shows that 3.3×10^6 g of coal must be burned each year at the power plant in order to furnish the needed 3.5×10^7 kJ of energy to heat the house.

This calculation assumed an efficiency of 37% at the coal plant. Higher efficiencies would mean that less fuel would have to be burned to generate the same amount of energy and that less carbon dioxide and other pollutants would be emitted. The next activity explores these connections.

Your Turn 4.4 Comparing Power Plants

Consider two coal-fired power plants that generate 5.0×10^{12} J of electricity daily. Plant A has an overall net efficiency of 38%. Plant B, a proposed replacement, would operate at higher temperatures with an overall net efficiency of 46%. The grade of coal used releases 30 kJ of heat per gram. Assume that coal is pure carbon.

a. If 1000 kg of coal costs $30, what is the difference in daily fuel costs for the two plants?
b. How many fewer grams of CO_2 are emitted daily by Plant B, assuming complete combustion?

Answer
a. Coal costs for Plant A = $13,150/day. Coal costs for Plant B = $10,900/day.

Cars and trucks also convert energy from one form to another. The internal combustion engine uses the gaseous combustion products (CO_2 and H_2O) to push a series of pistons, thus converting the potential energy of the gasoline or diesel fuel into mechanical energy. Other mechanisms transform that mechanical energy eventually into the kinetic energy of the vehicle's motion. Internal combustion engines are even less efficient than coal-fired power plants. Only about 15% of the energy released by the combustion of the gasoline actually is used to move the vehicle. Much of the energy is dissipated as waste heat, including about 60% lost from the internal combustion engine alone.

Sections 8.4 and 8.6 discuss more
efficient hybrid and fuel cell vehicles.

Consider This 4.5   Transportation Inefficiency

a. List some of the energy losses that take place when driving a car. Use the resources of the Internet to verify and expand your list if necessary.

b. Given the assumption that only 15% of the energy from fuel combustion is used to move the vehicle, estimate the percent used to move the passengers.

To bring this section to a close, we ask you to revisit the Newton's cradle. You would never expect the balls at rest to start knocking into one another on their own, right? For this to occur, all the heat energy dissipated when the balls were colliding would have to be gathered back together. The inability of a Newton's cradle to start up on its own relates to another concept—entropy. **Entropy** is a measure of how much energy gets dispersed in a given process. The **second law of thermodynamics** has many versions, the most general of which is that the entropy of the universe is constantly increasing. The Newton's cradle provides an example of the second law of thermodynamics. When we lift one of the balls of the Newton's cradle, we add potential energy. After the balls knock for awhile and come to rest, this potential energy has become transformed into the chaotic (and hence more random and dispersed) motion of heat energy and never the other way around. The entropy of the universe has increased.

Do you find it difficult to visualize how energy can disperse? If so, here is an analogy that might help. Imagine that you were sitting in the middle of a large auditorium and someone down in the front broke a bottle of perfume. You don't smell anything at first, because it takes time for the molecules of the perfume to diffuse to where you're sitting. This process of diffusion is predicted by the second law of thermodynamics. When the perfume molecules disperse into a larger volume (from the smaller volume of the bottle), the energy of the molecules gets dispersed as well. As with the Newton's cradle, the end result is an increase in the entropy of the universe. It is extremely unlikely that all of the perfume molecules would suddenly gather in one corner of the room. Rather, once dispersed they stay dispersed unless energy is expended to recollect them.

In the same way, it is essentially impossible for the Newton's cradle to begin to move on its own after the energy originally added was dissipated as heat. Though it may not be as obvious, the second law of thermodynamics also explains the inability of a power plant or an auto engine to convert energy from one type to another with 100% efficiency.

Consider This 4.6   More Entropy Examples

An input of energy can be used to decrease entropy "locally." Even so, energy expended in one place requires a net increase in entropy elsewhere in the universe.

a. Consider the energy input from burning coal. The entropy of the universe increased elsewhere. Give an example of how it could have increased.

b. Consider the decrease in entropy that occurs when somebody arranges the socks in a drawer. What must have accompanied this decrease in entropy?

Answer

b. This decrease in entropy must have been accompanied by an input of energy (by a human) and by an increase of entropy elsewhere in the universe (from the food burned as fuel by the human).

4.3 | The Chemistry of Coal

About two centuries ago, the Industrial Revolution began the great exploitation of fossil fuels that continues today. In the early 1800s, wood was the major energy source in the United States. Coal turned out to be an even better energy source than wood, because it yielded more heat per gram. Coal continued to provide more than 50% of the nation's energy until about 1940.

By the 1960s, most coal was used for generating electricity, and today the electrical power sector accounts for 92% of all U.S. coal consumption. Figure 4.6 displays the history of U.S. energy consumption.

Consider This 4.7   Changing Fuel Patterns

Use Figure 4.6 to:

a. Describe two ways in which fuel consumption in the United States has changed over time. Propose reasons for the changes.
b. Estimate the fraction of energy produced by the burning of coal.

In Your Turn 4.4, we assumed that coal was pure carbon. In fact, coal contains small amounts of other elements as well. Although not a single compound, coal can be approximated by the chemical formula $C_{135}H_{96}O_9NS$. This formula corresponds to a carbon content of about 85% by mass. The smaller amounts of hydrogen, oxygen, nitrogen, and sulfur come from the ancient plant material and other substances present when the plants were buried. In addition, some samples of coal typically contain trace amounts of silicon, sodium, calcium, aluminum, nickel, copper, zinc, arsenic, lead, and mercury.

Your Turn 4.8   Coal Calculations

a. Assuming the composition of coal can be approximated by the formula $C_{135}H_{96}O_9NS$, calculate the mass of carbon (in tons) in 1.5 million tons of coal. This quantity of coal might be burned by a typical power plant in 1 year.
b. Compute the amount of energy (in kilojoules) released by burning this mass of coal. Assume the process releases 30 kJ/g of coal. Recall that 1 ton = 2000 lb and that 1 pound = 454 g.
c. What mass of CO_2 would be formed by the complete combustion of 1.5 million tons of this coal?

Hint: In the balanced chemical equation, assume a mole ratio of coal to CO_2 of 1:135.

Answers

a. Calculate the approximate molar mass of coal. The subscripts for each element give the number of moles:

$$135 \text{ mol C} \times \frac{12.0 \text{ g C}}{1 \text{ mol C}} = 1620 \text{ g C}$$

$$96 \text{ mol H} \times \frac{1.0 \text{ g H}}{1 \text{ mol H}} = 96 \text{ g H}$$

$$9 \text{ mol O} \times \frac{16.0 \text{ g O}}{1 \text{ mol O}} = 144 \text{ g O}$$

$$1 \text{ mol N} \times \frac{14.0 \text{ g N}}{1 \text{ mol N}} = 14.0 \text{ g N}$$

$$1 \text{ mol S} \times \frac{32.1 \text{ g S}}{1 \text{ mol S}} = 32.1 \text{ g S}$$

The sum of these elemental contributions for $C_{135}H_{96}O_9NS$ is 1906 g/mol. Therefore, every 1906 g of coal contains 1620 g C. Similarly, 1906 tons of coal contains 1620 tons of carbon.

$$\text{Mass of carbon} = 1.5 \times 10^6 \text{ tons } C_{135}H_{96}O_9NS \times \frac{1620 \text{ tons C}}{1906 \text{ tons } C_{135}H_{96}O_9NS} = 1.3 \times 10^6 \text{ tons C}$$

b. 4.1×10^{13} kJ
c. 4.7 million tons

Coal occurs in varying grades, but all grades are better fuels than wood because they contain a higher percentage of carbon and a lower percentage of oxygen. Generally speaking, the more oxygen a fuel contains, the less energy per gram it releases on

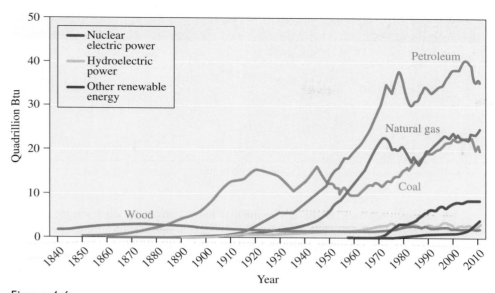

Figure 4.6

U.S. energy consumption by source, 1840–2010.

Source: U.S. Energy Information Administration, Energy Perspectives 2011, *September 27, 2012.*

In Figure 4.6, other renewable energy sources appear only recently. These include solar, wind, geothermal, and biofuels.

combustion. In other words, oxygen-containing fuels lie lower on the potential energy scale. For example, burning 1 mole of C to produce CO_2 yields about 40% more energy than is obtained from burning 1 mole of CO to produce CO_2.

Soft lignite, or brown coal, is the lowest grade (Figure 4.7). The plant matter from which it originated underwent the least amount of change, and its chemical composition is similar to that of wood or peat (Table 4.1). Consequently, the amount of energy released when lignite is burned is only slightly greater than that of wood. The higher grades of coal, bituminous and anthracite, have been exposed to higher pressures and temperatures for longer periods of time in the earth. During that process, they lost more oxygen and moisture and became a good deal harder, more mineral than vegetable (Figure 4.7). These grades of coal contain a higher percentage of carbon than lignite. Anthracite has a relatively high carbon content and a low sulfur content, both of which make it the most desirable grade of coal. Unfortunately, the deposits of anthracite are relatively small, and the supply of it in the United States is almost exhausted.

Although coal is available across the globe and remains a widely used fuel, it has serious drawbacks, the first of which relates to underground mining, which is both dangerous and expensive. Although mine safety has dramatically improved in the United States, since 1900 more than 100,000 workers have been killed by accidents, cave-ins, fires, explosions, and poisonous gases. Many more have been incapacitated by respiratory diseases. Worldwide, the picture is far worse.

Figure 4.7

Samples of lignite (*left*) and anthracite coal (*right*).

Table 4.1	Energy Content of U.S. Coals	
Type of Coal*	State of Origin	Energy Content (kJ/g)
anthracite	Pennsylvania	30.5
bituminous	Maryland	30.7
sub-bituminous	Washington	24.0
lignite (brown coal)	North Dakota	16.2
peat	Mississippi	13.0

*For comparison, the energy content of wood ranges from 10 to 14 kJ/g, depending on the type.

A second drawback is the environmental harm caused by coal mining. Many streams and rivers in Appalachia suffer from the effects of decades of mining operations. When groundwater floods abandoned mine shafts, or comes in contact with sulfur-rich rock often associated with coal deposits, it becomes acidified. This acid mine drainage also dissolves excessive amounts of iron and aluminum, making the water uninhabitable for many fish species and placing drinking water sources at risk for many communities.

When coal deposits lie sufficiently close to the surface, mining techniques safer for miners are possible, but they still have environmental costs. One technique, called mountaintop mining, is most common in West Virginia and eastern Kentucky. The process calls for scraping away the overlying vegetation and then blasting off the top several hundred feet of a mountain to reveal the underlying coal seam. Mountaintop mining creates massive quantities of rubble ("overburden") that often is disposed of by dumping the debris into nearby river valleys. In 2005, the U.S. EPA estimated that over 700 miles of Appalachian streams were completely buried as a result of mountaintop mining between 1985 and 2001. Furthermore, increased sediments and mineral content in the surrounding water systems has adversely affected many aquatic ecosystems.

A third drawback is that coal is a dirty fuel. It is, of course, physically dirty, but the issue here is the dirty combustion products. Soot from countless coal fires in cities in the 19th and early 20th centuries blackened both buildings and lungs. The oxides of nitrogen and sulfur are less visible but equally damaging. Although coal contains only minor amounts of mercury (50–200 ppb), mercury is concentrated in the fly ash that escapes as particulate matter into the atmosphere. In the United States, coal-fired power plants emit roughly 48 metric tons of mercury to the environment each year. The "bottom" ash left on site also presents a storage hazard. For example, Figure 4.8 shows the devastation caused by millions of gallons of fly ash sludge that spilled down a valley when the retaining walls of a storage pond failed.

In 2009, a U.S. district court in West Virginia issued an injunction against new mountaintop removal projects in the southern part of that state. Further legislation in other parts of the country is likely.

Mercury, a contaminant in soils and in drinking water, will be discussed in Section 5.5.

Your Turn 4.9   Coal Emissions

In the United States, coal–burning power plants are responsible for two thirds of the sulfur dioxide emissions and one fifth of the nitrogen monoxide emissions.
Hint: Revisit Chapter 1.

a. Why does burning coal produce SO_2? Name another source of SO_2 in the atmosphere.
b. Why does burning coal produce nitrogen monoxide? Name two other sources of NO.

A fourth drawback may ultimately be the most serious, that burning coal produces carbon dioxide, a greenhouse gas. Coal combustion produces more CO_2 per kilojoule of heat released than either petroleum or natural gas. In 2012, coal again was the world's fastest growing fossil fuel source.

Because of these drawbacks, and given that coal reserves are relatively plentiful in the United States, significant research efforts are underway to develop new coal technologies. Though it may sound like an oxymoron, "clean coal" is promoted by its supporters as an important step toward decreasing our reliance on petroleum imports and reducing air pollution. The term "clean coal technology" actually encompasses a variety of methods that aim to increase the efficiency of coal-fired power plants while decreasing harmful emissions. Here we list several technologies already implemented in selected power plants.

- "Coal washing" to remove sulfur and other mineral impurities from the coal before it is burned.
- "Gasification" to convert coal to a mixture of carbon monoxide and hydrogen (equation 4.10). The resulting gas burns at a lower temperature, thus reducing the generation of nitrogen oxides.
- "Wet scrubbing" to chemically remove SO_2 before it goes up the smokestack. This is accomplished by reacting the SO_2 with a mixture of ground limestone and water.

None of these technologies address greenhouse gas emissions. This requires the most ambitious clean coal technology: carbon capture and storage. Serious questions remain about the viability of the technology involved.

What does the future hold for the dirtiest of the fossil fuels? The answer depends on where you live. Figure 4.9 compares coal consumption in different regions of the globe between 1986 and 2011. Though most regions showed modest changes, the use

Figure 4.8

In December 2008, 300 million gallons of coal sludge buried homes near Knoxville, Tennessee.

Carbon dioxide capture and storage, also known as sequestration, was discussed in Section 3.11.

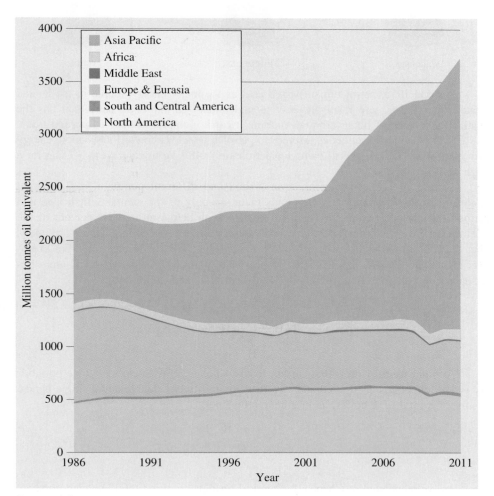

Figure 4.9

World consumption of coal by region, 1986–2011. *Source:* BP Statistical Review of World Energy, *June 2012.*

of coal in Asia is skyrocketing. On one hand, this makes sense, as China has enormous coal reserves to fuel its rapid growth. But on the other, coal burning (by any nation) clearly does not meet the criteria for sustainability.

Consider This 4.10   Clean Coal

In 2011, a newspaper columnist remarked that the idea of clean coal "remains a distant dream."

a. List three factors that contribute to making coal a dirty fuel.
b. Now that it is several years later, has the dream of clean coal come any closer to being realized? Select a format and use it to argue your case either way.

4.4 | Petroleum and Natural Gas

Crude oil, also known as petroleum, is the liquid that can gush out of oil wells. It also is found in tarry oil sands and shales. Depending on its origin, petroleum ranges from a clear golden oil to a black tarry liquid. Petroleum also may be accompanied by deposits of natural gas.

Caucasus

Middle East

France

Around 1950, petroleum surpassed coal as the major energy source in the United States. The reasons are relatively easy to understand. Unlike coal, petroleum has the distinct advantage of being a liquid, making it easily pumped to the surface and transported via pipelines to refineries. Moreover, petroleum yields about 40–60% more energy per gram than coal. A typical value for petroleum is 48 kJ/g in contrast to 30 kJ/g for a high grade coal.

Petroleum is a mixture of several thousand different compounds. The great majority are **hydrocarbons,** compounds made up only of the elements hydrogen and carbon. A few basic rules for chemical bonding can help you create order out of the seeming chaos of hydrocarbons. One is the **octet rule** introduced in Chapter 2; namely, that the C atoms in hydrocarbons bond to have a share in 8 outer electrons. For example, in methane (CH_4), the primary component of natural gas, the central C atom has a share in 8 electrons that are arranged to form 4 covalent bonds.

$$
\begin{array}{c}
\text{H} \\
| \\
\text{H}-\text{C}-\text{H} \\
| \\
\text{H}
\end{array}
$$

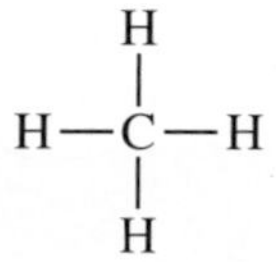

Another useful rule is that carbon forms 4 bonds in hydrocarbons. One possibility is 4 single bonds, as in methane. Another possibility is 1 double and 2 single bonds, again for a total of 4 bonds, as in ethene (ethylene).

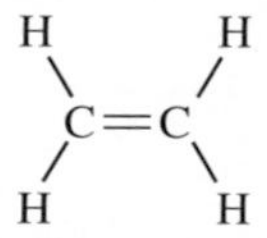

$$
\begin{array}{c}
\text{H} \qquad \text{H} \\
\diagdown \qquad \diagup \\
\text{C}=\text{C} \\
\diagup \qquad \diagdown \\
\text{H} \qquad \text{H}
\end{array}
$$

As we mentioned in Chapter 1, chemical formulas indicate the kinds and numbers of atoms present in a molecule but do not show how the atoms are connected. To get this level of detail, you need a structural formula. For example, here is the structural formula for n-butane, C_4H_{10}, a hydrocarbon used to fuel lighters and camp stoves. The n in the chemical name stands for normal, meaning that the carbon atoms are in a straight chain.

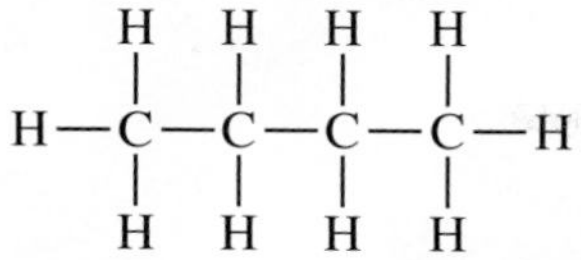

A drawback to structural formulas is that they take up a lot of space on the page. To convey the same information more compactly, use a **condensed structural formula** in which some bonds are not shown; rather, the structural formula is understood to contain an appropriate number of bonds. Here are two condensed structural formulas for n-butane, the second more "condensed" than the first.

$$CH_3—CH_2—CH_2—CH_3 \qquad CH_3CH_2CH_2CH_3$$

Although the H atoms in these structures appear to be part of the chain of C atoms, it is understood that they are not.

Many of the hydrocarbons in petroleum are **alkanes,** hydrocarbons with only single bonds between carbon atoms (Table 4.2). Gasoline is a mixture of hydrocarbons

Table 4.2	Selected Alkanes (Gases and Liquids)		
Name and Chemical Formula	Boiling Point (physical state at room temperature)	Structural Formula	Condensed Structural Formula
methane CH_4	−164 °C (gas)	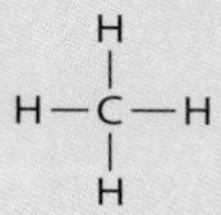	CH_4
ethane C_2H_6	−89 °C (gas)	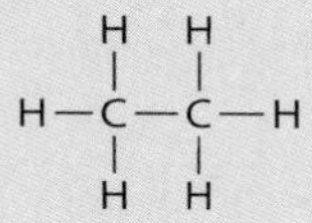	CH_3CH_3
propane C_3H_8	−42 °C (gas)	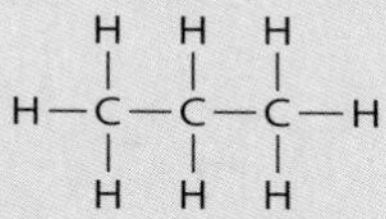	$CH_3CH_2CH_3$
n–butane C_4H_{10}	−0.5 °C (gas)	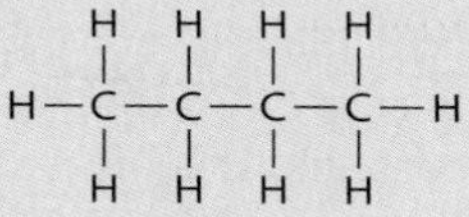	$CH_3CH_2CH_2CH_3$
n–pentane C_5H_{12}	36° C (liquid)	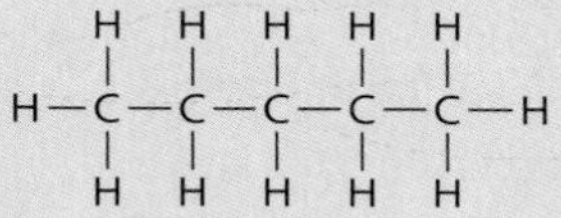	$CH_3CH_2CH_2CH_2CH_3$
n–hexane C_6H_{14}	69° C (liquid)	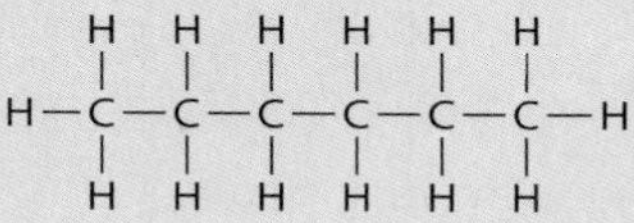	$CH_3CH_2CH_2CH_2CH_2CH_3$
n–heptane C_7H_{16}	98° C (liquid)	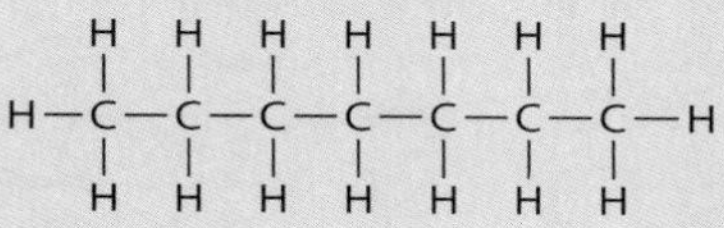	$CH_3CH_2CH_2CH_2CH_2CH_2CH_3$
n–octane C_8H_{18}	125° C (liquid)	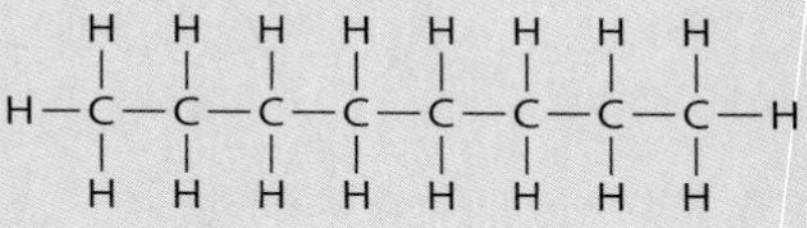	$CH_3CH_2CH_2CH_2CH_2CH_2CH_2CH_3$

Note: n–butane, n–pentane, n–hexane, n–heptane, and n–octane all have other isomers (see Section 4.7). The n stands for normal, the straight–chain isomer.

Figure 4.10
An oil refinery showing the tall distillation towers. Small amounts of natural gas are flared, as evidenced by the flames.

with 5–12 carbon atoms per molecule, including the alkanes pentane, hexane, and heptane. Although produced since the mid-1800s, gasoline became valuable in the early 20th century with the advent of the automobile. Look for more about gasoline later in this chapter.

How are gasoline and other hydrocarbons produced from petroleum? The process takes place at an oil refinery, the icon of the petroleum industry (Figure 4.10). During the initial step in the refining process, the crude oil is separated into fractions, including the gasoline fraction.

As of 2011, there were 137 oil refineries operating in the United States with 11 others idle.

In the context of water purification, look for more about distillation in Chapter 5.

Refineries work their magic on crude oil using several processes, including that of **distillation**, a separation process in which a solution is heated to its boiling point and the vapors are condensed and collected. Other processes include catalytic cracking, reforming, and coking, as shown on the distillation tower in Figure 4.11. We will describe these processes in more detail in Section 4.7.

To distill crude oil, first it must be pumped into a large vessel (the boiler in Figure 4.11) and heated.

- As the temperature in the boiler increases, compounds with lower boiling points (lower molar masses) begin to vaporize.
- As the temperature further increases, compounds with higher boiling points (higher molar masses) vaporize.
- Once vaporized, all compounds travel up the distillation tower.
- Compounds are condensed to liquids at different heights in the tower due to a decrease in temperature with height.

Figure 4.11 illustrates a distillation tower, showing the possible mixtures of compounds that can be obtained. These include gases such as methane, liquids such as

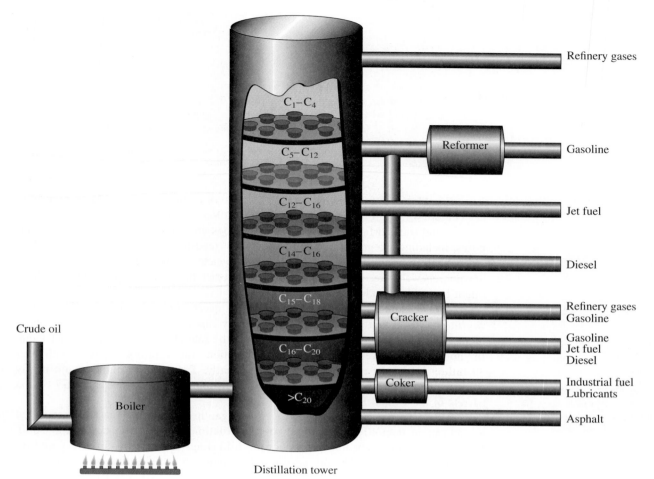

Refinery gases

Gasoline

Jet fuel

Diesel

Refinery gases
Gasoline

Gasoline
Jet fuel
Diesel

Industrial fuel
Lubricants

Asphalt

Reformer

Cracker

Coker

C_1–C_4

C_5–C_{12}

C_{12}–C_{16}

C_{14}–C_{16}

C_{15}–C_{18}

C_{16}–C_{20}

$>C_{20}$

Crude oil

Boiler

Distillation tower

Figure 4.11

Diagram of a distillation tower for crude oil that shows the fractions and typical uses.

gasoline, and solids such as asphalt. The amounts of each depend on the type of crude oil.

The "lightest" fraction collected is the "refinery gases." These compounds have 1–4 carbon atoms per molecule and include methane, ethane, propane, and butane. Refinery gases are flammable and often used as fuel at the refineries. They also can be liquefied and sold for home use. Chemical manufacturers also may use refinery gases as a starting material for making new compounds.

Refinery gases include methane, the main component of natural gas. However, most natural gas is obtained directly from oil and gas wells, rather than from distillation at a refinery. The natural gas piped to your home is practically pure methane, but also includes ethane (2–6%) and other hydrocarbons of low molar mass. Natural gas also may contain small quantities of water vapor, carbon dioxide, hydrogen sulfide, and helium. Before being transported by pipeline, natural gas must be scrubbed to remove impurities such as these.

Once in the pipeline, natural gas provides heat for more than half of the homes in the United States, either directly at the home or via electricity produced by burning natural gas at a power plant. Of the fossil fuels, natural gas is relatively clean. It releases essentially no sulfur dioxide and relatively little particulate matter, carbon monoxide, and nitrogen oxides. No ash residue containing toxic metals remains after combustion. Although burning natural gas does produce CO_2, a greenhouse gas, the amount is less per unit of energy released than for the other fossil fuels. Check the numbers yourself in Your Turn 4.11.

Methane is an odorless gas that can ignite explosively. To alert people to gas leaks, a compound with a distinctive odor is added to natural gas.

In addition to refinery gases, a wide range of compounds is produced at a refinery (Figure 4.12). From a barrel of crude (42 gallons), about 35 gallons are burned for heating and transportation. The remaining gallons are used primarily for nonfuel purposes, including the gallon or two that serve as "feedstocks" to produce plastics, pharmaceuticals, fabrics, and other carbon-based products. As these hydrocarbon feedstocks are nonrenewable resources, one easily can predict that one day petroleum products might become too valuable to burn.

Are we going to run out of oil? A better question to ask might be "When will we run out of oil that can be extracted relatively easily?" The issue is not the quantity of fossil fuels remaining on Earth, but rather the rate at which we can extract them. In the mid-1950s, yearly global oil consumption was 4 billion barrels, with over 30 billion barrels of new deposits found annually. Today, those numbers are nearly reversed. Globally, we use over 30 billion barrels annually, including about 6.7 billion barrels in the United States.

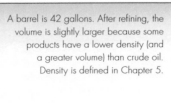
Since 2001, oil production in the United States has ranged between 7 and 9 million barrels of oil per day. In contrast, our oil consumption is ~20 million barrels of oil per day.

A recent large oil discovery was at Kashagan in the Caspian Sea and is expected to yield more than 10 billion barrels over its lifetime. Although discovered in 2000, Kashagan oil only went into production in 2013. Lags between oil discovery and oil production are typical. The oil we use today comes from fields that were discovered decades ago.

At some point, we no longer will find the fields that will insure future production. Given this, petroleum experts have predicted that oil production will peak and then decline. A 2011 article in *Science*, "Peak Oil Production May Already Be Here," reports:

> The problem up to this point, all agree, has been increasing difficulties extracting conventional oil. That's the easiest oil to get at, oil that freely flows out of a well of its own accord or with a minimum of

A barrel is 42 gallons. After refining, the volume is slightly larger because some products have a lower density (and a greater volume) than crude oil. Density is defined in Chapter 5.

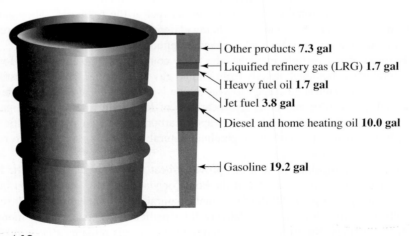
Other products **7.3 gal**
Liquified refinery gas (LRG) **1.7 gal**
Heavy fuel oil **1.7 gal**
Jet fuel **3.8 gal**
Diesel and home heating oil **10.0 gal**
Gasoline **19.2 gal**

Figure 4.12
Products (in gallons) from the refining of a barrel of crude oil.

Source: U.S. Energy Information Administration, 2009.

encouragement, such as pumping it out or pushing it out with water. Production of conventional oil from any one well or field typically increases, peaks, and then goes into decline.

In the same article, oil analyst Michael Rodgers (PFC Energy, Kuala Lumpur) comments, "Arguing that you're going to get continued and sustained growth of conventional oil is a very hard case to make."

Once we tap the easy sources, we are left with unconventional oil found in more difficult locations. It is found thousands of feet below seawater, extractable only with deep-water drilling rigs. It is found in the tarry oil sands of Canada (Figure 4.13). And it is found in the oil shales of Utah, Colorado, and Wyoming. The amounts involved—perhaps 3 trillion barrels—are impressive. Nonetheless, had this oil been easily recoverable, it would not today still lie embedded in the oil sands and shales.

Even so, there are surprises. One is the production of natural gas in the United States from reservoirs deep underground. To extract it, the process of hydraulic fracturing ("fracking") is used. Although first attempted in the 1940s, only more recently has fracking been carried out on a large scale. In 2004, the first well was drilled into the Marcellus Shale underlying Pennsylvania, West Virginia, and parts of states nearby. In 2010, production of natural gas from the Marcellus Shale reached a billion cubic feet per day.

Fracking involves drilling down into the gas-bearing shale that lies a mile or two beneath the Earth's surface. Water that contains a cocktail of substances is injected under pressure in order to create cracks into which the natural gas can flow. The water also carries fine sand that props open these cracks. The next activity gives you the opportunity to pin down some of the details of fracking.

Figure 4.13
The oil sand of Canada is a dense mixture that, unlike conventional oil sources, does not gush oil to the surface.

Consider This 4.12   Fracking!

a. The fracturing of the shale is done hydraulically rather than with dynamite. What does the term *hydraulic* mean? Suggest reasons why dynamite wouldn't work.

b. How much water typically is injected in a well? What are the ingredients of the "cocktail" that this water contains?

c. Some of the water returns to the surface as waste water. What are some of the options for handling this waste water?

Where does this discussion of conventional and unconventional fuels leave us? Some who propose the oil and gas scenarios of the future are optimistic; others are more pessimistic. The differences lie in the degree to which reserves worldwide are recoverable *and* to which they are feasible to burn, given the rise of CO_2 in our atmosphere. No predictions have us abruptly running out of oil and gas. Rather, dramatically higher prices, increasing scarcity, and perhaps even new social norms will characterize a time when oil production will peak. When this happens, we no longer will be able to rely on this "black gold" to the same extent.

4.5 | Measuring Energy Changes

The ability of a substance to release energy makes it a good fuel. As you have seen, both calories and joules can be used to express the energy contained in a food or fuel. In this section, you learn to quantify energy changes in chemical reactions. Your Turn 4.13 gives you practice with energy units.

Donuts contain lipids and carbohydrates, which are discussed in Sections 11.3 and 11.5, respectively.

Your Turn 4.13   Energy Calculations

a. When a donut is metabolized, 425 kcal (425 Cal) is released. Express this value in kilojoules.
b. Calculate the number of 1–kg books you could lift to a shelf 2 m off the floor with the amount of energy from metabolizing one donut.

Answers

a. 1 kcal is equivalent to 4.184 kJ.

$$425 \ \cancel{kcal} \times \frac{4.184 \ kJ}{1 \ \cancel{kcal}} = 1.78 \times 10^3 \ kJ$$

b. Earlier, we stated that one joule is approximately equal to the energy required to raise a 1–kg book a distance of 10 cm against Earth's gravity. We can use this information to calculate the number of 1–kg books that could be lifted 2 meters. First note that 2 m is equivalent to 200 cm. Next, calculate the energy (joules) required to lift one 1–kg book the entire 2 m.

$$200 \ cm \times \frac{1 \ J}{10 \ cm} = 20 \ J$$

Then, express this value in kilojoules.

$$20 \ J \times \frac{1 \ kJ}{10^3 \ J} = 0.020 \ kJ$$

Use this value to make the final calculation.

$$1.78 \times 10^3 \ kJ \times \frac{1 \ book}{0.020 \ kJ} = 8.9 \times 10^4 \ books$$

To work off one donut requires lifting almost 90,000 books!

Skeptical Chemist 4.14   Checking Assumptions

A simplifying (and erroneous) assumption was made in doing the calculations in part **b** of the preceding activity. What was the assumption and is it reasonable? Based on this assumption, is your answer too high or too low? Explain your reasoning.

The metabolism of foods, including minimally healthy ones such as donuts, helps keep our bodies at a constant temperature. **Temperature** is a measure of the average kinetic energy of the atoms and/or molecules present in a substance. Everything around us is at some temperature—hot, cold, or lukewarm. When we perceive a particular object as "cold," this means its atoms and molecules are moving more slowly on average relative to when we perceive this same object as "hot." Therefore, for the temperature of an object to increase, the kinetic energy of its atoms and molecules must increase. Where does that energy come from? **Heat** is the kinetic energy that flows from a hotter object to a colder one. When two bodies are in contact, heat always flows from the object at the higher temperature to one at a lower temperature.

Although the concepts of temperature and heat are related, they are not identical. Your bottle of water and the Pacific Ocean may be at the same temperature, but the ocean contains and can transfer far more heat than the bottle of water. Indeed, bodies of water can affect the climate of an entire region as a consequence of their ability to absorb and transfer heat.

The connections between oceans and climate are discussed further in Sections 3.10, 5.2, and 6.5.

The **calorimeter** is a device used to experimentally measure the quantity of heat energy released in a combustion reaction. Figure 4.14 shows a schematic representation of a calorimeter. To use it, you introduce a known mass of fuel and an excess of oxygen into the heavy-walled stainless steel container. The container is then sealed and submerged in a bucket of water. The reaction is initiated with a spark. The heat evolved by the reaction flows from the container to the water and the rest of the

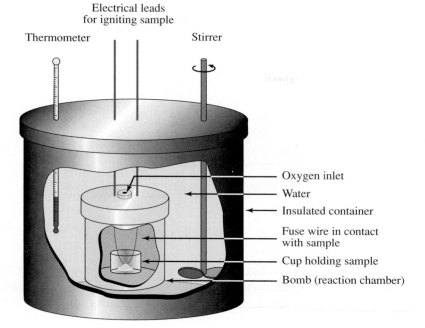

Figure 4.14
Schematic drawing of a calorimeter.

apparatus. As a consequence, the temperature of the entire calorimeter system increases. The quantity of heat given off by the reaction can be calculated from this temperature rise and the known heat-absorbing properties of the calorimeter and the water it contains. The greater the temperature increase, the greater the quantity of energy evolved from the reaction.

Experimental measurements of this sort are the source of most of the tabulated values of heats of combustion. As the name suggests, the **heat of combustion** is the quantity of heat energy given off when a specified amount of a substance burns in oxygen. Heats of combustion are typically reported as positive values in kilojoules per mole (kJ/mol), kilojoules per gram (kJ/g), kilocalories per mole (kcal/mol), or kilocalories per gram (kcal/g). For example, the experimentally determined heat of combustion of methane is 802.3 kJ/mol. This means that 802.3 kJ of heat is given off when 1 mole of $CH_4(g)$ reacts with 2 moles of $O_2(g)$ to form 1 mole of $CO_2(g)$ and 2 moles of $H_2O(g)$.

$$CH_4(g) + 2\,O_2(g) \longrightarrow CO_2(g) + 2\,H_2O(g) + 802.3 \text{ kJ} \qquad \textbf{[4.3]}$$

We can use this value to calculate the number of kilojoules released for a gram, rather than for a mole. The molar mass of CH_4, calculated from the atomic masses of carbon and hydrogen, is 16.0 g/mol. We then can calculate the heat of combustion per gram of methane.

$$\frac{802.3 \text{ kJ}}{1 \text{ mol } CH_4} \times \frac{1 \text{ mol } CH_4}{16.0 \text{ g } CH_4} = 50.1 \text{ kJ/g } CH_4$$

As fuels go, this is a high heat of combustion! Look ahead to Figure 4.16 to see how this value compares with those for other fuels.

Burning methane is analogous to water tumbling down from the top of a waterfall. Initially in a state of higher potential energy, the water drops down to one of lower potential energy. The potential energy is converted into kinetic energy, which is then released when the water hits the rocks below. Similarly, when methane is burned, energy is released when the atoms in the reactants "fall" to a state of lower potential energy as the products are formed. Figure 4.15 is a schematic representation of this process. The downward arrow indicates that the energy associated with 1 mole of

Heats of combustion, by convention, are tabulated as positive values *even though all combustion reactions release heat.*

The mole was defined in Section 3.7.

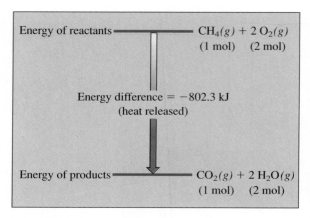

Figure 4.15

Energy difference in the combustion of methane—an exothermic reaction.

$CO_2(g)$ and 2 moles of $H_2O(g)$ is less than the energy associated with 1 mole of $CH_4(g)$ and 2 moles of $O_2(g)$. The combustion of methane is **exothermic,** a term applied to any chemical or physical change accompanied by the release of heat. In this reaction, the energy difference is −802.3 kJ. The negative sign attached to the energy change for all exothermic reactions signifies the decrease in potential energy going from reactants to products. Not surprisingly, the amount of energy released depends on the amount of fuel burned.

By now, it is probably clear that good fuels have high potential energies. The higher the potential energy of a fuel, the more heat it releases when it is burned to produce CO_2 and H_2O. Figure 4.16 compares the energy difference (in kJ/g) of several different fuels. We can make some interesting generalizations based on the chemical formulas of the fuels. First, the fuels with the highest heats of combustion are hydrocarbons. Second, as the ratio of hydrogen-to-carbon decreases, the heat of combustion decreases. And third, as the amount of oxygen in the fuel molecule increases, the heat of combustion decreases.

Consider This 4.15   Coal Versus Ethanol

On the basis of their chemical composition, explain why ethanol and coal have very different chemical formulas but similar heats of combustion.

See Section 4.9 for more about glucose and wood.

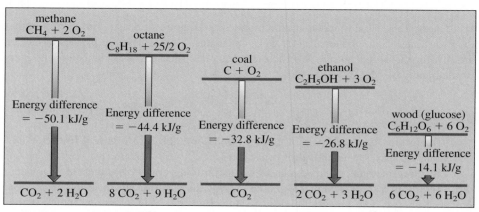

Figure 4.16

Energy differences (in kJ/g) for the combustion of methane (CH_4), *n*–octane (C_8H_{18}), coal (assumed to be pure carbon), ethanol (C_2H_5OH), and wood (assumed to be glucose). Carbon dioxide and water are formed in the gas phase.

Table 4.3	Endothermic Versus Exothermic Reactions
Endothermic Reaction	**Exothermic Reaction**
Energy$_{products}$ > Energy$_{reactants}$	Energy$_{products}$ < Energy$_{reactants}$
Net energy change is positive.	Net energy change is negative.
Energy is absorbed.	Energy is released.

Many naturally occurring reactions are not exothermic but rather *absorb* energy as they occur. We discussed two important examples in earlier chapters. One is the decomposition of O_3 to yield O_2 and O, and the other is the combination of N_2 and O_2 to yield two molecules of NO. Both reactions require energy in the form of an electrical discharge, a high-energy photon, or a high temperature. These reactions are **endothermic,** the term applied to any chemical or physical change that absorbs energy. A chemical reaction is endothermic when the potential energy of the products is *higher* than that of the reactants. The energy change for an endothermic reaction is always positive. Table 4.3 compares the energy changes in endothermic and exothermic reactions.

Photosynthesis also is endothermic. This process requires the absorption of 2800 kJ of sunlight per mole of $C_6H_{12}O_6$, or 15.5 kJ per gram of glucose formed. The complete process involves many steps, but the overall reaction can be described with this equation.

$$2800 \text{ kJ} + 6\,CO_2(g) + 6\,H_2O(l) \xrightarrow{\text{chlorophyll}} \underset{\text{glucose}}{C_6H_{12}O_6(s)} + 6\,O_2(g) \qquad \textbf{[4.4]}$$

The reaction requires the participation of the green pigment chlorophyll. The chlorophyll molecule absorbs energy from the photons of visible sunlight and uses this energy to drive the photosynthetic process, an energetically uphill reaction. Photosynthesis plays an essential role in the carbon cycle, as it removes CO_2 from the atmosphere.

The potential energy of any specific chemical species, and therefore the amount of energy released on combustion, is related to the chemical bonds in the molecules of the fuel. In the following section, we illustrate how knowledge of molecular structure can be used to calculate heats of combustion and can allow us to pinpoint the differences between fuels.

4.6 | Energy Changes at the Molecular Level

Chemical reactions involve the breaking and forming of chemical bonds. Energy is required to break bonds, just as energy is required to break chains or to tear paper. In contrast, forming chemical bonds releases energy. The overall energy change associated with a chemical reaction depends on the net effect of the bond breaking and bond forming. If the energy required to break the bonds in the reactants is greater than the energy released when the products form, the overall reaction is *endothermic;* energy is absorbed. If, on the other hand, the bond-making energy of the products is greater than the bond breaking in the reactants, then the net energy change is *exothermic;* energy is released by the reaction.

For example, consider the combustion of hydrogen. Hydrogen is desirable as a fuel because, compared with other fuels, it releases a large amount of energy per gram when it burns.

$$2\,H_2(g) + O_2(g) \longrightarrow 2\,H_2O(g) + \text{energy} \qquad \textbf{[4.5]}$$

To calculate the energy change associated with the combustion of hydrogen to form water vapor, let us assume that all the bonds in the reactant molecules are broken, and then the individual atoms are reassembled to form the products. In fact, the reaction does not occur this way, but we are interested in only the overall (net) change, not

Section 2.6 described the decomposition of O_3 with the absorption of UV light.
Section 1.9 described the formation of NO at high temperature.

When glucose is formed in equation 4.4, compare the value of 15.5 kJ/g with that of −14.1 kJ/g in Figure 4.16 for its combustion. The magnitudes are not the same because in the former, glucose is formed from CO_2 and water (liquid); in the latter, glucose burns to produce CO_2 and water (gas).

Look for more about hydrogen as a fuel in Sections 8.5 and 8.6.

Table 4.4 — Covalent Bond Energies (in kJ/mol)

	H	C	N	O	S	F	Cl	Br	I
Single Bonds									
H	436								
C	416	356							
N	391	285	160						
O	467	336	201	146					
S	347	272	—	—	226				
F	566	485	272	190	326	158			
Cl	431	327	193	205	255	255	242		
Br	366	285	—	234	213	—	217	193	
I	299	213	—	201	—	—	209	180	151
Multiple Bonds									
C=C	598			C=N	616		C=O*	803	
C≡C	813			C≡N	866		C≡O	1073	
N=N	418			O=O	498				
N≡N	946								

*in CO_2

the details. Therefore, we proceed with our convenient plan and see how well our calculated result agrees with the experimental value.

The covalent bond energies given in Table 4.4 provide the numbers needed for our computation. **Bond energy** is the amount of energy that must be absorbed to break a specific chemical bond. Thus, because energy must be absorbed, breaking bonds is an endothermic process, and all the bond energies in Table 4.4 are positive. The values are expressed in kilojoules per mole of bonds broken. Note that the atoms appear both across the top and down the left side of the table. The number at the intersection of any row and column is the energy (in kilojoules) needed to break a mole of the bonds between the two atoms.

The amount of energy required depends on the number of bonds broken: more bonds take more energy. Each value in Table 4.4 is for one mole of bonds. For example, the energy required to break 1 mole of H−H bonds, as in the H_2 molecule, is 436 kJ. Similarly, the energy required to break 1 mole of O=O double bonds, as in the O_2 molecule, is 498 kJ.

We need to keep track of whether energy is absorbed or released. To do this, we indicate the energy absorbed with a positive sign. This is the energy absorbed when the bond is broken. Forming a bond releases energy, and the sign is negative. For example, the bond energy for the O=O double bond is 498 kJ/mol. Accordingly, when 1 mole of O=O double bonds is broken, the energy change is +498 kJ, and when 1 mole of O=O double bonds is formed, the energy change is −498 kJ.

Now we are finally ready to apply these concepts and conventions to the burning of hydrogen gas, H_2. The next equation shows the Lewis structures of the species involved so that we can count the bonds that need to be broken and formed:

$$2\,\text{H——H} + \overset{..}{\underset{..}{\text{O}}}=\overset{..}{\underset{..}{\text{O}}} \longrightarrow 2\; \text{H}\overset{\overset{..}{\text{O}}..}{\diagup\diagdown}\text{H} \qquad \textbf{[4.6]}$$

Remember that chemical equations can be read in terms of moles. Both equation 4.5 and 4.6 indicate "2 moles of H_2 plus 1 mole of O_2 yields 2 moles of H_2O." To use bond energies, we need to count the number of moles of *bonds* involved. Here is a summary:

Molecule	Bonds per Molecule	Moles in Reaction	Moles of Bonds	Bond Process	Energy per Bond	Total Energy
H–H	1	2	1 × 2 = 2	breaking	+436 kJ	2 × (+436) = +872 kJ
O=O	1	1	1 × 1 = 1	breaking	+498 kJ	1 × (+498) = +498 kJ
H–O–H	2	2	2 × 2 = 4	forming	−467 kJ	4 × (−467) = −1868 kJ

From the last column, we can see that the overall energy change in breaking bonds (872 kJ + 498 kJ = 1370 kJ) and forming new ones (−1868 kJ) results in a net energy change of −498 kJ.

This calculation is diagrammed in Figure 4.17. The energy of the reactants, 2 H_2 and O_2, is set at zero, an arbitrary but convenient value. The green arrows pointing upward signify energy absorbed to break the bonds in the reactant molecules and form 4 H atoms and 2 O atoms. The red arrow on the right pointing downward represents energy released as these atoms bond to form the product molecules: 2 H_2O. The shorter red arrow corresponds to the net energy change of −498 kJ, signifying that the overall combustion reaction is strongly exothermic. The products are lower in energy than the reactants, so the energy change is negative. The net result is the release of energy, mostly in the form of heat. Another way to look at such exothermic reactions is as a conversion of reactants involving weaker bonds to products involving stronger ones. In general, the products are more stable (lower potential energy) and less reactive than the starting substances.

The energy change we just calculated from bond energies, −498 kJ for burning 2 mol of hydrogen, compares favorably with the experimentally determined value when all of the species are gases. This agreement justifies our rather unrealistic assumption that all the bonds in the reactant molecules are first broken and then all

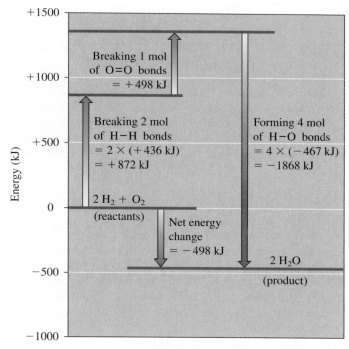

Figure 4.17

The energy changes during the combustion of hydrogen to form water vapor. See Figures Alive! for more about the energy changes of this reaction.

the bonds in the product molecules are formed. The energy change that accompanies a chemical reaction depends on the energy *difference* between the products and the reactants, not on the particular process, mechanism, or individual steps that connect the two. This is an extremely powerful idea when doing calculations related to energy changes in reactions.

Not all calculations come out as easily and well as this one did. For one thing, the bond energies in Table 4.4 apply only to gases, so calculations using these values agree with experiment only if all the reactants and products are in the gaseous state. Moreover, tabulated bond energies are average values. The strength of a bond depends on the overall structure of the molecule in which it is found; in other words, on what else the atoms are bonded to. Thus, the strength of an O−H bond is slightly different in HOH, HOOH, and CH_3OH. Nevertheless, the procedure illustrated here is a useful way of estimating energy changes in a wide range of reactions. The approach also helps illustrate the relationship between bond strength and chemical energy.

This analysis also helps clarify why products of combustion reactions (such as H_2O or CO_2) cannot be used as fuels. There are no substances into which these compounds can be converted that have stronger bonds and that are lower in energy. Bottom line: You cannot run a car on its exhaust fumes!

> Experimental values differ somewhat from those calculated using bond energies.

Your Turn 4.16   Heat of Combustion for Ethyne

Use the bond energies in Table 4.4 to calculate the heat of combustion for ethyne, C_2H_2, also called acetylene. Report your answer both in kilojoules per mole (kJ/mol) C_2H_2 and kilojoules per gram (kJ/g) C_2H_2. Here is the balanced chemical equation.

$$2\,H-C\equiv C-H \;+\; 5\,\ddot{O}=\ddot{O} \longrightarrow 4\,\ddot{O}=C=\ddot{O} \;+\; 2\,H-\ddot{O}-H$$

Hint: The coefficient for acetylene in the chemical equation is 2. The heat of combustion is for 1 mole.

Answer

Energy change = −1256 kJ/mol C_2H_2, or −48.3 kJ/g C_2H_2
Heat of combustion = 1256 kJ/mol C_2H_2, or 48.3 kJ/g C_2H_2

Your Turn 4.17 O_2 Versus O_3

As noted in Chapter 2, ozone absorbs UV radiation having wavelengths less than 320 nm, and oxygen absorbs electromagnetic radiation with wavelengths less than 242 nm. Use the bond energies in Table 4.4 plus information about the resonance structures of O_3 from Chapter 2 to explain why.

4.7 | The Chemistry of Gasoline

Equipped with our understanding of the molecular nature of fuels and the energy changes associated with combustion, we now return to petroleum. The distribution of compounds obtained by distilling crude oil does not correspond to the prevailing pattern of commercial use. For example, the demand for gasoline is considerably greater than that for higher boiling fractions. Chemists employ several processes to change the natural distribution and to obtain more gasoline of higher quality. These include cracking and reforming (see Figure 4.11).

Thermal cracking, a process that breaks large hydrocarbon molecules into smaller ones by heating them to a high temperature, was developed first. In this procedure, the heaviest crude oil fractions are heated between 400 and 450 °C. This heat "cracks" the heaviest tarry crude oil molecules into smaller ones useful for gasoline

> Coking, also shown in Figure 4.11, uses heat to break down the heavier fractions. The process leaves a residual of coke, which is almost pure carbon.

and diesel fuel. For example, at high temperature, one molecule of $C_{16}H_{34}$ can be cracked into two nearly identical molecules.

$$C_{16}H_{34} \xrightarrow{\text{heat}} C_8H_{18} + C_8H_{16} \qquad \text{[4.7]}$$

Thermal cracking also can produce different-sized molecules.

$$C_{16}H_{34} \xrightarrow{\text{heat}} C_{11}H_{22} + C_5H_{12} \qquad \text{[4.8a]}$$

In either case, the total number of carbon and hydrogen atoms is unchanged from reactants to products. The larger reactant molecules simply have been fragmented into smaller, more economically important molecules. We can use space-filling models to show the size difference more clearly.

The space–filling model of $C_{11}H_{22}$ shows a "bend" because of the geometry of the atoms at the C=C double bond.

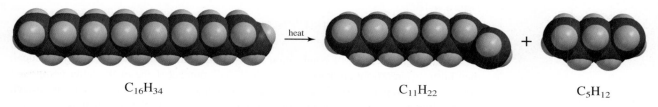

$$C_{16}H_{34} \qquad\qquad C_{11}H_{22} \qquad + \qquad C_5H_{12}$$

$$\text{[4.8b]}$$

Your Turn 4.18 More Practice with Cracking

a. Draw structural formulas for one pair of products formed when $C_{16}H_{34}$ is thermally cracked (see equation 4.7).
   Hint: Draw the atoms of the product molecules in a linear chain and include one double bond (only in one product).
b. Revisit the alkanes shown in Table 4.2. Look closely to find a pattern for the number of H atoms per C atom. Use this pattern to write the generic chemical formula.
c. Write the generic chemical formula for a hydrocarbon with one C=C double bond.

Answer
b. C_nH_{2n+2} (where n is an integer)

The problem with thermal cracking is the energy required to produce the high temperature. **Catalytic cracking** is a process in which catalysts are used to crack larger hydrocarbon molecules into smaller ones at relatively low temperatures, thus reducing energy use. Chemists at all major oil companies have developed important cracking catalysts and continue to find more selective and inexpensive processes. We discuss how catalysts affect the rates of chemical reactions in Section 4.8.

Catalysts were introduced in the context of automobile catalytic converters in Section 1.11.

Sometimes chemists want to combine molecules, rather than split them apart. To produce more of the intermediate-sized molecules needed for gasoline, catalytic combination can be used. In this process, smaller molecules are joined.

Using catalysts to produce *very large* molecules (polymers) from smaller ones (monomers) is discussed in Section 9.3.

$$4\,C_2H_4 \xrightarrow{\text{catalyst}} C_8H_{16} \qquad \text{[4.9]}$$

Another important chemical process is **catalytic reforming**. Here, the atoms within a molecule are rearranged, usually starting with linear molecules and producing ones with more branches. As we will see, the more highly branched molecules burn more smoothly in automobile engines.

It turns out that molecules with the same molecular formula are not necessarily identical. For example, octane has the formula C_8H_{18}. Careful analysis reveals 18 different compounds with this formula. Molecules with the same molecular formula but with different chemical structures and different properties are called **isomers**. In *n*-octane (normal octane) the carbon atoms are all in a continuous chain (Figure 4.18a). In iso-octane, the carbon chain has several branch points (Figure 4.18b). The chemical and physical properties of these two isomers are similar, but they are not identical. For example, the boiling point of *n*-octane is 125 °C, compared with 99 °C for iso-octane.

Combustion of branched hydrocarbons releases 2–4% more energy than combustion of their straight–chain isomers.

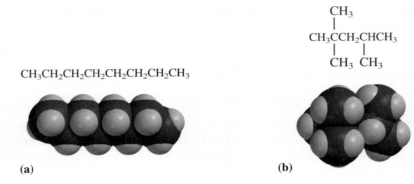

$$CH_3CH_2CH_2CH_2CH_2CH_2CH_2CH_3$$

(a)

(b)

Figure 4.18

Condensed structural formula and space–filling model for (a) *n*–octane and (b) iso–octane.

Although the heats of combustion for *n*-octane and iso-octane are nearly identical, they burn differently in an auto engine. The more compact shape of the latter compound imparts a "smoother" burn. In a well-tuned car engine, gasoline vapor and air are drawn into a cylinder, compressed by a piston, and ignited by a spark. Normal combustion occurs when the spark plug ignites the fuel–air mixture and the flame front travels rapidly across the combustion chamber, consuming the fuel. Sometimes, however, compression alone is enough to ignite the fuel before the spark occurs. This premature firing is called preignition. It results in lower engine efficiency and higher fuel consumption because the piston is not in its optimal location when the burned gases expand. "Knocking," a violent and uncontrolled reaction, occurs after the spark ignites the fuel, causing the unburned mixture to burn at supersonic speed with an abnormal rise in pressure. Knocking produces an objectionable metallic sound, loss of power, overheating, and engine damage when severe.

In the 1920s, knocking was shown to depend on the chemical composition of the gasoline. The "octane rating" was developed to designate a particular gasoline's resistance to knocking. Iso-octane performs exceptionally well in automobile engines and arbitrarily has been assigned an octane rating of 100. Like *n*-octane, *n*-heptane is a straight-chain hydrocarbon, but with one fewer –CH₂ group. It also has a high tendency to knock and is assigned an octane rating of 0 (Table 4.5). When you go to the gasoline pump and fill up with 87 octane, you are buying gasoline that has the same knocking characteristics as a mixture of 87% iso-octane (octane number 100) and 13% *n*-heptane (octane number 0). Higher grades of gasoline also are available: 89 octane (regular plus) and 91 octane (premium). These blends contain a higher percent of compounds with higher octane ratings (Figure 4.19).

Although *n*-octane has a poor octane rating, it is possible to catalytically re-form *n*-octane to iso-octane, thus greatly improving its performance. This rearrangement is accomplished by passing *n*-octane over a catalyst consisting of rare and expensive elements such as platinum (Pt), palladium (Pd), rhodium (Rh), and iridium (Ir). Re-forming isomers to improve their octane rating became important starting in the late 1970s because of the nationwide efforts to ban the use of tetraethyl lead (TEL) as an antiknock additive.

Younger people today may never have heard the sound of an engine "knocking" because it rarely occurs with current engine technology and gasoline blends.

Figure 4.19

Gasoline is available in a variety of octane ratings.

Table 4.5	Octane Ratings of Several Compounds
Compound	Octane Rating
n–octane	−20
n–heptane	0
iso–octane	100
methanol	107
ethanol	108
MTBE*	116

*MTBE, methyl tertiary–butyl ether

Consider This 4.19 Getting the Lead Out

The United States completed the ban on leaded gasoline in 1996 because of the hazards associated with lead exposure. But other sources of lead still exist. Be a detective on the Internet to identify:

a. an occupational source of lead exposure.
b. a hobby that is a source of lead exposure.
c. a source of lead exposure that particularly affects children.

In the United States, TEL was phased out during the 1970s because of the toxic effects of lead, especially to children. See Section 5.10 for more information on lead in the environment.

Elimination of TEL as an octane enhancer necessitated finding substitutes that were inexpensive, easy to produce, and environmentally benign. Several were tried, including ethanol and MTBE (*m*ethyl *t*ertiary-*b*utyl *e*ther), each with an octane rating greater than 100 (see Table 4.5). As we will see, however, MTBE did not turn out as well as expected.

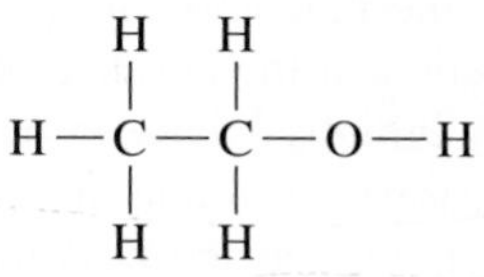

ethanol

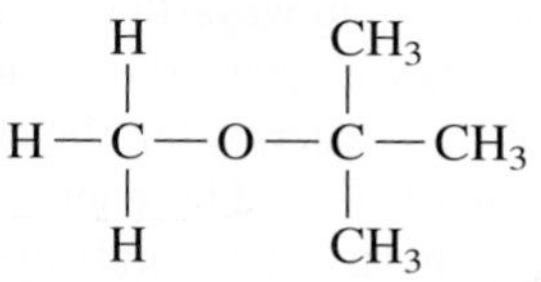

MTBE

Fuels containing these additives are referred to as **oxygenated gasolines**, blends of petroleum-derived hydrocarbons with added oxygen-containing compounds such as MTBE, ethanol, or methanol (CH_3OH). Because they contain oxygen, these gasoline blends burn more cleanly and produce less carbon monoxide than their nonoxygenated counterparts.

Since 1995, about 90 cities and metropolitan areas with the highest ground-level ozone levels have adopted the Year-Round Reformulated Gasoline Program mandated by the Clean Air Act Amendments of 1990. This program requires the use of **reformulated gasolines (RFGs)**, oxygenated gasolines that also contain a lower percentage of certain more volatile hydrocarbons found in nonoxygenated conventional gasoline. RFGs cannot contain more than 1% benzene (C_6H_6) and must be at least 2% oxygen. Because of their composition, reformulated gasolines evaporate less readily than conventional gasolines and produce less carbon monoxide emissions.

Benzene, C_6H_6, is a known carcinogen. Its molecular structure is introduced in Section 9.5 and further discussed in Section 10.2.

As pointed out earlier in Chapter 1, the volatile organic compounds (VOCs) in conventional gasoline play a role in tropospheric ozone formation, especially in high-traffic areas. When RFGs were introduced in the 1990s, MTBE was the oxygenate of choice. However, concerns over its toxicity and its ability to leach from gasoline storage tanks into the groundwater have led many states to ban MTBE and switch to ethanol. As an additive and a fuel in its own right, ethanol is described more fully in Section 4.9.

Volatile organic compounds and their role in ozone formation were explained in Section 1.12.

4.8 New Uses for an Old Fuel

World supplies of coal are predicted to last for hundreds of years, much longer than current estimates of remaining available oil reserves. Unfortunately, the fact that coal is a solid makes it inconvenient for many applications, especially as a fuel for vehicles. Therefore, research and development projects are underway aimed at converting solid coal into fuels that possess characteristics similar to petroleum products.

Before large supplies of natural gas were discovered and exploited, cities were lighted with water gas, a mixture of carbon monoxide and hydrogen. Water gas is formed by blowing steam over hot coke, the impure carbon that remains after volatile components have been distilled from coal.

$$C(s) + H_2O(g) \longrightarrow CO(g) + H_2(g) \qquad \textbf{[4.10]}$$
coke   water gas

This same reaction is the starting point for the Fischer–Tropsch process for producing synthetic gasoline from coal. German chemists Emil Fischer (1852–1919) and Hans Tropsch (1889–1935) developed the process during the 1920s. At that time, Germany had abundant coal reserves, but little petroleum.

The Fischer–Tropsch process can be described by this general equation.

$$n\ CO(g) + (2n + 1)\ H_2(g) \xrightarrow{\text{catalyst}} C_nH_{2n+2}(g,l) + n\ H_2O(g) \qquad \textbf{[4.11]}$$

The hydrocarbon products can range from small molecules like methane, CH_4 ($n = 1$), to the medium-sized molecules ($n = 5$–8) typically found in gasoline. This chemical reaction proceeds when the carbon monoxide and hydrogen are passed over a catalyst containing iron or cobalt.

To better understand the role of the catalyst, consider a typical exothermic reaction, as shown in Figure 4.20. The potential energy of the reactants (left side) is higher than the potential energy of the products (right side) because it is an exothermic reaction. Now examine the pathways that connect the reactants and products. The green line indicates the energy changes during a reaction in the absence of a catalyst. Overall, this reaction gives off energy, but the energy initially *increases* because some bonds break (or start to break) first. The energy necessary to initiate a chemical reaction is called its **activation energy** and is indicated by the green arrow. Although energy must be expended to get the reaction started, energy is given off as the process proceeds to a lower potential energy state. Generally, reactions that occur rapidly have low activation energies; slower reactions have higher activation energies. However, there is no direct relationship between the height of the activation barrier and the net energy change in the reaction. In other words, a highly exothermic reaction can have a large or a small activation energy.

Increasing the temperature often results in increased reaction rates; when molecules have extra energy, a greater fraction of collisions can overcome the required activation energy. Sometimes, however, increasing the temperature isn't a practical solution. The blue line shows how a catalyst can provide an alternative reaction pathway and thus a lower activation energy (represented by the blue arrow), without raising the temperature.

In the Fischer–Tropsch process, strong $C{\equiv}O$ triple bonds must be broken for the reaction to proceed. Breaking this bond corresponds to an activation energy so large the reaction simply does not proceed. This is the point at which the metal catalyst

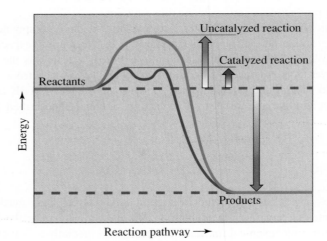

Figure 4.20

Energy–reaction pathway for the same reaction with (*blue line*) and without (*green line*) a catalyst. The green and blue arrows represent the activation energies. The red arrow represents the overall energy change for either pathway.

enters the reaction. Molecules of CO can form bonds with the metal surface, and when this happens, the C≡O bonds weaken. The hydrogen molecules also attach to the metal surface, completely breaking the H–H single bonds. The rest of the reaction proceeds quickly, producing the higher molecular weight hydrocarbons.

The beauty of a catalyst is that it is not consumed and thus only small amounts of it must be used. Green chemists value catalytic reactions not only because small amounts of catalysts are employed, but also because the reaction often can be carried out at lower temperatures.

Historically, commercialization of Fischer–Tropsch technology has been limited. South Africa, a coal-rich and oil-poor nation, is the only country that synthesizes a majority of its gasoline and diesel fuel from coal. Any spike in oil prices, coupled with a plentiful domestic coal supply, may spark increased use of the Fischer–Tropsch process in other energy-hungry countries. As of 2008, China is constructing a coal-to-liquid fuels plant in Inner Mongolia. In the United States, an Australian energy corporation announced plans to build a $7 billion coal-to-liquids plant in Big Horn County, Montana, home to the Crow Tribe. The deposits there are estimated to contain almost 9 billion tons of coal.

Coal, whether solid or converted to liquid fuels, still burns to produce CO_2. Recent work by the National Renewable Energy Laboratory indicates that greenhouse gas emissions over the entire fuel cycle for producing coal-based liquid fuels are nearly twice as high as their petroleum-based equivalent. Clearly, we need to search for fuels to replace coal.

4.9 | Biofuels I—Ethanol

"A sustainable society is one that is far-seeing enough, flexible enough, and wise enough not to undermine either its physical or social systems of support." These words from Donella Meadows, a biophysicist and the founder of the Sustainability Institute, were quoted in Chapter 0. We repeat them here, noting that the rapid rate at which we are burning fossil fuels is indeed undermining our physical and social support systems. This rate simply is *not* sustainable.

What are our options? Some people today believe that a more sustainable energy future will require the increased use of **biofuels**, a generic term for a renewable fuel derived from a biological source, such as trees, grasses, animal waste, or agricultural crops. Biofuels can replace fuels derived from crude oil, such as gasoline and diesel fuel. Although most biofuels today are not being produced in a sustainable manner, they could be in the future.

Donella Meadows 1941–2001

Like fossil fuels, all biofuels release CO_2 when burned. However, biofuels should release a lower net amount of CO_2 into the atmosphere than fossil fuels, definitely a plus. Why? The plants from which the biofuel originated absorbed CO_2 from the atmosphere while they were growing. Whether burned as a fuel or not, these plants would release this same amount of CO_2 back into the biosphere after they died. In contrast, fossil fuels would have kept their carbon "locked up" underground if not extracted and burned as fuels. The assertion that the net amount of CO_2 released is smaller assumes that the energy used to produce and transport the biofuel does not cancel out this benefit. As you will see in the next section, this assertion has been challenged.

Wood, the most common biofuel, has been used throughout human history for cooking and heating. Have you ever wondered why wood burns? Wood contains **cellulose**, a naturally-occurring compound composed of C, H, and O that provides structural rigidity in plants, shrubs, and trees. Similar to hydrocarbons, cellulose is made up of carbon and hydrogen. Unlike these, however, cellulose also contains oxygen, which lowers its energy content as a fuel. In fact, all of the biofuels that we will describe in this section contain some oxygen. As their oxygen content increases, biofuels release proportionately less energy per mass burned than hydrocarbons. Revisit Figure 4.16 to see the energy content of different fuels.

Cellulose is a natural polymer of glucose, that is, a chain of thousands of glucose molecules linked together. For this reason, earlier we equated burning wood to burning

Look for more about cellulose and other natural polymers in Chapter 9.

glucose in Figure 4.16. You may recognize glucose, $C_6H_{12}O_6$, as a sugar. Perhaps you have heard glucose called "blood sugar." It gives the familiar sweet taste to both grapes and sweet corn. Here is the chemical equation for burning wood, which is the same equation as the one we provided for respiration ("burning glucose") in your body:

$$C_6H_{12}O_6 + 6\,O_2 \longrightarrow 6\,CO_2 + 6\,H_2O + \text{energy} \qquad \textbf{[4.12]}$$
$$\text{glucose}$$

Even though widely available in many parts of the world, wood is in insufficient supply to meet our energy demands. Cutting down trees for fuel also destroys trees that effectively absorb CO_2 from our atmosphere. So instead of relying on wood, people in all sectors are eyeing liquid fuels such as ethanol.

Identical to the alcohol found in vodka, its higher-priced cousin, ethanol is a clear, colorless, and flammable liquid. Since ancient times, people have known how to ferment grain in order to produce ethanol. Admittedly, their purpose was to brew alcoholic beverages rather than to fuel automobile engines.

Which sugars and grains can be fermented? Almost any will do, although the latter may require an enzyme to nudge the process along. The choice depends on both availability and politics. Today in the United States, most of the ethanol is produced by fermenting the sugars and starches found in corn (Figure 4.21). However, in early human history, corn was not widely available. As you'll learn in Chapter 12 on genetic engineering, the people of the New World bred corn from a wild strain. Those living elsewhere brewed alcoholic beverages using other handy grains such as rice and barley. Accordingly, ethanol also goes by the name of grain alcohol.

In the context of oxygenated gasoline, we introduced ethanol in Section 4.7. For your convenience, we again provide its Lewis structure.

$$
\begin{array}{ccc}
& \overset{\displaystyle H}{\underset{\displaystyle |}{}} & \overset{\displaystyle H}{\underset{\displaystyle |}{}} \\
H - C\!\!\!& -\!\!\! C & -\ddot{O} - H \\
& \underset{\displaystyle H}{\overset{\displaystyle |}{}} & \underset{\displaystyle H}{\overset{\displaystyle |}{}}
\end{array}
$$

ethanol

Ethanol is an example of an **alcohol,** a hydrocarbon substituted with one or more $-OH$ groups (hydroxyl groups) bonded to its carbon atoms. Just like hydrocarbons, alcohols

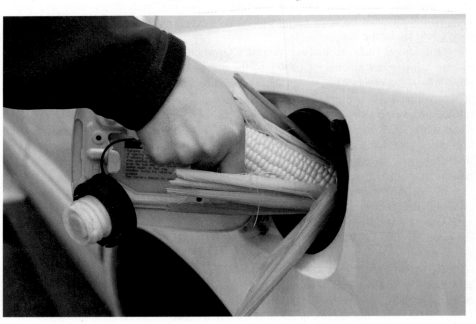

Figure 4.21

An advertisement for ethanol, a renewable fuel that can be produced from many different grains, including corn.

are flammable and burn to release energy. With complete combustion, the products are CO_2 and H_2O.

$$C_2H_5OH(l) + 3\,O_2(g) \longrightarrow 2\,CO_2(g) + 3\,H_2O(g) + 1240\,kJ \qquad \textbf{[4.13]}$$

Because alcohols contain one or more −OH groups, their properties differ from those of hydrocarbons. One difference is that humans can safely consume small amounts of ethanol in wine, beer, and other alcoholic drinks. In contrast, hydrocarbons have no appeal as a beverage. Another difference is their solubility. For example, ethanol dissolves readily in water. In contrast, hydrocarbons are insoluble. Look for more about solubility in the next chapter.

Alcohols provide us with an opportunity to mention the concept of a **functional group,** that is, a distinctive arrangement of a group of atoms that imparts characteristic properties to the molecules that contain this group. To emphasize the hydroxyl group (−OH) present in any alcohol, chemists typically write C_2H_5OH for ethanol rather than C_2H_6O. Another example of a functional group is C=C, the double bond, mentioned in Your Turn 4.18. In the next section on biofuels, we will give a sneak peak of another functional group, the ester.

Again, most of the ethanol produced in the United States comes from corn. Several steps are required. The first involves making a "soup" of corn kernels and water. The second step uses enzymes to catalyze the breakdown of the starch molecules found in these kernels, in essence, to "digest" the starch to make glucose. Like cellulose, starch is a carbohydrate that is found in many grains, such as corn and wheat. It is a natural polymer of glucose. Like a cellulose molecule, a starch molecule is a chain of thousands of glucose molecules linked together. But unlike cellulose molecules, the links are formed differently such that the enzymes in our bodies can break them. Thus, we can digest the starch in foods such as potatoes and rice. However, we cannot digest the cellulose found in leafy foods such as lettuce and thus refer to it as the "roughage" in our diets.

The third step (fermentation) converts glucose to ethanol. Yeast cells take over by releasing different enzymes that catalyze this conversion.

$$\underset{\text{glucose}}{C_6H_{12}O_6} \xrightarrow{\text{yeast enzymes}} \underset{\text{ethanol}}{2\,C_2H_5OH} + 2\,CO_2 \qquad \textbf{[4.14]}$$

The result is an alcoholic brew, not a very tasty one, with an alcohol content of about 10%. To separate the ethanol, the final step is to distill the mixture. Recall how the components of crude oil can be separated by their boiling points at an oil refinery. The same principles apply here. Ethanol and water differ in their boiling points and can be separated by distillation. Check out Figure 4.22 to see the tall distillation towers at an ethanol plant. As of January 2012, 209 ethanol plants were operating in the continental United States, but few others were under construction.

Look for more on the chemical properties of C=C bonds in Chapter 9 on polymers.

Enzymes (biological catalysts) are introduced in Section 10.4. Further examples are given in Chapters 11 and 12.

Figure 4.22

Archer Daniels Midland ethanol plant in Peoria, Illinois.

Source: Biofuels Atlas, NREL (2013).

Compare this ethanol production to the approximately 377 million gallons of ethanol burned daily in the United States in 2011.

Consider This 4.20   A Picture Is Worth . . . ?

This data table shows the annual ethanol production (millions of gallons) in the United States.

Year	Ethanol	Year	Ethanol	Year	Ethanol
1980	175	1991	950	2002	2130
1981	215	1992	1,100	2003	2800
1982	350	1993	1,200	2004	3400
1983	375	1994	1,350	2005	3904
1984	430	1995	1,400	2006	4855
1985	610	1996	1,100	2007	6500
1986	710	1997	1,300	2008	9000
1987	830	1998	1,400	2009	10,600
1988	845	1999	1,470	2010	13,230
1989	870	2000	1,630	2011	13,900
1990	900	2001	1,770	2012	13,300

Source: Renewable Fuels Association.

a. Find entries for more recent years to update this table.
b. Present this information to a public audience of your choice by some other visual means.

With over 13,000 million gallons of ethanol produced annually in 2011, the United States is the world's largest ethanol producer. Brazil is second, with about 7000 million gallons of ethanol. Together, these two countries account for about 85% of the world's production. Corn is the raw material in the United States. In contrast, Brazil derives almost all of its ethanol by fermenting sugarcane. Why the difference?

To answer this question, we again note that practically any sugar or grain can be fermented to produce ethanol. The substance fermented depends on its availability, economics, and politics. Sugarcane plants are rich in sucrose, also called "table sugar." Just as the glucose produced from the starch of corn kernels can be fermented to produce ethanol, so can sucrose. In Brazil, sugarcane is grown in areas that once were tropical rain forests. In the United States, corn is grown in the Midwest in areas that were once prairies and forests. In both cases, the use of land to produce biofuel is controversial.

Worldwide, another possible and less controversial source of ethanol is cellulose, a compound we mentioned earlier that gives support to plants, shrubs, and trees. **Cellulosic ethanol** is ethanol produced from any plant containing cellulose, typically cornstalks, switchgrass, wood chips, and other materials that are nonedible by humans. Although you may not recognize the name switchgrass, if you live east of the Rockies in the United States, Canada, or Mexico, most likely you have seen it. Switchgrass is a native plant; Figure 4.23 shows one of its varieties.

Derived from nonedible plants like switchgrass, cellulosic ethanol has a widespread appeal. For years, chemists have been successful at producing small amounts of cellulosic ethanol in the laboratory. But carrying out the process in batches large enough to obtain millions of gallons of ethanol has turned out to be another matter entirely. Like starch, cellulose does not ferment and therefore needs first to be broken down into sugars. As of 2012, the enzymes that catalyze the breakdown of cellulose were expensive and their rate of reaction was slow.

Figure 5.22 gives the structural formula for sucrose. Sugar beets also contain sucrose. Look to Chapter 11 for more about sugars, where they are found, and how sweet they are.

Figure 4.23

Switchgrass, a perennial plant that is native to North America.

Consider This 4.21   Biofuel from Nonfoods

List three desirable characteristics of sources of cellulosic ethanol, such as wood chips and switchgrass. Use the Triple Bottom Line to inform your answer.

The Triple Bottom Line was introduced in Chapter 0.

Figure 4.24

Gasoline is blended with ethanol to make E10 ("gasohol") that is 90% gasoline and 10% ethanol.

Regardless of its source, ethanol doesn't go straight into your gas tank because our automobiles are not engineered to burn it. However, auto engines can run on "gasohol," a blend of gasoline with ethanol. For many years, gasoline typically contained 10% ethanol. These blends now are labeled E10, as shown in Figure 4.24. E10 and other "oxygenated" fuels (see Section 4.7) have the added benefit of higher octane ratings and of reducing vehicle emissions that produce ground-level ozone.

Beginning with legislation launched in 2007, the United States sought to reduce dependence on oil imports and to increase the use of renewable fuels. As a result, a shift to E15 was proposed. As you might suspect, E15 is 15% ethanol, 85% gasoline. What you may not be anticipating, however, is the controversies that ensued given the relatively smooth transition to E10. Some constituencies were confident that the transition to a new fuel blend could be easily orchestrated. Others cited the need to carefully check whether increased concentrations of ethanol would corrode existing fuel tanks or adversely affect livestock feed prices. In addition, lawn mowers, boats, and snowmobiles currently cannot run on E15. As of 2013, the U.S. Environmental Protection Agency approved the use of E15 but did not mandate it.

Whether for E10 or E15, don't confuse octane rating with the gas mileage. The octane rating relates to how smoothly the fuel burns in the engine rather than to the energy content of the fuel. The octane rating of a gasoline increases as more ethanol is added. But with more ethanol, the gas mileage decreases slightly.

Why? Recall that ethanol releases a lower amount of energy per amount burned than do the hydrocarbons found in gasoline. Using *n*-octane as a representative hydrocarbon, here are the two combustion equations:

$$C_2H_5OH(l) + 3\,O_2(g) \longrightarrow 2\,CO_2(g) + 3\,H_2O(g) + 1240\text{ kJ} \qquad \textbf{[4.15]}$$

$$C_8H_{18}(l) + 25/2\,O_2(g) \longrightarrow 8\,CO_2(g) + 9\,H_2O(g) + 5060\text{ kJ} \qquad \textbf{[4.16]}$$

Per gram, the values are 26.8 kJ/g for C_2H_5OH and 44.4 kJ/g for C_8H_{18} (see Figure 4.16). Ethanol releases less energy because it contains oxygen. As a fuel, ethanol already is partially oxidized or "burned."

As we pointed out at the start of this section, ethanol is not the only biofuel in town. The next section is devoted to biodiesel, another renewable fuel.

4.10 | Biofuels II—Biodiesel

The production of biodiesel has grown dramatically in recent years. Its synthesis is so straightforward that you may have carried it out in your chemistry lab. Biodiesel is unique among transportation fuels in that it can be produced economically in small

(a)   **(b)**

Figure 4.25

(a) Restaurants purchase oil for frying in large amounts. Shown here is a 35–pound box.
(b) Hot oil out of the fryer. Depending on the chef, the cooking oil is changed frequently (shown here) or infrequently. In the latter case, the oil darkens with waste products.

batches by individual consumers, including students. As we will see later in this section, it is produced commercially as well.

Although biodiesel is made primarily from vegetable oils, animal fats work equally well. As you may already know, oils and fats are part of your diet and help fuel your body. When you dip your bread in olive oil or spread a roll with butter, you are preparing to consume an oil or a fat. Although biodiesel could be synthesized from olive oil or butter, both are too expensive (and too tasty) to use as a starting material. Instead, biodiesel is made from soy, rapeseed, or palm oil. It also can be produced from waste cooking oil, such as that used for French fries. Figure 4.25 shows a carton of oil that is destined for a restaurant fryer, together with the waste cooking oil.

To understand why fats and oils can serve as starting materials for biodiesel, we need to know more about **triglycerides**, a class of compounds that includes both fats and oils. **Fats** such as butter and lard are triglycerides that are solids at room temperature. In contrast, **oils** such as olive oil and soybean oil are triglycerides that are liquids. Either as liquids or solids, triglycerides are the starting material for biodiesel. They occur naturally in both plants and animals.

Here is the structural formula for glyceryl tristearate, a triglyceride found in animal fat.

Although we will not discuss it until Chapter 9, this structural formula for a triglyceride gives you a sneak preview of the **ester** functional group.

$$H_3C-(CH_2)_{16}-\overset{\overset{\displaystyle O}{\|}}{C}-O-CH_2-\overset{|}{CH}-CH_2-O-\overset{\overset{\displaystyle O}{\|}}{C}-(CH_2)_{16}-CH_3$$

Actually any triglyceride would serve our purposes because they all share common structural features. We picked this particular one because you will encounter it later in the context of nutrition (Chapter 11).

Glyceryl tristearate is a complex molecule! Even so, you should be able to spot the three hydrocarbon chains. Can you see their resemblance to hydrocarbon fuels? Each of these hydrocarbon chains, if snipped off, could serve as diesel fuel, a mixture of hydrocarbons with 14 to 16 carbon atoms (Figure 4.11). When you eat foods containing triglycerides, each "diesel-like" hydrocarbon chain is metabolized slowly in your body to release energy and produce CO_2 and H_2O. Although diesel fuel burns in an engine much more rapidly and at a higher temperature, the net result is the same. Energy is released, and CO_2 and H_2O are produced.

Although soybean oil and other triglycerides will burn, they should not go straight into your gas tank. Before triglycerides can be utilized as a fuel, first they need to be snipped into smaller pieces that are closer in size (and ease of evaporation) to the molecules in diesel fuel. One way to do this is to react them with an alcohol such as methanol (CH_3OH) and a catalytic amount of sodium hydroxide (NaOH). Here is the chemical reaction, using glyceryl tristearate (an animal fat) as the starting material.

Because of their viscosity and higher molar masses, oils would harden in colder weather and gum up your engine.

$$\text{glyceryl tristearate} + 3\ CH_3OH \xrightarrow{\text{NaOH}} 3\ CH_3(CH_2)_{16}\overset{\displaystyle O}{\overset{\displaystyle \|}{C}}OCH_3 + C_3H_8O_3$$

$$\text{(a triglyceride)} \qquad\qquad\qquad \underset{\text{methyl stearate}}{} \qquad \underset{\text{glycerol}}{}$$

$$\text{(a biodiesel molecule)}$$

[4.17]

One glyceryl stearate molecule produces 3 biodiesel molecules that each contain a long chain of carbon atoms. Depending on the fat or oil used as a starting material, other biodiesel molecules are possible, such as methyl lineolate.

$$CH_3CH_2CH_2CH_2CH_2CH=CHCH_2CH=CHCH_2CH_2CH_2CH_2CH_2CH_2CH_2\overset{\displaystyle O}{\overset{\displaystyle \|}{C}}OCH_3$$

In general:

- Biodiesel molecules contain a hydrocarbon chain, typically with 16–20 carbon atoms.
- The hydrocarbon chains usually contain one or more C=C bonds, especially if the triglyceride used as a starting material is an oil.
- In addition to the hydrocarbon chain, each biodiesel molecule also contains oxygen. The two O atoms form part of the ester functional group, which we will describe later in the context of polyesters in Chapter 9.
- Triglycerides (fats and oils) typically produce a mixture of different biodiesel molecules, unlike the triglyceride glyceryl stearate that produced just one product.

Also notice the 3 molecules of methanol in equation 4.17. Methanol provides the $-OCH_3$ group to "cap" each carbon chain at the point it was snipped from the larger triglyceride molecule. Other alcohols, including ethanol, can work equally well. No matter which alcohol is used, the net result is 3 molecules of biodiesel. The next activity is designed to refresh your memory about alcohols such as ethanol and methanol. It also sets the stage for glycerol, the alcohol that is a product of the biodiesel synthesis.

Just like ethanol, methanol (CH_3OH) contains the hydroxyl group, $-OH$. Like methane, methanol contains only one C atom.

Your Turn 4.22   More About Alcohols

In this chapter, you already have encountered two alcohols: ethanol and methanol.

a. Draw the structural formula for each.
b. Here is a new alcohol: $CH_3CH_2CH_2OH$. Suggest a name.
c. There is another alcohol with the same chemical formula as $CH_3CH_2CH_2OH$, that is, an isomer of this alcohol. Draw its structural formula.

Answers

b. Propanol, because (like propane) it has 3 carbon atoms. More properly, this compound is *n*–propanol or 1–propanol.

c. $CH_3 - CH - CH_3$
           $|$
          OH

This is isopropanol (2–propanol), better known as "rubbing alcohol." The reason for the numbers in 1– and 2–propanol is beyond the scope of our discussion.

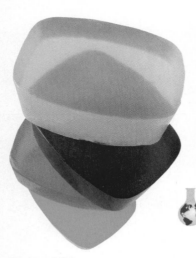

Figure 4.26
Glycerin (glycerol) is one of the ingredients in translucent soaps.

Section 1.13 listed propylene glycol and ethylene glycol as antifreezes in water–based interior paints. However, since both are volatile, low VOC paints no longer contain either.

If you worked through the previous activity, it should be evident that many different alcohols can be derived from hydrocarbons. All that you need to do is to substitute an −OH group for one of the H atoms. Furthermore, alcohols can contain more than one −OH group. The synthesis of biodiesel produces one such multifunctional alcohol, glycerol. In equation 4.17, we gave only its chemical formula, $C_3H_8O_3$. From its structural formula, you can see that glycerol is a "triple" alcohol.

$$\begin{array}{ccccc} & H & H & H & \\ & | & | & | & \\ H- & C- & C- & C- & H \\ & | & | & | & \\ & OH & OH & OH & \end{array}$$

Glycerol, a by-product of the synthesis of biodiesel, is used in many different consumer products. You may know it by the name of glycerin, a common ingredient in soaps and cosmetics (Figure 4.26). However, every 9 pounds of biodiesel nets 1 pound of glycerol, which has resulted in a glut of glycerol on the market. In 2006, Galen Suppes and coworkers at the University of Missouri earned a Presidential Green Chemistry Challenge Award for a process to convert glycerol to a different alcohol, propylene glycol.

$$\begin{array}{ccc} \begin{array}{ccc} H & H & H \\ | & | & | \\ H-C-C-C-H \\ | & | & | \\ OH & OH & OH \end{array} & \xrightarrow{\text{copper catalyst}} & \begin{array}{ccc} H & H & H \\ | & | & | \\ H-C-C-C-H \\ | & | & | \\ OH & OH & H \end{array} \end{array}$$

glycerol   propylene glycol   **[4.18]**

The FDA lists propylene glycol as "generally recognized as safe" and has approved it for use as a food additive. The compound also finds uses as a moisturizer in cosmetics and as a solvent for some drugs not soluble in water. As an antifreeze in vehicles and as a deicer at airports, it is far less toxic than ethylene glycol, another compound used as an antifreeze. Propylene glycol produced in this manner is from a renewable resource, not requiring petroleum as a feedstock. Conversion of the glycerol into value-added products lowers the cost of biodiesel production, making it more competitive with petroleum-derived diesel fuel.

Consider This 4.23   Heat of Combustion for Biodiesel

Revisit the structural formula for a biodiesel molecule.

a. Would you predict that the heat released per gram of biodiesel burned is higher or lower than that of octane? Explain your reasoning. *Hint:* Revisit Figure 4.16 to see the values for different fuels.

b. If instead the comparison were made on the basis of 1 mole of biodiesel vs. 1 mole of octane, which would release more heat if burned?

c. It is more useful to make comparisons per gram of fuel rather than per mole of fuel. Explain.

Biodiesel is blended with petroleum-based diesel fuel, just like ethanol is blended with gasoline. For example, B20 is 20% biodiesel and 80% diesel fuel (Figure 4.27a). Blends up to 20% are fully compatible with any diesel engine, including those in medium- and heavy-weight trucks. As of 2012, biodiesel blends were available at over 1600 retail locations in the United States that could easily be located via the Internet. For example, Figure 4.27b shows 32 locations for biodiesel in Tennessee in the vicinity of Knoxville, Memphis, and Nashville.

In this section and the previous one, we have discussed two biofuels: ethanol and biodiesel. In the process, we have hinted at the complexities and the controversies involved. In the final section of this chapter, we take a critical look not only at biofuels, but also at the larger energy picture. We need to find a way forward.

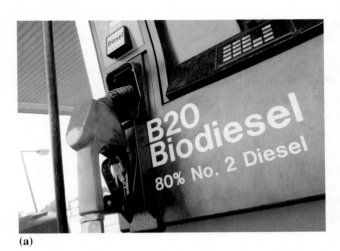

(a)

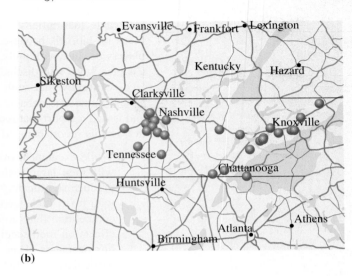

(b)

Figure 4.27

(a) B20 is a mixture of 80% petroleum diesel and 20% biodiesel. (b) Locations of the 36 biodiesel stations in Tennessee (2012).

Source: www.biodiesel.org.

4.11 | Biofuels and the Way Forward

Is growing our fuel a step on the path to a sustainable future? In this final section, we devote our full attention to this question. Underlying it are the economic, environmental, and societal costs of biofuels, in essence, the Triple Bottom Line. Many have pointed out that we need to proceed along this path deliberately and with due process. For example, the weekly journal of the American Chemical Society points out: "Governments need to pause, step back, and take a more nuanced and sophisticated view of biofuels, taking into consideration their sustainability and social costs" (*Chemical & Engineering News*, August 15, 2011).

Ethanol and biodiesel currently claim only a small share of global final energy consumption, that is, the energy delivered to consumers for all uses. According to a 2010 report issued on the status of biofuels (Figure 4.28), renewable fuels comprised just under 20% of the energy use, with biofuels a mere 0.6%. Nonetheless, biofuel production has increased in recent years, a trend that is expected to continue. Furthermore, many nations are setting political and economic wheels in motion to encourage the further use of biofuels. Figure 4.28 also reveals that biofuels are one of several

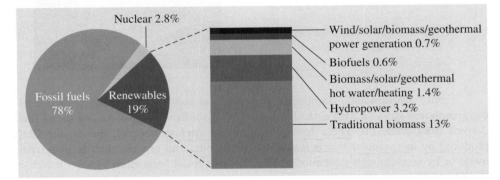

Biomass (in Figure 4.28) is a generic term that refers to any renewable fuel of biological origin, including wood and ethanol.

Figure 4.28

Renewable energy share of global final energy consumption, 2008. Traditional biomass includes wood, agricultural waste, and animal dung.

Source: Renewable Energy Policy Network for the 21st Century (2010), Renewables 2010: Global Status Report, Paris, REN21 Secretariat.

renewable fuel options. Others include wind, water, solar, and geothermal. Here, we focus on biofuels because of their connections to gasoline and diesel fuel, important players because as liquids, they can be pumped to fuel vehicles and aircraft. Later, in Chapter 8, we will discuss solar energy.

Currently and with good reason, biofuels are under debate. What principles should guide this debate? In April 2011, The Nuffield Council took up the challenge and issued a report that received wide attention: *Biofuels: Ethical Issues*. The introduction to this report plunged right into the controversies:

> While excitement over biofuels was still in full swing, important problems with their large-scale production began to emerge. The claims that biofuels produce significantly lower GHG [greenhouse gas] emissions compared with fossil fuels were contested. Concerns were also raised over the competition that biofuels pose to food production, and their consequent effects on food security and food prices. Moreover, many worried about infringements of the rights of farmers, farm workers and land holders, particularly in vulnerable populations in the developing world. There were also reports of severe environmental consequences, including pollution and the loss of biodiversity, for example through the destruction of rainforest, following large-scale biofuels production.

The report also listed moral values that apply to the use of biofuels: human rights, solidarity, sustainability, stewardship, and justice. From these values, ethical principles were constructed that could guide discussion, policy, and action (Table 4.6). While all of these principles warrant attention, two stand out as directly relevant to our discussion of the chemistry of biofuels: (1) a net reduction of greenhouse gas emissions and (2) the larger issues of environmental sustainability. We will address each in turn.

Do biofuels contribute to a net reduction of greenhouse gas emissions? To answer this question, remember that ethanol and biodiesel, like fossil fuels, contain carbon and thus produce carbon dioxide when burned. Try your hand at writing the combustion reactions in the next activity. Although the context is culinary, these chemical reactions also occur in automobile and truck engines.

> Based in the United Kingdom, the Nuffield Council has an international reputation for tackling ethical issues. As an independent agency, it is well-positioned to frame the debate on biofuels.

> "In the context of biofuels, the value of solidarity directs ethical attention to the most vulnerable people within societies, reminding us that we have a shared humanity, a shared life, and that those who are most vulnerable should be given special attention." (quoted from the Nuffield Report)

Your Turn 4.24   Cherries & Bananas

Have you ever been served cherries jubilee or bananas flambé? A chef first douses the fruit in brandy and then lights it with a match. The ethanol in brandy is what burns.

a. Write the chemical equation for the complete combustion of ethanol, that is, burning it with enough oxygen so that no carbon monoxide or soot is produced.

b. Although it wouldn't be very tasty, you also could pour cooking oil or biodiesel on fruit and set it afire. Write the chemical equation for the complete combustion of methyl stearate, $C_{19}H_{38}O_2$, the biodiesel product in equation 4.17.

From "field-to-tank," do ethanol and biodiesel contribute to a net reduction of the greenhouse gas CO_2? Here, the basis of comparison is with gasoline and diesel fuel derived from crude oil. These fossil fuels are not **carbon neutral,** that is, the CO_2 produced by their combustion is *not* offset by some natural process such as photosynthesis or by some human system of offsets. Burning fossil fuels leads to a net increase of CO_2 in the atmosphere.

In contrast, biofuels are potentially more carbon neutral because they are derived from modern-day crops, grasses, and trees. The carbon released on combustion of biofuels is at least partially offset by the carbon these plants once absorbed via photosynthesis. So where do biofuels stand in regard to reducing greenhouse gas emissions? The answer depends on the particular biofuel and how much energy was required to

Table 4.6	Ethical Principles to Apply to Current and Future Use of Biofuels

1. Biofuels development should not be at the expense of people's essential rights (including access to sufficient food and water, health rights, work rights and land entitlements).

2. Biofuels should be environmentally sustainable.

3. Biofuels should contribute to a net reduction of total greenhouse gas emissions and not exacerbate global climate change.

4. Biofuels should develop in accordance with trade principles that are fair and recognize the rights of people to just reward (including labor rights and intellectual property rights).

5. Costs and benefits of biofuels should be distributed in an equitable way.

6. If the first five Principles are respected and if biofuels can play a crucial role in mitigating dangerous climate change, then depending on additional key considerations, there is a duty to develop such biofuels. These additional key considerations are: absolute cost; alternative energy sources; opportunity costs; the existing degree of uncertainty; irreversibility; degree of participation; and the notion of proportionate governance.

Source: Nuffield Council on Bioethics, Biofuels: Ethical Issues, 2011, 84.

produce it, including the energy in producing the fertilizers and watering the crops. This is a moving target because, at least in some cases, the technologies have been improving with time.

Measuring the net reduction in CO_2 emissions for biofuels is challenging and controversial. To understand why, we again cite information from the Nuffield Council report on the ethics of biofuels.

- **Direct change in the use of land**
  This refers to converting natural land to cropland, such as deforestation or draining wetlands. Destroying existing natural lands to produce biofuels means removing an existing habitat that effectively sequesters a large amount of carbon and degrades the existing soil and vegetation. The challenge comes in determining both how much carbon is sequestered and by which land types.

- **Indirect change in the use of land**
  This refers to converting existing pastures or croplands to crops for biofuels. This switch can involve using more fertilizer, more herbicides, and more water, all accompanied by energy use and additional greenhouse gas emissions. The challenge comes in measuring these over the life cycle of a biofuel crop.

- **Waste products from biofuel production**
  This refers to agricultural and industrial wastes that have no value for food or fuel. The challenge comes not only in measuring the greenhouse emissions, but also in assigning the emissions correctly to their source.

In spite of the inherent challenges, several constituencies have proposed values for the CO_2 emissions. In 2011, the biofuel industry estimated 10–15% less CO_2 emissions for corn-based ethanol and 40–45% less CO_2 from soybean-based biodiesel. Both values were in comparison to petroleum-based gasoline. In contrast, other groups propose that biofuels result in net increases of CO_2 compared to petroleum-based gasoline, arguing that costs of land use and waste products needed to be more carefully accounted for. The debates are likely to continue, given the complexities in correctly assigning the CO_2 emissions to produce a fuel.

Are ethanol and biodiesel sustainable? Like the previous question of greenhouse gas emissions, this one cannot be answered in the abstract. Rather, the answers depend on where and how each particular biofuel is produced.

Let's begin with the tally for biodiesel because it is somewhat more straightforward than that of ethanol. Recall that biodiesel has several inherent advantages over ethanol. Its synthesis from oils is relatively easy and can be done either in small batches or large scale. Biodiesel blends well with existing diesel fuel and can be distributed via the same infrastructure. Like ethanol and because it contains oxygen, it burns more cleanly than diesel fuel releasing lower amounts of particulate matter, carbon monoxide, and volatile organic compounds. In the balance, it seems to be a winner for improving

(a)   (b)

Figure 4.29

(a) Palm oil plantation in Malaysia (young trees shown); (b) Palm oil factory in Malaysia.

public health, assuming that ethical principles (Table 4.6) have been followed for the local communities that produce biofuel. But can we assume this? Figure 4.29 shows a plantation and factory in Indonesia, one part of the world where palm oil is produced. The next activity offers the opportunity to further explore palm oil production.

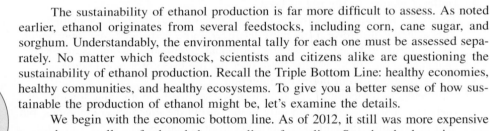

Consider This 4.25   Palm Oil, Biodiesel, and Ethics

Are there ethical issues with biodiesel that need attention? In 2008, an Oxfam report noted: "The big losers from the rich countries' biofuel boom are poor people, at risk from spiraling food prices, and a 'scramble to supply' that places their land rights, labor rights, and human rights under threat."

Use palm oil as a case study. It is produced in many parts of the world, including Indonesia and Malaysia. Prepare a one-page briefing that identifies the key issues for your classmates.

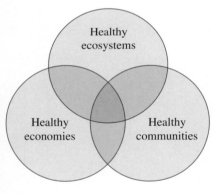

The sustainability of ethanol production is far more difficult to assess. As noted earlier, ethanol originates from several feedstocks, including corn, cane sugar, and sorghum. Understandably, the environmental tally for each one must be assessed separately. No matter which feedstock, scientists and citizens alike are questioning the sustainability of ethanol production. Recall the Triple Bottom Line: healthy economies, healthy communities, and healthy ecosystems. To give you a better sense of how sustainable the production of ethanol might be, let's examine the details.

We begin with the economic bottom line. As of 2012, it still was more expensive to produce a gallon of ethanol than a gallon of gasoline. So why the booming corn ethanol market? The answer varies by locale. In recent years, the U.S. government provided tax credits to ethanol producers. Although subsidies have encouraged the use of this fuel, they were controversial and ended in 2011 for ethanol produced from corn.

In terms of energy costs, the good news is that the Sun freely provides the energy for plants to grow. The bad news, however, is that growing corn requires additional energy inputs. Planting, cultivating, and harvesting all require energy. The same is true for watering the crops, producing and applying the fertilizers, manufacturing and maintaining the necessary farm equipment, and distilling the alcohol from the fermented grains. Currently, this energy is supplied by burning fossil fuels at a significant monetary cost and with significant carbon dioxide emissions. The overall energy cost for corn ethanol is difficult to quantify. Some studies estimate that for every joule put into ethanol production, 1.2 J is recovered. Others contend that the combined energy inputs outweigh the energy content of the ethanol produced.

Next, we consider the social bottom line. Many rural communities in the Midwest have benefited greatly from booming ethanol demand. Construction of a distillery provides not only jobs to local workers, but also a buyer for locally grown corn. Several communities, hit hard by the depressed viability of family farms, have experienced a resurgence thanks to demand for ethanol. There are certain drawbacks as well. Increased demand for corn leads to increased prices on many other products (especially foods); prices that everyone in that community (and others around the world) must pay.

Last, we turn to the environmental bottom line. Growing corn relies on the heavy use of fertilizers, herbicides, and insecticides. The manufacturing and transport of these chemicals requires the burning of fossil fuels, which in turn releases carbon dioxide. Furthermore, these chemicals, once introduced to the field, degrade the soil and water quality. Although corn growers can and do follow responsible practices, they certainly face challenges when called on to produce more corn.

Where to go from here? Clearly the choices are not easy. We have burned our way through many of the easy and conventional sources of oil. Our future choices are complex and involve trade-offs. We end this chapter by returning to words from the Nuffield Report. They call to mind the **precautionary principle** articulated in earlier chapters, reminding us that both to act and not to act carry risks. We hope these words not only will inspire you but also lead you to further investigate the issues and take action with appropriate caution.

The precautionary principle, discussed in Chapter 2, stresses the wisdom of acting, even in the absence of full scientific data, before the adverse effects to human health or the environment become significant or irreversible.

Exhorting people to make lifestyle changes will, of course, continue to be one approach to overall reduction of greenhouse gas emissions. However, this and other non-fuel-based power sources such as wind, wave and solar energy will not be sufficient to reduce global dependence on fossil fuels for the foreseeable future.

We will need new sources of liquid fuels and new ways of producing current biofuels more efficiently, and advanced biotechnology, including genetic modification, could be an important part of the tool kit to help deliver on these needs.

Precautionary safeguards have already been built in to the development of advanced biotechnologies and this will not present any new hazards. Indeed, it is important that precautionary approaches are implemented in a balanced and equitable way—we should be as precautionary about the risks of doing nothing as we are about the risks of developing new technologies. (Biofuels: Ethical Issues, Nuffield Council on Bioethics, 2011)

Consider This 4.26   A Sustainable Future

In 2002, then Secretary General of the United Nations, Kofi Annan, called sustainability ". . . an exceptional opportunity—economically to build markets, socially to bring people in from the margins, and politically to reduce tensions over resources that could give every man and woman a voice and a choice in deciding their own future." Expand on the Secretary General's remarks, giving some specifics for each area mentioned.

Conclusion

Fire! To early humans, fire was a source of security. It warded off animals, brought the ability to cook and preserve food, and minimized the spread of some diseases. Fires were an important social vehicle, a place to gather and share stories. Fire also allowed people to venture into colder regions of the planet.

Today, combustion still remains central to our human community. We use it daily to cook; to heat or cool our dwellings; to produce goods and crops; and to travel the roads, rails, waterways, and skies of our planet. Few chemical reactions have as far-reaching consequences for our health, well-being, and productivity as the ability to burn fuels.

As we have seen in this chapter, the process of combustion converts energy into less useful forms. For example, when we burn a mixture of hydrocarbons such as gasoline, we dissipate some of the potential (chemical) energy it contains in the form of heat. Although the *forms* of energy change, the total amount of energy before and after any transformation remains the same.

We have also seen that the process of combustion converts matter into less useful and sometimes even undesirable forms. For example, the products of complete combustion—carbon dioxide and water—are not usable as fuels. Furthermore, CO_2 is a greenhouse gas linked to global climate change. Products of incomplete combustion such as carbon monoxide and soot are undesirable because of their effects on human health. The same is true for the air pollutant NO that is formed in the high temperatures of flames.

Today, fossil fuels power the planet. So do renewable fuels, but to a much smaller extent. What will we use for energy sources tomorrow? Renewable biofuels such as ethanol and biodiesel will compose part of our energy future. Like all fuels, they need to align with our values, including stewardship and sustainability. Other possible ways of satisfying our ever-increasing appetite for energy include nuclear energy (Chapter 7) and solar energy (Chapter 8).

Recall the definition of sustainability from Chapter 0, "meeting the needs of the present without compromising the ability of future generations to meet their needs." We need the talents and good will of people in all walks of life to help create a sustainable society.

Chapter Summary

Having studied this chapter, you should be able to:

- Name the fossil fuels, describe the characteristics of each, and compare them in terms of how cleanly they burn and how much energy they produce (4.1–4.7)

- Apply the value of intergenerational justice to a discussion of energy choices, including fossil fuels and biofuels (4.0–4.2, 4.9–4.11)

- Explain how fossil fuels, photosynthesis, and the Sun are connected (4.1)

- Diagram the energy relationships between photosynthesis and combustion (4.1)

- Evaluate fossil fuels as a sustainable source of energy (4.1–4.7)

- Describe the process by which electricity is generated from the combustion of fossil fuels, listing each step in energy transformation (4.1)

- Compare and contrast kinetic energy and potential energy, both on the macroscopic and molecular level (4.1)

- Apply the concept of entropy to explain the second law of thermodynamics (4.2)

- Comment on the different grades of coal and how they connect to the environmental, economic, and social viability of coal (4.3)

- Describe "clean coal technologies" and comment on their viability, long-term and short (4.3)

- Explain the concept of a functional group and give three examples of compounds that are alcohols (4.4, 4.9)

- Explain how and why petroleum is refined (4.4)

- List the different fractions obtained by distilling petroleum. Compare and contrast these in terms of their chemical composition, chemical properties, boiling points, and end uses. (4.4)

- Describe how hydraulic fracturing ("fracking") is done, what it produces, and why it is controversial (4.4)

- Apply the terms *endothermic* and *exothermic* to chemical reactions based on calculations or chemical intuition (4.5)

- Calculate energy changes in reactions using bond energies (4.6)

- Assess how gasoline additives affect fuel economy, tailpipe emissions, human health, and the environment (4.7)

- Understand activation energy and catalysts and describe how these relate to reaction rates (4.8)

- Give examples of biofuels and describe what they all have in common (4.9)

- Differentiate between these terms: cellulose, starch, glucose, ethanol (4.9)

- Explain why there are several routes to the production of ethanol, some more sustainable than others (4.9)

- Compare and contrast ethanol with gasoline in terms of chemical composition, energy released on combustion, and solubility with water (4.9)

- Differentiate between these terms: fat, oil, triglyceride, biodiesel (4.10)

- Compare and contrast biodiesel with diesel fuel in terms of chemical composition, energy released on combustion, and energy required to produce (4.10)

- Compare ethanol and biodiesel in terms of source, chemical composition, ability to burn as a fuel, and promise as an alternative to fossil fuels (4.11)

- Take an informed stand on various energy conservation measures, including to what extent they are likely to produce energy savings (4.11)

Questions

Emphasizing Essentials

1. a. List five fuels. Name at least two properties that these fuels share.

   b. Of the fuels you listed, which are fossil fuels or derived from them?

   c. Of the fuels you listed, which are renewable?

2. The combustion of coal releases several substances into the air.

   a. Of these substances, one is a gas that is produced in large amounts. Give its chemical formula and name.

   b. In contrast, the amount of SO_2 (sulfur dioxide) released is relatively small. Even so, this SO_2 is of concern. Explain why.

c. Another gas produced in small amounts is NO (nitrogen monoxide). However, coal contains very little nitrogen. What is the origin of the nitrogen in NO?

d. When coal burns, fine particles of soot may be released. What are the health concerns with $PM_{2.5}$, the smallest of these particles?

3. This figure, reproduced from the first section of the chapter, depicts an electric power plant.

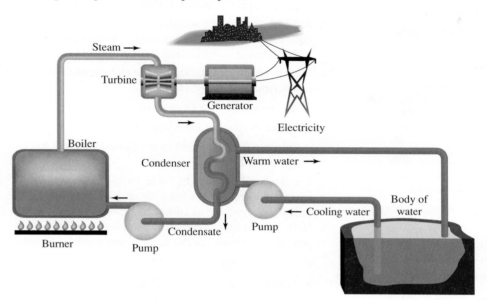

a. For a coal-fired power plant, where would the coal appear in this figure?

b. Water is part of two separate loops. One loop connects the boiler and turbine and is usually under pressure. Explain why.

c. Another loop brings in (and out) water from a lake or river. Explain why a large body of water is needed.

4. Energy exists in different forms in our natural world. In the figure shown in Question 3, identify where:

a. Potential (chemical) energy of the fuel is converted to heat.

b. Kinetic energy of water molecules is converted to mechanical energy.

c. Mechanical energy is converted to electrical energy.

d. Electrical energy is converted into forms such as heat and light.

5. A coal-burning power plant generates electrical power at a rate of 500 megawatts (MW), or 5.00×10^8 J/s. The plant has an overall efficiency of 37.5% (0.375) for the conversion of heat to electricity.

a. Calculate the electrical energy (in joules) generated in 1 year of operation and the heat energy used for that purpose.

b. Assuming the power plant burns coal that releases 30 kJ/g, calculate the mass of coal (in grams and metric tons) that is burned in 1 year of operation. *Hint:* 1 metric ton = 1×10^3 kg = 1×10^6 g.

6. The energy of sunlight can be converted into the potential (chemical) energy of glucose and oxygen.

a. Name the process by which this conversion occurs.

b. Name three fuels whose energy originates in sunlight.

7. Describe how grades of coal differ. What is the significance of these differences?

8. Although coal is an important fuel for producing electricity, it also has drawbacks. Name three of these.

9. Mercury (Hg) is present in trace amounts in coal, ranging from 50–200 ppb. Consider the amount of coal burned by the power plant in Your Turn 4.8. Calculate tons of mercury in the coal based on the lower (50 ppb) and higher (200 ppb) concentrations.

10. Name two ways in which all hydrocarbons are alike. Then name two ways in which they differ.

11. Here are the condensed structural formulas for two alkanes: CH_3CH_3 and $CH_3(CH_2)_2CH_3$.

a. What are the names for these compounds?

b. For each one, give the chemical formula and draw a structural formula that shows all bonds and atoms.

c. Comment on the relative advantages of chemical formulas, condensed structural formulas, and structural formulas in terms of convenience and information provided.

12. The structural formulas of straight-chain ("normal") alkanes containing 1 to 8 carbon atoms are given in Table 4.2.

a. Draw a structural formula for *n*-decane, $C_{10}H_{22}$.

b. Predict the chemical formula for *n*-nonane (9 C atoms) and for *n*-dodecane (12 C atoms).

13. Here is a ball-and-stick representation for one isomer of butane (C_4H_{10}).

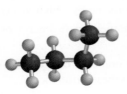

a. Draw a structural formula for this isomer.

b. Draw structural formulas for all other isomers. Watch out for duplicate structures.

14. Consider these three hydrocarbons.

Compound, Formula	Melting Point (°C)	Boiling Point (°C)
pentane, C_5H_{12}	−130	36
triacontane, $C_{30}H_{62}$	66	450
propane, C_3H_8	−188	−42

At room temperature (20 °C), categorize each one as a solid, liquid, or gas.

15. During petroleum distillation, kerosene and hydrocarbons with 12–18 carbons used for diesel fuel condense at position C marked on this diagram.

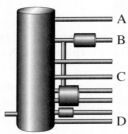

a. Separating hydrocarbons by distillation depends on differences in a specific physical property. Which one?

b. How does the number of carbon atoms in the hydrocarbon molecules separated at A, B, and D compare with those separated at position C? Explain your reasoning.

c. How do the uses of the hydrocarbons separated at A, B, and D differ from those separated at position C? Explain your reasoning.

16. The complete combustion of methane is given in equation 4.3.

a. By analogy, write a chemical equation for the combustion of ethane, C_2H_6.

b. Rewrite this equation using Lewis structures.

c. The heat of combustion for ethane, C_2H_6, is 52 kJ/g. How much heat is produced if 1.0 mol of ethane undergoes complete combustion?

17. a. Write the chemical equation for the complete combustion of *n*-heptane, C_7H_{16}.

b. The heat of combustion for *n*-heptane is 4817 kJ/mol. How much heat is released if 250 kg of *n*-heptane burns completely to produce CO_2 and H_2O?

18. A single serving bag of potato chips has 70 Cal (70 kcal). Assuming that all of the energy from eating these chips goes toward keeping your heart beating, how long can these chips sustain a heartbeat of 80 beats per minute? *Note:* 1 kcal = 4.184 kJ, and each human heart beat requires approximately 1 J of energy.

19. A 12-oz serving of a soft drink has an energy equivalent of 92 kcal. In kilojoules, what is the energy released when metabolizing this beverage?

20. State whether these processes are endothermic or exothermic.

a. Charcoal burns in an outdoor grill.

b. Water evaporates from your skin.

c. Glucose is synthesized in the leaves of a plant by photosynthesis.

21. Use the bond energies in Table 4.4 to calculate the energy changes associated with each of these reactions. Label each reaction as endothermic or exothermic. *Hint:* Draw Lewis structures of the reactants and products to determine the number and kinds of bonds.

a. $N_2(g) + 3\,H_2(g) \longrightarrow 2\,NH_3(g)$

b. $H_2(g) + Cl_2(g) \longrightarrow 2\,HCl(g)$

22. Use the bond energies in Table 4.4 to calculate the energy changes associated with each of these reactions. Label each reaction as endothermic or exothermic.

a. $2\,H_2(g) + CO(g) \longrightarrow CH_3OH(g)$

b. $H_2(g) + O_2(g) \longrightarrow H_2O_2(g)$

c. $2\,BrCl(g) \longrightarrow Br_2(g) + Cl_2(g)$

23. Ethanol can be produced by fermentation. Another way to produce ethanol is the reaction of water vapor with ethene (ethylene), a hydrocarbon containing a C=C:

$$CH_2CH_2(g) + H_2O(g) \longrightarrow CH_3CH_2OH(l)$$

a. Rewrite this equation using Lewis structures.

b. Use the bond energies in Table 4.4 to calculate the energy change for this reaction. Is the reaction endothermic or exothermic?

24. Here are structural formulas for ethane, ethene (ethylene), and ethanol.

H   H   H   H
| | H   H | |
H—C—C—H   \   /   H—C—C—O—H
| | C=C | |
H   H   /   \   H   H
                        H   H

ethane   ethene   ethanol

a. Is ethane an isomer of ethene? Of ethanol? Explain.

b. Are any other isomers possible for ethene? Explain.

c. Are any other isomers possible for ethanol? Explain.

25. These three compounds all have the same chemical formula of C_8H_{18}. The hydrogen atoms and C–H bonds have been omitted for simplicity.

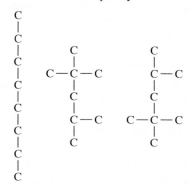

   a. For each compound, draw structural formulas that show the missing H atoms. All should have 18 H atoms.

   b. Which (if any) of these structural formulas are identical?

   c. Draw the structural formulas for any two additional isomers of C_8H_{18}.

26. Catalysts speed up cracking reactions in oil refining and allow them to be carried out at lower temperatures. Describe two other examples of catalysts given in the first three chapters of this text.

27. Explain why cracking is a necessary part of the refinement of crude oil.

28. Consider this equation representing the process of cracking.

$$C_{16}H_{34} \longrightarrow C_5H_{12} + C_{11}H_{22}$$

   a. Which bonds are broken and which bonds are formed in this reaction? Use Lewis structures to help answer this question.

   b. Use the information from part **a** and Table 4.4 to calculate the energy change during this cracking reaction.

29. What is a biofuel? Give three examples.

30. Consider these three alcohols: methanol, ethanol, and *n*-propanol (the straight-chain isomer).

   a. These compounds all contain a common functional group. Name it.

   b. These compounds all are flammable. Give names and chemical formulas for the products.

   c. Predict which one of these compounds has the lowest boiling point. Explain your reasoning.

   d. The chemical structure of one of these compounds is somewhat similar to glycerol. Which one and why? *Hint:* The structure for glycerol is shown in equation 4.18.

31. Cellulose and starch both can be fermented to produce ethanol.

   a. In terms of chemical structure, how are starch and cellulose similar?

   b. In terms of a food source for humans, how are starch and cellulose different?

32. When glucose, $C_6H_{12}O_6$, is "burned" (metabolized) in your body, the products are carbon dioxide and water.

   a. Write the balanced chemical equation.

   b. The chemical equation for burning wood is essentially the same as that of metabolizing glucose. Explain why.

33. As biofuels, biodiesel and ethanol warrant a close comparison. Use these parameters as the basis.

   a. The source

   b. The chemical reaction that produces the fuel

   c. The combustion products

   d. The solubility in water (more about this in Chapter 5)

34. Compare and contrast a molecule of biodiesel with a molecule of ethanol. Use these parameters as the basis of your comparison.

   a. The types of atoms each contains and their approximate relative proportions

   b. The number of atoms each contains

   c. The functional groups each contains

35. Use Figure 4.16 to compare the energy released for the combustion of 1 gallon of ethanol and 1 gallon of gasoline. Assume gasoline is pure octane (C_8H_{18}). Explain the difference.

36. Explain the terms *conventional* and *unconventional* with respect to crude oil as an energy source. Give an example of each.

Concentrating on Concepts

37. The sustainability of burning coal (and other fossil fuels) to produce electricity involves more than just the availability of coal. Explain.

38. In this chapter, we approximated the chemical formula of coal as $C_{135}H_{96}O_9NS$. However, we also noted that low-grade lignite (soft coal) has a chemical composition more similar to wood. Cellulose is a primary component in wood. Given this, predict an approximate chemical formula for lignite.

39. Use Figure 4.6 to compare the sources of U.S. energy consumption. Arrange the sources in order of decreasing percentage and comment on the relative rankings.

40. Compare the processes of combustion and photosynthesis in terms of energy released or absorbed, chemicals involved, and ability to remove CO_2 from the atmosphere.

41. How might you explain the difference between temperature and heat to a friend? Use some practical, everyday examples.

42. Write a response to this statement: "Because of the first law of thermodynamics, there can never be an energy crisis."

43. The concept of entropy and probability is used in games like poker. Describe how the rank of hands (from a simple high card to a royal flush) is related to entropy and probability.

44. Bond energies such as those in Table 4.4 are sometimes found by "working backward" from heats of reaction. A reaction is carried out, and the heat absorbed or evolved is measured. From this value and known bond energies, other bond energies can be calculated. For example, the energy change associated with the combustion of formaldehyde (H_2CO) is -465 kJ/mol.

$$H_2CO(g) + O_2(g) \longrightarrow CO_2(g) + H_2O(g)$$

Use this information and the values found in Table 4.4 to calculate the energy of the C=O double bond in formaldehyde. Compare your answer with the C=O bond energy in CO_2 and speculate on why there is a difference.

45. Use the bond energies in Table 4.4 to explain why chlorofluorocarbons (CFCs) are so stable. Also explain why it takes less energy to release Cl atoms from CFCs than it does to release F atoms and connect this to HFCs as replacements for CFCs.

46. Halons are similar to CFCs but also contain bromine. Although halons are excellent materials for fighting fires, they more effectively deplete ozone than CFCs. Here is the Lewis structure for Halon-1211.

$$:\ddot{B}r:$$
$$|$$
$$:\ddot{F}-C-\ddot{F}:$$
$$|$$
$$:\ddot{C}l:$$

   a. Which bond in this compound is broken most easily? How is that related to the ability of this compound to deplete ozone?

   b. In fire extinguishers, C_2HClF_4 is a possible replacement for halons. Draw its Lewis structure and identify the bond broken most easily.

47. The energy content of fuels can be expressed in kilojoules per gram (kJ/g), as shown in Figure 4.16. From these values, how do fuels containing oxygen compare to those that do not? Now calculate the energy content for each of these fuels in kilojoules per mole (kJ/mol). What trend do you now observe?

  Figures Alive! See Figures Alive! for related activities

48. A friend tells you that hydrocarbon fuels containing larger molecules liberate more heat per gram than those with smaller ones.

   a. Use these data, together with appropriate calculations, to discuss the merits of this statement.

Hydrocarbon	Heat of Combustion
octane, C_8H_{18}	5070 kJ/mol
butane, C_4H_{10}	2658 kJ/mol

   b. Based on your answer to part **a**, do you expect the heat of combustion per gram of candle wax, $C_{25}H_{52}$, to be more or less than that of octane? Do you expect the molar heat of combustion of candle wax to be more or less than that of octane? Justify your predictions.

49. The Fischer–Tropsch conversion of hydrogen and carbon monoxide into hydrocarbons and water was given in equation 4.11:

$$n\ CO + (2n + 1)\ H_2 \longrightarrow C_nH_{2n+2} + n\ H_2O$$

   a. Determine the heat evolved by this reaction when $n = 1$.

   b. Without doing a calculation, do you think that more or less energy is given off per mole in the formation of larger hydrocarbons ($n > 1$)? Explain your reasoning.

50. Here is a ball-and-stick model of ethanol, C_2H_5OH or C_2H_6O.

   a. Dimethyl ether is an isomer of ethanol. Draw its Lewis structure.

   b. People used to refer to "ether" as an anesthetic. What they meant was diethyl ether. Draw its structural formula.

   c. The ether is a functional group not described in this chapter. Based on your answer to the two previous parts, what common structural feature do all ethers have?

51. Octane ratings of several substances are listed in Table 4.5.

   a. What evidence can you give that the octane rating is not a measure of the energy content of a gasoline?

   b. Octane ratings measure a fuel's ability to minimize or prevent engine knocking. Why is this important?

   c. Why do higher octane blends cost more than lower octane ones?

   d. A premium gasoline available at most stations has an octane rating of 91. What does this tell you about whether the fuel contains oxygenates?

52. Both *n*-octane and iso-octane have essentially the same heat of combustion. How is this possible given that they have different chemical structures?

53. All of these terms fit under the heading of fuels: renewable fuel, nonrenewable fuel, coal, petroleum, biodiesel, natural gas, and ethanol. Use a diagram to show the relationship among them. Also find a way to show where the terms *fossil fuel* and *biofuel* fit.

54. Use a diagram to show the relationship among these terms that relate to foods we eat: fat, lard, oil, triglyceride, butter, olive oil, and soybean oil. Although biodiesel is not a food, it still connects to these terms. Find a way to represent this connection.

55. On a timescale of a few years, the combustion of ethanol derived from biomass releases a *lower* net amount of CO_2 into the atmosphere than does burning gasoline derived from crude oil. People argue whether this statement is true or not. What is the point of contention?

56. Revisit the Six Key Ideas in Green Chemistry found on the inside of the front cover. Which of these are met by the synthesis by Suppes of propylene glycol from glycerol? *Hint:* See equation 4.18.

57. Emissions of some pollutants are lower when biodiesel is used rather than petroleum diesel. In the case of biodiesel fuel, suggest a reason for lower emissions of

    a. sulfur dioxide, SO_2

    b. carbon monoxide, CO

Exploring Extensions

58. Although coal contains only trace amounts of mercury, the amounts released into the environment by the burning of coal have significant consequences. Defend or refute this statement by gathering the appropriate evidence.

59. According to a statement once made by the U.S. EPA, driving a car is "a typical citizen's most polluting daily activity."

    a. What pollutants do cars emit? *Hint:* Information on automobile emissions provided by the EPA (together with the information in this text) can help you fully answer this question.

    b. What assumptions does the truth of this statement depend on?

60. An article in *Scientific American* pointed out that replacing a 75-watt incandescent bulb with an 18-watt compact fluorescent bulb would save about 75% in the cost of electricity. Electricity is generally priced per kilowatt-hour (kW-h). Using the price of electricity where you live, calculate how much money you would save over the life of one compact fluorescent bulb (about 10,000 h). Note: Standard incandescent bulbs last about 750 h.

61. C. P. Snow, a noted scientist and author, wrote an influential book called *The Two Cultures,* in which he stated: "The question, 'Do you know the second law of thermodynamics?' is the cultural equivalent of 'Have you read a work by Shakespeare?' " How do you react to this comparison? Discuss his remark in light of your own educational experiences.

62. This chapter mentions several nonconventional sources of oil and gas, including drilling deep below seawater, hydraulic fracturing deep below the Earth, and extracting oil from shales and tarry oil sands. Pick one, describe it, and provide an analysis using the Triple Bottom Line: economic health, environmental health, and societal health.

63. Chemical explosions are *very* exothermic reactions. Describe the relative bond strengths in the reactants and products that would make for a good explosion.

64. The chapter pointed out that the FDA approved propylene glycol for use as a food additive. In which foods is it used and for what purposes?

65. Tetraethyl lead (TEL) was first approved for use in gasoline in the United States in 1926. It wasn't banned until 1986. Construct a timeline that includes any four events in the 60 years of its use, including some that led to its ban.

66. Tetraethyl lead (TEL) has an octane rating of 270. How does this compare with other gasoline additives? Examine a structural formula for TEL and propose a reason for the value of its octane rating in comparison to other additives.

67. Another type of catalyst used in the combustion of fossil fuels is the catalytic converter that was discussed in Chapter 1. One of the reactions that these catalysts speed up is the conversion of $NO(g)$ to $N_2(g)$ and $O_2(g)$.

    a. Draw a diagram of the energy of this reaction similar to the one shown in Figure 4.20.

    b. Why is this reaction important?
    Hint: See Sections 1.9 and 1.11.

68. Figure 4.17 shows energy differences for the combustion of H_2, an exothermic chemical reaction. The combination of N_2 and O_2 to form NO (nitrogen monoxide) is an example of an endothermic reaction:

$$N_2(g) + O_2(g) \longrightarrow 2\ NO(g)$$

The bond energy for N=O is 630 kJ/mol. Sketch an energy diagram for this reaction and calculate the overall energy change. *Hint:* NO has an unpaired electron. One way to represent its Lewis structure is

$$:\dot{N}=\ddot{O}:$$

69. Because the United States has large natural gas reserves, there is significant interest in developing uses for this fuel. List two advantages and two disadvantages of using natural gas to fuel vehicles.

"Of all our natural resources, water has become the most precious."

Rachel Carson, *Silent Spring*, Houghton Mifflin Co., 1962, p. 39.

Neeru, shouei, maima, aqua. In any language, water is the most abundant compound on the surface of the Earth. Images from space remind us that we live on a planet with oceans, rivers, lakes, and ice covering more than 70% of Earth's surface. Water indeed is precious to life.

Although oceans are home to a wealth of plant and animal life, they are not hospitable to the creatures that dwell on land. As Rachel Carson noted in *Silent Spring*, "By far the greater part of the earth's surface is covered by its enveloping seas, yet in the midst of this plenty we are in want. By a strange paradox, most of the earth's abundant water is not usable for agriculture, industry, or human consumption because of its heavy load of sea salts." We who live on land need fresh water and must obtain it either through natural processes such as rain and snowfall or though energy-intensive water purification technologies.

Unfortunately, fresh water is not an unlimited resource on our planet. Furthermore, it is not renewable fast enough to meet the needs of our increasing world population. As a result, water has become a strategic resource. Its scarcity brews conflicts and raises questions of who has the right to access and use it. Recognizing the importance of water, in 1993 the United Nations General Assembly proclaimed March 22 as International World Water Day. Each year's theme connects water to a social issue, promoting sustainable management of freshwater resources.

Whether found in oceans, lakes, or rivers, water is a compound with unique properties. Some of these are important in understanding large-scale processes on our planet, such as weather and climate. For example, water is the only common substance that can exist as a solid, a liquid, or a gas at average Earth temperatures. In its three forms—ice, liquid water, and water vapor (humidity)—water affects both the daily weather of a region and, over a longer time span, the climate.

Other properties of water help protect ecosystems. For example, unlike most solids, ice is less dense than its liquid counterpart. Because ice floats on water, ecosystems in lakes and streams can survive beneath the ice during frigid winter days. Water also absorbs more heat per gram than most other substances, allowing bodies of water on Earth to serve as heat reservoirs. As a result, oceans and lakes change their temperatures slowly, acting to moderate temperature swings.

Still other properties of water are important for smaller scale processes. For example, water dissolves many substances. It is the essential medium for the biochemical reactions in the cells of all living species, including humans. Your body can go weeks without food but only days without water. If the water content in your body were reduced by 2%, you would get thirsty. With a 5% water loss, you would feel fatigue and have a headache. At a 10–15% loss your muscles would become spastic and you would feel delirious; greater than 15% dehydration will kill you.

Before we launch into the details, we ask that you first consider how water is part of your daily routine. You may sip from a tap, bottle, or can. You may steam some vegetables, wash laundry, or flush a toilet. Or you may sit by a river, casting for fish. The next activity gives you the opportunity to document how water plays a role in your life.

Scientists look for water when they search for life on other planets.

Scientist, conservationist, and author Rachel Carson helped launch the environmental movement with the publication of *Silent Spring*.

Examples of past World Water Day themes.

2010-Water Quality
2009-Transboundary Waters
2008-International Year of Sanitation
2007-Water Scarcity
1996-Water for Thirsty Cities
1995-Women and Water

The amount of water you drink daily depends on your size, age, health, and level of physical activity.

Consider This 5.1   Keep a Water Log

Pick a 12-hour waking segment of your day. Record all of your activities that involve water by time and activity. Also capture:

a. The role the water played in your life. For example, are you consuming it? Are you using it in some process? Is it part of your outdoor experience?
b. The source of the water, the quantity involved, and where it went afterward.
c. The degree to which you got the water dirty.

Consider This 5.2 — — — — — no

> ### Consider This 5.2   Beyond Toilets
>
> Flushing a toilet is just one part of your daily water routine. Select a water–use calculator available on the Internet and investigate further your daily indoor water use.
>
> a. What surprised you about your water use?
> b. How does this information relate to your water log from the previous activity?

According to the U.S. Geological Survey, over 390 liters (~100 gallons) of water per day are required to support the lifestyle of the average U.S. citizen. As you undoubtedly discovered in your water log, we use water for many purposes.

In this chapter, we explore many facets of water, including where clean water comes from, how we use it, and which issues relate to its use. We also will revisit the key ideas of green chemistry that relate to keeping water from getting dirty in the first place. We begin by taking a closer look at the properties of water to see why it is such a special substance on this, our wet planet.

A liter (L) contains 1000 milliliters (mL). One gallon is about 3.8 L.

5.1 | The Unique Properties of Water

Clearly, water is essential to our lives. What may not be as apparent is that water has a number of unusual properties. In fact, these properties are quite peculiar, and we are *very* fortunate that they are. If water were a more conventional compound, life as we know it could not exist.

Let us begin with its physical state. Water is a liquid at room temperature (about 25 °C, or 77 °F) and normal atmospheric pressure. This is surprising, because almost all other compounds with similar molar masses are gases under those conditions. Consider these three gases found in air: N_2, O_2, and CO_2. Their molar masses are 28, 32, and 44 g/mol, respectively, all greater than that of water (18 g/mol). Yet none of these are liquids!

For covalent substances, as the molar mass increases, the boiling point generally increases as well.

Not only is water a liquid under these conditions, but also it has an anomalously high boiling point of 100 °C (212 °F). When water freezes, it exhibits another somewhat bizarre property—it expands. Most liquids contract when they solidify.

These and other unusual properties derive from the molecular structure of water. First, recall the chemical formula of water, H_2O. This is probably the world's most widely known bit of chemical trivia. Next, recall that water is a covalently bonded molecule with a bent shape. Figure 5.1 shows the same representations of the water molecule that we used in Chapter 3.

Revisit Sections 2.3 and 3.3 for more information about the water molecule.

New to our discussion in this chapter is the fact that the electrons are not shared equally in the O—H covalent bond. Experimental evidence indicates that the O atom attracts the shared electron pair more strongly than does the H atom. In chemical language, oxygen is said to have a higher electronegativity than hydrogen. **Electronegativity** is a measure of the attraction of an atom for an electron in a chemical bond. The scale runs from about 0.7 to 4.0. The values have no units and are set relative to each other. The greater the electronegativity, the more an atom attracts the electrons in a chemical bond toward itself.

Electronegativity values were developed by the chemist, peace activist, and Nobel Prize winner, Linus Pauling (1901–1994).

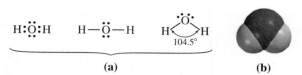

(a)   **(b)**

Figure 5.1

Representations of H_2O. **(a)** Lewis structures and structural formula; **(b)** Space–filling model.

Table 5.1	Electronegativity Values for Selected Elements						
1A	2A	3A	4A	5A	6A	7A	8A
H 2.1							He *
Li 1.0	Be 1.5	B 2.0	C 2.5	N 3.0	O 3.5	F 4.0	Ne *
Na 0.9	Mg 1.2	Al 1.5	Si 1.8	P 2.1	S 2.5	Cl 3.0	Ar *

*Noble gases rarely (if ever) bond to other elements

Table 5.1 shows electronegativity values for the first 18 elements. Examine it to see that:

- Fluorine and oxygen have the highest values.
- Metals such as lithium and sodium have low values.
- Values *increase* from left to right in a row of the periodic table (from metals to nonmetals) and *decrease* going down a group.

The greater the difference in electronegativity between two bonded atoms, the more polar the bond is. Accordingly, we can use electronegativity values to estimate bond polarities. For example, the electronegativity difference between oxygen and hydrogen is 1.4. The electrons in an O—H bond are pulled closer to the more electronegative oxygen atom. This unequal sharing results in a partial negative charge (δ^-) on the O atom and a partial positive charge (δ^+) on the H atom, as shown in Figure 5.2. An arrow is used to indicate the direction in which the electron pair is displaced. The result is a **polar covalent bond,** a covalent bond in which the electrons are not equally shared but rather are closer to the more electronegative atom. In contrast, a **nonpolar covalent bond** is a covalent bond in which the electrons are shared equally or nearly equally between atoms.

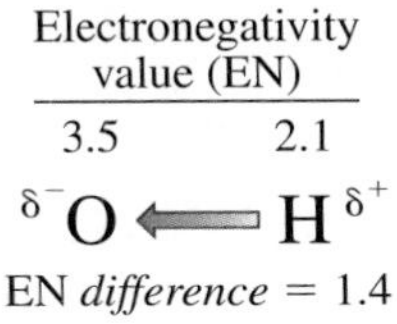

Electronegativity value (EN)

3.5   2.1

δ^-O ⟵══ Hδ^+

EN *difference* = 1.4

Figure 5.2

Representation of the polar covalent bond between a hydrogen and oxygen atom. The electrons are pulled toward the more electronegative oxygen atom.

If the electronegativity difference between two atoms is more than 1.0, the bond is considered polar covalent. If it is greater than 2.0, the bond is considered ionic. Use this information as a guideline rather than as a rule.

Your Turn 5.3   Polar Bonds

For each pair, which is the more polar bond? In the bond you select, the electron pair is more strongly attracted to one of the atoms. Which one? *Hint:* Use Table 5.1.

a. H—F or H—Cl
b. N—H or O—H
c. N—O or O—S
d. H—H or Cl—C

Answer
a. The H—F bond is more polar. The electron pair is more strongly attracted to the F atom.

We have made the case that bonds can be polar, some more than others. What about molecules? To help you predict if a molecule is polar, we offer two useful generalizations:

- A molecule that contains only nonpolar bonds *must be* nonpolar. For example, the Cl_2 and H_2 molecules are nonpolar.
- A molecule that contains polar covalent bonds *may or may not be* polar. The polarity depends on the geometry of the molecule.

For example, the water molecule contains two polar bonds, and the molecule is polar (Figure 5.3). Each H atom carries a partial positive charge (δ^+), and the oxygen atom carries a partial negative charge (δ^-). With these two polar bonds and a bent geometry, the water molecule is polar.

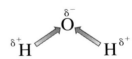

Figure 5.3

H_2O, a polar molecule with polar covalent bonds.

You can review why the water molecule is bent in Section 3.3.

Many of the unique properties of water are a consequence of its polarity. But before we continue the story of water, take a moment to complete this activity.

Consider This 5.4   The Carbon Dioxide Molecule

Revisit the carbon dioxide molecule. You can find its Lewis structure in Figure 3.14.

a. Are the covalent bonds in CO_2 polar or nonpolar? Use Table 5.1.
b. Analogous to Figure 5.3, draw a representation for CO_2.
c. In contrast to the H_2O molecule, the CO_2 molecule is *not* polar. Explain.

5.2 | The Role of Hydrogen Bonding

Consider what happens when two water molecules approach each other. Because opposite charges attract, a H atom (δ^+) on one of the water molecules is attracted to the O atom (δ^-) on the neighboring water molecule. This is an example of an **intermolecular force,** that is, a force that occurs between molecules.

But with more than two water molecules, the story gets more complicated. Examine each H_2O molecule in Figure 5.4 and note the two H atoms and two nonbonding pairs of electrons on the O atom. These allow for multiple intermolecular attractions. This set of attractions among molecules is called "hydrogen bonding." A **hydrogen bond** is an electrostatic attraction between a H atom bonded to a highly electronegative atom (O, N, or F) and a neighboring O, N, or F atom, either in another molecule or in a different part of the same molecule. Hydrogen bonds typically are only about one tenth as strong as the covalent bonds connecting atoms *within* molecules. Also, the atoms involved in hydrogen bonding are farther apart than they are in covalent bonds. In liquid water there may be three or four hydrogen bonds per water molecule, as shown in Figure 5.4.

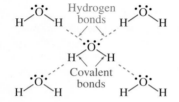

Figure 5.4

Hydrogen bonding in water (distances not to scale).

( ) Figures Alive!

Compare:

- *Intermolecular* forces are *between* molecules whereas *intramolecular* forces are *within* molecules.

- *Intercollegiate* sports are played *between* colleges whereas *intracollegiate* sports are played *within* colleges.

Sulfur is less electronegative than oxygen and nitrogen. Although H atoms bonded to N or O atoms can form hydrogen bonds, H atoms bonded to S atoms cannot.

Your Turn 5.5   Bonding in Water

a. Explain the dashed lines between water molecules in Figure 5.4.
b. In the same figure, label the atoms on two adjacent water molecules with δ^+ or δ^-. How do these partial charges help to explain the orientation of the molecules?
c. Are hydrogen bonds intermolecular or intramolecular forces? Explain.

Although hydrogen bonds are not as strong as covalent bonds, hydrogen bonds still are quite strong compared with other types of intermolecular forces. The boiling point of water gives us evidence for this assertion. For example, consider H_2S, a molecule that is analogous to water but does not hydrogen bond. H_2S boils at about -60 °C and so is a gas at room temperature. In contrast, water boils at 100 °C. Because of hydrogen bonding, water is a liquid at room temperature as well as at body temperature (about 37 °C). Life's very existence on our planet depends on this fact.

Consider This 5.6   Bonds Within and Between Water Molecules

Are any covalent bonds broken when water boils? Explain with drawings.
Hint: Start with molecules of water in the liquid state as shown in Figure 5.4. Make a second drawing to show water in the vapor phase.

Hydrogen bonding also can help you understand why ice cubes and icebergs float. Ice is a regular array of water molecules in which every H_2O molecule is hydrogen-bonded to four others. The pattern is shown in Figure 5.5. Note the empty space in the form of hexagonal channels. When ice melts, the pattern is lost, and individual H_2O

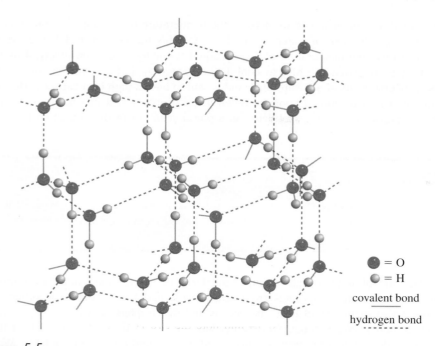

= O
= H

covalent bond

hydrogen bond

Figure 5.5

The hydrogen–bonded lattice structure of the common form of ice. Note the open channels between "layers" of water molecules that cause ice to be less dense than water.

molecules can enter the open channels. As a result, the molecules in the liquid state are more closely packed than in the solid state. Thus, a volume of one cubic centimeter (1 cm^3) of liquid water contains more molecules than 1 cm^3 of ice. Consequently, liquid water has a greater mass per cubic centimeter than ice. This is simply another way of saying that the **density,** the mass per unit volume, of liquid water is greater than that of ice.

People often confuse density with mass. For example, popcorn has a low density, and people say that a bag of popcorn feels "light." Similarly, you may hear someone say that lead is "heavy." Large pieces of lead are indeed often quite heavy, but it is more accurate to say that lead has a high density (11.3 g/cm^3).

We usually express the mass of water in grams. Expressing its volume is a bit trickier. We use either cubic centimeters or milliliters (mL)—the two units are equivalent. The density of water is 1.00 g/cm^3 at 4 °C and varies only slightly with temperature. So for convenience, we sometimes say that 1 cm^3 of water has a mass of 1 g. On the other hand, 1.00 cm^3 of ice has a mass of 0.92 g, so its density is 0.92 g/cm^3. The bottom line? The ice cubes in your favorite beverage float rather than sink.

Unlike water, most substances are denser as solids. The fact that water shows the reverse behavior means that in the winter, ice floats on lakes rather than sinking. This topsy-turvy behavior means that surface ice, often covered by snow, can act as an insulator and keep the lake water beneath from freezing solid. Aquatic plants and fish thus can live in a freshwater lake during cold winters. And when the ice melts in spring, the water formed sinks, helping to mix the nutrients in the freshwater ecosystem. Needless to say, water's unique behavior has implications both for the biological sciences and for life itself.

The phenomenon of hydrogen bonding is not restricted to water. It can occur in other molecules that contain covalent O—H or N—H bonds. The hydrogen bonds help stabilize the shape of large biological molecules, such as proteins and nucleic acids. For example, the double-helix structure of the DNA molecule is stabilized by hydrogen bonds between the two DNA strands. When DNA undergoes transcription, it "unzips" as the hydrogen bonds across the two strands break. Again, hydrogen bonding plays an essential role in the processes of life.

We end this section by examining one last unusual property of water, its uncommonly high capacity to absorb and release heat. **Specific heat** is the quantity of heat

For any liquid at any temperature, 1 cm^3 = 1 mL

To reiterate, water is most dense at 4 °C. At 0 °C, it is slightly less dense.

DNA molecules form hydrogen bonds between *different* strands of DNA. In contrast, proteins can form hydrogen bonds within different regions within the *same* molecule. Look for more about the structures of proteins and DNA in Chapter 12.

energy that must be absorbed to increase the temperature of 1 gram of a substance by 1 °C. The specific heat of water is 4.18 J/g · °C. This means that 4.18 J of energy is needed to raise the temperature of 1 g of liquid water by 1 °C. Conversely, 4.18 J of heat must be removed in order to cool 1 g of water by 1 °C. Water has one of the highest specific heats of any substance and is said to have a high heat capacity. Because of this, it is an exceptional coolant. When water evaporates, it can be used to carry away the excess heat in a car radiator, in a power plant, or in the human body.

The joule and the calorie, units of energy, were defined in Section 4.2. The specific heat of water can also be expressed (using calories) as 1.00 cal/g · °C.

Consider This 5.7   A Barefoot Excursion

Have you ever walked barefoot across a carpeted floor and then onto a tile or stone floor? If not, try it and see what you notice. Based on your observation, does carpet or tile have the higher heat capacity?

Because of water's high specific heat, large bodies of water influence regional climate. When water evaporates from seas, rivers, and lakes, heat is absorbed. By absorbing vast quantities of heat, the oceans and the droplets of water in clouds help moderate global temperatures. Since water has a higher capacity to "store" heat than the ground does, when the weather turns cold, the ground cools more quickly. Water retains more heat and is able to provide more warmth for a longer time to the areas bordering it. Such properties should be familiar to anyone who has ever lived near a large body of water.

We have just examined some of the critical properties of water that influence life on our planet. Before we explore its ability to dissolve many different substances, we seek a broader picture of where water comes from, how we use it, and which issues are related to its use.

5.3 | The Water We Drink and Use

Just as we need clean, unpolluted air to breathe, we also need **potable water**, that is, water safe for drinking and cooking. We also may bathe and wash dishes with potable water. In contrast, nonpotable water contains contaminants that include particulates from dirt, toxic metals such as arsenic, or bacteria that cause cholera. Although not drinkable, nonpotable water still has its uses. For example, water from rivers or lakes may be hauled in trucks (Figure 5.6a) and used to wash sidewalks, to reduce roadway dust, or to irrigate.

A devastating cholera outbreak followed the 2010 earthquake that leveled Port–au–Prince, Haiti.

(a)

(b)

Figure 5.6
(a) Water truck at the University of Alaska, Fairbanks, with a warning that the water is not fit to drink.
(b) Reclaimed water is pumped in purple pipes.

If first treated at a municipal water plant, nonpotable water finds additional uses. This reclaimed water, sometimes called recycled water, is distributed to communities through "purple pipes," as shown in Figure 5.6b. It can be used to irrigate athletic fields, flush toilets, or fight fires. To keep water flowing, community water utilities match the type of water available with its best use.

Look for more about water treatment in Section 5.11.

Consider This 5.8   Matching Form to Function

In some communities, reclaimed or recycled (nonpotable) water is used to wash cars, water gardens, and flush toilets.

a. List three other activities for which nonpotable water could be used.
b. What conditions might prompt a community to use nonpotable water?
c. Does your community use reclaimed or recycled water? Find out for which purposes, if any.

Where is fresh water found on our planet? The most convenient source for human activities is **surface water,** the fresh water found in lakes, rivers, and streams (Figure 5.7). Less convenient to access is **groundwater,** fresh water found in underground reservoirs also known as aquifers. People worldwide pump groundwater from wells drilled deep into these underground reservoirs. Fresh water is also found in our atmosphere in the form of mists, fogs, and humidity.

How much of the water on our planet is fresh water? Amazingly, only about 3%; the remainder is salt water. Although not shown in Figure 5.8, about two thirds of this fresh water is locked up in glaciers, ice caps, and snowfields. Additionally, about 30% is found underground and must be pumped to the surface in order to use it.

Lakes, rivers, and wetlands account for a mere 0.3% of the fresh water. Think of it this way. If all the water on our planet were represented by the contents of a 2-L bottle, only 60 mL of this would be fresh water. The water easily accessible to us in lakes and rivers would be about four drops!

Seawater is drinkable only if we remove its salt through a process called desalination. Look for more about desalination in Section 5.12.

Skeptical Chemist 5.9   A Drop to Drink

We just stated that 4 drops in 2 liters corresponds to the amount of fresh water available for our use. Is this accurate? Make a determination of your own.
Hint: Use the relationships shown in Figure 5.8 and assume 20 drops per milliliter.

Figure 5.7
Lakes and reservoirs provide much of our drinking water. This one, Hetch Hetchy, provides water to San Francisco, California.

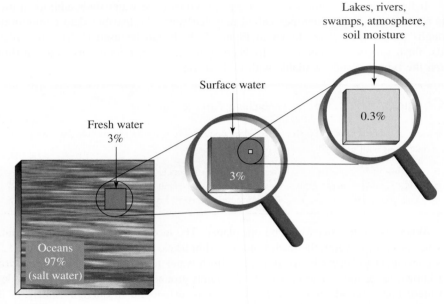

Figure 5.8
The distribution of fresh water on Earth.

How do we use fresh water? Predictably, the answer depends on where you live. In the United States, the U.S. Geological Survey estimates that of the 410 billion gallons of water withdrawn daily, 85% comes from fresh water and 15% from salt water. Figure 5.9 shows eight activities responsible for this water use, with the production of electricity being the largest. About 200 billion gallons of water daily, or 50% of the total water withdrawn, is used as a coolant in electric power plants—coal, natural gas, and nuclear. The next largest uses are for crop irrigation and for homes, schools, and businesses, accounting for another 31% and 12%, respectively.

Worldwide, agriculture takes the biggest gulp of water, accounting for about 70% of the global water consumption. Crops such as wheat, rice, corn, and soybeans are grown by farmers across the globe, each requiring several thousand liters of water on average in order to produce one kilogram of food. These values reported in Table 5.2 are examples of **water footprints,** that is, estimates of the volume of fresh water used to produce particular goods or to provide services.

The values in Table 5.2 are global averages. The actual value for a water footprint depends both on the country and on the particular region within the country in which

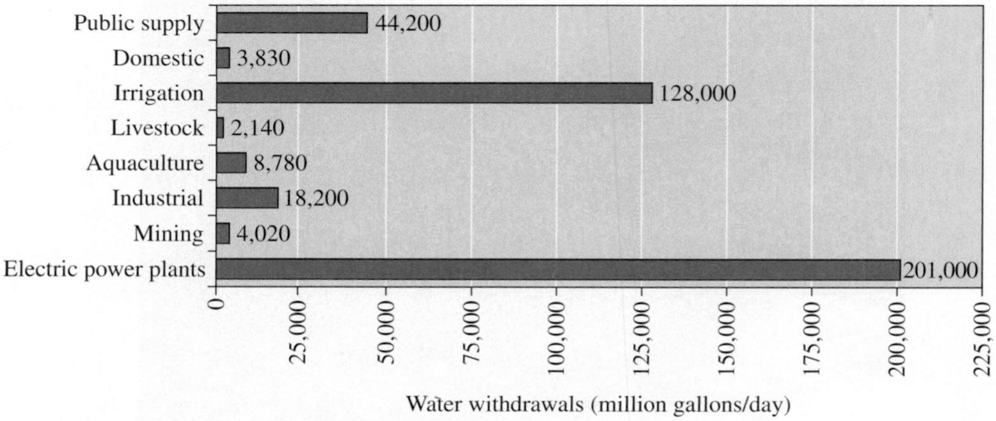

Look for how water is used as a coolant in power plants in Sections 4.1 and 7.3.

Look for information about ecological footprints in Section 0.5 and carbon footprint in Section 3.9.

Figure 5.9
Total fresh and salt water withdrawals in the United States, 2005.

Source: USGS.

Table 5.2	Water Footprints for Meats and Grains
Food (1 kg)	Water footprint (L, global average)
corn (maize)	1200
wheat	1800
soybeans	2100
rice	2500
chicken	4300
pork	6000
sheep meat	8700
beef	15,400

Source: Water Footprint Network, 2012.

the crop is grown. For example, according to the Water Footprint Network, corn grown in the United States has an average water footprint of 760 liters. In comparison, the values in China and India are 1160 liters and 2540 liters, respectively. Over time, footprint values change if there are changes in rainfall or in agricultural practices.

Table 5.2 also reveals the large difference in the amount of water, on average, needed to produce meats in comparison to grains. Highest in water footprint is beef, reflecting that cattle tend to be grain-fed. Again, remember the values are global averages. The actual water footprint of any particular kilogram of meat is dependent on how the animal was raised and brought to slaughter.

Water footprints also can be estimated for other products as well. For example, consider a 250-mL glass of cow's milk. On average, the volume of water used to *produce* this is 255 L, almost a thousand times the volume of one glass of milk! As in our example for beef, this includes the water to care for the cow and the water used to grow the food that it eats. It also includes the water used at a dairy farm to collect the milk and clean the equipment. You can check out the water needed to produce other beverages, foods, and consumer goods in Table 5.3.

Water footprint values are inexact and, as a result, controversial. Our intent in providing them is not to label items as good or bad. Rather, these values are meant to remind you that water is used to produce goods and to provide you with a more inclusive picture of water use. For example, on first inspection of Table 5.3, you might be tempted to forgo cotton T-shirts. Cotton is indeed a thirsty crop and has been grown in arid climates using imported water for irrigation. Huge amounts of water are required to process cotton fibers into the shirts that we wear. This large water footprint for cotton can encourage us to irrigate more efficiently and to design industrial practices that conserve water, as we'll see in the next section.

"The average water footprint per calorie for beef is 20 times larger than for cereals and starchy roots."
Source: Ecosystems (2012) 15:401–415.

 A green chemistry solution applied to the processing of cotton is discussed in Section 5.12.

Table 5.3	Water Footprints for Various Products
Product	Water footprint (L, global average)
1 cup of coffee (250 mL)	260
1 cup of tea (250 mL)	27
1 banana (200 g)	160
1 orange (150 g)	80
1 glass of orange juice (200 mL)	200
1 egg (60 g)	200
1 chocolate bar (100 g)	1700
1 cotton T–shirt (250 g)	2500

Source: Water Footprint Network, 2012.

5.4 | Water Issues

In some nations, water is truly a bargain right out of the faucet at home. For example, the average price for 1000 gallons (3800 L) of tap water in the United States is about two dollars. So inexpensive, this tap water is supplied free in drinking fountains along streets, in parks, or in public buildings (Figure 5.10). In nations where the cost of drinking water is low, people easily decide how frequently they drink, how much they drink, and from which source they will drink. Although for convenience or personal reasons some may select bottled water at a much higher price, in most cases this is a choice rather than a necessity.

What if you cannot turn on a tap or buy bottled water? Some people inhabit regions where they must walk miles to reach a water source, fill a container, and carry it home (Figure 5.11a). Others, because an emergency has interrupted their usual water supply, must depend on a water truck to supply their needs (Figure 5.11b). Still others need engineers to design megastructures that move water from one region of the country to where they live. For example, aqueducts in the United States move water from the Colorado River to the Southwest. Major diversions of water often are accompanied by unintended consequences, as we will discuss in a later section.

Unfortunately, the water found on our planet does not always match where people need to use it. Several issues, including global climate change, overconsumption and inefficient use of water, and contamination further complicate the availability of water. We now discuss each of these in turn.

Global Climate Change

Just as carbon cycles from place to place on our planet, so does water. For example, rain or snow falls on land and becomes part of lakes and rivers. Some of this water seeps through soils into aquifers. Other water finds its way to the ocean or is trapped for a time in snow or glaciers. Still other water evaporates and becomes the water vapor in our atmosphere. Natural processes continually recycle water on our planet.

Climate plays an important role in the timing of the water cycle and therefore the distribution of water on the planet. For example, glaciers accumulate snowpack

Figure 5.10

Some people (but not all) can take the safety of and access to drinking water for granted.

The carbon cycle was described in Chapter 3.

Weather describes the physical conditions of the atmosphere, such as its temperature, pressure, moisture, and wind. In contrast, climate describes weather patterns in a region over a longer time span.

(a)   (b)

Figure 5.11

(a) Young girls walking home with water vessels.
(b) An emergency water truck providing water for a community.

(a)   (b)

Figure 5.12

(a) Parched soils feed a dust storm approaching a town in southeastern Australia.
(b) Shrinking waters at a dam during the Big Dry left thousands of fish stranded.

during winter months and then release a regular stream of water during summer months. The great glaciers of the Himalayas feed seven of the largest rivers in Asia, ensuring a reliable water supply for 2 billion people—almost one third of the world's population. If climate is altered and these glaciers are not replenished annually, they will not sustain the rivers in the region, a scenario with devastating consequences to the people who depend on glaciers as water reservoirs.

Violent storms and floods bring water in ferocious abundance, as witnessed by periodic flooding across the globe. At the other extreme, drought creates crippling water shortages. For example, beginning in about 1997, the Millennium Drought covered much of Australia. Known as the "Big Dry" to Australians, the lack of significant rainfall over many regions of the continent contributed to widespread livestock loss, crop failures, bushfires, dust storms, and habitat loss (Figure 5.12). As rivers and lakes dried up, the Australian government, together with farmers and city dwellers, implemented water conservation measures and developed systems to use recycled water. Seeking to become more climate-independent, Australians are building desalination plants to convert the seawater from its coastal areas to fresh water.

The timing of the water cycle also affects events in Earth's ecosystems. As another example, insects, birds, and plants need to appear in the right order so that the birds can feed, the insects can pollinate, and the plants can grow. If birds migrate earlier in the spring, they may arrive before enough insects have hatched for food. Conversely, if too many insects hatch before the birds are present to eat them, the insects may devastate crops. Either way, water is a key variable supporting ecosystems in which these creatures live.

Consider This 5.10   Weather and Water

Identify a recent drought or flood that caused hardship for people and/or for an ecosystem. For an audience of your choice, write a paragraph that describes the hardship, who or what was impacted, and how some of the challenges were met.

Overconsumption and Inefficient Use

In many places, water is being pumped out of the ground faster than it is replenished by the natural water cycle. For example, much of the bountiful grain harvest from the central United States stems from using water from the High Plains Aquifer. This vast aquifer trapped water from the last ice age and runs from South Dakota to

Figure 5.13
One of the world's largest aquifers, the High Plains Aquifer, is shown in dark blue on this map.

In the context of air quality, the tragedy of the commons was first mentioned in Section 1.12.

Practices that can conserve water include using efficient ways to irrigate fields, replacing grass lawns with native vegetation, and repairing leaky pipes in aging water distribution systems.

Texas (Figure 5.13). It is an unsustainable practice to pump water from aquifers faster than they recharge. Continuous pumping can bring harmful outcomes as well. For example, if water is removed from a geologically unstable area near the coast, salt water may intrude into a freshwater aquifer.

Overdrawing reserves of surface water creates problems as well. For example, consider Kazakhstan and Uzbekistan, countries that border the Aral Sea. Until recently, this sea was the world's fourth largest inland body of fresh water. In the 1960s, workers in the former Soviet Union built a network of canals that diverted this water from the rivers that fed the Aral Sea in order to grow cotton in the arid climate. Not only were the rivers feeding the Aral Sea diverted, but also the water taken was used inefficiently. For example, the water for cotton irrigation was transported in open canals resulting in loss through evaporation.

Consequently, the Aral Sea dried up, as shown in Figure 5.14. Although the ecosystem once was rich as a fishery, today only a few salty pools of water remain. The United Nations has called this the greatest environmental disaster of the 20th century. Dust that is laden with toxins, pesticides, and salt now blows in the region, causing health problems and contributing to poverty.

Both of these water diversion stories present us with examples of the tragedy of the commons. The water from the aquifers and surface water is the resource used in common, yet no one in particular is responsible for its use. If water is overdrawn for agriculture or some other purpose, this act can be to the detriment of all who depend on this common and necessary resource.

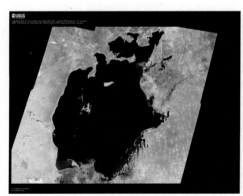
Aral Sea 1973

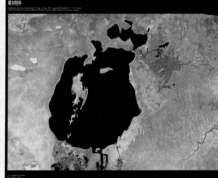
Aral Sea 1987

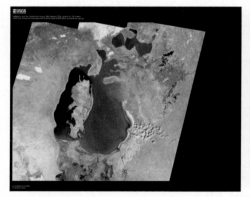
Aral Sea 1999

Aral Sea 2009

Figure 5.14
The Aral Sea has lost more than 80% of its water over a period of 30 years. The rivers that fed it were diverted to irrigate crops.

Figure 5.15
Water that is unsafe to drink may or may not appear to be contaminated.

Contamination

We expect access to water that is safe, that is, devoid of harmful chemicals and microbes. However, a 2010 joint report released by the World Health Organization/ United Nations Children's Fund (WHO/UNICEF) indicated that almost a billion people, primarily in developing nations, lacked safe drinking water. Each day, more than 3000 infants and children die because of contaminated water, sometimes indicated by its appearance but other times not (Figure 5.15).

In the 1980s, UNICEF responded to some of the global needs for water by sinking wells and providing pumps to tap underground aquifers. Although the water from aquifers usually is potable, tragically in India and Bangladesh this was not the case. Rather, the water contained naturally-occurring arsenic and fluoride ions, both cumulative poisons. Because their presence in the drinking water went undetected until it was too late, thousands of people were irreversibly poisoned.

The arsenic ion is positively charged; in contrast the fluoride ion is negatively charged. Look for more about ions in Section 5.6.

The unintended consequences from the UNICEF-sponsored project bring up an important question. What makes water safe to drink? Safe water isn't pure—it has substances dissolved in it. Many of these substances are part of the world's natural systems. For example, beneficial minerals found in groundwater contribute calcium and magnesium ions to the water. As we have seen, other natural substances can be harmful. The U.S. EPA defines a water contaminant as anything physical, chemical, biological, or radioactive that is harmful to human health or degrades the taste or color of the water. As we'll see in Section 5.10, the EPA regulates more than 90 substances known to contaminate drinking water.

Radioactive substances are discussed in Chapter 7.

Not all contaminants found in water are monitored or regulated. For example, personal care products such as cosmetics, lotions, and fragrances contribute thousands of chemicals to wastewater. In addition, trace amounts of pharmaceutical drugs end up in our wastewater stream and quite possibly in our drinking water as well. At present, we are in only the early stages of understanding the effects of these substances in our water. Consider This 5.11 will help you assess your use of personal care products.

Section 5.12 describes how green chemistry can be applied to the disposal of pharmaceuticals.

Consider This 5.11   To Clean or to Dirty?

We use personal care products with a goal in mind. For example, we use shampoo to clean hair, pat on shaving lotion to refresh the skin, or apply hand lotion to soften it. After the product has done its job, what happens to it?

a. List several personal care products that you use daily.
b. Suggest several routes by which these personal care products could end up in water.
c. Revisit your list from part **a**. How might you apply green chemistry key ideas in your daily use of personal care products? For example, would using less shampoo still be effective in cleaning your hair?

Answer

b. Personal care products enter wastewater through many routes, including bathing, washing clothes, and swimming.

We hope this section has increased your awareness of how water is used, is misused, and sometimes picks up contaminants, either natural or of human origin. This last point warrants our closer attention. What is it about water that allows contamination to happen so easily? We now turn to topics that help us better understand why water is able to dissolve and mix with so many substances.

5.5 | Aqueous Solutions

Water dissolves a remarkable variety of substances. As we will see, some of them, including salt, sugar, ethanol, and the air pollutant SO_2, are *very* soluble in water. In comparison, limestone rock, oxygen, and carbon dioxide dissolve only in tiny amounts. To build your understanding about water quality, you need to know *what* dissolves in water, *why* it dissolves, and *how* to specify the concentration of the resulting solution when it does dissolve. This section tackles solution concentrations; the section that follows addresses solubility.

Let's begin with some useful chemical terminology. Water is a **solvent,** a substance, often a liquid, that is capable of dissolving one or more pure substances. The solid, liquid, or gas that dissolves in a solvent is called the **solute.** The result is called a **solution,** a homogeneous (of uniform composition) mixture of a solvent and one or more solutes. In this section, we are particularly interested in **aqueous solutions,** solutions in which water is the solvent.

Because water is such a good solvent, it practically never is "100% pure." Rather, it contains impurities. For example, when water flows over the rocks and minerals of our planet, it dissolves tiny amounts of the substances that they contain. Although this usually causes no harm to our drinking water, occasionally the ions dissolved in water are toxic. For example, as we noted in the previous section, if the water contacts minerals that contain arsenic or fluoride ions, the water may be rendered nonpotable. The water on our planet also comes in contact with air. When it does, it dissolves tiny amounts of the gases in the air, most notably oxygen and carbon dioxide. Some air pollutants are *very* soluble in water. So when it rains, the water actually cleans some of the pollutants out of the air, including SO_2 and NO_2. As we will see in Chapter 6, the acidic solutions that form can have serious consequences for the environment.

Humans also contribute to the number of substances dissolved in water. When we wash clothes, we add not only the spent detergent, but also whatever made our clothing dirty in the first place. When we flush a toilet, we add liquid and solid wastes. Our urban streets add solutes to rainwater during the process of storm run-off. And our agricultural practices add fertilizers and other soluble compounds to water.

What does water's being a good solvent mean for our drinking water? In order to assess water quality, you need to know several things. One is a way to specify *how much* of a substance has dissolved, so that you can compare the value with a known standard. In other words, you need to understand the concept of concentration. This was first introduced in Chapter 1 in relation to the composition of air. For example, O_2 and N_2 are about 21% and 78% of dry air, respectively. We revisited concentration again in Chapters 2 and 3, exploring the concentrations of chlorine compounds in the stratosphere and greenhouse gases in the troposphere. For example, carbon dioxide has a concentration of about 400 ppm in the air. Now we examine this concept in terms of substances dissolved in water. As we will see, percent and parts per million are valid ways of expressing concentrations for aqueous solutions as well.

To get started with solution concentrations, let's use a familiar analogy—sweetening a cup of tea. If 1 teaspoon of sugar is dissolved in a cup of tea, the resulting solution has a concentration of 1 teaspoon per cup. Note that you would have this same concentration if you were to dissolve 3 teaspoons of sugar in 3 cups of tea, or half a teaspoon in half a cup of tea. If your recipe is tripled or halved, the sugar and tea are adjusted proportionally. Therefore, the **concentration,** the ratio of the amount of solute to the amount of solution—or in this case the ratio of sugar dissolved to make the solution—is the same in each case.

Solute concentrations in aqueous solution follow the same pattern but are expressed with different units. We use four ways to express concentration: percent, parts per million, parts per billion, and molarity. Three of these should already be familiar to you. The fourth, molarity, uses the mole concept introduced in Chapter 3.

Percent (%) means parts per hundred. For example, an aqueous solution containing 0.9 grams of sodium chloride (NaCl) in 100 grams of solution is a 0.9% solution by mass. This concentration of sodium chloride is referred to as "normal saline" in medical settings when given intravenously. You may find the antiseptic isopropyl alcohol in your medicine cabinet as a 70% aqueous solution by volume. It contains 70 milliliters of isopropyl alcohol in every 100 milliliters of aqueous solution. Percent is used to express the concentration of a wide range of solutions.

But when the concentration is very low, as is the case for many substances dissolved in drinking water, **parts per million (ppm)** is more commonly used. For example, water that contains 1 ppm of calcium ions contains the equivalent of 1 gram of calcium (in the form of the calcium ion) dissolved in 1 million grams of water. The water we drink contains substances naturally present in the parts per million range. For example, the acceptable limit for nitrate ion, found in well water in some agricultural areas, is 10 ppm; the limit for the fluoride ion is 4 ppm.

Although parts per million is a useful concentration unit, measuring 1 million grams of water is not very convenient. We can do things more easily by switching to the unit of a liter. One ppm of any substance in water is equivalent to 1 mg of that substance dissolved in a liter of solution. Here is the math:

$$1 \text{ ppm} = \frac{1 \text{ g solute}}{1 \times 10^6 \text{ g water}} \times \frac{1000 \text{ mg solute}}{1 \text{ g solute}} \times \frac{1000 \text{ g water}}{1 \text{ L water}} = \frac{1 \text{ mg solute}}{1 \text{ L water}}$$

Municipal water utilities may use the unit milligrams per liter (mg/L) to report the minerals and other substances dissolved in tap water. For example, Table 5.4 shows a tap water analysis from an aquifer that supplies a midwestern community in the United States.

Some contaminants are of concern at concentrations much lower than parts per million and are reported as **parts per billion (ppb).** Assuming that 1 ppm corresponds to 1 second in nearly 12 days, then 1 ppb corresponds to 1 second in 33 years. Another

For solutions at low concentration, the mass of the solution is approximately the mass of the solvent.

These limits for fluoride and nitrate ions reflect the U.S. standards. See Section 5.10.

1000 grams (1×10^3 g) of H_2O can be taken to have a volume of 1 liter. Strictly speaking, this is true only at 4 °C.

In aqueous solutions,
1 ppb = 1 µg/L
1 ppm = 1 mg/L

Table 5.4	Tap Water Mineral Report		
Cation	mg/L	Anion	mg/L
calcium ion	97	sulfate ion	45
magnesium ion	51	chloride ion	75
sodium ion	27	nitrate ion	4
		fluoride ion	1

way of looking at this is that one part per billion corresponds to a few centimeters on the circumference of the Earth!

One contaminant found in the range of parts per billion is mercury. For humans, the primary source of exposure to mercury is food, mainly fish and fish products. Even so, the concentration of mercury in water needs to be monitored. One part per billion of mercury (Hg) in water is equivalent to 1 gram of Hg dissolved in 1 billion grams of water. In more convenient terms, this means 1 microgram (1×10^{-6} g, or 1 μg) of Hg dissolved in 1 liter of water. The acceptable limit for mercury in drinking water is 2 ppb:

Mercury in water is present in a soluble form (Hg^{2+}) rather than as elemental Hg ("quicksilver").

$$2 \text{ ppb Hg} = \frac{2 \text{ g Hg}}{1 \times 10^9 \text{ g H}_2\text{O}} \times \frac{1 \times 10^6 \text{ μg Hg}}{1 \text{ g Hg}} \times \frac{1000 \text{ g H}_2\text{O}}{1 \text{ L H}_2\text{O}} = \frac{2 \text{ μg Hg}}{1 \text{ L H}_2\text{O}}$$

Convince yourself that the units cancel, as in the previous example.

Your Turn 5.12   Mercury Ion Concentrations

a. A 5-L sample of water contains 80 μg of dissolved mercury ion. Express the mercury ion concentration of the solution in ppm and ppb.
b. Would your answer in part a be in compliance with a federal maximum mercury concentration of 2 ppb? Explain.

Molarity (M), another useful concentration unit, is defined as a unit of concentration represented by the number of moles of solute present in 1 liter of solution.

$$\text{Molarity (M)} = \frac{\text{moles of solute}}{\text{liter of solution}}$$

The great advantage of molarity is that solutions of the same molarity contain exactly the same number of moles of solute and hence the same number of molecules (ions or atoms) of solute. The mass of a solute varies depending on its identity. For example, 1 mole of sugar has a different mass than 1 mole of sodium chloride. But if you take the same volume, all 1 M solutions (read as "one molar") contain the same number of moles of solute.

The molar mass of NaCl (58.5 g) is calculated by adding the molar mass of sodium (23.0 g) plus the molar mass of chlorine (35.5 g). Section 3.7 explains molar mass calculations.

As an example, consider a solution of NaCl in water. The molar mass of NaCl is 58.5 g; therefore, 1 mol of NaCl has a mass of 58.5 g. By dissolving 58.5 g of NaCl in some water and then adding enough water to make exactly 1.00 L of solution, we would have a 1.00 M NaCl aqueous solution (Figure 5.16). We have prepared a one-molar solution of sodium chloride. Note the use of a **volumetric flask,** a type of glassware that contains a precise amount of solution when filled to the mark on its neck. But because concentrations are simply ratios of solute to solvent, there are many ways to make a 1.00 M NaCl(*aq*) solution. Another possibility is to use 0.500 mol NaCl (29.2 g) in 0.500 L of solution. This requires the use of a 500-mL volumetric flask, rather than the 1-L flask shown in Figure 5.16.

(aq) is short for aqueous, indicating that the solvent is water.

$$1 \text{ M NaCl}(aq) = \frac{1 \text{ mol NaCl}}{1 \text{ L solution}} \text{ or } \frac{0.500 \text{ mol NaCl}}{0.500 \text{ L solution}}, \text{ etc.}$$

Remember that 1 ppm = 1 mg/L and that the molar mass of Hg is 200.6 g/mol.

Let's say you have a water sample with 150 ppm of dissolved mercury. What is this concentration expressed in molarity? You might do the calculation this way:

$$150 \text{ ppm Hg} = \frac{150 \text{ mg Hg}}{1 \text{ L H}_2\text{O}} \times \frac{1 \text{ g Hg}}{1000 \text{ mg Hg}} \times \frac{1 \text{ mol Hg}}{200.6 \text{ g Hg}} = \frac{7.5 \times 10^{-4} \text{ mol Hg}}{1 \text{ L H}_2\text{O}} = 7.5 \times 10^{-4} \text{ M Hg}$$

Thus, a sample of water containing 150 ppm of mercury also can be expressed as 7.5×10^{-4} M Hg.

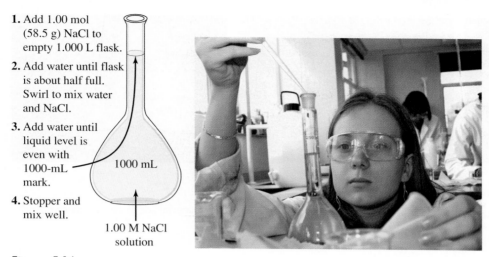

1. Add 1.00 mol (58.5 g) NaCl to empty 1.000 L flask.

2. Add water until flask is about half full. Swirl to mix water and NaCl.

3. Add water until liquid level is even with 1000-mL mark.

1000 mL

4. Stopper and mix well.

1.00 M NaCl solution

Figure 5.16

Preparing a 1.00 M NaCl aqueous solution.

Your Turn 5.13   Moles and Molarity

a. Express a concentration of 16 ppb Hg in units of molarity.

b. For 1.5 M and 0.15 M NaCl, how many moles of solute are present in 500 mL of each?

c. A solution is prepared by dissolving 0.50 mol NaCl in enough water to form 250 mL of solution. A second solution is prepared by dissolving 0.60 mol NaCl to form 200 mL of solution. Which solution is more concentrated? Explain.

d. A student was asked to prepare 1.0 L of a 2.0 M $CuSO_4$ solution. The student placed 40.0 g of $CuSO_4$ crystals in a volumetric flask and filled it with water to the 1000-mL mark. Was the resulting solution 2.0 M? Explain.

In this section, we made the case that water is an excellent solvent for a wide variety of substances and that we can express the concentration of these substances numerically. As promised, the next section helps you to build an understanding of how and why substances dissolve in water.

5.6 | A Closer Look at Solutes

Salt and sugar both dissolve in water. However, the solutions of these two solutes are quite different in nature—the former conducts electricity and the latter does not. Experimentally, we demonstrate this difference using a **conductivity meter,** an apparatus that produces a signal to indicate that electricity is being conducted. The conductivity meter shown in Figure 5.17 is built from wires, a battery, and a lightbulb. As long as the electrical circuit is not completed, the bulb does not glow. For example, if the two wires are placed into distilled water or a sugar solution in distilled water, the bulb does not light. However, if the separate wires are placed into an aqueous solution of salt, the bulb turns on. Perhaps the light also has gone on in the mind of the experimenter!

Distilled water does not conduct electricity. The same is true for an aqueous solution of sugar. Sugar is a **nonelectrolyte,** a solute that is nonconducting in an aqueous solution. But an aqueous solution of common table salt, NaCl, conducts electricity and the lightbulb glows. Sodium chloride is classified as an **electrolyte,** a solute that conducts electricity in an aqueous solution.

Distillation, a process to purify water, is discussed in Section 5.12.

The term *electrolyte* is used in connection with sports drinks. Some taste slightly salty because they contain sodium salts.

(a)   **(b)**   **(c)**

Figure 5.17

Conductivity experiments. **(a)** Distilled water (nonconducting). **(b)** Sugar dissolved in distilled water (nonconducting). **(c)** Salt dissolved in distilled water (conducting).

Remember to indicate ions in aqueous solution using *(aq)*.

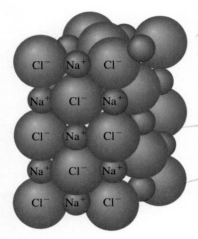

Figure 5.18

The arrangement of Na^+ and Cl^- in a crystal of sodium chloride.

Valence (outer) electrons were described in Section 2.2.

What makes salt solutions behave differently from sugar solutions or from pure water? The observed flow of electric current through a solution involves the transport of electric charge. The ability of aqueous NaCl solutions to conduct electricity suggests that they contain some charged species capable of moving electrons through the solution. When solid NaCl dissolves in water, it separates into $Na^+(aq)$ and $Cl^-(aq)$. An **ion** is an atom or group of atoms that has acquired a net electric charge as a result of gaining or losing one or more electrons. The term is derived from the Greek for "wanderer." Na^+ is an example of a **cation,** a positively charged ion. Similarly, Cl^- is an example of an **anion,** a negatively charged ion. No such separation occurs with covalently bonded sugar or water molecules, making these liquids unable to carry electric charge.

It may surprise you to learn that Na^+ and Cl^- exist both in crystals of salt (such as those in a salt shaker) and in an aqueous solution of NaCl. Solid sodium chloride is a three-dimensional cubic arrangement of sodium and chloride ions. An **ionic bond** is the chemical bond formed when oppositely charged ions attract. In the case of NaCl, ionic bonds hold the crystal together; there are no covalently bonded atoms, only positively charged cations and negatively charged anions held together by electrical attractions. An **ionic compound** is composed of ions that are present in fixed proportions and arranged in a regular, geometric structure. In the case of NaCl, each Na^+ is surrounded by six oppositely charged Cl^- ions. Likewise, each Cl^- is surrounded by six positively charged Na^+ ions. A single, tiny crystal of sodium chloride consists of many trillions of sodium ions and chloride ions in the arrangement shown in Figure 5.18.

We've described ionic compounds, but we still need to explain *why* certain atoms lose or gain electrons to form ions. Not surprisingly, the answer involves the distribution of electrons within atoms. For example, recall that a neutral sodium atom has 11 electrons and 11 protons. Sodium, like all metals in Group 1A, has one valence electron. This electron is rather loosely attracted to the nucleus and can be easily lost. When this happens, the Na atom forms Na^+, a cation.

$$Na \longrightarrow Na^+ + e^- \qquad\qquad [5.1]$$

The Na^+ has a 1+ charge because it contains 11 protons but only 10 electrons. It also has a complete octet, just like the neon atom. Table 5.5 shows the comparison between Na, Na^+, and Ne.

Table 5.5	Electronic Bookkeeping for Cation Formation	
Sodium Atom	Sodium Ion	Neon Atom
Na	Na^+	Ne
11 protons	11 protons	10 protons
11 electrons	10 electrons	10 electrons
net charge of 0	net charge of 1+	net charge of 0

Table 5.6	Electronic Bookkeeping for Anion Formation	
Chlorine Atom	Chloride Ion	Argon Atom
Cl	Cl⁻	Ar
17 protons	17 protons	18 protons
17 electrons	18 electrons	18 electrons
net charge of 0	net charge of 1−	net charge of 0

Unlike sodium, chlorine is a nonmetal. Recall that a neutral chlorine atom has 17 electrons and 17 protons. Chlorine, like all nonmetals in Group 7A, has seven valence electrons. Because of the stability associated with eight outer electrons, it is energetically favorable for chlorine to gain one electron.

$$Cl + e^- \longrightarrow Cl^-$$ [5.2]

The chloride ion (Cl⁻) has 18 electrons and 17 protons; thus the net charge is 1− (Table 5.6).

Sodium metal and chlorine gas react vigorously when they come in contact. The result is the aggregate of Na^+ and Cl^-, known as sodium chloride. In the formation of an ionic compound such as sodium chloride, the electrons are actually transferred from one atom to another, not simply shared as they would be in a covalent compound.

Is there evidence for electrically charged ions in pure sodium chloride? Experimental tests show that crystals of sodium chloride do not conduct electricity. This makes sense, because in the crystal, the ions are fixed in place and so are unable to move and transport charge. However, when a crystal is melted, the ions are free to move, and the hot liquid conducts electricity. This provides evidence that ions are present.

Like other ionic compounds, NaCl crystals are hard yet brittle. When hit sharply, they shatter rather than being flattened. This suggests the existence of strong forces that extend throughout the ionic crystal. Strictly speaking, there is no such thing as a specific, localized "ionic bond" analogous to a covalent bond in a molecule. Rather, ionic bonding holds together a large assembly of ions; in this case, Na^+ and Cl^-.

Generally speaking, electron transfer to form cations and anions occurs between metallic elements and nonmetallic elements. Sodium, lithium, magnesium, and other metals have a strong tendency to give up electrons and form positive ions. As shown in Table 5.1, they have low electronegativity values. On the other hand (or the other side of the periodic table), chlorine, fluorine, oxygen, and other nonmetals have a strong attraction for electrons and readily gain them to form negative ions. Nonmetals have relatively high electronegativity values.

Revisit Section 1.6 for more about metals and nonmetals.

Your Turn 5.14   Predicting Ionic Charge

a. Predict whether these atoms will form an anion or a cation based on their electronegativity values.

Li   S   K   N

b. Predict the ion that each of these will form. Then draw a Lewis structure for the atom and the ion, clearly labeling the charge on the ion.

Br   Mg   O   Al

Hint: Use the periodic table as a guide to the number of outer electrons. Then determine how many electrons must be lost or gained to achieve stability with an octet of electrons.

Answer

b. Bromine (Group 7A) gains one electron. The resulting ion has a charge of 1−, just as was the case for chlorine. Here are the Lewis structures for the atom and the ion.

:Br· and [:Br:]⁻

This section opened with a discussion of salt and sugar. The names *salt* and *sugar* are both in common use, and you knew what we were talking about. Salt is the stuff you sprinkle on French fries. And sugar is the stuff that some people use to sweeten coffee. In fact, ordinary table salt (NaCl) is such an important example of an ionic compound that chemists frequently refer to others simply as "salts," meaning crystalline ionic solids. As you will see in Chapter 11, sugars are another important class of compounds, and what we call "sugar" is really the compound sucrose.

To delve further into the issues of water quality, you need to know the names of other salts; that is, ionic compounds. As you might guess, chemists name them using a long and careful set of rules. Luckily, we won't discuss all of these rules here. Rather, we follow the "need-to-know" philosophy, helping you learn the ones that you need for understanding water quality.

5.7 | Names and Formulas of Ionic Compounds

In this section, we work on the "vocabulary" you need in order to work with ionic compounds. As we pointed out in Chapter 1, chemical symbols are the alphabet of chemistry and chemical formulas are the words. Earlier, we helped you to "speak chemistry" by correctly using chemical formulas and names for the substances in the air you breathe. Now we do the same for the substances in the water you drink.

Let's begin with the ionic compound formed from the elements calcium and chlorine: $CaCl_2$. The explanation for the 1:2 ratio of Ca to Cl lies in the charges of the two ions. Calcium, a member of Group 2A, loses its two outer electrons to form Ca^{2+}.

$$Ca \longrightarrow Ca^{2+} + 2\,e^- \qquad\qquad [5.3]$$

Chlorine, as we saw in equation 5.2, gains an outer electron to form Cl^-. In an ionic compound, the sum of the positive charges equals the sum of the negative charges. Hence, the formula for this compound is $CaCl_2$.

The logic is the same with MgO and Al_2O_3, two other ionic compounds. These both contain oxygen, but in different ratios. Recall that oxygen, Group 6A, has six outer electrons. Thus a neutral oxygen atom can gain two electrons to form O^{2-}. The magnesium atom loses two electrons to form Mg^{2+}. These two ions must then combine in a 1:1 ratio so the overall charge is zero; the chemical formula is MgO. Note that although the charge *always* must be written on an individual ion, we omit the charges in the chemical formulas of ionic compounds. Thus, it is *not* correct to write the chemical formula as $Mg^{2+}O^{2-}$. The charges are implied by the chemical formula.

Here is another example. Armed with the knowledge that aluminum tends to lose three electrons to form Al^{3+}, you can write the chemical formula of the ionic compound formed from Al^{3+} and O^{2-} as Al_2O_3. Here, a 2:3 ratio of ions is needed so that the overall electric charge on the compound is zero. Again, it is *not* correct to write the chemical formula as $Al_2^{3+}O_3^{2-}$.

Earlier in the chapter, we referred to several ionic compounds by their names, including sodium chloride, sodium iodide, and potassium chloride. Observe the pattern: name the cation first, then the anion, modified to end in the suffix *-ide*. Thus, $CaCl_2$ is calcium chloride, with each ion named for its element and with chlorine modified to read chloride. Similarly, NaI is sodium iodide and KCl is potassium chloride.

The elements presented thus far formed only one type of ion. Group 1A and 2A elements only form 1+ and 2+ ions, respectively. The halogens form only 1− ions. Lithium bromide is LiBr. The ratio of 1:1 is understood because lithium only forms Li^+ and bromine only forms Br^-. The prefixes *mono-, di-, tri-,* and *tetra-* are *not* used when naming ionic compounds such as these. There is no need to call it monolithium monobromide. $MgBr_2$ is magnesium bromide, not magnesium dibromide. Magnesium *only* forms Mg^{2+}, and the ratio of 1:2 is understood and so does not need to be stated.

Halogens were described in Sections 1.6 and 2.9.

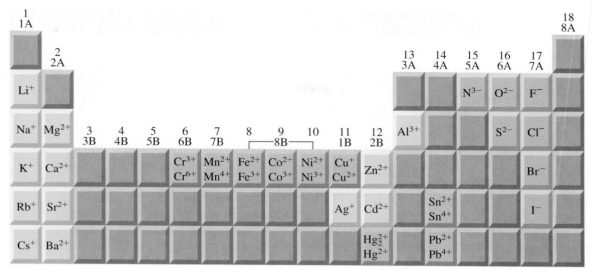

Figure 5.19

Common ions formed from their elements. Ions in green (cations) or blue (anions) have only one charge.
Ions in red (cations) have more than one possible ionic charge.

But some elements do form more than one ion, as you can see in Figure 5.19. Prefixes still are not used, but rather the charge on the ion must be specified using a Roman numeral. Take copper for example. If your instructor asks you to head down to the stockroom and grab some copper oxide, what do you do? You ask if what is wanted is copper(I) oxide or copper(II) oxide, right? Similarly, iron can form different oxides. Two forms are FeO (formed from Fe^{2+}) and Fe_2O_3 (commonly called rust and formed from Fe^{3+}). The names for FeO and Fe_2O_3 are iron(II) oxide and iron(III) oxide, respectively. Note the space after but not before the parenthesis enclosing the Roman numeral.

Again compare. The name $CuCl_2$ is copper(II) chloride, but the name of $CaCl_2$ is calcium chloride. Calcium only forms one ion (Ca^{2+}), whereas copper can form two ions: Cu^+ and Cu^{2+}.

> Prefixes such as *di–* and *tri–* generally are not used in naming ionic compounds. Roman numerals are used with the name of the cation if it has more than one possible charge.

Your Turn 5.15   Ionic Compounds

Each pair of elements forms one or more ionic compounds. For each, write the chemical formulas and names.

  a. Ca and S   **b.** F and K   **c.** Mn and O
  d. Cl and Al   **e.** Co and Br

Answer
  e. From Figure 5.19, Co can form Co^{2+} and Co^{3+}. Br forms only Br^-. The possible chemical formulas are $CoBr_2$, cobalt(II) bromide, and $CoBr_3$, cobalt(III) bromide.

One or both of the ions in an ionic compound can be a **polyatomic ion,** two or more atoms covalently bonded together that have an overall positive or negative charge. An example is the hydroxide ion, OH^-, with an oxygen atom covalently bonded to a hydrogen atom. The Lewis structure shown in Figure 5.20 reveals that there are 8 electrons, 1 more than the 7 valence electrons provided by one O atom and one H atom. The "extra" electron gives the hydroxide ion a charge of 1−. Table 5.7 lists common polyatomic ions. Most are anions, but polyatomic cations also are possible, as in the case of the ammonium ion, NH_4^+. Note that some elements (carbon, sulfur, and nitrogen) form more than one polyatomic anion with oxygen.

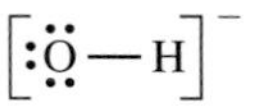

The rules for naming ionic compounds containing polyatomic ions are similar to those for ionic compounds of two elements. Consider, for example, aluminum sulfate,

$$\left[\ddot{\ddot{\mathrm{O}}} - \mathrm{H} \right]^-$$

Figure 5.20

The Lewis structure for the hydroxide ion, OH^-.

Table 5.7	Common Polyatomic Ions		
Name	Formula	Name	Formula
acetate	$C_2H_3O_2^-$	nitrite	NO_2^-
bicarbonate*	HCO_3^-	phosphate	PO_4^{3-}
carbonate	CO_3^{2-}	sulfate	SO_4^{2-}
hydroxide	OH^-	sulfite	SO_3^{2-}
hypochlorite	ClO^-	ammonium	NH_4^+
nitrate	NO_3^-		

*Also called the hydrogen carbonate ion

an ionic compound that is used in many water purification plants. The compound is formed from Al^{3+} and SO_4^{2-}. When you see $Al_2(SO_4)_3$, mentally read this chemical formula as a compound that contains two ions: aluminum and sulfate. These ions are in a 2:3 ratio. As is true for all ionic compounds, the name of the cation is given first.

The parentheses in $Al_2(SO_4)_3$ are meant to help you. The subscript 3 applies to the *entire* SO_4^{2-} ion that is enclosed in parentheses. Accordingly, "read" this as three sulfate ions. Similarly, in the ionic compound ammonium sulfide (Table 5.8), the NH_4^+ is enclosed in parentheses. The subscript of 2 indicates that there are two ammonium ions for each sulfide ion. Note that the charges are not shown in the chemical formula; they are assumed to be there. In some cases, though, the polyatomic ion is *not* enclosed in parentheses. Table 5.8 shows two examples. The PO_4^{3-} ion in aluminum phosphate has no parentheses; similarly, the NH_4^+ ion in ammonium chloride has no parentheses. Parentheses are omitted when the subscript of the polyatomic ion is 1. Nonetheless, you still have to "read" the chemical formula of $AlPO_4$ as containing the phosphate ion, and you have to "read" NH_4Cl as containing the ammonium ion.

The next three activities will help you practice using polyatomic ions.

Your Turn 5.16   Polyatomic Ions I

Write the chemical formula for the ionic compound formed from each pair of ions.

a. Na^+ and SO_4^{2-} b. Mg^{2+} and OH^- c. Al^{3+} and $C_2H_3O_2^-$ d. CO_3^{2-} and K^+

Answers
a. Na_2SO_4 b. $Mg(OH)_2$

Your Turn 5.17   Polyatomic Ions II

Name each of these compounds.

a. KNO_3 b. $(NH_4)_2SO_4$ c. $NaHCO_3$ d. $CaCO_3$ e. $Mg_3(PO_4)_2$

Answers
a. potassium nitrate   b. ammonium sulfate

Table 5.8	Ionic Compounds Containing Polyatomic Ions			
Chemical formula	$Al_2(SO_4)_3$	$(NH_4)_2S$	$AlPO_4$	NH_4Cl
Cation(s)	Al^{3+} Al^{3+}	NH_4^+ NH_4^+	Al^{3+}	NH_4^+
Anion(s)	SO_4^{2-} SO_4^{2-} SO_4^{2-}	S^{2-}	PO_4^{3-}	Cl^-

Your Turn 5.18   Polyatomic Ions III

Write the chemical formula for each of these compounds.

- a. sodium hypochlorite (used to disinfect water)
- b. magnesium carbonate (found in some limestone rocks, makes water "hard")
- c. ammonium nitrate (fertilizer, runoff can contaminate groundwater)
- d. calcium hydroxide (an agent used to remove impurities from water)

Answer

d. $Ca(OH)_2$. Two hydroxide ions (OH^-) are needed for each calcium ion (Ca^{2+}).

5.8 | The Ocean—An Aqueous Solution with Many Ions

Salt water! As we pointed out earlier, about 97% of the water on our planet is found in the oceans. This source of water contains much more than simple table salt (NaCl) dissolved in water. You are now in a position to understand why so many other ionic compounds can be found dissolved in our oceans.

Recall from Section 5.1 that water molecules are polar. When you take salt crystals and dissolve them in water, the polar H_2O molecules are attracted to the Na^+ and Cl^- ions contained in these crystals. The partial negative charge (δ^-) on the O atom of a water molecule is attracted to the positively charged Na^+ cations of the salt crystal. At the same time, the H atoms in H_2O, with their partial positive charges (δ^+), are attracted to the negatively charged Cl^- anions. Over time, the ions are separated and then surrounded by water molecules. Equation 5.4 and Figure 5.21 represent the process of forming an aqueous solution.

$$NaCl(s) \xrightarrow{H_2O} Na^+(aq) + Cl^-(aq) \qquad \textbf{[5.4]}$$

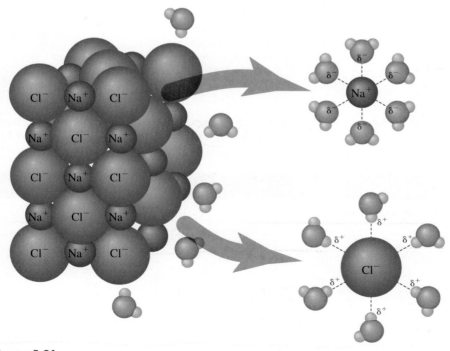

Figure 5.21

Sodium chloride dissolving in water.

  **Figures Alive!**

The process is similar for forming solutions of compounds containing polyatomic ions. For example, when solid sodium sulfate dissolves in water, the sodium ions and sulfate ions simply separate. Note that the sulfate ion stays together as a unit.

$$Na_2SO_4(s) \xrightarrow{H_2O} 2\,Na^+(aq) + SO_4^{2-}(aq) \qquad\qquad [5.5]$$

Many ionic compounds dissolve in this manner. This explains why almost all naturally occurring water samples contain various amounts of ions. The same is also true for our bodily fluids, as these also contain significant concentrations of electrolytes.

Consider This 5.19   Electricity and Water Don't Mix

Small electric appliances such as hair dryers and curling irons carry prominent warning labels advising the consumer not to use the appliance near water. Why is water a problem since it does not conduct electricity? What is the best course of action if a plugged-in hair dryer accidentally falls into a sink full of water?

If the principles we just described applied to *all* ionic compounds, our planet would be in trouble. When it rained, ionic compounds such as calcium carbonate (limestone) would dissolve and end up in the ocean! Fortunately, many ionic compounds are only slightly soluble or have extremely low solubilities. The differences arise because of the sizes and charges of the ions, how strongly they attract one another, and how strongly the ions are attracted to water molecules.

Table 5.9 is your guide to solubility. For example, calcium nitrate, $Ca(NO_3)_2$, is soluble in water, as are all compounds containing the nitrate ion. Calcium carbonate, $CaCO_3$, is insoluble, as are most carbonates. By similar reasoning, copper(II) hydroxide, $Cu(OH)_2$, is insoluble, but copper(II) sulfate, $CuSO_4$, is soluble.

Your Turn 5.20   Solubility of Ionic Compounds

Which of these compounds are soluble in water? Use Table 5.9 as your guide.

a. ammonium nitrate, NH_4NO_3, a component of fertilizers
b. sodium sulfate, Na_2SO_4, an additive in laundry detergents
c. mercury(II) sulfide, HgS, known as the mineral cinnabar
d. aluminum hydroxide, $Al(OH)_3$, used in water purification processes

Answer
a. Soluble. All ammonium compounds and all nitrate compounds are soluble.

The landmasses on Earth are largely composed of minerals, that is, ionic compounds. Most have extremely low solubility in water as we mentioned earlier. Table 5.10 summarizes some environmental consequences of solubility.

Table 5.9	Water Solubility of Ionic Compounds		
Ions	Solubility of Compounds	Solubility Exceptions	Examples
sodium, potassium, and ammonium	all soluble	none	$NaNO_3$ and KBr. Both are soluble.
nitrates	all soluble	none	$LiNO_3$ and $Mg(NO_3)_2$. Both are soluble.
chlorides	most soluble	silver and mercury(I)	$MgCl_2$ is soluble. $AgCl$ is insoluble.
sulfates	most soluble	strontium, barium, and lead sulfate	K_2SO_4 is soluble. $BaSO_4$ is insoluble.
carbonates	mostly insoluble*	Carbonates of Group 1A metals and NH_4^+ are soluble.	Na_2CO_3 is soluble. $CaCO_3$ is insoluble.
hydroxides and sulfides	mostly insoluble*	Hydroxides and sulfides of Group 1A metals and NH_4^+ are soluble.	KOH is soluble. $Al(OH)_3$ is insoluble.

*Insoluble means that the compounds have extremely low solubilities in water (less than 0.01 M). All compounds have at least a very small solubility in water.

Table 5.10	Environmental Consequences of Solubility	
Source	**Ions**	**Solubility and Consequences**
salt deposits	sodium and potassium halides*	These salts are soluble. Over time, they dissolve and wash into the sea. Thus, oceans are salty and seawater cannot be used for drinking without expensive purification.
agricultural fertilizers	nitrates	All nitrates are soluble. The runoff from fertilized fields carries nitrates into surface and groundwater. Nitrates can be toxic, especially for infants.
metal ores	sulfides and oxides	Most sulfides and oxides are insoluble. Minerals containing iron, copper, and zinc are often sulfides and oxides. If these minerals had been soluble in water, they would have washed out to sea long ago.
mining waste	mercury, lead	Most mercury and lead compounds are insoluble. However, they may leach slowly from mining waste piles and contaminate water supplies.

*Halides, such as Cl^- and I^-, are anions of the atoms in Group 7A.

5.9 | Covalent Compounds and Their Solutions

From the previous discussion, you might have gotten the impression that only ionic compounds dissolve in water. But remember that sugar dissolves in water as well. The white granules of "table sugar" that you use to sweeten your coffee or tea are sucrose, a polar covalent compound with the chemical formula $C_{12}H_{22}O_{11}$ (Figure 5.22).

When sucrose dissolves in water, the sucrose molecules disperse uniformly among the H_2O molecules. The sucrose molecules remain intact and do *not* separate into ions. Evidence for this includes the fact that aqueous sucrose solutions do not conduct electricity (see Figure 5.17b). However, the sugar molecules do interact with the water molecules, as they are both polar and are attracted to one another. Furthermore, the sucrose molecule contains eight −OH groups and three additional O atoms that can participate in hydrogen bonding (see Figure 5.22). Solubility is always promoted when an attraction exists between the solvent molecules and the solute molecules or ions. This suggests a general solubility rule: *Like dissolves like.*

Let's also consider two other familiar polar covalent compounds, both of which are highly soluble in water. One is ethylene glycol, the main ingredient in antifreeze; and the other is ethanol, or ethyl alcohol, found in beer and wine. These molecules both contain the polar −OH group and are classified as alcohols (Figure 5.23).

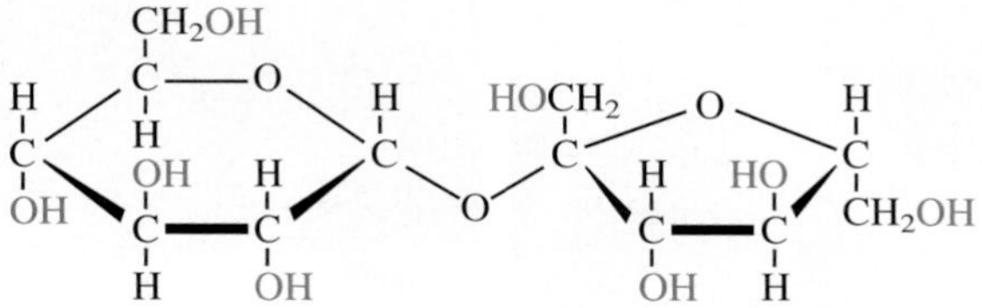

Look for more about sucrose and other sugars in Chapter 11.

Figure 5.22
Structural formula of sucrose. The −OH groups are shown in red.

Your Turn 5.21   Alcohols and Hydrogen Bonds

Some of the H and O atoms in the ethanol and the ethylene glycol molecule (see Figure 5.23) bear partial charges. Label these δ^+ and δ^-, respectively.

Hint: If the electronegativity difference between two atoms is more than 1.0, the bond is considered polar.

ethanol   ethylene glycol

Figure 5.23

Lewis structures of ethanol and ethylene glycol. The —OH groups are shown in red.

The H in the —OH group of an ethanol molecule can hydrogen bond, just as was the case for water (Figure 5.24). This is why water and ethanol have a great affinity for each other. Any bartender can tell you that alcohol and water form solutions in all proportions. Again, both molecules are polar and *like dissolves like*.

Ethylene glycol is another example of an alcohol, sometimes called a "glycol." Ethylene glycol is added to water, such as the water in the radiator of your car, to keep it from freezing. It also is one of the VOCs that some water-based paints emit when drying, an additive to keep the paint from freezing. Examine its structural formula in Figure 5.23 to see that it has two —OH groups available for hydrogen bonding. These intermolecular attractions give high water-solubility to ethylene glycol, a necessary property for any antifreeze.

It often has been observed that "oil and water don't mix." Water molecules are polar, and the hydrocarbon molecules in oil are nonpolar. When in contact, water molecules tend to attract to other water molecules; in contrast, hydrocarbon molecules stick with their own. Since oil is less dense than water, oil slicks float on top (Figure 5.25).

In connection with indoor air quality, Chapter 1 mentioned propylene glycol, a "glycol" used as an antifreeze in paints.

Your Turn 5.22   More About Hydrocarbons

Hydrocarbon molecules such as pentane and hexane contain C—H and C—C bonds. Use the electronegativity values in Table 5.1 to determine whether these bonds are polar or nonpolar.

Since water is a poor solvent for grease and oil, we cannot use water to wash these off. Instead, we wash our hands (and clothes) with the aid of soaps and detergents. These compounds are **surfactants,** compounds that help polar and nonpolar compounds to mix, sometimes called "wetting agents." The molecules of surfactants contain both polar and nonpolar groups. The polar groups allow the surfactant to dissolve in water while the nonpolar ones are able to dissolve in the grease.

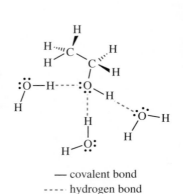

— covalent bond
---- hydrogen bond

Figure 5.24

Hydrogen bonding between an ethanol molecule and three water molecules.

Figure 5.25

Oil and water do not dissolve in each other.

Another way to dissolve nonpolar molecules is to use nonpolar solvents. Like dissolves like! Nonpolar solvents (sometimes called "organic solvents") are widely used, including in the production of drugs, plastics, paints, cosmetics, and cleaning agents. For example, dry cleaning solvents typically are chlorinated hydrocarbons. One example, "perc," is a cousin of ethene. Take ethene (sometimes called ethylene), a compound with a C=C double bond, and replace all the H atoms with Cl atoms. The result is tetrachloroethylene, also called perchloroethylene. Its nickname is perc.

Look for more about ethylene (ethene) in Chapter 9 on polymers.

ethylene   tetrachloroethylene ("perc")

Perc and other chlorinated hydrocarbons like it are carcinogens or suspected carcinogens. They have serious health consequences whether we are exposed to them in the workplace or as contaminants of our air, water, or soil.

Green chemists aim to redesign processes so that they don't require solvents. But if this is not possible, they try to replace harmful solvents like perc with ones that are friendly to the environment. One possibility is liquid carbon dioxide. Under conditions of high pressure, the gas you know as CO_2 can condense to form a liquid! Compared with organic solvents, $CO_2(l)$ offers many advantages. It is nontoxic, nonflammable, chemically benign, non-ozone-depleting, and it does not contribute to the formation of smog. Although you may be concerned with the fact that it is a greenhouse gas, carbon dioxide that is used as a solvent is a recovered waste product from industrial processes and it is generally recycled.

Adapting liquid CO_2 to dry cleaning posed a challenge, as it is not very good at dissolving oils, waxes, and greases found in soiled fabrics. To make carbon dioxide a better solvent, Dr. Joe DeSimone, a chemist and chemical engineer at the University of North Carolina–Chapel Hill, developed a surfactant to use with $CO_2(l)$. For his work, DeSimone received a 1997 Presidential Green Chemistry Challenge Award. His breakthrough process paves the way for designing environmentally benign, inexpensive, and easily recyclable replacements for conventional organic and water solvents currently in use. DeSimone was instrumental in the beginnings of Hangers Cleaners, a dry cleaning chain that uses the process that he developed.

Consider This 5.23   Liquid CO_2 as a Solvent

a. Which of the six key ideas in green chemistry (see inside front cover) are met by the use of liquid carbon dioxide as a solvent to replace organic solvents? Explain.

b. Comment on this statement: "Using carbon dioxide as a replacement for organic solvents simply replaces one set of environmental problems with another."

c. If a local dry cleaning business switched from "perc" to carbon dioxide, how might this business report a different Triple Bottom Line?

The tendency of nonpolar compounds to dissolve in other nonpolar substances explains how fish and animals accumulate nonpolar substances such as PCBs (polychlorinated biphenyls) or the pesticide DDT (dichlorodiphenyltrichloroethane) in their fatty tissues. When fish ingest these, the molecules are stored in body fat (nonpolar) rather than in the blood (polar). PCBs can interfere with the normal growth and development of a variety of animals, including humans, in some cases at concentrations of trillionths of a gram per liter.

The higher you go on the food chain, the greater concentrations of harmful nonpolar compounds like DDT you find. This is called **biomagnification,** the increase in concentration of certain persistent chemicals in successively higher levels of a food chain. Figure 5.26 shows a biomagnification process that was studied extensively in the 1960s. At that time, DDT was shown to interfere with the reproduction of peregrine

PCBs (mixtures of highly chlorinated compounds) were widely used as coolants in electrical transformers until banned in 1977. Like CFCs, they do not burn easily. They were released into the environment during manufacture, use, and disposal.

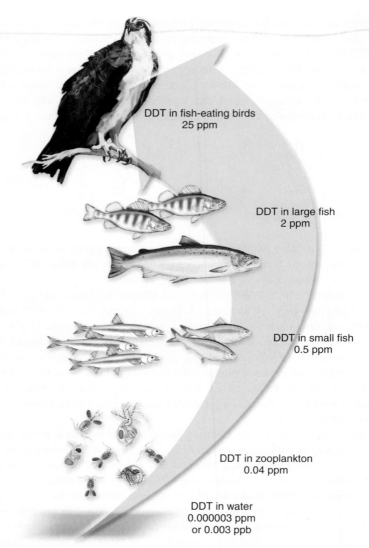

DDT in fish-eating birds
25 ppm

DDT in large fish
2 ppm

DDT in small fish
0.5 ppm

DDT in zooplankton
0.04 ppm

DDT in water
0.000003 ppm
or 0.003 ppb

Figure 5.26

Organisms in the water take up and store DDT. They are eaten by larger creatures that in turn are eaten by still larger ones. Creatures highest on the food chain have the highest concentration of DDT.

Source: From William and Mary Ann Cunningham. Environmental Science: A Global Concern, 10th ed., 2008. Reprinted with permission of the McGraw-Hill Education.

Rachel Carson (1907–1964)

falcons and other predatory birds at the top of their food chain. In 1962, Rachel Carson's publication of *Silent Spring* also linked a decline in the song bird populations with their exposure to pesticides.

5.10 | Protecting Our Drinking Water: Federal Legislation

One way or another, many different substances get added to fresh water. Is this water safe to drink? The answer depends on *what* is present in the water, *how much* of it is present, and *how much* of it you drink in a day. In this section, we address issues relating to water quality.

The need to keep public water supplies safe to drink has long been recognized. In 1974, the U.S. Congress passed the Safe Drinking Water Act (SDWA) in response to public concern about harmful substances in the water supply. The aim of this act, as amended in 1996, was to ensure potable water to those who depend on community water supplies. As required by the SDWA, contaminants that may be health risks are

The SDWA does not apply to the 10% of the people in the United States whose water comes from private wells.

Table 5.11	MCLGs and MCLs for Drinking Water	
Contaminant	MCLG (ppm)	MCL (ppm)
cadmium (Cd^{2+})	0.005	0.005
chromium (Cr^{3+}, CrO_4^{2-})	0.1	0.1
lead (Pb^{2+})	0.0	0.015
mercury (Hg^{2+})	0.002	0.002
nitrates (NO_3^-)	10.0	10.0
benzene (C_6H_6)	0.0	0.005
trihalomethanes ($CHCl_3$ and others)	varies	0.080

Look for more examples of trihalomethanes in the next section.

regulated by the Environmental Protection Agency (EPA). The EPA sets legal limits for contaminants according to their toxicities (Table 5.11). These limits also take into account the practical realities that water utilities face in trying to remove the contaminants with available technology.

For each water-soluble contaminant, the EPA established a **maximum contaminant level goal (MCLG),** the maximum level of a contaminant in drinking water at which no known or anticipated adverse effect on human health would occur. Expressed in parts per million or parts per billion, MCLGs allow for a margin of safety. Each MCLG allows for uncertainties in data collection and for how different people might react to each contaminant. An MCLG is *not* a legal limit to which water systems must comply; rather, it is a goal based on human health considerations. For known carcinogens, the EPA has set the health goal at zero under the assumption that *any* exposure presents a cancer risk.

Before regulatory action can be taken against a water utility, the concentration of an impurity must exceed the **maximum contaminant level (MCL),** the legal limit for the concentration of a contaminant expressed in parts per million or parts per billion. The EPA sets legal limits for each impurity as close to the MCLG as possible, keeping in mind any practical realities that may make it difficult to achieve the goals. Except for contaminants regulated as carcinogens (for which the MCLG is set at zero), most legal limits and health goals are the same. Even when less strict than the MCLGs, the MCLs still provide substantial public health protection.

Secondary maximum contaminant levels (SMCLs) are recommended but not required by the EPA. These are for substances that may affect taste, odor, or color, or cause cosmetic damage. For example, minerals such as manganese can stain laundry and add an unpleasant taste to water.

Consider This 5.24   What's in Drinking Water?

Table 5.11 is merely a starting point for information available about contaminants in drinking water. The EPA Office of Ground Water and Drinking Water offers a consumer fact sheet on dozens of contaminants. Both general summaries and technical fact sheets are available; the latter is recommended.

a. Select a contaminant listed in Table 5.11. How does it get into the water supply? List potential health effect(s) of this contaminant.
b. How would you know if it were in your drinking water? Is your state one of the top states that releases it?

Consider This 5.25   Understanding MCLGs and MCLs

Most people are unfamiliar with the terms MCLG and MCL from the Safe Drinking Water Act. How would you explain these abbreviations to the general public? Prepare an outline for a presentation. Be prepared to answer questions from the audience, including why MCLs are not set to zero for all carcinogens.
Hint: Search the Internet to find a water quality report published for a city near you.

Water legislation continually needs to be updated. In part, this need arises because water chemists keep improving their ability to detect what is in the water. But the need also arises because our knowledge base is growing. MCL limits should be raised or lowered as we learn more about toxicity. Currently more than 90 contaminants are regulated:

- metal ions such as Cd^{2+}, Cr^{3+}, Hg^{2+}, Cu^{2+}, and Pb^{2+}
- nonmetal ions such as NO_3^-, F^-, and various arsenic-containing ions
- miscellaneous compounds, including pesticides, industrial solvents, and compounds associated with plastics manufacturing
- radioisotopes, including uranium
- biological agents, including *Cryptosporidium* and intestinal viruses

Depending on the particular contaminant, MCLs range from about 10 ppm to less than 1 ppb. Some contaminants interfere with liver or kidney function. Others can affect the nervous system if ingested over a long period at levels consistently above the legal limit (MCL). For example, unlike many contaminants, lead is a cumulative poison. Lead pipes and solder were once commonly used in water distribution systems. When ingested by humans and animals, lead accumulates in bones and the brain, causing severe and permanent neurological problems. Severe exposure in adults causes symptoms such as irritability, sleeplessness, and irrational behavior. Lead is a particular problem for children because Pb^{2+} can be incorporated rapidly into bone along with Ca^{2+}. Since children have less bone mass than adults, some Pb^{2+} may remain in the blood where it can damage cells, especially in the brain. Children may suffer mental retardation and hyperactivity as a result of lead exposure, even at relatively low concentrations.

The chemical symbol Pb comes from the Latin name for lead, *plumbum*. The word *plumbing* comes from this Latin word as well and harkens back to the time when most water pipes were made of lead.

Fortunately, very little lead is present in most public water supplies. Amounts exceeding allowable limits are estimated to be present in less than 1% of public water supply systems, and these serve less than 3% of the U.S. population. Most of this lead comes from corrosion of plumbing systems, not from the source water itself. When lead is reported, consumers are advised to take simple steps to minimize exposure, such as letting water run before use and not cooking with hot water from the tap. Both actions minimize the chances of ingesting dissolved Pb^{2+}.

Cold water is recommended because some lead compounds, notably $PbCl_2$, are more soluble in hot water than in cold.

Regulatory values change as research yields new information about contaminants. For example, the MCL for Pb^{2+} in drinking water once had been set to 15 ppb. In 1992, however, the EPA converted this to an "action level," meaning that the EPA will take legal action if 10% of tap water samples exceed 15 ppb. The hazard from lead is so great that the EPA has established an MCLG of 0, even though lead is not a carcinogen.

Your Turn 5.26   Comparing Lead Content

Two samples of drinking water contained lead ion. One had a concentration of 20 ppb; the other a concentration of 0.003 mg/L.

a. Which sample has a higher concentration of lead ion? Explain.
b. How does each sample compare with the current acceptable limit?

Whereas contaminants such as lead cause chronic long-term health problems, other substances in drinking water present more immediate and acute effects. For example, in infants, nitrate ion (NO_3^-) may be converted into nitrite ion (NO_2^-), a substance that limits blood's ability to carry oxygen. Infants who drink formula made from water containing high levels of nitrate ion may experience difficulty breathing and possibly permanent brain damage from lack of oxygen. Although a maximum contaminant level (MCL) is set for nitrate ion in drinking water, this level may be exceeded for a variety of reasons, including fertilizer or manure runoff that gets into well water. Figure 5.27 shows water quality data for nitrate ion in California. As you can see, some water sources exceeded the MCL of 10 ppm. Because nitrate is toxic to infants, monitoring nitrate levels *and* informing communities of any violations are important.

Together with nitrates, phosphates from fertilizers can influence the types and numbers of plants and animals that live in aquatic ecosystems.

Water can also be contaminated by biological agents such as bacteria, viruses, and protozoa. Examples include *Cryptosporidium* and *Giardia*. News media warnings announcing a "boil-water emergency" are typically the result of a "total coliform" violation. Coliforms are a broad class of bacteria that live in the digestive tracts of humans and other

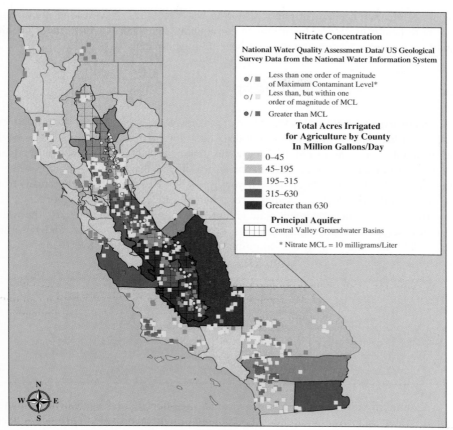

Figure 5.27

Map showing nitrate concentrations from California domestic groundwater wells and agricultural irrigation.

Source: Environmental Waikato, 2000.

animals. Most are harmless. The presence of a high coliform concentration in water usually indicates that the water-treatment or distribution system is allowing fecal contamination to enter the drinking water supply. Diarrhea, cramps, nausea, and vomiting—the symptoms of microbial-related illness—are generally not serious for a healthy adult but can be life-threatening for the very young, the elderly, or those with weakened immune systems.

Consider This 5.27   A Cryptic Microbe

The EPA surface water–treatment rules require systems using surface water or groundwater under the direct influence of surface water to remove or deactivate 99% of *Cryptosporidium*.

a. What is *Cryptosporidium* and how does it get into drinking water? What are its potential health effects?

b. What feature of *Cryptosporidium* allows it to survive disinfection? Because of this feature, how must water contaminated with *Cryptosporidium* be treated?

Hint: Use the Internet to research the Long Term 2 Enhanced Surface Water Treatment Rule.

In 1993, the drinking water of Milwaukee, WI, was contaminated with *Cryptosporidium*. This resulted in about 100 deaths, with over 400,000 sickened, triggering a change in how communities treat their drinking water.

In addition to the Safe Drinking Water Act, other federal legislation controls pollution of lakes, rivers, and coastal areas. The Clean Water Act (CWA), passed in 1974 by Congress and amended several times, provided the foundation for reducing surface water pollution. The CWA established limits on the amounts of pollutants that industry can discharge, removing over a billion pounds of toxic pollutants from U.S. waters every year. In keeping with the new trend toward green chemistry, industries are finding ways both to convert waste materials into useful products and to design processes that neither use toxic substances nor harm water quality. Improvements in surface water quality have at least two major beneficial effects. First, they reduce the amount of cleanup needed for public drinking water supplies. And second, they result in a more healthful natural environment for aquatic organisms. In turn, more healthy aquatic ecosystems have many indirect benefits for humans.

5.11 | Water Treatment

This section explores both what takes place to make water clean (at a local water treatment plant) and what happens after we make it dirty (at a sewage treatment plant). Let us begin with what takes place at a local drinking water treatment plant. We assume that the plant gets water from an aquifer or lake. For example, if you live in San Antonio, water is pumped from the Edwards Aquifer. Or if you live in San Francisco, the water comes from a reservoir in the Hetch Hetchy valley, over a hundred miles away (see Figure 5.7).

In a typical water treatment plant (Figure 5.28), the first step is to pass the water through a screen that physically removes items such as weeds, sticks, and beverage bottles. The next step is to add aluminum sulfate and calcium hydroxide. Take a moment to review these two chemicals.

Your Turn 5.28   Water Treatment Chemicals

a. Write chemical formulas for these ions: sulfate, hydroxide, calcium, and aluminum.
b. What compounds can be formed from these four ions? Write their chemical formulas.
c. The hypochlorite ion plays a role in water purification. Write chemical formulas for sodium hypochlorite and calcium hypochlorite.

Aluminum sulfate and calcium hydroxide are flocculating agents, that is, they react in water to form a sticky floc (gel) of aluminum hydroxide. This gel collects suspended clay and dirt particles on its surface.

$$Al_2(SO_4)_3(aq) + 3\,Ca(OH)_2(s) \longrightarrow 2\,Al(OH)_3(s) + 3\,CaSO_4(aq) \qquad \textbf{[5.6]}$$

As the $Al(OH)_3$ gel slowly settles, it carries particles with it that were suspended in the water (see Figure 5.28). Any remaining particles are removed as the water is filtered through charcoal or gravel and then sand.

The crucial step comes next—disinfecting the water to kill disease-causing microbes. In the United States, this is most commonly done with chlorine-containing

Chlorine only can kill the microorganisms with which it comes in contact. Chlorine does not kill bacteria or viruses that are enclosed inside particles of silt or clay. This is one reason why particles need to be removed before the chlorination step.

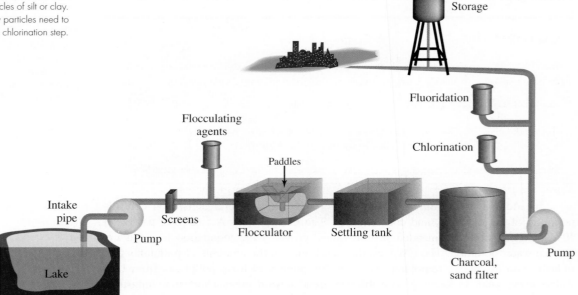

Figure 5.28

Typical municipal water treatment facility.

compounds. Chlorination is accomplished by adding chlorine gas (Cl_2), sodium hypochlorite (NaClO), or calcium hypochlorite (Ca(ClO)$_2$). All of these generate the antibacterial agent hypochlorous acid, HClO. A very low concentration of HClO, 0.075 to 0.600 ppm, remains to protect the water against further bacterial contamination as it passes through pipes to the user. **Residual chlorine** refers to the chlorine-containing chemicals that remain in the water after the chlorination step. These include hypochlorous acid (HClO), the hypochlorite ion (ClO$^-$), and dissolved elemental chlorine (Cl_2).

Before chlorination, thousands died in epidemics spread via polluted water. In a classic study, John Snow, an English physician, was able to trace a mid-1800s cholera epidemic in London to water contaminated with the excrement of cholera victims. Another example occurred in 2007 in war-torn Iraq. After extremists had put chlorine tanks on suicide truck bombs earlier that year, authorities kept tight controls on chlorine. The chlorine killed two dozen people in several attacks, sending up noxious clouds that left hundreds of people panicked and gasping for breath. At one point, a shipment of 100,000 tons of chlorine was held up for a week at the Jordanian border amid fears for its safe passage through Iraq. With the water infrastructure disrupted and the quality of water and sanitation poor, levels of fecal coliform bacteria increased dramatically, resulting in thousands of Iraqis contracting cholera.

Even in peacetime when the transportation of chlorine is relatively safe, chlorination has its drawbacks. The taste and odor of residual chlorine can be objectionable and is commonly cited as a reason why people drink bottled water or use filters to remove residual chlorine. A more serious drawback is the reaction of residual chlorine with other substances in the water to form by-products in drinking water at concentrations that may be toxic. The most widely publicized, **trihalomethanes (THMs),** are compounds such as $CHCl_3$ (chloroform), $CHBr_3$ (bromoform), $CHBrCl_2$ (bromodichloromethane), and $CHBr_2Cl$ (dibromochloromethane) that form from the reaction of chlorine or bromine with organic matter in drinking water. Like HClO, hypobromous acid (HBrO) used to disinfect spa tubs can generate trihalomethanes.

Your Turn 5.29   THMs at a Glance

a. Draw Lewis structures for any two THM molecules.
b. THMs differ from CFCs in their chemical composition. How?
c. THMs differ from CFCs in their chemical properties. How?

Answer

c. CFCs are chemically inert and nontoxic. In contrast, THMs are chemically reactive and quite toxic.

Many European and a few U.S. cities use ozone to disinfect their water supplies. In Chapter 1, we discussed tropospheric O_3 as a serious air pollutant. But in water treatment, the toxicity of O_3 serves a beneficial purpose. One advantage is that a lower concentration of ozone than chlorine is required to kill bacteria. Furthermore, ozone is more effective than chlorine against water-borne viruses.

But ozonation also comes with disadvantages. One is cost. Ozonation only becomes economical for large water-treatment plants. Another is that ozone decomposes quickly and hence does not protect water from possible contamination as it is piped through the municipal distribution system. Consequently, a low dose of chlorine must be added to ozonated water as it leaves the treatment plant.

Disinfecting water using ultraviolet (UV) light is gaining in popularity. By UV, we mean UV-C, the high-energy UV radiation that can break down DNA in microorganisms, including bacteria. Disinfection with UV-C is fast, leaves no residual by-products, and is economical for small installations, including rural homes with unsafe well water. Like ozone, however, UV-C does not protect the water after it leaves the treatment site. Again, a low dose of chlorine must be added.

Depending on local needs, one or more additional purification steps may be taken after disinfection at the water-treatment facility. Sometimes the water is sprayed into

NaClO is present in Clorox and other brands of laundry bleach. Ca(ClO)$_2$ is commonly used to disinfect swimming pools.

HClO is sometimes written as HOCl to show the order in which the atoms are bonded.

See Chapter 2 for more about UV light. See Chapter 12 for more about DNA.

the air to remove volatile chemicals that create objectionable odors and taste. If little natural fluoride ion is present in the water supply, some municipalities add fluoride ion (~1 ppm NaF) to protect against tooth decay. Learn more about fluoridation in the next activity.

In water, sodium fluoride dissolves to form $Na^+(aq)$ and $F^-(aq)$.

Consider This 5.30   Keep Your Teeth!

Until recently, losing your teeth was common as you grew older. The culprit was dental caries, a disease in which bacteria attack tooth enamel and cause infections.

a. Community water fluoridation is cited as one of 10 great public health achievements of the 20th century by the U.S. Centers for Disease Control and Prevention. Explain why.

b. Although important in all communities, water fluoridation is especially important for low income communities. Explain.

In 2011, the U.S. Department of Health and Human Services recommended the concentration of fluoride be lowered to 0.7 mg/L to reduce tooth discoloration in children. The MCL for fluoride is 4 mg/L.

We just described how water is treated before it is ready to drink out of the tap. But once we turn on this tap, we start the process of getting the water dirty again. We add waste to the water each time it leaves our bathrooms in a toilet flush, runs down the drain after a soapy shower, or goes down the sink after we wash the dishes. Clearly it makes sense to use as little water as possible because if we dirty it, it has to be cleaned again before it is released back to the environment. Remember green chemistry! It is better to prevent waste than to treat or clean up waste after it is formed.

How do we remove wastes from water? If the drains in your home are connected to a municipal sewage system, then the wastewater flows to a sewage treatment plant. Once there, it undergoes similar cleaning processes to those for water treatment, with the exception of end-stage chlorination before it is released back to the environment.

Cleaning sewage is more complicated, though, because it contains waste in the form of organic compounds and nitrate ions. To many aquatic organisms, this waste is a source of food! As these organisms feed, they deplete oxygen from surface waters. **Biological oxygen demand (BOD)** is a measure of the amount of dissolved oxygen that microorganisms use up as they decompose organic wastes found in water. A low BOD is one indicator of good water quality.

Nitrates and phosphates both contribute to BOD, as these ions are important nutrients for aquatic life. An overabundance of either can disrupt the normal flow of nutrients and lead to algal blooms that clog waterways and deplete oxygen from the water. In turn, this reduced oxygen can lead to massive fish kills. The problem of reduced oxygen in water is compounded by the fact that the solubility of oxygen in water is so very low in the first place.

Some treatment plants are using wetland areas to capture nutrients such as nitrates and phosphates before the water is returned to the surface water or recharges the groundwater. Plants and soil microorganisms in these wetland areas (marshes and bogs) facilitate nutrient recycling, thus reducing the nutrient load in the water.

If the water produced from treated sewage is clean enough, why not just use it as a source of drinking water? Singapore's growing population relies on several potable water sources. One of these, NEWater, is purified wastewater. The next activity gives you the opportunity to explore this controversial use of reclaimed water.

Typical BOD values: A pristine river, 1 mg/L; effluent from a municipal sewage treatment plant, 20 mg/L; and untreated sewage, 200 mg/L.

Flood waters and agricultural runoff containing nitrates and phosphates disrupt ecosystems in the Mississippi Delta. Chapter 11 (Figure 11.15) shows a stunning photo.

Consider This 5.31   Toilet to Tap?

Communities are considering using reclaimed water as a source of drinking water. If the quality of the water produced from the sewage treatment process matched the quality of the water in our current drinking water system, would you accept treated sewage water as drinking water? Comment either way.

5.12 | Water Solutions for Global Challenges

As pointed out in the opening of this chapter, World Water Day focuses attention on freshwater issues: "Water is crucial for sustainable development, including the preservation of our natural environment and the alleviation of poverty and hunger. Water is indispensable for human health and well-being" (United Nations website).

In this final section, we showcase four efforts that demonstrate the sustainable use of water. The first relates to the production of fresh water from salt water. The second describes how individuals in developing nations can purify their own drinking water. The third and fourth efforts employ green chemistry solutions, one for cotton production and one for drug disposal.

Fresh Water from Salt Water

"Water, water everywhere, nor any drop to drink." These words from *The Rime of the Ancient Mariner* are as true today as they were in 1798 when written by Samuel Taylor Coleridge. The high salt content (3.5%) of seawater makes it unfit for human consumption. While some creatures can live in salt water, neither the ancient mariner nor we can subsist on drinking it.

Today, we are able to tap the sea as a source of water for both agriculture and drinking. **Desalination** is any process that removes sodium chloride and other minerals from salty water, thus producing potable water. In 2011, the International Desalination Association reported that almost 16,000 desalination plants worldwide produced over 60 billion liters of water daily. With demand for fresh water ever increasing, we now are witnessing the construction of many new desalination facilities worldwide including in the Middle East, Spain, the United States, China, North Africa, and Australia. One of the world's largest in the United Arab Emirates is shown in Figure 5.29.

One means of desalination is **distillation,** a separation process in which a liquid solution is heated and the vapors are condensed and collected. Impure water is heated. As the water vaporizes, it leaves behind most of its dissolved impurities. Distillation requires energy! Figure 5.30 shows this energy being provided by a Bunsen burner in one case and by the Sun in the other. Recall from Section 5.2 that water has a high specific heat and requires an unusually large amount of energy to convert to a vapor. Both properties result from the extensive hydrogen bonding in water.

> Recall from the chapter opener that the average U.S. citizen uses (directly and indirectly) about 390 liters of water daily.

> A process similar to distillation occurs in the natural water cycle. Water evaporates, condenses, and then falls as rain or snow.

Figure 5.29
Desalination plant at Jebel Ali in the United Arab Emirates.

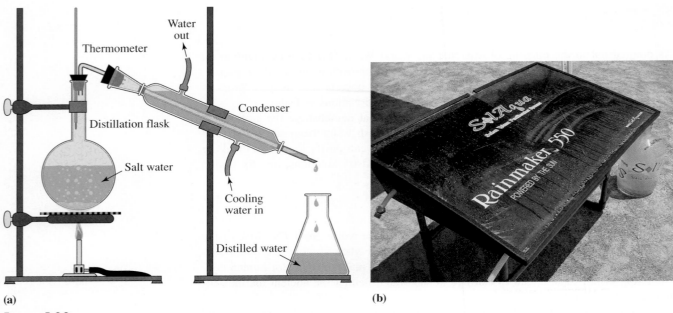

(a)

(b)

Figure 5.30

(a) Laboratory distillation apparatus. (b) Tabletop solar still.

Large-scale distillation operations employ new technologies with impressive names such as multistage flash evaporation. Although these technologies have increased energy efficiency over the basic distillation process shown in Figure 5.30a, their energy requirement is still high and usually provided by burning fossil fuels. An alternative is to purify water using smaller solar distillation units, as shown in Figure 5.30b.

Other desalination options exist. For example, **osmosis** is the passage of water through a semipermeable membrane from a solution that is less concentrated to a solution that is more concentrated. The water diffuses through the membrane and the solute does not. This is why the membrane is called "semipermeable."

However, with an input of energy, osmosis can be reversed. **Reverse osmosis** uses pressure to force the movement of water through a semipermeable membrane from a solution that is more concentrated to a solution that is less concentrated. To use this process to purify water, pressure is applied to the saltwater side, forcing water through the membrane to leave the salt and other impurities behind (Figure 5.31). As might be expected, producing the pressure is energy-intensive. Reverse osmosis

The "distilled water" on tap in chemistry labs most likely is deionized water, produced through reverse osmosis.

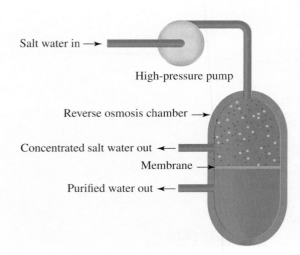

Figure 5.31

Water purification by reverse osmosis.

technology can be used to produce some bottled water and ultra-pure water used in the microelectronic and pharmaceutical industries. Portable units are suitable for use on sailboats (Figure 5.32).

Skeptical Chemist 5.32   At What Cost?

An Internet blogger proclaimed, "Desalination will make it possible for us to get and clean water. This will solve our water shortages." Revisit the green chemistry key ideas to help you refute these claims.

Figure 5.32
A small reverse osmosis apparatus for converting seawater to potable water.

Point-of-Use LifeStraws

With advances in sanitation and management of water-borne diseases over the past century, many in developed countries have access to high-quality drinking water that meets certain standards. However, worldwide a billion people are sickened or die each year due to cholera, typhoid, and other diseases caused by microbes in untreated water. A European company, Vestergaard Frandsen, developed the LifeStraw, which removes virtually all bacteria and protozoan parasites from water. LifeStraws are used in many parts of the globe, including in time of need following a natural disaster.

Aptly named, the personal LifeStraw is a type of pipe filter through which to suck water, as shown in Figure 5.33. This unit can be used to drink from a stream, river, or lake. Lasting about a year, it can purify about 1000 liters of water. The larger LifeStraw family unit contains a different filter that removes bacteria and further improves the quality of water. The family unit filters up to 18,000 liters of water for about 3 years.

The personal LifeStraw has limitations. It is not a long-term solution to the lack of potable water. In addition, it doesn't remove chemicals such as arsenic or fluoride or the viral microbes responsible for diarrhea. Both types of LifeStraws provide an interim solution in regions where fresh water is contaminated with microbes.

Figure 5.33
Children using personal LifeStraws to drink.

Skeptical Chemist 5.33   Periodic Error

The company that produces LifeStraws has a set of FAQs on the Internet. One reads: "Does LifeStraw filter heavy metals like arsenic, iron, and fluoride?" What might the Skeptical Chemist say about the phrasing of this answer: "No, the present version does not filter any of the heavy metals."

The Cotton Industry

A cotton T-shirt, anybody? Or perhaps pants, socks, or a baseball cap? The third effort that we describe targets the water use associated with cotton. Globally, over 40 billion pounds of this very popular material is produced each year. Currently, the United States exports almost 50% of the world's supply. Cotton serves not only as the fiber for clothing but also for many other consumer products. Explore these in Consider This 5.34.

Figure 5.34

Raw cotton has a waxy cuticle (outer layer) that must be removed.

From Section 5.11, recall that a low BOD (biological oxygen demand) indicates good water quality.

Consider This 5.34 — Water Footprint Content of a T–shirt

In Table 5.3, the water footprint of a 250–g cotton T–shirt was listed as 2500 liters.

a. List four ways that water is used in the production of a T–shirt.
b. Besides clothing, cotton has many other uses. Name three.
c. For these uses, estimate whether the water footprint is larger, smaller, or roughly the same as for cotton clothing.

Answers
b. Cotton uses include curtains, upholstery, netting, gauze bandages, and swabs.
c. These all can be expected to have a large water footprint because of the water used both to grow and clean the cotton.

Even though cotton is a natural fiber, its production leaves a significant footprint on the environment. In Section 5.3, we mentioned that cotton was a thirsty crop as it grew. Once produced, raw cotton must be treated to remove the cuticle, or outermost layer of cotton, before it can be bleached and dyed (Figure 5.34). The process of "scouring" the cotton requires copious quantities of caustic chemicals, water, and energy. The wastewater produced has a high BOD equal to that of raw sewage! In addition, the wastewater is contaminated with significant amounts of caustic chemicals, ones that weaken the cotton fibers.

 In 2001, Novozymes won a **Presidential Green Chemistry Challenge Award** for developing an alternative process to remove the waxy cotton cuticle. The milder process, "biopreparation," uses an enzyme that breaks down the cuticle. As a result, cotton's environmental footprint is improved. The BOD of wastewater dropped by more than 20%; the caustic chemicals were eliminated; and the amount of water, energy, and time required was reduced. Recall one of the key ideas of green chemistry: *It is better to use and generate substances that are not toxic.*

Your Turn 5.35 — Green Chemistry in Action

We just named one of the six green chemistry key ideas (see inside front cover) that is met through the Novozymes "biopreparation" process. Which others apply as well?

This is another example of how green chemistry improves the Triple Bottom Line (economic, societal, and environmental), moving us toward more sustainable practices. Reduced and less toxic waste benefits the environment. Using less energy and materials reduces the cost. And society gains a more robust cotton fiber and conserves water. Let's look at one other application for keeping water clean.

"Do Not Flush"

In the past, a quick way to get rid of unwanted medicines was to simply flush them down a sink or toilet. Through flushing, however, these drugs can end up in our waterways exposing those downstream to low drug concentrations. Is this a harmful practice? At this point, the answer is uncertain.

Good news! Together with the Food and Drug Administration, many communities have launched drug take-back programs. For example, in 2012, about 500,000 pounds of unwanted medications was collected at over 5,000 sites across the United States during a National Prescription Drug Take-Back Day. This is another application of green chemistry: *It is better to prevent waste than to treat or clean up waste after it is formed.*

Consider This 5.36   The Future of Water

a. Select two of the green chemistry key ideas listed on the inside front cover. For each, brainstorm an idea that might help us to keep water clean.

b. Identify an important global water issue. Suggest two factors that make it important. Name two ways in which people currently are addressing this issue.

Conclusion

Like the air we breathe, water is essential to our lives. It bathes our cells, transports nutrients through our bodies, provides most of our body mass, and cools us when it evaporates. Water also is central to our *way of life*. We drink it, cook with it, clean things in it, use it to irrigate our crops, and manufacture goods with it. As we do these things, we add waste to the water. Although fresh water purifies itself through a cycle of evaporation and condensation, we humans are dirtying water faster than nature can regenerate clean water.

Remember the first key idea of green chemistry: *It is better to prevent waste than to treat or clean up waste after it is formed.* So catch the rainwater and use it on a garden, rather than letting it run off and join the streams of runoff that pick up pollutants. Instead of using the garbage disposal to grind up food wastes, put the scraps in a compost pile and save the tap water. Turn off the faucet when you are brushing your teeth, limit your time in the shower, and fix that dripping faucet and running toilet!

You may feel like your efforts are a mere drop in a much larger bucket. Indeed they are. But remember that like the raindrop shown in the winning Earth Day poster (to the right), your efforts are part of the bigger water picture on this planet (Figure 5.35).

Although fresh water is a renewable resource, the demands of population growth, rising affluence, and other global issues are amplifying shortages of this essential commodity. If we are to achieve sustainability we must think water! Think water! Your life and the lives of other creatures depend on it.

One little raindrop
Falling from the darkened sky
Landing in the lake

Figure 5.35
An Earth Day Haiku Poster Winner, 2008.

Chapter Summary

Having studied this chapter you should be able to:

- Describe how water is linked to life on this planet (Introduction)
- Connect the electronegativity of atoms with the polarity of the bonds formed from these atoms (5.1)
- Describe hydrogen bonding and relate it to the properties of water (5.2)
- Compare the densities of ice and water and be able to account for the difference (5.2)
- Relate the specific heat of water to the roles played by water on the planet (5.2)
- Discuss the relationship between the properties of water and its molecular structure (5.2)
- Describe the major ways people use water on our planet (5.3)

- Discuss how the concept of water footprint shapes our view of water use (5.3)
- Connect global climate change with the supply and demand of water (5.4)
- Use concentration units: percent, ppm, ppb, and molarity (5.5)
- Discuss why water is such an excellent solvent for many (but not all) ionic and covalent compounds (5.5)
- Relate these terms: *cation, anion,* and *ionic compound* (5.6)
- Write the names and chemical formulas for ionic compounds, including those with common polyatomic ions (5.7)
- Describe what occurs when an ionic compound dissolves in water (5.8)

- Explain why some solutions conduct electricity and others do not (5.9)
- Describe the role of surfactants as solubility agents (5.9)
- Explain the saying "like dissolves like" and relate this to biomagnification (5.9)
- Understand the role of federal legislation in protecting safe drinking water (5.10)
- Contrast the maximum contaminant level goal (MCLG) and the maximum contaminant level (MCL) established by the EPA to ensure water quality (5.10)

- Discuss how drinking water can be made safe to drink (5.11)
- Describe the basic process for sewage treatment (5.11)
- Understand the processes of distillation and reverse osmosis for producing potable water (5.12)
- Describe how green chemistry and its applications can contribute to clean water (5.9, 5.12)
- Summarize at least two possible solutions to our global water challenges (5.12)

Questions

Emphasizing Essentials

1. The chapter opens with these words: "*Neeru, shouei, maima, aqua.* In any language, water is the most abundant compound on the surface of the Earth."

   a. Explain the term *compound* and also why water is *not* an element.

   b. Draw the Lewis structure for water and explain why its shape is bent.

2. Today we are creating dirty water faster than nature can clean it for us.

   a. Name five daily activities that dirty the water.

   b. Name two ways in which polluting substances naturally are removed from water.

   c. Name five steps you could take to keep water cleaner in the first place.

3. Life on our planet depends on water. Explain each of these.

   a. Bodies of water act as heat reservoirs, moderating climate.

   b. Ice protects ecosystems in lakes because it floats rather than sinks.

4. Why might a water pipe break if left full of water during extended frigid weather?

5. Here are four pairs of atoms. Consult Table 5.1 to answer these questions.

N and C	N and H
S and O	S and F

   a. What is the electronegativity difference between the atoms?

   b. Assume that a single covalent bond forms between each pair of atoms. Which atom attracts the electron pair in the bond more strongly?

   c. Arrange the bonds in order of increasing polarity.

6. Consider a molecule of ammonia, NH_3.

   a. Draw its Lewis structure.

   b. Does the NH_3 molecule contain polar bonds? Explain.

   c. Is the NH_3 molecule polar? *Hint:* Consider its geometry.

   d. Would you predict NH_3 to be soluble in water? Explain.

7. In some cases, the boiling point of a substance increases with its molar mass.

   a. Does this hold true for hydrocarbons? Explain with examples. *Hint:* See Section 4.4.

   b. Based on the molar masses of H_2O, N_2, O_2, and CO_2, which would you expect to have the lowest boiling point?

   c. Unlike N_2, O_2, and CO_2, water is a liquid at room temperature. Explain.

8. Both methane (CH_4) and water are compounds of hydrogen and another nonmetal.

   a. Give four examples of nonmetals. In general, how do the electronegativity values of nonmetals compare with those of metals?

   b. How do the electronegativity values of carbon, oxygen, and hydrogen compare?

   c. Which bond is more polar, the C–H bond or the O–H bond?

   d. Methane is a gas at room temperature, but water is a liquid. Explain.

9. This diagram represents two water molecules in a liquid state. What kind of bonding force does the arrow indicate?

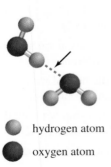

   🔵 hydrogen atom

   ⚫ oxygen atom

10. The density of water at 0 °C is 0.9987 g/cm³; the density of ice at this same temperature is 0.917 g/cm³.

   a. Calculate the volume occupied at 0 °C by 100.0 g of liquid water and by 100.0 g of ice.

   b. Calculate the percentage increase in volume when 100.0 g of water freezes at 0 °C.

11. Consider these liquids.

Liquid	Density, g/mL
dishwashing detergent	1.03
maple syrup	1.37
vegetable oil	0.91

   a. If you pour equal volumes of these three liquids into a 250-mL graduated cylinder, in what order should you add the liquids to create three separate layers? Explain.

   b. Predict what would happen if a volume of water equal to the other liquids were poured into the cylinder in part **a** and the contents then were mixed vigorously.

12. Let's say the water in a 500-L drum represents the world's total supply. How many liters would be suitable for drinking? *Hint:* See Figure 5.8.

13. Based on your experience, how soluble is each of these substances in water? Use terms such as *very soluble, partially soluble,* or *not soluble.* Cite supporting evidence.

   a. orange juice concentrate

   b. household ammonia

   c. chicken fat

   d. liquid laundry detergent

   e. chicken broth

14. a. Bottled water consumption was reported to be 29 gallons per person in the United States in 2011. The 2010 U.S. census reported the population as 3.1×10^8 people. Given this, estimate the total bottled water consumption.

   b. Convert your answer in part **a** to liters.

15. NaCl is an ionic compound, but $SiCl_4$ is a covalent compound.

   a. Use Table 5.1 to determine the electronegativity difference between chlorine and sodium, and between chlorine and silicon.

   b. What correlations can be drawn about the difference in electronegativity between bonded atoms and their tendency to form ionic or covalent bonds?

   c. How can you explain, on the molecular level, the conclusion reached in part **b**?

16. For each of these atoms, draw a Lewis structure. Also draw the Lewis structure for the corresponding ion. *Hint:* Consult Tables 5.5 and 5.6.

   a. Cl   b. S

   c. Ne   **d.** Ba

   e. Li

17. Give the chemical formula and name of the ionic compound that can be formed from each pair of elements.

   a. Na and Br   b. Cd and S

   c. Ba and Cl   **d.** Al and O

   e. Rb and I

18. Write the chemical formula for each compound.

   a. calcium bicarbonate   **b.** calcium carbonate

   c. magnesium chloride   d. magnesium sulfate

19. Name each compound.

   a. $KC_2H_3O_2$ b. LiOH

   c. CoO   d. ZnS

   e. $Ca(ClO)_2$ f. Na_2SO_4

   g. $MnCl_2$ h. K_2O

20. Explain why $CoCl_2$ is named cobalt(II) chloride, whereas $CaCl_2$ is named calcium chloride.

21. The MCL for mercury in drinking water is 0.002 mg/L.

   a. Does this correspond to 2 ppm or 2 ppb mercury?

   b. Is this mercury in the form of elemental mercury ("quicksilver") or the mercury ion (Hg^{2+})?

22. The acceptable limit for nitrate, often found in well water in agricultural areas, is 10 ppm. If a water sample is found to contain 350 mg/L, does it meet the acceptable limit?

23. A student weighs out 5.85 g of NaCl to make a 0.10 M solution. What size volumetric flask does he or she need? *Hint:* See Figure 5.16.

24. Solutions can be tested for conductivity using this type of apparatus.

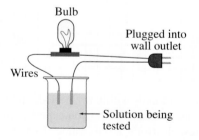

Predict what will happen when each of these dilute solutions is tested for conductivity. Explain your predictions briefly.

   a. $CaCl_2(aq)$ **b.** $C_2H_5OH(aq)$ c. $H_2SO_4(aq)$

25. An aqueous solution of KCl conducts electricity, but an aqueous solution of sucrose does not. Explain.

26. Based on the generalizations in Table 5.9, which compounds are likely to be water-soluble?

    a. $KC_2H_3O_2$ b. LiOH

    c. $Ca(NO_3)_2$ d. Na_2SO_4

27. For a 2.5 M solution of $Mg(NO_3)_2$, what is the concentration of each ion present?

28. Explain how you would prepare these solutions using powdered reagents and any necessary glassware.

    a. Two liters of 1.50 M KOH

    b. One liter of 0.050 M NaBr

    c. 0.10 L of 1.2 M $Mg(OH)_2$

29. a. A 5-minute shower requires about 90 L of water. How much water would you save for each minute that you shorten your shower?

    b. Running the water while you brush your teeth can consume another liter. How much water can you save in a week by turning it off?

30. Use the Internet to determine which has the higher water footprint, a 100-gram chocolate bar or a 16-ounce glass of beer. Explain the difference.

Concentrating on Concepts

31. Explain why water is often called the *universal solvent*.

32. Is there any such thing as "pure" drinking water? Discuss what is implied by this term, and how the meaning of this term might change in different parts of the world.

33. Some vitamins are water-soluble, whereas others are fat-soluble. Would you expect either or both to be polar molecules? Explain.

34. A new sign is posted at the edge of a favorite fishing hole that says "Caution: Fish from this lake may contain over 1.5 ppb Hg." Explain to a fishing buddy what this unit of concentration means, and why the caution sign should be heeded.

35. This periodic table contains four elements identified by numbers.

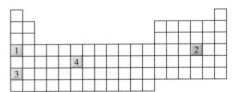

    a. Based on trends within the periodic table, which of the four elements would you expect to have the highest electronegativity value? Explain.

    b. Based on trends within the periodic table, rank the other three elements in order of decreasing electronegativity values. Explain your ranking.

36. A diatomic molecule XY that contains a polar bond *must* be a polar molecule. However, a triatomic molecule XY_2 that contains a polar bond *does not necessarily* form a polar molecule. Use some examples of real molecules to help explain this difference.

37. Imagine you are at the molecular level, watching water vapor condense.

    a. Sketch four water molecules using a space-filling representation similar to this one. Sketch them in the gaseous state and then in the liquid state. How does the collection of molecules change when water vapor condenses to a liquid?

    b. What happens at the molecular level when water changes from a liquid to a solid?

38. Propose an explanation for the fact that NH_3, like H_2O, has an unexpectedly high specific heat.
    Hint: See Figure 3.12 for the Lewis structure and bond geometry in NH_3.

39. a. What type of bond holds together the two hydrogen atoms in the hydrogen molecule, H_2?

    b. Explain why the term *hydrogen bonding* does *not* apply to the bond within H_2.

40. Consider ethanol, an alcohol with the chemical formula of C_2H_5OH.

    a. Draw the Lewis structure for ethanol.

    b. A cube of solid ethanol sinks rather than floats in liquid ethanol. Explain this behavior.

41. The unusually high specific heat of water helps keep our body temperature within a normal range despite age, activity, and environmental factors. Consider some of the ways the body produces and loses heat. How would these differ if water had a low specific heat?

42. Health goals for contaminants in drinking water are expressed as MCLG, or maximum contaminant level goals. Legal limits are given as MCL, or maximum contaminant levels. How are MCLG and MCL related for a given contaminant?

43. Some areas have a higher than normal amount of THMs (trihalomethanes) in the drinking water. Suppose that you are considering moving to such an area. Write a letter to the local water district asking relevant questions about the drinking water.

44. Infants are highly susceptible to elevated nitrate levels because bacteria in their digestive tract convert nitrate ion into nitrite ion, a much more toxic substance.

    a. Give chemical formulas for both the nitrate ion and nitrite ion.

    b. Nitrite ion can interfere with the ability of blood to carry oxygen. Explain the role of oxygen in respiration. *Hint:* Review Sections 1.1 and 3.5 for more about respiration.

    c. Boiling nitrate-containing water will not remove nitrate ion. Explain.

45. Water quality in a chemistry building on campus was continuously monitored because testing indicated water from drinking fountains in the building had dissolved lead levels above those established by the Safe Drinking Water Act.

   a. What is the likely major source of the lead in the drinking water?

   b. Do the research activities carried out in this chemistry building account for the elevated lead levels found in the drinking water? Explain.

46. Explain why desalination techniques, despite proven technological effectiveness, are not used more widely to produce potable drinking water.

Exploring Extensions

47. In 2005, the Great Lakes–St. Lawrence River Basin Sustainable Water Resources Agreement set the stage to coordinate water management and protect water from use by those outside the region.

   a. List states and provinces involved with this unique transboundary agreement.

   b. What was the impetus behind protecting these waters?

48. Liquid CO_2 has been used successfully for many years to decaffeinate coffee. Explain how and why this works.

49. How can you purify your water when you are hiking? Name two or three possibilities. Compare these methods in terms of cost and effectiveness. Are any of these methods similar to those used to purify municipal water supplies? Explain.

50. Hydrogen bonds vary in strength from about 4 to 40 kJ/mol. Given that the hydrogen bonds between water molecules are at the high end of this range, how does the strength of a hydrogen bond *between* water molecules compare with the strength of a H–O covalent bond *within* a water molecule? Do your values bear out the assertion made in Section 5.2 that hydrogen bonds are about one tenth as strong as covalent bonds? *Hint:* Consult Table 4.4 for covalent bond energies.

51. Levels of naturally occurring mercury in surface water are usually less than 0.5 μg/L.

   a. Name three human activities that add Hg^{2+} ("inorganic mercury") to water.

   b. What is "organic mercury"? This chemical form of mercury tends to accumulate in the fatty tissues of fish. Explain why.

52. We all have the amino acid glycine in our bodies. Here is the structural formula.

$$H-\underset{\underset{H}{|}}{\overset{\overset{H}{|}}{N}}-\underset{\underset{H}{|}}{\overset{}{C}}-\overset{\overset{O}{\|}}{C}-O-H$$

   a. Is glycine a polar or nonpolar molecule? Explain.

   b. Can glycine exhibit hydrogen bonding? Explain.

   c. Is glycine soluble in water? Explain.

53. Hard water may contain Mg^{2+} and Ca^{2+} ions. The process of water softening removes these ions.

   a. How hard is the water in your local area? One way to answer this question is to determine the number of water-softening companies in your area. Use the Internet, as well as ads in your local newspapers and yellow pages, to find out if your area is targeted for marketing water-softening devices.

   b. If you chose to treat your hard water, what are the options?

54. Suppose that you are in charge of regulating an industry in your area that manufactures agricultural pesticides. How will you decide if this plant is obeying necessary environmental controls? Which criteria affect the success of this plant?

55. Before the U.S. EPA banned their manufacture in 1979, PCBs were regarded as useful chemicals. What properties made them desirable? Besides being persistent in the environment, they bioaccumulate in the fatty tissues of animals. Use the electronegativity concept to show why PCB molecules are nonpolar and thus fat-soluble.

56. The PUR "Purifier of Water" is a point-of-use system.

   a. How does this system work?

   b. Compare it to the personal LifeStraw by listing benefits offered by each system.

57. In the United States, the EPA has set SMCLs (secondary maximum contaminant levels) for substances in drinking water that are not health threatening. Visit the EPA website to learn more about one of these substances and prepare a summary of your findings.

58. The EPA uses an extensive process to add contaminants to its list of regulated substances. Search the Internet for information on the Unregulated Contaminant Monitoring (UCM) program.

   a. What is the UCM, and when does it occur?

   b. What is the importance of its Contaminant Candidate List (CCL), and how does it relate to the precautionary principle?

   c. List some general categories of substances included in the CCL. Include one specific substance from the most current list.

59. List a recent theme for World Water Day. Prepare a short presentation of this theme in a format of your choice.

CHAPTER 6

Neutralizing the Threats of Acid Rain and Ocean Acidification

"I tell my son, go to see the corals now because soon it will be too late."
James Orr, Laboratory of Sciences of the Climate and Environment, France.

Source: *New Scientist*, August 5, 2006. Ocean Acidification: the *Other* CO_2 Problem.

Coral reefs are massive structures found in shallow ocean waters. Often called "the rain forests of the ocean," reefs provide habitat for countless species of marine creatures. Attached to a reef or in the water nearby you may find sponges, mollusks, clams, crab, shrimp, sea urchins, sea worms, jellyfish, and many species of fish. Of benefit to humans, reefs protect fragile coastlines from powerful ocean waves. In some countries, they single-handedly support the tourism industry.

Coral reefs are alive. With lifetimes of hundreds of thousands of years, reefs can grow thousands of kilometers long, millimeter by millimeter. The tiny animals that form the reef grow and develop using nutrients and other essential chemical compounds dissolved in the ocean water. Why does James Orr want his son to go see the corals? Simply put, today's reefs may not exist tomorrow. Scientists estimate that at least a quarter of the reefs are now lost; very few are pristine. As energy use worldwide has climbed, changes in both the temperature and chemical composition of our atmosphere have occurred. In turn, changes have occurred in our oceans. At best, these changes slow the growth of coral reefs; at worst they damage the ecosystems established within the reefs. Here we are witness to another example of the tragedy of the commons.

As you learned in earlier chapters, we burn fuels to harness their energy. Emissions from combustion include carbon dioxide, nitrogen oxides, and sulfur dioxide. These gases, especially the oxides of nitrogen and sulfur, are soluble in water, including the salt water of our oceans. They dissolve to produce acids; as a result, the water becomes more acidic. For example, over time oceans absorb 25–40% of the carbon dioxide that is emitted as a result of human activities. As more carbon dioxide is emitted, more carbon dioxide dissolves in the oceans. The resulting changes in the seawater have significant effects on ocean ecosystems. For example, the increase in acidity leads to a reduction in the amount of carbonate ion available to build and maintain coral reefs.

The emissions from combustion dissolve not only in the oceans but also in water anywhere on the planet, including the rain, snow, and mist of our atmosphere. For example, when SO_2 and NO_x dissolve in rainwater, they fall back to the Earth in the form of acid rain. Just as added acidity damages ocean ecosystems, it damages the ecosystems of rivers and lakes as well.

In Chapter 5 you learned about water's special properties, what water is used for, how it tends to get dirty, and how we clean it. In this chapter, you will learn how certain compounds dissolve in water to produce acidic and basic solutions. In the right context, acids and bases are extremely useful compounds. We depend on them in many agricultural and manufacturing processes. Acids also impart flavors to the foods we eat. However, in the wrong place at the wrong time, acids can have devastating effects. Ocean acidification and acid rain are two examples. This chapter tells the story of both with an eye to helping you understand what is happening and why. But this story would not be complete without a discussion of bases and of pH, so we touch on these topics as well.

Since people tend to be more familiar with acids than with bases, we begin with a discussion of acids and their properties. In what contexts have you already encountered acids? Before you read about acids in the next section, take a moment to do this activity.

Over time, healthy reefs repair themselves. So in part, the issue becomes how healthy the reefs were to begin with.

The tragedy of the commons was discussed in Chapter 1.

Ocean acidification is one of several factors that harm coral reefs. Physical damage occurs with storms and warming ocean temperature; chemical damage occurs due to waste products dumped in the ocean.

Recall from Chapter 1 that NO_x is a shorthand notation for NO and NO_2.

Recall from Chapter 5 that water is a polar compound. Nonpolar compounds such as CO_2 dissolve in water only to a small extent. In contrast, SO_2 is a polar compound and very soluble.

Your Turn 6.1   Acids You Have Encountered

a. List the names for any three compounds that are acids.
b. In what context do you know of these acids? For example, is it from reading ingredient labels on foods? Did you run across these acids in some sport or activity? Did you read about these acids in a news article?

6.1 | What Is an Acid?

Figure 6.1

Citrus fruit contains both citric acid and ascorbic acid.

We can approach acids either by listing their observable properties or by describing their behavior at the molecular level. Either way, the information is useful to our discussion, so we employ both approaches.

Historically, chemists identified acids by properties such as their sour taste. Although tasting is not a smart way to identify chemicals, you undoubtedly know the sour taste of acetic acid in vinegar. The sour taste of lemons comes from acids as well (Figure 6.1). Acids also show a characteristic color change with indicators such as litmus.

The plant dye litmus changes from blue to pink in acid. The term *litmus test* has also come to refer to something that quickly reveals a politician's point of view.

Another way to identify an acid is by its chemical properties. For example, under certain conditions acids can react with and dissolve marble, eggshell, or the shells of marine creatures. These materials all contain the carbonate ion (CO_3^{2-}) either as calcium carbonate or magnesium carbonate. An acid reacts with a carbonate to produce carbon dioxide. This gas is the "burp" when carbonate-containing stomach antacid tablets react with acids in your stomach. This chemical reaction also explains the dissolution of the skeletons of carbonate-based sea creatures such as coral in acidified oceans, as we will see in a later section.

You will see the term *proton* again in Chapter 8 (proton exchange membranes) and Chapter 10 (the protonated form of drug molecules).

At the molecular level, an **acid** is a compound that releases hydrogen ions, H^+, in aqueous solution. Remember that a hydrogen atom is electrically neutral and consists of one electron and one proton. If the electron is lost, the atom becomes a positively charged ion, H^+. Because only a proton remains, sometimes H^+ is referred to as a proton.

For example, consider hydrogen chloride (HCl), a compound that is a gas at room temperature. Hydrogen chloride is composed of HCl molecules. These dissolve readily in water to produce a solution that we name hydrochloric acid. As the polar HCl molecules dissolve, they become surrounded by polar water molecules. Once dissolved, these molecules break apart into two ions: $H^+(aq)$ and $Cl^-(aq)$. This equation represents the two steps of the reaction.

The notation *(aq)* is short for *aqueous.* Revisit equations 5.4 and 5.5, which show the formation of ions as a solute dissolves in water.

$$HCl(g) \xrightarrow{H_2O} HCl(aq) \longrightarrow H^+(aq) + Cl^-(aq) \qquad [6.1]$$

We also could say that HCl *dissociates* into H^+ and Cl^-. No HCl molecules remain in solution because they dissociate completely. Hydrochloric acid is a **strong acid,** that is, an acid that dissociates completely in aqueous solution.

There is a slight complication with the definition of acids as substances that release H^+ (protons) in aqueous solutions. By themselves, H^+ are much too reactive to exist as such. Rather, they attach to something else, such as water molecules. When dissolved in water, each HCl molecule donates a proton (H^+) to an H_2O molecule, forming H_3O^+, a hydronium ion. Here is a representation of the overall reaction.

Here is the Lewis structure for the hydronium ion:

$$\left[\begin{array}{c} H \\ H \!:\! \overset{\cdot\cdot}{O} \!:\! H \end{array} \right]^{+}$$

It obeys the octet rule.

$$HCl(aq) + H_2O(l) \longrightarrow H_3O^+(aq) + Cl^-(aq) \qquad [6.2]$$

The solution represented on the product side in *both* equations 6.1 and 6.2 is called hydrochloric acid. It has the characteristic properties of an acid because of the presence of H_3O^+. Chemists often simply write H^+ when referring to acids (for example, in equation 6.1), but understand this to mean H_3O^+ (hydronium ion) in aqueous solutions.

Your Turn 6.2   Acidic Solutions

For each of these strong acids dissolved in water, write a chemical equation that shows the release of a hydrogen ion, H^+.

Hint: Remember to include the charges on the ions. The net charge on both sides of the equation should be the same.

a. HI(aq), hydroiodic acid   b. HNO₃(aq), nitric acid   c. H₂SO₄(aq), sulfuric acid

Answer

c. $H_2SO_4(aq) \longrightarrow H^+(aq) + HSO_4^-(aq)$

Refer back to Chapter 5 to review
solubility. In general, "like dissolves like."

Consider This 6.3   Are All Acids Harmful?

Although the word *acid* may conjure up all sorts of pictures in your mind, every day you eat or drink various acids. Check the labels of foods or beverages and make a list of the acids you find. Speculate on the purpose of each acid.

Hydrogen chloride is but one of several gases that dissolves in water to produce an acidic solution. Sulfur dioxide and nitrogen dioxide are two others. These two gases are emitted during the combustion of certain fuels (particularly coal) to produce heat and electricity. As we mentioned in the introduction to this chapter, SO_2 and NO_2 both dissolve in rain and mist. When they do so, they form acids that in turn fall back to the Earth's surface in rain and snow. The increased acidity of the Earth's water due to anthropogenic emissions is the central focus of this chapter.

But before delving into the acidity in rain caused by nitrogen oxides and sulfur dioxide, let's focus on carbon dioxide. With an atmospheric concentration of about 400 ppm in 2013, and rising, carbon dioxide is at a far higher concentration than either sulfur dioxide or nitrogen dioxide. Just as solids vary in their solubility in water, so do gases. Compared with more polar compounds such as SO_2 and NO_2, carbon dioxide is far less soluble in water. Even so, it dissolves to produce a weakly acidic solution.

At this stage, you as a Skeptical Chemist should be raising an important question. Given that an acid is defined as a substance that releases hydrogen ions in water, how can carbon dioxide act as an acid? There are no hydrogen atoms in carbon dioxide! The explanation is that when CO_2 dissolves in water, it produces carbonic acid, $H_2CO_3(aq)$. Here is a way to represent the process.

$$CO_2(g) \xrightarrow{H_2O} CO_2(aq) \qquad \textbf{[6.3a]}$$

$$CO_2(aq) + H_2O(l) \longrightarrow H_2CO_3(aq) \qquad \textbf{[6.3b]}$$

The carbonic acid dissociates to produce H^+ and the hydrogen carbonate ion.

$$H_2CO_3(aq) \longrightarrow H^+(aq) + HCO_3^-(aq) \qquad \textbf{[6.3c]}$$

This reaction occurs only to a limited extent, producing only tiny amounts of H^+ and HCO_3^-. Accordingly, we say that carbonic acid is a **weak acid,** that is, an acid that dissociates only to a small extent in aqueous solution.

Although carbon dioxide is only slightly soluble in water, and then only a tiny amount of the dissolved carbonic acid dissociates to produce H^+, these reactions are happening on a large scale across the planet. The carbon dioxide can dissolve in water in the troposphere (making acids that may fall as acidic rain) or in the planet's oceans, lakes, and streams. We will return to this topic after we introduce bases.

6.2 | What Is a Base?

No discussion of acids would be complete without discussing their chemical counterparts—bases. For our purposes, a **base** is a compound that releases hydroxide ions, OH^-, in aqueous solution. Aqueous solutions of bases have their own characteristic properties attributable to the presence of $OH^-(aq)$. Unlike acids, bases generally taste bitter and do not lend an appealing flavor to foods. Aqueous solutions of bases have a slippery, soapy feel. Common examples of bases include household ammonia (an aqueous solution of NH_3) and NaOH, sometimes called lye. The cautions on oven cleaners (Figure 6.2) warn that lye can cause severe damage to eyes, skin, and clothing.

Many common bases are compounds containing the hydroxide ion. For example, sodium hydroxide (NaOH), a water-soluble ionic compound, dissolves in water to produce sodium ions (Na^+) and hydroxide ions (OH^-).

$$NaOH(s) \xrightarrow{H_2O} Na^+(aq) + OH^-(aq) \qquad \textbf{[6.4]}$$

Dilute basic solutions have a soapy feel because bases can react with the oils of your skin to produce a tiny bit of soap.

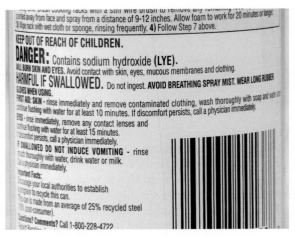

Figure 6.2
Oven cleaning products may contain NaOH, commonly called lye.

Although sodium hydroxide is very soluble in water, most compounds containing the hydroxide ion are not. Table 5.9 summarized the solubility trends for compounds containing specific types of anions. Bases that dissociate completely in water, such as NaOH, are called **strong bases.**

Your Turn 6.4   Basic Solutions

These solids dissolve in water to release hydroxide ions. For each, write a balanced chemical equation.

a. KOH*(s)*, potassium hydroxide
b. LiOH*(s)*, lithium hydroxide
c. Ca(OH)₂*(s)*, calcium hydroxide **Note:** Calcium hydroxide is a weak base. The reaction you have written will occur only to a small extent.

Some bases, however, do not contain the hydroxide ion, OH⁻, but rather react with water to form it. One example is ammonia, a gas with a distinctive sharp odor. Unlike carbon dioxide, ammonia is very soluble in water. It rapidly dissolves in water to form an aqueous solution.

> In some industrial applications, ammonia (rather than HCFCs) is used as a refrigerant gas. Great care needs to be taken to prevent the exposure of workers to ammonia, as the gas can dissolve in moist lung tissue and injure or kill.

$$NH_3(g) \xrightarrow{\text{H}_2\text{O}} NH_3(aq) \qquad \textbf{[6.5a]}$$

On a supermarket shelf, you may see a 5% (by mass) aqueous solution of ammonia called "household ammonia." This cleaning agent has an unpleasant odor; if it gets on your skin, you should wash it off with plenty of water.

The chemical behavior of aqueous ammonia is difficult to simplify, but we will do our best to represent it for you with a chemical equation. When an ammonia molecule reacts with a water molecule, the water molecule transfers H⁺ to the NH₃ molecule. An ammonium ion, $NH_4^+(aq)$, and a hydroxide ion, $OH^-(aq)$, are formed. However, this reaction only occurs to a small extent, that is, only a tiny amount of $OH^-(aq)$ is produced.

> The ammonium ion, NH_4^+, is analogous to the hydronium ion, H_3O^+, in that each was formed by the addition of a proton (H⁺) to a neutral compound.

$$NH_3(aq) + H_2O(l) \xrightarrow{\text{only to a small extent}} NH_4^+(aq) + OH^-(aq) \qquad \textbf{[6.5b]}$$

The source of the hydroxide ion in household ammonia now should be apparent. When ammonia dissolves in water, it releases small amounts of the hydroxide ion and the ammonium ion. Aqueous ammonia is an example of a **weak base,** a base that dissociates only to a small extent in aqueous solution.

To indicate more clearly that aqueous ammonia is a base, some people use the representation NH₄OH*(aq).* If you add up the atoms (and their charges), you will see that NH₄OH(*aq*) is equivalent to the left-hand side of equation 6.5b. It is unlikely, however, that this species exists as such in an aqueous solution of ammonia.

6.3 | Neutralization: Bases Are Antacids

Acids and bases react with each other—often very rapidly. This happens not only in laboratory test tubes, but also in your home and in almost every ecological niche of our planet. For example, if you put lemon juice on fish, an acid–base reaction occurs. The acids found in lemons neutralize the ammonia-like compounds that produce the "fishy smell." Similarly, if the ammonia fertilizer on a corn field comes in contact with the acidic emissions of a power plant nearby, an acid–base reaction occurs.

Let us first examine the acid–base reaction of solutions of hydrochloric acid and sodium hydroxide. When the two are mixed, the products are sodium chloride and water.

$$HCl(aq) + NaOH(aq) \longrightarrow NaCl(aq) + H_2O(l) \qquad \textbf{[6.6]}$$

This is an example of a **neutralization reaction,** a chemical reaction in which the hydrogen ions from an acid combine with the hydroxide ions from a base to form water molecules. The formation of water can be represented like this.

$$H^+(aq) + OH^-(aq) \longrightarrow H_2O(l) \qquad \textbf{[6.7]}$$

> Recall from Section 5.8 that NaCl is an ionic compound that dissolves in water to produce Na⁺(*aq*) and Cl⁻(*aq*).

What about the sodium and chloride ions? Recall from equations 6.1 and 6.4 that the HCl(*g*) and NaOH(*s*), when dissolved in water, completely dissociate into ions. We can rewrite equation 6.6 to show this.

$$H^+(aq) + Cl^-(aq) + Na^+(aq) + OH^-(aq) \longrightarrow Na^+(aq) + Cl^-(aq) + H_2O(l) \quad \textbf{[6.8]}$$

Neither Na⁺(*aq*) nor Cl⁻(*aq*) take part in the neutralization reaction; they remain unchanged. Canceling these ions from both sides again gives us equation 6.7, which summarizes the chemical changes taking place in an acid–base neutralization reaction.

Your Turn 6.5   Neutralization Reactions

For each acid–base pair, write a balanced neutralization reaction. Then rewrite the equation in ionic form and eliminate ions common to both sides. What is the relevance of the final simplified step in each case?

a. HNO₃(*aq*) and KOH(*aq*)

b. HCl(*aq*) and NH₄OH(*aq*)

c. HBr(*aq*) and Ba(OH)₂(*aq*)

Answer

c. $2\,HBr(aq) + Ba(OH)_2(aq) \longrightarrow BaBr_2(aq) + 2\,H_2O(l)$

$2\,H^+(aq) + \cancel{2\,Br^-(aq)} + \cancel{Ba^{2+}(aq)} + 2\,OH^-(aq) \longrightarrow \cancel{Ba^{2+}(aq)} + \cancel{2\,Br^-(aq)} + 2\,H_2O(l)$

$2\,H^+(aq) + 2\,OH^-(aq) \longrightarrow 2\,H_2O(l)$

Divide by 2 to simplify this last equation.

$H^+(aq) + OH^-(aq) \longrightarrow H_2O(l)$

In each case, the final step summarizes the reaction, that is, it shows that the hydrogen ion from the acid and the hydroxide ion from the base react with each other to form water.

A **neutral solution** is neither acidic nor basic, that is, it has equal concentrations of H⁺ and OH⁻. Pure water is a neutral solution. Some salt solutions also are neutral, such as the one formed by dissolving solid NaCl in water. In contrast, acidic solutions contain a higher concentration of H⁺ than OH⁻, and basic solutions contain a higher concentration of OH⁻ than H⁺.

> There is no such thing as "pure" water. Remember from Chapter 5 that water always contains impurities.

It may seem strange that acidic and basic solutions contain both hydroxide ions *and* hydrogen ions. But when water is involved, it is not possible to have H^+ without OH^- (or vice versa). A simple, useful, and very important relationship exists between the concentration of hydrogen ion and hydroxide ion in any aqueous solution.

$$[H^+][OH^-] = 1 \times 10^{-14} \qquad \textbf{[6.9]}$$

The square brackets indicate that the ion concentrations are expressed in molarity, and $[H^+]$ is read as "the hydrogen ion concentration." When $[H^+]$ and $[OH^-]$ are multiplied, the product is a constant with a value of 1×10^{-14} as shown in mathematical equation 6.9. This shows that the concentrations of H^+ and OH^- depend on each other. When $[H^+]$ increases, $[OH^-]$ decreases, and when $[H^+]$ decreases, $[OH^-]$ increases. Both ions are always present in aqueous solutions.

Knowing the concentration of H^+, we can use equation 6.9 to calculate the concentration of OH^- (or vice versa). For example, if a rain sample has a H^+ concentration of 1×10^{-5} M, we can calculate the OH^- concentration by substituting 1×10^{-5} M for $[H^+]$.

$$(1 \times 10^{-5}) \times [OH^-] = 1 \times 10^{-14}$$
$$[OH^-] = \frac{1 \times 10^{-14}}{1 \times 10^{-5}}$$
$$[OH^-] = 1 \times 10^{-9}$$

Since the hydroxide ion concentration (1×10^{-9} M) is smaller than the hydrogen ion concentration (1×10^{-5} M), the solution is acidic.

In pure water or in a neutral solution, the concentrations of the hydrogen and hydroxide ions both equal 1×10^{-7} M. Applying mathematical equation 6.9, we can see that $[H^+][OH^-] = (1 \times 10^{-7})(1 \times 10^{-7}) = 1 \times 10^{-14}$.

The product $[H^+][OH^-]$ is dependent on temperature. The value 1×10^{-14} is valid at 25 °C.

By definition, the product of the two concentrations is unitless.

acidic solution	$[H^+] > [OH^-]$
neutral solution	$[H^+] = [OH^-]$
basic solution	$[H^+] < [OH^-]$

Your Turn 6.6   Acidic and Basic Solutions

For parts **a** and **c**, calculate $[OH^-]$. For **b**, calculate $[H^+]$. Then, classify each solution as acidic, neutral, or basic.

   a. $[H^+] = 1 \times 10^{-4}$ M   **b.** $[OH^-] = 1 \times 10^{-6}$ M   **c.** $[H^+] = 1 \times 10^{-10}$ M

Answer
   a. $[H^+][OH^-] = 1 \times 10^{-14}$. Solving, $[OH^-] = 1 \times 10^{-10}$ M. The solution is acidic because $[H^+] > [OH^-]$.

Your Turn 6.7   Ions in Acidic and Basic Solutions

These solutions represent strong acids or strong bases. Classify each as acidic or basic. Then list all of the ions present in order of decreasing relative amounts in each solution.

   a. KOH*(aq)*   **b.** HNO_3*(aq)*   **c.** H_2SO_4*(aq)*   **d.** $Ca(OH)_2$*(aq)*

Answer
   d. When calcium hydroxide dissociates, two hydroxide ions are released for each calcium ion. The basic solution contains much more OH^- than H^+.

$$OH^-(aq) > Ca^{2+}(aq) > H^+(aq)$$

How can we know if the acidity of seawater and of rain is cause for concern? To make a judgment, we need a convenient way of reporting how acidic or basic a solution is. The pH scale is just such a tool because it relates the acidity of a solution to its H^+ concentration.

6.4 | Introducing pH

The term *pH* already may be familiar to you. For example, test kits for soils and for the water in aquariums and swimming pools report the acidity in terms of pH. Deodorants and shampoos claim to be pH-balanced (Figure 6.3). And, of course, articles about acid rain make reference to pH. The notation pH is always written with a small p and a capital H and stands for "power of hydrogen." In the simplest terms, **pH** is a number, usually between 0 and 14, that indicates the acidity (or basicity) of a solution.

As the midpoint on the scale, pH 7 separates acidic from basic solutions. Solutions with a pH less than 7 are acidic, and those with a pH greater than 7 are basic (alkaline). Solutions of pH 7 (such as pure water) have equal concentrations of H^+ and OH^- and are said to be neutral.

The pH values of common substances are displayed in Figure 6.4. You may be surprised that you eat and drink so many acids. Acids naturally occur in foods and contribute distinctive tastes. For example, the tangy taste of McIntosh apples comes from malic acid. Yogurt gets its sour taste from lactic acid, and cola soft drinks contain several acids, including phosphoric acid. Tomatoes are well known for their acidity, but with a pH of about 4.5, they are in fact less acidic than many other fruits.

Figure 6.3

This shampoo claims to be "pH–balanced," that is, adjusted to be closer to neutral. Soaps tend to be basic, which can be irritating to the skin.

Universal indicator paper is a quick way to estimate the pH of a solution. For more accurate results, pH meters are used.

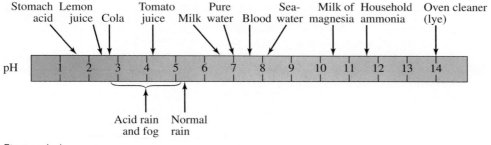

Figure 6.4

Common substances and their pH values.

(图) Figures Alive!

For highly acidic or basic solutions, the pH may lie outside the 0–to–14 range.

Consider This 6.8   Acidity of Foods

a. Rank tomato juice, lemon juice, milk, cola, and pure water in order of increasing acidity. Check your order against Figure 6.4.

b. Pick any other five foods and make a similar ranking. Search the Internet to find their actual pH values.

Is the water on the planet acidic, basic, or neutral? Water would be expected to have a pH of 7.0, but Figure 6.4 shows that the pH of water depends on where it is found. "Normal" rain is slightly acidic, with a pH value between 5 and 6. Even though the acid formed by dissolved carbon dioxide is a weak acid, enough H^+ is produced to lower the pH of rain. Seawater is slightly basic, with a pH of approximately 8.2.

As you might have guessed, pH values are related to the hydrogen ion concentration. If $[H^+] = 1 \times 10^{-3}$ M, then the pH is 3. Similarly, for $[H^+] = 1 \times 10^{-9}$ M, the pH is 9.

Equation 6.9 shows that the hydrogen ion concentration multiplied by the hydroxide ion concentration is a constant, 1×10^{-14}. When the concentration of H^+ is high (and the pH is low), the concentration of OH^- is low. Likewise, as pH values rise above 7.0,

The mathematical relationship is

$$pH = -\log[H^+]$$

More information can be found in Appendix 3.

the concentration of hydrogen ions decreases and the concentration of hydroxide ions increases. As the pH value *decreases*, the acidity *increases*. For example, a sample of water with a pH of 5.0 is 10 times *less* acidic than one with a pH of 4.0. This is because a pH of 4 means that the [H⁺] is 0.0001 M. By contrast, a solution with a pH of 5 is more dilute, with a [H⁺] = 0.00001 M. This second solution is *less* acidic with only 1/10 the hydrogen ion concentration of a solution of pH 4. Figure 6.5 shows the relationship between pH and the hydrogen ion concentration.

| [H⁺] | 10^{-1} 10^{-2} 10^{-3} 10^{-4} 10^{-5} 10^{-6} 10^{-7} 10^{-8} 10^{-9} 10^{-10} 10^{-11} 10^{-12} 10^{-13} 10^{-14} |
| pH | 1　2　3　4　5　6　7　8　9　10　11　12　13　14 |

Acidic　　　　　　　　　　Basic

Neutral

Figure 6.5

The relationship between pH and the concentration of H⁺ in moles per liter (M). As pH increases, [H⁺] decreases.

Your Turn 6.9　　Small Changes, Big Effects

Compare the pairs of samples below. For each, which one is more acidic? Include the relative difference in hydrogen ion concentration between the two pH values.

a. Rain sample, pH = 5, and lake water sample, pH = 4.
b. Ocean water sample, pH = 8.3, and tap water sample, pH = 5.3.
c. Tomato juice sample, pH = 4.5, and milk sample, pH = 6.5.

Answer

c. Although the pH values differ only by 2, the tomato juice sample is 100 times more acidic and (for an equal volume) would have 100 times more H⁺ than the milk sample.

Consider This 6.10　　On the Record

A legislator from the Midwest is on record with an impassioned speech in which he argued that the environmental policy of the state should be to bring the pH of rain all the way down to zero. Assume that you are an aide to this legislator. Draft a tactful memo to your boss to save him from additional public embarrassment.

6.5 | Ocean Acidification

How can seawater be basic when rain is naturally acidic? Indeed this is the case, as shown in Figure 6.4. Ocean water contains small amounts of three chemical species that play a role in maintaining the ocean pH at approximately 8.2. These three species—the carbonate ion, the bicarbonate ion, and carbonic acid—interact with each other as well. All arise from dissolved carbon dioxide (equations 6.3a, b, and c). These species also help maintain your blood at a pH of about 7.4.

Ocean pH can vary by ±0.3 pH units, depending on latitude and region.

Only one resonance form is shown for the bicarbonate ion and for the carbonate ion. For more about resonance, see Section 2.3.

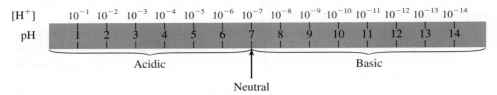

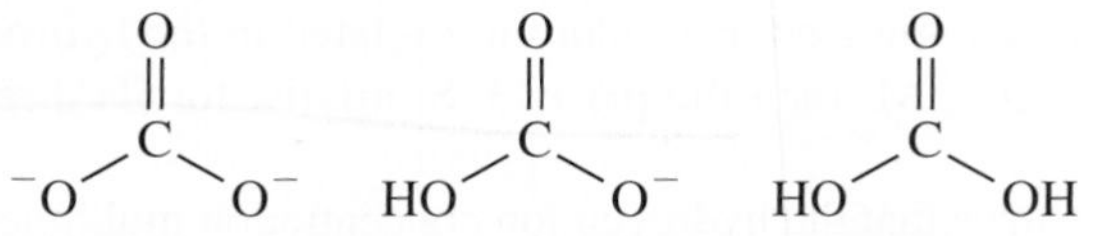

carbonate ion　　　bicarbonate ion　　　carbonic acid
CO_3^{2-}　　　　HCO_3^-　　　　　H_2CO_3

Many organisms, such as mollusks, sea urchins, and coral, have connections to this ocean chemistry because they build their shells out of calcium carbonate, $CaCO_3$. Changing the amount of one chemical species in the ocean (such as carbonic acid) can affect the concentration of the others, in turn affecting marine life.

Human industrial activity has rapidly increased the amount of carbon dioxide released into the atmosphere over the past 200 years. As a result, more carbon dioxide is dissolving into the oceans and forming carbonic acid. In turn, the pH of seawater has dropped by roughly 0.1 pH unit since the early 1800s. This may sound like a small number. Remember, though, that each full unit of pH represents a 10-fold difference in the concentration of H^+. A decrease of 0.1 pH unit corresponds to a 26% increase in the amount of H^+ in seawater. The lowering of the ocean pH due to increased atmospheric carbon dioxide is called **ocean acidification.**

How can such a seemingly small change in pH pose a danger to marine organisms? Part of the answer lies in the chemical interactions between $CO_3^{2-}(aq)$, $HCO_3^-(aq)$, and $H_2CO_3(aq)$. The H^+ produced by the dissociation of carbonic acid reacts with carbonate ion in seawater to form the bicarbonate ion.

$$H^+(aq) + CO_3^{2-}(aq) \longrightarrow HCO_3^-(aq) \qquad \text{[6.10]}$$

The net effect is to reduce the concentration of carbonate ion in seawater. The calcium carbonate in the shells of sea creatures begins to dissolve in response to the decreased concentration of carbonate ions in seawater.

$$CaCO_3(s) \xrightarrow{\text{H}_2\text{O}} Ca^{2+}(aq) + CO_3^{2-}(aq) \qquad \text{[6.11]}$$

The interaction of carbonic acid, bicarbonate ion, and carbonate ion are summarized in Figure 6.6. As carbon dioxide dissolves in ocean water, it forms carbonic acid. This in turn dissociates to produce "extra" acidity in the chemical form of H^+. The H^+ reacts with the carbonate ion, depleting it and producing more bicarbonate ion. Calcium carbonate then dissolves to replace the carbonate that was depleted.

Ocean scientists predict that within the next 40 years, the carbonate ion concentration will reach a low enough level that the shells of sea creatures near the ocean surface will begin to dissolve. In fact, one study has shown that the Great Barrier Reef off the coast of Australia is already growing at slower and slower rates. However, other factors could be to blame. For example, ocean warming also contributes to the poor health of coral reefs. One can examine growth rings in a slice of coral, much as one can view tree rings (Figure 6.7).

To date, only a small number of researchers have focused on the effects of thinning shells on sea creatures. However, negative effects on whole ecosystems have been

Recall (Section 3.2) that in recent decades, the concentration of CO_2 in the atmosphere has steadily risen a few parts per million each year.

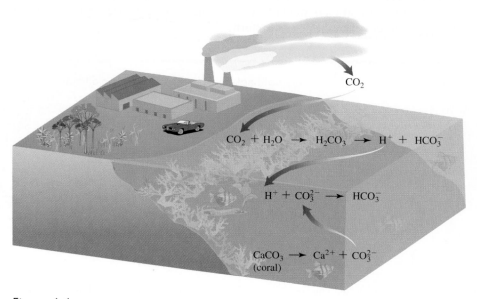

Figure 6.6

Chemistry of CO_2 in the ocean.

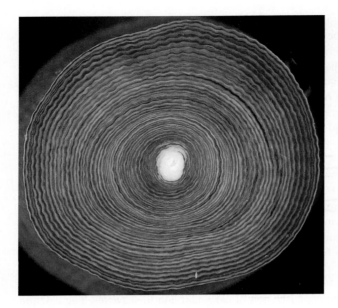

Figure 6.7
A thin slice of coral. Special lighting reveals annual growth rings. A recent study has shown that some corals have seen a dramatic decrease in their growth rate over the past 20 years.

projected. For example, weaker (or missing) coral reefs could fail to protect coastlines from harsh ocean waves. Coral reefs also provide fish species with their habitat, and damage to the reefs would translate into losses of marine life. Finally, a weakening of the reefs would make them more susceptible to further damage from storms and predators.

Can the ocean heal itself? Although we don't know the answer for sure, nonetheless we can speculate from what we know of past events. When changes in ocean pH have occurred over a very long period of time, the ocean has been able to compensate. This happens because large collections of sediment at the bottom of the ocean contain massive amounts of calcium carbonate, mostly from the shells of long-deceased marine creatures. Over long time periods, these sediments dissolve to replenish the carbonate lost to reaction with excess H^+. But today's changes in the pH of the oceans have happened rapidly on the geologic time scale. In just 200 years, the pH of the ocean has dropped to a level not seen in the past 400 million years. Because the acidification is occurring over a relatively short time and in water close to the surface, the sediment reserve has not had time to dissolve and counteract the effects of the added acidity.

Even if the amount of carbon dioxide in the atmosphere were to immediately level off, the oceans would take thousands of years to return to the pH measured in preindustrial times. Coral reefs would take even longer to regenerate, and any species lost to extinction, of course, would not return.

Consider This 6.11   International Response to Ocean Acidification

In 2008, a group of scientists met in Monaco to raise awareness about ocean acidification. They issued the Monaco Declaration, calling on the countries of the world to reverse carbon dioxide emissions trends by 2020. Have more recent gatherings of scientists and negotiators created a worldwide policy to address ocean acidification? Do research of your own and summarize your findings.

6.6 | The Challenges of Measuring the pH of Rain

Ours is a wet planet, as we saw in Chapter 5. Carbon dioxide not only has the opportunity to dissolve in the ocean but also can dissolve in rain and fresh water everywhere. The result is the same—when CO_2 dissolves, the pH drops slightly due to the formation

Figure 6.8

A pH meter with a digital display.

of carbonic acid. In the case of rain, the resulting pH is between 5 and 6. But at times the pH of rain can be even lower than this. We refer to this type of precipitation as **acid rain,** that is, rain with a pH below 5.

What are the levels of acidity in rain across the mainland United States, Alaska, Hawaii, and Puerto Rico? To measure acidity levels anywhere in the world, we need an analytical tool, the pH meter. Many types of pH meters are available. The pH meter that you are most likely to encounter has a special probe capped with a membrane that is sensitive to H^+. When the probe is immersed in a sample, the difference in H^+ concentrations between the solution and the probe creates a voltage across the membrane. The meter measures this voltage and converts it to a pH value (Figure 6.8).

Although it is straightforward to measure the pH of a rain sample, certain procedures are necessary to ensure accurate results. For example, the electrode of the pH meter needs to be carefully calibrated. Another challenge is to collect and measure rain samples without contaminating them. The collection containers must be scrupulously clean and free of minerals from the water in which they were washed. When a container is placed on site, it must be set high enough to prevent splash contamination either from the ground or surrounding objects. Even if elevated, contamination may still occur from the pollen of nearby plants, insects, bird droppings, leaves, soil dust, or even the ash of a fire.

One way to minimize contamination is to fit a rain collection bucket with a lid and a moisture sensor that opens this lid when it begins to rain. This is how samples are collected at the approximately 250 sites of the National Atmospheric Deposition Program/National Trends Network (NADP/NTN). Figure 6.9a shows the sensor and two buckets at a NADP/NTN monitoring station in Illinois that has been in operation for over 30 years. One bucket is for dry deposition (open when it is not raining) and the other is covered. A sensor opens this bucket (closing the other) when it rains.

Deciding where to locate the collection sites also is a challenge. Due to budgetary constraints, the test sites cannot go in as many places as researchers might like. The relative advantages of widely dispersing the sites versus putting several near each other in a special ecosystem (such as a national park) need to be weighed. Currently there are more collection sites in the eastern United States, as historically the acidity levels have been higher there due in large part to coal-fired electric power plants.

Rain samples have been collected routinely in the United States and Canada since about 1970. Since 1978, NADP/NTN has collected over 250,000 samples, analyzing them for pH and for these ions: SO_4^{2-}, NO_3^-, Cl^-, NH_4^+, Ca^{2+}, Mg^{2+}, K^+, and Na^+. Figure 6.9b shows the five active NADP/NTN sites in the state of Illinois. To discover how many sites are in your state, complete Consider This 6.12.

Section 8.5 describes how hydrogen fuel cells also create a voltage across a membrane.

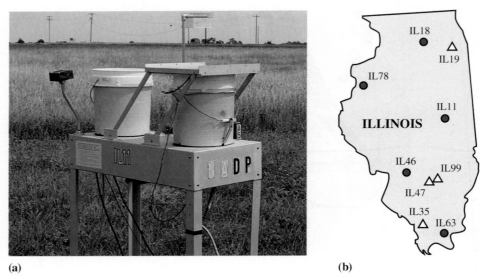

(a)   **(b)**

Figure 6.9

(a) The Bondville Monitoring Station in central Illinois (IL11) has been in operation since 1979. The black moisture sensor connected to the left of the table controls which bucket is open. It is not raining, so the right bucket for wet deposition is closed.

(b) The five active NTN precipitation monitoring sites in Illinois, including IL11 in Bondville. The sites marked with triangles are inactive.

Source: National Atmospheric Deposition Program, 2009. NADP Program Office, Illinois State Water Survey.

Consider This 6.12   The Rain in Maine . . . Oregon or Florida

Thanks to the NADP/NTN, almost every state plus Puerto Rico and the Virgin Islands has one or more precipitation monitoring sites.

a. In Figure 6.9a, name the precautions you see being taken to preserve the integrity of the rain samples.
b. How many monitoring sites are in your state?
c. Do you think the number and placement of collection sites in your state fairly represent the acidic deposition?
d. Find a collection site in your state (or in a neighboring one) that provides a photograph online. Compare the picture with Figure 6.9a. What additional ways of minimizing contamination (for example, a fence or signage) can you spot, if any?

Answer
a. The collection buckets are located up off the ground, one is fitted with a lid that opens when it rains, and the area around the site is mowed. Also, the location is far from people and roads.

Each week, researchers at the Central Analytical Laboratory in Champaign, Illinois, receive hundreds of rain samples. The photographs in Figure 6.10 indicate the magnitude of the operation. At the left are sample collection buckets waiting to be cleaned prior to being shipped back to the collection sites. The center photo shows a set of rain samples waiting to be analyzed, each assigned an alphanumeric label. A small portion of each sample is saved after analysis and stored under refrigeration. The photo on the right shows Chris Lehmann, director of the laboratory, standing inside a cold room in which samples are archived.

Each year, researchers at the Central Analytical Laboratory use the analytical data to construct maps such as the one shown in Figure 6.11. From these maps, we observe that all rain is slightly acidic. Remember that rain contains a small amount of dissolved carbon dioxide, and that the carbon dioxide dissolved in rainwater produces a weakly acidic solution.

 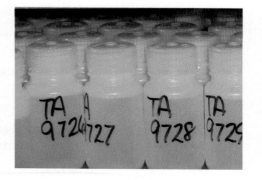 

Figure 6.10

Photographs from the Central Analytical Laboratory (CAL), Champaign, Illinois. *Left:* Sample collection buckets waiting to be cleaned. *Center:* Rain samples waiting to be analyzed. *Right:* Chris Lehmann, Director of the CAL.

Recall that rain naturally has a pH between 5 and 6. Figure 6.11 shows that the pH of rain samples is well below normal in the eastern third of the United States, especially in the Ohio River valley. Carbon dioxide is not the only source of H^+ in rain. Chemical analysis of rainwater confirms the presence of other substances that result in the formation of hydrogen ion: sulfur dioxide (SO_2), sulfur trioxide (SO_3), nitrogen monoxide (NO), and nitrogen dioxide (NO_2). These compounds are affectionately known as "Sox and Nox." Chemically, we write SO_x and NO_x, where $x = 2$ or 3 for SO_x, or $x = 1$ and 2 for NO_x.

Let's examine SO_x and NO_x in turn. First, here is a way to represent the process by which sulfur trioxide dissolves in water to form sulfuric acid.

Equation 6.12 is analogous to the reaction of CO_2 with water.

$$SO_3(g) + H_2O(l) \longrightarrow \underset{\text{sulfuric acid}}{H_2SO_4(aq)} \qquad \textbf{[6.12]}$$

Sites not pictured:
Alaska 01	5.3
Alaska 03	5.3
Alaska 06	5.2
Puerto Rico 20	5.2
Virgin Islands 01	5.2

Lab pH

≤ 4.1
4.5
4.9
5.3
≥ 5.7

Figure 6.11

The pH of rain samples. Measurements made at the Central Analytical Laboratory, 2011. Values at stations in Alaska, Puerto Rico, and the Virgin Islands are given at the lower left. Hawaii data not available.

Source: National Atmospheric Deposition Program/National Trends Network.

In water, sulfuric acid is a source of the hydrogen ion.

$$H_2SO_4(aq) \longrightarrow H^+(aq) + HSO_4^-(aq)$$

[6.13a]

hydrogen sulfate ion

Equations 6.13b and 6.13c are simplified versions of more complex equations.

The hydrogen sulfate ion also can dissociate to yield another hydrogen ion.

$$HSO_4^-(aq) \longrightarrow H^+(aq) + SO_4^{2-}(aq)$$

[6.13b]

sulfate ion

Adding equations 6.13a and 6.13b shows that sulfuric acid dissociates to yield two hydrogen ions and a sulfate ion (SO_4^{2-}).

$$H_2SO_4(aq) \longrightarrow 2\,H^+(aq) + SO_4^{2-}(aq)$$

[6.13c]

The sulfate ion can be detected in rainwater, providing a clue to the source of the additional acidity in the rain.

🌣 Your Turn 6.13   Sulfurous Acid

Sulfur dioxide dissolves in water to form sulfurous acid, H_2SO_3. Write equations for the formation of 2 $H^+(aq)$ from sulfurous acid, analogous to chemical equations 6.13a, 6.13b, and 6.13c for sulfuric acid. Visit Figures Alive! for a set of interactive activities relating to acids and bases.

Now let's turn to NO_x. Nitrogen oxides also dissolve in water to form acids, but the chemical reactions are more complex because O_2 also is a reactant. For example, NO_2 reacts in moist air to form nitric acid. This reaction is a simplification of the atmospheric chemistry that takes place.

$$4\,NO_2(g) + 2\,H_2O(l) + O_2(g) \longrightarrow 4\,HNO_3(aq)$$

[6.14]

nitric acid

In water, nitric acid dissociates to release H^+.

$$HNO_3(aq) \longrightarrow H^+(aq) + NO_3^-(aq)$$

[6.15]

nitrate ion

The nitrate ion that is produced in this reaction can be detected in rainwater.

Rain is only one of several ways that acids can be delivered to Earth's surface waters. Snow and fog obviously are others. The term **acid deposition** refers to both wet and dry forms of delivery of acids from the atmosphere to the surface of the Earth. Examples of wet deposition include rain, snow, and fog. Mountaintops are particularly susceptible to wet deposition resulting from direct contact with clouds containing microscopic water droplets. Because these droplets contain acids that are more concentrated than those found in larger raindrops, they are often more acidic and damaging than acid rain. If SO_x and NO_x are indeed responsible for the increased acidity of rain falling in the eastern part of the United States, these regions should show elevated levels of sulfate ion and nitrate ion in rainwater, from SO_x and NO_x, respectively. Indeed, this is the case. Figure 6.12 shows the nitrate and sulfate ion content for wet deposition.

Acid deposition also includes the "dry" forms of acids that deposit on land and water. For example, during dry weather, tiny solid particles (aerosols) of the compounds ammonium nitrate, NH_4NO_3, and ammonium sulfate, $(NH_4)_2SO_4$, are deposited. Dry deposition can be just as significant as the wet deposition of the acids in rain, snow, and fog. These aerosols also contribute to haze, as we will see in Section 6.12.

Aerosols consist of tiny particles that remain suspended in our atmosphere (Section 1.11) and can have a cooling effect on the Earth (Section 3.9).

Armed with the knowledge that oxides of sulfur and nitrogen contribute to acid rain, we now need to look more closely at how these oxides come to be released into the atmosphere. In the next section, we examine the chemistry of SO_2 and its connection to the burning of coal. In the two sections after, we turn our attention to nitrogen chemistry, including that of NO and NO_2.

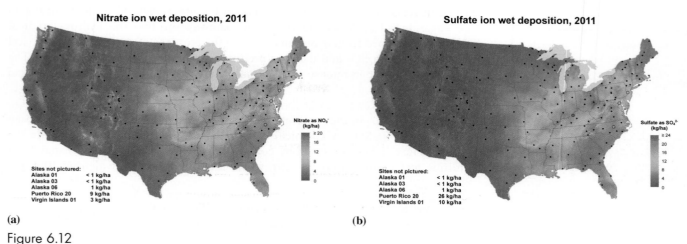

Figure 6.12

(a) 2011 wet deposition of nitrate ion in kilograms per hectare. (b) 2011 wet deposition of sulfate ion in kilograms per hectare.

Source: National Atmospheric Deposition Program/National Trends Network.

6.7 | Sulfur Dioxide and the Combustion of Coal

Let's look more closely at coal and its combustion products. At first glance, coal may not appear much different from charcoal or black soot, both of which are essentially pure carbon. When carbon is burned with plenty of oxygen, it forms carbon dioxide and liberates large amounts of energy, which of course is the reason for burning it.

$$C(\textit{in coal}) + O_2(g) \longrightarrow CO_2(g) + \text{energy} \qquad \textbf{[6.16]}$$

Coal also contains varying amounts of sulfur. How did the sulfur wind up in the coal? Several hundred million years ago, coal formed from decaying vegetation such as that found in swamps or peat bogs. Plants, like other living things, contain sulfur, so some of the sulfur in coal can be traced to this ancient vegetation. However, most of the sulfur in coal came from the sulfate ion (SO_4^{2-}) naturally present in seawater. Bacteria on the sea floors use the sulfate ion as an oxygen source, removing the oxygen and releasing the sulfide ion (S^{2-}). In the past, the sulfide ion became incorporated into the ancient rocks (including coal) that were in contact with seawater. In contrast, the coal formed in freshwater peat bogs has a lower sulfur content. Thus, the percent of sulfur in coal can vary from less than 1% to as much as 6% by mass.

> The movement of sulfur through the biosphere should remind you of the carbon cycle described in Section 3.5.

We can approximate its composition with the chemical formula $C_{135}H_{96}O_9NS$. Burning sulfur in air produces sulfur dioxide, a poisonous gas with an unmistakable choking odor (Figure 6.13).

$$S(s) + O_2(g) \longrightarrow SO_2(g) \qquad \textbf{[6.17]}$$

Because the sulfur content of coal varies, burning coal produces sulfur dioxide in varying amounts. This fact is central to the acid rain story. When coal is burned, the sulfur dioxide produced goes up the smokestack along with the carbon dioxide, water vapor, and small amounts of metal oxide ash. Emission control measures can reduce the amount of SO_2. Thus the levels of SO_2 emissions vary depending on how coal-burning electric utility plants are equipped.

Once in the atmosphere, SO_2 can react with oxygen to form sulfur trioxide, SO_3.

$$2\,SO_2(g) + O_2(g) \longrightarrow 2\,SO_3(g) \qquad \textbf{[6.18]}$$

This reaction, although extremely slow, is accelerated by the presence of tiny particles such as the ash that goes up the stack along with the SO_2. Once SO_3 is

Figure 6.13

Sulfur burns in air to produce SO_2. This gas produces an acidic solution when dissolved in water. In ancient times sulfur was known as brimstone, thus the biblical admonition about "fire and brimstone."

> Sulfur trioxide plays a role in aerosol formation, as we will see in Section 6.12.

The hydroxyl radical was first introduced in Section 1.1.

formed, it reacts rapidly with water vapor in the atmosphere to form sulfuric acid (see equation 6.12). A second important pathway involves the hydroxyl radical ($\cdot$OH) that is formed from ozone and water in the presence of sunlight. The hydroxyl radical reacts with SO_2 and then the product reacts with oxygen to form SO_3. The reaction goes faster in intense sunlight and thus is more important in summer and at midday.

Although pathways exist for the reaction of SO_2 with oxygen to form SO_3, the majority of SO_2 in the atmosphere directly contributes to acid rain by forming sulfurous acid, H_2SO_3. A chemical calculation can help us better appreciate the vast quantities of SO_2 produced by coal-burning power plants. A utility may burn 1 million metric tons of coal a year, where a metric ton is equivalent to 1000 kg.

Emissions data are given both in metric tons (1000 kg, 2200 lb) and in short tons (2000 lb). To add to the confusion, short tons usually are simply called tons.

$$\frac{1 \times 10^6 \text{ metric ton coal}}{\text{yr}} \times \frac{1000 \text{ kg coal}}{\text{metric ton coal}} \times \frac{1000 \text{ g coal}}{\text{kg coal}} = 1 \times 10^{12} \text{ g coal/yr}$$

For this discussion, we assume a coal that contains 2.0% sulfur, that is, 2.0 g sulfur per 100 g coal. First we can calculate the grams of sulfur burned each year from 1 million metric tons (1×10^{12} g) of coal.

$$\frac{1 \times 10^{12} \text{ g coal}}{\text{yr}} \times \frac{2.0 \text{ g S}}{100 \text{ g coal}} = \frac{2.0 \times 10^{10} \text{ g S}}{\text{yr}}$$

See Section 3.7 to review mole calculations.

Next, we use the fact that 1 mole of sulfur reacts with oxygen (O_2) to form 1 mole of SO_2 (see equation 6.17). The molar mass of sulfur is 32.1 g, and the molar mass of SO_2 is 64.1 g, that is, 32.1 g + 2(16.0 g). Therefore, 32.1 g of sulfur burn to produce 64.1 g of SO_2.

$$\frac{2.0 \times 10^{10} \text{ g S}}{\text{yr}} \times \frac{1 \text{ mol S}}{32.1 \text{ g S}} \times \frac{1 \text{ mol } SO_2}{1 \text{ mol S}} \times \frac{64.1 \text{ g } SO_2}{1 \text{ mol } SO_2} = \frac{4.0 \times 10^{10} \text{ g } SO_2}{\text{yr}}$$

This mass of SO_2 is equivalent to 40,000 metric tons, or 88 million pounds, of SO_2 per year per power plant. Power plants burning high-sulfur coal may emit more than twice this amount!

The connection between burning coal and sulfur dioxide emissions in the United States is evident in Figure 6.14. Most of the emissions arise from power plants ("fuel combustion") in which coal or other fossil fuels are burned to generate electricity for public or industrial consumption. Transportation is responsible only for a small percent of the emissions because gasoline and diesel fuel contain relatively low amounts of sulfur. Industrial processes, such as the producing of metals from their ores, account for the remainder of the emissions. For example, the ores of both copper and nickel are sulfides. When nickel sulfide is heated to a high temperature in a smelter, the ore decomposes and sulfur dioxide is released. Similarly, smelting copper sulfide releases SO_2. Although the large-scale production of nickel and copper contributes only a few percent to the total emissions, huge quantities of SO_2 are generated in some regions.

One of the world's largest smelters in Sudbury, Ontario, produces nickel from an ore that contains sulfur. The bleak, lifeless landscape in the immediate vicinity of the plant stands in mute testimony to past uncontrolled releases of SO_2. After a major renovation in 1993, the two major smelters in the area have decreased their sulfur dioxide emissions substantially. The smokestack is tall so that the emissions that still remain are carried away from Sudbury by the prevailing winds (Figure 6.15). Lest we point any fingers, Canadians report that more than half of acid deposition in the eastern portion of their country originates in the United States. The quantity of sulfur dioxide that drifts northward over the border into Canada is estimated at 4 million metric tons per year.

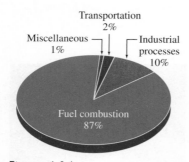

Figure 6.14

U.S. sulfur dioxide emission sources, 2011.

Source: EPA, National Emissions Inventory, Air Pollution Emissions Trends Data.

Figure 6.15
The smokestack in Sudbury, Ontario, is one of the world's tallest at 1250 ft (381 m).

Your Turn 6.14   Coal Calculations

a. Assume that coal has the chemical formula of $C_{135}H_{96}O_9NS$. Calculate the fraction and percent (by mass) of sulfur in the coal.
b. A certain power plant burns 1.00×10^6 tons of coal per year. Assuming the sulfur content calculated in part **a**, calculate the tons of sulfur released per year.
c. Calculate the tons of SO_2 formed from this amount of sulfur.
d. Once released into the atmosphere, the SO_2 is likely to react with oxygen to form SO_3. What can happen next if SO_3 encounters water droplets?

Answers
a. 0.0168, or 1.68%
b. 1.68×10^4 tons S

Having examined the chemistry of SO_2, we now return to that of NO and NO_2. In the next section, we describe NO emissions and the connection to automobiles and power plants. In the section following, we relate the bigger stories of nitrogen chemistry.

6.8 | Nitrogen Oxides and the Combustion of Gasoline

Those who live in southern California have experienced high levels of acid deposition. For example, in January 1982, the fog near the Rose Bowl in Pasadena was found to have a pH of 2.5. Breathing it must have been like inhaling a fine mist of vinegar! The acidity exceeded that of normal precipitation by at least 500 times. In this same year, the fog at Corona del Mar on the coast south of Los Angeles was 10 times more acidic than near the Rose Bowl, registering a pH of 1.5. However, the concentration of SO_2 was relatively low in both areas. Clearly, something else was the cause.

To find out what, we need to turn to the cars and trucks that jam the freeways of Los Angeles. At first glance, it may not be obvious how these thousands of vehicles contribute to acid precipitation. Gasoline burns to form CO_2 and H_2O, together with small amounts of CO, unburned hydrocarbons, and soot. But gasoline contains very little sulfur, so SO_2 is not the culprit. So what might be the source of the acidity?

Nitrogen oxides already have been identified as contributors to acid rain, but gasoline does not contain nitrogen. Therefore, logic and chemistry assert that nitrogen

Gasoline is a mixture of hydrocarbons. See Section 4.4.

oxides cannot be formed from burning gasoline. Literally, this is correct. Remember, however, that about 78% of air consists of N_2. This element is remarkably stable and for the most part unreactive. Nevertheless, if the temperature is high enough, nitrogen is able to react with a few elements. One of these is oxygen. Recall from Chapter 1 that with sufficient energy, nitrogen and oxygen combine to form nitrogen monoxide (nitric oxide).

$$N_2(g) + O_2(g) \xrightarrow{\text{high temperature}} 2\ NO(g) \qquad [6.19]$$

In an automobile, gasoline and air are drawn into the cylinders and compressed, bringing the N_2 and O_2 molecules closer together. The gasoline, once ignited, burns rapidly. The energy released powers the vehicle. But the unfortunate truth is that the energy also powers chemical equation 6.19.

The reaction of N_2 with O_2 is not limited to automobile engines. The same reaction occurs when air is heated in the furnace of a coal-fired electric power plant such that collectively these plants release huge amounts of NO_x. In the United States, the combustion of fossil fuels (particularly coal) in electric power plants accounts for over a third of the nitrogen oxide emissions (Figure 6.16). Transportation sources such as motor vehicles, aircraft, and trains account for over half. In an urban environment, an even greater proportion of NO_x arises from motor vehicles.

In the early 1990s, a green chemistry solution to reducing NO emissions and energy consumption was introduced by Praxair Inc. of Tarrytown, NY, a glass manufacturing company. The technology substitutes 100% oxygen for air in the large furnaces used to melt and reheat glass. Switching from air (78% nitrogen) to pure oxygen requires lower temperatures, thereby reducing overall plant NO production by 90% and cutting energy consumption by up to 50%. Glass manufacturers using the Praxair Oxy-Fuel technology save enough energy annually to meet the daily needs of 1 million Americans.

Once formed, nitrogen monoxide is highly reactive. As we noted in Chapter 1, through a series of steps, NO reacts with oxygen, the hydroxyl radical, and volatile organic compounds (VOCs) to form NO_2.

$$VOC + \cdot OH \longrightarrow A + O_2 \longrightarrow A' + NO \longrightarrow A'' + NO_2 \qquad [6.20]$$

The reactive intermediate species A, A′, and A″, present in trace amounts, are synthesized from the VOC molecules. The production of acid rain from NO_2 requires a trace amount of VOCs in the atmosphere.

Nitrogen dioxide is a highly reactive, poisonous, red-brown gas with a nasty odor. For our purposes, the most significant reaction of NO_2 is the one that converts it to nitric acid, HNO_3. Earlier, equation 6.14 was a simplification of this conversion. Actually, a series of reactions occurs in the presence of sunlight. These take place in the air surrounding Los Angeles, Phoenix, Dallas, and other sunny metropolitan areas. A key player is the hydroxyl radical. Once formed in the atmosphere, the hydroxyl radical can rapidly react with nitrogen dioxide to yield nitric acid.

$$NO_2(g) + \cdot OH(g) \longrightarrow HNO_3(aq) \qquad [6.21]$$

As you have already seen in equation 6.15, HNO_3 is a strong acid that dissociates completely in water to release aqueous H^+ and NO_3^-. The result is the alarmingly low pH values occasionally found in the rain and fog of cities like Los Angeles.

The bit of NO_x chemistry that we have described in this section fits into a larger picture involving agriculture, food, and actually all of the ecosystems of our planet. In the next section, we provide the details.

6.9 | The Nitrogen Cycle

Rarely a day goes by that you don't ingest food in one form or another. Clearly, you need to eat in order to stay alive. As you are reading this, men and women across the globe are producing food by planting fields of grain, harvesting fruits and vegetables by the truckload, and perhaps even growing oregano or chives on a sunny windowsill. To their credit, humans have become quite expert in raising both plants and animals.

You may have seen advertisements for "nitrogen–enriched" gasoline, referred to by one oil company as "a nitrogen–enriched cleaning system." The amount of nitrogen in this gasoline additive is quite low.

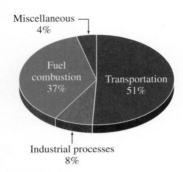

Figure 6.16

U.S. nitrogen oxides (NO_x) emission sources, 2011.

Source: EPA, National Emissions Inventory, Air Pollution Emissions Trends Data.

See Section 1.11 for more about equation 6.20.

However, producing food releases NO_x and adds to the acidity of the environment. Human activity is affecting both where nitrogen compounds are found and how they move through the air, water, and land of our planet.

The connection between food production and NO_x emissions arises because nitrates act as fertilizers and promote plant growth. Plants depend on other elements as well, including carbon, hydrogen, phosphorus, sulfur, and potassium. Many of these elements are readily available in the environment for uptake by plants. Since usable forms of nitrogen are scarce, we need to supply them in the form of fertilizers.

You might be wondering how nitrogen levels can be so low in soils when N_2 makes up so much of our atmosphere. Although abundant, the nitrogen molecule is *not* in a chemical form that most plants can use. N_2 is far less reactive than O_2.

Just as there is a "carbon cycle" (Chapter 3), there also is a "nitrogen cycle." Stay tuned!

All living things, not just plants, require nitrogen.

Your Turn 6.15   Unreactive Nitrogen

How does the bond energy of the triple bond in N_2 compare with other bond energies?
Hint: See Table 4.4.

In order to grow, plants need access to a form of nitrogen that reacts more easily, such as the ammonium ion, ammonia, or the nitrate ion. These and other forms are called **reactive nitrogen,** the compounds of nitrogen that cycle through the biosphere and interconvert with each other. Some reactive forms of nitrogen are listed in Table 6.1. As you might imagine, the air pollutants NO and NO_2 are included in the list. These forms of nitrogen all occur naturally and are present on our planet in relatively small amounts. Other forms of reactive nitrogen also exist, such as a group of compounds known as "amines" that contain the $-NH_2$ group. We introduce amines when we need them for our study of polymers, proteins, and DNA in Chapter 12.

Your Turn 6.16   Reactive Nitrogen

Select one of the compounds in Table 6.1. Give evidence, either in the form of an observation or a chemical equation, that this compound is reactive.
Hint: Revisit Chapters 1 and 2. Also draw on your personal knowledge.

Although we categorized N_2 as generally unreactive, one reaction involving the nitrogen molecule is of utmost importance: biological nitrogen fixation. Plants such as alfalfa, beans, and peas "fix" (remove) N_2 from the atmosphere (Figure 6.17). To be more accurate, it is not the plants themselves, but rather the bacteria living on or near the roots of these plants that fix the nitrogen. As part of their metabolism, **nitrogen-fixing bacteria** remove nitrogen gas from the air and convert it to ammonia. When the

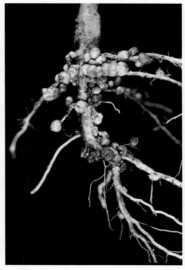

Figure 6.17

Nodules on the root of a soya plant that contain nitrogen–fixing bacteria.

Table 6.1	Some Reactive Forms of Nitrogen
Name	Chemical Formula
nitrogen monoxide	NO
nitrogen dioxide	NO_2
nitrous oxide	N_2O
nitrate ion	NO_3^-
nitrite ion	NO_2^-
nitric acid	HNO_3
ammonia	NH_3
ammonium ion	NH_4^+

Note: These forms of nitrogen all are naturally occurring.

ammonia dissolves in water, it produces the ammonium ion, NH_4^+. The reaction is shown in equations 6.5a and 6.5b. This ion is one of two forms of reactive nitrogen that most plants can absorb. Recall from Chapter 5 that compounds containing the ammonium ion tend to be water soluble. Here is the pathway.

This icon represents the bacteria responsible for the interconversion of nitrogen–containing species.

$$N_2 \xrightarrow[\text{nitrogen fixation}]{} NH_3 \xrightarrow{H_2O} NH_4^+ \qquad \text{[6.22]}$$

The other form of reactive nitrogen that plants can absorb is the nitrate ion. Again, compounds of the nitrate ion tend to be soluble. **Nitrification** is the process of converting ammonia in the soil to the nitrate ion. Bacteria are involved in this two-step process.

$$NH_4^+ \xrightarrow[\text{bacteria in the soil}]{} NO_2^- \xrightarrow[\text{bacteria in the soil}]{} NO_3^- \qquad \text{[6.23]}$$

Finally, to come full circle, bacteria help with **denitrification,** the process of converting nitrates to nitrogen gas. In so doing, these bacteria harness the energy released when the stable N_2 molecule forms. Recall from Chapter 4 the large amount of energy released in forming the triple bond found in the nitrogen molecule, a very stable molecule indeed!

Depending on the soil conditions, the pathway may occur in steps that include NO and N_2O. Thus, these reactive forms of nitrogen also can be converted to N_2 and released from the soil.

Of the oxides of nitrogen, N_2O is emitted naturally in the greatest amount. It is a potent greenhouse gas. See Section 3.8.

$$NO_3^- \xrightarrow[\text{bacteria in the soil}]{} NO \xrightarrow[\text{bacteria in the soil}]{} N_2O \xrightarrow[\text{bacteria in the soil}]{} N_2 \qquad \text{[6.24]}$$

All of these pathways are part of the **nitrogen cycle,** a set of chemical pathways whereby nitrogen moves through the biosphere. Figure 6.18 assembles the pathways shown in equations 6.22, 6.23, and 6.24 into a simplified version of the nitrogen cycle. In this cycle, all species are forms of reactive nitrogen except for N_2.

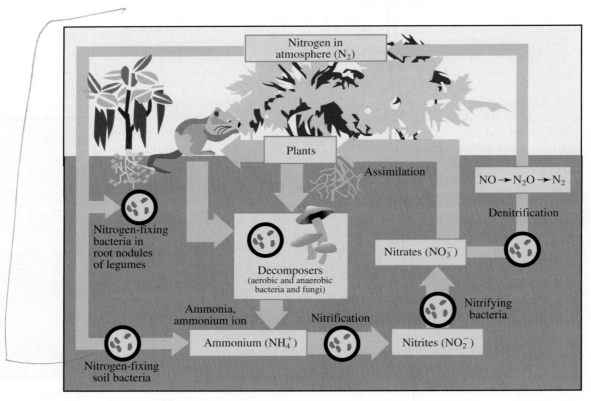

Figure 6.18

The nitrogen cycle (simplified).

Remember that reactive forms of nitrogen are needed for plant growth. Because bacteria in the soil cannot supply ammonia, ammonium ion, or nitrate ion in the amounts needed for optimal plant growth, farmers use fertilizers. A few centuries ago, fertilizers were obtained by mining deposits of saltpeter (ammonium nitrate) from the deserts of Chile or by collecting guano, a nitrogen-rich deposit from bird and bat droppings in Peru. Neither source, however, was sufficient to meet the demand of the growing world population. An additional drain on the supply of nitrates was their use in the production of gunpowder and other explosives such as TNT. By the early 1900s, the search was on for a way to synthesize reactive nitrogen compounds from the abundant N_2 in the air.

How are fertilizers obtained in the large quantities needed for present-day agriculture? The answer lies in a second important reaction of N_2, one that literally captures it out of the air to synthesize ammonia.

$$N_2(g) + 3\,H_2(g) \longrightarrow 2\,NH_3(g) \qquad \textbf{[6.25]}$$

This famous chemical reaction is known as the Haber–Bosch process. It allows the economical production of ammonia, which in turn enables the large-scale production of fertilizers and nitrogen-based explosives. As a fertilizer, ammonia can be directly applied to the soil or can be applied as ammonium nitrate or ammonium phosphate. The green line that starts around 1910 in Figure 6.19 represents the large increase in global reactive nitrogen from the Haber–Bosch process.

Also notice the orange line on this graph that indicates the amount of reactive nitrogen formed by the burning of fossil fuels. Recall that at the high temperatures of combustion, N_2 and O_2 react to form NO. The purple line on the graph represents reactive nitrogen from all sources, or the sum of the orange, blue, and green lines. The overlaid red line for population, of course, comes as no surprise. The increases in reactive nitrogen from burning fossil fuels (energy production) and fertilization (food production) parallel the growth in world population (people production).

The reactive forms of nitrogen in this cycle continuously change chemical forms. Thus, the ammonia that starts out as a fertilizer may end up as NO, in turn increasing the acidity of the atmosphere. Or the NO may end up as N_2O, a greenhouse gas that

In 1918, Fritz Haber received the Nobel Prize in Chemistry for synthesizing NH_3 from N_2 and H_2. In 1931, Carl Bosch received the Nobel Prize for using this synthesis commercially.

Increased access to fertilizers and large-scale farming equipment enabled an unprecedented expansion of agriculture called the Green Revolution that began worldwide around 1945. Look for more on the Green Revolution in Section 11.12.

Greenhouse gases were introduced in Section 3.1 and further described in Section 3.8.

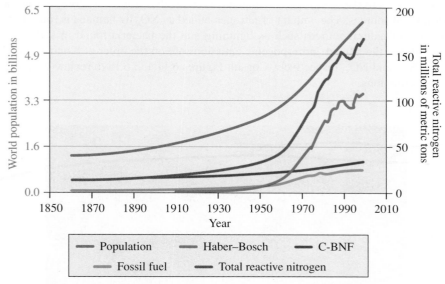

Figure 6.19

Global changes in reactive nitrogen produced by various sources (million metric tons, scale on the right). The top line is the world's population in 2000 (billions, scale on the left).

Note: C-BNF is the reactive nitrogen created from the cultivation of legumes, rice, and sugarcane.

Source: BioScience by American Institute of Biological Sciences, April 2003, Vol. 53, No. 4, p. 342. Copyright © 2003 by University of California Press-Journals. Reproduced with permission of University of California Press-Journals via Copyright Clearance Center.

is currently rising in atmospheric concentration. Or the ammonium ion, instead of being tightly bound to the soil, may end up being converted and leached out as the nitrite or nitrate ion, in turn contaminating a water supply.

Now we can begin to understand the full effects that NO emissions have on our environment. First, the oxides of nitrogen form ground-level ozone in the presence of sunlight, contributing to photochemical smog, as we saw in Chapter 1. Second, NO_x emissions are a form of reactive nitrogen, just like the fertilizers used for food production. NO is formed from unreactive N_2 in the air when fuels are burned. The more fuels are burned, the more N_2 is changed into a reactive form. Both NO_x and fertilizer use are affecting the balances within the nitrogen cycle on our planet. Finally, NO_x emissions increase the acidity of the precipitation falling from the sky.

6.10 | SO_2 and NO_x— How Do They Stack Up?

Having identified SO_2 and NO_x as the two major contributors to acid precipitation, we now examine their production over time and strategies for controlling anthropogenic emissions. In addition to anthropogenic sources, these oxides are naturally produced. Some volcanoes steadily emit SO_2, and under certain conditions, they produce beautiful crystals of elemental sulfur (Figure 6.20). When they erupt, they can release large amounts of SO_2. The June 1991 eruption of Mount Pinatubo in the Philippines was 10 times as large as the 1980 eruption of Mount St. Helens in the United States, emitting between 15 and 30 million tons of sulfur dioxide into the stratosphere.

Oceans are a second natural source of sulfur emissions. Marine organisms produce dimethyl sulfide gas as a by-product. The dimethyl sulfide enters the troposphere and reacts with OH· to form SO_2. NO is formed any time that high heat causes nitrogen and oxygen gases to react; in nature, this occurs during lightning strikes and forest fires. Bacteria in soil convert nitrogen gas in the air into nitrogen oxides that plants can use to build mass.

Anthropogenic SO_2 and NO_x emissions outpace natural emissions. The amount of sulfur added to the atmosphere by humans is twice that from volcanoes, oceans, and other natural sources. The amount of nitrogen added as NO_x by humans is roughly four times that of natural sources such as lightning and the bacteria found in soils. In the United States, the annual anthropogenic emissions are on the order of 8 and 12 million tons for SO_2 and NO_x, respectively. Consult Figures 6.14 and 6.16 to review the sources of these emissions.

The contamination of fresh water with excess nitrogen–containing compounds used in agriculture is discussed in Section 11.6.

An active volcano, such as Kilauea in Hawaii, emits varying amounts of SO_2. The values are in hundreds of metric tons per day.

1 ton (short ton) = 2000 lb
= 0.9072 metric tons
(tonnes)

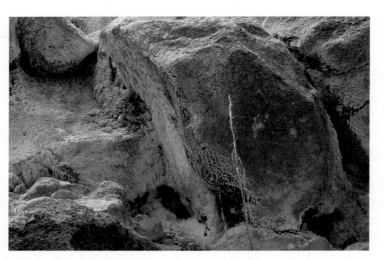

Figure 6.20

Elemental sulfur (*yellow*) occurring naturally in Hawaii Volcanoes National Park.

The levels of these two pollutants have changed dramatically over time. Before 1950, relatively small amounts of NO_x were present in rain, fog, and snow. Emissions of both pollutants reached their highest levels in the 1970s. Figure 6.21 shows NO_x and SO_2 emissions in the United States since 1970. In the past few decades, SO_2 and NO_x emissions in the United States have decreased substantially, a tribute to many efforts, including the 1990 Clean Air Act Amendments. In the final section of this chapter, we examine how costs, control strategies, and politics have influenced SO_2 and NO_x emissions in the United States.

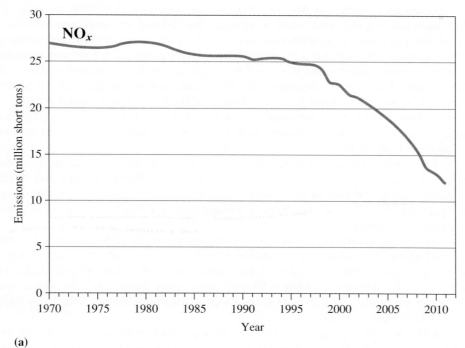

(a)

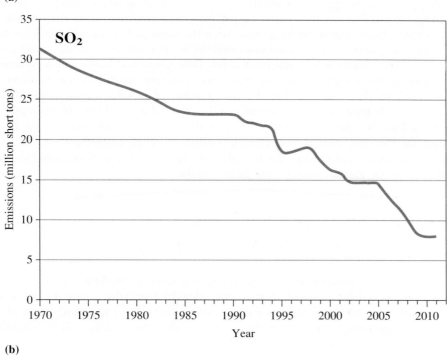

(b)

Figure 6.21

(a) U.S. nitrogen oxides emissions, 1970–2011. (b) U.S. sulfur dioxide emissions, 1970–2011. In both graphs, the data is the sum of fuel combustion, transportation, and industrial processes.

Source: EPA National Emissions Inventory.

Your Turn 6.17   SO$_2$ and NO$_x$ Emissions

Figure 6.21 depicts NO$_x$ and SO$_2$ emissions in the United States over a period of four decades. Which pollutant decreased more in this time period? Suggest a reason for the decrease.

Globally, the levels of SO$_2$ and NO$_x$ also are changing over time. Because the NO$_x$ emissions originate from millions of small, unregulated, and mobile sources, they are difficult to track. In contrast, emissions of SO$_2$ can be estimated with a reasonable degree of accuracy. National data on fossil fuel consumption and the refining of metal ores that contain sulfur make this possible. To get an estimate, researchers start with the amount of fossil fuels (together with their sulfur content) produced in a country, then add in imports of fossil fuels, and finally subtract out exports. Metal refining is a bit trickier to estimate, as the amount of sulfur released depends on the technologies used (which are not always known). Nonetheless, it is possible to reach conclusions using these types of data.

One such estimate published in 2011 shows good news—a decline in world SO$_2$ emissions over the past two decades. In the 1970s, Western Europe and North America shared the title of the world's largest emitters. Sulfur dioxide emissions levels in the United States and Western Europe declined rapidly as a result of environmental regulation.

Today, the continent of Asia leads in SO$_2$ emissions. In 1970, the United States emitted about 30 million tons of sulfur dioxide and China about 7 million tons. With the start of the year 2000, China emerged as the clear global leader in SO$_2$ emissions. However, China is closing some older inefficient coal plants and installing technology to reduce SO$_2$ emissions. China's annual SO$_2$ emissions have been decreasing since 2006.

China's economy continues to grow at a remarkable pace, in part driven by developed countries' appetite for inexpensive manufactured goods. To meet the massive demand for electricity, China's coal output more than doubled in the first decade of this century. India appears to be headed down the same path as energy needs hamper its economic growth. China's coal consumption in 2011 was 50% of the world total, with the United States at 14% and India at 8%. Both China and India, with a combined one third of the world's population, have seen a massive growth in the numbers of motor vehicles. If China alone had the same number of cars per person as the United States, it would have close to the world's total of more than 1 billion cars currently on the road. Clearly, a pattern of unchecked growth is not sustainable. As a result, many nations are pursuing sources of electricity powered by wind, geothermal, and the Sun. Such technologies that produce far less SO$_2$ and NO$_x$, coupled with conservation, are essential for our planet both now and in the future.

Even "green" technologies produce some SO$_2$ and NO$_x$. These gases are emitted during the manufacture, installation, and service of the wind turbines, solar cells, and electric transmission lines.

6.11 | Acid Deposition and Its Effects on Materials

As we have seen, much of the rain, mist, fog, and snow in the United States is more acidic than would be expected from carbon dioxide dissolution alone. In the worst cases, rain, fog, and dew can have a pH of 3.0 or lower. Does this really matter? To answer this question, we need to know something about the effects of acid deposition and how serious they really are.

National studies can help us. During the 1980s, the U.S. Congress funded a national research effort called the National Acid Precipitation Assessment Program (NAPAP). Over 2000 scientists were involved, with a total expenditure of $500 million. The project was completed in 1990, and the participating scientists prepared a 28-volume set of technical reports (NAPAP, *State of the Science and Technology,* 1991). Some of the material in the remainder of this chapter is drawn from the NAPAP Report. Other information is drawn from the proceedings of a conference in 2001 entitled "Acid Rain: Are the Problems Solved?" sponsored by the Center for Environmental Information. The purpose of that conference was "to put the acid rain problem squarely back on the forefront of the public agenda."

And we agree—acid rain should remain on the public agenda. One reason is the damage that acid rain causes. Another is what we would gain by reducing its formation (Table 6.2). In this section, we describe the effects of acid rain on metals, statues, and buildings. The effects of acid deposition on living things are explored in the section that follows.

Recall from Chapter 1 that about 80% of the elements on the periodic table are metals. Many of these metals are vulnerable to damage from acid precipitation. Metals typically are shiny and silvery; well, before they become tarnished or rusted.

Your Turn 6.18   Metals and Nonmetals

With the help of a periodic table, classify these elements as metals or nonmetals. Also give the chemical symbol for each.

a. iron   b. aluminum   c. fluorine
d. calcium   e. zinc   f. oxygen

Metals and nonmetals were defined in Section 1.6.

Although acid rain (pH 3–5) does not affect all metals, unfortunately iron is one that it does. Bridges, railroads, and vehicles of all kinds depend on iron and the steel that is made from it. Rods of steel are used to strengthen concrete buildings and roadways. In many parts of the country, decorative iron fences and latticework both ornament and protect city and rural homes.

Metals used in jewelry (gold, silver, and platinum) do not react with acidic depositions.

Table 6.2	Effects of Acid Rain and Benefits of Acid Rain Reduction
Effects	**Recovery Benefits**
Materials	
Acid deposition contributes to the corrosion and deterioration of buildings, cultural objects, and cars. This decreases their value and increases the cost of correcting and repairing damage.	Less damage to buildings, cultural objects, and cars. Lowering future costs to correct and repair such damage. See Section 6.11.
Human Health	
Sulfur dioxide and nitrogen oxides in the air increase deaths from asthma and bronchitis.	Fewer visits to the emergency room, fewer hospital admissions, and fewer deaths. See Section 6.12.
Visibility	
In the atmosphere, sulfur dioxide and nitrogen oxides form sulfate and nitrate aerosols that impair visibility and affect enjoyment of national parks and other scenic views.	Reduced haze, therefore the ability to view scenery at a greater distance and with greater clarity. See Section 6.12.
Surface Waters	
Acidic surface waters injure animal life in lakes and streams. In more severe instances, some or all types of fish and other marine organisms die.	Lower levels of acidity in the surface waters and a restoration of animal and plant life in the more severely damaged lakes and streams. See Section 6.13.
Forests	
Acid deposition contributes to forest degradation by impairing the growth of trees and increasing their susceptibility to winter injury, insect infestation, and drought. It also causes leaching and depletion of natural nutrients in forest soil.	Less stress on trees, thereby reducing the effects of winter injury, insect infestation, and drought. Less leaching of nutrients from soil, thereby improving the overall forest health.

Source: Adapted from Emission Trends and Effects in the Eastern U.S., *United States General Accounting Office, Report to Congressional Requesters, March, 2000.*

The problem with iron is that it rusts, as represented by this chemical equation.

This is an oxidation–reduction reaction. Look for more about this type of reaction in Chapter 8.

$$4\ Fe(s) + 3\ O_2(g) \longrightarrow 2\ Fe_2O_3(s) \qquad \text{[6.26]}$$

Rusting is a slow process. Iron combines rapidly with oxygen only if you heat or ignite it, such as with a sparkler or fireworks. But at room temperature, the rusting of iron is a two-step process that requires the presence of hydrogen ions. Equation 6.26 is the overall equation for the process. The role of H^+ is evident in equation 6.27, the first step of the process. In this step, iron metal dissolves.

$$4\ Fe(s) + 2\ O_2(g) + 8\ H^+(aq) \longrightarrow 4\ Fe^{2+}(aq) + 4\ H_2O(l) \qquad \text{[6.27]}$$

Even pure water (pH = 7) has a sufficient concentration of H^+ to promote slow rusting. In the presence of acid, the rusting process is greatly accelerated. In the second step, the aqueous Fe^{2+} further reacts with oxygen.

$$4\ Fe^{2+}(aq) + O_2(g) + 4\ H_2O(l) \longrightarrow 2\ Fe_2O_3(s) + 8\ H^+(aq) \qquad \text{[6.28]}$$

Adding the two steps together gives equation 6.26. The solid product, Fe_2O_3, is the familiar reddish brown material that we call rust.

Your Turn 6.19   Rust Adds Up

Add equations 6.27 and 6.28 together to show the overall reaction for rust formation (equation 6.26).

Your Turn 6.20   Careful with the Charges

On our planet, the element iron is found in several different chemical forms. This section just mentioned three: Fe, Fe^{2+}, and Fe^{3+}.

a. Which one of these is the familiar silvery iron metal?
b. With respect to iron metal, have Fe^{2+} or Fe^{3+} gained outer (valence) electrons? If so, which one(s) and how many electrons?
c. Have either lost valence electrons? If so, which one(s) and how many?

Answer

b. With respect to Fe, neither Fe^{2+} nor Fe^{3+} has gained outer electrons.

Because iron is inherently unstable when exposed to the natural environment, billions of dollars are spent annually to protect exposed iron and steel in bridges, cars, buildings, and ships. Paint is the most common means of protection, but even paint degrades, especially when exposed to acidic rain and gases. Coating iron with a thin layer of a second metal such as chromium (Cr) or zinc (Zn) is another means of protection.

Automobile paint can be spotted or pitted by acid deposition. To prevent this damage, automobile manufacturers now use acid-resistant paints. It is an irony that automobiles emit the very chemical that mars their paint. Follow the NO from your car's tailpipe and you may find that its reaction product (nitric acid) eventually ends up in droplets hitting the hood of your car.

Marble and limestone dissolve under acidic conditions. This is analogous to what happens to shellfish during ocean acidification (Section 6.5).

Acidic rain also damages statues and monuments made of marble. For example, those in the Gettysburg National Battlefield have suffered irreparable damage. Figure 6.22 shows a recognizable, but much deteriorated statue of George Washington in New York City. Marble limestone, composed mainly of calcium carbonate, $CaCO_3$, slowly dissolves in the presence of hydrogen ion.

$$CaCO_3(s) + 2\ H^+(aq) \longrightarrow Ca^{2+}(aq) + CO_2(g) + H_2O(l) \qquad \text{[6.29]}$$

In 1944   In 1994

Figure 6.22

Acid rain damaged this limestone statue of George Washington. It was erected in New York City in 1944.

Your Turn 6.21   Damage to Marble

Marble can contain both magnesium carbonate and calcium carbonate.

a. Analogous to equation 6.29, write the chemical equation for the reaction of acidic rain with magnesium carbonate.
b. Marble never contains sodium bicarbonate. Explain why.
   Hint: See Section 5.8 on the water solubility of ionic compounds.

Your Turn 6.22   Damage from SO_2

Suppose that the acid represented in equation 6.29 by $H^+(aq)$ is sulfuric acid. Write the balanced chemical equation for the reaction of sulfuric acid with marble.

Visitors to the Lincoln Memorial in Washington, D.C., learn that the huge stalactites growing in chambers beneath the memorial are the result of acid rain eroding the marble, again a material containing either calcium carbonate or magnesium carbonate (or both). Other monuments in the eastern United States are suffering similar fates. Some limestone tombstones are no longer legible. Worldwide, many priceless and irreplaceable marble statues and buildings are being attacked by airborne acids (Figure 6.23). The Parthenon in Greece, the Taj Mahal in India, and the Mayan ruins at Chichén Itzá all show signs of acid erosion. Ironically, some of the acid deposition at these sites is due to the NO_x produced by tour buses and other vehicles with minimal emissions controls.

Consider This 6.23   Deterioration and Damage

Reexamine Figure 6.22. Although it may be tempting to blame acid rain for the damage, other agents may be at work. View possible other culprits for yourself by taking a photo tour of our nation's capitol, courtesy of a website on acid rain provided by the United States Geological Survey. What kinds of damage do the photos show? What promotes damage by acid rain? What else has caused the deterioration?

Figure 6.23
Acid rain knows no geographic or political boundaries. Acid rain has eroded Mayan ruins at Chichén Itzá, Mexico.

Consider This 6.24   Acid Rain Across the Globe

The concerns of acid rain vary across the globe. Many countries in North America and Europe have websites dealing with acid rain. Choose a country. What are the issues in the country you selected? Does the acid deposition originate outside the borders of the country? How does your example connect to the tragedy of the commons?

6.12 | Acid Deposition, Haze, and Human Health

Haze! This phenomenon, often an indication of acid deposition, results from tiny liquid droplets or solid particles suspended in air. If you live in a congested urban area, you often can see haze simply by looking at the buildings down a long street. If you live in the country, you may be familiar with the summer haze that sometimes settles over the fields. Airline passengers, as they peer down from a cruising altitude, often notice that the features and colors of the landscape are blurred. Ironically, you become more aware of the haze on the occasional clear day when it really does seem that you can see forever.

The causes of haze are well understood, but they differ from region to region. In large cities such as Beijing, China (Figure 6.24), coal-burning power plants produce the smoke and particulate matter that in turn create the haze. In rural regions, a different set of particulates, including soil dust and the soot of wood-burning stoves, add to the haze.

East or west, power plants emit NO_x and SO_2. Although both contribute to haze, for the purposes of illustrating acid deposition we focus on the latter. As we mentioned earlier, coal contains a few percent sulfur, and when the coal is burned, a steady stream of sulfur dioxide is released. Sulfur dioxide is colorless, so this gas is not what we are peering through as "haze." Rather, SO_2 is the precursor to the formation of this haze.

Let's focus on a molecule of SO_2 as it exits the tall smokestack of a coal-fired power plant. As it moves downwind, via a series of steps it forms an aerosol of sulfuric acid. The first step is the reaction of SO_2 with oxygen to form SO_3, as we saw earlier in equation 6.18. Sulfur trioxide is also a colorless gas, but it has the property of being **hygroscopic,** that is, it readily absorbs water from the atmosphere and retains it. In a second step, a molecule of SO_3 can react rapidly with a water molecule to form sulfuric acid (see equation 6.12).

Similarly, acidic aerosols of nitric acid form from NO_x.

Figure 6.24

The Forbidden City in Bejing, China, as seen on two different days.

Your Turn 6.25   Droplets of Acid

As a review of the sulfur chemistry described, write a set of chemical equations that start with elemental sulfur in coal and eventually produce sulfuric acid.

Many molecules of sulfuric acid form a tiny droplet, and many of these droplets of sulfuric acid then coalesce to produce larger droplets. These droplets form an aerosol with droplets about a micrometer (1 μm = 10^{-6} m) in diameter. These droplets of sulfuric acid do not absorb sunlight. Rather, they scatter (reflect) sunlight, reducing visibility. The aerosols of sulfuric acid, which can persist for several days, can travel hundreds of miles downwind, which is why the haze can become so widespread. In addition, these fine droplets of acid are stable enough that they enter our buildings and become part of the air that we breathe indoors.

You also may have heard of sulfate aerosols. Recall that sulfuric acid, H_2SO_4, ionizes to produce H^+, HSO_4^-, and SO_4^{2-}. The concentrations of each can be measured in an aerosol. But these acidic aerosols may react with bases to produce salts that contain the sulfate ion. Typically this base is ammonia or in aqueous form, ammonium hydroxide. Thus, the particles or droplets in an aerosol may be a mixture of sulfuric acid, ammonium sulfate, $(NH_4)_2SO_4$, and ammonium hydrogen sulfate, NH_4HSO_4. Reporting the concentration of sulfate and hydrogen sulfate ions (rather than simply the pH) gives a better indication of how much sulfuric acid was initially present.

Your Turn 6.26   Sulfate Aerosols

As a review of the acid–base chemistry just described, write balanced chemical equations that show how sulfate compounds form in aerosols. Write reactants and products in their aqueous forms rather than dissociated into ions. For example, represent sulfuric acid as $H_2SO_4(aq)$.

a. The reaction of sulfuric acid with ammonium hydroxide to form ammonium hydrogen sulfate and water.
b. The reaction of sulfuric acid with ammonium hydroxide to form ammonium sulfate and water.

Hint: This requires 2 moles of base.

The summer sunshine plays a role in generating the hydroxyl radical in the atmosphere, which in turn catalyzes the SO_2-to-SO_3 conversion.

During hot and dry seasons, wild fires also contribute to haze.

Haze is most pronounced in summer when there is more sunlight to accelerate the photochemical reactions leading to the production of sulfuric acid. As a result, the average visibility in the eastern United States is now about 20 miles and occasionally as low as 1 mile. By contrast, visibility in the western states is now lessened from the natural visual range of about 200 miles to 100 miles or less. Where you formerly might have been able to see the mountains 100 miles away, these mountains may now have disappeared into the haze. The visibility in many national parks, including Yellowstone, the Grand Canyon, and the Great Smoky Mountains, has been affected.

In the United States, the Clean Air Act of 1970 and its subsequent amendments included provisions to improve the visibility in our national parks. Although the standards were set by federal law, the states were charged with their implementation. Visibility continued to drop in the national parks. In the last few days of his presidency, Bill Clinton signed a bill authorizing the EPA to issue regulations to help clear the skies in national parks and wilderness areas. These regulations, called the Regional Haze Rule (1999), required the hundreds of older power plants that emitted vast quantities of SO_2, NO_x, and particulates to retrofit their operations with pollution controls. A final set of amendments, the Clean Air Visibility Rule, was issued on June 15, 2005 by then President George W. Bush.

Consider This 6.27   Hazy at Mount Rainier?

Live on the Internet, see for yourself the haze (or lack thereof) at Mount Rainier. Dozens of other places have webcams as well, and the EPA posts a list of these.

a. During daylight hours, look up several webcams to see what's out there.
b. Find the current air quality for a location of your choice. Some websites provide this information together with the webcam photographs. For others, you can obtain the data from the EPA AIRNow website.
c. How well does the air quality correlate with the visibility?

When you can see haze on the horizon, you are most likely also breathing it. Once inhaled, the acidic droplets attack the sensitive tissue of your lungs. People with asthma, emphysema, and cardiovascular disease are the most sensitive. Mortality rates may increase, especially for those with bronchitis and pneumonia. But even people in good health feel the irritating effects of the acidic aerosols. Thus, breathing air contaminated with aerosols of sulfate and sulfuric acid clearly comes with a medical price tag! The low cost of electricity from burning coal fails to take into account the costs to the community of the health effects resulting from NO_x and SO_2 emissions.

A decrease in acidic aerosol levels would benefit many, both in real dollars and in quality of life. The problem is that the costs and savings are not directly borne by the same groups. Industry must pay to clean up; people must pay medical bills. Government, of course, is involved in paying both.

The EPA's Clean Air Visibility Rule of 2005 is expected to provide "substantial health benefits in the range of $8.4 to $9.8 billion each year—preventing an estimated 1600 premature deaths, 2200 nonfatal heart attacks, 960 hospital admissions, and more than 1 million lost school and work days." The cost-to-benefit ratio is thus exceedingly favorable. For some, the question is, Who is paying the cost, and who is reaping the benefit? For companies striving to reduce emissions, upgrading older equipment definitely comes with a cost. But there are savings as well. Fewer emissions translate to healthier communities (including employees) and lower health care costs and lost days at work. In terms of the Triple Bottom Line, reducing emissions translates to healthier ecosystems, healthier communities, and healthier economies.

Historically, polluted air has exacted a huge price. One of the worst recorded instances of pollution-related respiratory illness occurred in London in 1952. Periods of foggy bad air were nothing unusual to the British Isles, as factory chimneys had belched smoke into the air for several hundred years. But in December, 1952, the weather was colder than usual and people were burning large quantities of sulfur-rich coal in their home fireplaces. Due to unusual weather conditions, a deep layer of fog developed that trapped all the smoke and pollutants for five days, dropping visibility to practically zero. The deadly aerosol caused more than 4000 deaths, claiming 900 lives daily during its peak.

In 1948, a similar incident occurred in Donora, Pennsylvania, a steel mill town south of Pittsburgh. Again a layer of fog trapped industrial pollutants close to the ground. By noon, the skies had darkened with a choking aerosol of fog and smoke (Figure 6.25). An 81-year-old fireman who took oxygen door-to-door to the victims reported, "It may sound dramatic or exaggerated, but you could barely see." High concentrations of sulfuric acid and other pollutants soon caused widespread illness. During the fog, 17 people died, to be followed by 4 more later. Although Donora and London were extreme and unusual incidents from the past, people still breathe highly polluted air today. The U.S. EPA and the World Health Organization currently estimate that 625 million people are still exposed to unhealthy levels of SO_2 released by the burning of fossil fuels. Indeed, modern residents of Datong, China, the coal mining

Triple Bottom Line: healthy economies, healthy ecosystems, and healthy communities. For more about the Triple Bottom Line, see Chapter 0.

Figure 6.25

(a) A 1948 news headline from Donora, Pennsylvania. (b) Donora at noon during the deadly smog of 1948.

center of the country, have reported winter air quality so poor that "even during the daytime, people drive with their lights on."

Although acidic fogs can be immediately hazardous to one's health, public concern is growing over the indirect effects of acid deposition. For example, the solubilities of certain toxic metal ions, including lead, cadmium, and mercury, are significantly increased in the presence of acids. These elements are naturally present on Earth, often tightly bound in minerals that make up soil and rock. Dissolved in acidified water and conveyed to the public water supply, these metals can pose serious health threats.

Clearly there is a connection between burning fossil fuels, acidic precipitation, and human health. An article written in the journal *Science* in 2001 by an international team of authors bluntly assessed the situation this way: "For every day that policies to reduce fossil-fuel combustion emissions are postponed, deaths and illness related to air pollution will increase." These words are as true today as they were in 2001. Health care costs will be reduced if the air we breathe is clean.

Similarly, studies by the EPA have estimated that the reductions in SO_2 and associated acid aerosol pollution called for by the Clean Air Act Amendments of 1990 should result in saving billions of dollars in health care costs over time. The savings would come principally from reduced costs to treat pulmonary diseases such as asthma and bronchitis and from a decrease in premature deaths.

6.13 | Damage to Lakes and Streams

Humans are not the only creatures bearing the costs of acidic precipitation. Organisms in the world's surface waters experience a change in environment when acidic precipitation fills lakes and streams. Healthy lakes have a pH of 6.5 or slightly above. If the pH is lowered below 6.0, fish and other aquatic life are affected (Figure 6.26). Only a few hardy species can survive below pH 5.0. At pH 4.0, lakes become essentially dead ecosystems.

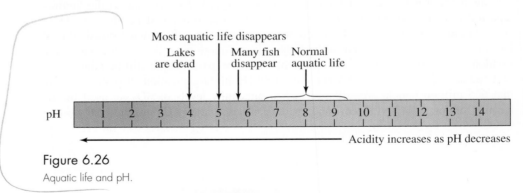

Figure 6.26
Aquatic life and pH.

Numerous studies have reported the progressive acidification of lakes and rivers in certain geographic regions, along with reductions in fish populations. In southern Norway and Sweden, where the problem was first observed, one fifth of the lakes no longer contain any fish, and half of the rivers have no brown trout. In southeastern Ontario, the average pH of lakes is now 5.0, well below the pH of 6.5 required for a healthy lake. In Virginia, more than a third of the trout streams are episodically acidic or at risk of becoming so.

Many areas of the midwestern United States have no problem with acidification of lakes or streams, even though the Midwest is a major source of acidic precipitation. This apparent paradox can be explained quite simply. When acidic precipitation falls on or runs off into a lake, the pH of the lake drops (become more acidic) unless the acid is neutralized or somehow used by the surrounding vegetation. In some regions, the surrounding soils contain bases that can neutralize the acid. The capacity of a lake or other body of water to resist a decrease in pH is called its **acid-neutralizing capacity.** The surface geology of much of the Midwest is limestone, $CaCO_3$. As a result, lakes in the Midwest have a high acid-neutralizing capacity because limestone slowly reacts with acid rain, as we saw earlier with marble statues and monuments (equation 6.29).

More importantly, the lakes and streams also have a relatively high concentration of calcium and hydrogen carbonate ions. This occurs as a result of the reaction of limestone with carbon dioxide and water.

$$CaCO_3(s) + CO_2(g) + H_2O(l) \longrightarrow \underset{\text{calcium ion}}{Ca^{2+}(aq)} + \underset{\text{hydrogen carbonate ion}}{2\ HCO_3^-(aq)} \qquad \textbf{[6.30]}$$

Because acid is consumed by the carbonate and hydrogen carbonate ions, the pH of the lake remains more or less constant.

Your Turn 6.28   The Bicarbonate Ion

The hydrogen carbonate ion produced in equation 6.30 also can accept a hydrogen ion.

a. Write the chemical equation.
b. Is the hydrogen carbonate ion functioning as an acid or a base?

Answer

a. $HCO_3^-(aq) + H^+(aq) \longrightarrow H_2CO_3(aq) \longrightarrow CO_2(g) + H_2O(l)$

In contrast to the Midwest, many lakes in New England and northern New York (as well as in Norway and Sweden) are surrounded by granite, a hard, impervious, and much less reactive rock. Unless other local processes are at work, these lakes have very little acid-neutralizing capacity. Consequently, many show a gradual acidification.

As it turns out, understanding the acidification of lakes is a good deal more complicated than simply measuring pH and acid-neutralizing capacities. One level of complexity is added by annual variations. Some years, for example, heavy winter snowfalls persist into the spring and then melt suddenly. As a result, the runoff may be more acidic than usual, because it contains all the acidic deposits locked away in the winter snows. A surge of acidity may enter the waterways at just the time when fish are spawning or hatching and are more vulnerable. In the Adirondack Mountains of northern New York, about 70% of the sensitive lakes are at risk for episodic acidification, in comparison with a far smaller percent that are chronically affected (19%). In the Appalachians, the number of episodically affected lakes (30%) is seven times those chronically affected.

When, if ever, will the lakes recover? The good news is that U.S. SO_2 emissions have been declining in recent years, and we have seen a corresponding decrease in the sulfate ion concentrations in the lakes of the Adirondacks. However, even though NO_x emissions have remained fairly constant, the concentration of nitrates in the Adirondacks is increasing in more lakes than not. Thus, it appears that nitrogen saturation has occurred in the surrounding vegetation, with more of the acidity ending up in the lakes. The soil in the region of these lakes most likely has lost some of its acid-neutralizing capacity.

Recent findings are mixed. In 2011, EPA reported to Congress that since 1994 "only an additional 10% of streams in the central Appalachian region are protected from ecological damage from acidic deposition." However, the EPA also acknowledges some improvements. For example, the number of lakes in the Adirondacks in which acid deposition exceeds the soil's acid-neutralizing capacity was reduced by a factor of one third between 1991 and 2008.

Conclusion

Emissions of acidic oxides—carbon dioxide, sulfur dioxide, and nitrogen oxides—are affecting the acidity of the world's oceans, rainfall, lakes, and rivers. In the United States, "acid rain" is not the dire plague once described by environmentalists and journalists. Nor is it a matter to be ignored. It was sufficiently serious that federal legislation, the Clean Air Act Amendments of 1990, were enacted to reduce SO_2 and NO_x emissions, precursors to acid deposition.

If you have learned anything from this chapter, we hope it has been the recognition that complex problems cannot be solved by simple or simplistic strategies. Any failure to acknowledge the intertwined relationships involving the combustion of coal and gasoline; the production of carbon, sulfur, and nitrogen oxides; and the reduced pH of seawater, fog, and precipitation is to deny some fundamental facts of chemistry. Knowledge of ecology and biological systems is needed as well, so that acid deposition can be understood in the context of entire ecosystems, a task that requires that experts from several disciplines collaborate.

Public health also is at issue. Economic analyses reveal that allocating funds to reduce sulfur and nitrogen emissions will have a huge payoff in terms of lower mortality rates, fewer illnesses, and higher quality of living.

One response that we as individuals and as a society might make to the problems of ocean acidification and acid precipitation has hardly been mentioned in this chapter, yet it is potentially one of the most powerful: to conserve energy and to transition to noncombustion sources of energy. Carbon dioxide, sulfur dioxide, and nitrogen oxides are by-products of our voracious demand for energy, especially for electricity and transportation. If our personal, national, and global appetite for fossil fuels continues to grow unchecked, our environment may well become a good deal warmer and a good deal more acidic. Moreover, the problem may be intensified as the supply of petroleum and low-sulfur coals diminishes and we become even more reliant on high-sulfur coal.

There are other sources of energy—nuclear fission, water and wind, renewable biomass, and the Sun itself. All currently are being utilized, and their use will no doubt increase. We explore nuclear fission in the next chapter. But we conclude this chapter with the modest suggestion that, for a multitude of reasons, the conservation of energy by industry and collectively by individuals could have profoundly beneficial effects on our environment.

Chapter Summary

Having studied this chapter, you should be able to:

- Define the terms *acid* and *base* and know how to use these definitions to distinguish acids from bases (6.1–6.3)

- Represent the dissociation (ionization) of acids and bases using chemical equations (6.1–6.2)

- Write neutralization reactions for acids and bases (6.3)

- Classify solutions as acidic, basic, or neutral based on their pH or concentrations of H^+ and OH^- (6.3–6.4)

- Calculate pH values given hydrogen or hydroxide ion concentrations in the form of 1×10 raised to whole-number values (6.4)

- Compare the pH of pure water, the pH of ordinary rain, the pH of acid rain, and the pH of seawater (6.4)

- Use chemical equations to relate increasing levels of carbonic acid in seawater to the dissolution of calcium carbonate shells (6.5)

- Locate on a map of the United States where the most acidic rain falls (6.6)

- Explain the role of sulfur oxides and nitrogen oxides in causing acid rain (6.7–6.8)

- Compare the causes of ocean acidification and acid precipitation (6.5–6.8)

- Explain why N_2 is a relatively inert element. Describe different forms of reactive nitrogen and how they are produced both naturally and by humans. Use the nitrogen cycle to explain the cascading effects of reactive nitrogen. (6.9)

- Describe how the industrial production of ammonia and the acidic deposition of nitrates both contribute to the buildup of reactive nitrogen on our planet (6.9)

- List the different sources of NO_x and of SO_2 and explain the variations in the levels of these pollutants over the past 30 years (6.10)

- Describe the production of acidic aerosols and their effects on building materials and human health (6.12)

- Explain why acid rain control is a wise investment in terms of the benefits to human health (6.12)

- Describe nitrogen saturation and its consequences for lakes (6.13)

Questions

Emphasizing Essentials

1. This chapter opens with a discussion of ocean acidification.

   a. Seawater contains many salts, including sodium chloride. Write its chemical formula.

   b. Sodium chloride is soluble in water. What chemical process takes place when solid sodium chloride dissolves? *Hint:* See Section 5.8.

   c. Is sodium chloride an electrolyte? Explain.

2. Calcium carbonate is another salt. Write its chemical formula. Would you expect calcium carbonate to be soluble or insoluble in water? *Hint:* See Section 5.8.

3. Carbon dioxide is a gas found in our atmosphere.

   a. What is the approximate concentration?

   b. Why is its concentration in the atmosphere increasing?

   c. Draw the Lewis structure for the CO_2 molecule.

   d. Would you expect carbon dioxide to be highly soluble in seawater? Explain.

4. The term *anthropogenic emissions* is used in the opening section of this chapter. Explain its meaning.

5. a. Draw the Lewis structure for the water molecule.

   b. Draw Lewis structures for the hydrogen ion and the hydroxide ion.

   c. Write a chemical reaction that relates all three structures from parts **a** and **b**.

6. a. Give names and chemical formulas for five acids of your choice.

   b. Name three observable properties generally associated with acids.

7. Write a chemical equation that shows the release of one hydrogen ion from a molecule of each of these acids.

   a. HBr*(aq)*, hydrobromic acid

   b. H_2SO_3*(aq)*, sulfurous acid

   c. $HC_2H_3O_2$*(aq)*, acetic acid

8. a. Give names and chemical formulas for five bases of your choice.

   b. Name three observable properties generally associated with bases.

   c. Draw Lewis structures for each species in equation 6.5b.

9. Write a chemical equation that shows the release of hydroxide ions as each of these bases dissolves in water.

   a. KOH*(s)*, potassium hydroxide

   b. $Ba(OH)_2$*(s)*, barium hydroxide

10. Which gas dissolved in water to produce each of these acids?

    a. carbonic acid, H_2CO_3

    b. sulfurous acid, H_2SO_3

11. Consider these ions: nitrate, sulfate, carbonate, and ammonium.

    a. Give the chemical formula for each.

    b. Write a chemical equation in which the ion (in aqueous form) appears as a product.

12. Write a balanced chemical equation for each acid–base reaction.

    a. Potassium hydroxide is neutralized by nitric acid.

    b. Hydrochloric acid is neutralized by barium hydroxide.

    c. Sulfuric acid is neutralized by ammonium hydroxide.

13. In each pair below, the $[H^+]$ is different. By what factor of 10?

    a. pH = 6 and pH = 8

    b. pH = 5.5 and pH = 6.5

    c. $[H^+] = 1 \times 10^{-8}$ M and $[H^+] = 1 \times 10^{-6}$ M

    d. $[OH^-] = 1 \times 10^{-2}$ M and $[OH^-] = 1 \times 10^{-3}$ M

14. Classify these aqueous solutions as acidic, neutral, or basic.

    a. HI*(aq)*

    b. NaCl*(aq)*

    c. NH_4OH*(aq)*

    d. $[H^+] = 1 \times 10^{-8}$ M

    e. $[OH^-] = 1 \times 10^{-2}$ M

    f. $[H^+] = 5 \times 10^{-7}$ M

    g. $[OH^-] = 1 \times 10^{-12}$ M

15. For parts **d** and **f** of question 14, calculate the $[OH^-]$ that corresponds to the given $[H^+]$. Similarly, for parts **e** and **g,** calculate the $[H^+]$.

16. Which of these has the *lowest* concentration of hydrogen ions: 0.1 M HCl, 0.1 M NaOH, 0.1 M H_2SO_4, or pure water? Explain your answer.

17. Write a balanced chemical equation for the reaction of elemental sulfur shown in Figure 6.13.

18. Assume that coal can be represented by the chemical formula $C_{135}H_{96}O_9NS$.

    a. What is the percent of nitrogen by mass in coal?

    b. If 3 tons of coal is burned, what mass of nitrogen in the form of NO is produced? Assume that all of the nitrogen in the coal is converted to NO.

    c. Actually more NO is produced than you just calculated. Explain.

19. In 2010, the United States burned about 1 billion tons of coal. Assuming that it was 2% sulfur by weight, calculate the mass (in tons) of sulfur dioxide emitted.

20. Acid rain can damage marble statues and limestone building materials. Write a balanced chemical equation using an acid of your choice.

21. Calculate the number of tons of $CaCO_3$ needed to react completely with 1.00 ton of SO_2.

22. A garden product called dolomite lime is composed of tiny chips of limestone that contain both calcium carbonate and magnesium carbonate. This product is "intended to help the gardener correct the pH of acid soils," as it is "a valuable source of calcium and magnesium."

a. Is the "calcium" in the form of calcium ion or calcium metal?

b. Write a chemical equation that shows why limestone "corrects" the pH of acidic soils.

c. Will the addition of dolomite lime to soils cause the pH to rise or fall?

d. Plants such as rhododendrons, azaleas, and camellias should not be given dolomite lime. Explain.

Concentrating on Concepts

23. Professor James Galloway, an expert on acid rain, wrote "Human activity is not making the world acidic, rather it is making the world *more* acidic."

a. Explain why the world is naturally acidic.

b. Explain how humans are making the world more acidic.

c. One large part of our planet is basic. Which one? *Hint:* Consult Figure 6.4.

24. A news reporter talked about how acidic the oceans currently are and that they were getting even more acidic. What email message would you send to the news station?

25. Assuming the ocean continues to acidify at the same rate that it has been over the past 200 years, how long will it take before the ocean actually becomes acidic?

26. Suppose you have a new mountain bike and accidentally spilled a can of carbonated cola on the metallic handlebars and paint.

a. Soft drinks are more acidic than acid rain. About how many times more acidic? *Hint:* Consult Figure 6.4.

b. In spite of the higher acidity, this spill is unlikely to damage your handle bars and paint (although the sugar probably isn't great on your gears). Why is damage unlikely?

27. a. On the label of a shampoo bottle, what does the phrase "pH-balanced" imply?

b. Does the phrase "pH-balanced" influence your decision to buy a particular shampoo? Explain.

28. Judging by the taste, do you think there are more hydrogen ions in a glass of orange juice or in a glass of milk? Explain your reasoning.

29. The formula for acetic acid, the acid present in vinegar, is commonly written as $HC_2H_3O_2$. Many chemists write the formula as CH_3COOH.

a. Draw the Lewis structure for acetic acid.

b. Show that both formulas represent acetic acid.

c. What are the advantages and disadvantages of each formula?

d. How many hydrogen atoms can be released as hydrogen ions per acetic acid molecule? Explain.

30. Television and magazine advertisements tout the benefits of antacids. A friend suggests that a good way to get rich quickly would be to market "antibase" tablets. Explain to your friend the purpose of antacids and offer some advice about the potential success of "antibase" tablets.

31. In Your Turn 6.7, you listed the ions present in aqueous solutions of acids, bases, and common salts. Now add water, a molecular species, to this list.

a. List all molecular and ionic species in order of decreasing concentration in a 1.0 M aqueous solution of NaOH.

b. List all molecular and ionic species in order of decreasing concentration in a 1.0 M aqueous solution of HCl.

32. Many gases, including CO, CO_2, O_3, NO, NO_2, SO_2, and SO_3, are associated with exhaust from jet engines.

  a. Which of these gases do jet engines emit *directly*?

  b. Which ones form secondarily, that is, resulting from the emissions of part **a**?

33. Figure 6.14 offers information about SO_2 emissions from fuel combustion (mainly from electric power production) and from transportation. Figure 6.16 offers information about NO_x emissions from fuel combustion (again mainly from power production) and from transportation. Relative to fuel combustion and transportation, how do the emissions of SO_2 and NO_x differ? Explain this difference.

34. Almost equal *masses* of SO_2 and NO_x are produced by human activities in the United States.

  a. How does their production compare in moles? Assume that all the NO_x is produced as NO_2.

  b. Suggest reasons why the U.S. percentage of global emissions is greater for NO_x than for SO_2.

35. Reactive nitrogen compounds affect the biosphere both directly and indirectly through other chemicals they help form.

  a. Name a direct effect of reactive nitrogen compounds that is a benefit.

  b. Name two direct effects of reactive nitrogen compounds that are harmful to human health.

  c. Ozone formation is a harmful indirect effect. Explain the connection between reactive nitrogen compounds and the formation of ozone.

36. Explain why rain is naturally acidic, but not all rain is classified as "acid rain."

37. Some local newspapers give forecasts for pollen, UV Index, and air quality. Why do you suppose that no forecast for acid rain is provided?

38. Here are examples of what an individual might do to reduce acid rain. For each, explain the connection to producing acid rain.

  a. Hang your laundry to dry it.

  b. Walk, bike, or take public transportation to work.

  c. Avoid running dishwashers and washing machines with small loads.

  d. Add additional insulation on hot water heaters and pipes.

  e. Buy locally grown produce and locally produced food.

39. As mentioned in Section 6.6, rain samples now are analyzed for acidity in the Central Analytical Laboratory in Illinois rather than out in the field.

  a. The pH values tend to be slightly higher in the lab than in the field. Did the acidity increase or decrease?

  b. Speculate on the causes of the pH increase.

40. Speaking of field measurements, in January 2006 those living in the metropolitan St. Louis area experienced a severe hail storm. Hail stones were still visible a day later, as shown in the photo. A chemistry professor took samples of the hail, analyzed them in her laboratory, and reported a pH of 4.8.

  a. How does this pH compare with the normal precipitation in the St. Louis area? To acidity levels further east and further west of St. Louis?

  b. What factors might lead to acid rain in St. Louis?

41. Mammoth Cave National Park in Kentucky is in close proximity to the coal-fired electric utility plants in the Ohio Valley. Noting this, the National Parks Conservation Association (NPCA) reported that this national park had the poorest visibility of any in the country.

  a. What is the connection between coal-fired plants and poor visibility?

  b. The NPCA reported "the average rainfall in Mammoth Cave National Park is 10 times more acidic than natural." From this information and that in your text, estimate the pH of rainfall in the park.

42. In the United States over the past few decades, agricultural emissions of ammonia have dramatically increased, although less so in the east than in the west.

  a. Show with a chemical equation that ammonia dissolves in rain to form a basic solution.

  b. Write the neutralization reaction for rain that contains both ammonia and nitric acid.

  c. Ammonium sulfate also is found in rain. Write a chemical equation that demonstrates how it could have formed.

43. Ozone in the troposphere is an undesirable pollutant, but stratospheric ozone is beneficial. Does nitric oxide, NO, have a similar "dual personality" in these two atmospheric regions? Explain. *Hint:* Consult Chapter 2.

44. The mass of CO_2 emitted during combustion reactions is much greater than the mass of NO_x or SO_2, but there is less concern about the contributions of CO_2 to acid rain than from the other two oxides. Suggest two reasons for this apparent inconsistency.

45. The average pH of precipitation in New Hampshire and Vermont is low, even though these states have relatively fewer cars and virtually no industry that emits large quantities of air pollutants. How do you account for this low pH?

46. Admittedly, global sulfur emissions are difficult to estimate, and you will find a range of values published in the literature. One set is shown in this figure for 1850–2005. These are estimates from a paper published in 2011. Gg stands for gigagrams, or 1×10^{12} grams.

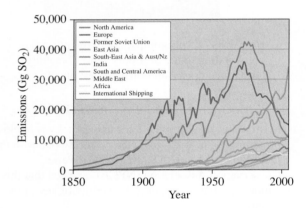

Source: S. J. Smith, J. van Aardenne, Z. Klimont, R. J. Andres, A. Volke, and S. Delgado Arias, Atmos. Chem. Phys., *2011, 3:* 1101–16.

a. According to the figure, in which years did the sulfur emissions peak?

b. List reasons for the decline in more recent years.

c. In 2005, which region of the world contributed the highest level of sulfur emissions?

d. Which regions were the largest contributors in the early 1970s?

47. The chemistry of NO in the atmosphere is complicated. NO can destroy ozone, as seen in Chapter 2. But remember from Chapter 1 that NO can react with O_2 to form NO_2. In turn, NO_2 can react in sunlight to produce ozone. Summarize these reactions, noting in which region of the atmosphere they each occur.

48. a. Efforts to control air pollution by limiting the emission of particulates and dust can sometimes contribute to an increase in the acidity of rain. Offer a possible explanation for this observation. *Hint:* These particulates may contain basic compounds of calcium, magnesium, sodium, and potassium.

b. In Chapter 2, stratospheric ice crystals in the Antarctic were involved in the cycle leading to the destruction of ozone. Is this effect related to the observations in part **a**? Explain.

Exploring Extensions

49. Discuss the validity of the statement, "Photochemical smog is a local issue, acid rain is a regional one, and the enhanced greenhouse effect is a global one." Describe the chemistry behind each issue. Do you agree that the magnitudes of the problems are really so different in scope?

50. In terms of taste, pH, and amount of dissolved gas, how does carbonated water differ from rain that contains dissolved carbon dioxide?

51. The compound $Al(OH)_3$ contains OH in its chemical formula. However, we do not write a reaction analogous to equation 6.4. Explain. *Hint:* Consult a solubility table.

52. In Your Turn 6.7, you listed the ions present in aqueous solutions of acids, bases, and common salts. In question 31, you added molecular substances to the list. To quantify this list,

a. calculate the molar concentration of all molecular and ionic species in a 1.0 M solution of NaOH.

b. calculate the molar concentration of all molecular and ionic species in a 1.0 M solution of HCl.

53. The chemical reaction in which NO reacts to form NO₂ in the atmosphere (see equation 6.20) involves intermediate species A′ and A″. Here are possible structures.

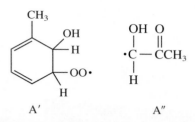

A′   A″

   a. In each, what does the dot (·) represent? For the atom with the dot, redraw to show all valence electrons, both bonding and nonbonding pairs. *Hint:* This atom does not have an octet of electrons.

   b. Name a chemical property that A′ and A″ have in common.

54. Equation 6.19 shows that energy (in the form of a hot engine or other source of heat) must be added to get N₂ and O₂ to react to form NO. A student wants to check this assertion and determine how much energy is required. Show the student how this can be done. *Hint:* Draw the Lewis structures for the reactants and products, noting that NO does not have an even number of electrons. The bond energy is 607 kJ/mol for the N=O double bond.

55. This chapter describes a green chemistry solution to reducing NO emissions for glass manufacturers.

   a. Identify the strategy.

   b. Which other industries similarly might make use of this green chemistry strategy?

56. One way to compare the acid-neutralizing capacity of different substances is to calculate the mass of the substance required to neutralize 1 mol of hydrogen ion, H^+.

   a. Write a balanced equation for the reaction of $NaHCO_3$ with H^+. Use it to calculate the acid-neutralizing capacity of $NaHCO_3$.

   b. If $NaHCO_3$ costs $9.50/kg, determine the cost to neutralize one mole of H^+.

Billboard with an advertisement for Madison Area Technical College (MATC, now called Madison College), Madison, WI.

Should you heed the warning on this billboard? Absolutely, at least in part. Covering up or retreating to the shade makes sense when the ultraviolet rays of the Sun are most harsh. As pointed out in Chapter 2, certain wavelengths of light damage many life forms on our planet, including humans. Ultraviolet light, in particular, can cause cataracts, cause aged and damaged skin, and ultimately lead to skin cancer.

But there is no need to avoid all radiation. In fact, you couldn't do this even if you tried to! For example, infrared radiation, which we feel as heat, is a source of warmth. Visible radiation—the colors in a rainbow—bathes our world in daylight hours.

Should you avoid nuclear radiation? Generally speaking, yes, although this isn't as easy as it may sound. Substances that emit nuclear radiation are found naturally on our planet and you encounter them daily. Furthermore, you have no built-in way of detecting these radioisotopes. For example, a freshly brewed cup of coffee laced with tritium would, of course, feel hot to the touch, but not due to the tritium! Your coffee would not reveal its radioactivity by glowing in the dark, although most likely you would feel the characteristic "glow" of caffeine after drinking it. Most definitely your coffee would not be ticking, even though the tritium present in it would be decaying according to its own nuclear clock. Furthermore, you would not be able to detect the radioactivity either by taste. So although most people can see a tree root and not trip over it, hear the wail of an ambulance, and feel the warmth of the Sun on their skin, they have no clue as to the proximity of a radioactive substance. Indeed, people did not even learn of the existence of radioactivity until the early 1900s.

Do we need a sixth sense for detecting nuclear radiation? Occasionally, this ability would come in handy. For example, all of us would benefit from the ability to sense the nuclear radiation emitted by radon. As an inert gas that is odorless, colorless, and tasteless, radon has no chemical characteristics that alert us to its presence. However, as pointed out in Chapter 1, radon causes lung cancer. We could more easily avoid it if we could detect it.

What about the radioactive isotopes present in a nuclear power plant near you? Would it be handy to be able to detect these with our senses as well? Possibly. More important, this brings up several related questions. Which radioisotopes are present in a nuclear reactor? Are any of these radioisotopes released into the surrounding countryside? If so, which ones and how much? Are any of these a cause for concern?

Questions such as these deserve answers, which in turn rest upon knowledge of the behavior of radioactive substances, of nuclear fission, and of nuclear power plants. Today, nuclear power is in the news, both because of its possible resurgence and because nuclear reactors emit neither greenhouse gases nor air pollutants such as sulfur dioxide and nitrogen monoxide.

Both supporters and opponents of nuclear power today have excellent tools with which to make their arguments. For example, a **cradle-to-cradle** analysis offers a more-inclusive picture of the economic, environmental, and societal costs of running a nuclear reactor, by taking into account what happens from the moment the uranium ore is mined to the ultimate fate of the spent nuclear fuel. Such an analysis includes not only the high economic costs of construction but also the eventual decommissioning of the nuclear reactor.

Should we build more nuclear power plants? The answer depends on both whom you ask and when you ask them. Some long-time opponents of nuclear energy are now in favor of it. Similarly, some who supported it now are questioning its societal costs, both to our current generation and those to come.

Whether citizens (and politicians) support or oppose nuclear power, they still must deal with some real and pressing questions. If not with nuclear, how are we going to produce electricity in the years to come? Do the benefits of nuclear power plants outweigh the costs and risks? How should we deal with the wastes that nuclear reactors produce? Can we prevent the diversion of nuclear materials to nuclear weapons? Is nuclear power sustainable?

As we'll point out in Section 7.4, the word *radiation* can mean electromagnetic radiation, which was introduced in Chapter 2, or nuclear radiation, depending on the context.

Tritium is hydrogen–3 or ^3H, a radioactive isotope of the element hydrogen. The other two isotopes of hydrogen (^1H and ^2H) are not radioactive.

The term *cradle–to–cradle* was introduced in Chapter 0. In the case of nuclear power, cradle–to–grave may be more appropriate in that most nuclear waste currently is stored rather than becoming the "cradle" for something else.

Decommissioning (shutting down) a nuclear plant is a complex operation. All parts must be analyzed for radioactive contamination and removed according to strict criteria.

As has been the case in earlier chapters, science, economic, and societal issues are tightly connected. In the next section, we will present an overview of nuclear power. But before we start, we ask you to consider your own position.

Consider This 7.1   Your Opinion of Nuclear Power

a. Given a choice between purchasing electricity generated by a nuclear plant or by a coal-burning plant, would you choose one over the other? Explain.

b. What circumstances, if any, would change your position on the use of nuclear power for generating electricity?

Save your answers to these questions, because you will revisit them at the end of the chapter.

We have a high demand for electricity (and caffeine).

7.1 | Nuclear Power Worldwide

Most people flip a light switch without thinking of the energy source that produced the electricity that caused the bulb to glow. But others, especially those who have lost electrical power because of a storm or a blackout, may not take electricity for granted. All too well they know the sensation of turning on the switch and remaining in the dark.

Let's say that you switch on your coffee pot. If you live in the United States, about one fifth of the electricity is coming from a nuclear power plant. If you live in France, Belgium, or Sweden, the percentage is even higher. In either case, you can brew your coffee!

Worldwide, nations differ in the extent to which they employ nuclear energy to generate electricity. For example, in the United States, 20% of commercial electrical power is produced from just over 100 nuclear reactors, all licensed by the Nuclear Regulatory Commission. As of 2012, these reactors were operating at 65 sites in 31 states. As you can see by Figure 7.1, the electricity generated by these nuclear plants has increased over the years, despite the drop in number of operating reactors from its peak of 112 in 1990.

The power increase over time in Figure 7.1 stems from both improved reactor efficiencies and upgrades to reactor components.

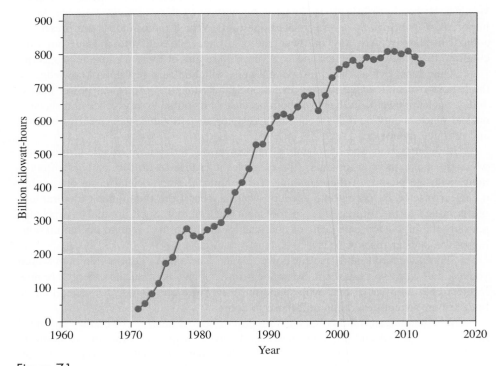

Figure 7.1

Nuclear power generation in the United States, 1971–2012.

Source: Energy Information Administration (EIA).

When you brew your coffee a decade from now, where will the electricity originate? Nuclear power plants surely will be one source. Although no new plants have been built in the United States since 1978, several reactors currently are under construction at existing plants. As of 2013, these include two new units in Georgia at Plant Vogtle that eventually will make this the largest nuclear plant in the United States. Construction also continues in South Carolina at two additional units at the Virgil C. Summer nuclear generating station. In Tennessee, construction on the Watts Bar unit 2 reactor has resumed.

Many nuclear plants are like Plant Vogtle (Figure 7.2), generating electricity using multiple reactors. As another example, the Palo Verde plant pictured in Consider This 7.11 has three reactors.

Consider This 7.2   Nuclear Power in the United States

This map shows the 31 states with nuclear power plants shaded in blue.

a. Select a state and prepare a summary of its nuclear power plants, their energy production, and any proposed changes.

b. As of 2011, Vermont was the state with the highest percent of nuclear energy (72.5%). Search the Internet to find at least two other states that use at least one third nuclear energy.

c. From the map, select a state with no nuclear power plants. How is that state's electricity generated?

Construction sites for new nuclear power plants are enormous. They cover hundreds of acres and employ a workforce in the thousands, essentially cities unto themselves. The construction site at Plant Vogtle, pictured in Figure 7.2, even has its own railway!

The construction and continued operation of a commercial nuclear power plant is not only a matter of energy supply and demand but also one of public acceptance. Depending on your age, you may have little recollection of the controversies surrounding some nuclear plants when they first were proposed back in the 1970s. People have been lining up on one side or the other of the nuclear fence for quite some time. Which side are you on?

Figure 7.2

Aerial view of the 550–acre construction site of the Vogtle nuclear power plant, units 3 and 4 (March 2012).

Source: Southern Company, Inc. Reprinted with permission.

Figure 7.3

Worldwide distribution of nuclear
power plants, including those under
construction (August 2012).

*Source: International Atomic Energy
Agency.*

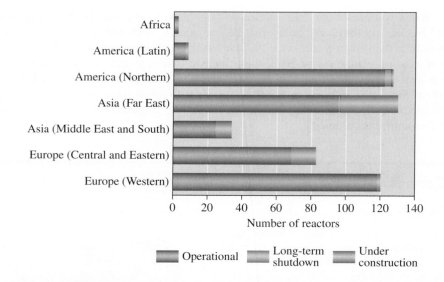

Consider This 7.3   Nuclear Signposts

As you can see in this photo taken during the
construction of the Seabrook nuclear power plant
in New Hampshire (1977), signs are one way to
convey a position. If a nuclear plant were being built
near your community today, sketch out what your sign
would say.

What is the larger picture of nuclear energy worldwide? In a word, changing. In part, the changes stem from increased energy demand. Major commercial development of nuclear energy is clearly on the agenda of many nations. For example, although India only generated 3.7% of its electricity from 20 reactors in 2011, construction was underway for 7 new plants, with others planned or proposed. In 2011, China had 16 operational nuclear power reactors, with 26 under construction, similarly with others planned or proposed.

However, as some nations move toward increased nuclear power, others are wary or even moving away from it. Most recently, this cautiousness results from the 2011 Tohoku earthquake and accompanying tsunami that damaged four nuclear reactors at the Fukushima Daiichi nuclear power plant in Japan.

Look for more about the Fukushima
Daiichi nuclear power plant in
Section 7.5.

Consider This 7.4   Nuclear Neighbors

a. Where are nuclear reactors located? Write a paragraph that summarizes the data of Figure 7.3.
b. Name three countries that currently do not have commercial nuclear reactors.
c. Suggest reasons why some countries develop nuclear energy more than others.

Although clearly nuclear power plants produce electricity, we have not yet described how this occurs. In the next section, we turn to the topic of nuclear fission, thus taking the first step in explaining both the controversies and the desires for nuclear energy as a power source.

7.2 | How Fission Produces Energy

The key to understanding fission is probably the most famous equation in all of the natural sciences, $E = mc^2$. This equation dates from the early years of the 20th century and is one of the many contributions of Albert Einstein (1879–1955). It summarizes the equivalence of energy, *E,* and matter, or mass, *m.* The symbol *c* represents the speed of light, 3.0×10^8 m/s, so c^2 is equal to 9.0×10^{16} m²/s². The large value of c^2 means that it should be possible to obtain a tremendous amount of energy from a very small amount of matter, whether in a power plant or in a weapon.

For over 30 years, Einstein's equation was a curiosity. Scientists believed that it described the source of the Sun's energy, but as far as anyone knew, no one on Earth had ever observed a transformation of a substantial fraction of matter into energy. But in 1938, two German scientists, Otto Hahn (1879–1968) and Fritz Strassmann (1902–1980), discovered otherwise. When they bombarded uranium with neutrons, they found what appeared to be the element barium (Ba) among the products. The observation was unexpected because barium has an atomic number of 56 and an atomic mass of about 137. Comparable values for uranium are 92 and 238, respectively. At first, the scientists were tempted to conclude that the element was radium (Ra, atomic number 88), a member of the same group in the periodic table as barium. But for Hahn and Strassmann, the chemical evidence for barium was too compelling to ignore.

The German scientists were unsure of how barium could have been formed from uranium, so they sent a copy of their results to their colleague, Lise Meitner (1878–1968), for her opinion (Figure 7.4). Dr. Meitner had collaborated with Hahn and Strassmann on related research, but was forced to flee Germany in March 1938 because of the Nazi government. When she received their letter, she was living in Sweden. She discussed the strange results with her physicist nephew, Otto Frisch (1904–1979), as the two of them went walking in the snow. In a flash of insight, she understood. Under the influence of the bombarding neutrons, the uranium atoms were splitting into smaller ones such as barium. The nuclei of the heavy atoms were dividing, like biological cells undergoing binary fission.

The word *fission* from biology is applied to a physical phenomenon in the letter that Meitner and Frisch published on February 11, 1939, in the British journal *Nature.* In the letter, entitled "Disintegration of Uranium by Neutrons: A New Type of Nuclear Reaction," the authors state the following:

> Hahn and Strassmann were forced to conclude that isotopes of barium are formed as a consequence of the bombardment of uranium with neutrons. At first sight, this result seems very hard to understand. . . . On the basis, however, of present ideas about the behavior of heavy nuclei, an entirely different . . . picture of these new disintegration processes suggests itself. . . . It seems therefore possible that the uranium nucleus . . . may, after neutron capture, divide itself into two nuclei of roughly equal size. . . . The whole "fission" process can thus be described in an essentially classical way.

Figure 7.4
Lise Meitner is pictured shortly after her arrival in New York in January, 1946.

Although just over a page long, this letter was immediately recognized for its significance. In fact, it would be difficult to think of a more important scientific communication. Niels Bohr (1885–1962), an eminent Danish physicist, learned of the news directly from Frisch and brought a copy of the letter to the United States on an ocean liner several days before its publication. Within a few weeks of Meitner and Frisch's letter in *Nature*, scientists in a dozen laboratories in various countries confirmed that the energy released by the splitting of uranium atoms was that predicted by Einstein's equation. Lise Meitner's contributions to the discovery of nuclear fission were honored by naming element 109 meitnerium.

Nuclear fission is the splitting of a large nucleus into smaller ones with the release of energy. Energy is released because the total mass of the products is slightly *less* than the total mass of the reactants. In spite of what you may have been taught, neither matter nor energy is individually conserved. Matter disappears and an equivalent quantity of energy appears. Alternatively, one can view matter as a very concentrated form of energy; nowhere is it more concentrated than in the atomic nucleus. Remember that an atom is mostly empty space. If a hydrogen nucleus were the size of a baseball, then its electron would be found within a sphere half a mile in diameter. Because almost all the mass of an atom is associated with its nucleus, the nucleus is incredibly dense. Indeed, a pocket-sized matchbox full of atomic nuclei would weigh over 2.5 billion tons! Given the energy–mass equivalence of Einstein's equation, the energy content of all nuclei is, relatively speaking, immense.

Only the nuclei of certain elements undergo fission and these only under certain conditions. Three factors determine whether a particular nucleus will split: its size, the numbers of protons and neutrons it contains, and the energy of the neutrons that bombard the nucleus to initiate the fission. For example, relatively light and stable atoms such as oxygen, chlorine, and iron do not split. Extremely heavy nuclei may fission spontaneously. And heavy nuclei, such as those of uranium and plutonium, can be made to split if hit hard enough with neutrons. Notably, one isotope of uranium fissions with neutrons of a more moderate speed, such as those employed in the reactor of a nuclear power plant.

Let's examine uranium more closely. *All* uranium atoms contain 92 protons. If these atoms are electrically neutral, these protons are accompanied by 92 electrons. In nature, uranium is found predominantly as two isotopes. The more abundant one (99.3%) contains 146 neutrons. The mass number of this isotope of uranium is 238, that is, 92 protons plus 146 neutrons. We represent this isotope as uranium-238, or more simply as U-238. The less abundant isotope (0.7%) contains 143 neutrons and 92 protons; namely, U-235.

The terms mass number and isotope were introduced in Section 2.2.

Your Turn 7.5   Another Isotope of Uranium

A trace amount of a third isotope, U–234, is also found in nature. How do U–238 and U–234 compare in terms of the number of protons and the number of neutrons?

More commonly, we specify an isotope with both its mass number and atomic number. The former is a superscript and the latter a subscript, both written to the left of the chemical symbol. Using this convention, uranium-238 becomes:

Mass number = number of protons + number of neutrons $\longrightarrow$ $^{238}_{92}U$

Atomic number = number of protons $\longrightarrow$

Similarly, U-235 is written as $^{235}_{92}U$. Although $^{235}_{92}U$ and $^{238}_{92}U$ differ by a mere three neutrons, this difference translates to one key difference in *nuclear* properties. Under the conditions present in a nuclear reactor, $^{238}_{92}U$ does *not* undergo fission, yet $^{235}_{92}U$ does.

The process of nuclear fission is initiated by neutrons and releases neutrons, as can be seen by this example.

$$\ _{0}^{1}\text{n} + \ _{92}^{235}\text{U} \longrightarrow [\ _{92}^{236}\text{U}] \longrightarrow \ _{56}^{141}\text{Ba} + \ _{36}^{92}\text{Kr} + 3\ _{0}^{1}\text{n} \qquad \textbf{[7.1]}$$

Let's examine the components from left to right. Initially, a neutron hits the nucleus of U-235. This neutron, $_{0}^{1}\text{n}$, has a subscript of 0, indicating no positive charges; the superscript is 1 because the mass number of a neutron is 1. The nucleus of $_{92}^{235}\text{U}$ captures the neutron, forming a heavier isotope of uranium, $_{92}^{236}\text{U}$. This isotope is written in square brackets indicating that it exists only momentarily. Uranium-236 immediately splits into two smaller atoms (Ba-141 and Kr-92) with the release of three more neutrons.

Nuclear equations are similar to, but not the same as "regular" chemical equations. To balance a nuclear equation, you count the protons and neutrons rather than counting atoms as you would do in a chemical equation. A nuclear equation is balanced if the sum of the subscripts (and of the superscripts) on the left is equal to the sum of those on the right. Coefficients in nuclear equations, such as the 3 preceding the $_{0}^{1}\text{n}$ in equation 7.1, are treated the same way as in chemical equations, multiplying the term that follows it. For example, examine the math to see why nuclear equation 7.1 is balanced.

Left	Right
Superscripts: $1 + 235 = 236$	$141 + 92 + (3 \times 1) = 236$
Subscripts: $0 + 92 = 92$	$56 + 36 + (3 \times 0) = 92$

When the nucleus of an atom of U-235 is struck with a neutron, many different fission products are formed. The activity that follows acquaints you with two other possibilities.

Your Turn 7.6   Other Examples of Fission

With the help of a periodic table, write these two nuclear equations. Both are initiated with a neutron.

a. U–235 fissions to form Ba–138, Kr–95, and neutrons.
b. U–235 fissions to form an element (atomic number 52, mass number 137), another element (atomic number 40, mass number 97), and neutrons.

Answer
a. $_{0}^{1}\text{n} + \ _{92}^{235}\text{U} \longrightarrow \ _{56}^{138}\text{Ba} + \ _{36}^{95}\text{Kr} + 3\ _{0}^{1}\text{n}$

Look again at nuclear equation 7.1. Both sides contain neutrons, which might lead you to think that we should cancel them. Although you might do this in a mathematical expression, don't do it here. The neutrons on both sides of the equation are important! The one on the left *initiates* the fission reaction; the ones on the right are *produced* by it. Each neutron produced can in turn strike another U-235 nucleus, cause it to split, and release a few more neutrons. This is an example of a **chain reaction**, a term that generally refers to any reaction in which one of the products becomes a reactant and thus makes it possible for the reaction to become self-sustaining. This particular rapidly branching nuclear chain reaction is self-sustaining and spreads in a fraction of a second (Figure 7.5). With exactly this chain reaction, the first controlled nuclear fission took place at the University of Chicago in 1942.

A **critical mass** is the amount of fissionable fuel required to sustain a chain reaction. For example, the critical mass of U-235 is about 15 kg, or 33 lb. Were this mass of pure U-235 to be brought together in one place, fission would spontaneously occur. And if the mass were held together, fission would continue. Nuclear weapons work on this principle, although the energy released quickly blows the critical mass apart, stopping the fission reaction. But as you will soon see, the uranium fuel in a nuclear power plant is far from pure U-235 and is unable to explode like a nuclear bomb. There simply aren't enough neutrons around (and enough fissionable nuclei for these neutrons to hit) to produce an uncontrolled chain reaction characteristic of a nuclear explosion.

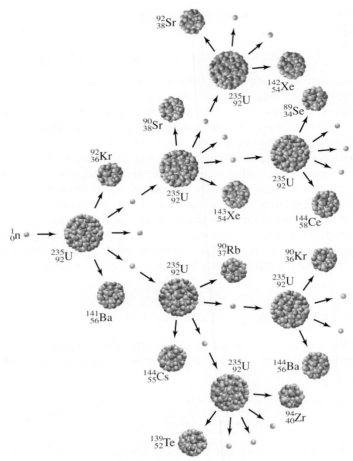

Figure 7.5

A neutron initiates the fission of uranium–235, starting a chain reaction.

 Figures Alive!

We mentioned earlier that energy is given off during fission because the mass of the products is slightly less than that of the reactants. However, from the nuclear equations we have just written, no mass loss is apparent because the sum of the mass numbers is the same on both sides. In fact, the actual mass does decrease slightly. To understand this, remember that the actual masses of the nuclei are not the mass numbers (the sum of the number of protons and neutrons); rather, they have measured values with many decimal places. For example, an atom of uranium-235 weighs 235.043924 atomic mass units. Were you to keep all six decimal places and compare the masses on both sides of the nuclear equation for the fission of U-235, you would find that the mass of the products is less by about 0.1%, or 1/1000th. As a consequence, the energy of the products is less than that of the reactants. This difference corresponds to the energy released.

How much energy would be released if all the nuclei in 1.0 kg (2.2 lb) of pure U-235 were to fission? We can calculate an answer by using an equation closely related to $E = mc^2$; namely, $\Delta E = \Delta mc^2$. Here the Greek letter delta (Δ) means "the change in," so now with a change in mass we can calculate a change in energy. Since 1/1000 of this mass is lost, the value for Δm, the change in mass, is 1/1000 of 1.0 kg, which is 1.0 g or 1×10^{-3} kg. Now substitute this value and $c = 3.0 \times 10^8$ m/s into Einstein's equation.

$$\Delta E = \Delta mc^2 = (1.0 \times 10^{-3} \text{ kg}) \times (3.0 \times 10^8 \text{ m/s})^2$$
$$\Delta E = (1.0 \times 10^{-3} \text{ kg}) \times (9.0 \times 10^{16} \text{ m}^2/\text{s}^2)$$

An atomic mass unit is 1/12 the mass of a C–12 atom, or 1.66×10^{-27} kg. This unit is convenient for expressing the mass of individual atoms.

Completing the calculation gives an energy change in what may appear to be unusual units.

$$\Delta E = (9.0 \times 10^{13} \text{ kg·m}^2/\text{s}^2)$$

The unit kg·m^2/s^2 is identical to a joule (J). Therefore, the energy released from the fission of an entire kilogram of uranium-235 is a whopping 9.0×10^{13} J, or 9.0×10^{10} kJ.

As described in Section 4.2, the joule (J) is a unit of energy.
$1 \text{ J} = 1 \text{ kg·m}^2/\text{s}^2$

To put things into perspective, 9.0×10^{13} J is the amount of energy released by the explosion of about 22 metric kilotons of the explosive TNT. By way of comparison, this is roughly twice that of the atomic bombs dropped on Hiroshima and Nagasaki in 1945. This energy originates from the fission of a single kilogram of U-235, in which a mass of approximately 1 gram (0.1% mass change) was transformed into energy.

Your Turn 7.7   Coal Equivalence

Select a grade of coal from Table 4.1. What mass of coal would be needed to produce the same amount of energy as would the fission of 1 kg of U–235?

As it turns out, one cannot fission a kilogram or two of pure U-235 in one fell swoop. In an atomic weapon, for example, the energy that is released blasts the fissionable fuel apart in a fraction of a second, thus halting the chain reaction before all the nuclei can undergo fission. Nonetheless, the energy released is enormous—on the order of 10 kilotons of TNT for the atomic bomb dropped on the city of Hiroshima in 1945. Figure 7.6 shows an atomic explosion at the U.S. Nevada Test Site. Code named Priscilla, this test in 1957 had more than twice the explosive power of the bombs at Hiroshima and Nagasaki in 1945.

Figure 7.6

The nuclear test "Priscilla" was exploded on a dry lake bed northwest of Las Vegas, Nevada, on June 24, 1957.

Recognize, though, that the energy of nuclear fission can be harnessed. This is exactly the objective of a nuclear power plant. Here, the energy is slowly and *continually* released under controlled conditions, as we shall see in the next section.

7.3 | How Nuclear Reactors Produce Electricity

Chapter 4 described how a conventional power plant burns coal, oil, or some other fuel to produce heat. The heat is then used to boil water, converting it into high-pressure steam that turns the blades of a turbine. The shaft of the spinning turbine is connected to large wire coils that rotate within a magnetic field, thus generating electric energy. A nuclear power plant operates in much the same way, except that the water is heated not by combustion of a fuel, but by the energy released from the fission of nuclear "fuel" such as U-235. Like any power plant, a nuclear one is subject to the efficiency constraints imposed by the second law of thermodynamics. The theoretical efficiency for converting heat energy to work depends on the maximum and minimum temperatures between which the plant operates. This thermodynamic efficiency, typically 55–60%, is significantly reduced by other mechanical, thermal, and electric inefficiencies.

A nuclear power station has parts that are both nuclear and nonnuclear (Figure 7.7). The nuclear reactor is the hot heart of the power station. The reactor, together with one or more steam generators and the primary cooling system, is housed in a special steel vessel within a separate reinforced concrete dome-shaped containment building. The nonnuclear portion contains the turbines that run the electric generator. It also contains the secondary cooling system. In addition, the nonnuclear portion must be connected to some means of removing excess heat from the coolants. Accordingly, a

> The second law of thermodynamics has many versions. The one relevant here might be to say that it is impossible to convert heat completely into work in a process that is a cycle. See Section 4.2.

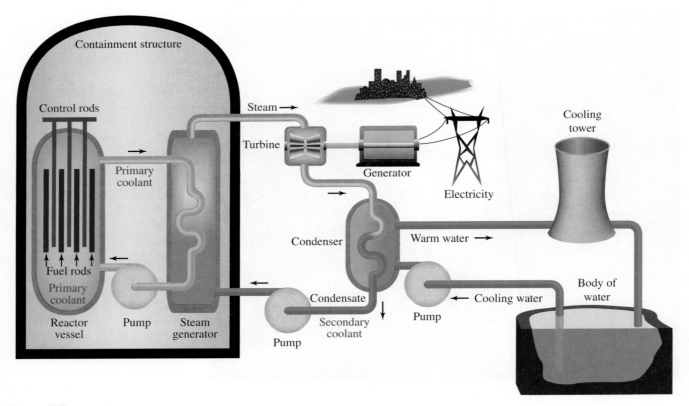

Figure 7.7

Diagram of a nuclear power plant. Components are not illustrated to scale.

nuclear power station has one or more cooling towers or is located near a sizeable body of water (or both). Look back at Figure 4.2, which shows a diagram of a fossil fuel power plant. This plant also requires a means of removing heat, as shown by the stream of cooling water.

The uranium fuel in the reactor core is in the form of uranium dioxide (UO_2) pellets, each comparable in height to a dime, as shown in Figure 7.8. These pellets are placed end-to-end in tubes made of an alloy of zirconium and other metals, which in turn are grouped into stainless-steel-clad bundles (Figure 7.9). Each tube contains at least 200 pellets. Although a fission reaction, once started, can sustain itself by a chain reaction, neutrons are needed to induce the process (see equation 7.1 and Figure 7.5). One means of generating neutrons is to use a combination of beryllium-9 and a heavier element such as plutonium. The heavier element releases alpha particles, $_2^4He$.

Figure 7.8

Nuclear fuel pellets and a U.S. dime.

$$_{94}^{238}Pu \longrightarrow \ _{92}^{234}U + \ _2^4He \qquad \textbf{[7.2]}$$
alpha particle

These alpha particles in turn strike the beryllium, releasing neutrons, carbon-12, and gamma rays, $_0^0\gamma$. Here is the nuclear equation.

$$_2^4He + \ _4^9Be \longrightarrow \ _6^{12}C + \ _0^1n + \ _0^0\gamma \qquad \textbf{[7.3]}$$
gamma ray

> Gamma rays were first introduced in Section 2.4. Alpha particles and gamma rays will be further discussed in Section 7.4.

The neutrons produced in this way can initiate the nuclear fission of uranium-235 in the reactor core.

Your Turn 7.8   Poo–Bee and Am–Bee

A neutron source constructed with Pu and Be is a PuBe ("poo–bee") source. Similarly, the AmBe ("am–bee") source is constructed from americium and beryllium. Analogous to the PuBe source, write the set of reactions that produce neutrons from an AmBe source. Start with Am–241.

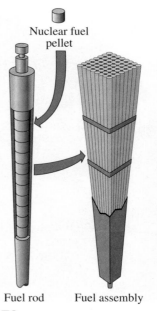

Nuclear fuel pellet

Fuel rod   Fuel assembly

Figure 7.9

Fuel pellet, fuel rod, and fuel assembly making up the core of a nuclear reactor (*left*). The fuel assembly is submerged under water in an active reactor core (*right*).

Remember—one fission event produces two or three neutrons. The trick is to "sponge up" these extra neutrons, but still leave enough to sustain the fission reaction. A delicate balance must be maintained. With extra neutrons, the reactor runs at too high a temperature; with too few, the chain reaction halts and the reactor cools down. To achieve the needed balance, one neutron from each fission event should in turn cause another.

Metal rods interspersed among the fuel elements serve as the neutron "sponges." These **control rods,** composed primarily of an excellent neutron absorber such as cadmium or boron, can be positioned to absorb fewer or more neutrons. With the rods fully inserted, the fission reaction is not self-sustaining. But as the rods are gradually withdrawn, the reactor can "go critical" and become self-sustaining, running at different rates depending on the exact position of the control rods. Over time, fission products that absorb neutrons build up in the fuel pellets. To compensate, the control rods can be withdrawn. Eventually, the reactor fuel bundles must be replaced.

Your Turn 7.9   Earthquake!

Look ahead to Figure 7.16 to see that earthquakes may occur in the vicinity of nuclear reactors. Reactors near the epicenter should automatically shut down. Should the software be programmed to fully insert the control rods into the reactor core, or should they be pulled out? Explain.

The fuel bundles and control rods are bathed in the **primary coolant,** a liquid that comes in direct contact with them and carries away heat. In the Byron nuclear reactor (Figure 7.10) and in many others, the primary coolant is an aqueous solution of boric acid, H_3BO_3. The boron atoms absorb neutrons and thus control the rate of fission and the temperature. Like the control rods, the solution serves as a **moderator** for the reactor, slowing the neutrons, thus making them more effective in producing fission. Another major function of the primary coolant is to absorb the heat generated by the nuclear reaction. Because the primary coolant solution is at a pressure more than 150 times normal atmospheric pressure, it does not boil. It is heated far above its normal boiling point and circulates in a closed loop from the reaction vessel to the steam generators, and back again. This closed primary coolant loop thus forms the link between the nuclear reactor and the rest of the power plant (see Figure 7.7).

Figure 7.10

The Byron nuclear power plant in Illinois. The two cooling towers (one with a cloud of condensed water vapor) are the most prominent features of this plant. The reactors, however, are located in the two cylindrical containment buildings with white roofs in the foreground.

The heat from the primary coolant is transferred to what is sometimes referred to as the **secondary coolant,** the water in the steam generators that does not come in contact with the reactor. At the Byron nuclear plant (see Figure 7.10), more than 30,000 gallons of water is converted to vapor each minute. The energy of this hot vapor turns the blades of turbines that are attached to an electric generator. To continue the heat transfer cycle, the water vapor is then cooled and condensed back to a liquid and returned to the steam generator. In many nuclear facilities the cooling is done using large cooling towers that commonly are mistaken for the reactors. The reactor buildings are not as large.

Cooling towers also are used in coal–fired plants.

Your Turn 7.10   Clouds (Not Mushroom–Shaped)

Some days you can see a cloud coming out of the cooling tower of a nuclear power plant, as shown in Figure 7.10. What causes the cloud? Does it contain radioisotopes produced from the fission of U–235? Explain.

Nuclear power plants also use water from lakes, rivers, or the ocean to cool the condenser. For example, at the Seabrook nuclear power plant in New Hampshire, every minute about 400,000 gallons of ocean water flows through a huge tunnel (19 feet in diameter and 3 miles long) bored through rock 100 feet beneath the floor of the ocean. A similar tunnel from the plant carries the water, now 22 °C warmer, back to the ocean. Special nozzles distribute the hot water so that the observed temperature increase in the immediate area of the discharge is only about 2 °C. The ocean water is in a separate loop from the fission reaction and its products. The primary coolant (water with boric acid) circulates through the reactor core inside the containment building. However, this boric acid solution is kept isolated in a closed circulating system, which makes the transfer of radioactivity to the secondary coolant water in the steam generator highly unlikely. Similarly, the ocean water does not come in direct contact with the secondary system, so the ocean water is well protected from radioactive contamination. Clearly, the electricity generated by a nuclear power plant is identical to the electricity generated by a fossil fuel plant; the electricity is not radioactive, nor can it be.

Consider This 7.11   The Palo Verde Reactors

One of the most powerful nuclear plants in operation in the United States is the Palo Verde complex in Arizona. At maximum capacity, just one of its three reactors generates 1243 million joules of electric energy every second. Calculate the total amount of electric energy produced per day and the loss of mass of U–235 each day.
Hint: Start by calculating the quantity of energy generated not per second, but per day. Then use the equation $\Delta E = \Delta mc^2$ and solve for the change in mass, Δm. Report the mass loss in grams.

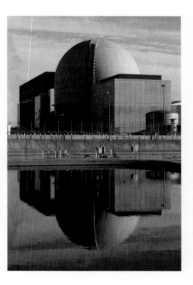

The topics we have been discussing—nuclear fission, uranium, nuclear fuel, nuclear weapons—all rest on an understanding of radioactivity. We now turn to this topic.

7.4 | What Is Radioactivity?

Our knowledge of radioactive substances is just over 100 years old. In 1896, the French physicist Antoine Henri Becquerel (1852–1908) discovered radioactivity. At the time, his research involved using photographic plates; film, of course, had not yet been invented. Prior to use, these plates were sealed in black paper to keep them from being exposed. By accident he left a mineral near one of these sealed plates and found that the plate's light-sensitive emulsion darkened. It was as though the plate had been

Figure 7.11

Marie Sklodowska Curie won two Nobel Prizes—one in chemistry, the other in physics—for her research on radioactive elements.

See Figure 2.7 for more information about the electromagnetic spectrum.

exposed to light! Becquerel immediately recognized that the mineral emitted powerful rays that penetrated the lightproof paper.

Further investigation by the Polish scientist Marie Sklodowska Curie (1867–1934) (Figure 7.11) revealed that the rays were coming from a constituent of the mineral—the element uranium. In 1899, Marie Curie applied the term **radioactivity** to the spontaneous emission of radiation by certain elements. Subsequent research by Ernest Rutherford (1871–1937) led to the identification of two major types of radiation. Rutherford named them after the first two letters of the Greek alphabet, alpha (α) and beta (β).

Alpha and beta radiation have strikingly different properties. A **beta particle (β)** is a high-speed electron emitted from the nucleus. It has a negative electric charge (1−) and only a tiny mass, about 1/2000 that of a proton or a neutron. If you are wondering how an electron (a beta particle) could possibly be emitted from a nucleus, stay tuned. We offer an explanation shortly.

In contrast, an **alpha particle (α)** is a positively charged particle emitted from the nucleus. It consists of two protons and two neutrons (the nucleus of a He atom) and has a 2+ charge since no electrons accompany the helium nucleus.

Gamma rays frequently accompany alpha or beta radiation. A **gamma ray (γ)** is emitted from the nucleus and has no charge or mass. It is a high-energy, short-wavelength photon. Just like infrared (IR), visible, and ultraviolet (UV) radiation, gamma rays are part of the electromagnetic spectrum and have energies similar to those of X-rays. Table 7.1 summarizes these three types of nuclear radiation.

The term *radiation* tends to be confusing, because people don't always specify whether they mean electromagnetic radiation or nuclear radiation. *Electromagnetic radiation* refers to all the different types of light: radio, X-rays, visible, infrared, ultraviolet, microwave, and, of course, gamma rays. For example, it is perfectly correct to say visible radiation instead of visible light. *Nuclear radiation,* however, refers to the radiation emitted by the nucleus, such as alpha, beta, or gamma radiation. Watch out for one more source of confusion. Gamma rays are *both* a type of electromagnetic radiation and of nuclear radiation. When emitted from the nucleus of a radioactive substance, we refer to gamma rays as nuclear radiation. In contrast, when emitted from a galaxy far away, we call these gamma rays electromagnetic radiation.

Your Turn 7.12   "Radiation"

For each sentence, use the context to decipher whether the speaker is referring to nuclear or electromagnetic radiation.

a. "Name a type of radiation that has a shorter wavelength than visible light."
b. "The gamma radiation from cobalt–60 can destroy a tumor."
c. "Watch out for UV rays! If you have lightly pigmented skin, this radiation may cause a sunburn."
d. "Rutherford detected the radiation emitted by uranium."

Answers

a. electromagnetic radiation   b. nuclear radiation

Table 7.1	Types of Nuclear Radiation			
Name	Symbol	Composition	Charge	Change to the Nucleus That Emits It
alpha	^4_2He or α	2 protons 2 neutrons	2+	mass number decreases by 4 atomic number decreases by 2
beta	$^0_{-1}e$ or β	1 electron	1−	mass number does not change atomic number increases by 1
gamma	$^0_0\gamma$ or γ	photon	0	no change in either the mass number or the atomic number

When either an alpha or beta particle is emitted, a remarkable transformation occurs—the atom that emitted the particle changes its identity. For example, earlier with the PuBe neutron source (see equation 7.2), you saw that alpha emission resulted in the nucleus of plutonium becoming that of uranium. Similarly, when uranium emits an alpha particle, it becomes the element thorium. This nuclear equation shows the process for uranium-238.

$$_{92}^{238}\text{U} \longrightarrow {}_{90}^{234}\text{Th} + {}_{2}^{4}\text{He} \qquad \qquad \textbf{[7.4]}$$

Notice that the sum of the mass numbers on both sides of the nuclear equation is equal: $238 = 234 + 4$. The same is true for the atomic numbers: $92 = 90 + 2$.

In some cases, the nucleus formed as the result of radioactive decay still is radioactive. For example, thorium-234, formed by the alpha decay of uranium-238, is radioactive. Thorium-234 undergoes subsequent beta decay to form protactinium (Pa).

$$_{90}^{234}\text{Th} \longrightarrow {}_{91}^{234}\text{Pa} + {}_{-1}^{0}\text{e} \qquad \qquad \textbf{[7.5]}$$

In contrast to alpha emission, with beta emission the atomic number *increases* by 1 and the mass number remains unchanged. Table 7.1 summarizes the changes that occur with both beta and alpha emission.

A model that can help you make sense of this seemingly unusual set of changes is to regard a neutron as a combination of a proton and an electron. Beta emission can be thought of as breaking a neutron apart. Equation 7.6 shows this process, giving us an explanation of how an electron can be emitted from the nucleus.

$$_{0}^{1}\text{n} \longrightarrow {}_{1}^{1}\text{p} + {}_{-1}^{0}\text{e} \qquad \qquad \textbf{[7.6]}$$

During beta emission, the mass number (neutrons plus protons) in the nucleus remains constant because the loss of the neutron is balanced by the formation of a proton. For example, a neutron in thorium "became" a proton in protactinium. Because of this proton, the atomic number increases by 1. Again, this model can help you to better visualize beta emission, but may not be exactly what is occurring.

Your Turn 7.13   Alpha and Beta Decay

a. Write a nuclear equation for the beta decay of rubidium–86 (Rb–86), a radioisotope produced by the fission of U–235.

b. Plutonium–239, a toxic isotope that causes lung cancer, is an alpha emitter. Write the nuclear equation.

Answer

a. $_{37}^{86}\text{Rb} \longrightarrow {}_{38}^{86}\text{Sr} + {}_{-1}^{0}\text{e}$

As we noted earlier, a nucleus may decay to produce another radioactive nucleus. In some cases we can predict this, because *all* isotopes of *all* elements with atomic number 84 (polonium) and higher are radioactive. Thus all the isotopes of uranium, plutonium, radium, and radon are radioactive because these elements all have atomic numbers greater than 83.

What about the lighter elements? Some of these are naturally radioactive, such as carbon-14, hydrogen-3 (tritium), and potassium-40. Whether an isotope is radioactive (a radioisotope) or stable depends on the ratio of neutrons to protons in its nucleus. With each emission of an alpha or a beta particle, this neutron-to-proton ratio changes. Eventually a stable ratio is achieved, and the nucleus is no longer radioactive. Most of the atoms that make up our planet are *not* radioactive. They are here today, and you can count on their being here tomorrow, although possibly not located in the same spot you last saw them (such as the atoms that make up your car keys).

In some cases, radioisotopes may decay many times before producing a stable isotope. For example, the radioactive decay of U-238 and Th-234 (see equations 7.4 and 7.5) are the first two steps of a 14-step sequence! As shown in Figure 7.12, lead-206

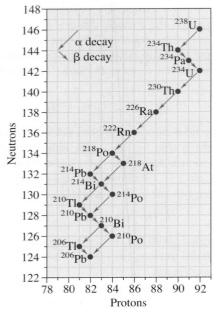

Figure 7.12
The naturally occurring radioactive decay series of uranium–238.

is the end product in this sequence. Similarly, lead-207 is the end product in a different sequence of 11 steps that begins with U-235. Each of these sequences is called a **radioactive decay series,** that is, a characteristic pathway of radioactive decay that begins with a radioisotope and progresses through a series of steps to eventually produce a stable isotope. Radon, a radioactive gas, is produced midway in both the U-238 and U-235 decay series. Thus, wherever uranium is present, so is radon.

7.5 | Looking Backward to Go Forward

We now examine the legacy of nuclear power with an eye to what we can learn from the past. All nuclear plants use the process of fission to produce energy; all produce radioactive fission products. Have these radioactive products posed a danger in the past? In this section, we consider the accidental release of radioisotopes into the environment. Although this is not the sole legacy of nuclear power, it nonetheless is a significant one.

In 1979, a film called *The China Syndrome* portrayed a near nuclear disaster in the United States. In a fictitious power plant, the heat-generating fission reaction went critical and a meltdown was imminent. Supposedly, the heat would melt the underlying rock all the way to China. But in the nick of time, the safety features of the system prevailed.

Seven years later on April 26, 1986, the engineers of the very real Chornobyl nuclear power plant in Ukraine, then part of the Soviet Union, were less fortunate (Figure 7.13). This plant had four reactors, two built in the 1970s and two more in the 1980s. Water from the nearby Pripyat River was used to cool the reactors. Although the surrounding region was not heavily populated, approximately 120,000 people lived within a 30-km radius, including the cities of Chornobyl (pop. 12,500) and Pripyat (pop. 40,000).

Even taking into consideration the radioactive releases of the Fukushima Daiichi nuclear power plant in Japan, Chornobyl still stands as the world's worst nuclear power plant accident. What went wrong in Ukraine? During an electrical power safety test at the Chornobyl Unit 4 reactor, operators deliberately interrupted the flow of cooling water to the core. The temperature of the reactor rose rapidly. In addition, the operators had left an insufficient number of control rods in the reactor and other control rods couldn't be reinserted quickly enough. Furthermore, the steam pressure was too low to provide coolant, due to both operator error and faulty reactor design.

The effects of uranium mining both on the workers and on the land are also part of the nuclear legacy. So is the storage of nuclear waste, the topic of a later section.

Chernobyl is the transliteration of the Russian pronunciation. Чорнобиль (Chornobyl) is the Ukrainian word.

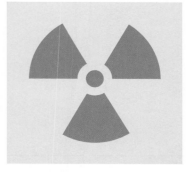

Figure 7.13

Chornobyl, Ukraine, in the former Soviet Union.

As shown in Figure 7.13, the black trefoil on a yellow background is the international radiation warning symbol. In the United States, magenta is used instead of black.

A chain of events quickly produced a disaster. An overwhelming power surge produced heat, rupturing the fuel elements and releasing hot reactor fuel particles. These, in turn, exploded on contact with the coolant water, and the reactor core was destroyed in seconds. The heat ignited the graphite used to slow neutrons in the reactor. When water was sprayed on the burning graphite, the water and graphite reacted to produce hydrogen gas.

$$2\ H_2O(l) + C(graphite) \longrightarrow 2\ H_2(g) + CO_2(g) \qquad \textbf{[7.7]}$$

In turn, the hydrogen exploded upon reaction with oxygen in the air.

$$2\ H_2(g) + O_2(g) \longrightarrow 2\ H_2O(g) \qquad \textbf{[7.8]}$$

The explosion blasted off the 4000-ton steel plate covering the reactor (Figure 7.14). Although a "nuclear" explosion never occurred, the fire and explosions of hydrogen blew vast quantities of radioactive material out of the reactor core and into the atmosphere.

The disaster at Chornobyl was caused by rapid chemical reactions, that is, the combustion involving hydrogen gas and the resulting fires fueled by the nuclear plant and its reactor materials. It was not a nuclear explosion.

Figure 7.14

An aerial view of the Chornobyl Unit 4 reactor taken shortly after the chemical explosion.

Fires started in what remained of the building. In a short time, the plant lay in ruins. The head of the crew on duty at the time of the accident gave an eyewitness report: "It seemed as if the world was coming to an end . . . I could not believe my eyes; I saw the reactor ruined by the explosion. I was the first man in the world to see this. As a nuclear engineer I realized the consequences of what had happened. It was a nuclear hell. I was gripped with fear" (*Scientific American*, April 1996, p. 44).

The disaster continued. For 10 days as fires kept burning the reactor spewed large quantities of radioactive fission products into the atmosphere. People living within 60 km of the power plant were permanently evacuated. The radioactive dust cut a swath across Ukraine, Belarus, and up into Scandinavia, affecting some who never had benefited from the power plant but nonetheless shared in its risks.

The human toll was immediate. Several people working at the plant were killed outright, and another 31 firefighters died in the cleanup process from acute radiation sickness, a topic we examine in a later section. An estimated 250 million people were exposed to levels of radiation that ultimately may cause illness.

One of the hazardous radioisotopes released was iodine-131, a beta emitter with an accompanying gamma ray.

$$^{131}_{53}\text{I} \longrightarrow {}^{131}_{54}\text{Xe} + {}^{0}_{-1}\text{e} + {}^{0}_{0}\gamma \qquad \textbf{[7.9]}$$

> The thyroid gland requires iodine in the form of iodide ion to make thyroxin, a hormone essential for growth and metabolism.

If ingested, I-131 can cause thyroid cancer. In the contaminated area near Chornobyl, the incidence of thyroid cancer increased sharply, especially for those younger than age 15 (Figure 7.15). As of 2001, more than 700 children in Belarus, a neighboring country, were treated for thyroid cancer. A few years later, the number had risen to more than 5000. Fortunately, with treatment, the survival rate for thyroid cancer is high and most have survived. As Dr. Akira Sugenoya, a Japanese physician who volunteered his expertise in Belarus to treat the children suffering from thyroid cancer, remarked, "The last chapter of the terrible accident is far from written."

Figure 7.15

At a clinic north of Minsk, the level of radioactivity is being checked in the thyroid gland of a child who lived in the path of Chornobyl's radioactive plume.

Your Turn 7.14   Iodine!

When people speak of iodine, they may be referring to an iodine atom, an iodine molecule, or an iodide ion, depending on the context.

  a. Draw Lewis structures to show the differences among of these chemical forms of iodine.
  b. Which one is the most chemically reactive and why?
  c. Which chemical form of iodine–131 is implicated in thyroid cancer?

Answer
  c. The element iodine (including its radioisotope, I–131) is taken up by the thyroid gland in the chemical form of I⁻, the iodide ion.

United Nations Scientific Committee on the Effects of Atomic Radiation

For the most recent findings on Chornobyl, we turn to UNSCEAR, the United Nations Scientific Committee on the Effects of Atomic Radiation. In 2011, UNSCEAR released an assessment of the health effects of Chornobyl.

> Apart from the dramatic increase in thyroid cancer incidence among those exposed at a young age, and some indication of an increased leukemia and cataract incidence among the workers, there is no clearly demonstrated increase in the incidence of solid cancers or leukemia due to radiation in the exposed populations. Neither is there any proof of other non-malignant disorders that are related to ionizing radiation. However, there were widespread psychological reactions to the accident, which were due to fear of the radiation, not to the actual radiation doses.

In 2012, construction of a steel arch, large enough to encompass a college football stadium with the Statue of Liberty at midfield, was begun at Chornobyl to encase the ruins of the plant. This will allow for robots to dismantle the ruins and permanently seal the remains. Recognizing that Chornobyl is a global problem, 29 countries have committed 2.9 billon dollars to this project. To this day, the area around the nuclear reactor has remained unsuitable for human habitation.

Underlying the solemn facts of Chornobyl is the inevitable question: "Could it happen again?" The closest brush with nuclear disaster in the United States occurred in March 1979, when the Three Mile Island power plant near Harrisburg, Pennsylvania, lost coolant and a partial meltdown occurred. Although some radioactive gases were released during the incident, no fatalities resulted. A 20-year follow-up study concluded in 2002 that the total cancer deaths among the exposed population were not higher than those of the general population. Nuclear engineers agree that no commercial nuclear reactors in the United States have the design defects that led to the Chornobyl catastrophe.

Preventing nuclear accidents involves more than the designing the safety features of the reactor. Accidents also can result from the complex interplay of human error, natural disasters, and political instability. In 2011, a pair of natural disasters, an earthquake and a tsunami, resulted in the meltdown of three units of a nuclear power plant in Japan.

Again we cast an eye backward in history, but this time to see what we can learn from what the author team wrote in the previous edition of this textbook: "Today, about 20% of the world's nuclear reactors are located in regions of seismic activity, such as the Pacific Rim. So even before the threat of terrorism, nuclear reactors had to be constructed to withstand a shock. Reactors are fitted with seismic detectors that immediately shut the reactor down if a quake occurs" (*Chemistry in Context*, 7th ed., p. 302). As it turned out, the quake was only part of the problem. More devastating was the tsunami that followed (Figure 7.16).

The tsunami delivered a one-two punch. First the flood waters knocked out the electrical generators necessary to pump the cooling water at the Fukushima power plant; as a result, the reactor cooling systems failed. The fuel inside reactors #1, #2, and #3 quickly heated, and the heat started a chemical reaction that generated hydrogen gas. Fearing an explosion, plant workers vented the hydrogen. At the same time, this action released some of the radioactive fission products, including I-131, to the surrounding countryside. Despite the venting, explosions occurred at several of the reactors.

The Fukushima plant contained six units. Reactors 1, 2, and 3 melted down. The building housing reactor 4 (and its spent fuel) suffered a hydrogen explosion. Units 5 and 6 were shut down at the time.

Figure 7.16

Flooding from the tsunami that followed the 2011 Tohoku earthquake, a 9.0 on the Richter scale.

Your Turn 7.15   Hydrogen!

Equation 7.8 represents the combustion of hydrogen, that is, hydrogen combines with oxygen to produce water vapor. Chapter 4 provided the Lewis structures for this chemical reaction.

$$2\ H\!-\!H + \ddot{\underset{..}{O}}\!=\!\ddot{\underset{..}{O}} \longrightarrow 2\ \ _{H}\!\diagup^{\overset{..}{\underset{..}{O}}}\!\diagdown_{H}$$

Using the bond energies for those bonds broken and formed, the energy change for this reaction can be estimated. As shown in Figure 4.17, the value is −498 kJ for burning 2 moles of H_2.

a. Calculate the energy change per mole and per gram of H_2.
b. Of the fuels listed in Figure 4.16, methane releases the most heat per gram upon combustion. Burning hydrogen releases even more heat. Approximately how many times more?

In Chapter 8, look for more about the energy released by the reaction of H_2 and O_2 in the context of fuel cells.

Consider This 7.16   Zirconium!

At the Chornobyl nuclear power plant, hydrogen was generated by a reaction of water with the hot graphite, as described earlier in this section. At Fukushima, however, the hydrogen was generated by a reaction of water with the element zirconium in the alloy in the outer casing of the fuel rods.

a. Zirconium is the metal of choice for reactors due to several reasons, including that it does not absorb neutrons. Why is this a desirable property?
b. Zirconium, if heated to a high temperature (such as in a nuclear accident), has two undesirable properties: (1) it will swell and crack, and (2) it will react with water to produce hydrogen. Explain the danger that these present.

Today, nuclear plants and their past operations continue to be under intense scrutiny, hence the title of this section, "Looking Backward to Go Forward." Indeed we must look to the past in order to gain the wisdom we need to move ahead. Undoubtedly, nuclear energy will be part of our future, but at present it is not clear just how much.

7.6 | Nuclear Radiation and You

The evidence of the past suggests that to dismiss nuclear radiation as harmless would be a mistake. Marie Curie, for example, died of a blood disorder that most likely was induced by her exposure to radiation. Many who worked underground in uranium mines suffered lung cancer. Others who accidently ingested radioactive substances were stricken ill or died of radiation sickness.

Even so, nuclear radiation is only weakly carcinogenic. Furthermore, when it damages your cells or tissues, your body uses a number of mechanisms to repair a certain level of radiation damage. We live on a planet that naturally contains radioactive substances and, for the most part, we survive. When the repair systems in our bodies are overwhelmed and damage accumulates, then we have reason for concern.

What causes the cell or tissue damage? The answer lies in the alpha particles, beta particles, and gamma rays that radioisotopes emit. All have enough energy to ionize the molecules they strike, that is, they eject electrons from the bonds or non-bonded pairs in these molecules. The same is true for X-rays, such as those used to produce medical images. For this reason, we use the term **ionizing radiation** to refer collectively to X-rays and nuclear radiation that can remove electrons from the atoms and molecules they hit. Cosmic rays from space are also ionizing radiation. In contrast, UV, visible, and infrared radiation have lower energies and are nonionizing types of radiation.

X-rays and gamma rays differ by their source. X-rays are emitted by machines that cause high energy changes in electronic configuration; in contrast, gamma rays are emitted from the nucleus.

When ionizing radiation penetrates your skin, it may set in motion a chain of events. Let's say the radiation hits a water molecule, knocking out an electron.

$$H_2O \xrightarrow{\text{ionizing radiation}} H_2O^+ + e^- \qquad\qquad \textbf{[7.10]}$$

The species formed, H_2O^+, has a positive charge. Furthermore, it has an unpaired electron. You can explore the details in the next activity

Section 11.2 points out that your body is about 60% water, making it likely that ionizing radiation will interact with a water molecule.

Consider This 7.17   Free Radicals

Chemical species with an unpaired electron are called free radicals. Here is equation 7.10 rewritten to show the unpaired electron with a dot.

$$H_2O \xrightarrow{\text{ionizing radiation}} [H_2O\cdot]^+ + e^-$$

As we have mentioned in earlier chapters, free radicals are highly reactive. The next equation shows how the free radical can react with another water molecule to produce yet another free radical, $\cdot OH$, the hydroxyl radical.

$$[H_2O\cdot]^+ + H_2O \longrightarrow H_3O^+ + HO\cdot$$

a. Draw Lewis structures for all reactants and products in these two equations.
b. Label the Lewis structures that are free radicals.
c. Based on these Lewis structures, why do you think free radicals are reactive?

Look for more about free radicals in other chapters.

Chapter 1: $\cdot OH$, formation of NO_2 and then tropospheric ozone
Chapter 2: $Cl\cdot$, $ClO\cdot$, and $\cdot NO$, depletion of stratospheric ozone
Chapter 6: $\cdot OH$, formation of SO_3 in acid rain
Chapter 9: $R\cdot$, polymerization of ethylene

As you saw in Consider This 7.17, one free radical can react to produce another one. And another! The hydroxyl radical continues to react with other molecules, including your DNA if it is nearby. Depending on how the DNA molecule is damaged by the free radical, the cell that contains this DNA may die, may repair itself, or may contain a mutation. Rapidly dividing cells, including some tumors, are particularly susceptible to damage by ionizing radiation. As a result, nuclear radiation and X-rays can treat certain types of cancer.

You will learn more about DNA in Chapter 12.

Ionizing radiation can treat other diseases as well. For example, people with Graves' disease have an overactive thyroid gland that produces excess hormone which boosts their metabolism, causing many complications. Although the idea of swallowing a radioactive pill may not sound appealing, such a pill provides a cure because it contains radioactive I-131 in the form of potassium iodide.

Just as dietary iodine is incorporated into the thyroid gland, so is the radioactive iodine. Once in the thyroid gland, the radioactive I-131 destroys the overactive thyroid tissue, in whole or in part (Figure 7.17). Then, to restore normal metabolic function, most patients take a supplement of a synthetic form of thyroxin, the iodine-containing hormone normally secreted by the thyroid gland.

End-of-chapter question #51 relates to taking potassium iodide (KI) tablets to minimize uptake of I–131.

Radiation can both heal and hurt. The trouble is, all rapidly dividing cells are susceptible to radiation, not just the ones in cancer cells. Healthy cells that rapidly divide include those in the bone marrow, the skin, hair follicles, stomach, and intestine. People who receive radiation treatments for cancer often experience a host of side effects that relate to the damage of these *healthy* cells. Collectively, these side effects are termed **radiation sickness,** the illness characterized by early symptoms of anemia, nausea, malaise, and susceptibility to infection that are the result of a large dose of radiation. Radiation sickness is a possibility whenever people are exposed to larger doses of ionizing radiation. For example, those near the Chornobyl accident, as well as those who survived the initial firestorm from the atomic bombs dropped on Japan experienced radiation sickness.

Our world naturally contains radioactive substances, so your radiation levels can never be reduced to zero. Scientists use the term **background radiation** to describe the level of radiation that, on average, is present at a particular location. It can arise from both natural and human-made sources. The largest natural source of background radiation is radon, a radioactive gas that is formed in the decay series of uranium. Your

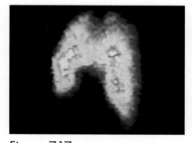

Figure 7.17
A thyroid image produced with I–131. Radioactive iodine has concentrated in the red and yellow areas.

exposure to radon depends both on the amount of uranium in the rocks and soils where you live and on whether your dwelling allows this radon to accumulate in living spaces. The next activity helps make clear the connection between radon and lung cancer.

See Section 1.13 for more about radon as an indoor air pollutant.

Your Turn 7.18   Radon and You

Produced in the radioactive decay series of U–238, radon–222 is an alpha emitter.

a. Write the nuclear equation for the radioactive decay of radon–222.
b. The product is a solid. You should expect it to be radioactive. Why?
c. Radon and its decay products may cause lung cancer. Explain why.

Answer

b. Polonium–218 is radioactive, as are all isotopes of all elements of atomic number 84 or higher.

The increased use of CT scans (and the dose of radiation they deliver) is a concern of many doctors. Alternatively, they realize the benefits of having a high quality image for diagnosis and treatment.

Radon, a naturally occurring radioisotope, is one of your largest exposures to ionizing radiation, as you can see in Figure 7.18. Decades ago, almost *all* of our exposure was from natural sources. In recent years, however, medical exposures have entered the picture, such as those from CT scans, X-rays, and diagnostic radioactive tracers. Consequently, about half the exposure to ionizing radiation today is medical. This exposure now greatly exceeds natural background radiation for some patients.

Each exposure can be quantified in terms of the dose of radiation received. Examine Figure 7.18 to see that the annual dose is given in two units, the **rem** and the **sievert (Sv)**. Both are a measure of the dose of radiation, taking into account the damage that occurs to human tissue when this dose is absorbed. 1 sievert = 100 rem. Although you may see both units in use, the rem is the older one, and most scientists now are using the sievert, the unit used internationally.

But a sievert is a high dose! Because most exposures to radiation are significantly less than a sievert or a rem, smaller units are necessary: microsieverts (μSv) and millirems (mrem).

$$1 \text{ microsievert (μSv)} = 1/1{,}000{,}000 \text{ of a sievert} = 1 \times 10^{-6} \text{ Sv}$$
$$1 \text{ millirem (mrem)} = 1/1000 \text{ of a rem} = 1 \times 10^{-3} \text{ rem}$$

1 microsievert = 0.1 millirem

When you take a pill, it's easy to calculate the drug dose for your body mass. It simply is a function of how much of the drug is in the pill and how much you weigh. With ionizing radiation, calculating the dose is far more complicated. One reason is that different types of radiation deliver different doses. For example, the alpha particle packs a big punch. Why? Alpha particles are larger and deposit a greater amount of energy in the tissue when they hit. It takes approximately 20 times as many beta particles to do the same tissue damage as a given number of alpha particles.

Another reason is that the same type of radiation may differ in the energy that it deposits in your tissue. For example, X-rays come in different wavelengths with

In Figure 7.18, internal refers to the radioisotopes present naturally in your body, such as tiny amounts of carbon–14 and potassium–40.

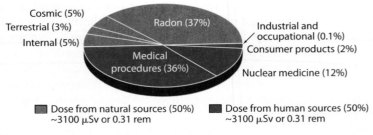

Figure 7.18

Sources of ionizing radiation exposure for people living in the United States, 2009.

Source: National Council on Radiation Protection and Measurements (NCRP) Report No. 160, Ionizing Radiation Exposure of the Population of the United States, 2009.

correspondingly different energies. So both the sievert and the rem are based on another unit, the **rad,** short for "radiation absorbed dose." The rad is a measure of the energy deposited in tissue and is defined as the absorption of 0.01 joule of radiant energy per kilogram of tissue. Thus, if a 70-kg person were to absorb 0.70 J of energy, a dose of 1 rad would be received. Although this is not very much energy, it is localized in a small region where the radiation hits.

We hope this brief discussion has helped you see that all radiation is not created equal. The dose you receive depends on the type, as well as whether it is inside or outside of your body.

Let's now examine the annual dose shown in Figure 7.18 in more detail. A sample calculation based on a nonsmoking individual living in the U.S. Midwest is shown in Table 7.2. Given that this individual had minimal exposure from medical procedures, the annual dose of 3581 μSv fits well with the data of Figure 7.18 that show an annual dose of 6200 μSv. Consider This 7.19 allows you to do your own calculation.

Consider This 7.19   Your Annual Dose of Radiation

If you search for annual radiation dose on the Internet, you'll find several calculators. Depending on when they were created, they may or may not give options to input medical exposures to radiation. Pick an annual dose calculator and run the numbers. How close is your value to the total annual radiation dose in the example calculation above? Account for any differences.

Table 7.2 Annual Radiation Dose (Sample Calculation)*	
Sources of Radiation	**(μSv/yr)**
1. Cosmic radiation	
a. Sea level (U.S. average)	260
b. Additional dose if you are above sea level	
up to 1000 m (3300 ft) add 20 μSv	20
1000–2000 m (6600 ft) add 50 μSv	
2000–3000 m (9900 ft) add 90 μSv	
3000–4000 m (13,200 ft) add 150 μSv	
4000–5000 m (16,500 ft) add 210 μSv	
2. Building material(s) used in your dwelling	
Stone, brick, or concrete add 70 μSv	
Wood or other add 20 μSv	20
3. Rocks and soil	460
4. Food, water, and air (K and Rn)	2400
5. Fallout from nuclear weapons testing	10
6. Medical and dental X-rays	
a. Chest X-ray, add 100 μSv each	0
b. Gastrointestinal tract X-ray, add 5000 μSv each	0
c. Dental X-rays, add 100 μSv each	100
7. Airplane travel	
5-hour flight at 30,000 feet, add 30 μSv/flight	300
8. Other	
a. Live within 50 miles of a nuclear plant, add 0.09 μSv	0.09
b. Live within 50 miles of a coal–fired power plant, add 0.3 μSv	0.3
c. Use a computer terminal, add 1 μSv	1
d. Watch TV, add 10 μSv	10
Total Annual Radiation Dose	**3581**

* Sample calculation is for an adult nonsmoker living in the Midwest.
If you smoke one pack of cigarettes per day, add 10,000 μSv.

Sources: Adapted from information provided by the U.S. Environmental Protection Agency and the American Nuclear Society.

What about nuclear power plants? If you examine Table 7.2 closely, you will see that the radiation dose you receive from a properly operating nuclear power plant is negligible. It is less than that of your "internal dose," that is, the dose from radioisotopes that occur naturally in your own body. For example, about 0.01% of all the potassium ions (K^+) in your body are radioactive K-40. This radioactive potassium yields a dose of about 200 µSv per year, approximately 2000 times the exposure from living within 50 miles of a nuclear power plant. Although bananas are rich in potassium (K^+), you need not worry that eating bananas will increase your dose. Why? As quickly as the potassium ions move into your body, they also move out with no net accumulation.

Carbon-14 is another naturally occurring radioisotope in our food. This radioisotope is produced in our upper atmosphere by the interaction of nitrogen with cosmic rays. Carbon-14 gets incorporated into carbon dioxide molecules that diffuse down into the troposphere where we live. The late Isaac Asimov, a prolific science writer, pointed out that a human body contains approximately 3.0×10^{26} carbon atoms, of which 3.5×10^{14} are C-14. Each breath you inhale contains carbon dioxide, including about 3.5 million carbon dioxide molecules that contain C-14 atoms. This number of atoms is so insignificant that Table 7.2 contains no entry for it. Check the math in the next activity.

Your Turn 7.21   Radioactive Carbon and You

Assume that Isaac Asimov's figures are correct and that 3.5×10^{14} of the 3.0×10^{26} carbon atoms in your body are radioactive. Calculate the percent that is C–14.

How does your annual dose of ionizing radiation affect you? Nobody can give you a detailed personal answer to this question. Even so, we can make some helpful observations.

First, even with diagnostic medical tests, your annual dose is likely to be relatively low. Only those who are in the wrong place at the wrong time (or have a serious illness) receive higher doses. Examples include being in the fallout path of a nuclear weapon or in an area contaminated by a serious nuclear power plant accident. Having a bone marrow transplant also would put you in the high dose category.

Second, scientists have reasonably good data on the effects of a single dose of radiation. As you can see in Table 7.3, an average annual dose on the order of 6200 µSv, if received all at one time, would have no immediate physiological effects. In contrast, higher doses lead to radiation sickness and death. The cause is the damage done to

The average estimated doses that those at Chornobyl received:

120 mSv — 530,000 recovery operation workers

30 mSv — 115,000 evacuated persons

Source: United Nations Scientific Committee on the Effects of Atomic Radiation (UNSCEAR)

An annual dose of 6200 µSv is equivalent to 0.0062 Sv (0.62 rem).

Table 7.3	Likely Effects of a Single Dose of Radiation	
Dose (Sv)	Dose (rem)	Likely Effect
0–0.25	0–25	No observable effect
0.25–0.50	25–50	White blood cell count decreases slightly
0.50–1.00	50–100	Significant drop in white blood cell count, lesions
1.00–2.00	100–200	Nausea, vomiting, loss of hair
2.00–5.00	200–500	Hemorrhaging, ulcers, possible death
5.00	>500	Death

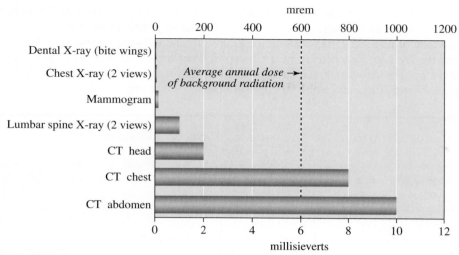

Figure 7.19

Doses from medical procedures that use ionizing radiation. The average annual background radiation in the United States (6200 μSv or 6.2 mSv) is shown for comparison.

Source: Michael G. Stabin, Health Physics Society, *2011.*

rapidly dividing cells, such as ones in the bone marrow and ones in the gastrointestinal tract that you need in order to live.

Third, in spite of the fact that your annual dose of ionizing radiation is low, nonetheless it can have an effect on you. The most likely one is cancer. For example, radon is the second leading cause of lung cancer with perhaps as many as 20,000 deaths per year in the United States. Medical exposures to ionizing radiation cause excess cancers over what would be expected without this exposure. To help you put these medical tests in perspective, Figure 7.19 shows typical values. Keep in mind that the dose depends on the particular machine that is used and its manufacturer, as well as body weight. Although the risk (or probability) of developing cancer from a CT scan is low, an unlikely cancer is still a serious consequence.

Finally, the long-term effects of low doses of radiation are still topics of debate. The difficulty lies in extrapolating from the known high-dose data to lower doses. The process of extrapolation is necessary because we cannot do experiments on humans to make reliable measurements. Additionally, the effects of low doses would be small, showing up over a long time span.

To finish up our discussion, we need to explore the units for measuring radioactivity. To do this, we must switch our focus. Up until now, the emphasis has been on doses of radiation and how these damaged your cells, causing illness or even death. Now we switch to what radioisotopes do, that is, they emit nuclear radiation.

The radioactivity of a sample is measured by counting the number of disintegrations in a given time period. The **becquerel (Bq)**, pronounced BEK-uh-rel, is the international unit of radioactivity equivalent to one disintegration (alpha, beta, or gamma) per second. This is a tiny unit, so another unit is commonly used, the **curie (Ci)**. Named in honor of Marie Curie, the curie is a measure of the radioactivity of a sample, approximately equivalent to the activity of one gram of radium.

$$1 \text{ curie (Ci)} = 3.7 \times 10^{10} \text{ disintegrations/second}$$

$$= 3.7 \times 10^{10} \text{ Bq}$$

Since radium is highly radioactive, one curie is a large amount of radiation! Accordingly, people typically refer to radioactivity levels in terms of *milli*curies (mCi), *micro*curies (μCi), *nano*curies (nCi), or even *pico*curies (pCi). For example, household radon measurements are quoted in picocuries, as you will see in Your Turn 7.27. Chemists working with radioisotopes in the lab typically use millicurie or microcurie amounts. If a laboratory worker spilled an amount as large as 100 mCi, serious cleanup procedures would be needed. In contrast, a spill of 100 μCi would be considered far less dangerous.

milli
1×10^{-3}
1/1000
micro
1×10^{-6}
1/1,000,000
nano
1×10^{-9}
1/1,000,000,000
pico
1×10^{-12}
1/1,000,000,000,000

To put these values in perspective, the explosion at Chornobyl spewed 100–200 *million* curies into the atmosphere. In terms of the amount of radioactivity itself, this is the equivalent of dispersing 100–200 million grams of radium. In the months after the accident, the levels of radioactivity near Chornobyl were from 5 to over 40 Ci per square kilometer. The amount of radiation released by the atomic bombs that exploded on Nagasaki and Hiroshima was lower by two orders of magnitude.

Consider This 7.22   Assessing Radioactive Releases

It is not sufficient to just report the amount of a radioactive release. Rather, the *identity* of the radioisotopes also should be reported. Explain why, using the nuclear fission products I–131, Sr–90, and Cs–137 as examples.

Answer

Radioactive Cs–137 is particularly dangerous because it is taken up in the food chain in the form of Cs^+, the cesium ion. The same is true for Sr–90 in the form of Sr^{2+}, which is a calcium mimic, and I–131, which accumulates in the thyroid gland. Cs–137 and Sr–90 also are dangerous because they have half–lives long enough to persist for decades. Look for more about half–life in Section 7.8 and more about Sr–90 in Consider This 7.28.

We conclude this section by directing your attention back to Table 7.2, the calculation for your personal dose of ionizing radiation. As we pointed out in Skeptical Chemist 7.20, versions of this calculation differ in terms of the parameters they include. At least one version includes an item called *the nuclear fuel cycle*, a term we define in the next section. Although the dose you receive annually from this source is small (0.1%), nuclear fuel warrants our closer attention. In the next section, we explore the connection between nuclear fuel and weapons. In the section that follows, we begin a much longer discussion of nuclear half-lives that will enable us to tackle questions relating to nuclear waste.

7.7 | The Weapons Connection

Although hydrogen bombs are initiated by nuclear fission, they derive their energy primarily from nuclear fusion, a topic not explored in this chapter.

Most commercial reactors worldwide use enriched uranium as fuel. However, some British and Canadian reactors are designed to run on natural (unenriched) uranium.

Although both nuclear power plants and atomic bombs derive their energy from fission, each requires that energy be released at a different rate. A nuclear power plant needs a slow, controlled energy release; in contrast, a nuclear weapon requires one that is rapid and uncontrolled. In either case, the fission reaction is essentially the same. Both are fueled by **enriched uranium,** that is, uranium that has a higher percent of U-235 than its natural abundance of about 0.7%. The difference lies in the *extent* of the enrichment. Commercial nuclear power plants typically operate with 3–5% U-235, whereas atomic weapons use fuel that may be as high as 90% U-235. The latter is sometimes referred to as highly enriched or weapons-grade uranium.

Your Turn 7.23   Enriched Uranium

The fuel pellets in a nuclear power plant are enriched to 3–5% uranium–235.

a. Another isotope of uranium is present in the pellets. Which one?
b. Is this isotope fissionable under the conditions in a nuclear reactor?
c. After use in a reactor, spent fuel pellets contain radioisotopes of many different elements, including strontium, barium, krypton, and iodine. Explain the origin of these radioisotopes.

 Hint: See Figures Alive! for more about fuel pellets.

In a nuclear reactor, the concentration of fissionable U-235 is low. Most of the neutrons given off during fission of U-235 are absorbed by U-238 nuclei in the fuel pellets and by other elements such as cadmium and boron in the control rods. Consequently, the neutron stream cannot build up sufficiently to cause a nuclear explosion. In contrast, atomic weapons use highly enriched uranium in which neutrons are likely to encounter another U-235 nucleus. As we noted earlier, an explosive fission reaction (that is, the explosion of an atomic bomb) occurs only if a critical mass of U-235 (about 33 lb) is quickly assembled all in one place.

Enriching uranium is no easy task! U-235 and U-238 behave essentially the same in all chemical reactions, so they cannot be separated by using one. Rather, the trick to separating them lies in their tiny mass difference of three neutrons. How can this difference be exploited to achieve a separation? On average, lighter gas molecules move faster than heavier ones. Therefore gas molecules containing U-235 should travel slightly more rapidly than their analogs containing U-238. One way to separate molecules is by **gaseous diffusion,** a process in which gases with different molecular weights are forced through a series of permeable membranes. Lighter gas molecules diffuse more rapidly through the membranes than do heavier ones.

But uranium ore clearly is not a gas; rather, it is a mineral that contains UO_3 and UO_2. Most other uranium compounds are solids as well. However, the compound uranium hexafluoride (UF_6) has a notable property. Known as "hex," UF_6 is a solid at room temperature but readily vaporizes when heated to 56 °C (about 135 °F). To produce hex, the uranium ore is converted to UF_4, which in turn is reacted with more fluorine gas.

$$UF_4(g) + F_2(g) \longrightarrow UF_6(g) \qquad \textbf{[7.11]}$$

Equation 7.11 is a *chemical* equation, not a *nuclear* equation.

On average, a $^{235}UF_6$ molecule travels about 0.4% faster than a $^{238}UF_6$ molecule. If the gaseous diffusion process is allowed to occur repeatedly through a long series of permeable membranes, significant amounts of $^{235}UF_6$ and $^{238}UF_6$ can be separated. Prior to World War II and then during the Cold War, U.S. scientists separated uranium isotopes by gaseous diffusion at the Oak Ridge National Laboratory in Tennessee.

The process of gaseous diffusion is used to enrich uranium at commercial plants in a few nations, including France and the United States. However, enrichment now is more commonly carried out using large gas centrifuges. Like gaseous diffusion, the gas centrifuge process makes use of the small mass difference between $^{235}UF_6$ and $^{238}UF_6$. However, it has the advantage of requiring significantly less energy than gaseous diffusion for the same degree of enrichment. For this reason, newer commercial enrichment plants use centrifuges. For example, in 2006, the Nuclear Regulatory Commission issued a license to a consortium of U.S. and European energy companies to build a state-of-the-art gas centrifuge facility near Eunice, New Mexico (Figure 7.20). In 2010, officials held a ribbon-cutting ceremony at the plant; it is expected to reach full capacity in 2015.

Figure 7.20

The new state-of-the-art uranium enrichment plant to fuel commercial reactors in the United States is located near Eunice, New Mexico. The plant was built by URENCO, an international nuclear fuel company.

Source: URENCO.

Regardless of the enrichment method, once the U-235 has been separated, the U-238 that remains is now "depleted." Nicknamed DU, **depleted uranium** is composed almost entirely of U-238 (~99.8%) because much of the U-235 that it once naturally contained has been removed. Estimates indicate that over 1 billion metric tons of DU is stored currently in the United States. In recent years, the military has deployed DU in armor-piercing munitions. The next activity gives you an opportunity to learn more about DU.

Consider This 7.24   Depleted Uranium

Depleted uranium is used to tip antitank shells. These first were used in the Gulf War in 1991 and later in other armed conflicts, including Kuwait, Bosnia, Afghanistan, and Iraq. Research the properties of DU in order to explain why it can pierce armor. Also summarize the controversies involved.

At enrichment levels of 3–5%, nuclear fuel rods cannot be incorporated into functional atomic bombs. However, the technology to transform the uranium ore into weapons-grade uranium (about 90% U-235) is essentially identical to that used to produce reactor-grade fuel. In recognition of this fact, only certain countries are authorized to produce enriched uranium according to the Nuclear Non-Proliferation Treaty of 1968. That agreement bestows on signatory sovereign nations the right to pursue nuclear power (and hence uranium enrichment) for peaceful purposes. Iran, a signer of the treaty, restarted its uranium enrichment program in the summer of 2005, despite protests from the United States and other countries.

A more likely scenario for clandestine weapon manufacturing would be to use the plutonium-239 formed from U-238 in a conventional reactor. Analogous to U-235 in equation 7.1, U-238 absorbs a neutron and forms the unstable species U-239. In this case, fission does *not* occur, but rather in a matter of hours U-239 undergoes beta decay.

$$^1_0n + {}^{238}_{92}U \longrightarrow [{}^{239}_{92}U] \longrightarrow {}^{239}_{93}Np + {}^{0}_{-1}e \qquad \textbf{[7.12]}$$

The new element formed, neptunium-239, also is a beta emitter and decays to form plutonium-239.

$$^{239}_{93}Np \longrightarrow {}^{239}_{94}Pu + {}^{0}_{-1}e \qquad \textbf{[7.13]}$$

This transformation was discovered early in 1940. The chemical and physical properties of plutonium were determined with an almost invisible sample of the element on the stage of a microscope. The chemical processes devised on such minute samples were scaled up a billion-fold and used to extract plutonium from the spent fuel pellets from a reactor built on the Columbia River at Hanford, Washington. The plutonium was chemically separated from the uranium and used in the first test explosion of a nuclear device on July 16, 1945, near Alamogordo, New Mexico. The bomb dropped on Nagasaki a little less than a month later also was fueled by plutonium.

Depleted uranium, enriched uranium, and plutonium all are components of the **nuclear fuel cycle,** a way of conceptualizing all the different processes that can happen when uranium ore is mined, processed, used to fuel a reactor, and then dealt with as waste. Examine Figure 7.21 to see the connection with plutonium. As equations 7.12 and 7.13 show, plutonium-239 is produced ("bred") in nuclear reactors and thus is a component of the spent fuel. Reactors can be designed to breed more (or less) plutonium. We return to the nuclear fuel cycle later in the chapter.

Look for more about breeder reactors in Section 7.9.

Plutonium-239 poses an international security problem because the plutonium produced in nuclear power reactors could possibly be incorporated into nuclear bombs. Given the risks associated with Pu-239 and U-235, it is essential that both national and international organizations carefully monitor the supplies and distribution of these two isotopes throughout the world. Safeguarding existing nuclear materials has taken on a new meaning since the end of the Cold War and the demise of the former Soviet Union. One part of the problem is the plutonium and highly enriched uranium in Russia's

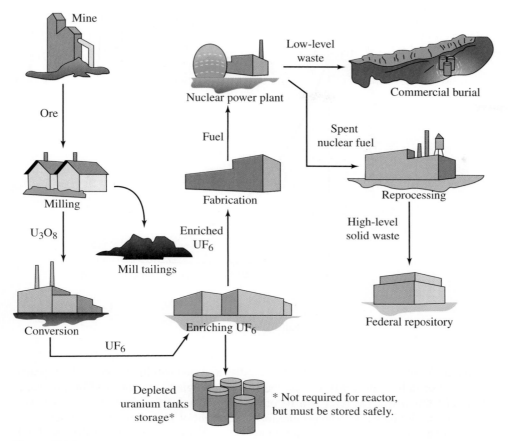

Figure 7.21

One representation of the nuclear fuel cycle. Currently, some of the cycle stages are not in operation. *Note:* U_3O_8 is uranium oxide, or "yellow cake," a uranium compound produced from the refining of uranium ore.

Source: W. Cunningham and M. Cunningham, Environmental Science: A Global Concern, *12th ed., McGraw-Hill, 2012.*

Look for more about yellow cake and parts of the nuclear fuel cycle in Section 7.10.

nuclear arsenal (about 20,000 warheads). Another problem stems from Russia's legacy from the Cold War, a stockpile of highly enriched uranium and plutonium (about 600 metric tons). Both of these pose a threat to world security (Figure 7.22). The fissionable materials stored in labs, research centers, and shipyards across the former Soviet Union are vulnerable to theft. These 600 tons of fissionable material translate into the capacity to construct approximately 40,000 new nuclear weapons.

The world community clearly recognizes the dangers of nuclear trafficking and the need for effective safeguards. In recognition of the global threat, the Nobel Peace Prize for 2005 was shared equally between the International Atomic Energy Agency (IAEA) and its Director General, Mohamed ElBaradei. The Nobel committee cited ". . . their efforts to prevent nuclear energy from being used for military purposes and to ensure that nuclear energy for peaceful purposes is used in the safest possible way." The future safety of nations, if not of our planet, may depend on our ability to safeguard and ultimately recycle plutonium and highly enriched uranium.

Figure 7.22

A smuggled canister of military grade Pu–239 captured in Germany.

7.8 | Nuclear Time: The Half-Life

How long does a radioactive sample "last"? The answer depends on the radioisotope. Some radioisotopes decay quickly over a short period of time; others undergo radioactive decay much more slowly. Each radioisotope has its own **half-life ($t_{1/2}$),** the time required for the level of radioactivity to fall to one half of its initial value. For example, plutonium-239, an alpha emitter formed in nuclear reactors fueled with uranium, has a half-life of about 24,110 years. Accordingly, it will take 24,110 years for the

Figure 7.23
Decay of a sample of Pu–239
over time.

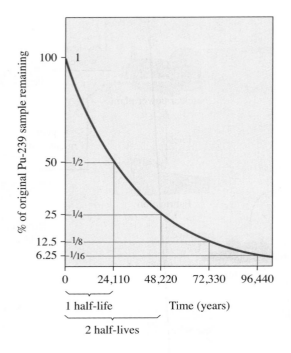

Revisit nuclear equations 7.12 and
7.13 to see how Pu–239 can be
produced from U–238 in a
nuclear reactor.

radioactivity of a sample of Pu-239 to halve. After a second half-life (another 24,110 years), the level of radioactivity will be one fourth of the original amount. And in three half-lives (72,330 years), the level will be one eighth (Figure 7.23). From these times, you can see that it takes a very long time for the amount of plutonium to decrease!

Other radioisotopes decay even more slowly. For example, the half-life of U-238 is 4.5 billion years. Coincidentally, this is approximately the age of the oldest rocks on Earth, a determination made by measuring their uranium content. The half-life for each particular isotope is a constant and is independent of the physical or chemical form in which the element is found. Moreover, the rate of radioactive decay is essentially unaltered by changes in temperature and pressure. From Table 7.4 you can see that half-lives range from milliseconds to millennia.

From Table 7.4, you also can see that Pu-239 and Pu-231 have different half-lives. Other isotopes of plutonium have different half-lives as well. For example, in 1999

Table 7.4	Half–life of Selected Radioisotopes	
Radioisotope	Half–life ($t_{1/2}$)	Found in the Spent Fuel Rods of Nuclear Reactors?
uranium–238	4.5×10^9 years	Yes. Present originally in fuel pellet.
potassium–40	1.3×10^9 years	No.
uranium–235	7.0×10^8 years	Yes. Present originally in fuel pellet.
plutonium–239	24,110 years	Yes. See equation 7.13.
carbon–14	5715 years	No.
cesium–137	30.2 years	Yes. Fission product.
strontium–90	29.1 years	Yes. Fission product.
thorium–234	24.1 days	Yes. Small amount generated in natural decay series of U–238.
iodine–131	8.04 days	Yes. Fission product.
radon–222	3.82 days	Yes. Small amount generated in natural decay series of U–238.
plutonium–231	8.5 minutes	No. Half-life is too short.
polonium–214	0.00016 seconds	No. Half-life is too short.

Carola Laue, Darleane Hoffman, and a team at Lawrence Berkeley National Laboratory characterized plutonium-231. These researchers had to work fast because the half-life of Pu-231 is a matter of mere minutes! In general, each radioisotope has its own unique half-life, including isotopes of the same element.

We can use the half-life ($t_{1/2}$) of a radioisotope to determine the percent of a sample that remains at some later point in time. For example, once Pu-231 is generated in a laboratory, what percent of the original sample *remains* after 25 minutes? To answer this, first recognize that 25 minutes is roughly three half-lives or 3×8.5 minutes. After one half-life, 50% of the sample has decayed and 50% remains. After two half-lives, 75% of the sample has decayed and 25% remains. And after three half-lives, 87.5% has decayed and 12.5% remains. These values are not exact, because 25 minutes is not exactly three half-lives. Nonetheless, quick back-of-the-envelope calculations can be useful.

This question also could have been phrased in this way: "After 25.5 minutes what percent of a sample of Pu-231 has *decayed*?" This question requires one more step. To find the amount decayed, simply subtract the percent that remains from 100%. If 12.5% remains, then $100\% - 12.5\% = 87.5\%$ has decayed. Table 7.5 summarizes these changes for any radioisotope.

Your Turn 7.25   Here Today . . .

. . . and gone tomorrow? People sometimes use the value of 10 half–lives to indicate when a radioisotope will be gone, that is, when only a negligible amount of it will be present. What percent of the original sample remains after 10 half–lives? Add rows to Table 7.5 so that it shows the mathematics of decay to 10 half–lives.

Let's do another back-of-the-envelope calculation with a different radioisotope. For example, if you had a sample of U-238 ($t_{1/2} = 4.5 \times 10^9$ years), what percent of it would remain after 25 minutes? To answer this, recognize that minutes, days, or even months would be a mere instant in the span of a 4.5-billion-year half-life. Thus, essentially all of the uranium-238 would remain. The next two activities offer you more practice with half-life calculations.

Your Turn 7.26   Tritium Calculation

Hydrogen–3 (tritium, H–3) sometimes is formed in the primary coolant water of a nuclear reactor. Tritium is a beta emitter with $t_{1/2} = 12.3$ years. For a given sample containing tritium, after how many years will about 12% of the radioactivity remain?

Table 7.5	Half–life Calculations	
# of Half–lives	% Decayed	% Remaining
0	0	100
1	50	50
2	75	25
3	87.5	12.5
4	93.75	6.25
5	97.88	3.12
6	98.44	1.56

Your Turn 7.27   Radon Calculation

Radon–222 is a radioactive gas produced from the decay of radium, a radioisotope naturally present in many rocks.

a. What is the most likely origin for the radium present in rocks?
   Hint: See Figure 7.12.
b. Radon activity is usually measured in picocuries (pCi). Suppose that the radioactivity from Rn–222 in your basement were measured at 16 pCi, a high value. If no additional radon entered the basement, how much time would pass before the level dropped to 0.50 pCi?
   Hint: In dropping from 16 to 1 pCi, the radioactivity level halves four times: 16 to 8 to 4 to 2 to 1.
c. Why is it incorrect to assume that no more radon will enter your basement?

One final difficulty with reactor waste is that the fission products, if released, may enter and accumulate in your body, with potentially fatal consequences. One culprit is strontium-90, a radioactive fission product that entered the biosphere in the 1950s from the atmospheric testing of nuclear weapons. Strontium ions are chemically similar to calcium ions; both elements are in Group 2A of the periodic table. Hence, like Ca^{2+}, Sr^{2+} accumulates in milk and in bones. Thus, once ingested, radioactive strontium with its half-life of 29 years poses a lifelong threat. Like I-131, Sr-90 was among the harmful fission products released in the vicinity of the Chornobyl reactor.

Your Turn 7.28   Strontium–90

Sr–90 is one of the fission products of U–235 listed in Table 7.4. It forms in a reaction that produces three neutrons and another element. Write the nuclear equation.

Hint: Remember to include the neutron that induces the fission of U–235.

On a cheerier note, we end this section with carbon-14, a radioisotope mentioned in the previous section. Carbon-14 has a half-life of 5715 years and decays to nitrogen-14 through the process of beta decay. Our atmospheric carbon dioxide contains a constant steady-state ratio of one radioactive C-14 atom for every 10^{12} atoms of nonradioactive C-12. Living plants and animals incorporate the isotopes in that same ratio. However, when the organism dies, exchange of CO_2 with the environment ceases. Thus, no new carbon is introduced to replace the C-14. As a consequence, the concentration of C-14 in any material that once was alive decreases with time, halving every 5715 years.

In the 1950s, W. Frank Libby (1908–1980) first recognized this decrease by experimentally measuring the C-14/C-12 ratio in a sample. The ratio provided an estimate of when the organism died. Human remains and many human artifacts contain carbon, and fortunately, the rate of decay of C-14 is a convenient one for measuring human activities. Charcoal from prehistoric caves, ancient papyri, mummified human remains, and suspected art forgeries have all revealed their ages by this technique. The C-14 technique provides ages that agree to within 10% of those obtained from historical records, thus validating the legitimacy of the radiocarbon-dating technique.

Steady–state was defined in Chapter 2.

With high confidence, carbon–14 dating was used to establish the age of the famous Shroud of Turin as approximately 1300 CE.

Skeptical Chemist 7.29   Ancient Shroud

Using carbon–14 dating, a burial cloth from a tomb was estimated to have an age of 100,000 years. Does this determination seem reasonable to you, given that the half–life of C–14 is 5715 years?

Hint: After more than 10 half–lives have passed, consider the amount of radioisotope that remains. Revisit Your Turn 7.25 to see this.

The nuclear decay process cannot be hastened; we can neither make the nuclear clocks run fast nor slow. Radiocarbon dating depends on the unerring "ticking" of carbon-14. The same principles apply to nuclear waste. As we see in the next section, we can do nothing to make any particular radioisotope decay more quickly. We have to deal with what we have—perhaps for millennia.

7.9 | Nuclear Waste: Here Today, Here Tomorrow

Of the issues surrounding nuclear power, safely dealing with nuclear waste is the most pressing. There is no apparent "silver bullet" (or silver waste canister). In a June 1997 *Physics Today* article, John Ahearne, past chair of the U.S. Nuclear Regulatory Commission, reminds us that, "Like death and taxes, radioactive waste is with us—it cannot be wished away."

Before we discuss the options, it makes sense first to define the types of nuclear waste materials. **High-level radioactive waste (HLW),** as the name implies, has high levels of radioactivity and, because of the long half-lives of the radioisotopes involved, requires essentially permanent isolation from the biosphere. HLW comes in a variety of chemical forms, including ones that are highly acidic or basic. It also can contain toxic metals. Thus, HLW is sometimes labeled as a "mixed waste" in that it is hazardous *both* because of the chemicals *and* their radioactivity. Furthermore, as we noted in Section 7.7, this waste also poses a national security risk because it contains plutonium that could be extracted and used to construct a nuclear weapon. Huge quantities of HLW also were created during the Cold War because reactor fuel was reprocessed to produce plutonium for nuclear warheads. This military waste tends to be in the inconvenient form of solutions, suspensions, slurries, and salt cake stored in barrels, bins, and underground tanks.

In contrast, **low-level radioactive waste (LLW)** contains smaller quantities of radioactive materials than HLW and specifically excludes spent nuclear fuel. LLW includes a wide range of materials, including contaminated laboratory clothing, gloves, and cleaning tools from medical procedures using radioisotopes, and even discarded smoke detectors. As you might guess, the hazards associated with LLW are significantly less than those from HLW. Nearly 90% of the volume of all nuclear waste is low level.

Consider This 7.30   Compact It! Incinerate It!

An elected state representative visited a chemistry class to address questions relating to the radioactive waste that was being sent to local landfills. She proposed compacting the waste to reduce its radioactivity and then incinerating it. In her view, this was preferable to filling the landfills with radioactive waste. Assume that you were one of her staff members. Draft a tactful memo to set her straight.

Commercial and military nuclear power plants are the primary source of HLW. For example, each of the 100+ commercial nuclear reactors in the United States produces about 20 tons of spent fuel annually. **Spent nuclear fuel (SNF)** is the radioactive material remaining in fuel rods after they have been used to generate power in a nuclear reactor. After removal from the reactor, the spent fuel rods are still "hot," both in temperature and their radioactivity. These rods contain primarily U-238 with about 1% of the U-235 that did not fission. They also contain fission products, that is, many highly radioactive isotopes including iodine-131, cesium-137, and strontium-90. In addition, the spent fuel rods contain plutonium. Pu-239 is formed from U-238, as we saw earlier in equation 7.13. Refer back to Table 7.4 for the values of half-lives for some radioisotopes present in spent nuclear fuel.

Figure 7.24

A cask containing spent fuel is lowered into a deep underwater storage pool at the Savannah River Site in Aiken, South Carolina. This site is for interim storage.

Source: U.S. Department of Energy, Office of Civilian Radioactive Waste Management.

At each nuclear reactor in the United States, approximately 30% of the fuel rods are replaced annually on a rotating schedule. After the spent rods are removed from the reactor, they are transferred to deep basins of water for temporary storage (Figure 7.24). The water serves both to cool the fuel and to absorb alpha and beta radiation, thus shielding any nearby workers.

These pools are not intended for permanent storage of spent nuclear fuel. They are expensive to operate, and some corrosion of the metal rods occurs under water. Furthermore, most of the pools in the United States have reached their capacity, so the fuel rods need to be removed to make room for new ones. So for many reasons, after a year or so of "wet" storage in pools, the spent nuclear fuel is removed, dried, and transferred to casks.

Dry cask storage typically involves putting the spent reactor fuel into leak-tight steel cylinders that are enclosed by additional layers of steel or concrete to provide additional shielding. These casks are then stored in a concrete vault. Like the deep pools, this option for storage is temporary and requires continual maintenance (Figure 7.25).

Today, almost all reactor waste is being stored on site where it was generated. The storage facilities, not built for the long term, are hardly ideal. In the 1950s and early 1960s, the plan had been to reprocess the spent fuel to extract plutonium and uranium from it and to recycle these elements as nuclear fuel. On-site storage capacity for spent fuel rods was designed with such reprocessing in mind. However, only one of several planned reprocessing plants ever went into operation and then only briefly (1967–1975). Thus, reprocessing never was capable of keeping up with the rate of spent fuel production, about 2000 tons every year. In 1977, then President Jimmy Carter, a nuclear engineer, declared a moratorium on commercial nuclear fuel reprocessing that continues to this day.

The restrictions vary by nation. France, the United Kingdom, Germany, and Japan all reprocess some of their SNF. An option that is becoming more and more attractive is the use of a **breeder reactor,** a nuclear reactor that can produce more fissionable fuel (usually Pu-239) than it consumes (usually U-235). This seems like a dream come true to an energy-hungry planet. Imagine if your car synthesized gasoline as you drove! Scientists in the United States and elsewhere have figured out how to recover plutonium from the spent fuel of breeder reactors. In the 1970s, several factors

Figure 7.25

The dry cask system for storage of nuclear waste at a reactor site.

Source: U.S. Nuclear Regulatory Commission.

led the United States to stop pursuing breeder reactor technology, including the objection to plutonium reprocessing and the more complicated reactor design required. We take a more detailed look at the possible future of reprocessing in the final section of this chapter.

In the absence of reprocessing, two options exist for the storage of HLW: monitored storage on or near the surface and storage in geological repositories deep underground. These differ in a key variable: *active management* (Figure 7.26). In surface storage, human societies over thousands of years must commit resources to maintaining the integrity of the wastes. In geological repository storage, the wastes may be accessible and retrievable (although less easily) or sealed "forever," requiring minimal human vigilance. In a report published by the National Academies in 2000, the option of deep-underground storage was favored, noting that it was not prudent to assume that future societies on Earth would be able to maintain surface storage facilities.

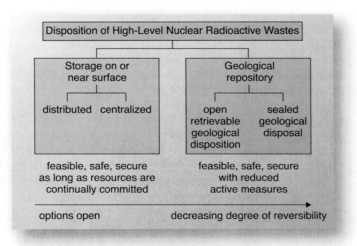

Figure 7.26

Strategies for high–level nuclear waste disposition.

Source: Disposition of High–Level Wastes and Spent Nuclear Fuel, *National Academy Press, 2000.*

Figure 7.27

Encapsulating reprocessed HLW in glass canisters (vitrification).

With either strategy for storage, HLW must remain isolated from the groundwater for at least 10,000 years to allow the high levels of radioactivity to decrease significantly. Some plans employ a method known as **vitrification,** in which the spent fuel elements or other mixed waste are encased in ceramic or glass. First, the waste is dried, pulverized, and then mixed with finely ground glass and melted at about 1150 °C. Then the molten glass and wastes are poured into stainless-steel canisters, cooled, and capped for on-site storage. More than 1 million pounds of waste already has been treated in this way and awaits the development of a long-term underground repository (Figure 7.27). The radioactivity remains, but the nuclear materials are trapped in solid glass.

Whatever physical form it may take, at present nuclear waste has no final resting place. In 1997, the Nuclear Waste Policy Amendments Act designated Yucca Mountain (Figure 7.28) in Nevada as the sole site to be studied as an underground long-term, high-level nuclear waste repository. In the years that followed, billions of dollars were spent to fund the development of such a repository. As of 2010, however, it appeared that the Yucca Mountain depository would not become operational.

Congress (or its successor) may still be debating the issue 24,110 years from now, when the plutonium-239 we create today completes its *first* half-life. Other disposal methods seem even less promising. Disposal in deep-sea clay sediments beneath 3000–5000 meters of water was investigated. Proposals to bury the radioactive waste under the Antarctic ice sheet or to rocket it into space have largely been discredited. But one thing is sure. Whatever disposal methods are ultimately adopted, they must be effective over an extremely long time. Nuclear engineers William Kastenberg and Luca Gratton conclude their 1997 article in *Physics Today* with a sobering thought that still rings true today:

> For a high-level waste depository of the type proposed for Yucca Mountain, it is clear that natural processes will eventually redistribute the waste materials. Present design efforts are directed toward ensuring that, at worst, the degraded waste configurations will eventually resemble stable, natural ore deposits, preferably for periods exceeding the lifetimes of the more hazardous radionuclides. Perhaps that's the best we can hope for.

(a)

(b)

Figure 7.28

(a) Map of Yucca Mountain and state of Nevada. (b) Yucca Mountain, looking south into the desert.

Source: (a) *U.S. Department of Energy.*

Consider This 7.31   Nuclear Waste Warning Markers

On February 15, 2007, the International Atomic Energy Agency (IAEA) unveiled the new symbol pictured to the right to warn the public about the dangers of radiation. You can read the details at the IAEA website.

a. Describe what this new symbol conveys to you.
b. Suppose you were asked to design markers to be installed near an underground nuclear waste repository. These markers must warn future generations of the existence of nuclear waste and must last for at least 10,000 years (more than four times the age of the pyramids of Egypt). The message must be intelligible to Earthlings of the future. Try your hand at designing these warning markers, keeping in mind the changes that have occurred in *Homo sapiens* during the past 10,000 years and those that might occur in the next 10 millennia.

7.10 | Risks and Benefits of Nuclear Power

In earlier sections, we noted the markedly different degree to which countries around the world employ nuclear power to generate electricity. Regardless of whether a country contains many nuclear-powered electric generators or only a few, the associated risks and benefits must be weighed by all involved.

Although a risk–benefit analysis may seem daunting, we actually make these kinds of assessments every day. Many types of risks are possible. Risks can be voluntary, such as those associated with wind surfing or bungee jumping; or they can be involuntary, such as inhaling someone else's cigarette smoke. When we drive a car, we can control some of the risks by using defensive driving techniques. But aboard a flight to Toledo or Tokyo, we have no control over the increased risk of radiation exposure at cruising altitude. Counterbalancing risks are many types of benefits. These include the improvement of health, increased personal comfort or quality of life, cost savings, or a lower ecological footprint.

> The 19th century poet William Wordsworth spoke of technological risks and benefits as "weighing the mischief with the promised gain." He was speaking, in this case, about the railroad, a technology new in his time.

Consider This 7.32   Informed Citizens

"Nuclear plants are no problem! I get a higher dose of radiation from flying for 5 hours than I do from working in a nuclear power plant. No worker has ever lost his or her life on the job."

a. In what sense is this assessment valid?
b. In what sense is this nuclear worker missing the point?

Hint: Use Table 7.2 to help formulate your answer. When it comes to radiation, also remember that the identity of the radioisotope (and whether it is inside or outside of your body) is a factor to consider.

There is no such thing as zero risk! Everyday living inevitably involves risks and their related benefits: crossing a street, riding a motorcycle, driving a car, cooking a meal or eating one, and even the simple act of getting up in the morning. Because there is some element of risk in everything we do, automatically we make judgments about what level of risk we consider acceptable. Most people do not intentionally put themselves at high risk. On the other hand, expecting "zero risk" in whatever we do is impossible to achieve.

Clearly, one of the desired benefits of nuclear power is electricity. Along with this, we desire minimal risks, including those to local, regional, and global economies,

Figure 7.29

The "green zone" in which we have healthy ecosystems, healthy economies, and healthy communities.

those to workers in all parts of the nuclear fuel cycle (see Figure 7.21), and those to the environment. This should sound reminiscent of the Triple Bottom Line: the nuclear power industry should promote health for our economy, for our communities, and for our ecosystems. In essence, we want to operate in the "green zone" where all three overlap (Figure 7.29, reproduced from Chapter 0 of this book).

How does nuclear power stack up against the alternatives? This is no easy question! Even so, we explore the answers, at least in part. For example, one alternative to "burning" uranium in a nuclear reactor is to burn coal in a conventional power plant. Here are some of the risks associated with coal-fired power plants, including some we described earlier in Chapter 4.

- **Mine worker safety**
  Over 100,000 workers have been killed in American coal mines since 1900, most prior to the 1950s when higher safety standards were instituted. Once mined, however, the coal does not require further refining. Mine workers also die from black lung disease. Although the overall rate in the United States is dropping, it still claims the lives of several hundred per year.

- **Greenhouse gas generation**
  Coal-fired power plants produce carbon dioxide, a waste product of combustion. Annually, a 1000-MW coal-fired electric power plant releases about 4.5 million tons of CO_2. The total release in the United States from burning coal is on the order of 2 billion tons yearly.

- **Air pollutant generation**
  A typical 1000-MW coal-fired power plant burns over 10,000 tons of coal and could easily release 300 tons of SO_2 and perhaps 100 tons of NO_x daily. Deaths attributed to poor air quality are numbered annually in the tens of thousands.

- **Ash generation**
  In a year, a 1000-MW coal-fired power plant generates about 3.5 million cubic feet of waste ash, a substantial volume. Revisit Figure 4.8 (reproduced in margin) to see the devastation caused when millions of gallons of fly ash sludge spilled down a valley in Tennessee.

- **Mercury release**
  Coal contains trace quantities of mercury. When coal is burned, mercury is released into the air in the form of elemental mercury. Although Hg emissions are slowly dropping, the amount emitted yearly worldwide is still on the order of hundreds of tons. Each year, about 50 tons of mercury is released in the United States.

- **Uranium and thorium release**
  Trace quantities of uranium in coal can be as high as 10 ppm, and the amount of thorium is usually higher. In the United States, at an annual coal consumption of over 1100 million tons, over 1300 tons of uranium and 2600 tons of thorium are being released into the environment yearly, exceeding the amount of uranium consumed in nuclear plants. Although much of the radioactive metals are collected in the fly ash, this too must be disposed of.

By way of contrast, here are some of the risks associated with nuclear power plants. Note that there is some overlap.

- **Mine worker safety**
  Uranium ore is mined and then chemically processed at a uranium mill to produce "yellow cake" (Figure 7.30). Mine and mill workers are at risk for cancer (especially lung cancer) both from the uranium dust and from the radon that it emits. After World War II in the United States, most uranium mining took place on the Colorado Plateau. Hundreds of workers later died of lung cancer. Family members of the workers sometimes were affected as well, as the workers carried home the uranium dust. Today, a stricter set of safety regulations for ventilation and radiation exposure is in place.

Figure 7.30

A sample of yellow cake, U_3O_8. This product is then refined to produce uranium metal, which in turn is enriched in U–235 (see Section 7.7).

- **Greenhouse gas generation**
  Nuclear power plants produce no carbon dioxide, although CO_2 emissions are associated with the mining, milling, enriching, and transporting of uranium and handling of spent reactor fuel. CO_2 emissions also accompany cement manufacture, used in power plant construction.

- **High-level nuclear waste generation**
  A 1000-MW nuclear power reactor produces about 70 cubic feet of high-level waste (HLW) per year (see previous section). In the United States, the total is on the order of 2000 tons annually.

- **Releases of fission products**
  Releases from almost all nuclear power plants have been tiny. Revisit Table 7.2 to see that living within 50 miles of a reactor contributes little to your annual radiation dose. However, accidents like the one in 2011 at the Fukushima reactor in Japan remind us of the devastation that is possible.

- **Mine tailings and mill waste**
  Uranium mining and milling operations produce radioactive tailings and waste. These rock tailings, because they contain uranium, also emit radon, so must be capped. Mining spills have occurred in the United States, most notably in 1979 at Church Rock, New Mexico. Today this is a Superfund cleanup site.

As we noted early in this chapter, nuclear energy carries tremendous emotional overtones. In part, these stem from mystery, misunderstandings, and the powerful image of the mushroom-shaped cloud. The possibility of a major disaster, however remote, looms large in human consciousness. The accidents at Chornobyl and Fukushima have brought public outcry. We have limited trust in technology and perhaps even less in people. We are apprehensive about human error in the design, construction, and management of nuclear power plants. After all, human errors and technicians' responses to them were the weak points in the prescribed safety procedures that caused the accidents at Three Mile Island and Chornobyl.

What about the risks in comparison with other sources of energy, such as wind, solar, and geothermal? The next activity offers an opportunity to explore some of the risks and benefits of wind power, a topic otherwise not discussed in *Chemistry in Context*.

> About 1 pound of CO_2 is emitted for each pound of cement manufactured.

> Recall from Section 7.9 that high–level radioactive waste (HLW) requires essentially permanent isolation from the biosphere.

> Look for the details of solar energy in Chapter 8.

Skeptical Chemist 7.33   Wind Power Safety

The author of a 2009 article on wind versus nuclear energy wrote: "The wind turbine industry, on the other hand, has quite a treacherous track record."

a. According to 2009 data from the World Nuclear Association, nuclear plants account for about 15% of the generation of electricity worldwide. How does wind compare?
b. Prepare a bullet point list of the risks associated with constructing wind turbines.
c. Now list the benefits of wind power. What do you conclude?

The risks associated with energy produced by nuclear plants clearly are different from those associated with other types of power generation. Remember, though, that "zero risk" is impossible for any energy source. Clearly, conservation and the efficient use of natural resources and energy are the best options of all. With this thought in mind, we now address the more general question of whether we can design nuclear power plants that meet the criteria for sustainability in the future.

7.11 | A Future for Nuclear Power

People across the globe share the dream of clean and sustainable sources of energy for the future. Does this dream include nuclear energy? If so, should we build more nuclear power plants to achieve this dream? The answers depend on both whom you ask and when you ask them.

If you had asked this question in the United States back in the early 1960s, the answer would have been yes. At this time, the United States experienced a dramatic growth in the nuclear power industry, one that lasted until 1979 when the malfunction at Three Mile Island occurred. The fear that accompanied this incident certainly contributed to the end of the growth phase. More important at that time, however, were the economics of nuclear energy. With the retreat of fossil fuel prices and the added costs of nuclear safety and oversight imposed in the 1980s, it simply was not economically feasible for utilities to construct new nuclear plants.

What are the economic realities today? Again, the answer depends on whom you ask and when you ask them. Two things, however, are clear. The first is that any new reactors will be built with improved designs, especially in light of the earthquake and tsunami that disabled reactors in Japan. And the second is that these designs will have a higher price tag.

In terms of design, the near future of nuclear power, especially in the United States, is primarily focused on ensuring current nuclear power plants are prepared for extraordinary disasters such as that which occurred at the Fukushima Daiichi power plant. The United States Nuclear Regulatory Commission (NRC) stated in a report that "a sequence of events like the Fukushima, Japan incident is unlikely to occur in the U.S." but an "accident involving core damage and uncontrolled release of radioactivity to the environment, even one without significant health consequences, is inherently unacceptable."

The NRC issued three orders to U.S. nuclear power facilities in reaction to the events in Japan. The orders include the requirements:

- that all facilities "obtain sufficient equipment to support all reactors and spent fuel pools at a given site simultaneously." This is to ensure that if a disaster affects multiple reactors, there will be protection.
- that certain facilities improve their venting systems for boiling water reactors to ensure protection against a backup of steam and to control the temperature.
- that new equipment be installed in order to monitor water levels in each plant's spent fuel pool. This will ensure that facilities will know water levels throughout the plant.

These orders must be addressed by December 2016. These changes will increase cost as well as other factors in current nuclear energy technology. Some of these are presented in the following paragraphs.

In his editorial in the May 9, 2011, issue of *Chemical & Engineering News*, then Editor-in-Chief Rudy Baum stated, "Despite the severity of the situation in Japan, nuclear power remains an essential component of our overall energy mix for the near to mid-term because it will help us avert the worst impacts of global climate change." Do you agree? Opponents of nuclear power cite current issues with waste disposal, noting that the only country in the world that has a long-term plan for dealing with nuclear waste is Finland. Also noted was the environmental damage caused by uranium mining, the high cost of nuclear reactors (approximately $12 billion for a new plant), fear among people, and the need to develop alternative energies. The examples of wind and solar energy continue to be a topic of both debate and humor as shown in Figures 7.31a and 7.31b.

Baum counters these arguments by acknowledging the nuclear waste issue but also stating, "at least nuclear waste is in temporary repositories and remains under human control which is more than can be said of the waste from burning fossil fuel." He also counters the mining concern with comparisons to the extraction techniques and current methods for fossil fuels, mentioning oil spills, coal mining, and natural gas extraction. Finally Baum addresses the other concerns with the following statement, "For the next 50 years or so, alternative energy sources cannot fuel civilization. Nuclear power can make a contribution that doesn't contribute to climate disruption."

(a)

(b)

Figure 7.31

(a) A photograph depicting many of the topics currently debated about nuclear energy
(b) a cartoon depicting thoughts on nuclear, wind, and solar power.

Consider This 7.34   Into the Future

In the previous paragraphs we have analyzed arguments both for and against using nuclear energy as a power source.

a. Reread the discussion on Rudy Baum's editorial and explain your thoughts on nuclear waste, mining, effects on climate change, cost, and human fear.
b. What does the cartoon (*right*) show about future energy concerns?
c. What do you feel is the future of nuclear power?

So where does that leave us? As you can see, there are no easy answers for the issue of nuclear power. Global demand for energy expands daily, as does the mass of radioactive waste from nuclear power plants with which we must cope. The era of climate change has dawned. Yet both real and perceived hazards associated with radioactivity, with mining and enriching uranium, and with nuclear weapons still remain. This presents a classic risk–benefit situation, and the final compromise has yet to be reached. For now, it is clear that nuclear power is not the cure-all for the world's energy woes. It is the cause of some environmental and societal woes. Even so, it will remain a piece of the energy pie in the years to come.

Consider This 7.35   Second Opinion Survey

Now that you are near the end of your study of nuclear power, return to the personal opinion survey of Consider This 7.1 and answer the questions again. Then compare your new answers with your earlier ones. Are there any striking differences in your opinions? If so, what changed and how do you account for the difference(s)?

Conclusion

Over 50 years have passed since the first commercial nuclear power plant began producing electricity in the United States. The glittering promise of boundless, unmetered electricity, drawn from the nuclei of uranium atoms, has proved illusory. But the needs of our nation and our world for safe, abundant, and inexpensive energy are far greater today than they were in 1957. Therefore, scientists and engineers continue their atomic quest.

Where the search will lead is uncertain, but it is clear that people and politics will have a major say in ultimately making the decision. Reason, together with a regard for those who will inhabit our planet in both the near and far future, must govern our actions. Maybe Homer Simpson was right when he proclaimed, "Lord, we are especially thankful for nuclear power, the cleanest, safest energy source there is. Except for solar, which is just a pipe dream." As it just so happens, we explore a little of the rationality behind that pipe dream—and other alternative energy sources as well—in the next chapter.

Chapter Summary

Having studied this chapter, you should be able to:

- Give an overview of the past and current use of nuclear power in the United States or another country of your choice (7.1)

- Report on the use of nuclear power for electricity generation worldwide (7.1)

- Explain the process of nuclear fission, the role of neutrons in sustaining a chain reaction, and the source of the energy it produces (7.2)

- Compare and contrast how electricity is produced in a conventional power plant and in a nuclear power plant (7.3)

- Compare the processes of alpha, beta, and gamma decay in terms of the changes that occur in the nucleus of the radioactive atom (7.4)

- Interpret the meaning of the word *radiation,* depending on the context (7.4)

- Explain how the radioactive decay of uranium-238 leads to the production of a series of radioisotopes. Also explain why naturally occurring radioisotopes such as carbon-14 and hydrogen-3 are *not* part of this series. (7.4)

- Describe the accident at Chornobyl and explain why radioactive iodine was released and was hazardous to people (7.5)

- Rank the sources that contribute to your annual dose of radiation, both natural and human-made (7.6)

- Explain why nuclear radiation is also termed *ionizing radiation.* In your body, explain the connection between ionizing radiation and the production of free radicals. (7.6)

- Use the curie, the rad, and the rem to illustrate that some measurement units describe the radioactive sample while others describe the damage done to tissue (7.6)

- Describe the terms *enriched uranium* and *depleted uranium* in such a way that the general public could more easily grasp the similarities and differences. (7.7)

- Do "back-of-the-envelope" half-life calculations for radioisotopes, being able to quickly determine how much radioactivity is left after time has passed (7.8)

- Apply the concept of half-life to the storage of nuclear waste (7.8)

- Evaluate radioisotopes in terms of their health hazards, discussing factors such as half-life, type of radioactive decay, effect once in the body, and route of entry into the body. For example, compare radon-222, iodine-131, and strontium-90. (7.8)

- Describe the issues associated with the production and storage of high-level radioactive waste, including spent nuclear fuel (7.9)

- Take an informed stand on how high-level radioactive wastes should be handled and stored (7.9)

- Evaluate news articles on nuclear power and nuclear waste with confidence in your ability to understand the scientific principles involved (7.9–7.11)

- Describe the connections between nuclear power and nuclear weapons proliferation (7.9)

- Assess the risks and benefits in regard to the use of nuclear power (7.10)

- Take an informed stand on the use of nuclear power for electricity production (7.11)

- Outline the factors that favor or oppose the growth of nuclear energy in the next decade (7.11)

Questions

Emphasizing Essentials

1. Name two ways in which one carbon atom can differ from another. Then name three ways in which *all* carbon atoms differ from *all* uranium atoms.

2. The representations ^{14}N or ^{15}N give more information than simply the chemical symbol N. Explain.

3. a. How many protons are in the nucleus of this isotope of plutonium: $^{239}_{94}Pu$?

   b. The nuclei of all atoms of uranium contain 92 protons. Which elements have nuclei with 93 and 94 protons, respectively?

   c. How many protons do the nuclei of radon-222 contain?

4. Determine the number of protons and neutrons in each of these nuclei.

   a. ^{14}C, a naturally occurring radioisotope of carbon

   b. ^{12}C, a naturally occurring stable isotope of carbon

   c. ^{3}H, tritium, a naturally occurring radioisotope of hydrogen

   d. Tc-99, a radioisotope used in medicine

5. $E = mc^2$ is one of the most famous equations of the 20th century. Explain the meaning of each symbol in it.

6. Give an example of a nuclear equation and of a chemical equation. In what ways are the two equations alike? Different?

7. This nuclear equation represents a plutonium target being hit by an alpha particle. Show that the sum of the subscripts on the left is equal to the sum of the subscripts on the right. Then do the same for the superscripts.

$$^{239}_{94}Pu + {}^{4}_{2}He \longrightarrow [{}^{243}_{96}Cm] \longrightarrow {}^{242}_{96}Cm + {}^{1}_{0}n$$

8. For the nuclear equation shown in the question 7,

   a. suggest the origin of the $^{4}_{2}He$ particle.

   b. $^{1}_{0}n$ is a product. What does this symbol represent?

   c. curium-243 is written in square brackets. What does this notation convey? *Hint:* See equation 7.1.

9. Californium, element number 98, was first synthesized by bombarding a target with alpha particles. The products were californium-245 and a neutron. What was the target isotope used in this nuclear synthesis?

10. Explain the significance of neutrons in initiating and sustaining the process of nuclear fission. In your answer, define and use the term *chain reaction*.

11. Nuclear fission occurs through many different pathways. For the fission of U-235 induced by a neutron, write a nuclear equation to form:

    a. bromine-87, lanthanum-146, and more neutrons.

    b. a nucleus with 56 protons, a second with a total of 94 neutrons and protons, and 2 additional neutrons.

12. This schematic diagram represents the reactor core of a nuclear power plant.

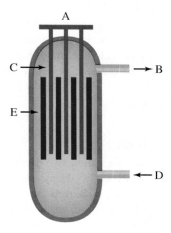

Match each letter in the figure with one of these terms.

   fuel rods

   cooling water into the core

   cooling water out of the core

   control rod assembly

   control rods

13. Identify the segments of the nuclear power plant diagrammed in Figure 7.7 that contain radioactive materials and those that do not.

14. Explain the difference between the primary coolant and the secondary coolant. The secondary coolant is not housed in the containment dome. Why not?

15. Boron can absorb neutrons.

    a. Write the nuclear equation in which boron-10 absorbs a neutron to produce lithium-7 and an alpha particle.

    b. Boron, like cadmium, can be used in control rods. Explain.

16. What is an alpha particle and how is it represented? Answer these same questions for a beta particle and a gamma ray.

17. Plutonium-239 decays by alpha emission (with no gamma ray), and iodine-131 decays by beta emission (with an accompanying gamma ray).

   a. Write the nuclear equation for each.

   b. Plutonium is most hazardous when inhaled in particulate form. Explain.

   c. Iodine-131 can be hazardous if ingested. Where do all isotopes of iodine accumulate in the body?

   d. Would you expect the radioactivity of a sample of each isotope to decrease to background level on a timescale of hours, days, years, or thousands of years? Explain. *Hint:* See Table 7.4.

18. Radioactive decay is accompanied by a change in the mass number, a change in the atomic number, a change in both, or a change in neither. For the following types of radioactive decay, which change(s) do you expect?

   a. alpha emission

   b. beta emission

   c. gamma emission

19. Figure 7.12 shows the radioactive decay series for U-238. Analogously, U-235 decays through a series of steps (α, β, α, β, α, α, α, β, α, β, α) to reach a stable isotope of lead. For practice, write nuclear reactions for the first six. Although some steps are accompanied by a gamma ray, you may omit this. *Hint:* The result is an isotope of radon.

20. Given that the average U.S. citizen receives 3600 μSv of radiation exposure per year, use the data in Table 7.2 to calculate the percentage of radiation exposure the average U.S. citizen receives from each of these sources.

   a. food, water, and air

   b. a dental X-ray

   c. the nuclear power industry

21. What percent of a radioactive isotope would remain after two half-lives, four half-lives, and six half-lives? What percent would have decayed after each period?

22. Estimate the half-life of radioisotope X from this graph.

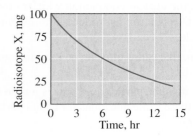

23. a. Is depleted uranium (DU) radioactive? Explain.

   b. Is spent nuclear fuel (SNF) radioactive? Explain.

Concentrating on Concepts

24. Alchemists in the Middle Ages dreamed of converting base metals, such as lead, into precious metals—gold and silver. Why could they never succeed? Today could we convert lead into gold? Explain.

25. Make a time line of nuclear history, putting at least a dozen dates on your line. For example, start with Becquerel's discovery of radioactivity in 1896. Other candidates for inclusion are Chornobyl, Hiroshima, Fukushima, the opening of the first commercial reactor, the discovery of various medical isotopes, the use of uranium glazes in Fiestaware, and the Nuclear Test Ban Treaty.

26. The isotopes U-235 and U-238 are alike in that they are both radioactive. However, these two isotopes have very different abundances in nature. List their natural abundances and explain the significance of this difference.

27. Consider the uranium fuel pellets used in commercial nuclear power plants.

   a. Describe one way in which U-235 and U-238 can be separated.

   b. Why is it necessary to enrich the uranium for use in the fuel pellets?

   c. Fuel pellets are enriched only to a few percent, rather than to 80–90%. Name three reasons why.

   d. Explain why it is not possible to separate U-235 and U-238 by chemical means.

28. a. Why must the fuel rods in a reactor be replaced every few years?

   b. What happens to the fuel rods after they are taken out of the reactor?

29. At full capacity, each reactor in the Palo Verde power plant uses only a few pounds of uranium to generate 1243 megawatts of power. To produce the same amount of energy would require about 2 million gallons of oil or about 10,000 tons of coal in a conventional power plant. How is energy produced in the Palo Verde plant, compared with conventional power plants?

30. One important distinction between the Chornobyl reactors and those in the United States is that those in Chornobyl used graphite as a moderator to slow neutrons, whereas U.S. reactors use water. In terms of safety, give two reasons why water is a better choice.

31. If you look at nuclear equations in sources other than this textbook, you may find that the subscripts have been omitted. For example, you may see an equation for a fission reaction written this way.

$$^{235}U + {^1}n \longrightarrow [{^{236}}U] \longrightarrow {^{87}}Br + {^{146}}La + 3\,{^1}n$$

   a. How do you know what the subscripts should be? Why can they be omitted?

   b. Why are the superscripts *not* omitted?

32. Using the model of a neutron presented in equation 7.6, explain how a high-speed electron can be ejected from the nucleus in beta decay.

33. Coal can contain trace amounts of uranium. Explain why thorium must be found in coal as well.

34. Suppose somebody tells you that a radioisotope is gone after 10 half-lives. Critique this statement, explaining why it could be a reasonable assumption for a small sample, but might not be for a large one.

35. "Bananas are radioactive!" A vice president of nuclear services made this comment in a public lecture in the context of comparing the different sources of radiation to which people are exposed.

    a. Why might he have made such an assertion?

    b. Suggest a better way to have phrased this.

    c. Should you stop eating bananas because they are radioactive? Explain.

36. A website describing an X-ray procedure reports, "Despite its negative connotations, people are exposed to more radiation on a daily basis than they may realize. For example, infrared radiation is released whenever there is extreme heat. The Sun generates ultraviolet radiation, and a little exposure to it will tan a lighter skinned person. In addition, the body contains naturally radioactive elements." Examine the three examples given in this explanation. Do they refer to nuclear or electromagnetic radiation?

37. Consider this representation of a Geiger–Müller counter (also called a Geiger counter), a device commonly used to detect ionizing radiation. The probe contains a gas under low pressure.

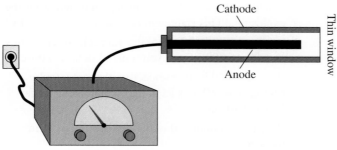

    a. How does radiation enter the Geiger–Müller counter?

    b. Why does this device only detect radiation that is capable of ionizing the gas contained in the probe?

    c. What other methods are used to detect the presence of ionizing radiation?

38. Rapidly dividing cells are present in several places in the adult body. These include the skin, the hair follicles, the stomach and intestines, the lining of your mouth, and your bone marrow. Match the symptoms listed in Table 7.3 with the type of cell affected by the radiation.

39. Exposure to ionizing radiation can cause cancer. A beam of ionizing radiation also can be used to cure certain types of cancer. Explain.

40. Fluorine has only one naturally occurring radioisotope, F-19. If fluorine also occurred in nature as F-18, would this necessarily complicate the separation of $^{238}UF_6$ and $^{235}UF_6$? Explain.

41. It is generally believed that terrorists would be more likely to construct a nuclear bomb using Pu-239 reclaimed from breeder reactors than using U-235. Use your knowledge of nuclear chemistry to explain why.

42. Weapons-grade plutonium is almost completely Pu-239. In contrast, the plutonium produced in the normal operation of a water-cooled power reactor (reactor-grade plutonium) generally has a higher concentration of heavier isotopes such as Pu-240 and Pu-241. Propose an explanation for this observation.

43. a. What are the characteristics of high-level radioactive waste (HLW)?

    b. Explain how low-level waste (LLW) differs from HLW.

Exploring Extensions

44. In Consider This 7.1, you were asked to answer several questions about nuclear power. Ask the same questions of someone at least one generation older than you and someone younger. In comparison with your answer, what similarities and differences do you find?

45. The film *King Corn* opens with a scene from Professor Stephen Macko at the University of Virginia, a forensic chemist. He analyzed hair samples from two college students, reporting that much of the carbon in their body originated from corn. His analysis was based on carbon-13.

    a. Is this a stable or a radioactive isotope of carbon?

    b. What can be learned about your diet by analyzing samples of hair?

46. Explain the term *decommission*, as in "decommissioning a nuclear power plant." What technical challenges are involved? The resources of the Internet can help you.

47. Einstein's equation, $\Delta E = \Delta mc^2$ applies to chemical reactions as well as nuclear ones. An important chemical change studied in Chapter 4 was the combustion of methane, which releases 50.1 kJ of energy for each gram of methane burned.

    a. What mass loss corresponds to the release of 50.1 kJ of energy?

    b. To produce the same amount of energy, what is the ratio of the mass of methane burned in a chemical reaction to the mass loss converted into energy according to the equation $\Delta E = \Delta mc^2$?

    c. Use your results in parts **a** and **b** to comment on why Einstein's equation, although correct for both chemical and nuclear changes, usually is only applied to nuclear changes.

48. When 4.00 g of hydrogen nuclei undergoes fusion to form helium in the Sun, the change in mass is 0.0265 g and energy is released. Use Einstein's equation, $\Delta E = \Delta mc^2$, to calculate the energy equivalent of this mass change.

49. Under conditions like those on the Sun, hydrogen can fuse with helium to form lithium, which in turn can form different isotopes of helium and of hydrogen. The mass of one mole of each isotope is given.

$$\,^2_1\text{H} + \,^3_2\text{He} \longrightarrow [\,^5_3\text{Li}] \longrightarrow \,^4_2\text{He} + \,^1_1\text{H}$$

2.01345 g   3.01493 g   4.00150 g   1.00728 g

    a. In grams, what is the mass difference between the reactants and the products?

    b. For one mole of reactants, how much energy (in joules) is released?

50. Lise Meitner and Marie Curie were both pioneers in developing an understanding of radioactive substances. You likely have heard of Marie Curie and her work, but may not have heard of Lise Meitner. How are these two women related in time and in their scientific work?

51. Taking potassium iodide tablets can protect your thyroid from exposure to radioactive iodine, thus reducing your risk of thyroid cancer.

    a. Give the chemical formula for potassium iodide.

    b. By what mechanism does potassium iodide protect you?

    c. How long does the protection last?

    d. Are the tablets expensive? *Hint:* The FDA website is a good source of information for parts **b** and **c**.

52. A stockpile of approximately 50 metric tons of plutonium exists in the United States as a result of disassembling warheads from the nuclear arms race. What is the likely fate of this plutonium? *Hint:* Search for *plutonium disposal*. Try also including *United States* and *Department of Energy* in your search string.

    a. Some propose that the plutonium be sent to local nuclear power plants to "burn" as fissionable fuel. What are the advantages and disadvantages of such a course of action?

    b. Others propose that it be stored permanently in a repository. Again, list the advantages and disadvantages.

53. Advertisements for Swiss Army watches stress their use of tritium. One ad states that the "hands and numerals are illuminated by self-powered tritium gas, 10 times brighter than ordinary luminous dials." Another advertisement boasts that the "tritium hands and markers glow brightly making checking your time a breeze, even at night." Evaluate these statements and, after doing some Internet research, discuss the chemical form of tritium in these watches, and what its role is.

54. Nuclear weapons are not the only threat. Consider also "the dirty bomb," a device that employs a conventional explosive to disperse a radioactive substance. No fission is involved with a dirty bomb; only a conventional explosive.

    a. What radioisotopes might be used in a dirty bomb?

    b. A brochure on nuclear terrorism makes this assertion: "A nuclear weapon, if exploded, would create more radioactive substances than originally present in the weapon. In contrast, if a dirty bomb were to be exploded, the amount of radioactivity would be the same before, during, and right after the explosion." This statement is accurate. Explain why.

55. According to Table 7.2, smoking 1.5 packs of cigarettes a day adds 15,000 μSv to your annual radiation dose.

    a. Polonium-210 is the radioactive element largely responsible. What is its mode of radioactive decay and its half-life?

    b. Why is polonium-210 found (in tiny amounts) in tobacco?

56. MRI, or magnetic resonance imaging, is an important tool for some types of medical diagnoses.

   a. The science behind MRI is complex. You should, however, be able to pin down whether or not MRI uses ionizing radiation to produce an image. Does it?

   b. How does an MRI compare with a CT (computed tomography) scan in terms of the image produced and the radiation used?

   c. MRI is based on NMR, nuclear magnetic resonance. Speculate why the abbreviation MRI is used to denote the medical tool rather than NMR.

57. Deciding where to locate a nuclear power plant requires analysis of both risks and benefits associated with the plant. If you were to play the role of a CEO of a major electric utility considering whether to pursue permits for the construction of a nuclear power plant in your area, what risks and benefits would you cite?

58. Provide at least two similarities and two differences between a nuclear-fueled power plant (Figure 7.7) and a coal-fueled power plant (Figure 4.2).

"In going on with these Experiments, how many pretty systems do we build, which we soon find ourselves oblig'd to destroy! If there is no other Use discover'd of Electricity, this, however, is something considerable, that it may help to make a vain Man humble."

Benjamin Franklin, statesman, scientist, inventor, diplomat (1706–1790)

We hope you never tempt fate by flying a kite in a thunderstorm with a key attached to the string. Ben Franklin probably never sent a key aloft either, although he did prove that lightning was electric in nature. As Franklin himself commented, the power of electricity is something "*to make a vain Man humble*." Indeed, a bolt of lightning is one of nature's grandest displays of electrical energy. You may have jumped at the crack of a nearby lightning strike. Inside your body, a cascade of electrons as part of cellular metabolism powered your startled response. Thus both a lightning strike and your physiological response to it involve processes driven by the flow of electrons. Clearly, our world is naturally electric!

People also have built additional electric systems. We rely on a flow of electrons— better known as electricity—to heat or cool our living and workspaces, to provide light to read by, and to power our TV sets. For most of us, the electricity we use is generated at centralized power plants, such as those fueled by fossil fuels (see Chapter 4) or fissionable isotopes (see Chapter 7). To a lesser extent, we also rely on wind, sun, and geothermal, as well as the potential energy of water trapped by dams as sources to generate electric power.

Additionally, we have created convenient-sized portable sources of electricity, better known as batteries. These long-lasting and reliable devices fill a special energy niche. They power our cell phones, MP3 players, laptops, and perhaps even our hearing aids and motorized wheelchairs. In order to start thinking about your own personal battery use, complete this activity.

Look for more about metabolism in Chapter 11, the food chapter.

Consider This 8.1   Personal Battery Use

Many devices, both large and small, contain electrochemical cells that people usually call "batteries." Create a table with four columns. Head these with the labels: device, battery use, rechargeable, and recyclable.

a. Fill in the "Device" column with at least four items powered by batteries.
b. Some devices use a battery as the main source of power; others use it as a backup. Categorize the items in your table.
c. Some batteries are rechargeable; others are not. Again categorize the items.
d. When the battery runs down, do you throw it out, recycle it, or give it to a dealer to recycle? Fill out the last column of your table. We explore the challenges of battery recycling later in this chapter.

If you are like many students we know, you may carry a cellular phone (lithium-ion battery, rechargeable), own a wristwatch (mercury battery), snap photos with a digital camera (nickel–cadmium, or Ni-Cd, battery, rechargeable), and punch numbers into a calculator (alkaline battery). You may even own a laptop computer with a lithium-ion rechargeable battery and perhaps drive a car with a lead–acid storage battery.

Not everyone in the world has access to these consumer items. In fact, the International Energy Agency estimated in 2009 that 1.3 billion people, approximately a fifth of the world's population, lacked access to electricity. Increasingly, people worldwide want home appliances and electronic devices. Indeed, in 2011 the U.S. Energy Information Administration projected that electricity will supply an increasing share of the world's total energy demand and is the fastest growing use of energy worldwide.

This growth will place an ever-increasing demand on our natural resources. There are practical limits to the long-term availability of both fossil fuels and the metals used to power batteries. Fissionable isotopes, though available, are a difficult fuel to obtain. Moreover, all fuels come with environmental and societal price tags, sometimes referred to as their "external costs." The combustion of coal, petroleum products, and natural gas releases vast quantities of carbon dioxide, a significant contributor to global warming. The combustion of fossil fuels also releases sulfur dioxide and nitrogen oxides, leading to decreases in air quality and increases in health costs. Processing uranium or breeding plutonium create both low-level and high-level nuclear waste. Additional high-level nuclear waste from spent nuclear fuel must be safely stored for generations to come (see Chapter 7).

The conclusion seems obvious. If we are to continue to inhabit this planet and not compromise the ability of future generations to meet their needs, we must develop and depend on other sources of energy. We also must better match our current batteries (and other sources of electricity) with their end uses. The key ideas in green chemistry and cradle-to-cradle stewardship can help inform our national approaches as well as our day-to-day activities.

Electron transfer! In this chapter we look at several power sources that derive energy through electron transfer technology. These include batteries for portable devices, automobiles, fuel cells, and solar photovoltaic power. We begin with the basics of batteries.

8.1 | Batteries, Galvanic Cells, and Electrons

Batteries are a big and growing business worldwide due to consumer demand for products that require them (Figure 8.1). Many consumer products require batteries, spurring continued growth in the battery industry. Although we commonly use the word *battery*, a standard flashlight "battery" is more correctly called a **galvanic cell.** This is a type of electrochemical cell that converts the energy released in a spontaneous chemical reaction into electrical energy. A collection of several galvanic cells wired together constitutes a true battery.

> Think of a battery as a collection of related things, such as a battery of tests or a battery of artillery cannons.

All galvanic cells produce useful energy through the transfer of electrons from one substance to another. For this transfer process, you can write an overall chemical equation. In turn, this can be divided—split if you like—into two parts. One is for **oxidation,** a process in which a chemical species loses electrons. The other is for **reduction**, a process in which a chemical species gains electrons. We refer to these two parts as "half-reactions" in the sense that each represents half of the overall process occurring in the galvanic cell. More formally, a **half-reaction** is a type of chemical equation that shows the electrons either lost or gained by the reactants.

> oxidation = loss of electrons
> reduction = gain of electrons

Half-reactions are a bit different from the chemical equations that we used earlier in this text. First, they always occur in pairs. Secondly, they include electrons! Even though electrons cannot be poured from a bottle into a flask, it still is helpful to show them in half-reactions so that you can better understand what is taking place. Note that the electrons show up either on the right or the left side of the half-reaction, but not on both. If on the right side, then the reactant has lost electrons; this is an oxidation half-reaction. In contrast, if the electrons are on the left side of the half-reaction, then the reactant is gaining electrons, and this is a reduction half-reaction.

Frank and Ernest

Figure 8.1

A humorous although realistic view of how batteries link to consumer products.

As an example, consider a simplified version of the reaction that takes place in a nickel–cadmium (Ni-Cd, or "nicad") battery:

Ni–Cd is an abbreviation, not a chemical formula for the nickel–cadmium battery. It is pronounced "NYE–cad."

$$\text{oxidation half-reaction:} \quad Cd \longrightarrow Cd^{2+} + 2\,e^- \qquad \textbf{[8.1]}$$

$$\text{reduction half-reaction:} \quad 2\,Ni^{3+} + 2\,e^- \longrightarrow 2\,Ni^{2+} \qquad \textbf{[8.2]}$$

In this case, two electrons are given off, or "lost," in the oxidation half-reaction. Where do they go? These electrons were transferred to the ion being reduced. The number of electrons given off during oxidation must equal the number of electrons gained through reduction for the overall equation to balance. For this reason, the coefficient "2" appears in the reduction half-reaction (see equation 8.2).

We now can add the two half-cell reactions to obtain the overall equation:

$$Cd + 2\,Ni^{3+} + \cancel{2\,e^-} \longrightarrow Cd^{2+} + \cancel{2\,e^-} + 2\,Ni^{2+} \qquad \textbf{[8.3]}$$

The electrons that appear on both sides of equation 8.3 cancel, as the electrons "lost" by the cadmium metal are gained by the nickel ions. So we can rewrite the overall cell equation as:

$$\text{overall cell equation:} \quad Cd + 2\,Ni^{3+} \longrightarrow Cd^{2+} + 2\,Ni^{2+} \qquad \textbf{[8.4]}$$

Your Turn 8.2   Electrons in Half–Reactions

Categorize each as an oxidation half–reaction or a reduction half–reaction. Explain your reasoning.

a. $Al^{3+} + 3\,e^- \longrightarrow Al$
b. $Zn \longrightarrow Zn^{2+} + 2\,e^-$
c. $Mn^{7+} + 3\,e^- \longrightarrow Mn^{4+}$
d. $2\,H_2O \longrightarrow 4\,H^+ + O_2 + 4\,e^-$
e. $2\,H^+ + 2\,e^- \longrightarrow H_2$

Answer

a. Reduction. The aluminum ion gained three electrons to become aluminum in its elemental form, that is, aluminum metal (no charge).

Figure 8.2

This 7.2–V Ryobi portable power drill comes with two Ni–Cd battery packs and a recharging unit.

The movement of electrons through an external circuit produces **electricity,** the flow of electrons from one region to another that is driven by a difference in potential energy. The electrochemical reaction provides the energy needed to drive a cordless razor, a power tool, or countless other battery-operated devices. The chemical species oxidized and reduced in the cell must be connected in such a way to allow electrons released during the oxidation to transfer to the reactant being reduced while following an appropriate electrical path for the desired application.

Potential energy was first introduced in Section 4.1.

Electrodes, electrical conductors within a cell that serve as sites for chemical reactions, facilitate this electron transfer. At the **anode,** oxidation takes place and is the source of electrons in the current flow. At the **cathode,** reduction takes place. The cathode receives the electrons sent from the anode through the external circuit to complete the reduction. Once the electrical circuit is completed, then a **voltage** can be measured across the cell, that is, the difference in electrochemical potential between the two electrodes. Voltage is measured in units called volts (V). The greater the difference in potential between the two electrodes, the higher the voltage and the greater the energy associated with the electron transfer. For example, with a Ni-Cd cell, the maximum difference in electrochemical potential under the conditions specified is measured as 1.2 V. In contrast, alkaline cells deliver 1.5 V, mercury cells 1.35 V, and lithium ion cells are capable of potentials in excess of 4 V! In order to produce the higher voltages necessary to power larger devices (for example, power tools or automobile starter motors) several cells must be connected (Figure 8.2).

anode = oxidation
cathode = reduction

The chemical reaction that takes place in a Ni-Cd cell is more complicated than represented in equations 8.1–8.4. Cadmium metal, at the anode, contains atoms of cadmium that are oxidized to Cd^{2+}. These in turn combine with OH^- to form $Cd(OH)_2$.

The unit "volt" honors the Italian physicist Alessandro Volta (1745–1827). He is credited with inventing the first electrochemical cell in 1800.

Electrolytes were first introduced
in Section 5.6.

Simultaneously, Ni^{3+}, present in the hydrated form of $NiO(OH)$ on the nickel cathode, is reduced to Ni^{2+} in the chemical form of $Ni(OH)_2$. A water-based electrolyte paste containing a highly concentrated solution of the strong base $NaOH$ or KOH separates the electrodes and allows the flow of charge.

oxidation half-reaction (anode):

$$Cd(s) + 2\ OH^-(aq) \longrightarrow Cd(OH)_2(s) + 2\ e^- \qquad \textbf{[8.5]}$$

reduction half-reaction (cathode):

$$2\ NiO(OH)(s) + 2\ H_2O(l) + 2\ e^- \longrightarrow 2\ Ni(OH)_2(s) + 2\ OH^-(aq) \qquad \textbf{[8.6]}$$

overall cell equation (sum of the two half-reactions):

$$Cd(s) + 2\ NiO(OH)(s) + 2\ H_2O(l) \longrightarrow 2\ Ni(OH)_2(s) + Cd(OH)_2(s) \qquad \textbf{[8.7]}$$

These three equations show exactly the same transfer of electrons represented in equations 8.1–8.4, but now different states and chemical forms are indicated. Figure 8.3 illustrates an inner view of a Ni-Cd galvanic cell (a "battery").

Your Turn 8.3   Checking Balance and Charge

Consider equations 8.1–8.7, which include both chemical equations and half–reactions.

  a. Is each equation balanced in terms of the number of atoms, that is, by the law of conservation of matter and mass? Explain.
  b. Does each equation have the same amount of electrical charge on both sides? Explain.
  c. Name a quick way to distinguish an overall cell equation from a half–reaction.

A Ni-Cd "battery" is rechargeable, an added advantage for many applications. A rechargeable battery employs electrochemical reactions that can run in both directions. The transfer of electrons takes place both during the forward (discharging) and the reverse (recharging) processes.

$$Cd(s) + 2\ NiO(OH)(s) + 2\ H_2O(l) \xrightleftharpoons[\text{recharging}]{\text{discharging}} 2\ Ni(OH)_2(s) + Cd(OH)_2(s) \qquad \textbf{[8.8]}$$

What feature makes a battery rechargeable? The key is that both the reactants and products are solids. Furthermore, the solid products cling to a stainless-steel grid within the battery rather than dispersing. If a voltage is applied to this grid, these products can be converted back to reactants, thus recharging the battery. Although a rechargeable battery can be discharged and recharged many times, eventually the accumulation of impurities, breakdown of the separators, or generation of unwanted side-reaction by-products ends its useful life.

Batteries come in many shapes and sizes, each one uniquely matched to its use. For example, in an application like a hearing aid, the size and weight of the cell is of paramount importance. In contrast, an automobile battery must last for years and perform over a range of temperatures. To be successful in the eyes of today's consumers, batteries must be affordable, last a reasonable length of time, and be safe to use and recharge. Ultimately, to be successful in the years to come, batteries also must be designed so that their materials can be recycled in a sustainable way.

Most electrochemical cells convert chemical energy into electric energy with an efficiency of about 90%. Compare this with the much lower efficiencies of 30–40% that characterize coal-fired power plants that generate electricity. Recognize, though, that electricity from these plants is used to recharge batteries. This is but one of many incentives to explore renewable energy sources.

With the exception of lead–acid batteries used for automobile starter motors, aqueous solutions usually are too hazardous to use in batteries because sooner or later they leak from the battery casing. For example, you may have seen the corrosive mess inside of a flashlight or child's toy from a leaking battery. However, in the chemistry

A Ni–Cd "battery" is really a single galvanic cell, rather than several cells (a battery). But given the common use of the word battery, from now on we will simply refer to it as a battery.

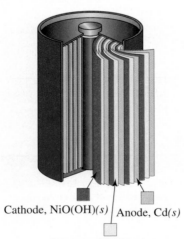

Cathode, $NiO(OH)(s)$ | Anode, $Cd(s)$

Separator, $KOH(aq)$ paste

Figure 8.3

Representation of a Ni–Cd galvanic cell showing how the components are layered to increase the surface area of the electrodes.

laboratory, you can safely use aqueous solutions to build a galvanic cell. Many different combinations are possible! For example, ask your instructor if you can set up the copper–zinc cell shown in the next activity.

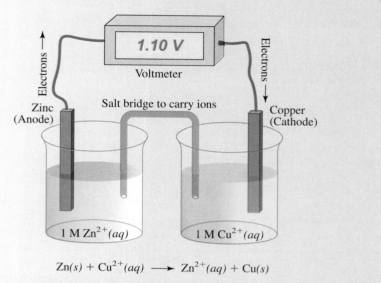

Your Turn 8.4   Galvanic Cells in the Lab

As this cell operates, a reddish coating of copper metal begins to appear on the surface of the copper cathode. The overall equation for the chemical reaction is given below the diagram.

$$Zn(s) + Cu^{2+}(aq) \longrightarrow Zn^{2+}(aq) + Cu(s)$$

a. Write the oxidation half–reaction taking place at the anode.
b. Write the reduction half–reaction taking place at the cathode.
c. This laboratory galvanic cell is not rechargeable. Explain why.

The overview of galvanic cells provided in this section is the start of a much longer story. We continue the tale in the next section.

8.2 | Other Common Galvanic Cells

You can review alkaline (basic) solutions in Section 6.4.

Almost everyone has inserted an alkaline battery into a flashlight, calculator, or digital camera. You may recognize the ones shown in Figure 8.4. One end of each of these batteries is marked with a + sign; the other end with a − sign. These markings point to the fact that electron transfer is at work. Alkaline cells each produce 1.5 V, but the larger ones can sustain a current through the external circuit for a longer time. The **current,** or rate of electron flow, is measured in amperes (amps, A) or likely in milliamps (mA) for smaller cells.

Current is measured in amperes (amps, A) to honor André Ampère (1775–1836). He was a self–taught French mathematician who worked on electricity and magnetism.

The voltage of a battery is primarily determined by its chemical composition. The alkaline cell is based on chemical reactions involving zinc and manganese (Figure 8.5). The cell is called "alkaline" because it operates in a basic, rather than acidic medium. The half-reactions for this cell are:

oxidation half-reaction (anode):
$$Zn(s) + 2\,OH^-(aq) \longrightarrow Zn(OH)_2(s) + 2\,e^- \qquad \text{[8.9]}$$

reduction half-reaction (cathode):
$$2\,MnO_2(s) + H_2O(l) + 2\,e^- \longrightarrow Mn_2O_3(s) + 2\,OH^-(aq) \qquad \text{[8.10]}$$

overall cell equation (sum of the two half-reactions):
$$Zn(s) + 2\,MnO_2(s) + H_2O(l) \longrightarrow Zn(OH)_2(s) + Mn_2O_3(s) \qquad \text{[8.11]}$$

Figure 8.4

These alkaline cells of size AAA to D all produce 1.5 V.

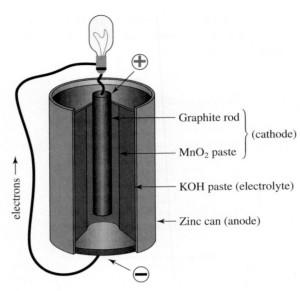

Figure 8.5

Representation of an alkaline cell.

Note that the cell voltage is not a function of the size of the cell. All alkaline batteries, from the tiny AAA size to the large D cells, produce the same voltage, 1.5 V. However, larger cells contain more material and so can sustain the transfer of a large number of electrons either in a short burst or with a smaller current over a longer time.

However, the voltage *is* a function of the chemicals involved. You can see from the examples listed in Table 8.1 that different voltages are produced using different chemical systems. Only a few volts are possible with a single galvanic cell. But as we noted in the previous section, higher voltages are possible by connecting cells. For example, in order to run a 14.4 or 19.2 V power drill, manufacturers sell a "battery pack" that contains multiple cells.

Compact, long-lasting cells may find their way into your body. For example, the widespread use of cardiac pacemakers is largely due to the improvements made in the electrochemical cells rather than in the pacemakers themselves. Lithium–iodine cells are so reliable and long-lived that they are often the battery of choice for this application, lasting as long as 10 years before needing to be replaced.

Lithium batteries take advantage of the low density and large oxidation potential of lithium metal to make a lightweight battery with large energy output.

Table 8.1	Some Common Galvanic Cells		
Type	Voltage (V)	Rechargeable	Examples of Uses
alkaline	1.5	no	flashlights, small appliances, some calculators
lithium–iodine	2.8	no	pacemakers
lithium–ion	3.7	yes	laptop computers, cell phones, digital music players, power tools
lead–acid	2.0	yes	automobile batteries
nickel–cadmium (Ni–Cd)	1.3	yes	toys and portable electronic devices including digital cameras, power tools
nickel–metal hydride (NiMH)	1.3	yes	replacing Ni–Cd for many uses; hybrid vehicles batteries
mercury	1.3	no	once widely used in cameras, watches, and hearing aids, but now are banned or being phased out

Consider This 8.5   Can You Swing a Hammer?

Shifting baselines, introduced in Chapter 0, is the idea that what people perceive as normal has changed over time, especially with regard to the ecosystems on our planet. The idea also can be applied more generally.

a. "Carpenters today no longer know how to swing a hammer!" Of course a good carpenter can still drive a nail with a single blow, but this lament indeed has some truth to it. Power tools now provide much of the muscle. With an eye to shifting baselines, interview someone old enough to be able to tell you stories of carpentry before power tools. Write a brief summary.

b. Power tools are but one of the many uses for batteries listed in Table 8.1. Select a different use and propose at least three ways in which what people consider as normal has shifted because batteries are used.

Parking meters were unknown before 1935.

Found under the front hood of a car, the lead–acid battery is the workhorse of today's rechargeable batteries. It is an excellent example of a battery that has changed what is "normal" for people now as compared with a century ago, as it was one of several technological advances that allowed the rise of the automobile. Cars indeed have changed our world! For example, parking ramps and parking meters were unknown a hundred years ago. You could not have bought an infant car seat or windshield washer fluid, because these items did not yet exist. Gas stations did not dot the landscape. And the waste products of gasoline combustion were not dirtying the air we breathe or warming our planet.

Today, however, we take the lead–acid battery for granted. In an automobile, it powers an electric motor that replaced the hand crank that people once used to start their cars. It is a true battery since it consists of six electrochemical cells, each generating 2.0 V for a total of 12.0 V (Figure 8.6). Here is the overall chemical equation, the sum of the two half-reactions.

$$\underset{\text{lead}}{Pb(s)} + \underset{\text{lead dioxide}}{PbO_2(s)} + \underset{\text{sulfuric acid}}{2\,H_2SO_4(aq)} \underset{\text{recharging}}{\overset{\text{discharging}}{\rightleftarrows}} \underset{\text{lead(II) sulfate}}{2\,PbSO_4(s)} + \underset{\text{water}}{2\,H_2O(l)} \qquad \textbf{[8.12]}$$

As the arrows in equation 8.12 indicate, when the chemical reaction proceeds to the right, the battery is discharging. For example, using the battery to start the car

Lead dioxide is the common name for lead(IV) oxide. We will use the common name in this chapter.

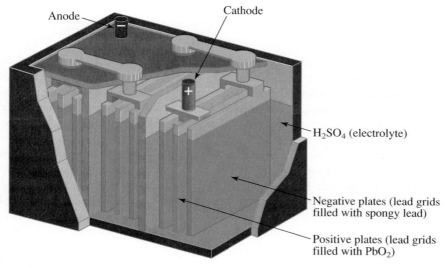

Figure 8.6

Cutaway view of a lead–acid storage battery.

Older lead–acid batteries required addition of water and therefore were designed with removable screw caps.

discharges the battery. Running the lights or radio without the engine on also discharges it. But once the engine is running, an alternator, turned by the engine, provides the current needed to reverse the chemical reaction and recharge the battery. Fortunately, the battery can discharge and be recharged many times before it needs to be replaced. A high-quality battery can perform for five years or more!

Your Turn 8.6   The Battery in Your Car

Let's take a closer look at the lead–acid storage battery, the one found in most cars (see equation 8.12).

a. Lead occurs in this equation as Pb, PbO_2, and $PbSO_4$, all solids. In which of these is lead in an ionic form? What is the ion? Which one of these represents lead in its metallic form?

b. When lead is converted from its metallic form to an ionic form, are electrons lost or gained? Is this oxidation or reduction?

c. When the battery is discharging, is metallic lead oxidized or reduced?

Answer

a. $Pb(s)$ is lead in its elemental form (a metal), whereas both $PbO_2(s)$ and $PbSO_4(s)$ are compounds that contain the lead ions, Pb^{4+} and Pb^{2+} respectively.

Because lead–acid batteries have the advantage of being rechargeable and low in cost, they may be used together with wind turbine electric generators. The generator recharges the batteries during favorable winds; the batteries discharge during unfavorable wind conditions. You can also find lead–acid batteries in environments where the emissions from internal combustion engines cannot be tolerated. The forklifts in warehouses, the passenger carts in airports, and the electric wheelchairs in supermarkets typically are powered by lead–acid storage batteries. Their weight may even be an advantage in stabilizing these vehicles.

In an automobile, however, the weight of the lead–acid battery is a disadvantage. Another disadvantage is the chemical components of the battery. The anode (lead metal), cathode (lead dioxide), and the electrolyte (sulfuric acid solution) pose disposal challenges as toxic or corrosive chemicals. If batteries are to be used sustainably, we must meet these challenges. The next section speaks more directly to the components of batteries and where they do (and should) end up when the battery is disposed of.

8.3 | Battery Ingredients: Cradle-to-Cradle

Can you recall when you last went an entire day without using a device powered by a battery? Batteries have made cell phones, MP3 players, laptops, and hand-held calculators so commonplace that we tend to take them for granted. Developing technologies also rely heavily on batteries. For example, batteries are a key component of hybrid vehicles. Off-grid scale solar energy installations also require the use of batteries to deliver power at night.

Yet the battery in your cell phone, car, or even in a solar installation costs more than what you pay for it in the store. There also is an environmental price tag, that is, an "external cost" that is borne by all. Part of this stems from the "ingredients" found in just about any battery, namely, one or more metals. These metals must be mined from the Earth and refined from the ores in which they occur. The process of mining is energy-intensive and produces mine tailings and other waste. The refining process also requires energy and produces pollutants. For example, metal refining often results in the release of sulfur dioxide because so many metals occur naturally as sulfides. Your Turn 8.7 gives you the opportunity to examine the details of a metal-refining process.

Smelting is the process of heating and chemically processing an ore. The smelting of sulfide ores was mentioned in the context of air quality (see Section 1.11) and acid rain (see Section 6.7).

Your Turn 8.7   Metal Refining (Smelting)

The Ni–Cd battery in your digital camera requires two metals: nickel and cadmium. These metals are smelted from sulfur–containing ores such as NiS and CdS.

a. Name three attributes that distinguish a metal from a nonmetal.
   Hint: Review Sections 1.6 and 5.6.
b. To produce elemental nickel, oxygen gas is reacted with an ore of nickel and sulfur, represented as NiS.

$$NiS(s) + O_2(g) \longrightarrow Ni(s) + SO_2(g)$$

Is Ni in the ore oxidized or reduced?
c. Write the analogous chemical equation for cadmium, and again identify the species oxidized and reduced.
d. Why is the release of SO_2 a serious problem? *Hint:* Revisit both Chapter 1 and Chapter 6.

Answer
b. NiS contains Ni^{2+}, which is reduced. This ion gains two electrons to form Ni metal.

The environmental price tag also includes the disposal of "dead" batteries. Even rechargeable batteries eventually have to be replaced because at some point the voltage drops below usable levels, and electrons no longer flow. Although the battery may be dead, the chemicals still can be hazardous. Thus communities eventually either must pay the cost of cleaning up the landfills where batteries are improperly disposed of, or they must pay to properly recycle the batteries.

Remember in Chapter 1 that we commented on the logic of prevention. It makes more sense not to dirty the air we breathe than it does to clean it up after the fact. In essence, take off your muddy boots rather than laundering the carpet! Thus we urge you to use this same logic when it comes to batteries. Companies should take responsibility—as should you—for items from the moment the natural resources used to make them were taken out of the ground to their point of ultimate "disposal." Throwing batteries that contain mercury, lead, or cadmium into the trash, ultimately into the landfill, is a poorly planned scenario. An easy way to reduce the number of batteries that wind up as trash is to switch to using rechargeable ones. Investing in a battery charger should easily pay for itself if used properly.

Another way to reduce battery waste is to think "cradle-to-cradle." The end of the life cycle of one item should dovetail with the beginning of the life cycle of another, so that everything is reused rather than added to the waste stream. If each battery served as the starting material for a new product, then the metals these batteries contain would not be lost to the landfill. This also is called "closed-loop recycling."

The economics make sense, especially when it is cheaper to extract and reuse a metal (such as from a discarded battery) than to mine new ore and refine it. With a cradle-to-cradle approach, the item to be recycled is sent to a company that pulls out the desired metal and then returns it to another manufacturer. Unfortunately, far too few batteries are recycled in this manner worldwide.

Keeping toxic materials out of the environment also makes sense. For example, the components of an automobile battery—metallic lead, lead dioxide (PbO_2), and sulfuric acid—are toxic or corrosive. Other metals commonly used in batteries, including cadmium and mercury, are equally if not more toxic. Disposing of these batteries in landfills eventually contaminates the land, the surface water, and ultimately the groundwater with these metals. In addition, the metals become lost to the manufacturing supply chain as they are too widely dispersed to effectively mine. Consider This 8.8 explores a possible future scenario if we continue along this path.

The term *cradle–to–cradle* was introduced in Section 0.4.

Lead toxicity was mentioned earlier both in the context of paint (Section 1.13) and water quality (Section 5.10).

Consider This 8.8   Could Metals Become Extinct?

In 2009, this very question was posed in an article called "Future of Metals." It was published in *Chemical & Engineering News*, the weekly magazine of the American Chemical Society.

  a. Why is it not possible for metals to become extinct, at least as such?

  b. Nonetheless, the author has a point. Explain.

  c. The authors pinpointed copper, zinc, and platinum as the currently "endangered species." Which, if any, of these metals currently are in demand for batteries?

The lead–acid battery represents one success story. Today most state laws require retailers that sell lead–acid batteries to collect them for recycling. The EPA reports that since 1988, greater than 90% of lead–acid batteries have been recycled in the United States. The next activity enables you to learn more about battery recycling.

Consider This 8.9   Battery Recycling

What can you do to keep the metals used in batteries from being lost to a landfill? The answer depends on the battery type. Search the Internet to answer the following.

  a. Which types of batteries currently are more commonly recycled: rechargeable ones or the nonrechargeable (single-use) ones?

  b. Why is recycling a Ni–Cd battery more critical than recycling an alkaline one?

  c. List some reasons why household battery-recycling programs have not been as effective as those for recycling car batteries.

Lithium (stored in oil)

Sodium (removed from oil, being cut)

Potassium (in sealed glass tube)

Rubidium (in sealed glass tube)

Figure 8.7

Selected Group 1A elements.

In the same article on the future of metals, Thomas Graedel, an industrial ecologist at Yale, points out that "Metals have limits in the same way that crude oil and clean water do." His point is well taken. If metals are to remain available for use in the future, we all need smarter battery designs that allow for efficient recycling of the metals they contain. It makes no sense for cadmium, mercury, nickel, and lead to end up in landfills. Rather, they should end up in new batteries.

There is precedent and good reason for recycling metals. Recall from Chapter 1 that catalytic converters typically contain platinum. Chemical and petroleum industries already have set protocols in place for recycling platinum catalysts. The item to be recycled is sent to a company that extracts the platinum and then returns the metal for reuse by a manufacturer. Although rechargeable batteries can and are being recycled, such is not yet the norm for single-use batteries.

Lithium is an interesting case in point. Recall from Chapter 2 that lithium is an alkali metal in Group 1A of the periodic table, just like sodium and potassium (Figure 8.7), and that Li, Na, and K all are highly reactive metals, with one outer electron. Finally, recall from Chapter 5 that these metals occur in nature as ions: Li^+, Na^+, and K^+.

However, lithium is different from other Group 1A elements in several important ways. In comparison with the atoms of sodium and potassium, those of lithium are smaller and lighter. Having less mass is an advantage when it comes to building portable batteries. And being smaller also is an advantage in that lithium ions are small enough to fit within certain types of electrode materials, in contrast to Na^+ and K^+, which may be too large. Lithium also is far less abundant in the Earth's crust than sodium and potassium, both of which are readily available. Furthermore, lithium deposits tend to be found in remote locations, such as the one shown in Figure 8.8. At present, lithium is mined primarily from salt lakes (brine lakes) that once were ancient sea beds.

The future availability of lithium is a key point for discussion. As you will see in the next section, the batteries under development for the next generation of hybrid electric cars are slated to contain lithium. The use of these batteries in millions of cars—each with about 4.5 kg (10 lb) of lithium per battery pack—may severely test

Figure 8.8
One of the world's largest lithium deposits, a salt lake in a desert area of Chile. Lithium is in the form of soluble chloride and carbonate salts, LiCl and Li_2CO_3.

our ability to supply lithium to battery manufacturers. At the moment, people are arguing over whether we will be able to do this. On one hand, the lithium on our planet appears to be present in sufficient quantity to meet our needs. On the other, only certain of the lithium deposits are of high enough quality and in accessible enough regions to be extracted economically.

 Clearly, it is in everybody's best interest to follow the key ideas in green chemistry as we manufacture batteries now and in the future. This means that we must minimize or avoid the use of toxic metals in batteries *and* use smart battery designs that enable metals in short supply to be efficiently recycled. With an eye to how batteries can be one component of a more sustainable energy picture, we now turn to the topic of hybrid vehicles.

> Check green chemistry key ideas #3 and #5 printed on the inside front cover.

8.4 | Hybrid Vehicles

As concerns grow about the cost and availability of gasoline and about the pollutants that gasoline-powered vehicles emit, more car owners are considering **hybrid electric vehicles (HEVs),** better known as "hybrids." These vehicles are propelled by a combination of a conventional gasoline engine and an electric motor run by batteries. Honda and Toyota have led the way in developing hybrids (Table 8.2). In 1999, the Honda Insight, a small two-seater, was the first sold in the United States. The Toyota Prius (Figure 8.9) became available in Japan in 1997 and then three years later in the United States. Today, other manufacturers now produce hybrid cars, SUVs, trucks, and even luxury models.

> In Latin, *prius* means "to go before."

Consider This 8.10   The NiMH Battery

As of 2010, the Prius gasoline–electric hybrid car employed two batteries, one a conventional lead–acid storage battery and the other a nickel–metal hydride (NiMH).

a. Which features of NiMH batteries make them superior to lead–acid storage batteries?
b. Search the Internet to find out what advantages newer lithium–ion batteries might offer over NiMH batteries in hybrid vehicles.

Figure 8.9
(a) A 2010 Toyota Prius, a gasoline–electric hybrid.
(b) The NiMH batteries under the back seat and in the trunk area.

(a)

(b)

In delivering about 50 miles to the gallon, the Prius burns about half the gasoline and thus emits about half of the carbon dioxide of a conventional car. It has a 1.8-L gasoline engine working together with nickel–metal hydride batteries, an electric motor, and an electric generator. The electric motor draws power from the batteries to start the car moving and to power it at low speeds. Using a process called regenerative braking, the energy of the car's motion is transferred to the alternator, which in turn charges the batteries during deceleration and braking. The gasoline engine assists the electric motor during normal driving, with the batteries boosting power when extra acceleration is needed.

Given that each gallon of gasoline burned releases about 18 pounds of CO_2 into the atmosphere, the average vehicle emits from 6 to 9 tons of CO_2 each year. Unlike other vehicle emissions, such as NO and CO, pollution control technologies currently do not reduce CO_2 emissions. Rather, we must reduce the amount of carbon dioxide either by burning less fuel *or* by burning a fuel such as H_2 that does not contain carbon. Doing the math, each increase of 5 miles per gallon a year (for example, improving from 20 to 25 miles per gallon) can reduce CO_2 emissions by about 18 tons over a vehicle's lifetime. This calculation assumes a vehicle lifetime of 200,000 miles, which results in burning about 2000 fewer gallons of gasoline by increasing the fuel efficiency by 5 miles per gallon.

Kinetic energy was first introduced in Section 4.1.

Many hybrids, unlike conventional gasoline–powered cars, deliver better mileage in city driving than at highway speeds.

Table 8.2	Fuel Economy Leaders for the 2010 Model Year	
Rank	Manufacturer/Model	Miles per Gallon (city/highway)
1	Toyota Prius (hybrid)	51/48
2	Ford Fusion Hybrid FWD Mercury Milan Hybrid FWD	41/36
3	Honda Civic Hybrid	40/45
4	Honda Insight (hybrid)	40/43
5	Lexus HS250h (hybrid)	35/34

Source: U.S. EPA.

Skeptical Chemist 8.11   Yes, Tons of CO_2!

Could an automobile really emit 7 tons of carbon dioxide in a year? Do a calculation to prove or disprove this. State all the assumptions that you make.

Automobile manufacturers now provide more than one option for fuel-efficient, low-emission vehicles, allowing customers to choose the option that best meets their transportation needs. One such option is a **plug-in hybrid electric vehicle (PHEV)**. These vehicles use rechargeable batteries for short daily commutes to run an electric motor and switch to a combustion engine to travel longer distances. The electric energy provided by the battery decreases the direct emissions out the tailpipe, a major selling point. In addition, proponents argue that PHEVs would cost 2–4¢/mile to operate, a bargain compared with the 8–20¢/mile cost of a regular car. However, according to a 2009 study by the U.S. National Research Council, PHEVs are still a few decades away from mass introduction into the U.S. automobile market.

In 2010, the cost to manufacture a plug-in hybrid was estimated at about $18,000 more than that of an equivalent gasoline-powered vehicle. The larger lithium-ion batteries were one factor in driving up the price tag. To recoup the upfront cost of a PHEV, given the current price of gasoline it would take several decades before the saving in fuel cost, a mile driven on electricity versus a mile driven on gasoline, could be seen. As a result, PHEVs are not expected to be players in reducing gasoline consumption or carbon emissions until the energy picture changes. However, nearly every major automotive manufacturer currently has major research and development teams working on PHEVs. Most of these companies agree that in the future, plug-in electric cars could easily number in the millions on U.S. city streets, provided that battery technologies continue to improve and suitable economic incentives are developed. Even so, the numbers are daunting. Assuming that the number of vehicles continues to increase, these PHEVs would still be outnumbered by the 300 million cars that we expect to find on U.S. highways a few decades from now.

With such advantages offered by both HEVs and PHEVs, has the United States turned into a hybrid nation? The answer most certainly is no. Although the annual sales of HEVs surged in 2012 to over 380,000 vehicles, this is a mere drop in the fuel economy bucket. In each of the past five years, U.S. customers purchased roughly 13 million cars, vans, SUVs, and light pickup trucks. Although the United States has the highest count of HEVs on its roads, these vehicles represent only 2–3% of the total. In contrast, new car sales in Japan are over 20% HEVs. As of 2012, over 4.5 million hybrid vehicles had been sold worldwide, including 2.2 million in the United States and 1.5 million in Japan.

Consider This 8.12   Electric Vehicles

A car totally powered by electricity has been in the human imagination, on the drawing boards, and even in a few automobile showrooms during the past decade.

a. List three advantages that an electric vehicle (EV) would have over an HEV or a PHEV.
b. Give three reasons why EVs are not yet the norm today.
c. Search the Internet to locate the latest Fuel Economy Guide. How prominent are EVs in this report?

At this point, a major limitation to EV, HEV, and PHEV development is in the battery technology and in the economics of battery development and cost of the vehicle. It remains to be seen how hybrid vehicles will affect your mode of transportation. In the next section, we examine another way in which we might power our vehicles, hydrogen fuel cells.

8.5 | Fuel Cells: The Basics

With fuel cells, we take another step on our journey to find fuels that release high amounts of energy and low amounts of pollutants. In Chapter 4, we compared the energy released, gram for gram, in the combustion of coal, hydrocarbons, and other combustible fuels. As we saw, methane was clearly the winner. Assuming the combustion products to be $CO_2(g)$ and $H_2O(g)$, the heats of combustion of coal (anthracite or bituminous) and *n*-octane, $C_8H_{18}(l)$, (a major component in gasoline) are 30 and 45 kJ per gram of fuel, respectively. In comparison, the heat of combustion of methane is 50 kJ/g.

However, when paired against methane, hydrogen easily wins the competition, as you can see from this equation.

$$H_2(g) + 1/2\, O_2(g) \longrightarrow H_2O(g) + 249 \text{ kJ} \qquad \textbf{[8.13]}$$

In equation 8.13, the heat of combustion, 249 kJ, is per mole of H_2. This is equivalent to 124.5 kJ per gram of H_2.

Therefore, hydrogen releases almost three times as much energy as methane per gram when burned! In addition to its superior energy production, using hydrogen raises another tantalizing prospect—the powering of motor vehicles with a fuel that would produce only water vapor as a product. Neither CO nor CO_2 would be produced, although depending on the engine conditions and temperatures, some NO conceivably could form.

Skeptical Chemist 8.13   Hydrogen Versus Methane

Is hydrogen really that good of a fuel? Use the bond energy values from Table 4.4 to find out. Clearly show how you performed your calculation, noting any assumptions you needed to make. Does the value you calculated match that of equation 8.13?

Hint: You'll find most of the work done for you in Section 4.6, except that the calculation is done on a mole basis.

As with other flammable fuel sources, like methane or gasoline, when hydrogen is directly mixed with oxygen, a mere spark can set off an explosion. With its 7 million cubic feet of hydrogen gas, the Hindenburg was to airspace as the Titanic was to the high seas. When the air ship caught fire in 1937 and plunged its passengers and crew to their deaths, hydrogen was indelibly stamped in our consciousness as an explosive fuel.

But suppose someone were to suggest a way to combine H_2 and O_2 to form H_2O without the hazards of combustion. Furthermore, let's suppose that this person also claimed that the reaction could be carried out with no direct contact between the hydrogen and the oxygen. The Skeptical Chemist might well dismiss such assertions as sheer nonsense—an outright impossibility. And yet, the operation of a fuel cell is a case in point. A **fuel cell** is an electrochemical cell that produces electricity by converting the chemical energy of a fuel directly into electricity without burning the fuel. William Grove, an English physicist, invented fuel cells in 1839. However, these cells remained a mere curiosity until the dawn of the Space Age. It was only in the 1980s, when the U.S. Space Shuttle carried three sets of 32 cells fueled with hydrogen, that fuel cells came into public view. The electricity generated by these cells powered the lights, motors, and computers onboard the shuttle.

Unlike conventional batteries such as those in flashlights, under the hood of a car, or powering your laptop computers, fuel cells operate on an external supply of fuel that is electrochemically oxidized inside the fuel cell. They also require an external supply of oxygen gas or other "oxidant" material to accept the electrons that are lost by the fuel. With the supply of fuel and oxidant continually being replenished, these "flow batteries" produce electricity. They do not run down or need to be recharged in the same manner as conventional batteries do. Check out the location of the hydrogen fuel supply in Figure 8.10, a schematic drawing of a fuel cell vehicle (FCV). The hydrogen tanks are pressurized up to 5000 pounds/inch^2 (psi). FCVs can travel up to 200 miles before needing to be refueled.

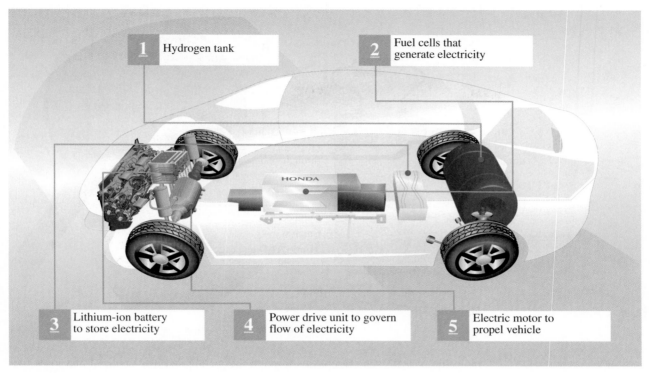

Figure 8.10

Schematic of Honda FCX, powered by fuel cells, that shows the location of the fuel cell, hydrogen storage tank, and lithium–ion storage battery.

Source: American Honda Motor Company.

What may surprise you about fuel cells is that the chemicals being oxidized and reduced are physically separated, that is, they do not come in direct contact with each other. Oxidation still occurs at the anode and reduction at the cathode. However, instead of the anode *itself* being the source from which electrons are released, the anode is merely an electric conductor that provides a physical location in the cell at which the oxidation of the fuel takes place. Similarly, the cathode is an electric conductor where reduction of the oxygen takes place and does not enter into the reaction itself.

The electrolyte that separates the anode from the cathode serves the same purpose as in a traditional electrochemical cell, that is, to allow the flow of ions and hence the flow of charge. The earliest commercially available fuel cells used a strong corrosive acid, H_3PO_4, as an electrolyte. As a result, these fuel cells were closed systems that fully contained the liquid, not unlike the closed system of a conventional alkaline battery. Current designs of fuel cells are open systems that require a continued flow of fuel and oxidant, adding complexity and cost.

Today, fuel cells based on different electrolyte materials have been developed for a variety of applications. One type incorporates a solid polymer electrolyte separating the reactants. We use this type to explain the general operation of fuel cells. The polymer electrolyte membrane, also called a proton exchange membrane (PEM), is permeable to H^+ ions and is coated on both sides with a platinum-based catalyst. These electrolytes operate at reasonably low temperatures, typically from 70 °C to 90 °C, and transfer electrons to rapidly provide electric power. As a result, PEM fuel cells currently are popular with automakers for new fuel cell prototype vehicles and for personal consumer applications. A typical design is shown in Figure 8.11.

In fuel cells hydrogen is used as the fuel in conjunction with oxygen; the oxidation and reduction half-reactions are represented by equations 8.14 and 8.15. As a

Look for more about polymers in Chapter 9.

The H^+ ion is a proton, the simplest cation (Section 6.1).

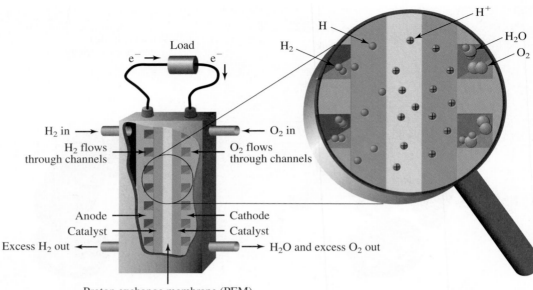

Figure 8.11

A PEM fuel cell in which H_2 and O_2 combine to form water without combustion.

molecule of hydrogen (H_2) passes through the membrane, it is oxidized and loses two electrons to form two hydrogen ions.

oxidation half-reaction (anode): $H_2(g) \longrightarrow 2\,H^+(aq) + 2\,e^-$ **[8.14]**

The hydrogen ions, H^+, flow through the proton exchange membrane and combine with oxygen (O_2). At the same time, they combine with two electrons to form water.

reduction half-reaction (cathode):

$$^{1}/_{2}\,O_2(g) + 2\,H^+(aq) + 2\,e^- \longrightarrow H_2O(g)$$ **[8.15]**

As with galvanic cells, the overall cell equation is the sum of the two half-reactions.

$$H_2(g) + {}^{1}/_{2}\,O_2(g) + 2\,H^+(aq) + 2\,e^- \longrightarrow 2\,H^+(aq) + H_2O(g) + 2\,e^-$$ **[8.16]**

The 2 e^- and 2 H^+ appearing on both sides of the arrow can be cancelled.

overall cell equation (sum of the two half-reactions):

$$H_2(g) + {}^{1}/_{2}\,O_2(g) \longrightarrow H_2O(g)$$ **[8.17]**

In Chapters 4 and 7, we showed this chemical equation with whole–number coefficients as $2\,H_2(g) + O_2(g) \rightarrow 2\,H_2O(g)$.

The electrons flowing from the anode to the cathode of a fuel cell move through an external circuit to do work, which is the whole point of the device. Thus, in a fuel cell, a transfer of electrons occurs from H_2 to O_2. This occurs with no flame, with relatively little heat, and without producing any light. Because of these characteristics, the reaction is not classed as combustion. If only the power-producing step is considered (admittedly omitting other parts of the energy picture), hydrogen fuel cells are judged to be a more environmentally friendly way to produce electricity than are coal-fired or nuclear power plants. No carbon-containing greenhouse gases are produced, no air pollutants are emitted, and no spent nuclear fuel needs to be disposed of. Water is the only chemical product if hydrogen is the fuel, an added benefit for the astronauts on the Space Shuttle, who relied on it as their source of water while in space.

Note that it *requires* energy to produce H_2 from compounds containing hydrogen.

The overall cell equation (see equation 8.17) releases 249 kJ of energy per mole of water formed. But instead of liberating most of this energy in the form of heat, the fuel cell converts 45–55% of it to electric energy. This direct production of electricity eliminates the inefficiencies associated with using heat to do work to produce electricity. Internal combustion engines are only 20–30% efficient in deriving energy from fossil fuels. Table 8.3 shows a comparison of fuel combustion with fuel cell technology.

Table 8.3	Combustion Versus Hydrogen Fuel Cell Technology			
Process	Fuel	Oxidant	Products	Other Considerations
combustion	hydrocarbons, alcohols, H_2, wood, etc.	O_2 from air	H_2O, CO/CO_2, heat, light, and possibly even sound	rapid process, flame present, lower efficiency, most useful for producing heat
hydrogen fuel cell	H_2	O_2 from air	H_2O, electricity, and some heat	slower process, no flame, quiet, higher efficiency, most useful for generating electricity

ⓨ Consider This 8.14   Revisiting the PEM Fuel Cell

Spend time exploring the animations of a PEM fuel cell at Figures Alive!. Then answer these questions.

a. How is a fuel cell different from other batteries described earlier in this chapter?
b. Can a PEM fuel cell be recharged? Explain.
c. Why is the combination of H_2 and O_2 in a fuel cell not classified as combustion? Explain.

Just as batteries, motors, and electric generators come in different sizes and types, so do fuel cells. Though the fuels and principles of operation are essentially the same, different electrolytes give each type of fuel cell unique characteristics that are appropriate for a given application. Many companies are experimenting with fuel cell vehicles. Like EVs, fuel cell vehicles (FCVs) are powered by electric motors. But they differ in that FCVs create their own electricity, whereas EVs draw electricity from an external source, storing that energy in an onboard battery.

An alternative to hydrogen gas is to use a hydrogen-rich fuel such as methanol or natural gas. These fuels must be converted into hydrogen gas by a reformer. This device uses heat, pressure, and catalysts to run a chemical reaction that yields hydrogen as one of the products (Figure 8.12). As liquid fuels, methanol and ethanol could be pumped at conventional gas stations. However, the onboard reformers add cost and maintenance demands to the vehicle. They also emit greenhouse gases and other air pollutants generated in the reforming process.

Section 4.7 discussed reforming in a different context, that of reforming n–octane to produce iso–octane, an isomer that burns more smoothly.

As a source of electricity, fuel cells have a broad range of applications. Hospitals, airports, banks, police stations, and military installations all now make use of them for standby and backup power applications. Fuel cells are a form of **distributed generation,** that is, they generate electricity on-site right where it is used, avoiding the losses of energy that occur over long electric transmission lines. As such, they serve as an alternative to central electric utility power plants. Also under development is the powering of portable electronic devices such as cell phones and laptop computers with

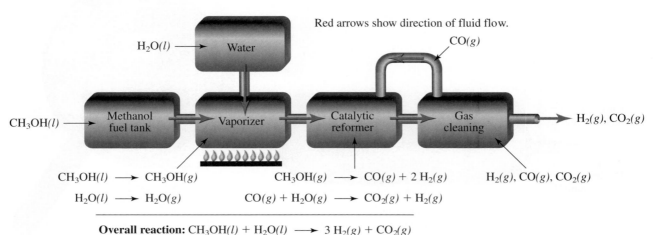

Figure 8.12
Hydrogen obtained from methanol via a reforming process.

miniature fuel cells. Such devices offer an advantage over batteries because they would not require time-consuming electric recharging but rather could be refueled by simply swapping out or refilling a fuel cartridge.

Before our societies can fully benefit from hydrogen fuel cell technologies, scientists and engineers need to meet several technological challenges. The first is to store, transport, and eventually distribute hydrogen to the consumer. A second challenge is to produce enough hydrogen to meet the projected demand. The next section examines both of these challenges in more depth.

8.6 | Hydrogen for Fuel Cell Vehicles

Imagine needing to refuel your fuel cell vehicle with hydrogen at a "gas station." Currently, refueling stations are few and far between. As of 2013, the U.S. Department of Energy reported about 60 fueling stations were approved for operation in the United States. An FCV can travel about 300 miles before refueling, which is certainly competitive with mileage achieved with a conventional gasoline-fueled engine.

Since hydrogen is a gas, it requires a different system for storage and transfer from that used for gasoline. As a gas, hydrogen also takes up a lot of space. For example, at sea level and room temperature, H_2 occupies a volume of about 11 L (almost 4 gal) per gram! In order to avoid having an enormous fuel tank, your vehicle must store hydrogen in a gas cylinder under pressure. To replenish the hydrogen in this cylinder, you must refuel with an airtight connection through a hose that can withstand higher pressures, as shown in Figure 8.13. Although the refueling process does require a different system than a gasoline pump used for a gasoline-powered vehicle, the process is similar in that there is a nozzle and you squeeze a trigger to start the flow of hydrogen.

Instead of compressing H_2 into metal cylinders, which in the past have been heavy and somewhat unwieldy, chemical engineers are investigating other methods for storing and transporting H_2 that could reduce space and the need for high-pressure gas compression. One promising technology is that some compounds, if subjected to hydrogen under high pressure, can absorb the hydrogen molecules like a sponge absorbs water. Then, by either reducing the hydrogen pressure or increasing the temperature, the H_2 can be re-released on demand (Figure 8.14). For example, metal hydrides can perform

By way of comparison, 12 L of gasoline has a mass of 9 kg.

Figure 8.13

Refueling a Honda FCX Clarity, a hydrogen–powered vehicle.

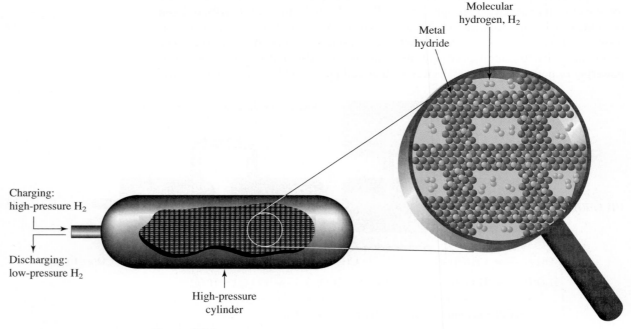

Figure 8.14

Absorption and release of hydrogen from a metal hydride.

in this way. Lithium hydride, LiH, is one example. A chemical formula of LiH may appear strange to you and for good reason. The problem is not the lithium ion (Li^+), as this should be an old friend by now. Rather, it is the hydride ion, H^-, a chemical species that differs markedly from the hydrogen ion, H^+. The hydride ion, with two electrons instead of one for neutral hydrogen, plays an important role in battery chemistry. Unlike H^+, the hydride ion is not stable in aqueous solution and hence we had no need to mention it earlier in our chapter on water chemistry.

Metal hydride storage systems are ideally suited for PEM fuel cells that require high-purity hydrogen. Because metal hydrides are selective and absorb only hydrogen and not larger gas molecules such as CO, CO_2, or O_2, they act simultaneously as a storage material and a way of filtering out other gases. New storage technologies must meet the challenge of taking up less vehicle space needed for people and cargo while allowing designers to put more fuel on board for longer-range travel.

A second challenge is the projected demand for hydrogen as a fuel. Where is all the hydrogen going to come from? On one hand, things look promising because hydrogen is the most plentiful element in the universe. Over 93% of all atoms are hydrogen atoms! Although hydrogen is not nearly this abundant on Earth, still there is an immense supply of the element. On the other hand, essentially all of the hydrogen on our planet is in some form other than H_2. Hydrogen gas is too reactive to exist for long in this form and so primarily is found in its oxidized form of H_2O, better known as water. Therefore, to obtain hydrogen for use as a fuel, we must form it from water or other hydrogen-containing compounds, a process that requires energy.

Fossil fuels, including natural gas and coal, as hydrocarbons, are one possible source of hydrogen. In particular, methane, the major component of natural gas, currently is the chief source of hydrogen. Hydrogen can be produced from CH_4 via an endothermic reaction with steam.

$$165 \text{ kJ} + CH_4(g) + 2\,H_2O(g) \longrightarrow 4\,H_2(g) + CO_2(g) \qquad \textbf{[8.18]}$$

Another possible way of producing hydrogen from methane is via a reaction with carbon dioxide.

$$247 \text{ kJ} + CO_2(g) + CH_4(g) \longrightarrow 2\,H_2(g) + 2\,CO(g) \qquad \textbf{[8.19]}$$

You can see the downside of this reaction—it requires a significant energy input. But the Hydrogen Energy Corporation now uses a solar mirror array that can focus sunlight to heat the reactants, CO_2 and CH_4. Not only can this technology produce hydrogen, but it can also do so from a waste gas generated by a landfill.

Your Turn 8.15   Back to Bond Energies

a. Use the average bond energy values in Table 4.4 to check the energy required by the reactions in equations 8.18 and 8.19. Show your work.
b. Are the chemical reactions endothermic or exothermic?
c. Did the values you calculated in part **a** match the values given in the equations? Explain.
Hint: Revisit Section 4.6.

Answer

a. In equation 8.18, 4 mol of C–H bonds and 4 mol of O–H bonds are broken.

= 4 mol (416 kJ/mol) + 4 mol (467 kJ/mol)
= 1664 kJ + 1868 kJ
= 3532 kJ

In equation 8.18, 4 mol of H–H bonds and 2 mol of C=O bonds are formed.

= 4 mol (436 kJ/mol) + 2 mol (803 kJ/mol)
= 1744 kJ + 1606 kJ
= 3350 kJ

For the overall reaction, (+3532 kJ) + (−3350 kJ) = 182 kJ.
A similar calculation for equation 8.19 gives 252 kJ.

Still, each of the reactions just described contains a major flaw; either carbon dioxide or carbon monoxide is produced. Is there another source of hydrogen around? In Jules Verne's 1874 novel, *Mysterious Island,* a shipwrecked engineer speculates about the energy resource that will be used when the world's coal supply has been used up. "Water," the engineer declares, "I believe that water will one day be employed as fuel, that hydrogen and oxygen which constitute it, used singly or together, will furnish an inexhaustible source of heat and light."

Is this simply science fiction, or is it energetically and economically feasible to break water into its elemental components? To assess the credibility of the claim by Verne's engineer, we need to examine the energy requirements of this chemical reaction. In Section 8.4, we noted that the formation of 1 mol of water from hydrogen and oxygen releases 249 kJ of energy (see equation 8.13). An identical quantity of energy must be absorbed to reverse the reaction to produce hydrogen.

$$249 \text{ kJ} + H_2O(g) \longrightarrow H_2(g) + 1/2 \, O_2(g) \qquad \textbf{[8.20]}$$

The most convenient method of decomposing water into hydrogen and oxygen is by **electrolysis,** the process of passing a direct current of electricity of sufficient voltage through water to decompose it into H_2 and O_2 (Figure 8.15). This process takes place in an **electrolytic cell,** a type of electrochemical cell in which electrical energy is converted to chemical energy. An electrolytic cell is the opposite of a galvanic cell, where chemical energy is converted to electric energy. When water is electrolyzed in an electrolytic cell, the volume of hydrogen generated is twice that of the oxygen as shown in equation 8.20. This suggests that a water molecule contains twice as many hydrogen atoms as oxygen atoms, testimony to the formula H_2O.

Water electrolysis requires about half the energy input per mole of H_2 than does using methane to produce hydrogen and produces no CO_2 (see equation 8.19). From a thermodynamic point of view, it takes energy to split water into oxygen and hydrogen. Figure 8.16 shows the energy differences involved.

Of course, the question remains: How will the electricity be generated for large-scale electrolysis? Most electricity in the United States is produced by burning fossil fuels in conventional power plants. If we only had to contend with the first law of thermodynamics, the best we could possibly achieve would be to burn an amount of fossil fuel equal in energy content to the hydrogen produced in electrolysis. But we must also deal with the consequences of the second law of thermodynamics. Because

Revisit Sections 4.1 and 4.2 for more about the first and second laws of thermodynamics.

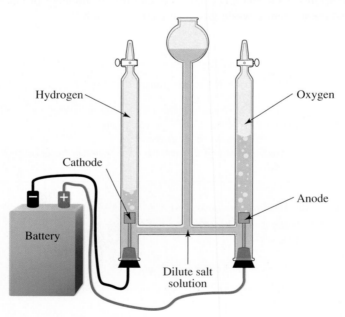

Figure 8.15

Electrolysis of water.

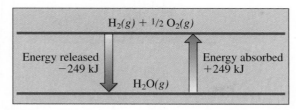

Figure 8.16
Energy differences in the hydrogen–oxygen–water system.

of the inherent and inescapable inefficiency associated with transforming heat into work, the maximum possible efficiency of an electric power plant is 63%. When we add the additional energy losses caused by friction, incomplete heat transfer, and transmission over power lines, it would require at least twice as much energy to produce the hydrogen than we could obtain from its combustion. This is comparable to buying eggs for 10¢ each and selling them for 5¢, which is no way to do business.

Another way to produce hydrogen is to use heat energy to decompose water. Simply heating water to decompose it thermally into H_2 and O_2 is not commercially promising. To obtain reasonable yields of hydrogen and oxygen, temperatures of over 5000 °C are required. To attain such temperatures is not only extremely difficult, but also requires enormous amounts of energy—at least as much as is released when the hydrogen burns. Thus, we have again reached a point where we are investing a great deal of time, effort, money, and energy to generate a quantity of hydrogen that, at best, returns only as much energy as we invested. In practice, a good deal less energy results.

Instead of burning fossil fuel to generate the enormous amount of heat needed to split water, another option is to use a sustainable source of energy, the radiant energy of the Sun. Photons of visible light have enough energy to split water. Unfortunately, water doesn't absorb light at these wavelengths (which is why water is colorless). New materials are being designed to use the power of the Sun to help drive the splitting of water. One photoelectrochemical cell, or a galvanic cell, is constructed containing a Pt cathode and an anode covered with nanoparticles of TiO_2 and coated with dye molecules. The dye molecules are tuned to absorb light in the most intense part of the solar spectrum. When submerged in an aqueous electrolyte solution and exposed to light, some of the electrons in the dye are promoted to higher energy states, high enough that they are transferred quickly to the TiO_2. Once there, the electrons can leave the electrode and move through an electric circuit (Figure 8.17).

The loss of electrons, as you have learned, corresponds to oxidation, and in this case the oxygen in water can be oxidized to O_2. After passing through the external circuit, the electrons arrive at the platinum cathode where they reduce hydrogen ions to H_2. Efficiencies of modern devices are less than 10% but are expected to increase.

Figure 2.9 shows UV radiation breaking bonds within molecules.

Consider This 8.16   Light That Splits Water

The energy required for equation 8.20 corresponds to a wavelength of 420 nm.

a. Which region of the electromagnetic spectrum does this fall in?
   Hint: Refer to Figure 2.7.
b. It is advantageous to use light energy directly, as opposed to the heat energy of the Sun to split water. Explain.

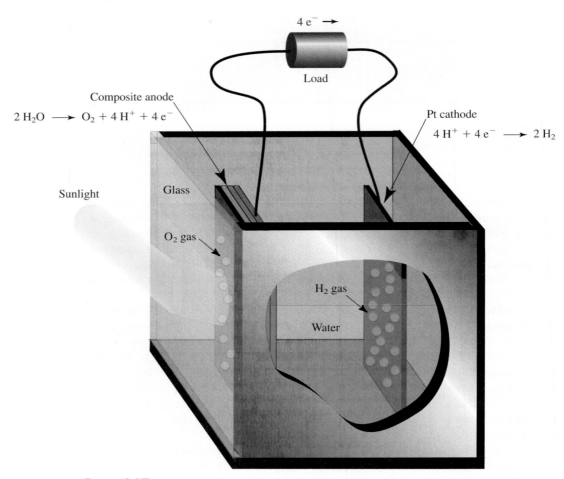

$$4\,e^- \rightarrow$$

Load

Composite anode

$$2\,H_2O \longrightarrow O_2 + 4\,H^+ + 4\,e^-$$

Pt cathode

$$4\,H^+ + 4\,e^- \longrightarrow 2\,H_2$$

Sunlight

Glass

O_2 gas

H_2 gas

Water

Figure 8.17
A schematic diagram of a photoelectrochemical cell for splitting water.

Figure 8.18
Some kinds of algae can produce hydrogen via photosynthesis.

In a vividly green example of green chemistry, scientists are looking to biological organisms to produce hydrogen. Certain species of unicellular green algae produce hydrogen gas during photosynthesis (Figure 8.18). The advantage here is that sunlight provides the energy, rather than fossil fuel combustion. At present, the efficiency of the process is far too low to be commercially viable. However, having new strains of algae that are more efficient in utilizing sunlight could tip the economic balance. A current area of research is to genetically engineer such types of algae—both a promising and a controversial area of inquiry.

Green plants, including algae, harness the energy of the Sun in order to grow and reproduce. However, we humans are not nearly as efficient in doing so as plants. In the next section, we turn to the successful technology we have developed to generate electricity from sunlight—photovoltaics—perhaps better known as "solar cells."

8.7 | Photovoltaic Cells: The Basics

It surely would make sense to take advantage of sunlight, a renewable energy source. The rays of our Sun hit the Earth every hour with enough energy to meet the world's energy demand for an entire year! Currently, however, less than 1% of the electric power generated in the United States comes directly from solar energy. Why does solar energy currently account for such a small part of the larger energy picture?

Although remarkable amounts of sunshine hit the Earth daily, the rays do not strike any one site on the planet for 24 hours a day, 365 days a year. Furthermore, some parts of the planet receive too low an intensity of light to be practical for solar

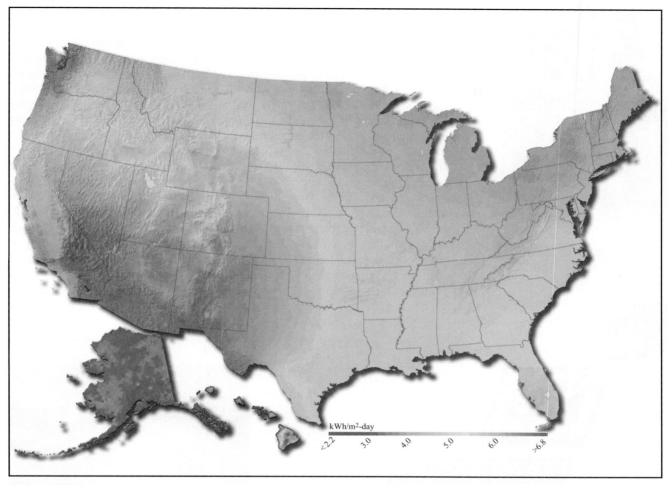

Figure 8.19

The average amount of daily solar energy received by a fixed photovoltaic panel oriented due south.

Source: Billy Roberts, National Renewable Energy Laboratory (NREL) for the U.S. Department of Energy, 2008.

collecting. The differences arise because of the geographical location and because of local factors such as cloud cover, aerosols, smog, and haze. For example, examine the map shown in Figure 8.19. The data in the figure are reported in kilowatt-hours (kWh, a unit of energy) per square meter per day for a flat-panel solar collector that is stationary. The next activity helps you explore the differences in daily solar energy over a calendar year.

1 kWh = 3,600,000 joules

The energy values in Figure 8.19 would be higher if the panels tracked the path of the Sun, rather than being stationary.

Consider This 8.17   Solar Maps

Thanks to a website provided by the U.S. National Renewable Energy Laboratory, you can view solar maps for different parts of the United States.

a. Select a state of your choice and view the data for each month of the year. What do you notice about how energy varies throughout the year?

b. It should come as no surprise that California, Arizona, New Mexico, and Texas lead the United States in average annual solar radiation. Why do some parts of these states have higher values than others?

The challenge, then, is to locate the areas in which the incident average solar energy is high and to collect this energy in sufficient quantities to produce electricity. One possibility is to convert sunlight *directly* into electricity, the topic of this section.

Figure 8.20

Photovoltaic (solar) cells are used to improve security, enhance safety, and direct pedestrians and vehicles.

Another is to trap the heat generated from solar radiation, a topic to be addressed in the next section.

One way to tap into the Sun's energy is to use a **photovoltaic cell (PV),** a device that converts light energy directly to electric energy, sometimes called a solar cell. It takes only a few PV cells to produce enough electricity to power your calculator or digital watch. Other common uses of photovoltaic cells include communication satellites, highway signs, security and safety lighting (Figure 8.20), automobile recharging stations, and navigational buoys. Cost savings can be substantial. For example, using solar cells rather than batteries in navigational buoys saves the U.S. Coast Guard several million dollars annually through reduced maintenance and repair.

If more power is required, PV cells can be combined into modules or arrays to make up solar panels, as shown in Figure 8.21. Many people today power their homes and businesses with solar PV systems. Depending on the size of a home, it may use a dozen or more solar panels for power. These panels are usually mounted facing due south. Installing them on a system that rotates to track the Sun's path, thus maximizing their exposure to sunlight, optimizes the efficiency, but has a higher initial cost. For electric utility or industrial applications, hundreds of solar arrays are interconnected to form a large-scale PV system, such as the one shown in a field in Bavaria, Germany (see Figure 8.21).

How does a photovoltaic cell generate electricity? The answer lies in the behavior of the electrons in the cell material. When light shines onto a PV cell, it may pass right

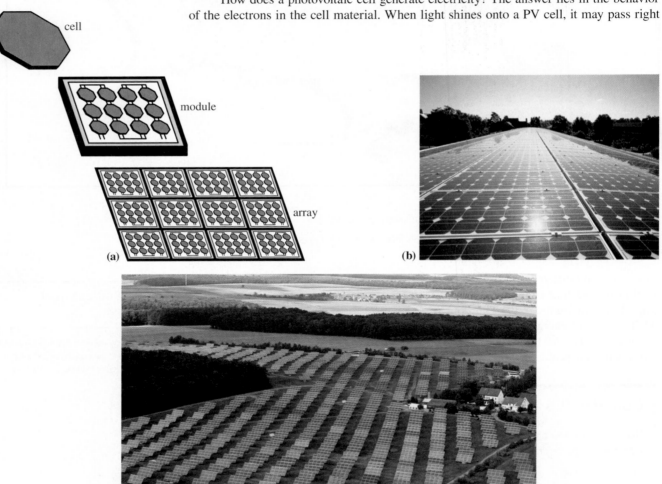

Figure 8.21

(a) Arrangement of photovoltaic cells used to make a module and an array. **(b)** A silicon solar array installed on a roof. **(c)** An aerial view of the Solarpark Gut Erlasee in Bavaria, Germany. At peak capacity, it can generate 12 MW. A typical nuclear power plant generates 1000 MW of electricity.

Source: NREL.

through the cell, be reflected, or be absorbed. If absorbed, the energy may cause an excitation of the electrons in the atoms of the cell. These excited electrons escape from their normal positions in the cell material and become part of an electric current.

Only certain materials behave this way in the presence of light. Photovoltaic cells are made from a class of materials called **semiconductors,** materials that have a limited capacity of conducting an electric current. Most semiconductors are made from a crystalline form of silicon, a metalloid. To induce a voltage in a PV cell, two layers of semiconducting materials are placed in direct contact. An ***n*-type semiconductor** is a layer with an abundance of electrons. The ***p*-type semiconductor** is the other layer with a deficit of electrons, sometimes referred to as "holes". In order to generate an electric current, the light hitting the PV cell must have enough energy to set the electrons in motion from the *n*-type side to the *p*-type side through the electric circuit. The transfer of electrons generates a current of electricity that can be intercepted to do all the things electricity does, including being stored in batteries for later use. As long as the cell is exposed to light, the current continues to flow, powered only by solar energy.

The element silicon was one of the first semiconducting materials developed for use in computers and in PV cells. In fact, many of the high-tech businesses that developed semiconductors were clustered in California's "Silicon Valley." A crystal of silicon consists of an array of silicon atoms, each bonded to four other atoms by means of shared pairs of electrons (Figure 8.22a). These shared electrons are normally fixed in the bonds and unable to move through the crystal. Consequently, silicon is not a very good electric conductor under ordinary circumstances. However, if a valence electron absorbs sufficient energy, it can be excited and released from its bonding position (Figure 8.22b). Once freed, the electron can move throughout the crystal lattice, making the silicon an electric conductor.

In actuality, pure silicon semiconductors do not allow an electric current to flow unless they are doped. **Doping** is a process of intentionally adding small amounts of other elements, "dopants" (or sometimes called impurities), to pure silicon. These dopants are chosen for their ability to facilitate the transfer of electrons. For example, about 1 ppm of gallium (Ga) or arsenic (As) is often introduced into the silicon. These two elements and others from the same groups on the periodic table are used because their atoms differ from silicon by a single outer electron. Silicon has four electrons in its outer energy level, gallium has three, and arsenic has five. Thus, when an atom of As is introduced in place of Si in the silicon lattice, an extra electron is added. The replacement of a Si atom with a Ga atom means that the crystal is now one electron "short." Figure 8.23 illustrates doped *n*- and *p*-type semiconductors. Both types of doping increase the electric conductivity of silicon because electrons can now move from an electron-rich to an electron-deficient environment.

In 1839, A. E. Becquerel, a French physicist, discovered the process of using sunlight to produce electricity in a solid material.

Conductivity in aqueous ionic solution was discussed in Section 5.6. Metalloids (semimetals) were introduced in Section 1.6.

At most, an individual solar cell produces 0.5 V.

A crystalline structure has a regular repeating array of atoms or ions, as shown in Figure 5.18 for NaCl.

Ga is in Group 3A.
Si is in Group 4A.
As is in Group 5A.

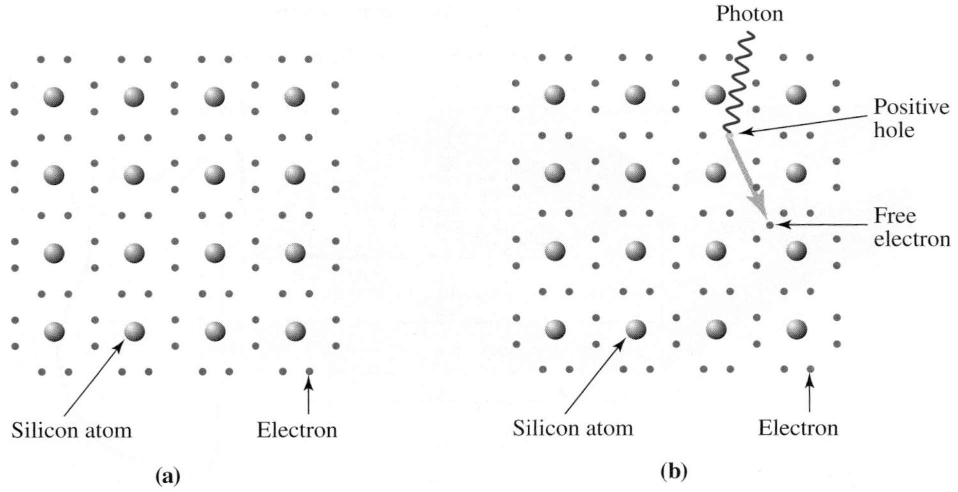

Figure 8.22

(a) Schematic of bonding in silicon. (b) Photon–induced release of a bonding electron in a silicon semiconductor.

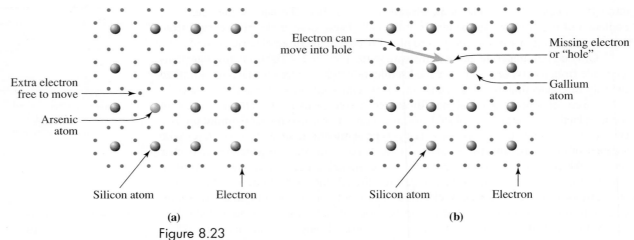

Figure 8.23

(a) An arsenic–doped *n*–type silicon semiconductor. (b) A gallium–doped *p*–type silicon semiconductor.

Your Turn 8.18   Other Dopants

Some solar cell designs use phosphorus and boron to dope silicon crystals.

a. Which will form an *n*–type semiconductor? Explain your reasoning.
b. Which will form a *p*–type semiconductor? Explain your reasoning.

A photovoltaic cell typically includes multiple layers of doped *n*- and *p*-type semiconductors in close contact (Figure 8.24). The *p*–*n* junctions not only make possible the conduction of electricity but also ensure that the current flows in a specific direction through the cell. Only photons with enough energy can knock electrons free from the dopants. These electrons then become part of the electric circuit. For a PV cell to convert as much sunlight as possible into electricity, the semiconductors must be constructed in such a way to make the best use of the photon's energy. If not, the energy of the Sun is lost as heat or not trapped at all.

The fabrication of photovoltaic cells poses some significant challenges. The first is that although silicon is the second most abundant element in Earth's crust, it is most frequently found combined with oxygen as silicon dioxide, SiO_2. You know this material by its common name, sand, or more correctly as quartz sand. The good news is

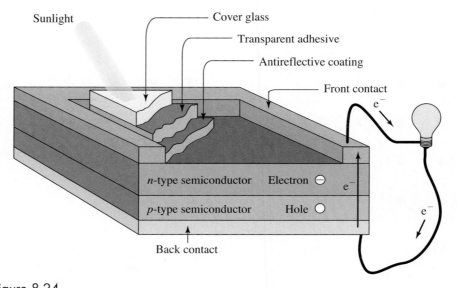

Figure 8.24

Schematic diagram of one layer of a solar cell showing the *n*–type and *p*–type semiconductors.

that the starting material from which silicon is extracted is cheap and abundant. The not-so-good news is that processes to extract and purify silicon are expensive. Many of the early PV cell designs required ultrapure 99.999% silicon.

A second challenge is that the direct conversion of sunlight into electricity is not very efficient. A photovoltaic cell could, in principle, transform up to 31% of the radiant energy to which it is sensitive into electricity. However, some of the radiant energy is reflected by the cell or absorbed to produce heat instead of an electric current. Typically, a commercial solar cell now has an efficiency of only 15%, but even this is a significant increase over the first solar cells built in the 1950s, which had efficiencies of less than 4%. In Chapter 4, we lamented the 35–50% efficiency of converting heat to work in a conventional power plant. It might seem that we should be even more distressed at the lower limits that can be achieved by photovoltaics. Remember, however, that the first use of solar cells was to provide electricity in NASA spacecraft. For that application, the intensity of radiation was so high that low efficiency was not a serious limitation and costs were not of paramount concern. For commercial use on Earth, costs and efficiency are issues. Our Sun is an essentially unlimited energy source, and converting its energy to electricity, even inefficiently, is free from many of the environmental problems associated with burning fossil fuels or storing spent fuel from nuclear fission. These considerations add impetus to research and development of solar cells.

One approach to increasing commercial viability is to replace crystalline silicon with the noncrystalline form of the element. Photons are more efficiently absorbed by less highly ordered Si atoms, a phenomenon that permits reducing the thickness of the silicon semiconductor to 1/60th or less of its former value. The cost of materials is thus significantly reduced.

Other researchers are developing multilayer solar cells. By alternating thin layers of p-type and n-type doped silicon, each electron has only a short distance to travel to reach the next p–n junction. This lowers the internal resistance within the cell and raises the efficiency of the cells. Maximum theoretically predicted efficiencies could improve to 50% for 2 junctions, to 56% for 3 junctions, and to 72% for 36 junctions. As of 2007, the maximum efficiency actually demonstrated with a multijunction solar cell was 40.7%. Figure 8.25 gives a sense of just how thin these layers actually are. Multilayer technology, compared with single-cell technology, uses smaller quantities of silicon, and the production process can become highly automated.

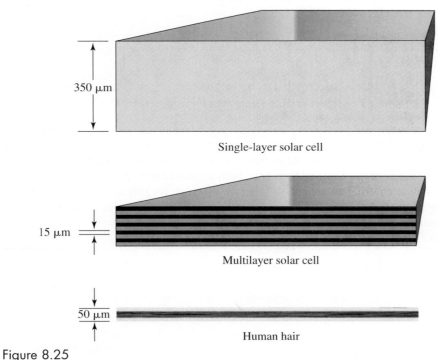

350 μm

Single-layer solar cell

15 μm

Multilayer solar cell

50 μm

Human hair

Figure 8.25

A comparison of the relative thickness of a solar cell layer, either in a single–layer or multilayer cell, to the diameter of an average human hair. *Note:* 1 μm = 10^{-6} m.

Figure 8.26

Thin–film solar tiles on a roof.

Source: NREL.

Thin-film solar cells are made from amorphous silicon or nonsilicon materials such as cadmium telluride (CdTe). These thin films use layers of semiconductor materials only a few micrometers thick. For comparison, a typical human hair is about 50 μm! Thin-film solar cells can even be incorporated into rooftop shingles and tiles, building facades, or the glazing for skylights due to their flexibility compared with more rigid traditional cells (Figure 8.26). Other solar cells are being made using various materials, such as solar inks using conventional printing press technologies, solar dyes, and conductive plastics. Solar modular units use plastic lenses or mirrors to concentrate sunlight onto small but very highly efficient PV materials. Utilities and industries experimenting with these solar lens materials find that despite their higher cost, using a small amount of these more efficient materials is becoming more cost-effective.

Your Turn 8.19   Solar PV Use

How are people today using solar photovoltaics? Search the Internet to answer this question for each group listed below.

a. farmers and ranchers   b. small–business owners   c. homeowners

Answer

a. Uses include pumping water for livestock and lighting in areas without electricity. Even on farms and ranches with electricity, solar PVs can reduce electric utility bills.

Long-range prospects for photovoltaic solar energy are encouraging. Its cost is decreasing while the cost of electricity generated from fossil fuels is increasing. But there is still the question of land use. At currently attainable levels of operating efficiency, the electricity needs of the United States have been estimated to require a photovoltaic generating station covering an area of 85 miles by 85 miles, roughly the size of New Jersey. Although photovoltaic power is steadily growing, it still represents a minute fraction of global power supplies.

Consider This 8.20   If Not New Jersey, . . .

Last we heard, New Jersey was not volunteering to be converted wholesale into a solar farm to power the rest of the United States.

a. Would New Jersey be a reasonable geographic location? *Hint:* Revisit Figure 8.19.
b. Which locations in the United States show the most promise for solar energy collection?
c. Location isn't everything. Name two other factors that come into play in dedicating land to solar energy collection.

Figure 8.27
Photovoltaics can power water pumps in remote areas of the world where there is no access to electricity.

Source: NREL.

Consider This 8.21   A Million Solar Roofs

Distributed generation! Use the resources of the Internet to learn more about how people are using solar energy locally, such as the Million Solar Roofs project. Then propose a solar energy project in a community of your choice. List at least five factors to consider before proceeding with the project.

Because of the diffuse nature of sunlight, photovoltaic technology is well suited to distributed generation, just as was described earlier for fuel cells (see Section 8.5). More than a third of Earth's population is not hooked into an electric network because of the costs associated with constructing and maintaining equipment and supplying the fuel to generate the electricity. Because PV installations are relatively maintenance-free, they are particularly attractive for electric generation in remote regions. For example, the highway traffic lights in certain parts of Alaska, far from power lines, operate on solar energy. A similar but more significant application of photovoltaic cells may be to bring electricity to isolated villages in developing countries. In recent years, more than 200,000 solar lighting units have been installed in residential units in Colombia, the Dominican Republic, Mexico, Sri Lanka, South Africa, China, and India. Photovoltaic cells currently are affecting the lives of millions of people across our planet (Figure 8.27).

Electricity generated by photovoltaic cells during the day must be stored using batteries for use at night. Nevertheless, the direct conversion of sunlight to electricity has many advantages. In addition to relieving some of our dependence on fossil fuels, an economy based on solar electricity would reduce the environmental damage of extracting and transporting these fuels. Furthermore, it would help to lower the levels of air pollutants such as sulfur oxides and nitrogen oxides. It would also help avert the dangers of global warming by decreasing the amount of carbon dioxide released into the atmosphere. Fossil fuels will certainly remain the preferred form of energy for certain applications. However, for the longer term, we can turn to many renewable energy sources, many of which are driven directly by the Sun or as result of solar heating of our atmosphere and water. The next section takes a brief look at how we can generate electricity from these sustainable renewable resources.

8.8 | Electricity from Renewable (Sustainable) Sources

No single source can meet our global energy needs. We also know that no energy source comes without a cost, such as mining, pollution, greenhouse gases, or setting up distribution networks. Clearly it is to our advantage to further develop and add a greater percentage of renewable sources than it is to continue to rely on fossil fuels and nuclear power. We discussed renewable sources, such as biofuels, ethanol, biodiesel, garbage, and biomass in Chapter 4. In this section, we turn to the heat of the Sun, wind, water, and the heat given off by the core of our planet as renewable energy sources.

Solar Thermal

In addition to emitting light, the Sun gives off heat. Concentrating the Sun's energy to heat water is called a solar-thermal process and is also known as concentrating solar power (CSP). Unlike solar voltaic technologies that rely on radiant energy to knock electrons loose from a semiconductor, CSP depends on solar collector devices such as the ones shown in Figure 8.28. These mirrored arrays concentrate sunlight in much the same way that a magnifying glass can focus light to burn a hole in a piece of paper.

Your Turn 8.22   Solar–Thermal Collectors I

Revisit Figure 4.2, reproduced here. It is a diagram of an electric power plant illustrating the conversion of energy from the combustion of fuels into electricity.

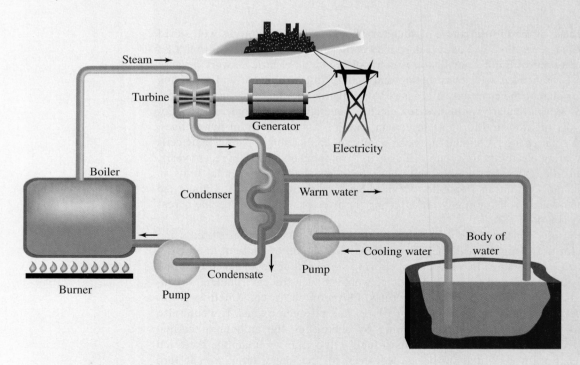

a. What part of this figure would change if solar energy were to be used?
b. Name two advantages that collecting solar energy locally (distributed generation) offers over a centralized system. Then answer this question in the reverse.

(a)

(b)

Figure 8.28

(a) An aerial view of the Solar Millennium Andasol project in Spain, which will have an approximate capacity of 150 MW of solar–thermal power. (b) A close–up of a portion of the mirrored array.

Source: Chemical & Engineering News, *February 1, 2010.*

Consider This 8.23   Solar–Thermal Collectors II

All solar collectors focus and concentrate the Sun's rays for the purpose of producing heat. However, they do so in different ways.

a. Describe the designs for three different types of collectors.
   Hint: Search the Internet for helpful links.
b. How is each design matched to its end use? As part of your answer, include the scale of use—that is, for a single home, for a community, or for a business.
c. Name at least one limitation for each.

Wind

The Sun's heat ultimately drives the large-scale movements of the air on our planet that we know better as "wind." For centuries, humans relied on various forms of windmills that, in turn, spun wheels to grind grain or pump water. Wind turbines today make use of large blades, sometimes nicknamed by the locals as the "pinwheels" that dot the landscape. These spin a shaft that turns a generator to produce electricity. Wind farms are located around the world in order to take advantage of prevailing winds. Such a farm is shown at Ka Lae (South Point) on the Big Island of Hawaii (Figure 8.29).

Figure 8.29

Pakini Nui Wind Farm, completed in 2007, supplied 20.5 MW of power in 2013.

Water

For centuries, humans have harnessed the movement of water with devices such as water wheels. When water flows over a wheel, this wheel can turn other wheels, including stones that can grind grain into flour. Similarly, small- and large-scale hydroelectric dams harness the movement of water. When water falls across turbine blades, the potential energy of water trapped in reservoirs is converted into kinetic energy which in turn is converted to electricity. Although worldwide a few dams are still being constructed, most large reservoirs of water are already in the service of hydroelectric projects.

The movement of ocean water in tides, currents, and waves can be harvested by a variety of principles to generate electricity. Some involve turning blades of a turbine, others involve forcing compressed air through a turbine. All involve the kinetic energy of motion to turn a generator to produce electricity.

Geothermal

Another renewable energy source is the heat given off from the core of our planet. Literally "earth heat," geothermal energy relies on drilling into underground reservoirs containing hot water or steam and thus drawing heat from the Earth. These heated sources of water can then be used to drive generators to produce electricity or the hot water may be used directly to heat a home. Geothermal works well in locations known for volcanic activity that have "hot rock," such as Hawaii, which generates 25% of its energy from geothermal sources.

Consider This 8.24   Our Energetic Future

We can obtain renewable energy from the wind, the oceans, or geothermal sources, not only from the Sun or biomass. Pick one of these renewable energy sources and learn more about the technologies available to harness it.

a. Name the geographic restrictions (if any) to its use.
b. Prepare a list of the reasons to support this technology. Prepare a similar list for the nay–sayers.
c. Predict how this technology will affect the energy production capacity where you live.

This section merely offered a renewable energy sampler, and no world view of energy resources would be complete without considering these and other sustainable sources of energy. To increase the share that renewable sources occupy on the world's energy scene, their economics, availability, and ease of use must be improved.

Conclusion

We look to many different forms of electron transfer to meet our energy needs. Batteries can store chemical energy and convert it to a flow of electrons useful for many applications. Hybrid vehicles use new battery technologies combined with internal combustion engines to improve fuel efficiency. Fuel cells are one of the most efficient ways to produce electricity and may become a major energy source for future personal power use, transportation, and perhaps even large-scale electricity production.

Photovoltaic cells can tap the energy of the Sun. Advances in research together with changes in global economies may make it both fiscally and energetically feasible to use solar energy to extract hydrogen from water or another hydrogen-containing compound. Thus in the years to come, we look forward to new developments that will improve each of these energy options, making their use suitable not only for our generation but for generations to come.

We hope that our discussions of energy in this book have provided you with enough background that you have gained a perspective on the complexity of energy issues that we face. We also hope you are in a position to take stock of the situation and look ahead to the future. A few facts seem beyond debate. The world's thirst for energy will not abate; it most assuredly will continue to grow. Moreover, the ways in which we currently generate energy are not sustainable. The coal, petroleum, and natural gas from which we now derive the vast majority of our power are destined to become scarce or difficult to extract in the not-too-distant future. In addition, their use is not without an environmental cost. Nuclear power, though not directly responsible for the emission of greenhouse and acid-rain-causing gases, carries its own risks and challenges as a long-term energy solution. A transformation is required.

But the laws of thermodynamics and human nature are such that these transformations will not occur spontaneously. A transition to sustainable energy alternatives and their applied uses cannot be developed without hard work and the investment of intellect, time, and money. The sacrifices and compromises that "kicking our fossil fuel habit" require depend heavily on the choices we make today. We need to establish global, national, and personal priorities, and to muster and sustain the will to act on them.

We have been the beneficiaries of a bountiful resource base from the Earth. In turn, we have an obligation to ensure energy sources for generations yet to come.

Chapter Summary

Having studied this chapter, you should be able to:

- Discuss the principles governing the transfer of electrons in galvanic cells, including the processes of oxidation and reduction (8.1)

- Identify oxidation and reduction half-reactions and be able to distinguish which chemical species is oxidized and which is reduced (8.1)

- Describe the design, operation, applications, and advantages of several different types of batteries (8.1–8.3)

- Compare and contrast the principles, advantages, and challenges of producing and using hybrid vehicles (8.4)

- Describe the design, operation, applications, and advantages of typical fuel cells (8.5)

- Explain the energy costs and gains of producing hydrogen and using it as a fuel (8.6)

- Describe the principles governing the operation of photovoltaic (solar) cells and their current and future uses (8.7)

- Describe advantages of renewable energy sources over traditional energy sources and how they are tied to energy through electron transfer (8.8)

Questions

Emphasizing Essentials

1. a. Define the terms *oxidation* and *reduction*.

   b. Why must these processes take place together?

2. Which of these half-reactions represent oxidation and which reduction? Explain your reasoning.

   a. $Fe \longrightarrow Fe^{2+} + 2\,e^-$

   b. $Ni^{4+} + 2\,e^- \longrightarrow Ni^{2+}$

   c. $2\,Cl^- \longrightarrow Cl_2 + 2\,e^-$

3. Which chemical species gets oxidized and which gets reduced in the following overall chemical equation:

   $$2\,Zn(s) + O_2(g) \longrightarrow 2\,ZnO(s)$$

4. What is the difference between a galvanic cell and a true battery? Give an example for each.

5. Two common units associated with electricity are the volt and the amp. What does each unit measure?

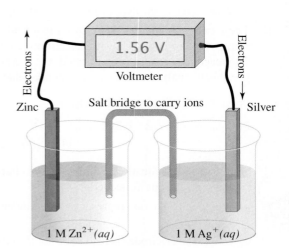

6. Consider the galvanic cell pictured. A coating of impure silver metal begins to appear on the surface of the silver electrode as the cell discharges.

   a. Identify the anode and write the oxidation half-reaction.

   b. Identify the cathode and write the reduction half-reaction.

7. In the lithium–iodine cell, Li is oxidized to Li^+; I_2 is reduced to $2 I^-$.

   a. Write the oxidation half-reaction and the reduction half-reaction that take place in this cell.

   b. Write the overall cell equation.

   c. Identify the half-reactions that occur at the anode and at the cathode.

8. a. How does the voltage from a tiny AAA alkaline cell compare with that from a large D alkaline cell? Explain.

   b. Can both batteries sustain the flow of electrons for the same amount of time? Explain.

9. Identify the type of galvanic cell commonly used in each of these consumer electronic products. Assume none uses solar cells.

   a. laptop computer

   b. MP3 player

   c. digital camera

   d. calculator

10. The mercury battery has been used extensively in medicine and industry. Its overall cell reaction can be represented by this equation.

$$HgO(l) + Zn(s) \longrightarrow ZnO(s) + Hg(l)$$

   a. Write the oxidation half-reaction.

   b. Write the reduction half-reaction.

   c. Why is the mercury battery no longer in common use?

11. a. What is the function of the electrolyte in a galvanic cell?

   b. What is the electrolyte in an alkaline cell?

   c. What is the electrolyte in a lead–acid storage battery?

12. These two *incomplete* half-reactions in a lead–acid storage battery do not show the electrons lost or gained. The reactions are more complicated, but it is still possible to analyze the reactions that take place.

$$Pb(s) + SO_4^{2-}(aq) \longrightarrow PbSO_4(s)$$

$$PbO_2(s) + 4 H^+(aq) + SO_4^{2-}(aq) \longrightarrow$$
$$PbSO_4(s) + 2 H_2O(l)$$

   a. Balance both equations with respect to charge by adding electrons as needed.

   b. Which half-reaction represents oxidation and which reduction?

   c. One of the electrodes is made of lead; the other is lead dioxide. Which is the anode and which is the cathode?

13. During the conversion of $O_2(g)$ to $H_2O(l)$ in a fuel cell (see equation 8.13), the following half-reaction takes place.

$$1/2 O_2(g) + 2 H^+(aq) + 2 e^- \longrightarrow H_2O(l)$$

   Does this half-reaction represent an example of oxidation or reduction? Explain.

14. How does the reaction between hydrogen and oxygen in a fuel cell differ from the combustion of hydrogen and oxygen?

15. This diagram represents the hydrogen fuel cell that was used in some of the earlier space missions.

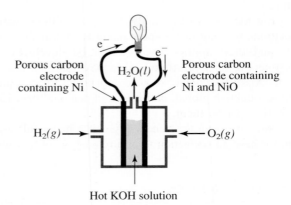

   The chemistry in the hydrogen–oxygen fuel cell can be represented by these half-reactions:

$$H_2(g) \longrightarrow 2 H^+(aq) + 2 e^-$$
$$1/2 O_2(g) + 2 H^+(aq) + 2 e^- \longrightarrow H_2O(l)$$

   Which half-reaction takes place at the anode and which at the cathode? Explain.

16. What is a PEM fuel cell? How does it differ from the fuel cell represented in question 15?

17. In addition to hydrogen, methane also has been studied for use in PEM fuel cells. Balance the given oxidation and reduction half-reactions, and write the overall equation for a methane-based fuel cell.

   Oxidation half-reaction:

$$\_\_ CH_4(g) + \_\_ OH^-(aq) \longrightarrow$$
$$\_\_ CO_2(g) + \_\_ H_2O(l) + \_\_ e^-$$

   Reduction half-reaction:

$$\_\_ O_2(g) + \_\_ H_2O(l) + \_\_ e^- \longrightarrow \_\_ OH^-(aq)$$

18. Relative to a vehicle with an internal combustion engine, list two advantages offered by hydrogen FCVs.

19. Potassium and lithium both are reactive Group 1A metals. Both form hydrides, highly reactive compounds.

   a. Potassium reacts with H_2 to form potassium hydride, KH. Write the chemical equation.

   b. KH reacts with water to produce H_2 and potassium hydroxide. Write the chemical equation.

   c. Offer a reason why LiH (rather than KH) has been proposed as a means of storing H_2 for use in fuel cells.

20. What challenges keep hydrogen fuel cells from being a primary energy source for vehicles?

21. Every year, 5.6×10^{21} kJ of energy comes to Earth from the Sun. Why can't this energy be used to meet all of our energy needs?

22. This *unbalanced* equation represents the last step in the production of pure silicon for use in solar cells.

$$\_\_ \; Mg(s) + \_\_ \; SiCl_4(l) \longrightarrow \_\_ \; MgCl_2(l) + \_\_ \; Si(s)$$

  a. How many electrons are transferred per atom of pure silicon formed?

  b. Does the Si in $SiCl_4(l)$ get oxidized or reduced in the formation of $Si(s)$? Explain your reasoning.

23. The symbol • represents an electron and the symbol ● represents a silicon atom. The darker purple sphere in the center of the diagram represents either a gallium or an arsenic atom. Does this diagram represent a gallium-doped *p*-type silicon semiconductor or an arsenic-doped *n*-type silicon semiconductor? Explain your answer.

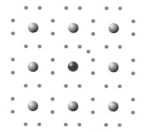

24. Describe the main reasons why solar cells have solar energy conversion efficiencies significantly less than the theoretical value of 31%.

Concentrating on Concepts

25. Explain the significance of the title of this chapter, "Energy from Electron Transfer."

26. Consider these three sources of light: a candle, a battery-powered flashlight, and an electric light bulb. For each source, provide

  a. the origin of the light.

  b. the immediate source of the energy that appears as light.

  c. the original source of the energy that appears as light. *Hint:* Trace this back stepwise as far as possible.

  d. the end-products and by-products produced from using each.

  e. the environmental costs associated with each.

  f. the advantages and disadvantages of each light source.

27. Explain the difference between a rechargeable battery and one that must be discarded. Use a Ni-Cd battery and an alkaline battery as examples.

28. What is the difference between an electrolytic cell and a fuel cell? Explain, giving examples to support your answer.

29. List some differences between a lead–acid storage battery and a fuel cell.

30. "The Earth is a metal-rich rock. I can't see the human race running out of metals when it will be possible to mine in new places or recycle or simply reduce consumption. We probably won't be able to live on the planet due to global warming or other environmental problems before we run into a metal supply problem." These comments were offered by geologist Maurice A. Tivey of Woods Hole Oceanographic Institution in an article in *Chemical & Engineering News* published in June 2009.

  a. Do you agree with the writer's sentiment about not running out of metals? Explain.

  b. Name two challenges connected with increasing the recycling of batteries.

31. The company ZPower is promoting its silver–zinc batteries as replacements for lithium–ion batteries in laptops and cell phones.

  a. What advantages do silver–zinc batteries have over the current lithium–ion batteries?

  b. Write the oxidation and reduction half-reactions using this overall cell equation as a guide. Indicate which reactant gets oxidized and which gets reduced.

$$Zn + Ag_2O \longrightarrow ZnO + 2\,Ag$$

32. The battery of a cell phone discharges when the phone is in use. A manufacturer, while testing a new "power boost" system, reported these data.

Time, min:sec	Voltage, V
0:00	6.56
1:00	6.31
2:00	6.24
3:00	6.18
4:00	6.12
5:00	6.07
6:35	6.03
8:35	6.00
11:05	5.90
13:50	5.80
16:00	5.70
16:50	5.60

  a. Prepare a graph of these data.

  b. The manufacturer's goal was to retain 90% of its initial voltage after 15 minutes of continuous use. Has that goal been achieved? Justify your answer using your graph.

33. Assuming that HEVs are available in your area, draw up a list of at least three questions you would ask the auto dealer before deciding to buy or lease one. Offer reasons for your choices.

34. You never need to plug in Toyota's gasoline–battery hybrid car to recharge the batteries. Explain.

35. Occasionally, the power goes out. When there is no electricity for an extended period of time, are HEVs, PHEVs, and EVs affected any differently than gasoline-powered vehicles?

36. What is *the tragedy of the commons*? How does this concept apply to our practice of using metals such as mercury and cadmium in batteries?

37. Hydrogen is considered an environmentally friendly fuel, producing only water when burned in oxygen. Name two positive effects that the widespread use of hydrogen would have on urban air quality.

38. Fuel cells were invented in 1839 but never developed into practical devices for producing electric energy until the U.S. space program in the 1960s. What advantages did fuel cells have over previous power sources?

39. Hydrogen and methane both can react with oxygen in a fuel cell. They also can be burned directly. Which has greater heat content when burned, 1.00 g of H_2 or 1.00 g of CH_4? *Hint:* Write the balanced chemical equation for each reaction and use the bond energies in Table 4.4 to help answer this question.

40. Engineers have developed a prototype fuel cell that converts gasoline to hydrogen and carbon monoxide. The carbon monoxide, in contact with a catalyst, then reacts with steam to produce carbon dioxide and more hydrogen.

   a. Write a set of reactions that describes this prototype fuel cell, using octane (C_8H_{18}) to represent the hydrocarbons in gasoline.

   b. Speculate as to the future economic success of this prototype fuel cell.

41. How can the key ideas in green chemistry be applied during the development of new technologies for batteries, photovoltaic cells, and fuel cells? Give three specific examples.

42. Consider this representation of two water molecules in the liquid state.

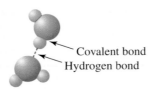

Covalent bond
Hydrogen bond

   a. What happens when water boils? Does boiling break covalent bonds within molecules or does it disrupt hydrogen bonds between molecules? *Hint:* Revisit Chapter 5.

   b. What happens when water undergoes electrolysis? Does this break covalent bonds within molecules or does it disrupt hydrogen bonds between molecules?

43. Why isn't the electrolysis of water the best method to produce hydrogen gas?

44. Small quantities of hydrogen gas can be prepared in the lab by reacting metallic sodium with water, as shown in this equation.

$$2\,Na(s) + 2\,H_2O(l) \longrightarrow H_2(g) + 2\,NaOH(aq)$$

   a. Calculate the grams of sodium needed to produce 1.0 mol of hydrogen gas.

   b. Calculate the grams of sodium needed to produce sufficient hydrogen to meet an American's daily energy requirement of 1.1×10^6 kJ.

   c. If the price of sodium were \$165/kg, what would be the cost of producing 1.0 mol of hydrogen? Assume the cost of water is negligible.

45. a. As a fuel, hydrogen has both advantages and disadvantages. Set up parallel lists for the advantages and disadvantages of using hydrogen as the fuel for transportation and for producing electricity.

   b. Do you advocate the use of hydrogen as a fuel for transportation or for the production of electricity? Explain your position in a short article for your student newspaper.

46. Fossil fuels have been called "Sun's ancient investment on Earth." Explain this statement to a friend who is not enrolled in your course.

47. The cost of electricity generated by solar thermal power plants currently is greater than that of electricity produced by burning fossil fuels. Given this economic fact, suggest two strategies that might be used to promote the use of environmentally cleaner electricity from photovoltaics.

48. Name two current applications of photovoltaic cells *other* than the production of electricity in remote areas.

Exploring Extensions

49. Although Alessandro Volta is credited with the invention of the first electric battery in 1800, some feel this is a reinvention. Research the "Baghdad battery" to evaluate the merit of this claim.

50. Oxidation and reduction also take place during combustion, the process of burning a fuel in oxygen. Because no metal electrodes are present during combustion, the electron transfer is harder to track. In this case, oxidation occurs when a chemical species loses H atoms or gains O atoms. Similarly, reduction occurs when a chemical either gains H atoms or loses O atoms.

   a. Use these new definitions to determine which species is oxidized and which is reduced in the equation below, the combustion of hydrogen. Explain.

$$H_2(g) + {}^1\!/_2\,O_2(g) \longrightarrow H_2O(g)$$

   b. Determine which species is oxidized and which is reduced in each of the following combustion reactions. Explain.

$$C + O_2 \longrightarrow CO_2$$
$$2\,C_8H_{18} + 17\,O_2 \longrightarrow 16\,CO + 18\,H_2O$$

51. If all of today's technology presently based on fossil fuel combustion were replaced by hydrogen fuel cells, significantly more H_2O would be released into the environment. Is this of concern? Research other consequences that might be anticipated from switching to an economy powered by hydrogen, a so-called hydrogen economy.

52. Iceland is taking bold steps to cut its ties to fossil fuels. Part of the plan is to demonstrate that the country can produce, store, and distribute hydrogen to power both public and private transportation.

   a. Name three factors that motivate Iceland to cut its ties to fossil fuels.

   b. What tangible outcomes have resulted to date?

   c. Can lessons learned in Iceland be relevant where you live? Explain.

53. At the cutting edge of technology, the line between science and science fiction often blurs. Investigate the "futuristic" idea of putting mirrors in orbit around Earth to focus and concentrate solar energy for use in generating electricity.

54. Although silicon, used to make solar cells, is one of the most abundant elements in Earth's crust, extracting it from minerals is costly. The increased demand for solar cells has some companies worried about a "silicon shortage." Find out how silicon is purified and how the PV industry is coping with the rising prices.

55. Figure 8.21 shows an array of photovoltaic cells installed at the Solarpark Gut Erlasee in Bavaria, Germany.

   a. At present, where is the largest photovoltaic power plant located in your country?

   b. Name two other locations of large-scale photovoltaic cell installations.

   c. Name two factors that promote a centralized array rather than individual rooftop solar units.

CHAPTER 9

The World of Polymers and Plastics

Golden orb spider and web.

"Nature doesn't have a design problem. People do."

William McDonough and Michael Braungart, *Cradle–to–Cradle*, 2002.

The cover of this book shows an image of a spiderweb. The same spiderweb motif has been present on the earlier editions of *Chemistry in Context*. What's with all the spiderwebs? The word *context* derives from a Latin word meaning "to weave." The spiderwebs exemplify the complex connections woven in each chapter between chemistry and society.

In this chapter, however, we take the spiderweb one step further because it provides us with an example of a natural polymer. To a spider, this polymer has many useful properties including strength, the ability to stretch, and enough stickiness to ensnare prey. Anyone who has accidentally walked into a spiderweb can attest to these properties!

Orb spiders, like the one shown in the photograph that opens this chapter, are notoriously picky builders and spin new webs each day. This daily web building easily could exhaust the resources available to the spider. So how does an orb spider manage to spin so much silk and still survive? Most simply, it recycles! Orb spiders have the ability to ingest old spider silk and recover the raw materials from which they are constructed. While the actual chemical processes are not fully understood, up to two thirds of the existing web goes into making a new one.

Humans have long sought the ability to make fibers as strong and versatile as spider silk. We've come a long way in synthesizing polymers that rival the strength of steel. However, we have yet to design polymers that can be used over and over again like the silk spun by the orb spider. Revisit the quote that opened this chapter, *"Nature doesn't have a design problem. People do."* In order to understand the design process for polymers, first you will need to know how to recognize them, where to find them, how they are made, and something about their properties. Let's get started!

Some polymers are natural, such as spider silk; others are synthetic, such as polyester. In either case, polymers are big molecules made from many smaller ones. The term *polymer* is defined in the next section.

9.1 | Polymers Here, There, and Everywhere

Polymers have revolutionized the world of sports. Football is played on artificial turf by players wearing plastic helmets. Tennis balls are made from synthetic polymers. Carbon fibers embedded in plastic resins provide the strength, flexibility, and lightweight construction required in bicycles, fishing rods, and sailboat hulls. Hockey players skate on rinks of Teflon or high-density polyethylene. Although wooden canoes still have their appeal, most canoes today are made of polymers.

In the previous paragraph, notice that we referred both to *polymers* and *plastics*. These two terms are related and sometimes used interchangeably. The word *polymer* tends to encompass both natural and synthetic polymers. Spider silk is an example of the former; polyethylene is an example of the latter. In contrast, synthetic (human-made) polymers are sometimes called plastics. Look for examples in the next activity.

Artificial turf now can be recycled; in fact, it sometimes is made from recycled plastic. In some climates, artificial turf lowers water use as well.

Consider This 9.1   Tennis Anyone?

Examine this photo of a tennis player. The clothing, racket, ball, and net are all likely to contain polymers, either as fibers in fabrics or as larger pieces. Choose three polymers from the photo. Describe the properties that make each one well-suited for its intended use.

Although polymers are everywhere, you may need to train your eye (and chemical mind) to recognize them. Not all have the look and feel of a rubber yellow ducky! Some are transparent like the clear plastic wrap on food; others are opaque, such as the container that holds liquid laundry detergent. Some are rigid, such as nylon automotive parts; others are more flexible such as a plastic spatula. Some polymers are drawn into fibers to weave clothing and carpet; others are molded into different shapes like a yellow rubber ducky.

Some polymers are easily recognized by their names, because they start with *poly:* polyester, polypropylene, and polystyrene. Others are more difficult to recognize because they have been given trade names: Gore-Tex, Kevlar, and Styrofoam. Still other polymers are coatings or resins generally referred to as epoxides and acrylics. Try your hand at recognizing polymers in the next activity.

Consider This 9.2   Polymers for Recreation

Choose a favorite activity on the land, in the water, or up in the air. Search the Internet to find a company that sells clothing or equipment for this activity. Which types of polymers are mentioned on the website? Prepare a table of the items, the polymers used, and any desirable properties.

In principle, polymers can be made from many different starting materials. In practice, most come from a single raw material: crude oil. As you learned earlier, oil is no longer as easy to obtain on our planet as it used to be. Today, crude oil is the starting material for many plastics, pharmaceuticals, fabrics, and other carbon-based products. Polymers also can come from renewable materials, as we will discuss toward the end of this chapter.

Both the origin and fate of polymers are of interest to us. Remember the orb spider. Although it ingests old spider silk to recover the raw materials, humans aren't nearly as efficient in the design process. In 2010, only 8% of the plastic discarded in the United States was recycled. To understand the complexities surrounding the sources and ultimate fate of polymers, you first need to know something about their chemical structures and how they are made, the topic of the next section.

> Dmitri Mendeleev, the great Russian chemist who proposed the periodic table, remarked that burning petroleum as a fuel "would be akin to firing up a kitchen stove with bank notes."

9.2 | Polymers: Long, Long Chains

Rayon, nylon, and polyurethane. Teflon, Lycra, Styrofoam, and Formica. These seemingly different materials all are synthetic polymers. What they have in common is most easily evident at the molecular level. **Polymers** are large molecules consisting of a long chain or chains of atoms covalently bonded together. A polymer molecule can contain thousands of atoms and have a molar mass of over a million grams.

Monomers (*mono* meaning "one"; *meros* meaning "unit") are the small molecules used to synthesize polymers. Each monomer is analogous to a link in a chain. Polymers (*poly* means "many") can be formed from one monomer or from a combination of two or more different monomers. The long chain shown in Figure 9.1 may help you to imagine a polymer made from identical monomers, that is, identical links in a chain.

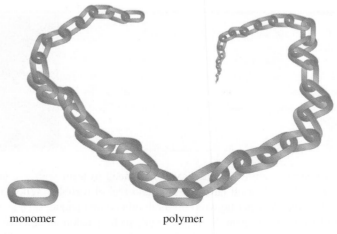

monomer   polymer

Figure 9.1

Representations of a monomer (*single link*) and a polymer (*long chain*) made from one type of monomer.

Figure 9.2

Oak logs and grass both contain the natural polymer cellulose. Glucose is the monomer.

Keep in mind that chemists did not invent polymers. For example, the natural polymers of glucose, **cellulose** and **starch,** were described earlier in the context of biofuels (Chapter 4). Other natural polymers include wool, cotton, silk, natural rubber, skin, and hair. Like synthetic polymers, natural ones exhibit a stunning variety of properties. They give strength to an oak tree, delicacy to a spider's web, softness to goose down, and flexibility to a blade of grass (Figure 9.2).

Some early synthetic polymers were developed as substitutes for expensive or rare natural polymers such as silk and rubber. Others were developed to deliver comparable strength at a lower mass. For example, contrast the density of steel, about 8 g/cm^3, with that of plastics, 1–2 g/cm^3. As a result, an automobile body constructed with plastics weighs less than its steel counterpart and requires less fuel to operate. Similarly, plastic packaging reduces weight and helps save fuel during shipping.

The concept of *density* was introduced in Section 5.2.

Synthetic polymers sometimes are called plastics, a term that applies to materials with a broad range of properties and applications. The word *plastic* is both an adjective (capable of being molded) and a noun (something capable of being molded). The *Merriam-Webster Collegiate Dictionary,* 11th edition, refers to plastics as "any of numerous organic synthetic or processed materials that are mostly . . . polymers of high molecular weight and that can be molded, cast, extruded, drawn, or laminated into objects, films, or filaments." Some metals also have plastic-like properties because they can be "cast, extruded, and drawn." Because the word *plastic* has many applications beyond those of describing synthetic polymers, we primarily will use the word *polymer* in this chapter.

9.3 | Adding Up the Monomers

How do monomers combine to make a polymer? In the previous section, we used a chain to represent a polymer but made no mention of how the chain was formed. In this section, we will provide the details of how chemical covalent bonds connect the monomers.

Polyethylene is our first example. As the name indicates, polyethylene is a polymer of ethylene, $H_2C=CH_2$. Ethylene is a common name for ethene, the smallest member in the family of hydrocarbons containing a C=C double bond. In the polymerization reaction, *n* molecules of the ethylene (ethene) monomer combine to form polyethylene.

Polyethylene is also called polyethene or polythene in the United Kingdom, reflecting the fact that ethene (not ethylene) is the systematic name. "Eth" indicates 2 carbon atoms, and "–ene" indicates a C=C bond.

$$n \; \begin{matrix} H \\ \diagdown \\ C \end{matrix}=\begin{matrix} H \\ \diagup \\ C \end{matrix} \quad \xrightarrow{\; R\cdot \;} \quad \left[\begin{matrix} H & H \\ | & | \\ C - C \\ | & | \\ H & H \end{matrix} \right]_n \qquad \text{[9.1]}$$

The coefficient *n* in front of the ethylene monomer specifies the number of molecules reacting. In turn, this determines the molecular mass of the polymer, typically between 10,000 and 100,000 g/mol, but can run into the millions. On the right side, the *n*

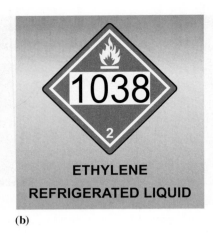

(a)   (b)

Figure 9.3

(a) Bottles made from polyethylene. (b) A sign posted on a railway tank car that transports liquefied ethylene. The 1038 identifies it as ethylene, the red diamond indicates high flammability, and the 2 indicates moderate reactivity.

appears as a subscript, indicating that each monomer has become part of the long chain. The large square brackets enclose the repeating unit of the polymer.

Polyethylene is the sole product. The monomers add to one another to form a long chain of *n* units. As a result, we call this **addition polymerization,** a type of polymerization in which the monomers add to the growing chain in such a way that the polymer contains all the atoms of the monomer. No other products are formed.

Notice the R· over the arrow in equation 9.1. So that you can better appreciate its significance, we will tell you a bit more about ethylene, the monomer. Produced at oil refineries, ethylene is a flammable, colorless gas with a faint gasoline-like odor and is unlike the odorless solid, polyethylene (Figure 9.3a). Although not classified as an air pollutant, ethylene nonetheless is a VOC (volatile organic compound). As you learned in Chapter 1, VOCs in the atmosphere are precursors to the buildup of photochemical smog. Accordingly, safety precautions are needed when transporting ethylene from refineries to sites at which polyethylene is produced. To conserve space, the ethylene gas is pressurized and refrigerated to liquefy it. In this form, it is transported in tank cars that bear labels like the one shown in Figure 9.3b.

Does liquid ethylene polymerize in the tank car? Fortunately, no. Clearly the end user of the ethylene would be distressed to receive a tank car full of solid polyethylene! In order to initiate the polymerization reaction, a free radical (R·) is required, as shown over the arrow in equation 9.1. This free radical represents one of a variety of chemical species, all with an unpaired electron.

To initiate the process of forming the polymer chain, R· attaches to $H_2C=CH_2$ (Figure 9.4). To understand what happens next, recall that the double bond in ethylene contains *four* electrons. After an ethylene molecule reacts with R·, only *two* of these

Recall that the hydroxyl free radical, ·OH, was described earlier in Sections 1.11, 2.8, and 6.7.

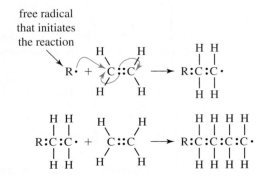

Figure 9.4

The polymerization of ethylene.

Figures Alive!

electrons remain in a C–C bond. The other *two* electrons move (shown by the red arrows) to form two new bonds, one to R· and the other to an ethylene molecule, thus adding another unit to the chain. An unpaired electron at the end of the chain provides the site at which another monomer can add.

As each ethylene monomer adds, a new C–C bond forms and the chain grows. This process repeats many times. Occasionally, the ends of two polymer chains join and stop the chain growth. The process stops when the supply of monomers is exhausted. The result of all this chemistry is that gaseous ethylene is converted to solid polyethylene.

Although we placed R· over the arrow in equation 9.1, we also could have represented the reaction in this way.

$$2 \text{ R·} + n \begin{array}{c} H \\ \diagdown \\ C=C \\ \diagup \\ H \end{array} \begin{array}{c} H \\ \diagup \\ \diagdown \\ H \end{array} \longrightarrow R\left[\begin{array}{cc} H & H \\ | & | \\ C & C \\ | & | \\ H & H \end{array}\right]_n R \qquad [9.2]$$

Because the R group that "caps" each end of the molecule is such a small part of the much longer chain, we will continue our practice of omitting R· as a reactant, as we did in equation 9.1.

The numerical value of *n* and hence the length of the chain can vary. During the manufacturing process, *n* will be adjusted in order to create specific properties for the polymer. Moreover, within a single sample the individual polymer molecules can have varying lengths. In every case, however, the molecules contain a chain of carbon atoms. In essence, the molecules in polyethylene resemble those in a hydrocarbon such as octane, except that they are much, much longer.

Industrial chemists use several synthetic routes to produce polyethylene. The most common uses a metal catalyst and mild temperatures.

Your Turn 9.3   Polymerization of Ethylene

In equation 9.1, the polymerization of ethylene, assume that *n* = 4.

a. Rewrite equation 9.1 to indicate this change.
b. Draw the structural formula of the product without using brackets. Remember to put an R group at each end of the chain.
c. In terms of its molecular structure, how does the product differ from octane?

Answer
c. Octane is C_8H_{18}. Although the product molecule similarly has eight carbon atoms, it has two fewer hydrogen atoms and two R groups at the ends of the molecule.

9.4 | Polyethylene: A Closer Look

Polyethylene is found in many packaging materials, including plastic milk jugs, detergent containers, and baggies (Figure 9.5). Yet, as we have seen in the previous section, all polyethylene is made from the monomer ethylene. How can polyethylene have so many different properties?

Your Turn 9.4   Polyethylene Hunt

As described in this section, polyethylene containers, baggies, and packaging materials are marked either as low density (LDPE) or as high density (HDPE). Using the recycling code as your guide, locate several items made of each. Do LDPE and HDPE differ in flexibility? Is one more translucent? Is one more often colored with a pigment than the other? Summarize your findings in a brief report.

♻ 4
LDPE

♻ 2
HDPE

Figure 9.5

Packing material and containers made from polyethylene.

Hydrogen bonding was explained in Section 5.2, as were the unique properties of water.

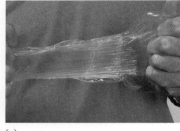

(a)

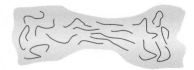

(b)

Figure 9.6

(a) A plastic bag stretched until it "necks." (b) A representation of "necking" at the molecular level.

The different properties of polyethylene stem largely from differences in the long molecular chains. Relatively speaking, these molecules are very long indeed. Imagine a polyethylene molecule to be as wide as a piece of spaghetti. If this were the case, the molecule would be almost a half mile long! To continue the analogy, the polyethylene used to make plastic bags contains molecular chains arranged somewhat like cooked spaghetti on a plate. The strands are not very well aligned, although in some regions the molecular chains run in parallel. Moreover, the polyethylene chains, like the spaghetti strands, are not covalently bonded to one another.

Recall that in Chapter 5 we used the concept of hydrogen bonding to describe an attractive force *between* water molecules in the liquid phase. The hydrogen bond is not a covalent bond. Rather, hydrogen bonds are **intermolecular forces,** that is, an attractive or repulsive force among molecules. Intermolecular forces differ from the covalent bonds that exist *within* molecules arising from shared pairs of electrons. Although intermolecular forces are much weaker than covalent bonds, they still have measurable effects. For example, in water these forces help to keep the molecules close together, sliding past and around one another as water flows, unlike in steam where the water molecules are far apart and bump into one another less frequently.

Polymers containing only atoms of H and C—such as HDPE, LDPE, and polypropylene—cannot form hydrogen bonds. Rather, another type of intermolecular attractive force keeps the molecules close to one another. This force arises because each atom in the long polymeric chain contains its own electrons. These electrons are attracted to the atoms on neighboring chains; the degree of attraction between strands of polyethylene results from the large number of atoms involved. The attraction is a bit like that between the two halves of Velcro. The larger the surface area of one Velcro strip, the better it will hold to the other. The intermolecular attractive forces that hold polyethylene molecules together are called **dispersion forces,** attractions between molecules that result from a distortion of the electron cloud that causes an uneven distribution of the negative charge. Dispersion forces are significant in large molecules, such as polymers.

Evidence of the molecular arrangement of polyethylene can be obtained by doing a short experiment. Cut a strip from a heavy-duty polyethylene bag, grab the two ends of the strip, and pull. A fairly strong pull is required to start the plastic stretching, but once it begins, less force is needed to keep the stretch going. The length of the plastic strip increases dramatically as the width and thickness decrease (Figure 9.6a). A small shoulder forms on the wider part of the strip and a narrow neck almost seems to flow from it in a process called "necking." Unlike the stretching of a rubber band, the necking effect is not reversible. Eventually the plastic thins to the point that it tears.

Figure 9.6b represents the necking of polyethylene from a molecular point of view. As the strip narrows, the molecular chains shift, slide, and align parallel to one another in the direction of pull. In some plastics, such stretching (sometimes called "cold drawing") is carried out as part of the manufacturing process to alter the three-dimensional arrangement of the chains in the solid. As the force and stretching continue, the polymer eventually reaches a point at which the strands can no longer realign and the plastic breaks. Paper, a natural polymeric material, tears when pulled because the strands (fibers) in paper are rigidly held in place and are not free to slip like the long molecules in polyethylene.

Consider This 9.5   "Necking" Polyethylene

Necking permanently changes the properties of a piece of polyethylene.

 a. Does necking affect the number of monomer units, n, in the average polymer?
 b. Does necking affect the bonding between the monomer units within the polymer chain?

Differences in the physical properties of polymers also can arise as a result of the extent of branching of the polymer chain. This is the case with high-density polyethylene (HDPE) and low-density polyethylene (LDPE), as shown in Figure 9.7.

As you may have discovered in Your Turn 9.4, the plastic bags dispensed in the produce aisles of supermarkets are usually LDPE. These bags are stretchy, transparent, and not very strong. Their molecules consist of about 500 monomeric units, and the central polymeric chain has numerous branches, like limbs radiating from a central tree trunk (see Figure 9.7a).

This low-density form was the first type of polyethylene to be manufactured. About 20 years after its discovery, chemists were able to adjust reaction conditions to prevent branching and HDPE was born. In their Nobel Prize-winning research, Karl Ziegler (1898–1973) and Giulio Natta (1903–1979) developed catalysts that enabled them to make linear (unbranched) polyethylene chains of about 10,000 monomer units. With no side branches, these long chains arranged in parallel, unlike the irregular tangle of the polymer chains in LDPE (see Figure 9.7b). HDPE, with its more highly ordered molecular structure, has a slightly higher density, greater rigidity, more strength, and a higher melting point than LDPE.

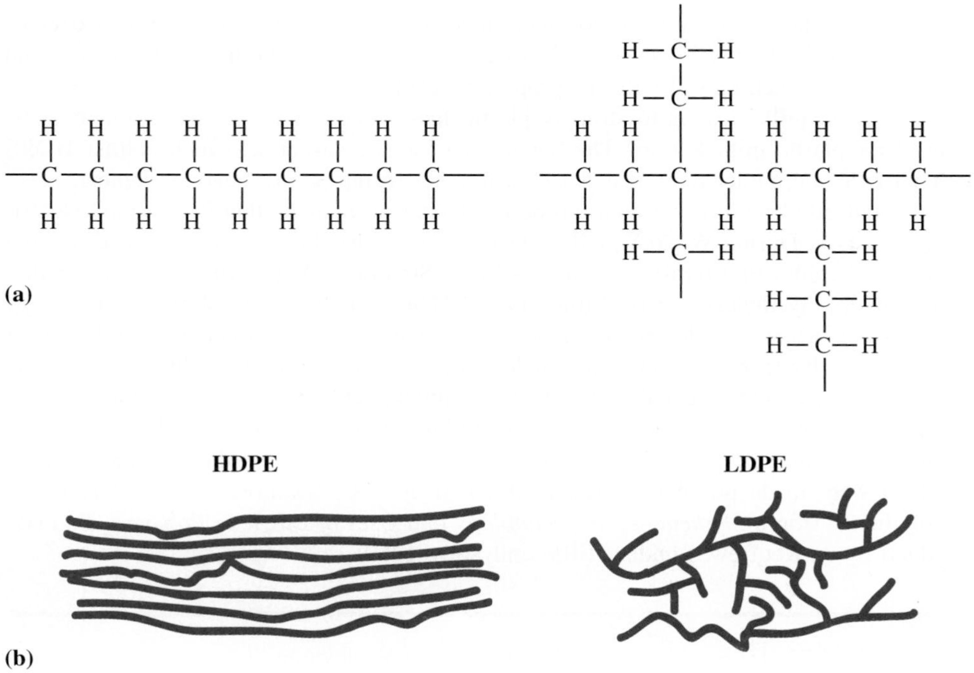

(a)

HDPE   **LDPE**

(b)

Figure 9.7

High–density (linear) polyethylene and low–density (branched) polyethylene.
(a) Details of the bonding. (b) Schematic representations.

Consider This 9.6   HDPE and LDPE

The densities of HDPE and LDPE are 0.96 g/cm^3 and 0.93 g/cm^3, respectively. Use Figure 9.7 to rationalize the slight difference in densities.

In 1999, AlliedSignal and Honeywell merged to form Honeywell International.

As you might expect, HDPE and LDPE have different uses. High-density polyethylene is used to make many different types of plastic bottles, toys, stiff or "crinkly" plastic bags, and heavy-duty pipes. A newer use of HDPE was spurred by surgery patients with blood-borne diseases, such as HIV/AIDS. Without suitable protection, surgeons would run the risk of being infected. AlliedSignal Inc. produced a linear polyethylene fiber called Spectra that could be fabricated into liners for surgical gloves. These gloves are reported to have 15 times more resistance to cuts than medium-weight leather work gloves but are still thin enough to allow a keen sense of touch. A sharp scalpel can be drawn across the glove with no damage to the fabric. Such strength is in marked contrast to the properties of everyday plastic gloves used by health professionals.

Consider This 9.7   Shopping for Polymers

The *Macrogalleria*, a "Cyberwonderland of Polymer Fun," was created with the support of many sponsors, including the American Chemical Society.

a. Search for *The Macrogalleria* on the Internet and find its virtual shopping mall. Visit stores to locate at least six different items made from LDPE or HDPE. List your findings.

b. Why do you think this site was named the *Macrogalleria*? *Hint:* Read ahead in Chapter 11 to learn about macronutrients and micronutrients.

Answer

b. *Macro* means large. The site is a gallery of large molecules. Similarly, macronutrients are foods that we eat in large quantities.

It would be a mistake to conclude that polyethylene is restricted to the extremes represented by highly branched or strictly linear forms. By modifying the extent and location of branching in LDPE, its properties can be varied from the soft and wax-like coatings on milk cartons to stretchy plastic food wrap. HDPE is rigid enough to be used for plastic milk bottles. The hot water of a dishwasher will melt neither HDPE nor LDPE, but either may melt if left near a hot frying pan or heating element.

Polyethylene has one more property of interest, namely, that it is a good electrical insulator. During World War II, polyethylene was used by the Allied Forces to coat electrical cables in aircraft radar installations. Sir Robert Watt, who discovered radar, described polyethylene's critical importance. "The availability of polythene [polyethylene] transformed the design, production, installation, and maintenance problems of airborne radar from the almost insoluble to the comfortably manageable. . . . A whole range of aerial and feeder designs otherwise unattainable was made possible, a whole crop of intolerable air maintenance problems was removed. And so polythene played an indispensable part in the long series of victories in the air, on the sea, and on land, which were made possible by radar" (Quoted by J. C. Swallow in "The History of Polythene" from *Polythene—The Technology and Uses of Ethylene Polymers*, 2nd ed., edited by A. Renfrew. London: Iliffe and Sons, 1960).

Consider This 9.8   Other Types of Polyethylene

In addition to LDPE and HDPE, polyethylene is manufactured as MDPE and LLDPE. Use the Internet to find out about these and other types of polyethylene. How do their properties differ?

9.5 | The "Big Six": Theme and Variations

Today, more than 60,000 synthetic polymers are known. Although polymers were developed for many specialized uses, six types account for roughly 75% of those used in both Europe and the United States. We refer to these everyday polymers as the "Big Six" and you can find them in Table 9.1: polyethylene (low- and high-density), polyvinyl chloride, polystyrene, polypropylene, and polyethylene terephthalate.

Table 9.1 also lists properties of these six polymers. All are solids that can be colored with pigments. All also are insoluble in water, although some dissolve or soften in the

Terephthalate is pronounced "ter–eh–THAL–ate." The "ph" is silent.

Table 9.1	The Big Six		
Polymer	**Monomer(s)**	**Properties of Polymer**	**Uses of Polymer**
Polyethylene (LDPE) — LDPE, ♺ 4	Ethylene	Translucent if not pigmented. Soft, flexible, and moderately tough. Unreactive to acids and bases. Softens with some oils and solvents.	Bags, films, sheets, bubble wrap, toys, wire insulation.
Polyethylene (HDPE) — HDPE, ♺ 2	Ethylene	Similar to LDPE but more rigid, usually opaque, tougher, slightly more dense.	Containers, such as those for milk, juice, detergent, and shampoo. Low–cost plastic items such as buckets, crates, and fencing.
Polyvinyl chloride — PVC, or V, ♺ 3	Vinyl chloride	Variable. Rigid if not softened with a plasticizer. Clear and shiny, but often pigmented. Resistant to most chemicals, including oils, acids, and bases.	Rigid: Plumbing pipe, house siding, charge cards, hotel room keys. Softened: Garden hoses, waterproof boots, shower curtains, IV tubing.
Polystyrene — PS, ♺ 6	Styrene	Variable. "Crystal" form transparent, sparkling, somewhat brittle. "Expandable" form lightweight foam. Both forms rigid and dissolve in many organic solvents.	"Crystal" form: Food wrap, CD cases, transparent cups. "Expandable" form: Foam cups, insulated containers, food packaging trays, egg cartons, packaging peanuts.
Polypropylene — PP, ♺ 5	Propylene	Opaque, tough, weathers well. Higher melting point. Resistant to most oils, acids, and bases.	Bottle caps. Yogurt, cream, and margarine containers. Carpeting, casual furniture, luggage.
Polyethylene terephthalate — PETE, or PET, ♺ 1	Ethylene glycol: HO—CH₂CH₂—OH; Terephthalic acid	Transparent, strong, shatter–resistant. Impervious to acids and atmospheric gases. Most costly of the six.	Soft–drink bottles, clear food containers, beverage glasses, fleece fabrics, carpet yarns, fiber–fill insulation.

Note: The structures of the first five monomers differ only by the atoms shown in blue.

presence of hydrocarbons, fats, and oils. All are **thermoplastic polymers,** meaning that with heat, they can be melted and reshaped over and over again. However, they exhibit a range of melting points depending on the route by which they were manufactured. Of the Big Six, polyethylene has the lowest melting point, with LDPE and HDPE melting at about 120 °C and 130 °C, respectively. In contrast, polypropylene (PP) melts at 160–170 °C.

Depending on the arrangement of their molecules, polymers have varying degrees of strength. At the microscopic level, the molecules in some parts of the polymer may have an orderly repeating pattern, such as one would find in a crystalline solid. In these **crystalline regions,** the long polymer molecules are arranged neatly and tightly in a regular pattern. In other parts of the same polymer, you can find **amorphous regions.** Here, the long polymer molecules are found in a random, disordered arrangement and are packed more loosely. Because of their structural regularity, the crystalline regions impart strength and resistance to abrasion, such as in HDPE and PP. Although some polymers are highly crystalline, most still include amorphous regions. These regions impart flexibility. For example, the amorphous regions in PP give it the ability to be bent without breaking. The range of properties among polymers means that they are differently suited for specific applications. The next exercise provides an opportunity to match polymers with their uses.

Consider This 9.9   Uses of the Big Six

Use Table 9.1 and other information provided about the Big Six to answer these questions.

  a. Which polymer would not be suitable for margarine tubs because it softens with oil?
  b. Which polymers are transparent? Which one is used in clear soft–drink bottles?
  c. Which one is tough and used for bottle caps? Name another application in which toughness counts.
  d. Which ones are listed as unreactive to acids and can serve as containers for acidic beverages, such as orange juice?

From Table 9.1, you also can see that six monomers are used to make six different polymers, but perhaps not in the way you might expect. PET uses *two* monomers; look for an explanation in the next section. HDPE and LDPE use *the same* monomer ethylene, as we mentioned in the previous section. Here, we focus on the *three* monomers closely related to ethylene: vinyl chloride, propylene, and styrene.

ethylene   vinyl chloride   propylene   styrene

In vinyl chloride, one of the H atoms of ethylene is replaced by a Cl atom. Similarly, in propylene, one of the H atoms of ethylene is replaced by a methyl group ($-CH_3$).

In styrene, a phenyl group, $-C_6H_5$, replaces one of the H atoms. The phenyl group consists of six carbon atoms arranged to form a hexagon:

Because the first structural formula for the phenyl group is tedious to draw, the ring sometimes is simplified, as shown second. Shown third is a space-filling model for the phenyl group.

As you might suspect, vinyl chloride, propylene, and styrene undergo addition polymerization just like ethylene. But the results are somewhat different. To see why, let's look at what happens when *n* molecules of vinyl chloride polymerize to form polyvinyl chloride (PVC).

$$n \quad \overset{H}{\underset{H}{}}C=C\overset{H}{\underset{Cl}{}} \quad \xrightarrow{R\cdot} \quad \left[\begin{matrix} H & H \\ | & | \\ C & C \\ | & | \\ H & Cl \end{matrix} \right]_n \qquad [9.3]$$

In equation 9.3, the Cl atom could be drawn in any of the four positions that attach to the C atoms in the vinyl chloride monomer. They are all equivalent due to the symmetry of the molecule.

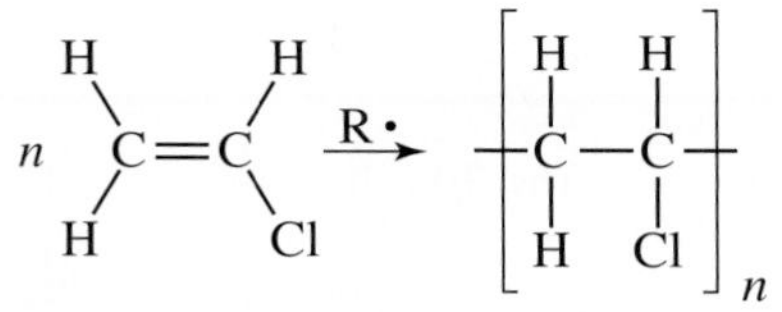

The Cl atom creates an asymmetry in the monomer. Arbitrarily, think of the carbon atom bearing two H atoms as the "tail" and the carbon with the Cl atom as the "head."

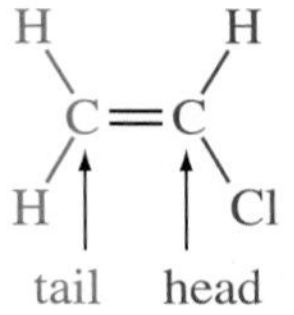

When vinyl chloride monomers add to form polyvinyl chloride, they orient in one of three ways, as shown in Figure 9.8:

- head-to-tail, with the Cl atoms on every other C atom
- alternating head-to-head/tail-to-tail, with the Cl atoms next to each other
- a random mix of the previous two arrangements

tail   head

The head-to-tail arrangement is the usual product for polyvinyl chloride.

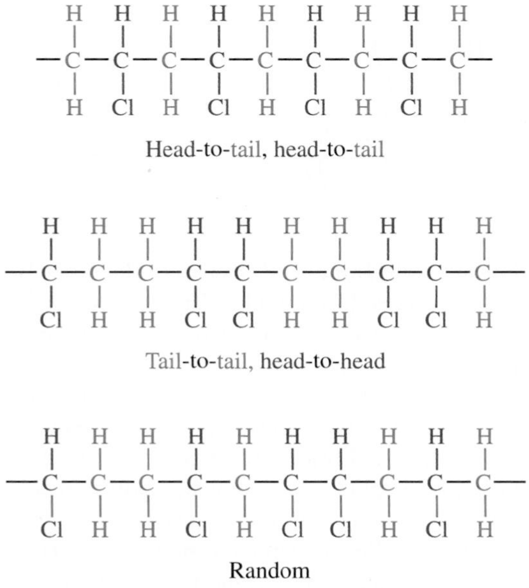

$$\begin{matrix} & H & H & H & H & H & H & H & H & H \\ & | & | & | & | & | & | & | & | & | \\ -C & -C & -C & -C & -C & -C & -C & -C & -C- \\ & | & | & | & | & | & | & | & | & | \\ & H & Cl & H & Cl & H & Cl & H & Cl & H \end{matrix}$$

Head-to-tail, head-to-tail

$$\begin{matrix} & H & H & H & H & H & H & H & H & H & H \\ & | & | & | & | & | & | & | & | & | & | \\ -C & -C & -C & -C & -C & -C & -C & -C & -C & -C- \\ & | & | & | & | & | & | & | & | & | & | \\ & Cl & H & H & Cl & Cl & H & H & Cl & Cl & H \end{matrix}$$

Tail-to-tail, head-to-head

$$\begin{matrix} & H & H & H & H & H & H & H & H & H & H \\ & | & | & | & | & | & | & | & | & | & | \\ -C & -C & -C & -C & -C & -C & -C & -C & -C & -C- \\ & | & | & | & | & | & | & | & | & | & | \\ & Cl & H & H & Cl & H & Cl & Cl & H & Cl & H \end{matrix}$$

Random

Figure 9.8
Three possible arrangements of the monomers in PVC.

The arrangement of monomers in the chain is one factor that affects the flexibility of the polymer. Thus each arrangement of PVC has somewhat different properties, with the most regular one, repeating head-to-tail, being the stiffest because the molecules pack more easily together to form crystalline regions. The stiffer PVC finds use in drain and sewer pipes, credit cards, house siding, furniture, and various automobile parts. The random arrangement is still stiff, but somewhat less so.

PVC can be further softened with **plasticizers**, compounds that are added in small amounts to polymers to make them softer and more pliable. Plasticizers work by fitting in between the large polymer molecules, thus disrupting the regular packing of the molecules. Flexible PVC that contains plasticizers is familiar in shower curtains, "rubber" boots, garden hoses, clear IV bags for blood transfusions, artificial leather ("patent leather"), and flexible insulation coatings on electrical wires. Additives to plastics are controversial for several reasons, as we'll see in Section 9.11.

Next, let us consider the polymerization of propylene to form polypropylene. Again, several arrangements are possible because of the asymmetry of the monomer. A particularly useful form of polypropylene is the repeating head-to-tail, head-to-tail arrangement. This regularity imparts a high degree of crystallinity and makes the polymer strong, tough, and able to withstand higher temperatures. These properties are reflected in the uses. For example, indoor–outdoor carpeting is often made using the strong fibers of polypropylene.

Just as ethylene also is called ethene, propylene also is called propene.

Consider This 9.11   "The Tough One"

Polypropylene may not be as familiar to you as polyethylene, or PET, in part because many polypropylene items don't carry a recycling symbol.

a. As just mentioned, polypropylene can be drawn into fibers such as those used in indoor–outdoor carpeting. Suggest two other uses for polypropylene fiber where toughness is desired.

b. Although HDPE is used in many food containers, polypropylene is used for margarine containers. Toughness is not the issue; rather, what is? *Hint:* Consult Table 9.1.

Finally, let us examine the polymerization of n molecules of styrene to form polystyrene (PS), an inexpensive and widely used plastic. Here is a representation of the addition polymerization.

Visit Figures Alive! to learn more about other addition polymers.

$$[9.4]$$

Polystyrene is a hard plastic with little flexibility. Like the other Big Six, it melts when heated (thermoplastic) and casts well into molds. Transparent cases for DVDs and clear plastic party glasses and plates also are made from polystyrene. So are hard exteriors of many laptop computers and cell phones.

Most commercial polystyrene has the random arrangement of the monomers shown in Figure 9.9a. In this form, sometimes referred to as general purpose or "crystal" polystyrene, the polymer is hard and brittle. Have you ever squeezed too hard on a clear plastic party glass causing it to split? It probably was polystyrene (see Figure 9.9b).

The familiar foam hot beverage cups, egg cartons, and "peanuts" also are made from polystyrene, sometimes called expandable polystyrene (EPS). These items are made from small hard "expandable" polystyrene beads. These beads contain 4–7% of a **blowing agent,** that is, either a gas or a substance capable of producing a gas to manufacture a foamed plastic. For PS, the blowing agent typically is a low-boiling

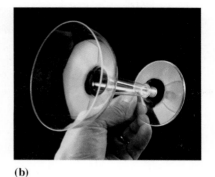

Figure 9.9

(a) Random arrangement of polystyrene monomers. (b) Partyware made from "crystal" (general purpose) polystyrene.

liquid such as pentane. If the beads are placed in a mold and heated with steam or hot air, the pentane vaporizes. In turn, the expanding gas expands the polymer. The expanded particles are fused together into the shape determined by the mold. Because it contains so many bubbles, this plastic foam not only is light but also is an excellent thermal insulator.

Chlorofluorocarbons, better known as CFCs, were once on the list of compounds used as blowing agents. Because CFCs destroy stratospheric ozone (see Chapter 2), this use was phased out in 1990. Pentane, C_5H_{12}, in its vapor form and carbon dioxide were two possible replacements. For example, the Dow Chemical Company developed a process that uses pure carbon dioxide as a blowing agent to produce Styrofoam for packaging material. Using the Dow 100% CO_2 technology eliminated the use of CFC-12 as a blowing agent. The CO_2 used is a by-product from existing commercial and natural sources, such as cement production and natural gas wells. Thus, it does not contribute additional CO_2, a greenhouse gas, to the atmosphere. Dow received a 1996 Presidential Green Chemistry Challenge Award for developing these alternative reaction conditions.

> Styrofoam is a brand name of polystyrene foam insulation produced by the Dow Chemical Company.

> Using CO_2 in place of CFCs as blowing agents illustrates green chemistry key idea #3 listed on the inside cover of this text. *It is better to use and generate substances that are not toxic.*

Your Turn 9.12   Polystyrene Possibilities

Show the arrangement of atoms in a polystyrene chain in the repeating head–to–tail arrangement. Why do you think this arrangement is favored rather than the head–to–head arrangement?

9.6 | Condensing the Monomers

Monomers make the polymer! As you saw in the previous section, changes in the monomer lead to changes in the properties of the polymer. To understand different monomers, we need to revisit the concept of **functional groups,** that is, distinctive arrangements of groups of atoms that impart characteristic chemical properties to the molecules that contain them (Table 9.2). For example, the hydroxyl functional group (−OH) was introduced earlier in the context of ethanol, a biofuel (Chapter 4). This group is present in all compounds classified as alcohols, including one that is of interest in this chapter, ethylene glycol.

> Chapters 4 and 10 mention functional groups in the context of biofuels and drug molecules, respectively.

We will now introduce several new functional groups, starting with the carboxylic acid group.

$$\underset{\displaystyle \diagdown}{\overset{\displaystyle O}{\underset{\displaystyle C}{\|}}}\diagdown_{O}\diagdown H$$

Although the carboxylic acid group contains an −OH group, it is *not* an alcohol. Rather, think of −COOH as a single unit.

Table 9.2	Selected Functional Groups	
Name	Chemical Formula	Structural Formula
hydroxyl (in alcohols)	–OH	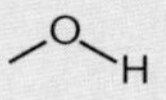
carboxylic acid	–COOH	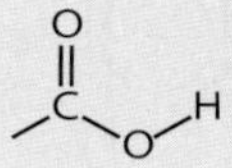
ester	–COOC–	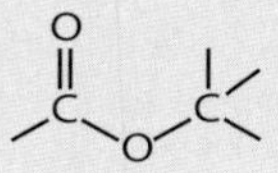
amine	–NH_2	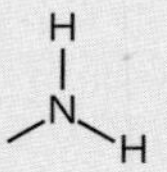
amide	–CONH_2	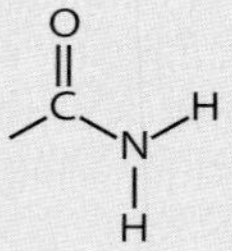

Table 9.3 shows that carboxylic acid groups naturally occur in foods such as vinegar and cheese. If you examine the entries in the table closely, you will see that a molecule can contain more than one carboxylic acid functional group, for example, terephthalic acid and adipic acid. A molecule can also have two different functional groups, such as the final entry, lactic acid.

Table 9.3	Selected Carboxylic Acids	
Name	Structural Formula	Information
ethanoic acid	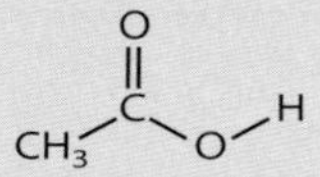	Naturally occurring in vinegar. Also called acetic acid.
propanoic acid	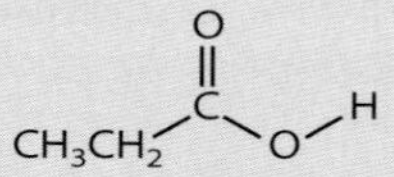	Naturally occurring in some cheeses, providing a "sharp" taste. Also called propionic acid.
benzoic acid	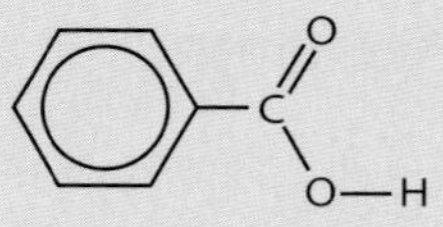	Naturally occurring carboxylic acid. Used as a food preservative.
terephthalic acid	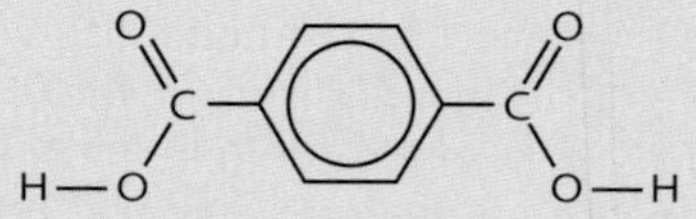	One of the monomers used to produce PET.
adipic acid	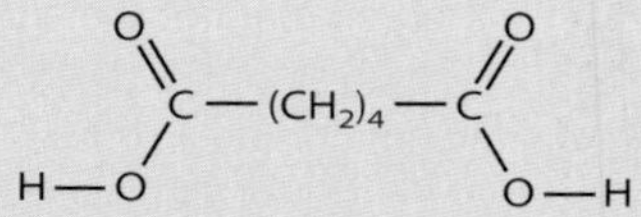	One of the monomers used to produce one type of nylon.
lactic acid	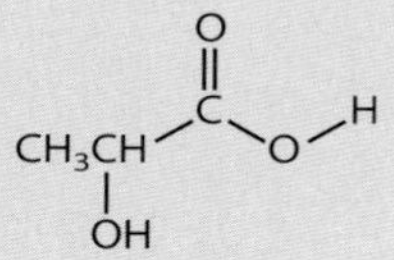	The monomer for PLA, a bio–based polymer.

Carboxylic acids are closely related to another new functional group, the ester. An ester can be represented by this structural formula.

Armed with the ability to recognize alcohols, carboxylic acids, and esters, you are now ready to explore polyesters, the topic of this section.

The star on the polyester stage is PET, also written as PETE. Both abbreviations stand for polyethylene terephthalate ester, which explains why people opt for the abbreviation. Because PET is semirigid, clear, and reasonably gas-tight (Figure 9.10), its most common use is in beverage bottles. Polyester also can be drawn into sheets and fibers. For example, Mylar is a trade name for thin plastic sheets of PET such as those used to make shiny festive balloons. When filled with helium, these balloons remain aloft for many hours because polyester is so impervious to gases. Eventually, however, the tiny helium atoms escape and the balloons deflate.

In contrast to polyethylene, PET is *not* formed by addition polymerization. Rather, it is formed by **condensation polymerization,** a process in which the monomers join by eliminating (splitting out) a small molecule, usually water. Thus, condensation polymerization always has a second product in addition to the polymer itself. Many natural polymers are formed by condensation reactions, including cellulose, starch, wool, silk from spiders, and proteins. Synthetic polymers include Dacron, Kevlar, and different types of nylon.

Also in contrast to polyethylene, PET is *not* formed from a single monomer. Rather, PET is a **copolymer,** a polymer formed by the combination of two or more different monomers. With two monomers, we have either double the trouble or double the fun, depending on how you look at things. One monomer, ethylene glycol, $HOCH_2CH_2OH$, is an alcohol that contains two hydroxyl groups, one on each carbon atom. The other monomer, terephthalic acid, contains two carboxylic acid groups, one on each side of the benzene ring. In essence, each monomer is "armed" with two functional groups. Revisit Table 9.1 to see structural formulas for each of the two monomers.

To understand how copolymers form, let's work with only one molecule of each monomer. Here is how these monomers can join.

Because polyethylene terephthalate contains no polyethylene, it is sometimes written as poly(ethylene terephthalate). This reduces the confusion, at least when the name is read. Spoken, the two names still sound the same.

terephthalic acid   ethylene glycol   **[9.5]**

Figure 9.10
Two-liter soft-drink bottles made from PET.

Highlighted in red, the −OH in the carboxylic acid group and the H atom in the hydroxyl group react to produce water, HOH. The remaining portions of the alcohol and the carboxylic acid connect through the ester functional group, highlighted in blue.

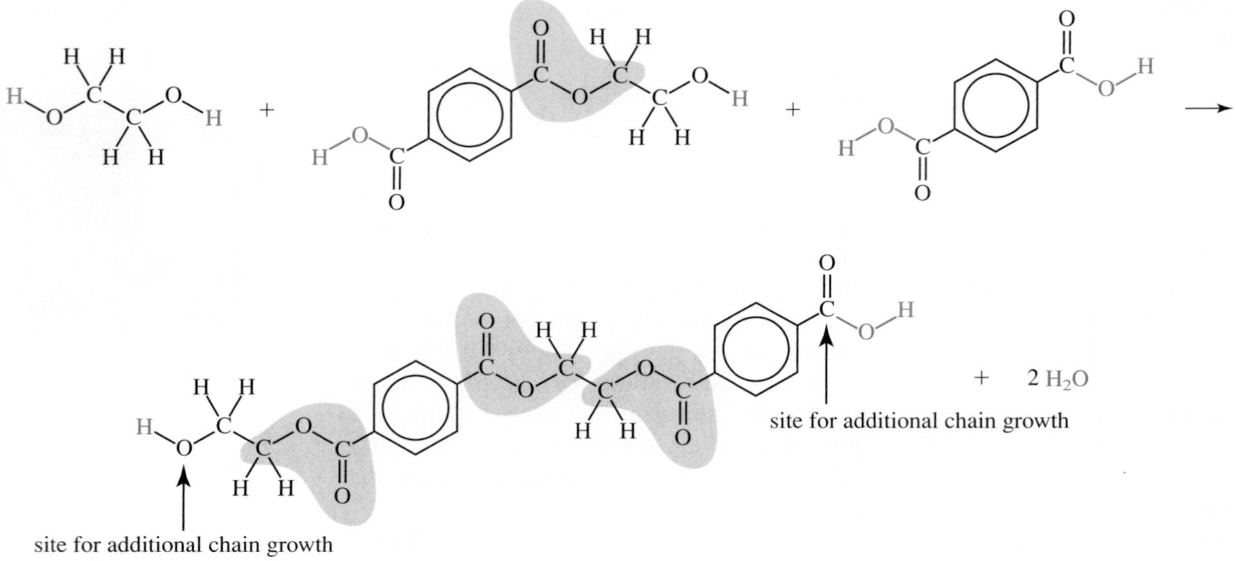

Figure 9.11
Two different monomers are added to the product in Equation 9.5 to further build PET, a polyester. The ester functional group is highlighted in blue.

Notice that the product has functional groups that are sites for additional chain growth: −COOH on the left end and −OH on the right. The former can react with the −OH of another ethylene glycol molecule; the latter can react with the −COOH of another terephthalic acid molecule. Each time, a molecule of water is released and an ester group is formed. This process, represented in Figure 9.11, occurs multiple times to yield polyethylene terephthalate. The result is a polyester, so named because the ester group connects the monomers.

Consider This 9.13   Esters and Polyesters

You have seen that terephthalic acid and ethylene glycol can react. Now consider ethanoic acid (acetic acid) and ethanol (ethyl alcohol):

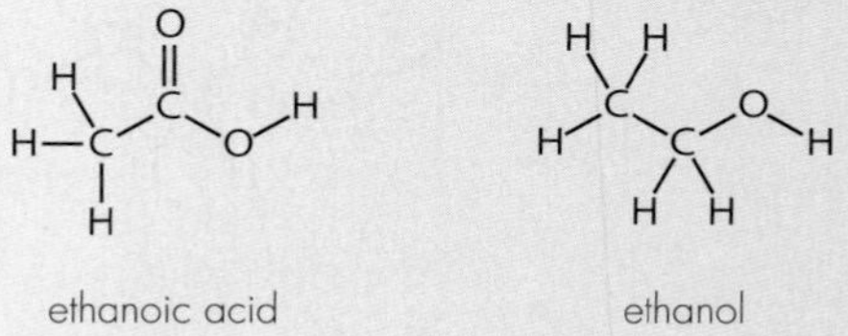

ethanoic acid   ethanol

a. Show how this carboxylic acid and alcohol can react to form an ester.
   Hint: Remember a water molecule is formed as a product.
b. Could ethanoic acid and ethanol react to form a polyester? Explain your reasoning.

PET is not the only polyester in town! By varying the number and type of carbon atoms in the monomers, chemists have synthesized other polyesters with trade names such as Dacron, Polartec, Fortrel, and Polarguard. Polyester spins readily into fibers that are easy to wash and quick to dry. Polyester also blends well with other fibers, such as cotton or wool. Consider This 9.14 describes polyethylene naphthalate (PEN), a polyester that has better temperature resistance than PET.

Consider This 9.14   From PET to PEN

In both PET and PEN, the alcohol monomer is ethylene glycol, but the organic acid monomers differ slightly. Here is the organic acid monomer in PEN, naphthalic acid:

Use structural formulas to show the reaction of two molecules of naphthalic acid with two molecules of ethylene glycol.

9.7 | Polyamides: Natural and Nylon

No discussion of condensation polymerization can be complete without examining two specific types of polymers. The first is proteins, which are natural polymers such as those in our muscles, fingernails, and hair; the second is nylons, which are synthetic substitutes that brilliantly duplicate some of the properties of silk, a naturally occurring protein. In 2011, according to the Chemical Heritage Foundation, manufacturers worldwide produced around 8 million pounds of nylon, roughly 12% of all synthetic fibers.

Amino acids are the monomers from which our body builds proteins. Each amino acid molecule contains two functional groups: an amine ($-NH_2$) and a carboxylic acid ($-COOH$). Twenty different amino acids occur naturally, each differing in one of the groups bonded to the central carbon atom. This side chain is represented with an R, as shown in this general structural formula for an amino acid.

In some amino acids, R consists of only carbon and hydrogen atoms; in others, R may include additional atoms, such as oxygen, nitrogen, and even sulfur. Some R groups have acidic properties, others are basic.

As monomers, amino acids join to form a long chain via condensation polymerization. However, keep in mind four key differences between a condensation polymer such as PET and any given protein:

- PET is a polyester. In contrast, proteins are **polyamides,** that is, condensation polymers that contain the amide functional group.
- PET is built from two monomers, ethylene glycol and terephthalic acid, that are in a 1:1 ratio. In contrast, proteins can contain up to 20 different amino acids (monomers) in any ratio.
- In proteins, each amino acid has two *different* functional groups, $-NH_2$ and $-COOH$.
- In PET, the two monomers have two *identical* functional groups, either $-OH$ or $-COOH$.

To see how these differences play out, examine this reaction between two amino acids. One has the side chain R, the side chain on the other amino acid is labeled as R′.

See Sections 11.7, 12.4, and 12.5 for more about amino acids and proteins.

Chemists use **R** as a place holder in a molecule. With amino acids, **R** represents one of 20 side chains. Earlier in this chapter, R· was used to represent a free radical such as Cl· or ·OH.

The amide functional group is shown in Table 9.2.

$$[9.6]$$

peptide bond

In this reaction, an amide is formed and a molecule of water is eliminated. This amide contains a C–N bond, referred to as a **peptide bond,** the covalent bond that forms when the $-COOH$ group of one amino acid reacts with the $-NH_2$ group of another, thus joining the two amino acids. In the sophisticated chemical factories of the cells of any organism, this condensation reaction is repeated many times to form the long polymeric chains that we call proteins. Given the 20 different amino acids that exist in nature, a great variety of proteins can be synthesized. Some contain hundreds of amino acids, others only a few.

Chemists sometimes attempt to replicate the chemistry of nature. For example, a brilliant chemist working for the DuPont Company, Wallace Carothers (1896–1937) (Figure 9.12), was studying many polymerization reactions, including the formation of peptide bonds (equation 9.6). Instead of using amino acids, Carothers tried combining adipic acid and hexamethylenediamine.

Figure 9.12

Wallace Carothers, the inventor of nylon.

adipic acid　　　　hexamethylenediamine

Note that adipic acid has a carboxylic acid at each end of the molecule. Similarly, hexamethylenediamine has an amine group on each end. As in protein synthesis, the acid and amine groups react to form an amide and release water. But unlike protein synthesis, the resulting polymer, better known as nylon, is formed from only two monomers. Here is how the monomers join.

site for additional chain growth

$$[9.7]$$

adipic acid　　　hexamethylenediamine

site for additional chain growth

DuPont executives decided that nylon had promise, especially after company scientists learned to draw it into thin filaments. These filaments were strong and smooth and very much like the protein spun by silkworms. Therefore, nylon was first introduced to the world as a substitute for silk. Nylon was one of the first **biomimetic materials,** materials that try to replicate specific properties of biological materials for use in human applications. The world greeted it with bare legs and open pocketbooks. Four million pairs of nylon stockings were sold in New York City on May 15, 1940,

Figure 9.13
Customers eagerly lined up to buy nylon stockings in 1940, when they were first available commercially.

the first day they became available (Figure 9.13). But, in spite of consumer passion for "nylons," the civilian supply soon dried up, as the polymer was diverted from hosiery to parachutes, ropes, clothing, and hundreds of other wartime uses. By the end of World War II in 1945, nylon had repeatedly demonstrated that it was superior to silk in strength, stability, and resistance to rot. Today this polymer, with its many modifications, continues to find wide applications in carpets, sportswear, camping equipment, the kitchen, and the laboratory.

Your Turn 9.15   Kevlar

Kevlar is a polyamide used in bulletproof vests. Like PET, one of the monomers is terephthalic acid. The other monomer, phenylenediamine, contains two amine functional groups.

terephthalic acid   phenylenediamine

Draw a segment of a Kevlar molecule built from two of each of these monomers.

The silk of an orb spider ranks among the toughest biological materials ever studied, an order of magnitude stronger than a similar piece of Kevlar.

Kevlar ends our tales of condensation polymers. We remind you that it is a polyamide, just like the silk spun by silkworms and spiders. Speaking of spiders, we now return to the story of the one that opened this chapter.

9.8 | Dealing with Our Solid Waste: The Four Rs

As you learned earlier, the orb spider recycles the material in its web to avoid running out of resources. Humans need to mimic the spider lest we, too, run out of resources and create an overwhelming amount of waste. As a 2010 report from multiple European plastics industries points out, "Plastic is simply too valuable to throw away."

Indeed, we humans have produced a lot of plastic! In 1950, the value was just under 2 million metric tons worldwide. Over the years, the amount of plastic produced has increased steadily, reaching 265 million metric tons worldwide in 2012. Without question, we need sustainable answers to the question of how to deal with plastic waste.

Most likely, you have taken the garbage to the curb for pickup. You also may have watched the waste being driven away in a truck, never to be seen again (by you at least). Plastics are part of this waste, and sending plastic to a landfill is far from an ideal solution. Although recycling is a good idea, even better options exist. Here are the Four Rs, ranked in order of their desirability.

- **Reduce** the amount of materials used (e.g., use less plastic in the production of a bottle)
- **Reuse** materials (e.g., repeatedly use your own plastic bag at the grocery store)
- **Recycle** materials (e.g., don't throw beverage bottles away, recycle them)
- **Recover** either the materials or the energy content from materials that cannot be recycled (e.g., burn plastics with high energy content)

How much plastic do you use and recycle? The next activity asks you to keep a tally.

Consider This 9.16   Plastic You Toss: Part I

Keep a journal of all the plastic you either throw away or recycle in one week. Include plastic packaging from food and other products that you purchase.

a. Estimate the mass of this plastic—is it a few grams, a kilogram, or more?
b. Which is greater, the mass of the plastic you throw away or the mass you recycle?

Keep the journal handy because you will be asked to revisit it.

Let's now examine each of the Four Rs as options for dealing with plastics.

Reduce! Source reduction is always the option of choice. This means using less material and generating less waste later on. Source reduction conserves resources, reduces pollution, and minimizes toxic materials in the waste stream. As an example, consider beverage bottles. Through an improved design, a 2-L soda bottle now uses about a third less plastic than when it was introduced in 1970; similarly, a 1-gallon milk jug now weighs less than it did a few decades ago.

> Chapter 11 (the food chapter!) will offer a perspective on why it makes sense to reduce your consumption of sugared beverages. In turn, this reduces your use of plastics.

Reduced packaging also is part of the equation. Corporations are recognizing that reduced packaging offers economic incentives, such as lower costs for shipping and lower landfill costs for waste. For example, *Force of Nature*, a book published in 2011, described Walmart's goal of reducing packaging by 5% for the 329,000 items on its shelves by 2013, with 2008 as the baseline year. The author pointed out that corporation leaders realized that "sustainability wasn't just a way of being cleaner and more efficient. It also seemed to be driving innovation."

Speaking of packaging, keep an eye out for innovations. **Sustainable packaging** is the design and use of packaging materials to reduce their environmental impact and improve the sustainability of all practices. Criteria established in 2011 by the Sustainable Packing Coalition include that such packaging is:

- "beneficial, safe and healthy for individuals and communities throughout its life cycle"
- "manufactured using clean production technologies and best practices"
- "effectively recovered and utilized"

As you might expect, polymer chemists and chemical engineers are key players in this endeavor.

Reuse! Reusing something means not disposing of it after one use. In the checkout line, supermarket clerks once gave their customers only two choices, "Paper or plastic?" Today, however, they may ask if you brought your own bag. Consider This 9.17 expands on the idea of reusing bags.

Consider This 9.17   Paper, Plastic . . . Neither?

Grocery stores are not the only place in which people could rethink their use of plastic and paper bags. List three other possibilities. For each, tell whether or not you would be willing to change your "bag habits" and reuse your own bag.

As another example, consider how polystyrene foam packing "peanuts" can be reused. While only a tiny part of the waste stream, these peanuts are a huge nuisance once they escape their intended use. They end up just about everywhere, including waterways, roads, and fields. Because they are only about 5% polystyrene by weight, they have little recycling value. Reusing these peanuts definitely is the option of choice. Actually, the same is true for all polystyrene foam packing materials. If you have worked at a retail store or shipping desk, chances are you have seen some type of "in-house" reuse or recycling.

Recycle! You probably now are seeing recycling containers just about everywhere—in campus buildings, sports centers, airports, and hotels. Reasons for recycling include that it:

- reduces waste at landfills and incinerators
- prevents the pollution of air, water, and soil during the manufacturing process
- decreases emissions of greenhouse gases during manufacturing
- conserves natural resources such as petroleum, timber, water, and minerals

How well are we doing? First the good news. In 2010, the Environmental Protection Agency reported that, on average, each person in the United States recycled 1.1 pounds of material a day. Furthermore, the percentage of waste recycled is increasing. Items that people deposit in bins or at curbside include aluminum cans, office paper, cardboard, glass, and plastic containers. In addition, about 0.4 pounds per person of waste such as grass clippings and food scraps is composted, and another 0.5 pounds of waste per person is incinerated to produce energy daily. Given these reductions, the amount of waste sent to the landfill is now averaging 2.3 pounds per person per day.

But now the bad news. As you will see in the next section, roughly 12% of what we discard is plastic. Depending on the type of plastic, our recycling efficiency varies, as the next activity will reveal.

"Expanded" polystyrene that is used in packing peanuts was described in Section 9.5.

Incineration and landfills create relatively few jobs in comparison to recycling programs. A commitment to increasing recycling can benefit a local economy.

Consider This 9.18   Plastics Recycling Scorecard

According to the EPA, here is the U.S. recycling scorecard for 2010. Durable goods include items such as luggage, plastic furniture, and garden hoses. Nondurable goods include plastic pens and safety razors.

Use of Plastic	Weight Generated (millions of tons)	Weight Recovered (millions of tons)
Durable goods	10.65	0.40
Nondurable goods	6.65	Negligible
Containers/Packaging	12.53	1.72

a. For each type of plastic, calculate the plastic recovered as a percent of the waste generated.
b. Nondurable and durable goods tend to have low recycling rates. List three other examples of each and suggest reasons why.

If you did the calculations, you saw that we recycle plastics at a surprisingly low rate. This may seem at odds with all the milk jugs and plastic bottles you see being recycled in your own community. Indeed, you are correct. Certain plastics are recycled more consistently than others. For example, in the United States polyethylene milk containers are recycled at a rate of 29% and clear PET soft drink bottles at 28%. While these numbers may seem high, nonetheless more than 70% of these containers still is being tossed out.

Skeptical Chemist 9.19   Plastic You Toss: Part II

Earlier, in Consider This 9.17, you kept a journal of all the plastic you discarded in a week. Revisit what you wrote. Do the yearly recycling figures just cited ring true? That is, do you throw out far more plastic than you recycle? Briefly report on how your own plastic use stacks up against the national averages. Remember that your journal may not reveal your use of durable and nondurable goods over a longer period of time.

Recover! What about incineration, that is, recovering the energy in plastics by burning them as fuels? Because the Big Six and most other polymers closely resemble hydrocarbon fuels, incineration would seem to be an excellent way to dispose of them, reducing demand on landfills. The chief products of combustion are carbon dioxide, water, and a good deal of energy. In fact, pound for pound, plastics have a higher energy content than coal. Although in the United States plastics accounted for only about 12% of the weight of municipal solid waste in 2010, they represent approximately 30% of its energy content.

But incineration of plastics has drawbacks. The repeated message of Chapters 1–4, that burning does not destroy matter, applies here as well. The gases produced by combustion may be "out of sight," but they best not be "out of mind." Burning plastics produces CO_2, a greenhouse gas. Of special concern in incineration are chlorine-containing polymers such as polyvinyl chloride that release hydrogen chloride during combustion. Because HCl dissolves in water to form hydrochloric acid, such smokestack exhaust could make a serious contribution to acid rain. Burning chlorine-containing plastics can produce other toxic gases. So in terms of the overall benefit, including the energy involved, recycling is always preferable to incineration.

Your Turn 9.20   Burning a Plastic

Under conditions of complete combustion, polypropylene burns to produce carbon dioxide and water.

a. Write a balanced chemical equation. Assume an average chain length of 2500 monomers.
b. If the combustion is incomplete, other products form. Name two possibilities.

Answer
b. Incomplete combustion produces CO and particulate matter (soot), both air pollutants.

The plastic that we do not reuse, recycle, or recover eventually ends up in a landfill (the "out of sight, out of mind" approach) or as trash in the environment. Both are problematic. Although landfill space is still available, landfills have drawbacks. They take up space in congested areas; they have costs associated with their construction and upkeep; they leak; they attract vermin; and they emit methane, a greenhouse gas.

The majority of plastics do not biodegrade in the landfill (or anywhere else). Most bacteria and fungi lack the enzymes necessary to break down synthetic polymers. Some microbes, however, possess the enzymes to break down naturally occurring polymers, such as cellulose. For example, in Chapter 3 you read about the release of methane by cattle. Actually, the methane is produced when bacteria obtain energy by decomposing cellulose in the cow's rumen. In the same chapter, you also learned that methane is generated by natural decomposition of organic materials in landfills, another result of bacterial activity.

Even natural polymers do not decompose completely in landfills. Modern waste disposal facilities are covered and lined to deter leaching of waste and waste by-products into the surrounding ground. Landfill linings and coverings also create anaerobic (oxygen-free) conditions that impede the breakdown of these wastes. As a result, many supposedly

Ideally, landfill liners last forever. However, over time, liners break down or rupture.

Figure 9.14

Some buried wastes can remain intact for a long time. This newspaper from 1952 was excavated 37 years later.

biodegradable substances decompose slowly or not at all. Excavation of old landfills has unearthed old newspapers that are still readable (Figure 9.14) and 5-year-old hot dogs that, while hardly edible, are at least recognizable.

Consider This 9.21   Landfill Liners

Landfill liners include natural clay and human–made plastics. For example, thick sheets of high–density polyethylene may be employed. Even the best HDPE liners, however, can crack and degrade.

   a. From Table 9.1, which types of chemicals soften HDPE?
   b. Name five substances sent to the landfill that could degrade a HDPE liner over time.

Answer
   b. Cooking oil, shoe polish, and alcohol, to name a few.

Given the problems associated with landfill disposal and incineration of natural and synthetic polymers, *recycling* has an important role to play. However, in contrast to incineration, recycling polymers requires an input of energy. Furthermore, if the waste plastic is dirty or of low quality, more energy may be needed to recycle it than to manufacture it from new plastic. Nonetheless, recycling is one of several ways to divert plastic from landfills and incinerators. In the next section, we examine the bigger picture of garbage.

9.9 | Recycling Plastics: The Bigger Picture

Together with other waste, the plastic that you discard is part of a bigger picture. In the United States, the EPA has been keeping statistics about municipal solid waste—better known as garbage—for over 30 years. **Municipal solid waste** (MSW) includes everything you discard or throw into your trash, including food scraps, grass clippings, and old appliances. MSW does not include all sources, such as waste from industry, agriculture, mining, or construction sites. In the United States, municipal solid waste has been averaging about 250 million tons per year. What is the largest single item? Paper, as you can see from Figure 9.15. Materials of biological origin such as paper, wood, food scraps, and yard trimmings make up the majority of the materials classified as municipal solid waste. All of these can be dealt with by one of the Four Rs (reduce, reuse, recycle, recover).

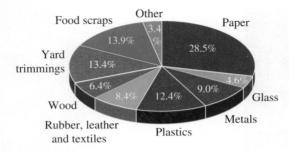

Figure 9.15

What's in your garbage? Composition by weight of municipal solid waste before recycling (250 million tons, 2010).

Source: U.S. Environmental Protection Agency, EPA-530-F-11-005, November 2011.

How much of this MSW is plastic? Consult Figure 9.15 to see that plastic is roughly 12% of what U.S. citizens discard. The U.S. EPA reports data for three types of plastics:

- durable items, such as plastic furniture, bowls, and garden hoses
- nondurable items, such as plastic cups, plates, trash bags, pens, and safety razors
- packaging, such as beverage bottles and food containers

In 2010, altogether, these plastics added up to about 31 million tons, or 12.4% of the 250 million tons of MSW generated.

How much of this plastic do we recycle? The graph in Figure 9.16a shows the amount in millions of tons over the years for *total* MSW recycling in the United States, not just for plastics. The overall rate of recycling of MSW in recent years has reached 34% (Figure 9.16b).

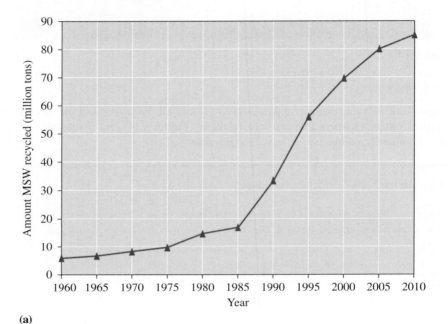

(a)

Figure 9.16

(a) Amount of municipal solid waste recycled in million tons, 1960–2010.
(b) Percent of municipal solid waste recycled, 1960–2010.

Source: U.S. Environmental Protection Agency, EPA-530-F-11-005, November 2011.

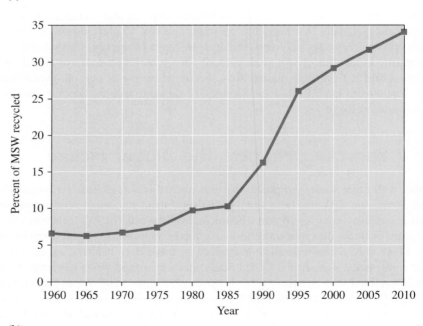

(b)

Table 9.4	Recycled Plastic Bottles in 2010	
Plastic	Amount Recycled in 2010 (million pounds)	Recycling Rate
PET	1557.0	29.1%
HDPE	984.0	29.9%
PVC	1.4	2.0%
PP	35.4	18.3%
LDPE	1.0	1.9%

Source: American Chemistry Council, National Post–Consumer Plastic Bottle Recycling Report, 2010.

By way of comparison, in 2010 only 7.6% of the plastic in the United States was recycled. Why so little? The devil is in the details! Some items can be easily recycled; others present nothing short of a logistical nightmare. Furthermore, some types of plastics have a ready market; others do not. Table 9.4 reveals the relatively high success currently achieved for plastic bottles in comparison to the overall 7.6% plastic recycling rate.

Skeptical Chemist 9.22   Pounds or Tons Recycled

Examine the values in Table 9.4 from the American Chemistry Council (ACC).

a. Are these values comparable to those quoted by the EPA in Consider This 9.18? Assume that the tons quoted were short tons, that is, 2000 pounds per ton.

b. The EPA reported the amounts recycled using one unit (million tons), and the ACC reported in another (million pounds). Several explanations are possible. Propose one.

Answer

a. 1557 + 984 + 1.4 + 35.4 + 1.0 = 2579 million pounds recycled, or 1.29 million tons. This is in the ballpark of the 1.72 million tons quoted by the EPA, especially considering that data for polystyrene are not included in the ACC set.

For recycling to be successful and self-sustaining, a number of factors must be coordinated. These involve not only science and technology but also economics and sometimes politics, especially at the local level. The best recycling involves a closed loop (Figure 9.17) in which plastics are collected, sorted, and then converted into products that consumers buy, use, and later recycle.

In order to recycle, it is necessary to collect the plastic. Several options include: collecting at curbside, at local drop-off centers, and through bottle bill programs involving a deposit and refund. For recycling to be successful, a dependable supply of used plastic must be consistently available at designated locations.

Once collected, the plastic needs to be transported to a facility at which it can be sorted and prepared for some marketable commodity. The codes that appear on plastic objects (see Table 9.1) help facilitate the sorting process. Because of the large volume of material, automated sorting methods have been developed. Once sorted, the polymer is melted. The molten polymer can be used directly in the manufacturing of new products. Alternatively, it can be solidified, pelletized, and stored for future use.

If a mixture of various polymers is melted, the product tends to be darkly colored and has different properties depending on the nature of the mixture. This type of reprocessed material is generally good enough to "downcycle" meaning to convert it to lower grade uses such as parking lot bumpers, disposable plastic flower pots, and cheap plastic lumber. Such mixed material is not as valuable as the pure, homogeneous recycled polymer. This underscores the importance of sorting plastics. For similar reasons, manufacturers prefer to use only a single polymer in a product to avoid the need to separate.

Given a supply of plastic (ideally clean and sorted), the manufacturers can get to work. The items produced contain varying percentages and types of recycled materials. The terminology is confusing. **Recycled-content products** are those made with materials that otherwise would have been in the waste stream. These include items manufactured from discarded plastic as well as rebuilt items, such as plastic toner cartridges

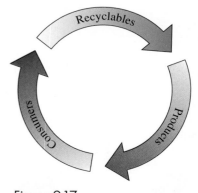

Figure 9.17

Recycling ideally is a never–ending loop.

Source: Reprinted by permission of the National Association for PET Container Resources.

that are refilled. Trash bags, laundry detergent bottles, and carpeting are common plastic items that may qualify as recycled-content products. Some playground equipment and park benches also are made from discarded plastic.

Recycled products are now beginning to provide the origin of the recycled material. **Postconsumer content** is material that previously was used individually that otherwise would have been discarded as waste. Recycling this waste—office paper, foam packing, and beverage bottles—is one way to keep it out of the landfill. **Preconsumer content** is waste left over from the manufacturing process itself, such as scraps and clippings. Preconsumer fabrics, such as polyester fabric scraps from the clothing industry, can be recycled rather than discarded.

The term *recyclable product* simply means that the product *can be* recycled. The term may be misleading because a recycling pathway may not exist. Recyclable products do not necessarily contain any recycled materials.

Your Turn 9.23   Recyclable and Recycled

Give three examples of items that you might purchase and recycle. Also give three examples of recycled-content products. Can an item fall into both categories?

To complete the cycle shown in Figure 9.17, the recycled items are marketed and (ideally) purchased by consumers. Without a product and buyers, recycling programs are doomed to fail. In fact, recycling laws in a number of cities have not been implemented and enforced because one of the links in this polymeric chain of supply, collecting, sorting, processing, manufacturing, and marketing was missing.

Consult Table 9.4 to see that as consumers, we are moderately adept in dropping PET beverage bottles into recycling bins (Figure 9.18). Over 1 billion pounds of PET is recycled in the United States! Since PET is more successfully recycled than most plastics, it warrants a closer look. PET soft-drink bottles need special handling before they can be melted and reused. The bottles usually are sorted to remove other types of plastic, such as PVC. If left in the batch, PVC can weaken the final product. Any labels, bottle caps, or food that adhered to the plastic also must be separated or scrubbed off. Bottle caps, for example, are usually made out of the tougher polypropylene. The next exercise shows how PET can be separated from other polymers by density. This is helpful in the case of PET mixed with PVC because these can look alike.

Figure 9.18
PET beverage bottles are widely recycled.

Consider This 9.24   Float or sink?

Here are density values for PET and for three other plastics likely to be found with it in a recycling bin.

Plastic	Density (g/cm^3)
PET	1.38–1.39
HDPE	0.95–0.97
PP	0.90–0.91
PVC	1.18–1.65

When dropped into a liquid, a plastic will float or sink depending on the density of the liquid. Here are the densities for several liquids that do not dissolve the four plastics just listed.

Liquid	Density (g/mL)
methanol	0.79
42% ethanol/water mixture	0.92
38% ethanol/water mixture	0.94
water	1.00
saturated solution of MgCl$_2$	1.34
saturated solution of ZnCl$_2$	2.01

Given a PET sample contaminated with HDPE, PP, and PVC, propose a way to separate the PET from the other three plastics. Assume that all density values were measured at the same temperature. *Note:* 1 cm^3 = 1 mL

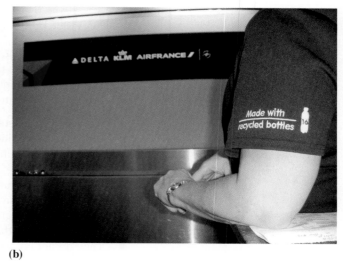

(a)   (b)

Figure 9.19

(a) Activewear made from recycled PET. (b) Airline uniform made from recycled PET bottles.

When you recycle a PET beverage bottle, it may come back to life as part of another beverage bottle. More likely, though, the polyester is downwardly recycled (downcycled) to produce items of lower purity. For example, the PET may be melted and spun into polyester carpeting, T-shirts, "fleece" (Figure 9.19), bed sheets, and the fabric uppers in jogging shoes. Five recycled 2-L bottles can be converted into a T-shirt or the insulation for a ski jacket; it takes just about 450 such bottles to make polyester carpeting for a 9 × 12-foot room.

A reasonable question to ask at this point is what happens to all of these products made from recycled PET. Shaw Industries won a 2003 Presidential Green Chemistry Challenge Award for providing an answer with its development of EcoWorx broadloom carpet and carpet tiles. By removing the PVC from the backing of these carpets, the product became 100% recyclable into other products. Additional environmental benefits of this carpeting include lower VOC emissions and lower transportation costs, because the carpet tiles are lighter in weight. As of 2012, this carpeting contained 40% recycled content and was labeled "We want it back." As more of this carpet is used, recycled, and again recycled, this percent is expected to grow. This is another example of the concept of cradle-to-cradle; in fact, this line of carpet was awarded a silver cradle-to-cradle award from MBDC (McDonough Braungart Design Chemistry).

This section explored the complexities of recycling. But remember that recycling is not the only game in town. There is no single, best solution to the problems of plastic waste, or more generally, *all* solid waste. Incineration, reuse, recycling, and source reduction all provide benefits, and all have costs. Therefore, it is likely that the most effective response will be an integrated waste management system that employs multiple strategies. Ultimately, such a system would optimize efficiency, conserve energy and material, and minimize cost and environmental damage.

Architect William McDonough and chemist Michael Braungart are the authors of the book *Cradle–to–Cradle* that was mentioned in Chapter 0.

Consider This 9.25   In a Store Near You

Unless people buy products made from recycled plastics, manufacturers will have little financial incentive to produce them. Find five recycled–content plastic items available for sale.

a. Identify the polymer(s) in each and the % recycled content, if provided.
b. Comment on the consumer appeal of the item, including whether or not you would purchase it.

9.10 | From Plants to Plastics

As we mentioned earlier, most polymers are produced from petroleum, a nonrenewable resource. Even so, some polymers find their origin in renewable materials such as wood, cotton fibers, straw, starch, and sugar. What makes these plant-based polymers different from their petroleum-based cousins?

- They are **compostable,** that is, under the conditions of either a home composter or an industrial composter, they are able to undergo biological decomposition to form a material (compost) that contains no materials toxic to plant growth.
- Some polymers can be "unzipped" and converted back into monomers and remade into virgin polymer.
- Their synthesis generally requires fewer resources, results in less waste, and uses less energy than petroleum-based polymers.
- They do not contain chlorine or fluorine, as do petroleum-based polymers such as Teflon, Saran, or PVC.

Because of characteristics such as these, these polymers are termed "eco-friendly." However, employ this term with caution. As you will see, the composting of biopolymers is not as straightforward as it may sound. In addition, in order to compare different polymers, the waste and energy costs from manufacture, use, and the end of a product's life all need to be considered. Again, the best solution is to *reduce* what you consume rather than to switch to any particular type of plastic.

While polylactic acid (PLA) is not the only plastic produced from plants, it serves as the poster child for eco-friendly plastics. Like the Big Six, PLA is a thermoplastic polymer that softens with heating and can be molded. Because PLA is a polyester that has a similar look and feel to PET, it is used to produce some of the same items as PET including clear shiny bottles, transparent food packaging, fibers for clothing, and plasticware (Figure 9.20). PLA also is used as a coating on paper cups and plates to make them water resistant.

Unlike PET, PLA softens around 140 °F (60 °C). As a result, if you leave an item made from PLA in a car on a sunny day, you may return to find that it has melted. So unless blended with other resins to improve its temperature stability, PLA is limited to uses at lower temperatures.

As the name suggests, polylactic acid is a polymer of lactic acid. This monomer has two functional groups: a carboxylic acid group and a hydroxyl group. Here is its structural formula.

$$HO-CH-\overset{\displaystyle O}{\overset{\displaystyle \|}{C}}-OH$$
$$\underset{\displaystyle CH_3}{|}$$

Like PET, polylactic acid is a condensation polymer and releases a molecule of water each time a covalent bond forms in the polymer chain.

Lactic acid is naturally present in the biosphere. It gives sour milk its taste and is partly responsible for making your muscles ache after vigorous exercise.

Figure 9.20

(a) PLA cups can be colorless, transparent, and water resistant, just like PET.
(b) PLA can be pigmented, again like PET.
(c) Paper cups coated with PLA.

(a)   (b)   (c)

Your Turn 9.26   Chemistry of PLA

We don't show the chemical reaction for the formation of PLA from lactic acid because it does not proceed in a single step and is complicated. Even so, you should be able to write a chemical formula for PLA.

a. Circle and label the functional groups in the monomer, lactic acid.
b. When lactic acid polymerizes, is this an addition or a condensation reaction? Explain.
c. What is the repeating unit in PLA?

Answer

b. A condensation reaction. The OH from the carboxylic group and the H from the hydroxyl group form a water molecule that is a product.

As an eco-friendly polymer, PLA has its share of controversies. One set arises from its synthesis from corn. Like ethanol, also produced from corn (Chapter 4), PLA competes with the corn that is used as animal food. Furthermore, the runoff from cornfields may produce nutrient-rich waterways (Chapter 11), and the corn may be genetically engineered to resist pests (Chapter 12). PLA also can be produced from plants other than corn that contain carbohydrates. For example, a Dutch company uses sugarcane and a Japanese manufacturer uses tapioca root. In the United States, PLA is largely manufactured from the starch of corn kernels leading to the nickname of "corn plastic."

Unlike petroleum-based polymers, PLA is compostable, but the process goes slowly without the heat supplied by an industrial composter. How slowly? In a backyard compost heap, the process takes up to a year. In contrast, industrial composters do the job in 3–6 months. However, many communities do not have access to such composters, at least not at present. Note that there is no ecological benefit to tossing PLA in a landfill. If you revisit Figure 9.14, you will see that the actual breakdown of anything in a landfill is slow.

Can PLA be recycled? In theory, yes, but at present no. In fact, having PLA in the recycling stream is of concern to those who recycle PET, because, as one recycler quipped, "the two mix as well as oil and water." Recyclers currently collect and bale PET bottles and then process the plastic, eventually making it into new containers, fiberfill, or carpeting. PLA, if present in more than small amounts, needs to be separated from the PET recycling stream.

As of 2012, PLA was primarily manufactured in the U.S. by NatureWorks, a subsidiary of Cargill. It is also manufactured in the Netherlands by PURAC Biomaterials and by several manufacturers in Japan and China.

In the biowaste stream (as part of municipal solid waste), PLA makes up only about 1%. Yard trimmings and food scraps are the major items.

Consider This 9.27   Detective Work on Your Campus

Meals are served on most college campuses, up to thousands each day. Most likely, professionals in your campus food service have given serious thought to which cups, plates, forks, spoons, chopsticks, and napkins to use. Be a detective and learn about the sustainable practices on your campus. What happens to plates, cups, and utensils? Are they washed and reused? Are they discarded? If so, are any made from PLA? What are the controversies? Prepare a one-page briefing on a particular item, for example, hot beverage cups.

9.11 | Shifting Baselines

In the opening chapter of this text, we introduced the concept of **shifting baselines,** that is, the idea that what people expect as "normal" on our planet has changed over time. Our use of plastics is a good example. Many people are still alive who remember "how it used to be" before the advent of plastics. Today, they are likely to have gray hair and were children back perhaps as early as the 1930s. Even the baby boomers of the 1950s remember collecting the glass bottles shown in Figure 9.21b to reclaim the two-cent deposit.

Take plastic pens, for example. Less than 50 years ago, most people—including children in elementary schools—wrote with refillable fountain pens. A bottle of blue

(a)   **(b)**

Figure 9.21

(a) 1970s 2–liter bottle with cup at the base for additional strength. (b) 1960s 10–ounce glass bottle, returnable.

Vending machines that dispensed aluminum cans were invented around 1965.

or black ink was something that you kept handy in your wooden desk and tightly capped. You worked arithmetic problems with a yellow No. 2 pencil, gradually wearing down the eraser. Disposable ball-point and gel pens were yet to appear on the writing landscape.

Think also about plastic beverage bottles. It wasn't until 1970 that the first 2-liter (64-oz) bottles appeared on supermarket shelves. The early models were made from PET and fitted with an opaque base cup for added strength (Figure 9.21a). PepsiCo was the first to sell soft drinks in 2-liter bottles and other beverage companies quickly followed suit.

Before the advent of plastic, most beverages were bottled in glass. Even as late as the 1970s, milk was brought to homes in glass bottles, with the empty bottles collected at the time of delivery. Portion sizes were smaller as well. For example, Coca-Cola bottles once held 10 ounces (Figure 9.21b); in contrast, aluminum cans today hold 12 ounces and plastic bottles are larger still. Rather than dispensing cans, vending machines of the past dispensed bottles, and wooden racks stood nearby to receive the empties. However, glass bottling is not necessarily "greener" or more sustainable than bottling in plastic. The next activity invites you to explore the two options.

Your Turn 9.28   Glass or Plastic?

a. Even though selling milk in glass bottles may be coming back in vogue, plastic jugs or plastic–coated cartons are still the norm in most places. List two advantages and disadvantages of using glass bottles. Do the same for using plastic bottles.

b. Today, if not sold in aluminum cans, soft drinks are sold in plastic bottles and beer is sold in ones made of glass. Research and report on at least two reasons for the difference.

Plastic debris! Not only has our use of plastic become the norm, but also it has become the norm to find plastic debris everywhere—streets, backyards, streams, beaches, and even wilderness areas. The trouble is, plastic is durable. Once a piece of plastic finds its way into the local environment, it does not dissolve, break down in sunlight, or decompose, at least not at any appreciable rate. Rather, it tends to break into smaller and smaller pieces that widely disperse. The very properties that made plastics so useful in the first place mean that the pieces of plastic persist for years and years. Does this sound familiar? See if the next activity helps jog your memory.

Consider This 9.29   Lessons from Refrigerators Past

Chlorofluorocarbons, better known as CFCs, were once widely used in refrigerators, aerosol sprays, foams, and medical inhalers.

a. Why were CFCs phased out?

b. Some CFCs remain in the atmosphere for 100 years or more. Explain how this property of CFCs is connected to the fact that they have been phased out.

c. Name some properties that polymers such as HDPE, LDPE, PVC, and PS share with CFCs.

d. Unlike CFCs, it is highly unlikely that plastics will be phased out. Offer some reasons why.

e. Even so, we cannot sustain our current use of plastics. Give evidence that supports this statement.

Plastic debris! It is not just the plastic bottles and wrappers that you see around you on the landscape. Also ubiquitous in nature—including in our bodies—are the invisible substances that leach out of plastics. Do the environmental math. What is added to a polymer is slowly subtracted with the passage of time. Why? Plasticizers are not chemically bonded to the plastic. Rather, they are mixed in to make plastics softer and more pliable. Over time, they slowly leach out into the biosphere. The next activity introduces you to DEHP, a controversial plasticizer.

Your Turn 9.30   Meet DEHP

DEHP belongs to a common class of plasticizers called *phthalates* (THAL–ates). Phthalates are esters of phthalic (THAL–ic) acid, an isomer of terephthalic acid, one of the monomers used to synthesize PET.

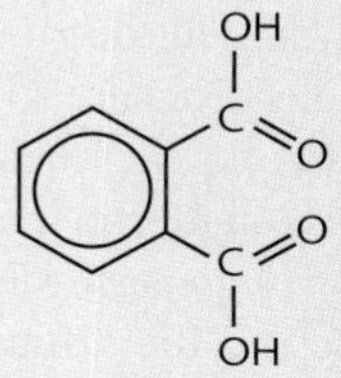

phthalic acid

a. Explain the meaning of the term *ester*.
b. Here is the structural formula for DEHP. Circle the two ester groups in this molecule.

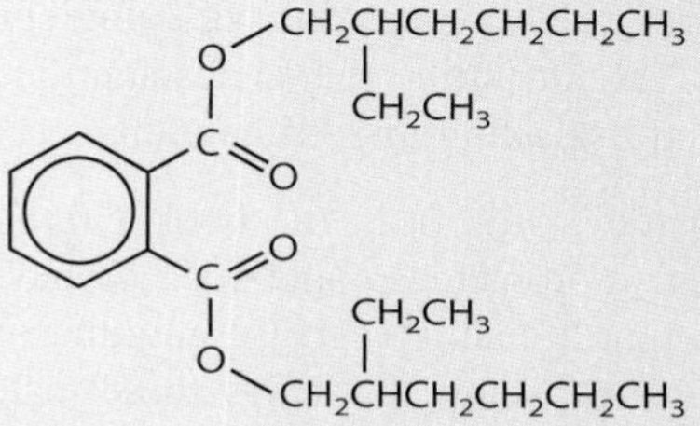

DEHP

c. Draw a structural formula for the alcohol that reacted with terephthalic acid to form this ester.

As you saw in the previous activity, the DEHP molecule has two long "wavy" side chains attached to a benzene ring. Imagine what happens when DEHP, perhaps as much as 30% by weight, is mixed in with a repeating head-to-tail arrangement of PVC. This arrangement of PVC tends to be stiff because its molecules pack well together and form crystalline regions. However, with the addition of DEHP, the regular packing of the PVC polymer chains is disrupted and the polymer becomes much more flexible.

Why is there a controversy? DEHP, like other phthalates, is a suspected **endocrine disrupter**, a compound that affects the human hormone system, including hormones for reproduction and sexual development. Estrogen is one such hormone, and unfortunately DEHP seems to have biological activity similar to that of estrogen. DEHP also is a suspected human carcinogen.

And why is it difficult to resolve the controversy? Although the evidence against DEHP has been mounting for decades, the research dots have been difficult to connect. Part of the difficulty lies in the low concentrations involved—parts per billion. Even so, in 2011, the U.S. Food and Drug Administration set the allowable limit for DEHP in bottled water at 0.006 mg/liter or 6 ppb. The very fact that DEHP might be present in bottled water may come as a surprise to you! But remember what we stated earlier: Compounds that originate in plastics have made their way almost everywhere in the environment, including our bodies.

Another reason that it is difficult to resolve the controversy is that not one, but many endocrine disrupters are present in our environment. Some are naturally present, others have been added by humans. As an example of the latter, you may have heard of BPA, a compound that mimics estrogen. BPA is transferred to the environment from several sources, including some plastic bottles.

In the next chapter on drugs, we'll examine the chemical structure and biological activity of estrogen.

Bisphenol A (BPA) has been known to mimic the effects of estrogen since the 1930s. Look for more about estrogen in Chapter 10, the drug chapter.

A third difficulty lies in the fact that it is unethical to test compounds like BPA on humans. Although such research quickly could resolve the arguments, it is neither possible nor desirable. One way to get around this is to study those who inadvertently already were exposed to BPA.

In spite of the difficulties, in some cases potentially harmful substances have been banned by law. For example, it made sense to ban DEHP in infant pacifiers because babies receive repeated exposure by sucking on them and because research on animals showed that DEHP affected male sexual development. Similarly, DEHP and other related plasticizers have been banned in children's toys. These bans are an example of the **precautionary principle,** mentioned earlier in Chapter 2. This principle stresses the wisdom of acting, even in the absence of complete scientific data, before the adverse effects on human health or the environment become significant or irrevocable.

In most other cases, though, the choices are still being debated. The extremes range from banning the chemicals entirely to allowing their indiscriminate use. Neither extreme currently is in practice. So now it is a matter of reaching consensus on allowable uses. A report about BPA in *Chemical & Engineering News*, the weekly news magazine of the American Chemical Society, assessed the difficulties that you and all citizens face:

> As this debate has unfolded, the public has been bombarded with a steady flow of studies, reports, claims, counter claims, conflicts of interest, lawsuits, and congressional inquiries regarding BPA. Both sides of the debate have been active in promoting their views to the media and the public. And both sides accuse each other of using spin tactics to create uncertainty about BPA, not unlike the socioscientific debates that have unfolded over cigarette smoking and climate change. (June 6, 2011, p. 13)

We end this chapter with the words from the book *Cradle-to-Cradle* that opened it: "Nature doesn't have a design problem. People do." We have designed marvelous plastics that serve us in ways that a century ago we couldn't even dream of. At the same time, we have failed to design systems that carry these materials smoothly, safely, and economically from cradle to cradle.

Conclusion

Synthetic polymers are at the very center of modern living, yet their existence depends on a precious resource that we are consuming—crude oil. We have come not only to depend on synthetic polymers, but also in many cases to take them for granted to the point of being wasteful. Once more, we encounter a chemical topic that has the potential to inspire us to revisit the issue of our lifestyle and its sustainability.

Over time, chemists have created an amazing array of polymers and plastics—new materials that have made our lives more comfortable and more convenient. In many cases, these plastics represent a significant improvement over the natural polymers they replace. Furthermore, products that we use today would be impossible without synthetic polymers: DVDs, cell phones, breathable contact lenses, fleece clothing, kidney dialysis equipment, and artificial hearts. We have become dependent on polymers, and it verges on the impossible to abandon their use.

The chemical industry has responded to consumers. But the response now appears to be the production of more plastic items than we would like or perhaps than we can deal with responsibly. Together with those who work in the corporate world, we must learn to cope with plastic waste while at the same time save raw materials and energy for tomorrow. To create a new world of plastics and polymers will require the intelligence and efforts of policy planners, legislators, economists, manufacturers, consumers, and, of course, chemists. This chapter showed that efforts at reducing, reusing, recycling, and recovering are well under way.

As we've seen in previous chapters, everything is connected, just like the web of the orb spider that opened this chapter. In this chapter, we looked at the connections of polymers to their raw materials—petroleum or plants—as well as at their connections to waste (or compost) in the environment. The chapter ended with an unexpected connection, that of additives to plastics that leach into the environment and have drug-like properties similar to estrogens. What exactly are drugs? Which other pharmaceutically active compounds are found in the environment, either naturally or from human sources? These questions connect us to the next chapter.

Chapter Summary

Need-to-know chemical principles in this chapter:

  Natural versus synthetic polymers (9.1, 9.7)

  Structure of polymers and monomers (9.2)

  Polymerization reactions (9.3, 9.6)

  Intermolecular forces (9.3)

  Molecular arrangement and observable properties (9.4)

  Functional groups and reactivity (9.5, 9.6)

  Amino acids and proteins (9.7)

  Environmental persistence and material design (9.8–9.11)

Having studied this chapter, you should be able to:

- Give examples of natural and petroleum-based as well as plant-based synthetic polymers (9.1, 9.10)

- Show the relationship between polymers and the monomers from which they are synthesized (9.2)

- Compare and contrast addition and condensation polymerization (9.3, 9.6)

- Compare and contrast low-density polyethylene and high-density polyethylene, in terms of molecular structure and observable properties (9.4)

- Recognize and describe the Big Six polymers in terms of uses and properties as well as the molecular structures of their monomers and polymers (9.4–9.6)

- Explain the uses and discuss the controversies surrounding plasticizers (9.5, 9.10, 9.11)

- Identify functional groups in monomers and polymers (9.6)

- Name and draw structural formulas for several different carboxylic acids (9.6)

- Show how an ester can be produced from an alcohol and carboxylic acid (9.6)

- Use structural formulas to write the chemical equation for polymerization reactions (9.6, 9.7)

- Explain the relationship between amino acids and proteins (9.7)

- Compare and contrast the origins and structures of nylons and proteins (9.7)

- Give examples of the Four Rs: Reduce, Reuse, Recycle, and Recover (9.8)

- Explain why the Four Rs have an order of preference (9.8)

- Describe the differences between recycled-content products, postconsumer content, and preconsumer content (9.9)

- Interpret trends in plastics recycling over the decade (9.9)

- Discuss the different activities involved in recycling and their inherent complexities (9.9)

- Discuss the sources and components of Municipal Solid Waste (MSW) (9.9)

- Compare and contrast the eco-friendliness and the limits of plant-based and petroleum-based polymers (9.10)

- Using plastics, give examples of shifting baselines and of the precautionary principle (9.11)

- Compare and contrast plastics and CFCs in terms of the issues that arise because of their environmental persistence (9.11)

Questions

Emphasizing Essentials

1. Give two examples of natural polymers and two of synthetic polymers.

2. Think about your intended profession or career path. How can you contribute in a meaningful way to reducing our solid waste? Suggest three ways. *Hint:* Thinking about the Four Rs may be of help.

3. Equation 9.1 contains an n on both sides of the equation. The one on the left is a coefficient; the one on the right is a subscript. Explain.

4. In equation 9.1, explain the function of the R· over the arrow.

5. Describe how each of these strategies would be expected to affect the properties of polyethylene. Also provide an explanation at the molecular level for each effect.

   a. increasing the length of the polymer chain

   b. aligning the polymer chains with one another

   c. increasing the degree of branching in the polymer chain

6. Figure 9.3a shows two bottles made from polyethylene. How do the two bottles differ at the molecular level?

7. Ethylene (ethene) is a hydrocarbon. Give the names and structural formulas of two other hydrocarbons that, like ethylene, can serve as monomers.

8. Why is a repeating head-to-tail arrangement not possible for ethylene?

9. Determine the approximate number of $H_2C=CH_2$ monomeric units, n, in one molecule of polyethylene with a molar mass of 40,000 g. How many carbon atoms are in this molecule?

10. A structural formula for styrene is given in Table 9.1.

    a. Redraw it to show all of the atoms present.

    b. Give the chemical formula for styrene.

    c. Calculate the molar mass of a polystyrene molecule consisting of 5000 monomers.

11. Vinyl chloride polymerizes to form PVC in several different arrangements, as shown in Figure 9.8. Which example is shown here?

12. Here are two segments of a larger PVC molecule. Do these two structures represent the same arrangement? Explain your answer by identifying the orientation in each arrangement. *Hint:* See Figure 9.8.

and

13. Butadiene, $H_2C=CH-HC=CH_2$, can be polymerized to make a synthetic rubber. Would this be by addition or condensation polymerization?

14. Which of the "Big Six" most likely would be used for these applications?

    a. clear soda bottles

    b. opaque laundry detergent bottles

    c. clear, shiny shower curtains

    d. tough indoor–outdoor carpet

    e. plastic baggies for food

    f. packaging "peanuts"

    g. containers for milk

15. a. Analogous to equation 9.3, write the polymerization reaction of n monomers of propylene to form polypropylene.

    b. Analogous to Figure 9.8, show a random arrangement of the monomers in a segment of polypropylene.

16. Many containers are made from plastic. Check the recycling code on 10 containers of your choice (see Table 9.1). In your sample, which polymer did you most frequently encounter?

17. Name the functional group(s) in each of these monomers.

    a. styrene

    b. ethylene glycol

    c. terephthalic acid

    d. the amino acid in which R = H

    e. hexamethylenediamine

    f. adipic acid

18. Circle and identify all the functional groups in this molecule:

19. Kevlar is a type of nylon called an *aramid*. It contains rings similar to that of benzene. Because of its great mechanical strength, Kevlar is used in radial tires and in bulletproof vests. Your Turn 9.15 gives the structures for the two monomers, terephthalic acid and phenylenediamine. Name the functional groups in both the monomers and in the polymer.

20. Table 9.3 gives structural formulas for ethanoic acid and propanoic acid. From these two names, you should be able to determine the naming pattern.

    a. How would a carboxylic acid containing five carbon atoms be named?

    b. Methanoic acid is the smallest carboxylic acid. Also known as formic acid, it is one of the components in the sting of an ant bite. Draw the structural formula for methanoic acid.

    c. Butanoic acid, like propanoic acid, has a sharp smell. Draw the structural formula for butanoic acid.

21. Silk is an example of a natural polymer. Name three properties that make silk desirable. Which synthetic polymer has a chemical structure modeled after silk?

22. The Dow Chemical Company won a Presidential Green Chemistry Challenge Award for developing a process that uses CO_2 as the blowing agent to produce Styrofoam packaging material.

    a. What is a blowing agent?

    b. What compound does CO_2 likely replace in the process, and why is this substitution environmentally beneficial?

23. Suggestions for reducing your waste include (1) buying in bulk and/or economy sizes and (2) avoiding individually packaged servings. Let's say that you followed this practice for these cases. Which plastic would you use less of? Would you use more of something else?

    a. For use in your refrigerator, buying a half-gallon plastic jug of milk rather than 2 quarts.

b. For guests at a reception, purchasing 2-liter bottles of lemonade rather than individual bottles.

c. Buying more concentrated laundry detergent in a smaller plastic bottle.

24. Recycled products now are beginning to provide the origin of the recycled material.

a. Give examples of postconsumer content and of preconsumer content.

b. Do recyclable products contain recycled materials?

Concentrating on Concepts

25. Draw a diagram to show the relationships among these terms: *natural, synthetic, polymer, nylon, protein.* Add other terms as needed.

26. Currently, many 2-liter beverage bottles are made of PET with polypropylene caps. Why is polypropylene a good choice for a bottle cap? What difficulty does using polypropylene present in the recycling of PET bottles?

27. Glucose from corn is the source of some new bio-based polymer materials. Glucose also is the monomer in cellulose. Earlier in this text you encountered glucose in the chemical reaction of photosynthesis. What is photosynthesis and from what compounds is glucose produced?

28. The properties of a polymer depend, in part, on which chemical elements it contains. Name three additional things that influence the properties of a particular polymer.

29. Many monomers contain a C=C double bond. Select such a monomer and draw its structural formula together with the corresponding polymer. Describe the similarities and differences between the monomer and the polymer.

30. What structural features must a monomer possess to undergo addition polymerization? Explain, giving an example. Do the same for condensation polymerization.

31. This equation represents the polymerization of vinyl chloride. At the molecular level as the reaction takes place, how does the Cl−C−H bond angle change?

$$n \quad \overset{H}{\underset{H}{\diagdown}}C=C\overset{H}{\underset{Cl}{\diagup}} \quad \xrightarrow{R\cdot} \quad \left[\begin{array}{cc} \overset{|}{\underset{|}{H}} & \overset{|}{\underset{|}{H}} \\ -C\!-\!C- \\ \underset{H}{|} & \underset{Cl}{|} \end{array} \right]_n$$

32. Polyacrylonitrile is a polymer made from the monomer acrylonitrile, CH_2CHCN.

a. Draw the Lewis structure for this monomer.
Hint: The N atom is attached via a triple bond.

b. Polyacrylonitrile is used in making Acrilan fibers used widely in rugs and upholstery fabric. If ignited, this fiber can release a poisonous gas. In the case of a fire, what danger might rugs and upholstery made of this polymer present?

33. Roy Plunkett, a DuPont chemist, discovered Teflon while experimenting with gaseous tetrafluoroethylene. Here is the monomer.

$$\overset{F}{\underset{F}{\diagdown}}C=C\overset{F}{\underset{F}{\diagup}}$$

a. Analogous to equation 9.1, write the chemical reaction for the polymerization of *n* molecules of tetrafluoroethylene to form Teflon.

b. Why is a repeating head-to-tail arrangement not possible for this polymer?

c. Teflon is a solid and CFC-12 (CCl_2F_2) is a gas. Nonetheless, they both contain C−F bonds. What other characteristics do Teflon and CFC-12 have in common?

34. Equation 9.1 shows the polymerization of ethylene. From the bond energies of Table 4.4, is this reaction endothermic or exothermic?

35. Would your answer from question 34 differ if tetrafluoroethylene were used as the monomer? See question 33 for the monomer.

36. Do you expect the heat of combustion of polyethylene, as reported in kilojoules per gram (kJ/g), to be more similar to that of hydrogen, coal, or octane, C_8H_{18}? Explain your prediction.

37. Recycling is not the same as waste prevention. Explain.

38. Here is a recycling symbol that is more colorful than the standard ones used on many plastic containers.

PLA

a. What is PLA?

b. Why is corn depicted in the center of the symbol?

c. This symbol is printed in green ink, presumably to convey that this polymer is "green." Give two reasons why PLA is considered an eco-friendly polymer.

d. For each of your reasons in the previous part, provide information counter to your argument.

39. Consider the polymerization of 1000 ethylene molecules to form a large segment of polyethylene.

$$1000\ CH_2\!\!=\!\!CH_2 \xrightarrow{R\cdot} \left(CH_2CH_2 \right)_{1000}$$

a. Calculate the energy change for this reaction.
Hint: Use the bond energies in Table 4.4.

b. To carry out this reaction, must heat be supplied or removed from the polymerization vessel? Explain.

40. Here is the structural formula for Dacron, a condensation polyester.

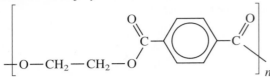

Dacron is formed from 2 monomers, one with 2 hydroxyl groups (−OH) and the other with 2 carboxylic acids (−COOH). Draw a structural formula for each monomer.

41. When you try to stretch a piece of plastic bag, the length of the piece of plastic being pulled increases dramatically and the thickness decreases. Does the same thing happen when you pull on a piece of paper? Why or why not? Explain on a molecular level.

42. Consider Spectra, AlliedSignal Inc.'s HDPE fiber, used as liners for surgical gloves. Interestingly, Spectra is linear HDPE, which is usually associated with being rigid and not very flexible.

    a. Suggest a reason why LDPE cannot be used in this application.

    b. Name two other possible uses of a fabric made of Spectra.

43. The Four Rs are reduce, recycle, reuse, and recover.

    a. Give an example of each, naming the plastic involved.

    b. A possible fifth R is "rethink." For example, plastic waste can be rethought in terms of benefits to public health. Give an example of a connection between waste reduction and public health.

44. All the Big Six polymers are insoluble in water, but some dissolve or at least soften in hydrocarbons (see Table 9.1). Use your knowledge of molecular structure and solubility to explain this behavior.

45. When polystyrene foam packing peanuts are immersed in acetone (a solvent in some nail-polish removers), they dissolve. If the acetone is allowed to evaporate, a solid remains. What is this solid? Explain what happened. *Hint:* Remember that polystyrene foam is made with blowing agents.

46. Today, some packing peanuts are made from plant-based materials rather than polystyrene foam.

    a. Starch is one of the options. What is starch and what is its source?

    b. Name two advantages and two disadvantages of starch packing peanuts.

    c. Name an option for disposing of starch packing peanuts.

47. Explain the concept of shifting baselines. Then give two examples each in regards to:

    a. plastic items used in packaging.

    b. plastic item contamination in waterways.

48. DEHP is a plasticizer that is an example of a phthalate, an ester of phthalic acid.

    a. What is a plasticizer?

    b. Why are plasticizers such as DEHP added to PVC?

    c. DEHP has been banned for some uses. Name two and explain why.

Exploring Extensions

49. a. Name two functional groups not discussed in this chapter. Give an example of a molecule containing each one. *Hint:* Look ahead to Chapter 10.

    b. Find the structural formula for the acetone molecule mentioned in question 45. What functional group does it contain?

50. Cotton, rubber, silk, and wool are natural polymers. Consult other sources to identify the monomer in each of these polymers. Which are addition polymers and which are condensation polymers?

51. The Great Pacific Garbage Patch ("Plastic Trash Vortex") supposedly consists of plastic broken into small fragments that lie below the surface of the ocean and wreak havoc on marine life and on those that eat it, including humans. In 2011, a high-ranking person in the plastics industry informally offered an opinion to an author of this textbook. "Personally," he said, "I think it's a hoax." Is he correct or is he misinformed about the facts? Use well-credentialed sources to make your case.

52. A Teflon ear bone, fallopian tube, or heart valve? A Gore-Tex implant for the face or to repair a hernia? Some polymers are biocompatible and are now used to replace or repair body parts.

    a. List four properties desirable for polymers used *within* the human body

    b. Other polymers are used *outside* your body but in close contact with it, such as contact lenses. What are contact lenses made of? What properties are desirable?

53. PVC, also known as "vinyl," is a controversial plastic. Comment on the controversies, either from the standpoint of a consumer or a worker in the vinyl industry.

54. Learn the story of the discovery of Kevlar. This polymer was originally sought for use in radial tires but found other applications as well. Write a short report citing your sources.

55. Isoprene polymerizes to form polyisoprene, a natural rubber. Here is the structural formula of isoprene, with its carbons numbered.

$$CH_2 \overset{2}{=} C \overset{3}{\underset{1}{\diagup}} CH \overset{4}{=} CH_2$$
$$\underset{CH_3}{|}$$

When isoprene monomers add, polyisoprene has a C=C between carbon atoms 2 and 3. How does this double bond form? *Hint:* Each C=C contains four electrons. Each new C–C bond that forms to link two monomers only needs two electrons, one from each of the monomers that joined to form it.

56. Synthetic rubber is usually formed through addition polymerization. An important exception is silicone rubber, which is made by the condensation polymerization of dimethylsilanediol. Here is a representation of the reaction.

$$n\ HO \overset{CH_3}{\underset{CH_3}{-\ Si\ -}} OH \longrightarrow \left[\overset{CH_3}{\underset{CH_3}{-O\ -\ Si\ -\ O-}} \right]_n + n\ H_2O$$

a. Predict two properties for this polymer. Explain the basis for your predictions.

b. Silly Putty is a popular form of silicone rubber. Name two of its properties.

c. Name two other household uses for silicone rubber.

57. Given the number of personal computers in use today, there is good reason to keep keyboards, monitors, and "mice" out of the landfill.

a. Which polymers do your computer and its accessories contain?

b. What are the options for recycling the plastics in computers?

58. Some regions in the United States have bottle bills that require a deposit on some or all containers. Some grocers, beverage companies, and bottle associations stand strongly against bottle bills. In contrast, some consumer groups and environmental groups argue strongly for them. Draft a one-page position statement that speaks either for or against bottle bills.

59. Cargill won a 2007 Presidential Green Chemistry Challenge Award for using soybeans instead of petroleum to produce polyols. What is a polyol? How are polyols used to produce "soybean plastics"?

CHAPTER **10** Manipulating Molecules and Designing Drugs

An ancient medicinal plant, Ephedra sinica, *also called* ma huang *(above).*
Shown as a tincture, twigs, powdered twigs, and dried roots (below).

Drugs. This word elicits hope, relief, fear, intrigue, outrage, or maybe simply disdain. Pharmaceuticals (drugs) are substances intended to prevent, moderate, or cure illnesses. Medicinal chemistry is the science that deals with the discovery or design of new therapeutic chemicals and their development into useful medicines.

Modern pharmacology has its origins in folklore, and the history of medicine is full of herbal and folk remedies. The use of herbs, roots, berries, and barks for relief from illness can be traced to antiquity as illustrated in documents recorded by ancient Chinese, Indian, and Near East civilizations. The Rig-Veda (compiled in India between 4500 and 1600 BCE), one of the oldest repositories of human learning, refers to the use of medicinal plants. The Chinese emperor Shen Nung prepared a book of herbs over 5000 years ago. In it, he described a plant called *ma huang* (now called *Ephedra sinica*), used as a heart stimulant. This plant contains ephedrine, a drug we will consider later in this chapter.

More recently, chemists have designed, synthesized, and characterized a vast array of prescription and over-the-counter drugs. Today, drugs help patients regulate their blood sugar, blood pressure, cholesterol, and allergies. They help AIDS patients stay alive while scientists search for a cure. Effective anticancer drugs and powerful analgesics now exist. Other drugs can even manage mental disorders that once were thought to be untreatable.

People have long taken drugs for the purpose of altering their perceptions and moods. The famed philosopher Nietzsche said that no art could exist without intoxication. Many writers and artists have found that drugs act as a creative and destructive force in their lives and work. People abuse drugs primarily because of the promise of instant relief or pleasure and the possibility of heightened awareness. It is a common misconception that today's problem with drug abuse is a recent phenomenon. The reality is that human history has been marked with drug use and abuse.

In discussing drugs, we will consider these questions: Where do the ideas and resources to develop new drugs come from? What is the process by which pharmaceuticals make it to market? Why does a drug have a certain effect, and which features of its molecular structure contribute to the biological activity? How do drugs move from being available by prescription only to being sold over the counter? What are the merits and pitfalls of herbal medicines, and are naturally occurring drugs "safer" than synthetic ones? Which drugs are most commonly abused? Chemistry concepts key to answering these questions will be presented in this chapter. Understanding some basic chemistry can go a long way toward staying healthy in today's complicated world.

Consider This 10.1   Today's Drugs

a. Consider the pharmaceuticals prescribed in the United States today. List what you think are the top five most frequently prescribed drugs.
b. List what you think are the top five most frequently abused drugs.
c. Share your lists with a small group of students. Do some of the drugs that you or others listed appear in both parts **a** and **b**?

10.1 | A Classic Wonder Drug

In the fourth century BCE, Hippocrates, perhaps the most famous physician of all time, described a "tea" made by boiling willow bark in water. The concoction was said to be effective against fevers. Over the centuries, that folk remedy, common to many different cultures, ultimately led to the synthesis of a true "wonder drug," one that has aided millions of people.

One of the first systematic investigators of willow bark (Figure 10.1) was Edmund Stone, an English clergyman. His report to the Royal Society (1763) set the stage for

Figure 10.1

The white willow tree, *Salix alba*, source of a miracle drug.

a series of further chemical and medical investigations. Chemists were subsequently able to isolate small amounts of yellow, needle-shaped crystals of a substance from the willow bark extract. Because the tree species was *Salix alba,* this new substance was named salicin. Experiments showed that salicin could be chemically separated into two compounds. Clinical tests provided evidence that only one of these components reduced fevers and inflammation. It also was demonstrated that the active component was converted to an acid in the body. Unfortunately, the clinical testing revealed some troubling side effects. The active component not only had a very unpleasant taste, but also its acidity led to acute stomach irritation in some individuals.

The active acidic compound was used to treat pain, fever, and inflammation. But recognizing its serious side effects, chemists set out to find a derivative that still would be effective but not cause stomach distress and lack the undesirable taste. The first attempt took a very simple approach. The acid was neutralized with a base, either sodium hydroxide or calcium hydroxide, to form a salt of the acid. It turned out that the resulting salts had fewer side effects than the parent compound. Based on this finding, chemists correctly concluded that the acidic part of the molecule was responsible for the undesirable properties. Consequently, the next step was to seek a structural modification that would lessen the acidity of the compound without destroying its medicinal effectiveness.

One of the chemists working on the problem was Felix Hoffmann, an employee of a major German chemical firm. Hoffmann's motivation was more than just scientific curiosity or assigned task. His father regularly took the acidic compound as treatment for arthritis. It worked, but he suffered nausea. The younger Hoffmann succeeded in converting the original compound into a different substance, a solid that reverted back to the active acid once it was in the bloodstream. This molecular modification greatly reduced nausea and other adverse reactions; a new drug had been discovered (1898).

Extensive hospital testing of Hoffmann's compound began along with simultaneous preparation for its large-scale manufacture by a well-known pharmaceutical company. The new drug itself could not be patented because it was already described in the chemical literature. However, the company hoped to recoup its investment by patenting the manufacturing process. Clinical trials showed the drug to be nonaddicting. Its toxicity is classified as low, but 20–30 g ingested at one time may be lethal. At the suggested dose of 325–650 mg every 4 hours, it is a remarkably effective antipyretic (fever-reducing), analgesic (pain-relieving), and anti-inflammatory agent. Data from clinical tests uncovered the side effects noted in Table 10.1. The drug was also found

Acid–base neutralization reactions were discussed in Section 6.3.

Table 10.1	Side Effects of the "Wonder Drug"	
Symptoms	Frequency	Severity*
nausea, vomiting, abdominal pain	common	2
heartburn	common	4
ringing in the ears	common	5
black or bloody vomit	rare	1
blood in the urine	rare	1
rash, hives, itch	rare	3
diminished vision	rare	3
jaundice	rare	3
shortness of breath	rare	3
drowsiness	rare	4

*The severity scale ranges from 1, life–threatening: seek emergency treatment immediately to 5, continue the medication and tell the physician at the next visit.

Source: H. W. Griffith, The Complete Guide to Prescription and Non–Prescription Drugs, 1983, HP Books, Tucson, Arizona.

to inhibit blood clotting and to cause at least some small, almost always medically insignificant, amounts of stomach bleeding in about 70% of users.

Consider This 10.2   Miracle Drug

In the United States, the final step for approval of a drug is the submission of all of its clinical test results to the Food and Drug Administration (FDA) for a license to market the product.

a. If you were an FDA panel member presented with the information in Table 10.1, would you vote to approve this drug that treats pain, fever, and inflammation?

b. If approved, should this drug be released as an over-the-counter drug or should its availability be restricted as a prescription drug? Write a one-page position paper.

Perhaps you have already guessed the identity of the miracle drug related to willow bark tea. Its chemical name, 2-acetyloxybenzoic acid or (more commonly) acetylsalicylic acid, may not help much. But the power of advertising is such that, had we revealed that the firm that originally marketed the drug was the Bayer division of I. G. Farben, we would have let the tablet out of the bottle. The compound in question is the world's most widely used drug, even a century after its discovery. People in the United States annually consume nearly 80 billion tablets of this miracle medicine. You know it as aspirin.

Admittedly, we have only given the highlights in the history of aspirin. Most of the development, testing, and design of aspirin occurred in the 18th and 19th centuries. Stone's letter to the Royal Society was written in 1763, and Felix Hoffmann's modification of salicylic acid to yield aspirin was done in 1898. Furthermore, the clinical testing of aspirin was somewhat less systematic than our account implies. But the basic facts and the steps that led to aspirin's full development are essentially correct. We must also add one more very important fact. Aspirin did not have to receive drug approval before being put on the market; no such certifying process was in place at the time. Had approval based on clinical test results been necessary, it is quite likely that aspirin would have been available only on a prescription basis.

Consider This 10.3   What Should a Drug Be Like?

Make a list of the properties you think a drug should have. Then compare your list with those of your classmates. Note similarities and differences.

a. Are any items missing from your list that you now think you should include?

b. Are any items present on your list that you now think you should delete?

10.2 | The Study of Carbon–Containing Molecules

Anybody who has watched reruns of *Star Trek* knows that carbon is the basis of life-forms on our planet. This element is so ubiquitous in nature that one of the largest subdisciplines of chemistry, **organic chemistry,** is devoted to the study of carbon compounds. The name *organic* is historical and suggests a biological origin but this is not necessarily true. In practice, most organic chemists investigate compounds, of biological origin or human design, in which carbon is combined with a relatively small number of other elements: hydrogen, oxygen, nitrogen, sulfur, chlorine, phosphorus, and bromine. Even with this restriction, over 12 million of the 27 million total known compounds are considered organic.

To specify an organic compound from among the myriad of possibilities, you must be able to name it correctly. An international committee called the International Union of Pure and Applied Chemistry (IUPAC) established and periodically updates a formal set of nomenclature rules so each of the known compounds can be uniquely named. However, many of these compounds have been known for a long time by common names such as alcohol, sugar, or morphine. When a headache strikes, even chemists do not call out for 2-acetyloxybenzoic acid; they simply say "Give me some aspirin!" Likewise, prescriptions specify penicillin-G rather than 3,3-dimethyl-7-oxo-6-(2-phenylacetamido)-4-thia-1-azabicyclo[3.2.0]heptane-2-carboxylic acid. A mouthful like this is the cause of great merriment to those who like to satirize chemists. Nonetheless, chemical names are important and unambiguous to those who know the system. You can rest easy because in this chapter, we will use common names in almost all cases.

We remind you that a few basic rules for bonding in organic molecules can help you find order in the chaos of millions of organic compounds. We introduced one of these in Chapter 2, the octet rule. When bonded, each carbon atom has a share in eight electrons, an octet. Eight electrons can be arranged to form four bonds, with a pair of shared electrons in each covalent bond. In Chapter 4, we introduced a second useful rule: carbon almost always forms four bonds. The possibilities include (a) four single bonds, or (b) some combination of single, double, and triple bonds. These possibilities are illustrated in Figure 10.2.

The octet rule was discussed in Section 2.3.

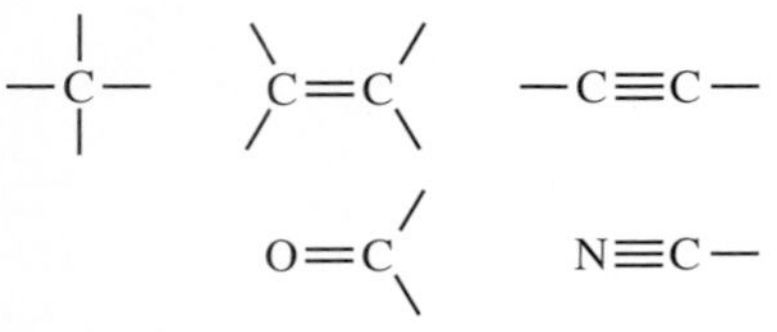

Figure 10.2

Common bonding arrangements for carbon.

Your Turn 10.4   Checking on Carbon

a. Examine the carbon atoms illustrated in Figure 10.2. Does each one follow the octet rule?
b. Can you recall a molecule in which carbon does not form four bonds?
   Hint: This molecule is one of the air pollutants discussed in Chapter 1.

Other elements exhibit different bonding behavior in organic compounds. A hydrogen atom is always attached to another atom by a single covalent bond. An oxygen atom typically attaches either with two single bonds (to two different atoms) or one double bond (to a single atom). A nitrogen atom commonly forms three single bonds (to three different atoms), but also can form either a triple bond (to one other atom), or a single and a double bond.

The same number and kinds of atoms can be arranged in different ways, helping to explain why there are so many different organic compounds. **Isomers** are molecules with the same chemical formula (same number and kinds of atoms), but with different structures and properties. In Chapter 4, you encountered two of the isomers of C_8H_{18}: *n*-octane (straight chain) and *iso*octane (branched).

Isomers were also described in Section 4.7.

In this chapter, we revisit the concept of isomers, this time using C_4H_{10}. Analogous to C_8H_{18}, we draw both a straight chain and a branched isomer. Here are the structural formulas. Note that *n*-butane is here represented in a more realistic zigzag form.

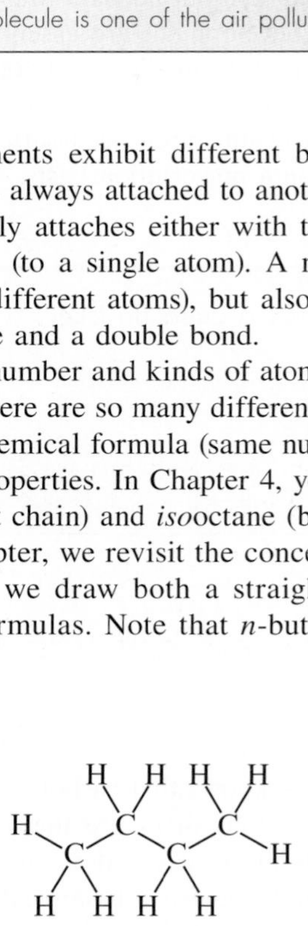

n-butane 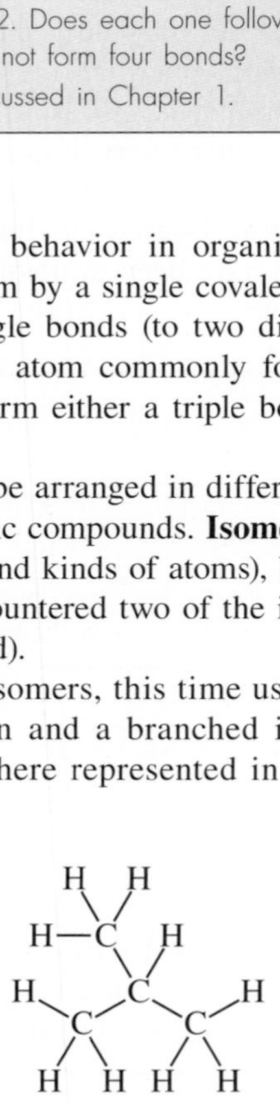   *iso*butane

Convince yourself that although these compounds both have the same chemical formula, the way in which the atoms are connected is different.

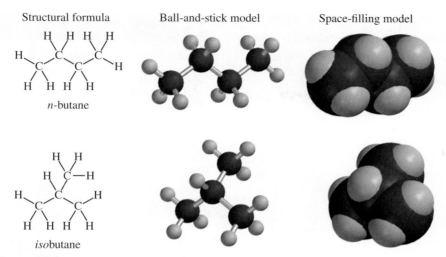

Figure 10.3

Three representations of the isomers *n*–butane and *iso*butane.

Although a CH_3 group at the left end of a chain could be drawn as H_3C-, for ease we often reverse the order to CH_3- with the understanding that the bond is to the C atom, not to the H atoms.

Both the linear isomer and the more complex *iso*butane can be represented with a condensed structural formula. Here we show the options for *iso*butane.

$$CH_3 - CH - CH_3 \quad \text{or} \quad CH_3CH(CH_3)CH_3 \quad \text{or} \quad CH_3CH(CH_3)_2$$

with CH_3 attached above the central CH.

These condensed structural formulas are trickier to interpret. The parentheses around the $-CH_3$ groups indicate that they are attached to the C atom to their left. Note that with three $-CH_3$ groups attached to the central C atom, a "branch" has been introduced into the molecule.

Figure 10.3 shows three representations of *n*-butane and *iso*butane. The first column shows the simple structural formula, the second a ball-and-stick model. The third column shows a space-filling model that presents a more realistic view of the molecular shape.

Only two isomers of C_4H_{10} exist. As the number of atoms in a hydrocarbon increases, so does the number of possible isomers. In addition to *n*-octane and *iso*octane, you can draw 16 other isomers for C_8H_{18}. And for $C_{10}H_{22}$, you could draw 75 isomers if you had the patience! Given a chemical formula, no simple calculation can be performed to obtain the number of isomers.

Your Turn 10.5   Switching Representations

Expand each of these condensed structural formulas into a structural formula.

a. $CH_3CH_2CH_2CH(CH_3)_2$

b. $CH_3CH(CH_3)CH_2CH_3$

c. $CH_3CH_2C(CH_3)_3$

d. $CH_3CH(CH_2CH_3)CH_3$

Answers

a. [structural formula]   b. [structural formula]

Chemists also routinely use a **line-angle drawing** to represent the structure of a molecule. This is a simplified version of a structural formula that is most useful for representing larger molecules. Line-angle drawings help the viewer to focus on the backbone of carbon atoms. One carbon atom is assumed to occupy each vertex position.

Table 10.2	Molecular Representations		
Compound	Chemical Formula	Structural Formula	Line–Angle Drawing
n–butane	C_4H_{10}		
*iso*butane	C_4H_{10}		
n–hexane	C_6H_{14}		
cyclohexane	C_6H_{12}		

Any line extending from the backbone signifies another carbon atom (actually a –CH_3 group), unless the symbol for another element is given. Hydrogen atoms are not indicated in the line-angle drawing, but are implied as required by the octet rule. Remember that each carbon atom will have four bonds to it, sharing a total of eight electrons. Table 10.2 shows line-angle drawings for *n*-butane, *iso*butane, and two other simple molecules.

Your Turn 10.6   Practice with Line–Angle Drawings

Revisit the compounds in Your Turn 10.5. For all four, draw line–angle representations.

Answers

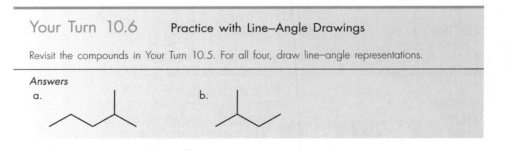

a.

b.

Your Turn 10.7   Practice with Isomers

a. Are *n*–butane and *iso*butane isomers? Explain.
b. Are *n*–hexane and cyclohexane isomers? Explain.
c. Three isomers have the formula C_5H_{12}. For each, draw a structural formula, a condensed structural formula, and a line–angle drawing.

Many molecules, including aspirin, have carbon atoms arranged in a ring. For example, examine the structure of cyclohexane, C_6H_{12}, in Table 10.2. The ring in cyclohexane has six carbons, and rings most commonly contain five or six carbon atoms. In aspirin, however, the six-membered ring is based on benzene, C_6H_6, rather than on cyclohexane. The structural formula for benzene is shown in Figure 10.4a.

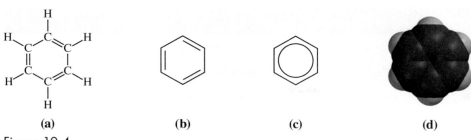

Figure 10.4
Representations of benzene, C_6H_6.

Structure (b) in Figure 10.4 is a line-angle drawing for benzene. Although this structure has alternating single and double bonds, experimental evidence indicates that all the C-to-C bonds in benzene actually have the same length. Since C–C single bonds are longer than C=C double bonds, benzene cannot have alternating single and double bonds. Consequently, the electrons must be uniformly distributed around the ring. The circle within the hexagon in structure (c) is an effort to convey this. Both structures (c) and (d) represent the uniformly distributed electrons around the ring, as described by resonance theory (see Section 2.3). This same hexagonal structure is found in the $-C_6H_5$ phenyl group that is part of many molecules, including styrene and polystyrene (Section 9.5).

> A C–C single bond length is 0.154 nm, and a C=C double bond length is 0.134 nm. In benzene, the C-to-C bond lengths are 0.139 nm.

10.3 | Functional Groups

Central to the study of drug discovery and interactions are functional groups. **Functional groups** are distinctive arrangements of groups of atoms that impart characteristic physical and chemical properties to the molecules that contain them. Indeed, these groups are so important that we often show them in structural formulas and represent the remainder of the molecule with an "R." The R is generally assumed to include at least one carbon or hydrogen atom. You already encountered some functional groups in Chapter 9. The generic formula for an alcohol is ROH, as in methanol, CH_3OH (an alcohol derived from degradation of wood), and ethanol, CH_3CH_2OH (alcohol derived from fermentation of grains and sugar). The presence of the –OH group attached to a carbon makes the compound an alcohol.

> An alcohol has an –OH group *covalently* bonded to the rest of the molecule. This is different from the hydroxide ion, OH^-, which is *ionically* bonded to a cation.

Similarly, a carboxylic acid group, commonly written as $\overset{\overset{\displaystyle O}{\|}}{\underset{\displaystyle O}{C}}\diagup H$, –COOH, or –CO₂H, confers acidic properties. In aqueous solution, a H^+ ion (a proton) is transferred from the –COOH group to an H_2O molecule to form a hydronium ion, H_3O^+. We represent an organic acid with the general formula RCOOH, or RCO₂H. In acetic acid (CH_3COOH), the acid in vinegar, the R group is $-CH_3$, the methyl group.

Table 10.3 lists eight functional groups found in drugs and other organic compounds. Each functional group is characteristic of an important class of compounds.

Your Turn 10.8   Line–Angle Drawings

For each of these condensed structural formulas, make a line–angle drawing. Name the functional group in each one.

a. $CH_3CH_2CH_2COCH_3$ b. $CH_3CH_2CH(CH_3)CH_2OH$
c. $CH_3CH(NH_2)CH_2CH_3$ d. $CH_3COOCH_2CH_3$
e. CH_3CH_2CHO

Answers

a.   (ketone)   b.   OH (hydroxyl)

Table 10.3 Some Important Organic Functional Groups

Functional Group	Generic Formula	SPECIFIC EXAMPLES		
		Name*	Structural Formula	Condensed Structural Formula
hydroxyl	O–H	ethanol (ethyl alcohol)	[structure]	CH_3CH_2OH
ether	C–O–C	dimethyl ether	[structure]	$CH_3{-}O{-}CH_3$ or CH_3OCH_3
aldehyde	[structure]	propanal	[structure]	$CH_3CH_2{-}\overset{O}{\underset{}{C}}{-}H$ or CH_3CH_2CHO
ketone	[structure]	2–propanone (dimethyl ketone, acetone)	[structure]	$CH_3{-}\overset{O}{\underset{}{C}}{-}CH_3$ or CH_3COCH_3
carboxylic acid	[structure]	ethanoic acid (acetic acid)	[structure]	$CH_3{-}\overset{O}{\underset{}{C}}{-}OH$ or CH_3CO_2H or CH_3COOH
ester	[structure]	methyl ethanoate (methyl acetate)	[structure]	$CH_3{-}\overset{O}{\underset{}{C}}{-}OCH_3$ or CH_3COOCH_3
amine	[structure]	ethylamine	[structure]	$CH_3CH_2NH_2$
amide	[structure]	propanamide	[structure]	$CH_3CH_2{-}\overset{O}{\underset{}{C}}{-}NH_2$ or $CH_3CH_2CONH_2$

*IUPAC names, common names in parentheses

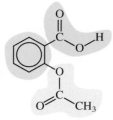

Figure 10.5
Structural formula of aspirin.

Functional groups are responsible for the action of all drugs. Aspirin has three functional groups, as shown in Figure 10.5. The green area encloses a benzene ring. The presence of this functional group makes aspirin soluble in fatty compounds that are important cell membrane components. The other two functional groups are responsible for the activity of the drug. The blue area encloses a –COOH group, a carboxylic acid, and the yellow area is an ester.

Felix Hoffmann prepared aspirin by modifying the structure of salicylic acid. But note that he did not modify the carboxylic acid group on the molecule. Salicylic acid also contains an –OH group that Hoffmann reacted with acetic acid as shown in equation 10.1. The product was an ester of acetic acid and salicylic acid, which accounts for one of aspirin's names: acetylsalicylic acid.

Formation of an ester was shown for condensation polymers in Section 9.6.

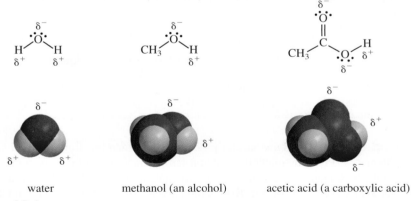

| salicylic acid | acetic acid | acetylsalicylic acid | water |

[10.1]

Because aspirin retains the –COOH group of the original salicylic acid, it still has some of the undesirable acidic properties of the parent compound. However, the ester group (yellow area in Figure 10.5) makes the compound more palatable and less irritating to the stomach lining. Once aspirin is ingested and reaches the site of its action, equation 10.1 is reversed. The ester splits into acetic acid and salicylic acid, and the latter compound exerts its antipyretic (fever-reducing) and analgesic (pain-reducing) properties.

Your Turn 10.9   Ester Formation

Draw structural formulas for the esters that form when these alcohol and acid pairs react.

a. CH_3CH_2OH + [structure] $\xrightarrow{H^+}$ b. [structure] + CH_3OH $\xrightarrow{H^+}$

Functional groups can play a role in the solubility of a compound, an important consideration in the uptake, rate of reaction, and residence time of drugs in the body. The general solubility rule, "like dissolves like," applies in the body as well as in the test tube. A polar molecule has a nonsymmetrical distribution of electric charge. This means that a partial negative charge builds up on some part (or parts) of the molecule, and other regions of the molecule bear a partial positive charge. Water is an excellent example of a polar molecule. Relatively speaking, the oxygen atom is slightly negatively charged and the hydrogen atoms are slightly positive. Because the molecule is bent, it has a nonsymmetrical charge distribution. This is represented in Figure 10.6; the δ^+ and δ^- symbols represent partial charges. Functional groups containing oxygen and

The concept of *like dissolves like* was introduced in Section 5.9.

| water | methanol (an alcohol) | acetic acid (a carboxylic acid) |

Figure 10.6

Examples of polar molecules.

nitrogen atoms (for example, –OH, –COOH, and –NH$_2$) usually increase the polarity of a molecule. This in turn enhances its solubility in a polar substance such as water, which is advantageous for drug molecules.

By contrast, hydrocarbons that do not contain such functional groups are typically nonpolar and will not dissolve in polar solvents. For example, *n*-octane, C$_8$H$_{18}$ is nonpolar and insoluble in water. However, it does dissolve in nonpolar solvents such as hexane (C$_6$H$_{14}$) and dichloromethane (CH$_2$Cl$_2$). For the same reasons, drugs with significant nonpolar character tend to accumulate in cell membranes and fatty tissues that are largely hydrocarbon and nonpolar.

The water solubility of a drug that is either acidic or basic can be improved by neutralizing it and forming a salt. For example, many drugs contain nitrogen and are basic. When such a drug is neutralized with HCl or H$_2$SO$_4$, the nitrogen accepts an H$^+$ from the acid. As a result, the nitrogen becomes positively charged and paired with the negative charge on the chloride or hydrogen sulfate (HSO$_4^-$) ion. Prior to taking on an extra H$^+$, the compound is electronically neutral and is said to be in its freebase form. A **freebase** is a nitrogen-containing molecule in which the nitrogen is in possession of its lone pair of electrons.

Consider the drug pseudoephedrine, a common decongestant used in over-the-counter remedies for the common cold:

pseudoephedrine (freebase)   pseudoephedrine hydrochloride salt

[10.2]

The nitrogen of the amino group reacts as a base when treated with hydrochloric acid. Pseudoephedrine can thus be converted to its hydrochloride salt (an ionic compound) in which the nitrogen bears a positive charge and the chloride ion a negative charge. The salt form of pseudoephedrine is preferable as a drug because it is more stable, has less of an odor, and is water-soluble. An estimated half of all drug molecules used in medicine are administered as salts that improve their water-solubility and stability, which in turn increase their shelf life. Conversion of a salt back into its freebase form may be accomplished by treating the salt with a base such as NaOH.

Drugs with similar physiological properties often have similar molecular structures and include some of the same functional groups. Of the approximately 40 alternatives to aspirin that have been produced, ibuprofen and acetaminophen are the most familiar. Figure 10.7 gives the structural formulas of the three leading analgesics. All are based on a benzene ring with two **substituents,** an atom or functional group that has been substituted for a hydrogen atom, but these substituents differ. In Your Turn 10.10, you have an opportunity to identify the structural similarities and differences of these analgesics.

Your Turn 10.10   Common Structural Features of Analgesics

Look at the structural formulas in Figure 10.7. Identify the structural features and functional groups that aspirin, ibuprofen, and acetaminophen have in common.

The current commercial method for producing ibuprofen is a stunning application of green chemistry. Previous methods of ibuprofen production required six steps, used large amounts of solvents, and generated significant quantities of waste. By using a catalyst that also serves as a solvent, BHC Company, a 1997 Presidential Green Chemistry Challenge Award winner, makes ibuprofen in just three steps with a minimum of solvents and waste. In the BHC process, virtually all the reactants are converted to

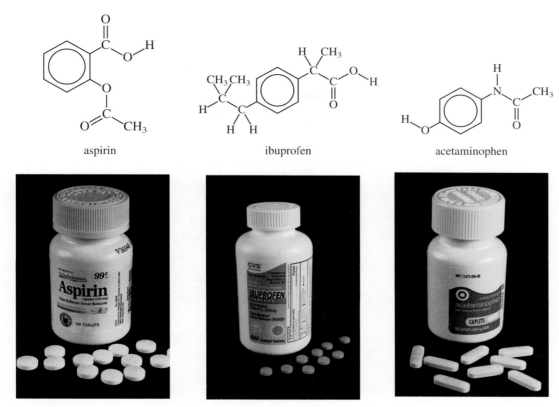

Figure 10.7
Structural formulas and samples of some common analgesics.

ibuprofen or another usable by-product; any unreacted starting materials are recovered and recycled. Nearly 8 million pounds of ibuprofen, enough to make 18 billion 200-mg pills, is produced annually in Bishop, Texas, at the BHC facility, built specifically for the commercial production of the drug.

10.4 | How Aspirin Works: Function Follows Form

To understand the action of aspirin, you need to know something about the body's chemical communication system. We normally think of internal communication as consisting of electrical impulses traveling along a network of nerves. This is true for the system that triggers movement, breathing, heartbeats, and reflex actions. Most of the body's messages, however, are conveyed not by electrical impulses, but through chemical processes. In fact, your very first communication with your mother was a chemical signal saying "I'm here; better get your body ready for me." It is much more efficient to release chemical messengers into the bloodstream where they can be circulated to appropriate body cells, than to "hardwire" each individual cell with nerve endings.

The chemical messengers produced by the body's endocrine glands are called **hormones.** Figure 10.8 is a representation of such chemical communication. Hormones encompass a wide range of functions and a similarly wide range of chemical composition and structure. Thyroxine, a hormone secreted by the thyroid gland, is essential for regulating metabolism. The ability of the body to use glucose (blood sugar) for energy depends on insulin. This hormone, a small protein built from only 51 polymerized amino acids, is secreted by the pancreas. Persons who suffer from diabetes are often required to take daily injections of insulin. Yet another well-known hormone is adrenaline (epinephrine), a small molecule that prepares the body to "fight or flight" in the face of danger.

Section 12.7 describes the use of genetic engineering to obtain human insulin from bacteria.

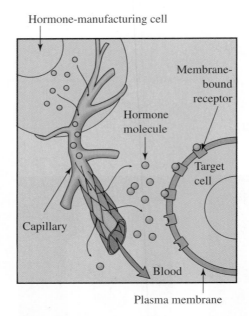

Figure 10.8

Chemical communication in the body. Hormone molecules travel through the bloodstream from the cell where they are made to the target cell.

Steroids are covered in Section 10.7.

You encountered catalysts in several other contexts, including automobile emissions control (Section 1.11), petroleum refining (Section 4.7), and addition polymerization (Section 9.3).

Aspirin and other drugs that are physiologically active are almost always involved in altering the chemical communication system of the body. A significant problem is that this system is very complex, allowing many compounds to be used to send more than one message simultaneously. The wide range of aspirin's therapeutic properties, as well as its side effects, is clear evidence that the drug is involved in several chemical communication systems. It works in the brain to reduce fever and pain, it relieves inflammation in muscles and joints, and it appears to decrease the chances of stroke and heart attack. It may even lessen the likelihood of colon, stomach, and rectal cancer.

In large measure, the versatility of aspirin and similar nonsteroidal anti-inflammatory drugs (NSAIDs) is related to their remarkable ability to block the actions of other molecules. Research on the activity of aspirin indicates that one of its modes of action involves blocking cyclooxygenase (COX) enzymes. **Enzymes** are proteins that act as biochemical catalysts, influencing the rates of chemical reactions. Most enzymes speed up reactions and channel them so that only one product (or a set of related products) is formed. Cyclooxygenases catalyze the synthesis of a series of hormone-like compounds called prostaglandins from arachidonic acid (Figure 10.9).

Prostaglandins cause a variety of effects. They produce fever and swelling, increase the sensitivity of pain receptors, inhibit blood vessel dilation, regulate the production of acid and mucus in the stomach, and assist kidney functions. By preventing prostaglandin production, aspirin reduces fever and swelling. It also suppresses pain receptors and so functions as a painkiller. Because the benzene ring conveys high fat solubility, aspirin is also taken up into cell membranes. In certain specialized cells, the drug blocks the transmission of chemical signals that trigger inflammation. This process also appears to be related to aspirin's effectiveness as a pain reliever and may explain why daily aspirin use may reduce some types of cancer.

The NSAIDs exhibit these same properties in varying degrees. For example, because acetaminophen blocks COX enzymes, but does not affect the specialized cells, it reduces fever but has little anti-inflammatory action. On the other hand, ibuprofen is a better enzyme blocker and specialized cell inhibitor. Consequently, ibuprofen is both a better pain reliever and fever reducer than aspirin. With fewer polar functional groups, ibuprofen is more fat-soluble than aspirin. Its anti-inflammatory activity is 5 to 50 times that of aspirin.

Interestingly, aspirin is unique among these three compounds in its ability to inhibit blood clotting. This property has led to the suggestion that low regular doses of aspirin can help prevent strokes or heart attacks. Of course, these anticoagulation

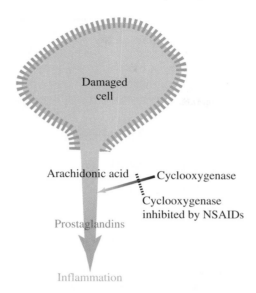

Figure 10.9
Aspirin's mode of action.

characteristics also mean that aspirin is not the painkiller of choice for surgical patients, or those suffering from ulcers or blood-clotting problems. Another drawback of aspirin is that in rare cases in the presence of certain viruses, it can trigger a sometimes fatal response known as Reye's syndrome, particularly in children younger than 15. Furthermore, in some patients aspirin can trigger acute episodes of asthma.

Consider This 10.11   COX–2 Inhibitors

In 1992 researchers discovered that there were two separate types of COX enzymes, COX–1 and COX–2. The COX–2 enzyme is responsible for the production of the prostaglandins that regulate inflammation, pain, and fever, thereby reducing these symptoms. The COX–1 enzyme catalyzes the production of the prostaglandins responsible for maintaining proper kidney function and for keeping the stomach lining intact. Aspirin blocks the activity of both COX enzymes so it has the unwanted side effects of producing stomach pain and bleeding.

After this discovery, new "super aspirins" that would affect only the COX–1 enzymes were developed. Touted as drugs that would cause fewer gastrointestinal problems, they entered the market with great fanfare. They became instant blockbuster drugs, selling in the billions of dollars per year. Use the Internet to find the names of two of these drugs. Why have they disappeared from the pharmaceutical radar screen?

A few final comments about NSAIDs seem appropriate. Because it is a specific chemical compound, aspirin is aspirin—acetylsalicylic acid, regardless of its brand. Indeed, about 70% of all acetylsalicylic acid produced in the United States is made by a single manufacturer. But, although all aspirin molecules are identical, not all aspirin tablets are the same. The products are mixtures of various components, including inert fillers and bonding agents that hold the tablet together. Buffered aspirin tablets also include weak bases that counteract the natural acidity of the aspirin. Some coated aspirins keep the tablet intact until it leaves the stomach and enters the intestine. These differences in formulation can influence the rate of uptake of the drug and hence, how fast it acts, and the extent of stomach irritation it produces. Furthermore, although standards for quality control are high, it is conceivable that individual lots of aspirin may vary slightly in purity. Aspirin also decomposes with time, and the smell of vinegar can signify that such a process has begun. Fortunately, none of this poses a significant threat to health, and the benefits of aspirin far outweigh the risks for the great majority of people.

Consider This 10.12   Supersize My Aspirin

A friend who suffers from heart disease has been told by the doctor to take one aspirin tablet a day. To save money, your friend often buys the large 300–tablet bottle of aspirin. You, on the other hand, rarely take aspirin, but cannot pass up a good bargain. You also buy the large bottle.

    a. Why is the "giant economy size" bottle of aspirin not as good a deal for you as it is for your friend?
    b. What chemical evidence supports your opinion?

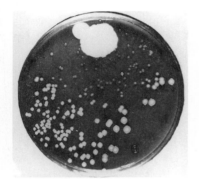

Figure 10.10

Photograph of the original culture plate of the fungus *Penicillium notatum*. This image was photographed by Sir Fleming for his 1929 paper on penicillin. The large white area at 12 o'clock is the mold *Penicillium notatum;* the smaller white spots are areas of bacterial growth.

Figure 10.11

A sign pasted at the entrance of a new facility for penicillin production during World War II.

10.5 | Modern Drug Design

The evolution of "willow bark tea" to aspirin and further modifications to this pain-killer's structure to enhance its beneficial effects and decrease its side effects represent stages in historical drug design. Penicillin is another example of a miracle drug whose origin lies in "natural" sources. Molds had been used for treating infections for 2500 years, although their effects were unpredictable and sometimes toxic. The penicillin story includes an accidental discovery by the British bacteriologist Alexander Fleming in 1928. Fleming's curiosity was aroused by the chance observation that in a container of bacterial colonies, the area contaminated by the mold *Penicillium notatum* was largely free of bacteria (Figure 10.10). He correctly concluded that the mold produced a substance that inhibited bacterial growth, and he named this biologically active material penicillin.

    A careful reconstruction has indicated that a series of critical, but fortuitous events had to occur for the discovery to be made. Spores from the mold, part of an experiment in a nearby lab, drifted into Fleming's laboratory and accidentally contaminated some Petri dishes containing *Staphylococcus* (bacteria) growing on a nutrient medium. Then came a series of chance incidents involving poor laboratory housekeeping, a vacation, and the effects of weather. Fleming fortunately noticed among a pile of dirty glassware the dish in which the *Staphylococcus* had been killed. His experience allowed him to interpret the phenomenon, recognizing that some unknown substance produced by the *Penicillium* was a potential antibacterial agent. "The story of penicillin," Fleming wrote, "has a certain romance in it and helps to illustrate the amount of chance, of fortune, of fate, or destiny, call it what you will, in anybody's career." But of course, the discovery would not have happened without Fleming's powers of observation and insight. The episode illustrates the often misquoted maxim of the great French scientist, Louis Pasteur: "In the fields of observation, chance favors only the prepared mind." Most versions of this famous aphorism neglect the "only." It was only because Fleming's mind was prepared that he was able to capitalize on this chain of unlikely events.

    The process of taking penicillin from the Petri dish to the pharmacy was not much different from what is done today. The first step was a systematic effort to isolate the active agent produced by *Penicillium notatum*. Once identified, the substance had to be purified and concentrated by sophisticated techniques. Also, the efficacy of penicillin in treating humans had to be demonstrated. World War II gave increased impetus to this research and to the development of new methods for preparing large quantities of penicillin. Because the scientists were successful in doing so, thousands of lives were saved during the war, and millions since then (Figure 10.11).

    Treatments of infections once considered incurable—pneumonia, scarlet fever, tetanus, gangrene, and syphilis—were revolutionized by Fleming's discovery. The discovery of penicillin may have been serendipitous, but the development of the next several "generations" of antibiotics in this class involved systematic and careful research. Small changes are made to a drug and the resulting substances are tested with the goal of optimizing desired activity and decreasing side effects. More than a dozen different penicillins are currently in clinical use including: penicillin G (the original discovered by Fleming and the form that causes an allergic reaction in about 20% of the population), ampicillin, oxacillin, cloxacillin, penicillin O, and amoxicillin (the pink, bubble-gum-flavored concoction you might have been given as a child). Amoxicillin is still available in capsule form; it is commonly prescribed for being effective against a broad spectrum of bacteria and is usually well tolerated.

Consider This 10.13   Drugs by Chance

Modern methods of drug discovery involve systematic studies of compounds with only small variations in structure and computer modeling, among other techniques. Sometimes side effects of a drug may open the door for its usefulness in treating other illnesses. There are many examples where a new drug was discovered by "chance." Use the resources of the Internet to find an example of a drug that was discovered by unusual circumstances.

The effectiveness of penicillin has unfortunately led to extreme overuse. As a result, cunning bacterial bugs have developed mechanisms for rendering penicillin (along with other antibiotics) useless. We are now witnessing strains of resistant bacteria or "superbugs," a phenomenon Fleming predicted back in 1945. Bacteria develop resistance to penicillin by secreting an enzyme that attacks the penicillin molecule before it can act. Some of the newer antibiotics differ in their effectiveness at killing certain bacteria and their susceptibility to the enzymes the organisms produce. Closely related to the penicillins are the cephalosporins (cephalexin, or Keflex) that are particularly effective against some resistant strains of bacteria. Careful research on structural modifications has led to other important medicines like cyclosporine, a drug that prevents tissue rejection. Its development made possible the revolutionary success of organ transplant surgery.

So how do chemists know which structural features are important to a drug's function? The modern approach to chemotherapy and drug design probably began early in the 20th century with Paul Ehrlich's search for an arsenic compound that would cure syphilis without doing serious damage to the patient. His quest was for a "magic bullet," a drug that would affect only the diseased site and nothing else. He systematically varied the structure of many arsenic compounds, simultaneously testing each new compound for activity and toxicity on experimental animals. He finally achieved success with arsphenamine (Salvarsan 606), so named because it was the 606th compound investigated. Since then, medicinal chemists have adopted Ehrlich's strategy of carefully relating chemical structure and drug activity. Systematic changes made to a drug molecule and assessment of the resulting changes in activity is known as a **structure–activity relationship (SAR) study.**

Drugs can be broadly classified into two groups: those that produce a physiological response in the body and those that inhibit the growth of substances that cause infections. You already learned that aspirin falls in the first group. So do synthetic hormones and psychologically active drugs. These compounds typically initiate or block a chemical action that generates a cellular response, such as a nerve impulse or the synthesis of a protein. Antibiotics exemplify drugs that prevent the reproduction of foreign invaders. They do so by inhibiting an essential chemical process in the infecting organism. Thus, they are particularly effective against bacteria.

Consider This 10.14   Friend or Foe?

Make two lists of drugs for each of the two broadly classified groups: those that bring about a desired physiological response and those that kill foreign invaders. Propose three drugs for each list, using examples not given in this section.

Although drugs vary in their versatility, many of them act only against particular diseases or infections. This specificity is consistent with the relationship that exists between the chemical structure of a drug and its therapeutic properties. Both the general shape of the molecule and the nature and location of its functional groups are important factors in determining its physiological efficacy. This correlation between form and function can be explained in terms of the interaction between biologically important molecules. Although many of these molecules are very large, consisting of hundreds of atoms, each molecule often contains a relatively small active site or receptor site that is of crucial importance in the biochemical function of the molecule. A drug is often designed to either initiate or inhibit this function by interacting with the receptor site.

An example is provided by a receptor site that controls whether a cell membrane is permeable to certain chemicals. In effect, such a site acts as a lock on a cellular door. The key to this lock may be a hormone or drug molecule. The drug or hormone bonds to the receptor site, opening or closing a channel through the cell membrane. Whether the channel is open or closed can significantly influence the chemistry that occurs in the cell. In fact, under some circumstances, the cell may be killed, which may or may not be beneficial to the organism.

This lock-and-key analogy is often used to describe the interaction of drugs and receptor sites. Just as specific keys fit only specific locks, a molecular match between a drug and its receptor site is required for physiological function. The process is illustrated in Figure 10.12. But if a perfect lock-and-key match were required in the body, it would mean that each of the millions of physiological functions would have a unique receptor site and a specific molecular segment to fit it. Simple logic suggests that such rigid demands would not be very efficient. Consequently, the lock-and-key model, although a good starting point that works in a limited number of cases, must be modified.

Using another analogy, a receptor site is like a size 9 right footprint in the sand. Only one foot will fit it exactly, and many feet (all left feet and any right feet larger than size 9) will not fit. But many other right feet can fit into the print reasonably well. So it is with receptor sites and the molecules (or their functional groups) that bind to them. Some active sites can accommodate a variety of molecules including drugs. Indeed, the way most drugs function is by replacing a normal protein, hormone, or other substance in the invading organism. The general term **substrate** refers to the substances whose reactions are catalyzed by an enzyme. In the substrate inhibition model of enzyme activity, the presence of the drug molecule prevents the enzyme from carrying out its required chemistry. As a result, the growth of an invading bacterium is inhibited, or the synthesis of a particular molecule is turned off (Figure 10.13).

Generally speaking, the drug that best fits the receptor site has the highest therapeutic activity. In some cases, however, a drug molecule does not need to fit the receptor site particularly well. The bonding of functional groups of the drug to the receptor site may even alter the shape of the drug, the site, or both. Often what counts is for the drug to have functional groups of the proper polarity in the right places. Therefore, one important strategy in designing drugs is to determine its **pharmacophore,** the three-dimensional arrangement of atoms or groups of atoms responsible for the biological activity of a drug molecule. Medicinal chemists then synthesize a molecule having that specific active portion, but with a much simpler, nonactive remainder. These researchers custom design the molecule to meet the requirements of the receptor site. In effect, they design feet to fit footprints.

An outstanding example of this approach is provided by opiate drugs such as morphine. Morphine, a complex molecule, is difficult to synthesize. However, the pharmacophore responsible for opiate activity has been identified and is highlighted in Figure 10.14. The flat benzene ring fits into a corresponding flat area of the receptor, and the nitrogen atom binds the drug molecule to the site. Incorporating this particular portion into other less complex molecules, such as meperidine (more commonly known by its brand name, Demerol), creates opiate activity. Meperidine is much less addictive than morphine but also less potent.

The lock–and–key analogy was first proposed in 1894 by the biochemist Emil Fischer.

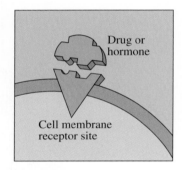

Figure 10.12

Lock–and–key model of biological interactions.

The term *pharmacophore* was originally described by Paul Ehrlich more than 100 years ago. Ehrlich was a German physician and biochemist who won the Nobel Prize in Physiology or Medicine in 1908 for his work on immunization.

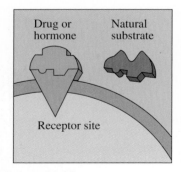

Figure 10.13

Drug molecule displacing a natural substrate on receptor site.

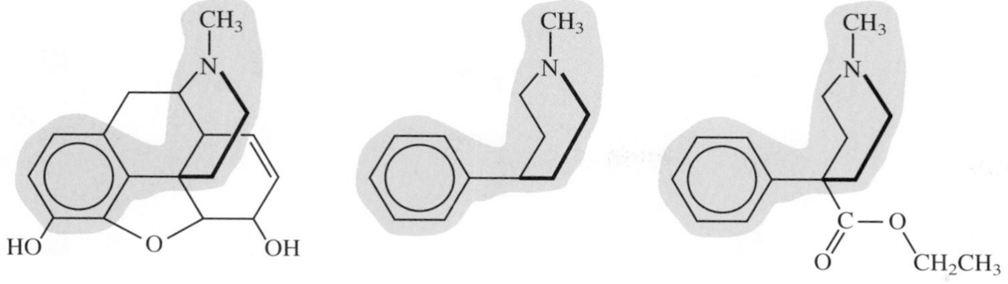

morphine   active area   meperidine

Figure 10.14

Molecular structures of morphine and meperidine. The highlighted "active areas," or pharmacophores, are the portions of the molecule that interact with the receptor. The darker lines indicate that these bonds are in front of the rings, or coming out in front of the plane of the page.

Consider This 10.15   3D Drugs

See for yourself the shapes of drug molecules by visiting 3Dchem.com. On screen, you can rotate 3-dimensional representations of best-selling drugs such as amoxicillin, lipitor, and ibuprofen.

a. Select several drugs and examine their three-dimensional structure. How do these computer representations differ from the structural formulas of drugs shown in this chapter?

b. What advantages do the computer representations have over two-dimensional drawings? What are their limitations compared with "real" molecules? Are there any disadvantages?

The discovery that only certain functional groups are responsible for the therapeutic properties of pharmaceutical molecules was an important breakthrough in drug design. Sophisticated computer graphics are now used to model potential drugs and receptor sites. Thanks to these representations with their three-dimensional character, medicinal chemists can "see" how drugs interact with a receptor site. Computers can then be used to search for compounds that have structures similar to that of an active drug. Chemists can also modify structures in computer models and visualize how the new compounds will function.

Such techniques help to minimize the cost and time it takes to prepare a so-called **lead compound,** a drug (or a modified version of that drug) that shows high promise for becoming an approved drug. An important new methodology is **combinatorial chemistry,** the systematic creation of large numbers of molecules in "libraries" that can be rapidly screened in the lab for biological activity and the potential for becoming new drugs. Drug companies have created large populations of molecules, or libraries, with sort of a "shotgun" approach. The sheer volume of compounds in the libraries increases the likelihood that lead compounds will be discovered. Advances in automation, robotics, and computer programming have refined the technique, making it one that no drug company can afford to ignore (Figure 10.15).

Although complex protocols for combinatorial chemistry exist, let's look at the concept in its simplest form. Consider a molecule with three different functional groups as shown in Figure 10.16. When a sample of this compound is reacted with some reagent (step 1), a set of products is formed. After the addition of a second reagent (step 2), it is easy to see that many compounds can be formed rapidly. Again, different protocols may involve splitting products at various points, but simple statistics show that a great number of new compounds can be made in short order. The process can be repeated numerous times, with the products being screened for desired activity at each step. Unpromising reactions can be screened out quickly. Used in conjunction with computers, combinatorial chemistry can minimize the trial-and-error aspects and expense, thus speeding up drug design and development. Using traditional methods, a medicinal chemist could prepare perhaps four lead compounds per month at an estimated cost of $7000 each. With combinatorial chemical methods, the chemist can prepare nearly 3300 compounds in that same time for about $12 each.

The term *lead compound*, pronounced differently, would refer to a compound containing the element Pb.

Figure 10.15

A scientist working with a combinatorial synthesis instrument.

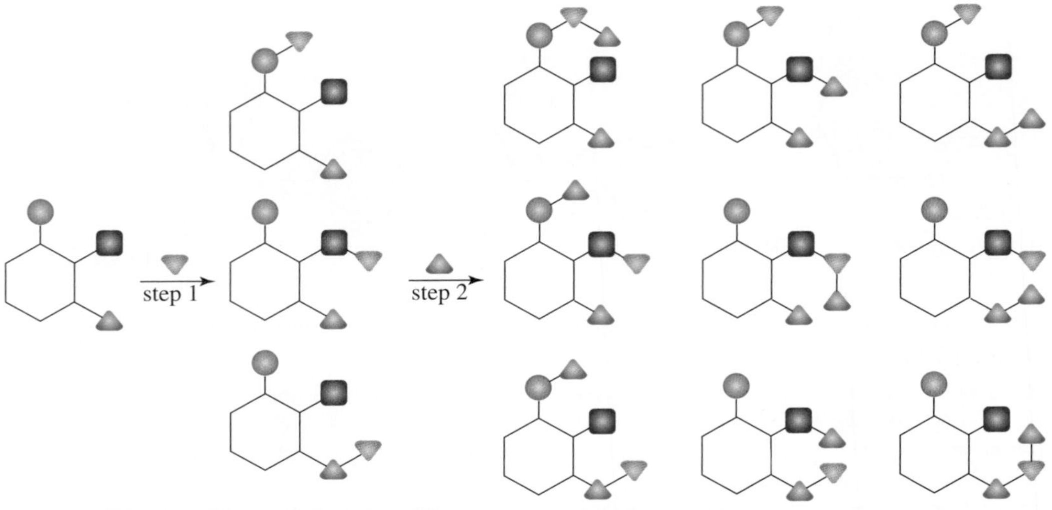

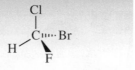

Figure 10.16

Illustration of a combinatorial synthesis process. Different colored shapes represent different functional groups.

10.6 | Give These Molecules a Hand!

Drug design is further complicated when drug–receptor interaction involves a common but subtle phenomenon called optical isomerism, or chirality. **Chiral,** or **optical, isomers** have the same chemical formula, but they differ in their three-dimensional molecular structure and their interaction with polarized light. Chirality most frequently arises when four different atoms or groups of atoms are attached to a carbon atom. A compound having such a carbon atom can exist in two different molecular forms that are nonsuperimposable mirror images of each other. One optical isomer will rotate polarized light in a clockwise manner, and this is called the dextro or (+) isomer. The other isomer is called the levo or (−) isomer, and it rotates polarized light in a counterclockwise manner.

Nonsuperimposable mirror images should be familiar to you. You carry two of them around with you all the time—your hands. If you hold them palms up, you can recognize them as mirror images. For example, the thumb is on the left side of the left hand and on the right side of the right hand. Your left hand looks like the reflection of your right hand in a mirror. But your two hands are not identical. Figure 10.17 illustrates this relationship for both hands and molecules.

Note that the four atoms or groups of atoms bonded to the central carbon atom are in a tetrahedral arrangement (Figure 10.18). The positions of these four atoms correspond to the corners of a three-dimensional figure with equal triangular faces. The "handedness" of these molecules gives rise to the term *chiral,* from the Greek word for hand.

Chemists often use a formalism called a wedge–dash drawing when representing a central chiral carbon atom. For example, the molecule in Figure 10.17 could be drawn as the figure on the left. Here, the Cl and the H are in the plane of the page. The dashed line to the Br indicates that the Br atom is behind the page, extending away from the viewer. The solid wedge going to the F indicates that the F atom is in front of the page, oriented toward the viewer. Similar to a line-angle drawing, the central carbon atom may be implied but not drawn.

Many biologically important molecules, including sugars and amino acids, exhibit chirality. This is significant because, although most chemical and physical properties of a pair of optical isomers are very nearly identical, their biological behavior can differ markedly. Generally, the explanation for this difference is related to the necessity of a good molecular fit between a molecule and its receptor site. Maybe Lewis Carroll's Alice had some inkling of this when, in *Through the Looking Glass,* she remarked to her cat, "Perhaps looking-glass milk isn't good to drink."

Polarized light waves move in a single plane; nonpolarized light waves may move in any plane.

$$H - \underset{\underset{F}{|}}{\overset{\overset{Cl}{|}}{C}} \cdots Br$$

Wedge–dash drawing of one of the molecules in Figure 10.17.

Sugars and amino acids are discussed in Sections 11.5 and 11.7.

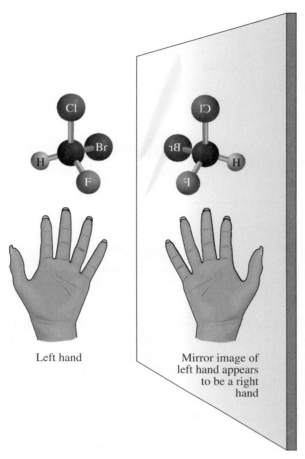

Figure 10.17

Mirror image of a molecular model and a hand. The molecule CHBrClF is chiral and its shape is tetrahedral.

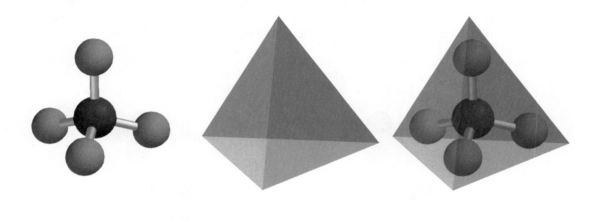

tetrahedral molecule   tetrahedron   tetrahedral molecule inside tetrahedron

Figure 10.18

A tetrahedron has four equilateral triangular faces.

Your Turn 10.16   Chiral Molecules

Use an asterisk to identify the chiral carbon in these molecules. Then draw both chiral isomers using wedge–dash drawings. Place the chiral carbon as the central atom.

a. phenylalanine, an essential amino acid

b. $CH_3CH(OH)CH_2CH_3$ 2–butanol, an alcohol

c. $CHClFCH_3$ 1–chloro–1–fluoroethane, a hydrochlorofluorocarbon

d. methamphetamine, a notoriously dangerous street drug

Answer

a.

You can illustrate the relationship between chirality and biological activity by taking things in your own hands. Your right hand fits only a right-handed glove, not a left-handed one. Similarly, a right-handed drug molecule fits only a receptor site that complements and accommodates it. Any drug containing a carbon atom with four different atoms or groups attached to it will exist in chiral isomers, only one of which usually fits into a particular asymmetrical receptor site (Figure 10.19).

The extreme molecular specificity created by chirality complicates the medicinal chemist's task of synthesizing drugs. A drug molecule must include the appropriate functional groups, and these groups must have the three-dimensional configuration that gives the molecule its desired biological activity. In many chemical reactions, the "right" and "left" optical isomers are produced simultaneously. Such a situation results in a **racemic mixture** consisting of equal amounts of each optical isomer. But frequently, only one optical isomer is pharmaceutically active. For example, many opiate drugs exist as optical isomers, only one of which may have opiate activity. In Figure 10.20, levomethorphan, the left-handed (levo, or −) isomer of methorphan, is an addictive opiate. On the other hand, its right-handed (dextro, or +) mirror image is a nonaddictive cough suppressant. This permits the use of dextromethorphan in many over-the-counter cough remedies, but the right-handed isomer must either be synthesized in pure dextro form or separated from a mixture with its levo isomer. The latter task can prove to be very difficult since the physical properties of the isomers are often identical.

The vitamin E sold in stores is generally a racemic mixture of (+) and (−) isomers. The (+) isomer is the physiologically active one that can be purchased in pure form at a significantly higher price.

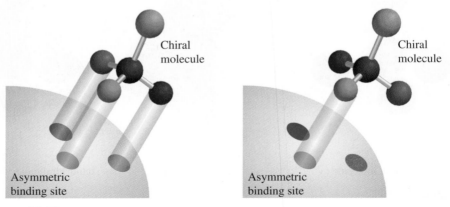

Figure 10.19

A chiral molecule binding (*left*) or not binding (*right*) to an asymmetrical site.

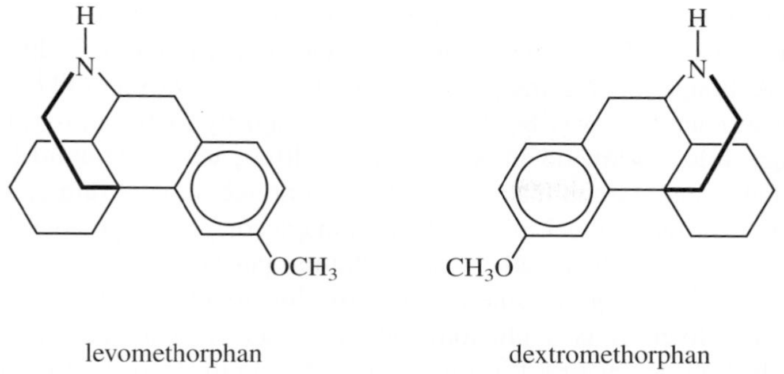

levomethorphan   dextromethorphan

Figure 10.20

Levo– and dextromethorphan.

Many other drugs exhibit chirality and are active only in one of the isomeric forms. This is true for some antibiotics and hormones and for certain drugs used to treat a wide range of conditions: inflammation, cardiovascular disease, central nervous system disorders, cancer, high cholesterol levels, and attention deficit disorder. Among the widely used chiral drugs are ibuprofen, cyclosporine (the drug used to prevent rejection in organ transplants), and the lipid-reducing drug atorvastatin (Lipitor). Ibuprofen is sold as a racemic mixture of (+) and (−) isomers (Figure 10.21 shows the (+) isomer). Only (−)-ibuprofen acts as a pain reliever; (+)-ibuprofen does not. However, in the body the (+) isomer is converted to the (−) form. Therefore, it is likely that someone taking ibuprofen is just as well off taking the racemic mixture rather than the more expensive (−)-ibuprofen.

Naproxen, a common pain reliever, is one example of many in which one isomer is preferred, even required. One form of naproxen relieves pain; the other causes liver damage. One last example involves a treatment for Parkinson's disease. The initial use of racemic dopa for treatment of this disease brought on adverse effects such as anorexia, nausea, and vomiting. The use of the single isomer (−)-dopa greatly reduced these side effects and the desired effect was achieved using half the initial doses.

Your Turn 10.17   Examining (+)–Ibuprofen and (−)–Dopa

Carefully examine the structural formulas for (+)–ibuprofen and (−)–dopa given in Figure 10.21.

a. For each drug, which is the chiral carbon atom?
b. Identify all of the functional groups present in both drugs.
c. Draw the structural formula of (−)–ibuprofen and (+)–dopa.

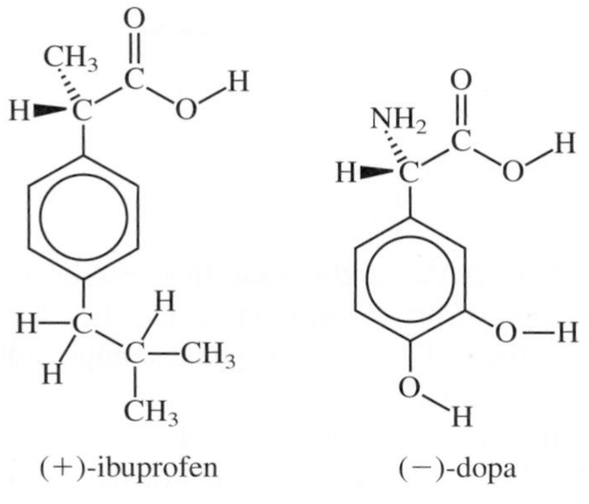

(+)-ibuprofen   (−)-dopa

Figure 10.21

Two chiral drug molecules.

William Knowles, Barry Sharpless, and Ryoji Noyori shared the 2001 Nobel Prize in Chemistry for their research that developed new catalytic methods for synthesizing chiral drugs.

Consequently, drug companies have active research programs designed to create chirally "pure" drugs, those having only the beneficial isomer of a drug as a single chiral form. Although making the proper, single isomer might seem like an exercise of interest only to chemists, it is big business. The majority of the most successful prescription drugs sold worldwide are single-isomer drugs, with total annual sales around $50 billion and rising, a trend that will no doubt continue into the future. These include the chiral "blockbuster" drugs Lipitor, simvastatin (Zocor), esomeprazole (Nexium), and sertraline (Zoloft), with global sales over $1 billion per year.

Lipitor, a chiral drug classified as a statin, lowers cholesterol by preventing its synthesis in the liver. It is a phenomenal bestseller with annual worldwide sales topping $10 billion. Producing Lipitor requires the synthesis of hydroxynitrile (HN), another chiral molecule. Until recently, HN had been produced only as a racemic mixture, thus requiring the separation of the two isomers. Worse still, this process involved large quantities of hydrogen bromide and cyanide. These chemicals are toxic to say the least, and the process produced enormous quantities of unwanted side products.

Enter Codexis, a company that won one of the 2006 Presidential Green Chemistry Challenge Awards. Chemists at Codexis developed an elegantly green route to the HN intermediate using enzymes to carry out highly specific reactions. Their green process increases yields, reduces the formation of by-products, reduces the generation of waste and use of solvents, reduces the use of purification equipment, and increases worker safety. The widespread use of Lipitor creates an annual demand for the HN intermediate of about 200 metric tons. This indeed is an invention worthy of a Presidential award!

New chiral drugs are big business, and drug companies have recently devised a novel strategy for increasing profits in this area. A number of proven medicines formerly sold as racemic mixtures are being reevaluated and remarketed as single isomers, a strategy known as a "chiral switch." The economic reasons for this are obvious: pharmaceutical companies are able to extend patent protection on their bestseller drugs and give them a hedge against generic competition. The therapeutic rationale for the switch is that the single isomer may provide benefits such as a wider margin of safety, fewer side effects, and more simple interactions in the body. Methylphenidate, sold under the trade name Ritalin, is a drug used for treating attention-deficit hyperactivity disorder (ADHD). Formerly prescribed as a racemate (racemic mixture), it has made the chiral switch and is now marketed as a single isomer; it is reported to be equally effective at half the dose compared with the racemate, and has an improved side effect profile.

Consider This 10.18   Chiral Switch

In principle, the strategy of chiral switching should afford a therapeutic advantage for the single-isomer drug over the racemic mixture. But is this always the case? Use the Internet to identify one drug (other than Ritalin) that has made the chiral switch and report on the relative merits of the single isomer versus the racemic mixture.

10.7 | Steroids

Consider cholesterol, contraceptives, and muscle-mass enhancers. What do these chemically have in common? The surprising answer is that they are all **steroids,** a class of naturally occurring or synthetic fat-soluble organic compounds that share a common carbon skeleton arranged in four rings.

As a family of compounds, steroids arguably best illustrate the relationship of form and function. Certainly no other group of chemicals is more controversial because their commonly known uses range from contraception to vanity promoters. The naturally occurring members of this ubiquitous group of substances include structural cell

Table 10.4	Steroid Functions
Function	**Examples**
Regulation of secondary sexual characteristics	estradiol (an estrogen), testosterone (an androgen)
Regulation of the female reproductive cycle	progesterone, RU-486 (the "abortion pill")
Regulation of metabolism	cortisol, cortisone derivatives
Digestion of fat	cholic acid
Component of cell membranes	cholesterol
Stimulation of muscle and bone growth	gestrinone, trenbolone

components, metabolic regulators, and the hormones responsible for secondary sexual characteristics and reproduction. Among the synthetic steroids are drugs for birth control, abortion, and bodybuilding. Table 10.4 lists some of the functions.

In spite of their tremendous range of physiological functions, all steroids are built on the same molecular skeleton. Thus, these compounds also provide a marvelous example of the economy with which living systems use and reuse certain fundamental structural units for many different purposes. The common characteristic of steroids is a molecular framework consisting of 17 carbon atoms arranged in four rings. The steroid skeleton is illustrated here.

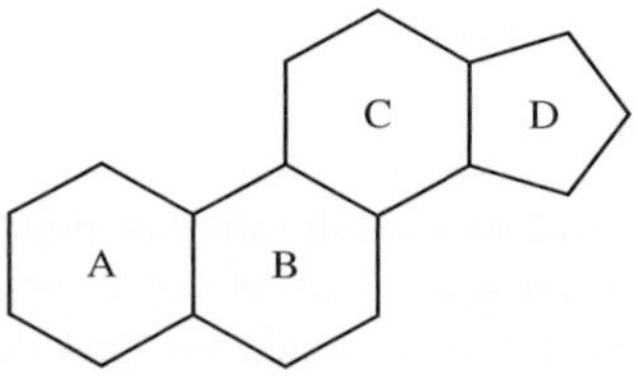

Recall that in such a representation (a line-angle drawing), carbon atoms are assumed to occupy the vertices of the rings but are not explicitly drawn. The three six-membered carbon rings of the steroid skeleton are designated A, B, and C, and the five-membered ring is designated D. Although the steroid nucleus appears flat as drawn, it actually is three-dimensional in shape. The dozens of natural and synthetic steroids are all variations on this theme. Some differ only slightly in structural detail, but have radically different physiological function. Extra carbon atoms or functional groups at critical positions on the rings are responsible for this variation.

The steroid cholesterol is a major component of cell membranes and is shown in Figure 10.22. The figure on the left includes all the atoms in the molecule; the one on the right gives the skeletal representation using a line-angle drawing.

Careful examination of Figure 10.23 illustrates how subtle molecular differences can result in profoundly altered physiological properties. The difference between a molecule of estradiol and one of testosterone lies only in one of the rings. Are the only differences between men and women due to a carbon atom and a few hydrogen atoms? You be the judge.

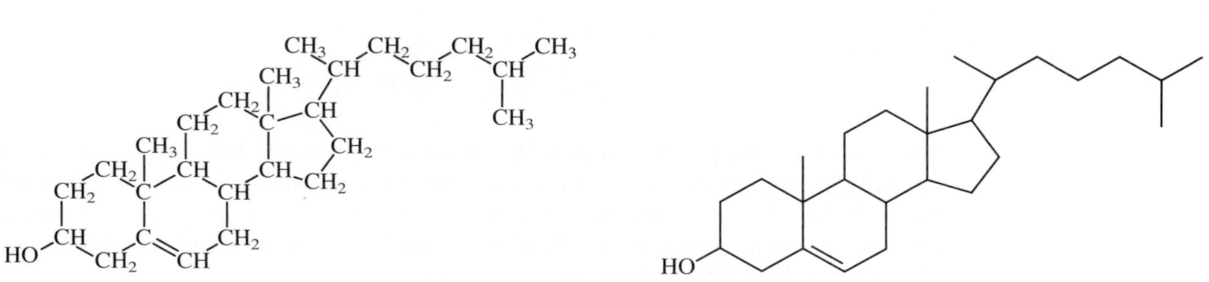

Figure 10.22

Figures Alive! Representations of cholesterol.

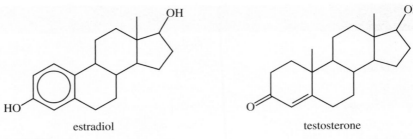

estradiol   testosterone

 Figure 10.23
Estradiol and testosterone.

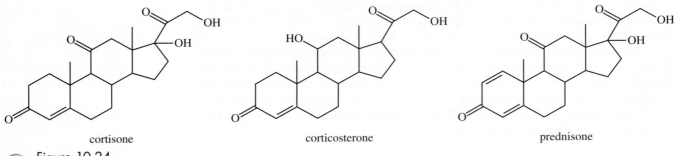

cortisone   corticosterone   prednisone

 Figure 10.24

Cortisone, corticosterone, and prednisone.

Some other common natural steroids are the hormones cortisone and corticosterone (Figure 10.24). You may have used some form of cortisone preparation for treating rashes and other minor skin disorders. Corticosteroids are produced in the adrenal cortex and play a wide range of roles such as regulation of inflammation, immune response, stress response, and carbohydrate metabolism. Steroidal anti-inflammatory drugs are the most often used treatment option for people with asthma; one synthetic choice is prednisone.

Your Turn 10.19   Structural Similarities of Steroids

Here are pairs of steroids. Their structures are given either here in the text or in Figures Alive! on Connect.

a. Identify the structural similarities in each pair.

estradiol and progesterone   corticosterone and cortisone
cholic acid and cholesterol   prednisone and cortisone
estradiol and testosterone

b. Write the chemical formula for five of the drugs in part **a**.

10.8 | Prescription, Generic, and Over-the-Counter Medicines

Enter customer. The pharmacist asks "Brand name or generic?" This scenario is played out daily in thousands of pharmacies across the country. How is the person to decide? For millions of Americans, the cheaper generic version can mean the difference between getting the necessary medication and not being able to afford it, although not all approved drugs are available in generic form.

The two forms can be differentiated rather simply. A pioneer drug is the first version of a drug that is marketed under a brand name, such as Xanax, an antianxiety

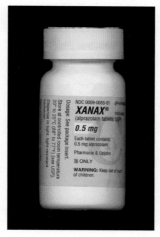
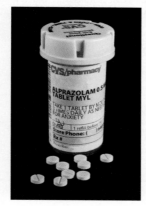

Figure 10.25

A brand–name drug (Xanax) and its generic counterpart (alprazolam).

or sedative drug. A **generic drug** is chemically equivalent to the pioneer drug, but cannot be marketed until the patent protection on the pioneer drug has run out after 20 years. The lower priced drug is commonly marketed under its generic name, in this case alprazolam instead of Xanax. The 20-year patent protection on the pioneer drug begins when it is patented, not when it's first put on the market. In cases requiring a long preapproval time, the actual marketing period can be relatively short, even less than six years. In such a situation, a drug company has very little time to recoup its research and development costs before a generic competitor can be manufactured. However, almost 80% of generic drugs are produced in brand-name equivalents (Figure 10.25). Like pioneer drugs, generic drugs must also be approved by the FDA.

In 1984, Congress passed the Drug Price Competition and Patent Restoration Act that greatly expanded the number of drugs eligible for generic status. This act eliminated the need for generics to duplicate the efficacy and safety testing done on counterpart pioneer drugs. Doing so saves generic drug manufacturers considerable time and money. The FDA also issued specific guidelines for a generic drug's comparability to the pioneer drug. By FDA mandate, the generic and pioneer versions must be bioequivalent in dosage form, safety, strength, route of administration, quality, performance characteristics, and intended use. In other words, they must deliver the same amount of active ingredient into a patient's bloodstream at the same rate. Once a generic drug is proven to be bioequivalent, companies can begin to drive the high price of a brand-name drug down through competition.

Consider This 10.20   Your Local Pharmacist

When it comes to generic drugs, pharmacists are on the front line. With your classmates, draft two or three short questions that relate to generic drugs. Then interview a local pharmacist and share your findings with your classmates. *Note*: If you have a school of pharmacy nearby, you might also want to interview pharmacy students.

Over-the-counter (OTC) drugs allow people to relieve many annoying symptoms and cure some ailments without the need to see a physician. Nonprescription medications now account for about 60% of all medications used in the United States. More than 80 therapeutic categories of OTC drugs exist, ranging from acne products to weight control products. Table 10.5 contains several major categories of OTC products and their chief components. In accordance with the laws and regulations prevailing in this country, drugs including OTC drugs are subjected to an intensive, extensive, and expensive screening process before they can be approved for sale and public use. Just

Table 10.5	Examples of Over–the–Counter Drugs
Analgesics and Anti–Inflammatory Drugs	**Cough Remedies**
aspirin	guaifenesin, expectorant
ibuprofen (Advil)*	dextromethorphan, suppressant
naproxen (Aleve)	benzonatate, suppressant
acetaminophen (Tylenol)	
Antacids and Indigestion Aids	**Antihistamines**
aluminum and magnesium salts (Maalox)	brompheniramine
calcium carbonate (Tums)	chlorpheniramine
calcium and magnesium salts (Rolaids)	diphenhydramine

*Names are shown as chemical name followed by common or brand name in parentheses.

Revisit Section 5.12 for a discussion of another safety issue, the disposal of unwanted drugs.

as in the case of prescription drugs, the ultimate question to be answered with over-the-counter drugs is "Do the benefits outweigh the risks?" The answer for an OTC drug depends on whether a consumer is using it properly. Therefore, the FDA and pharmaceutical manufacturers must try to balance OTC safety and efficacy.

Earlier we described OTC pain relievers and NSAIDs and their mode of action. Their side effects include increased stomach bleeding (aspirin), gastrointestinal upset (aspirin, ibuprofen), aggravating asthma (aspirin), and kidney or liver damage (acetaminophen) at high dosage or with chronic use.

More than 100 viruses are responsible for the misery accompanying the common cold. A whole host of cold remedies, most with multiple components, are designed to help the sufferer. Decongestants reduce swelling when viruses invade the mucous membranes, but the adverse effects include nervousness and insomnia. Nasal sprays relieve the swollen nasal tissues, but their use beyond a three-day limit often leads to a rebound effect, or a return of the runny nose.

Antihistamines relieve the runny nose and sneezing associated with allergies, but cause drowsiness and often light-headedness. Because they induce drowsiness, it is not surprising that approved sleep aids are often antihistamines. However, children often experience insomnia and hyperactivity after taking them.

Coughing is a natural way to rid the lungs of excess secretions. Expectorants make the phlegm thinner and therefore easier to cough up, while cough suppressants provide relief and restful sleep. The presence of both in most cough remedy preparations seems senseless! Codeine and dextromethorphan have equally good cough-suppressing potential, but the former has a reputation for being habit-forming, a property that limits its over-the-counter availability in some states.

Heartburn, indigestion, and "acid" stomach are targets of antacids and related drugs. Antacids are basic compounds containing aluminum, magnesium, or calcium hydroxides (or combinations of them) that neutralize excess stomach acid. The popularity of the calcium-containing alternatives has grown with the promotion of the need for younger and older adults to maintain a regular supply of dietary calcium to prevent degradation of bones (osteoporosis).

Consider This 10.21   Using Common Sense

Many people are of the opinion that it is best to only take the medicines that are indicated for a particular illness. This makes plain sense. Yet some companies selling OTC preparations seem to throw in everything but "the kitchen sink," hoping to give their product some sort of "value–added" feature. Check the contents of several cold remedies found at your local drug or grocery store (or go online to find the same information). In particular, look at several cough remedy preparations. Do you find the use of both guaifenesin and dextromethorphan in one product? List the names of the products that include both and then explain why a product containing both of these medicines makes no sense.

The self-care revolution of the last several decades has encouraged the availability of safe and effective OTC drugs and has provided additional pressure for the reclassification of many prescription drugs to OTC status. According to the Consumer Healthcare Products Association, about 80 ingredients or reduced dosages of drugs have made the OTC switch since 1976. Recent prescription to OTC switches include loratidine and cetirizine (Claritin and Zyrtec, antihistamines, 2002 and 2008, respectively), and omeprazole (Prilosec, acid reducer, 2003), and orlistat (Alli, weight loss, 2007). Right now, more than 700 OTC products have ingredients that were once only available by prescription. Additional pressure to have the switch occur comes from the health insurance industry. Changing widely used prescription drugs to OTC status greatly diminishes the insurance companies' share of payments. The conditions for which the drugs are prescribed must be common, non-life-threatening, and self-diagnosable by the average consumer. The FDA can change the status of an OTC drug back to prescription status if significant safety problems are uncovered.

From the drug manufacturer's standpoint, changing the status of a product from prescription to OTC often allows the manufacturer to market the product for several more years without generic competition. Sales volume also increases when a product is reclassified to OTC status. For the consumer, out-of-pocket expense in some cases may actually increase when going with OTC therapeutics because few third-party health insurance payers provide reimbursement for OTC products. But overall it is estimated that prescription to OTC switches save the American public over $20 million each year.

10.9 | Herbal Medicine

Worldwide, a growing number of people are using herbal products for preventive and therapeutic purposes. Herbal remedies and folk medicines abound in most cultures. This should not be surprising or astounding; nature is a very good chemist. Some (but not all) compounds found in plants and simple organisms are likely to have positive physiological effects in humans. U.S. sales of such popular herbal remedies as ginkgo biloba, St. John's wort, echinacea, ginseng, garlic, and kava kava have steadily risen over the past decade to $5 billion in 2010. Table 10.6 lists some herbs and plants and reasons for ingesting them.

Many people have been taking St. John's wort for its reported mood-elevating activity (Figure 10.26). The Herb Research Foundation reports data from over 2000 patients in 23 clinical studies that have consistently found that a preparation of St. John's wort, a plant, is just as effective against mild to moderate depression as standard antidepressant drugs. In April 2001, however, a study published in the *Journal of the American Medical Association* reported that St. John's wort is ineffective against severe depression. The herb worked no better than the placebo in over 200 adults diagnosed with severe depression. The study was funded partly by the National Institutes of

Table 10.6	Common Herbs and Their Possible Benefits
Herb or Plant	**Symptoms to Be Relieved**
Valerian, passion flower	anxiety
Licorice, wild cherry bark, thyme	coughs
Echinacea, garlic, goldenseal root	colds, flu
St. John's wort	depression
Chamomile, peppermint, ginger	nausea, digestive problems
Valerian, passion flower, hops, lemon balm	insomnia
Ginkgo biloba	memory loss
Valerian, passion flower, kava kava, Siberian ginseng	stress, tension

Figure 10.26

St. John's wort plant (*Hypericum perforatum*) and an extract in tablet form.

Mental Health and partly by Pfizer Incorporated, which makes sertraline (Zoloft), the most commonly prescribed multibillion dollar a year antidepression drug in the United States. Dr. Richard Skelton from Vanderbilt University, a coauthor of the new study, recommended further studies on the use of the herb for mild depression, saying: "I would like to see people with mild depression studied, and see if it works in those folks. If it works, that would be great." He recommended against using the herbal medicine until further studies are done.

Consider ephedra (Figure 10.27), a naturally occurring substance derived from the Chinese herb *ma huang* as well as from other plant sources. Although ephedra has long been used to treat certain respiratory symptoms in traditional Chinese medicine, in recent years it has been heavily promoted and used for the purposes of aiding weight loss, enhancing sports performance, and increasing energy.

Figure 10.27

Ephedra's source and a common formulation.

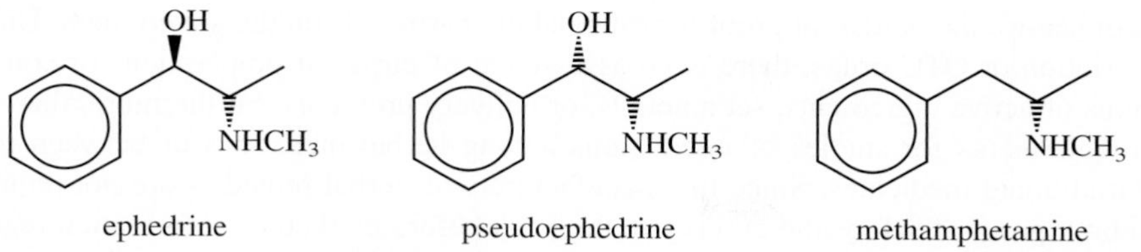

ephedrine   pseudoephedrine   methamphetamine

Figure 10.28

Chemical structures of ephedrine and two related drugs.

A solid wedge indicates a group coming out toward you. A dashed wedge indicates that the group is pointing away from you. These conventions were first introduced in Section 3.3.

Ephedra contains six amphetamine-like alkaloids including ephedrine and pseudo-ephedrine. Ephedrine, the main constituent, is a bronchodilator (opens the airways) and stimulates the sympathetic nervous system. It has valuable antispasmodic properties, acting on the air passages by relieving swelling of the mucous membranes. Pseudo-ephedrine (Sudafed) is a nasal decongestant and has less stimulating effect on the heart and blood pressure.

In their synthetic form, these drugs were regulated as OTC drugs and used as a decongestant for the short-term treatment of runny nose, asthma, bronchitis, and allergic reactions by opening the air passages in the lungs. Figure 10.28 shows three related structures; methamphetamine is presented so you can see the structural similarities between ephedra drugs and this potent and dangerous stimulant. Ephedra does not contain methamphetamine.

Dietary supplements that contained ephedra made big headlines in 2003. The deaths of well-known athletes were linked to rare but serious side effects of ephedra use. Side effects reported by ephedra users included nausea and vomiting, psychiatric disturbances such as agitation and anxiety, high blood pressure, irregular heartbeat, and, more rarely, seizures, heart attack, stroke, and even death.

No evidence currently supports the claim that ephedra enhances athletic performance. And only preliminary evidence suggests that ephedra aids in modest, temporary weight loss. However, evidence does indicate that ephedra is associated with an increased risk of side effects, possibly even fatal ones. In 2003, the International Olympic Committee, the National Football League, the National Collegiate Athletic Association, minor league baseball, and the U.S. Armed Forces banned the use of ephedra.

In December 2003, the FDA issued a consumer alert on the safety of dietary supplements containing ephedra. Consumers were advised to immediately stop buying and using ephedra products. In February 2004, the FDA published a final rule stating that dietary supplements containing ephedra present an unreasonable risk of illness or injury. The rule effectively banned the sale of these products, which took effect 60 days after its publication. However, the FDA ban does not apply to teas that contain ephedra (these are regulated as foods) and to traditional Chinese herbal remedies when prescribed by a traditional Chinese physician.

The St. John's wort and ephedra examples illustrate important concerns about herbal medicines. Are they effective, and are they safe? Psychiatrists report that many of their patients with depression have tried St. John's wort before coming for medical help. One estimate suggests that over a million people in the United States alone have tried it or are using St. John's wort. Irrespective of the accuracy of the estimate, large numbers of Americans are apparently using herbal medicines under circumstances with little or no medical supervision.

Herbal remedies are only loosely regulated by the FDA. The Dietary Supplement Health and Education Act (DSHEA) of 1994 changed their classification from "food or drug" to "dietary supplement." **Dietary supplements** by definition include vitamins, minerals, amino acids, enzymes, and herbs and other botanicals. Many dietary supplements have shown no adverse effects and in fact have proven to be beneficial to good health. Others, like ephedra, have been shown to be problematic.

Under the DSHEA, the FDA does not review dietary supplements for safety and effectiveness before they are marketed. Rather, the law allows the FDA to prohibit sale of a dietary supplement if it "presents a significant or unreasonable risk of injury." When the FDA seeks to take regulatory action against a supplement (such as in the ephedra case), the burden of proof for establishing harm falls on the government. Unlike prescription or OTC drugs, there is no assessment of purity of preparations or concentrations of active ingredients, set amounts, or delivery protocols. Furthermore, there are no requirements for studies of interactions among herbal medicines or between them and traditional medicines. Since the manufacturers of herbal remedies are not required to submit proof of safety and efficacy to the FDA before marketing, information regarding the interactions between herbal remedies and other drugs is largely unknown.

In the spring of 2001, representatives from the American Society of Anesthesiologists reported concerns that patients undergoing surgery may risk unexpected bleeding when they take certain herbs within two weeks before surgery. To this point, no scientific studies linking the bleeding and a specific herb have been published. According to Dr. John Neeldt, president of the American Society of Anesthesiologists, the familiar question "Are you taking any medications?" should be augmented with, "Are you taking any herbal remedies?"

Consider This 10.22   Does Natural Mean Safer?

The legal standard of "significant or unreasonable risk" implies a risk–benefit calculation based on the best available scientific evidence. This suggests that the FDA must determine if a product's known or supposed risks outweigh any known or suspected benefits, based on the available scientific evidence. This must be done in light of the claims the manufacturer makes and with the understanding that the product is being sold directly to consumers without medical supervision.

When deciding to take any medication a consumer makes a risk–benefit analysis, sometimes unconsciously. One element of such an analysis is the *perceived* risk. Do you think that the general population perceives naturally occurring drugs as safer than synthetic ones? Explain using examples of your choice.

10.10 | Drugs of Abuse

Before concluding our foray into the world of drugs, we should take time to examine their abuse. According to the National Survey on Drug Use and Health (NSDUH), the number of people illegally using one or more drugs ranks in the millions. In 2010, 8.9% of the population, or an estimated 22.6 million Americans of age 12 or older, reported that they used an illicit drug during the month prior to the survey. Details from the 2010 survey included that:

An illicit drug is one not sanctioned by law or custom.

- Marijuana was the most common illicit drug, with an estimated 17.4 million users. The extent of use among young adults (aged 18 to 25) is particularly high and continues to increase, from 16.5% in 2008 to 18.5% in 2010.
- Second highest was the nonmedical use of prescription-type drugs (pain relievers, tranquilizers, stimulants, and sedatives) at an estimated 7 million users. Again, among young adults aged 18 to 25, the rate of abuse was notable at 5.9% in 2010.
- 1.5 million people (0.6% of the population) were reported cocaine users, though use of both cocaine and methamphetamine has decreased in recent years.
- During 2010, 10.6 million people reported that they had operated a vehicle while under the influence of an illicit drug. In 2010, the rate was highest among young adults aged 18 to 25 (12.7%).

Consider This 10.23   Consequences

Legal or illegal, the drugs that humans use have consequences. People usually can point a finger at a drug that is disruptive in the home and workplace. Which drug would you pick? Make your choice and be prepared to defend it in a group discussion.

Table 10.7	Drug Schedules			
Class	Has Current Accepted Medical Uses	Potential for Abuse	Examples	
Schedule I	no	high	heroin LSD marijuana*, hashish mescaline MDMA ("ecstasy")	
Schedule II	yes	high	oxycodone (in OxyContin and Percocet) morphine, opium methadone cocaine (as a topical anesthetic) methamphetamine	
Schedule III	yes	medium	hydrocodone with acetaminophen (Vicodin) codeine with acetaminophen anabolic steroids	
Schedule IV	yes	low	alprazolam (Xanax) propoxyphene and acetaminophen (Darvocet) diazepam (Valium)	
Schedule V	yes	lowest	cough suppressants with small amounts of codeine diphenoxylate and atropine (Lomotil) promethazine (Phenergan)	

*Legal status of marijuana currently is complicated because federal and state laws may differ.

Although tobacco and alcohol are not illegal in the United States, their use was included in the NSDUH as well.

- Approximately one quarter of the population aged 12 and older reported binge drinking, meaning that they consumed five or more drinks at a time at least once in the past month.
- Among young adults aged 18 to 25, the rate of binge drinking was 40.6%.
- About 70 million people were tobacco users, including 58 million cigarette smokers. The overall rate of tobacco use was about 27% of the population.

In 1970, the Comprehensive Drug Abuse Prevention and Control Act was passed into law. Title II of this law, the Controlled Substances Act, is the legal foundation of narcotics enforcement in the United States. The Controlled Substance Act regulates the manufacture and distribution of drugs and places all drugs into one of five schedules (Table 10.7).

Consider This 10.24   Low Potential for Abuse?

The sedatives diazepam (Valium) and alprazolam (Xanax) are currently listed as Schedule IV drugs, indicating that they have a low potential for abuse. Search the Internet for information on addiction to these powerful sedative drugs. Do you agree with the current scheduling? Explain.

Marijuana, an example of a Schedule I drug, is the most commonly used illicit drug in the United States. It is a mixture of the dried leaves, stems, seeds, and flowers of the hemp plant, *Cannabis sativa* (Figure 10.29). The drug is usually smoked and occasionally eaten. The first known record of marijuana use dates back to the time of the Chinese Emperor Shen Nung (ca. 2737 BCE), who prescribed use of the plant for the treatment of malaria, gas pains, and absentmindedness.

Figure 10.29
Hemp plants.

Cannabis sativa means useful (*sativa*) hemp (*cannabis*).

Hemp is the plant whose botanical name is *Cannabis sativa*. Other plants are called hemp, but *Cannabis* hemp is the most useful of these plants. Fiber is its most well-known product, and the word *hemp* can mean the rope or twine made from the hemp plant, as well as just the stalk of the plant that produced it. The major psychoactive drug in *Cannabis sativa* is concentrated in the leaves and flowers of the hemp plant, so one cannot get high from smoking hemp rope or wearing clothing woven from hemp fibers.

Extracts of marijuana were employed by physicians in the early 1800s for a tonic and euphoriant. But in 1937, the Marijuana Tax Act prohibited its use as an intoxicant and its medical use was regulated as national concern of its use emerged. The Marijuana Tax Act required anyone producing, distributing, or using marijuana for medical purposes to register and pay a tax that effectively prohibited nonmedical use of the drug. Although the act did not make medical use of marijuana illegal, it did make it expensive and inconvenient.

In 1942, marijuana was removed from the U.S. Pharmacopoeia, the official government compendium of drugs, because it was believed to be harmful, addictive, and cause psychosis, mental deterioration, and violent behavior. The current legal status of marijuana was established in 1970 with the passage of the Controlled Substances Act.

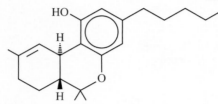

Figure 10.30

Structural formula for THC.

The major psychoactive chemical in marijuana is Δ^9-tetrahydrocannabinol, or THC, as shown in Figure 10.30. The concentration of THC varies depending on how the hemp is grown: temperature, amount of sunlight, and soil moisture and fertility. High-potency varieties of marijuana are grown across the United States, with THC levels as high as 7%. In hashish, or hash, the dried and pressed flowers and resin of the plant, THC concentrations can be as high as 12%.

When marijuana smoke is inhaled, THC rapidly passes from the lungs into the bloodstream, which carries the chemical to organs throughout the body, including the brain. In the brain, THC connects to specific sites called cannabinoid receptors on nerve cells and influences the activity of those cells. Some brain areas have many cannabinoid receptors; others have few or none. Many cannabinoid receptors are found in the parts of the brain that influence pleasure, memory, thought, concentration, sensory and time perception, and coordinated movement. THC leaves the blood rapidly through metabolism and uptake into the tissues. The chemical may remain stored in body fat for long periods; research has indicated that a single dose can take up to 30 days for complete elimination. The short-term effects of marijuana use can include problems with memory and learning, distorted perception, difficulty in thinking and problem solving, loss of coordination, decreased blood pressure, and increased heart rate.

Medicinal marijuana may be indicated for treatment of nausea, glaucoma, pain management, and appetite stimulation. Such treatment may be a last resort when all other medications have failed, such as with the unrelenting nausea and vomiting that may accompany weeks of chemotherapy in treating diseases such as leukemia and AIDS. Clinical studies on the usefulness of marijuana are difficult to conduct as many barriers discourage researchers. The scarcity of funding combined with complicated regulations enforced by both federal and state agencies make research in this area daunting.

At its heart, the debate over the medical use of marijuana pits benefits against risks. Underlying this debate, however, are the complex moral and social judgments relating to drug control policies in the United States. Supporters of medical marijuana argue that it is far less risky than some drugs currently in use and may succeed at relieving unpleasant symptoms where other drugs fail. Opponents argue that it is dangerous, unnecessary, and that its use leads to the use of other drugs.

In the United States, the Institute of Medicine of the National Academies has weighed in on the issue. In 1999, the Institute published a review that found marijuana to be "moderately well suited for particular conditions, such as chemotherapy-induced nausea and vomiting, and AIDS wasting." As of 2013, 18 states and the District of Columbia allowed legal use of marijuana for medical purposes and two states approved recreational use.

Consider This 10.25   THC in a Legal Form

A legal form of marijuana exists in the form of a prescription drug, dronabinol (Marinol). It is a synthetic form of THC.

a. Marinol is swallowed rather than smoked. The 1999 report from the Institute of Medicine labels smoking "a primitive drug delivery system." What are the disadvantages of smoking (as opposed to swallowing) a drug such as marijuana?

b. Even if primitive, inhaling a drug does have key advantages in treating nausea or vomiting. Name at least one.

OxyContin is an example of a Schedule II drug (Figure 10.31). Known on the street as "oxy," OxyContin is the trade name for oxycodone hydrochloride, a morphine-like narcotic. OxyContin tablets contain up to 80 mg of oxycodone with a time release mechanism. For those enduring acute and long-term pain, this drug delivers much-needed relief. Percocet and Percodan contain the same chemical, but in much smaller amounts (5–7.5 mg/tablet).

Abusers of OxyContin are able to get around the time release mechanism by crushing the tablet and either snorting it or dissolving it in water and injecting the solution. The effect is similar to that achieved from using heroin. Obviously, absorbing this much of the powerful narcotic can have dramatic consequences, very often emergency room overdoses.

The problem was first observed in rural areas of Kentucky, Virginia, West Virginia, and Maine and was given the derogatory slang names of "hillbilly heroin" and "poor man's heroin." But it has since spread to other areas in the United States, and in March 2002, an 18-year-old female became the first U.K. fatality attributed to OxyContin.

Purdue Pharma, the manufacturer of the product, has come under fire for allegedly turning a blind eye to the mounting reports of abuse of the drug. In an effort to educate healthcare providers about these risks, the drug manufacturer issued a warning in the form of a "Dear Healthcare Professional" letter. The company's other efforts have included discontinuing the most powerful pill, a 160-mg form of the drug; stamping pills from Mexico and Canada to help authorities trace illicit supplies; passing out tamper-proof prescription pads to doctors; and instituting educational programs aimed at doctors as well as potential abusers, with a particular focus in the Appalachian region.

> Oxycodone is a Schedule II drug under the Controlled Substances Act because of its high propensity to cause dependence and abuse.

Your Turn 10.26   Oxycodone Formulation

The oxycodone in an OxyContin pill is not a freebase but rather is formulated as a salt. Which acid is neutralized to form this salt? Draw a structural formula for the drug in its salt form.

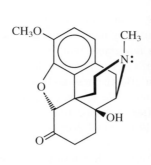
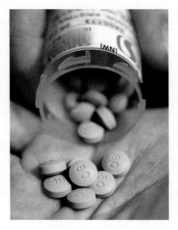

Figure 10.31

Oxycodone molecular structure and OxyContin pills. *Source: Photo © 2004, Publishers Group.*

Morphine, oxycodone, hydrocodone (found in Vicodin, Lortab, and Lorcet), and codeine belong to a class of drugs known as opiates. Morphine and codeine are extracted from *Papaver somniferum,* the opium poppy. The other opiates listed are synthesized from morphine. They vary in their strength and thus their drug scheduling. But they all have the same mode of action. These drugs bind to a chemical receptor called *mu* that interrupts the transmission of pain in the spinal cord. Opiates also stimulate areas of the brain involved in pleasure, called the reward, or endorphin, pathways. In a normal brain, the chemical dopamine crosses between brain cells in the reward pathway, producing pleasurable feelings. Opiates stimulate the release of higher levels of dopamine, strengthening reward signals, and producing intense euphoria. Repeated use of opiates causes the brain of a user to become accustomed to an over-stimulated reward pathway. This in turn brings about the phenomenon of tolerance—greater amounts of opiates are required to achieve the euphoria the user once experienced.

Consider This 10.27   House!

Gregory House, MD, the doctor in a popular TV series, in some episodes is addicted to Vicodin. An ABC News interview reports "In watching Dr. House on TV, one gets the impression that his addiction has no consequences other than affecting his medical judgment."

a. Research the effects of Vicodin abuse. Then interview one of the millions of viewers who watched this series. Do their impressions of Dr. House match what you found out about the realities of Vicodin abuse?

b. Is there a connection between Vicodin and hearing loss? Report your findings.

The drugs just described are but a few of today's commonly abused substances. There are many more, including alcohol, which is possibly the most damaging of all drugs when taken to excess. Just as for prescribed medicines, the choice to take illicit drugs involves a risk–benefit analysis. All drug users should have this basic information before making this choice.

Conclusion

Molecular modifications by chemists have created a vast new pharmacopoeia of wonder drugs that have significantly increased the number and quality of our days. Prior to penicillin, an infection could mean a death sentence. Now thanks to penicillin, sulfa drugs, and other antibiotics, the great majority of bacterial infections are easily controlled. Dreaded killers such as typhoid, cholera, and pneumonia have been largely eliminated—at least in many nations of the world. New methods of drug discovery are allowing vast libraries of novel compounds to be built. These can be stored for future testing by assays that have not yet been dreamed of.

But no drug can be completely safe, and almost any drug can be misused. These issues become the focus when the FDA is asked to change the status of a drug from prescription to over-the-counter. Taking any medication (generic or brand name) is a conscious choice between the benefits derived from the drug and the risks associated with its side effects and limits of safety. Because most drugs have very wide, carefully established margins of safety, their benefits far outweigh their risks for the general population. For some drugs, however, the trade-off between effectiveness and safety involves a different balance. A drug with severe side effects may be the only treatment available for a life-threatening disease. Someone suffering from HIV/AIDS or advanced, inoperable cancer understandably has a different perspective on drug risks and benefits than a person with a cold. And the impersonal anonymity of averages involved in clinical drug trials takes on new meaning at the bedside of a loved one.

Herbal and alternative medicines raise new questions. Who is responsible for defining their efficacy, monitoring their purity, and developing contraindications to their use with other drugs? Doctors must be advised of all medicines their patients are taking, including herbal remedies. The abuse of herbal and synthetic drugs continues to cause major problems throughout our society. Advances are being made in all of these areas. When chemistry is applied to medicine, science must be guided by morality, and reason must be tempered with compassion.

Chapter Summary

Having studied this chapter, you should be able to:

- Describe the discovery, development, and physiological properties of aspirin (10.1)
- Understand bonding in carbon-containing (organic) compounds (10.2)
- Apply the concept of isomerism to organic molecules (10.2)
- Convert chemical formulas of carbon-containing compounds to structural formulas, condensed structural formulas, and line-angle drawings (10.2)
- Recognize functional groups and the classes of organic compounds that contain them; draw structural formulas for organic molecules containing various functional groups (10.3)
- Understand that functional groups may be chemically modified to change a molecule's properties (10.3)
- Predict the products of ester formation reactions and describe how amines may be converted to their salt forms (10.3)
- Relate the molecular structure of aspirin to other analgesics (10.3)
- Understand the mode of action of aspirin and other analgesics (10.4)
- Describe the discovery of penicillin (10.5)

- Explain the lock-and-key mechanism of drug action (10.5)
- Describe how combinatorial synthesis can be employed in the creation of large collections of new drugs at lower costs than previous methods (10.5)
- Understand differences in molecular structure between a pair of chiral (optical) isomers (10.6)
- Appreciate the economic effect of chiral drugs (10.6)
- Identify the basic carbon skeleton arrangement of steroids (10.7)
- Recognize that minor changes in steroid structure may result in large changes in bioactivity (10.7)
- Compare and contrast brand-name and generic drugs (10.8)
- Identify some of the over-the-counter drug categories and their uses (10.8)
- Understand the process of a drug going from prescription to OTC (10.8)
- Describe some of the potential benefits and risks of herbal medicines (10.9)
- Explain the scheduling of prescription drugs (10.10)
- Discuss the use of marijuana and oxycodone in terms of their physiological and social effects (10.10)

Questions

Emphasizing Essentials

1. Give the intended effect of each. Can one drug exhibit all of these effects?

   a. an antipyretic drug
   b. an analgesic drug
   c. an anti-inflammatory drug

2. The field of chemistry has many subdisciplines. What do organic chemists study?

3. Write condensed structural formulas and line-angle drawings for the three isomers of C_5H_{12} assigned in Your Turn 10.7.

4. Write the structural formula and line-angle drawings for each different isomer of C_6H_{14}. *Hint:* Watch out for duplicate structures.

5. Consider the isomers of C_4H_{10}. How many different isomers could be formed by replacing a single hydrogen atom with an –OH group? Draw the structural formula for each.

6. For each compound, identify the functional group present.

   a. CH_3–O–CH_3

   b. CH_3CH_2–C(=O)–O–H

   c. CH_3CH_2–C(=O)–CH_3 d. CH_3CH_2–C(=O)–NH_2

   e. CH_3CH_2–C(=O)–OCH_3

7. Draw the simplest compound that can contain each of these functional groups. In some cases, only one carbon atom is required; in other cases two.

   a. an alcohol   d. an ester
   b. an aldehyde   e. an ether
   c. a carboxylic acid   f. a ketone

8. For each of these, identify the functional group. Then, draw an isomer that contains a different functional group.

   a. CH_3CH_2—OH   b. CH_3CH_2–C(=O)–H

   c. CH_3CH_2–C(=O)–OCH_3

9. In allergy sufferers, histamine causes runny noses, red eyes, and other symptoms. Here is its structural formula.

   a. Give the chemical formula for this compound.

   b. Circle the amine functional groups in histamine.

   c. Which part (or parts) of the molecule make the compound water-soluble?

10. Figure 10.7 shows a somewhat condensed structural formula for acetaminophen, the active ingredient in Tylenol.

   a. Draw the structural formula for acetaminophen, showing all atoms and all bonds.

   b. Give the chemical formula for this compound.

   c. Children's Tylenol is a flavored aqueous solution of acetaminophen. Predict what part (or parts) of the molecule make acetaminophen water-soluble.

11. Identify the functional groups in each of these.

   a. Barbital (a sedative)

   b. Penicillin-G (an antibiotic)

   c. Amyl dimethylaminobenzoate (an ingredient in sunscreens)

12. Ibuprofen is relatively insoluble in water but readily soluble in most organic solvents. Explain this solubility behavior based on its structural formula. *Hint:* See Figure 10.7.

13. Here is the structural formula for diazepam, the sedative found in Valium.

Judging from its structure, do you expect it to be more soluble in fats or in aqueous solutions? Explain.

14. Draw structural formulas for the esters formed when acetic acid reacts with these alcohols.

   a. *n*-propanol, $CH_3CH_2CH_2OH$

   b. *iso*propanol, $(CH_3)_2CHOH$

   c. *t*-butanol, $(CH_3)_3COH$

15. Interpret this sentence by giving the meaning of each acronym and explaining the effect. "NSAIDs have an effect on COX enzymes."

16. Usually carbon forms four covalent bonds, nitrogen three, oxygen two, and hydrogen only one bond. Use this information to draw structural formulas for:

   a. A compound that contains one carbon atom, one nitrogen atom, and as many hydrogen atoms as needed.

   b. A compound that contains one carbon atom, one oxygen atom, and as many hydrogen atoms as needed.

17. Would aspirin be more active if it were to interact with prostaglandins directly, rather than by blocking the activity of COX enzymes? Explain your reasoning.

18. Examine the combinatorial synthesis process diagrammed in Figure 10.16. If you started with a molecule that had two active functional groups, how many products could form after two synthetic steps, where each step adds a molecule with one functional group? How many products could be formed if the reagent in the first step had two reactive functional groups itself?

19. The text states that 80 billion tablets of aspirin a year are consumed in the United States. If the average tablet contains 500 mg of aspirin, how many pounds of aspirin does this consumption represent?

20. Identify the functional groups in morphine and meperidine. Can these molecules be assigned to a particular class of compound (i.e., an alcohol, ketone, or amine)? Explain. *Hint:* See Figure 10.14 for structural formulas.

21. What is meant by the term *pharmacophore?*

22. Sulfanilamide is the simplest sulfa drug, a type of antibiotic. It appears to act against bacteria by replacing *para*-aminobenzoic acid, an essential nutrient for bacteria, with sulfanilamide. Use these structural

formulas to explain why this substitution is likely to occur.

sulfanilamide

para-aminobenzoic acid

23. Which of these molecules has chiral forms?

a. $CH_3-\overset{\overset{\displaystyle NH_2}{|}}{\underset{\underset{\displaystyle OH}{|}}{C}}-CH_3$

b. $H-\overset{\overset{\displaystyle OH}{|}}{\underset{\underset{\displaystyle CH_3}{|}}{C}}-CO_2H$

c. $CH_3-\overset{\overset{\displaystyle NH_2}{|}}{\underset{\underset{\underset{\underset{\displaystyle N}{|||}}{C}}{|}}{C}}-CO_2H$

d. $CH_3-\overset{\overset{\displaystyle OH}{|}}{\underset{\underset{\displaystyle CH_3}{|}}{C}}-CO_2H$

24. Which of these molecules has chiral forms?

a. $CH_3-\overset{\overset{\displaystyle NH_2}{|}}{\underset{\underset{\displaystyle OH}{|}}{C}}-CH_2CH_3$

b. $H-\overset{\overset{\displaystyle OH}{|}}{\underset{\underset{\displaystyle H}{|}}{C}}-C_2H_5$

c. $CH_3-\overset{\overset{\displaystyle NH_2}{|}}{\underset{\underset{\displaystyle CH_2OH}{|}}{C}}-CO_2H$

d. $CH_3-\overset{\overset{\displaystyle OH}{|}}{\underset{\underset{\displaystyle CH_2SH}{|}}{C}}-CO_2H$

25. Methamphetamine hydrochloride is a powerful stimulant that is dangerous and highly addictive. This drug also goes by the street names "crystal," "crank," or "meth." This structural formula shows its salt form.

The freebase form of this drug, called "ice," is also abused. What does the term *freebase* mean, and how might the drug be converted to this form?

26. Examine the structures of levo- and dextromethorphan (Figure 10.20). Identify any chiral carbons and list any functional groups present.

27. Molecules as diverse as cholesterol, sex hormones, and cortisone contain common structural elements. Use a line-angle drawing to show the structure they share.

Concentrating on Concepts

28. The text states that some remedies based on the medications of earlier cultures contain chemicals that are effective against disease, others are ineffective but harmless, and still others are potentially harmful. How might it be determined into which of these three categories a recently discovered substance fits?

29. Draw structural formulas for each of these molecules and determine the number and type of bonds (single, double, or triple) for each carbon atom.

  a. H_3CCN (acetonitrile, used to make a type of plastic)

  b. $H_2NC(O)NH_2$ (urea, an important fertilizer)

  c. C_6H_5COOH (benzoic acid, a food preservative)

30. Compare the physiological effects of aspirin with those of acetaminophen and ibuprofen. Relate differences to the nature of each compound at the molecular and cellular levels.

31. In Your Turn 10.7, you were asked to draw structural formulas for the three isomers of C_5H_{12}. One student submitted this set, with a note saying that six isomers had been found. (*Note:* The hydrogen atoms have been omitted for clarity.) Help this student see why some of the answers are incorrect.

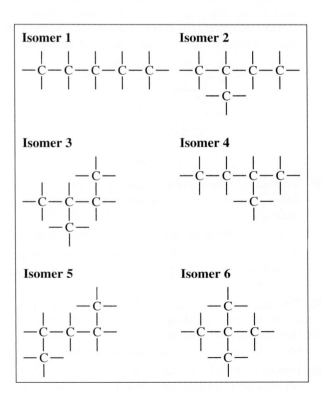

32. Styrene, $C_6H_5CH=CH_2$, the monomer for polystyrene described in Chapter 9, contains the phenyl group, $-C_6H_5$. Draw structural formulas to show that this molecule, like benzene, has resonance structures.

33. Aspirin is a specific compound, so what justifies the claims for the superiority of one brand of aspirin over another?

34. Figure 10.8 represents chemical communication within the body. Write a paragraph explaining what this figure means to you in helping to explain chemical communication.

35. Consider this statement. "Drugs can be broadly classed into two groups: those that produce a physiological response in the body and those that inhibit the growth of substances that cause infections." Into which class does each of these drugs fall?

  a. aspirin   **c.** (Keflex) antibiotic   **e.** amphetamine

  b. morphine   d. estrogen   f. penicillin

36. Consider the structure of morphine in Figure 10.14. Codeine, another strong analgesic with narcotic action, has a very similar structure in which the $-OH$ group attached to the benzene ring is replaced by an $-OCH_3$ group.

  a. Draw the structural formula for codeine and label its functional groups.

  b. The analgesic action of codeine is only about 20% as effective as morphine. However, codeine is less addictive than morphine. Is this enough evidence to conclude that replacement of $-OH$ groups with $-OCH_3$ groups in this class of drugs will always change the properties in this way? Explain.

37. Dopamine is found naturally in the brain. The drug $(-)$-dopa is found to be effective against the tremors and muscular rigidity associated with Parkinson's disease. Identify the chiral carbon in $(-)$-dopa, and comment on why $(-)$-dopa is effective, whereas $(+)$-dopa is not.

$(-)$-dopa

38. Vitamin E is often sold as a racemic mixture of $(+)$ and $(-)$ isomers. Use the Internet to find answers to these questions.

  a. Which is the more physiologically active isomer?

  b. How does the cost of the racemic mixture compare with the price of the pure, physiologically active isomer?

39. Consider the fact that levomethorphan is an addictive opiate, but dextromethorphan is safe enough to be sold in many over-the-counter cough remedies. From a molecular point of view, how is this possible?

40. Describe the lock-and-key analogy for the interaction between drugs and receptor sites. Use the analogy in a discussion as if you were explaining this to a friend.

41. Why are many projects to isolate or synthesize new drugs started in this country, but few drugs actually receive FDA approval for general use?

42. Until the early 19th century, it was believed that organic compounds had some sort of "life force" and could only be produced by living organisms. This was the basis of a concept called vitalism. This view was dispelled in the late 1800s. Use the Internet to find out what changed that opinion.

Exploring Extensions

43. One avenue for successful drug discovery is to use the initial drug as a prototype for the development of other similar compounds called analogs. The text states that cyclosporine, a major antirejection drug used in organ transplant surgery, is an example of a drug discovered in this way. Research the discovery of this drug to verify this statement. Write a brief report describing your findings, citing your sources.

44. Dorothy Crowfoot Hodgkin first determined the structure of a naturally occurring penicillin compound. What in her background prepared her to make this discovery? Write a short report on the results of your findings, citing your sources.

45. Before the cyclic structure of benzene was determined (see Figure 10.4), there was a great deal of controversy about how the atoms in this compound were arranged.

  a. Count outer electrons for C and H in C_6H_6. Then draw the structural formula for a possible linear isomer.

  b. Give the condensed structural formula for your answer in part **a**.

  c. Compare your structure with those drawn by classmates. Are they all the same? Why or why not?

46. Antihistamines are widely used drugs for treating symptoms of allergies caused by reactions to histamine compounds. This class of drug competes with histamine, occupying receptor sites on cells normally occupied by histamine. Here is the structure for a particular antihistamine.

  a. Give the chemical formula for this compound.

  b. What similarities do you see between this structure and that of histamine (shown in Question 9) that would allow the antihistamine to compete with histamine?

47. Over the next few years, the FDA may consider deregulating more than a dozen drugs, nearly as many as have already been approved for over-the-counter sales during the past decade. The products that have led this trend have been the widely advertised drugs for heartburn.

  a. What questions need to be answered before a drug is deregulated?

b. Will these questions change if you are considering this need from the viewpoint of the FDA, a pharmaceutical company, or as a consumer?

48. Find out more about the new process for the manufacture of hydroxynitrile (HN), a precursor to Lipitor that won a 2006 Presidential Green Chemistry Challenge Award. How does this process differ from the earlier one for manufacturing HN? Write a brief report on your research, citing your sources.

49. The steroids testosterone and estrone were first isolated from animal tissue. One ton of bull testicles was needed to obtain 5 mg of testosterone and 4 tons of pig ovaries was processed to yield 12 mg of estrone.

   a. Assuming complete isolation of the hormones was achieved, calculate the mass percentage of each steroid in the original tissue.

   b. Explain why the calculated result very likely is incorrect.

50. Herbal remedies are prominently displayed in supermarkets, drug stores, and discount stores.

   a. What influences your decision to buy one of these remedies?

   b. Choose a remedy and carefully examine its label for information about the active ingredients, inert ingredients, anticipated side effects, the suggested dosage, and the cost per dose.

   c. How confident are you that the safety and efficacy of these remedies are ensured? Explain your answer.

51. Habitrol was the most successful smoking-cessation prescription until the introduction of bupropion (Zyban) in 1997, which quickly claimed 50% of the market. How are these two approaches to drug therapy different?

52. Over-the-counter drugs allow consumers to treat a myriad of symptoms and ailments. An advantage is that the user can purchase and administer the treatment without the effort or the expense of consulting a physician. To provide a wider margin of safety for these circumstances, the OTC versions of drugs are often administered in lower doses. See if this is true by looking at information for prescription and OTC versions of painkillers like ibuprofen (Motrin) and heartburn treatments like nizatidine (Axid) and famotidine (Pepcid). Report on your findings.

53. Herbal or alternative medicines are not regulated in the same way as prescription or OTC medicines. In particular, the issues of concern are identification and quantification of the active ingredient, quality control in manufacture, and side effects when the herbal remedy is used in conjunction with another alternative or prescription medicine. Look for evidence from herbal supplement manufacturers that addresses these issues, and write a report documenting your findings, giving your references.

54. Danco Laboratories, the U.S. company that produces RU-486 (mifeprex, the "abortion pill") makes claims about the safety of this steroidal drug, including a comparison to aspirin. Do some research on RU-486, and write a short report on the drug. Include its structure, mode of action, and safety record.

55. The antibiotic ciprofloxacin hydrochloride (Cipro) treats bacterial infections in many different parts of the body. This drug made headlines in 2001 for use in patients who had been exposed to the inhaled form of anthrax. Use the Internet or another source to obtain the structure of Cipro. Draw its structure and identify the functional groups.

56. Direct-to-consumer advertising of prescription drugs has proved to be a successful marketing tool for pharmaceutical companies. Twenty percent of consumers say that advertisements prompted them to call or visit their doctor to discuss the drug, according to PharmTrends, a patient-level syndicated tracking study of consumer behavior by market research organization Ipsos-NPD. Make a list of the pros and cons of this type of marketing from both the patient's and physician's point of view.

57. In 2003, a series of spot examinations of mail shipments of foreign drugs to U.S. consumers conducted by the FDA and U.S. Customs and Border Protection revealed that these shipments often contain unapproved or counterfeit drugs that pose serious safety problems. Although many drugs obtained from foreign sources purport to be, and may even appear to be, the same as FDA-approved medications, these examinations showed that many are of unknown quality or origin. Of the 1153 imported drug products examined, the overwhelming majority, 1019 (88%), were illegal because they contained unapproved drugs. Many of these imported drugs could pose clear safety problems. Use the FDA website to determine which drugs were most commonly counterfeited and their countries of origin.

58. Thalidomide was first marketed in Europe in the late 1950s. It was used as a sleeping pill and to treat morning sickness during pregnancy. At that time it was not known to cause any adverse effects. By the late 1960s, however, the drug was banned after it was found to be a teratogen, causing deformed limbs in the children of women who took it early in pregnancy. Use the Internet for information to write a short paper that describes the optical isomers of thalidomide and why the FDA did not approve thalidomide for use in the United States until recently. For what purpose has the FDA recently approved the use of thalidomide?

59. Conventional acne treatments are maintenance therapies. Antibiotics, such as tetracycline and erythromycin, are not expected to result in long-term improvement once they are stopped. Some individuals may not respond to any of the conventional medications for acne. A possible solution for those patients is the vitamin A derivative known as isotretinoin (Accutane). However, Accutane is by no means a frontline therapy. Using the Internet, find the serious side effects that may accompany the use of Accutane.

CHAPTER 11

Nutrition: Food for Thought

"Even if you do not want to become a vegetarian, it's a desirable direction to move towards. Going vegetarian one day a week is a good beginning."

Dr. Andrew A. Weil, Director, Center for Integrative Medicine, University of Arizona.

Imagine never eating another hamburger. Put the thought out of your mind of picking up a piece of fried chicken. And your eggs definitely will come without bacon from now on. Would this be your worst nightmare? To some, being a vegetarian is akin to being deprived of those foods they most crave; well, with the exception of coffee and chocolate.

All too often, though, we set up our food selection in terms of all or nothing. No ice cream, because it has too many Calories. No red meat, because it is unhealthy. Actually, no meat at all because feeding animals requires an inordinate amount of grain that could better be used to feed people. No soft drinks, because they are loaded with sugar. And no diet soft drinks either, because they contain artificial sweeteners. No, no, NO!

Could your choices possibly be more nuanced? Unless dictated by an allergy, a specific health concern, or a deeply held belief, what you eat need not be an all-or-nothing proposition. For example, a person who eats meat "sometimes" is called a flexatarian. If you were to become a flexatarian and eat no meat one day a week, you could improve the odds that as you age, you would have a higher quality of life. Why? As a vegetarian, you are likely to get more of the whole grains, fruits, and vegetables that your body needs. At the same time, you are likely to get less saturated fat. Do the math—one day a week does matter. One day in seven is just short of a 15% change in your food intake. Make that two days a week and you have changed your diet by over 25%.

Look for more about saturated fats in Section 11.3.

Consider also that if you switch to eating less meat, you are taking a necessary step to improve the health of the planet. Why? Food not only has a price tag in the supermarket, but also it may be costly for the environment. For example, in the context of biofuels (see Chapter 4), we mentioned the energy and environmental costs of growing and harvesting corn and other grains. In the context of water use (see Chapter 5), we made the case for the high "water footprint" costs of producing food items.

In this chapter, we will make the case that both what you dine on and what you skip not only has an effect on your health, but also affects the health of our planet. To get started, let's examine what you ate for breakfast, lunch, and dinner yesterday. While you are at it, add in your snack breaks as well.

Consider This 11.1   Take a Bite

This activity gives you the opportunity to reflect on your food choices. What did you eat yesterday . . . ?

a. Make a list starting with the first cup of coffee (or however you chose to start your day).
b. From your list, select the three food items that you believe ranked *highest* in promoting your health. Name the criteria on which you based your ranking.
c. Select from your list the three food items that you believe ranked *highest* in terms of promoting the health of the land, air, and water on our planet. Again, name your criteria.

If you are one of the people on the planet fortunate enough to have adequate food to eat, some very good reasons exist to eat simply and to vary your diet. In fact, both *what* you eat and *how much* you eat may be two of the most important decisions you make over the course of your life. At stake here is both your health and the health of the planet. In the next section, we look at the bigger picture of producing food on our planet.

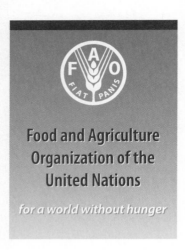

Food and Agriculture Organization of the United Nations

for a world without hunger

In the United States, water is diverted upstream from the Rio Grande and the Colorado River, thus reducing the volume downstream.

11.1 | Food and the Planet

Throughout history, food has played a pivotal role in human health and well-being. Millions have starved from a lack of food, while others have died from eating too much of it. Wars have been fought over food, and countries destabilized by the lack of it. We previously have discussed how the air we breathe and the water we drink are connected to regional and global issues. We now do the same for food.

Producing massive amounts of food affects the ecosystems that sustain life on our planet. Later in the chapter, we'll discuss the connections to energy and climate change. Here, we will examine food production, water use, and land use. Much of the data that we will cite are courtesy of the FAO, the Food and Agriculture Organization. As part of the United Nations, the FAO is an intergovernmental "knowledge network" that provides information about achieving food security.

Earlier in Chapter 5, we took a close look at water, including its availability and use. Producing food connects to several water-related issues, including:

- Depletion of aquifers by pumping water out of them for irrigation
- Drying up of rivers downstream because of irrigation upstream
- Contamination of groundwater by insecticides and herbicides
- Increase of nutrients in water as a result of fertilizer runoff

Keep these water-related issues in mind as you do the next activity.

Consider This 11.2　　World Water Day

Examine the words on the graphic: *The World is Thirsty Because We are Hungry.* Held on March 22, 2012, the theme of World Water Day was water for food security.

a. From a more distant part of the globe, give an example of how food production connects to water shortages.
b. Provide details for one example closer to home.

Water and Food Security – 22 March 2012
UN WATER
World Water Day 2012
The World is Thirsty Because We are Hungry

Answers
a. One example is the diversion of water from the Aral Sea for crop use (see Figure 5.14).
b. A possible example is the depletion of the Ogalalla Aquifer in the United States (see Figure 5.13).

Every day you drink water, perhaps as much as a few liters. You also indirectly consume water daily because water is used to produce the food you eat. For example, a 2010 UNESCO report indicated that it requires about 15,000 liters of water to bring one kilogram of beef protein to the table, enough to make nine quarter pounders. It's not that cattle drink this much water. Rather, this value reflects how much water is used to produce the grain that feeds the cattle. Thus by changing the foods you eat, you can alter your water consumption.

In the opening section of this chapter, we suggested that you consider eating vegetarian meals more frequently. Not only can this practice provide more whole grains and vegetables in your diet, but also it can reduce the amount of water you indirectly "eat." But before we fully weigh in on the value of vegetarian meals, first let's examine the connections between food and land use.

We use land both for raising crops and grazing animals. In turn, these connect to many issues, including:

- Loss of forest ecosystems to create land for agriculture
- Erosion of topsoil from overplanting and overgrazing
- Loss of biodiversity from the repeated planting of single crops

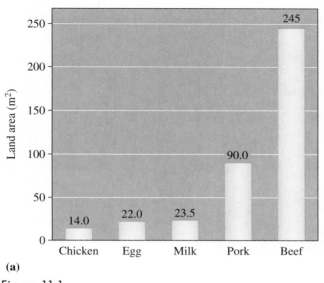

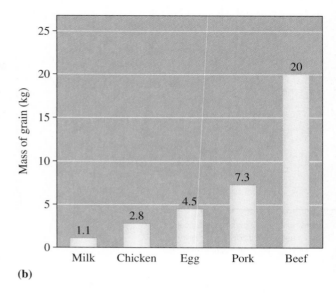

(a)   (b)

Figure 11.1

Land and Grain Estimates for Food Production.

(a) Square meters of land required to bring 1 kilogram of each food to the table. (b) Kilograms of grain required to bring 1 kilogram of each food to the table.

Source: Feeding the World: A Challenge for the Twenty-First Century, Smil, V., MIT Press, 2001.

As you can see from the bar graph of Figure 11.1a, foods differ in the amount of land required to produce them. One reason for the differences is that grain may be needed to feed the animals, as shown in Figure 11.1b. However, as estimates, these values do not necessarily apply to all meat and dairy products. For example, in some regions animals are grass-fed and consume little or no grain.

Estimates, such as those shown in Figure 11.1, are based on a set of assumptions. Depending on which assumptions, the values are higher or lower. For example, this particular set of values is somewhat high because the food (in kg) brought to the table includes only the edible parts of the animal, not the whole animal. No matter which assumptions are used, the trend is clear: beef requires more grain unless you are talking about grass-fed animals. The next activity helps you to be more discerning as you evaluate values such as those shown in Figure 11.1.

Skeptical Chemist 11.3   Checking the Assumptions

Here are some of the factors that affect an estimate of the amount of land or of feed grain needed to bring one kilogram of beef to the table. Examine each factor. Does it raise or lower the estimate?

a. The yield in grain (corn or soy) per acre.
b. The portion of the animal's lifespan included in the estimate.
c. Whether the entire animal or just the edible parts of it are included in the calculation.

Answer

b. Early in life, beef cattle may graze before heading to the feedlot. Estimates for land use are higher if more of a cow's lifespan is included. *Note:* Depending on the land quality and the practices of the farmer or rancher, a cow may require from a few acres to over 30 acres of grazing land.

In general, meat consumption is increasing worldwide, as shown in Figure 11.2. Fueled in large part by the rising affluence of people in developing countries, this trend is expected to continue through 2030.

Can the Earth feed its people a few decades from now if we continue on this path of increased meat consumption? To answer this question, let's do some math. From Figure 11.2, we can obtain the approximate values for the projected meat consumption

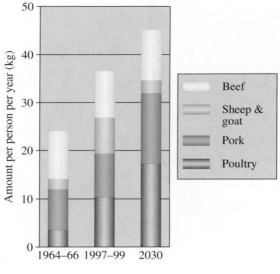

Figure 11.2
World Average Meat Consumption. The units are in kg/person per year.

Source: Agriculture, FAO. 2012.

From Figure 11.2, the projected increases in meat consumption are in poultry and pork, rather than in beef.

In this calculation, we omitted the grain used for sheep and goat meat production because it is so small.

A metric ton is 1000 kilograms.

These and other interesting properties of water were discussed in Chapter 5.

(in kg/person per year) in 2030. We then can pair each type of meat with its corresponding grain requirement from Figure 11.1.

10 kg beef/person-year × 20 kg grain/kg beef = 200 kg grain/person-year
15 kg pork/person-year × 7.3 kg grain/kg pork = 110 kg grain/person-year
17 kg chicken/person-year × 2.8 kg grain/kg chicken = 48 kg grain/person-year

Doing the math, this gives us 358 kg of grain per person in 2030. If we assume a world population of 8 billion people (a low estimate) for 2030, the world grain production would need to be about 2.9 trillion kilograms to produce this much meat. By way of comparison, in 2009 the world grain production *for all uses* was approximately 2 trillion kilograms (2 billion metric tons). Even if a lower set of values for estimated grain requirements were used than those supplied in Figure 11.1, there still would not be enough grain available. Although the shortfall possibly could be made up by increasing crop yields, this is unlikely, as we will see in the final section.

We bring this section to a close by returning to the theme of this section: *The food that we eat affects the health of our planet.* The trends are clear. Our land and water both are impacted by food production and are greater for meat than for a vegetarian diet.

So is the solution to switch to eating vegetarian? If only the answer were that simple! Yes, decreasing your meat consumption makes sense. So does substituting other meats for beef. As we will see, it also makes sense to increase your servings of certain foods and limit those of others. In the sections that follow, we will explore how *the food we eat affects our health.* At the end of this chapter, we will return to the issues connected to food production and the planet. Again, the answers are not simple.

11.2 | You Are What You Eat

Whether you sit down to a gourmet meal or gobble junk food on the run, you eat because you need the water, energy sources, raw materials, and micronutrients that food provides. Yes, water! This compound serves both as a reactant and a product in metabolic reactions, as a coolant and thermal regulator, and as a solvent for the countless substances that are essential for life. Our human bodies are approximately 60% water.

Water, however, cannot be burned as a fuel in the body or anywhere else, for that matter. We need food as an energy source to power muscles, to send nerve impulses, and to transport molecules and ions in our bodies. In addition, food serves as the raw material for bodies, including new bone, blood cells, enzymes, and hair. Food also supplies nutrients essential for **metabolism,** the complex set of chemical processes that are essential in maintaining life.

Eating properly means more than filling your stomach. It is possible to eat, even to the point of being overweight, and still be malnourished. **Malnutrition** is caused by a diet lacking in proper nutrients, even though the energy content of the food may be adequate. Contrast malnutrition with **undernourishment,** a condition in which a person's daily caloric intake is insufficient to meet metabolic needs. Today, people worldwide are malnourished and undernourished, yet increasingly others are more overweight than ever before. In 2010, the Centers for Disease Control and Prevention reported that 68% of all adults in the United States are classified as overweight with nearly half of that population classified as obese. This epidemic of obesity is caused by several factors, including eating the wrong foods, eating too much of any foods, and the lack of physical activity.

Skeptical Chemist 11.4   A Lifetime of Food

During your lifetime, it has been claimed that you will eat about 700 times your adult body weight. Is this statement in the ballpark? Do a calculation to find out. State your assumptions clearly.

Hint: You might assume a life span of 78 years and that your present weight is your adult weight. Estimate the weight of food eaten daily at present, and use these data to project your lifetime food consumption.

Think about the foods you ate yesterday. Did they come to you with minimal or no processing, such as an apple, a baked potato, or a juicy pork chop? Or did you obtain these same foods as apple sauce, a bag of frozen French fries, or sliced smoked bacon? The latter are **processed foods,** foods that have been altered from their natural state by techniques such as canning, cooking, freezing, and adding chemicals such as thickeners or preservatives. The typical diet in many countries contains numerous processed foods.

Processed foods in the United States must list nutritional information on their labels. These labels, such as the one shown in Figure 11.3, include the **macronutrients,** the fats, carbohydrates, and proteins that provide essentially all of the energy and most of the raw material for body repair and synthesis. Sodium and potassium ions are present in much lower concentrations, but these ions are essential for the proper electrolyte balance in the body. Several other minerals and an alphabet soup of vitamins (see Section 11.8) are listed in terms of the percent of recommended daily requirements supplied by a single serving of the product. All these substances, whether naturally occurring or added during processing, are chemicals. In fact, all food is inescapably and intrinsically chemical, even food claiming to be organic or "natural."

Table 11.1 indicates the mass percentages (grams of component per 100 g of food item) of water, fat, carbohydrate, and protein in several familiar foods. For this particular

Nutrition Facts

Serving Size 1 oz
(28 grams or about 30 whole nuts)

Amount Per Serving

Calories 170	Calories from Fat 140

	% Daily Value*
Total Fat 15g	23%
Saturated Fat 1.5g	8%
Trans Fat 0g	
Polyunsaturated Fat 5g	
Monounsaturated Fat 8g	
Cholesterol 0mg	0%
Sodium 50mg	2%
Potassium 200mg	6%
Total Carbohydrate 5g	2%
Dietary Fiber 3g	12%
Sugars 1g	
Protein 6g	
Vitamin A	0%
Vitamin C	0%
Calcium	4%
Iron	6%

*Percent Daily Values are based on a 2,000 calorie diet. Your Daily Values may be higher or lower depending on your calorie needs:

	Calories:	2,000	2,500
Total Fat	Less than	65g	80g
Sat Fat	Less than	20g	25g
Cholesterol	Less than	30mg	300mg
Sodium	Less than	2,400mg	2,400mg
Total Carbohydrates		300g	375g
Dietary Fiber		25g	30g

Figure 11.3

Nutrition facts from a can of mixed nuts.

Although widely used, the term *fat* is too narrow. The next section describes both fats and oils, also termed *triglycerides.*

Table 11.1	Percent Water, Fat, Carbohydrate, and Protein in Selected Foods			
Food	**Water**	**Fat**	**Carbohydrate**	**Protein**
white bread	37	4	48	8
2% milk	89	2	5	3
chocolate chip cookies	3	23	69	4
peanut butter	1	50	19	25
sirloin steak	57	15	0	28
tuna fish	63	2	0	30
black beans (cooked)	66	<1	23	9

Source: U.S. Department of Agriculture, Agricultural Research Service, Home and Garden Bulletin 72, 2002.

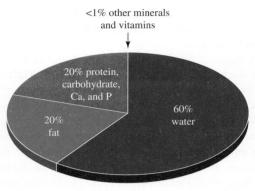

Figure 11.4

Composition of the human body.

selection of foods, the variation in composition is considerable. But in every case, these four components account for almost all of the mass present. Water ranges from a high of 89% in 2% milk to a low of 1% in peanut butter. Peanut butter is comparable to steak and fish in percent of protein. In this table, it leads in fat content. Chocolate chip cookies are the highest in carbohydrates because of their high sugar and refined flour content.

Compare this table with similar data for the human body (Figure 11.4). You are what you eat, but only to a certain extent. You are more like steak than chocolate chip cookies. You are wetter and fatter than bread, and you contain more protein than milk. From these data, you can determine that a 150-pound (68-kg) person consists of about 90 pounds (41 kg) of water and about 30 pounds (14 kg) of fat. The remaining 30 pounds is almost all protein, carbohydrate, and the calcium and phosphorus in the bones. The other minerals and the vitamins weigh less than 1 pound (0.5 kg), indicating that a little bit of each goes a long way, a point that will be discussed in Section 11.8.

In the next five sections, we take a look at each macronutrient in turn—fats, carbohydrates, and proteins. As you will see, each one is unique in several regards.

11.3 | Fats and Oils

From your experiences with ice cream, butter, and cheese, you probably know that fats can help impart a desirable flavor and texture to food. More generally, fats are greasy, slippery, and low-melting solids that are not soluble in water. When melted, they float on the top of broth or soup. Sour cream, frosting, and most pastries are loaded with fats (and Calories). Most fats are of animal origin, although meats vary in their fat content.

You may also know about oils, such as those obtained from corn and soybeans. You may have seen peanut oil forming a layer on top of your peanut butter. You may enjoy eating bread dipped in olive oil. Or you may prepare a loaf of nut bread using canola oil as the shortening. Many oils are of plant origin. Oils exhibit many of the properties of animal-based fats; but unlike fats, they are liquids at room temperature.

As we pointed out earlier when describing biodiesel in Chapter 4, the molecules that make up fats and oils share a common structural feature. They both are **triglycerides,** that is, molecules that contain three ester functional groups. They are formed from a chemical reaction between three fatty acids and the alcohol glycerol. **Fats** are triglycerides that are solids at room temperature, whereas **oils** are triglycerides that are liquids at room temperature. In turn, all triglycerides are **lipids,** a class of compounds that includes not only triglycerides, but also related compounds such as cholesterol and other steroids. Figure 11.5 shows the lipid family tree.

We introduced several new terms in the previous paragraph, and we will now work through them with you one by one. First up is *fatty acids,* an interesting class

This group is characteristic of an ester:

For more about esters, see Sections 4.10 and 9.6.

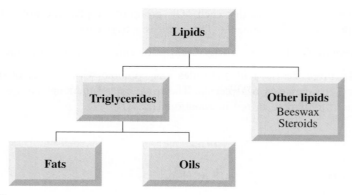

Figure 11.5
Types of lipids.

of compounds. Examine Figure 11.6 to see an example of a fatty acid, stearic acid. Like all fatty acids, the stearic acid molecule has two important characteristics. One is a long hydrocarbon chain with an even number of carbon atoms, typically 12 to 24 (including the −COOH group). This hydrocarbon chain gives fats and oils their characteristic greasiness. The other is the carboxylic acid group, −COOH, at the end of the hydrocarbon chain. The carboxylic acid group accounts for the "acid" in the name fatty acid.

You can review hydrocarbons in Section 4.4 and carboxylic acids in Section 9.6.

$CH_3(CH_2)_{16}COOH$
condensed structural formula

$CH_3CH_2CH_2CH_2CH_2CH_2CH_2CH_2CH_2CH_2CH_2CH_2CH_2CH_2CH_2CH_2CH_2—C$
$\quad\quad\quad\quad\quad\quad\quad\quad\quad\quad\quad\quad\quad\quad\quad\quad\quad\quad\quad\quad\quad\quad\quad\quad\quad\quad\quad\quad\quad\quad O \atop OH$

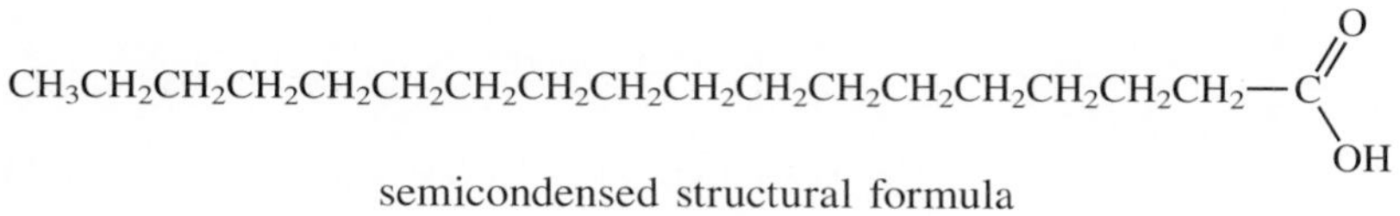

semicondensed structural formula

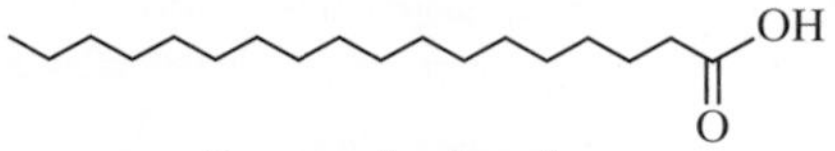

line-angle drawing

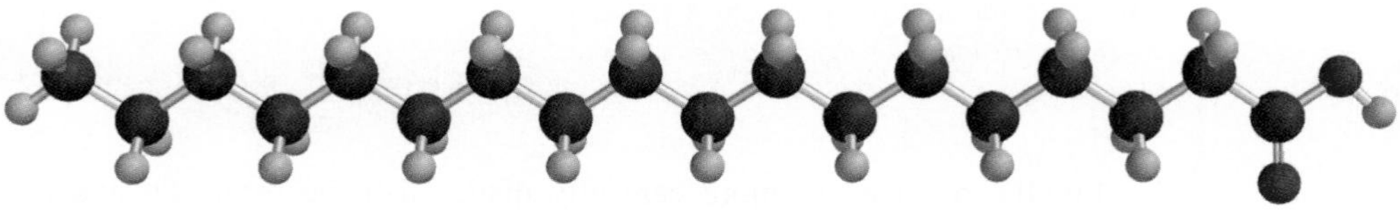

ball-and-stick model

Figure 11.6
Representations of stearic acid, $C_{17}H_{35}COOH$, an example of a fatty acid.

Line–angle drawings were introduced in Section 10.2.

Next we turn to the term *glycerol*, an alcohol that we briefly mentioned in Chapter 4 when describing biodiesel. Glycerol is a sticky, syrupy liquid that is sometimes added to soaps and hand lotions. The representations of a molecule of glycerol (Figure 11.7) show that it is an alcohol with three −OH groups.

$CH_2(OH)CH(OH)CH_2OH$

condensed structural formula

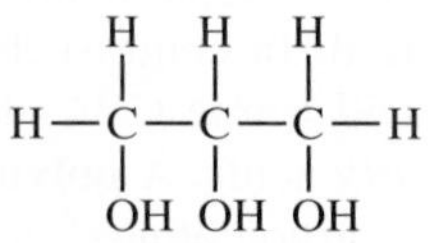

structural formula

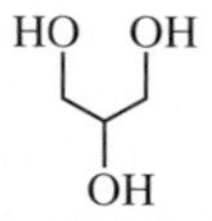

line-angle drawing

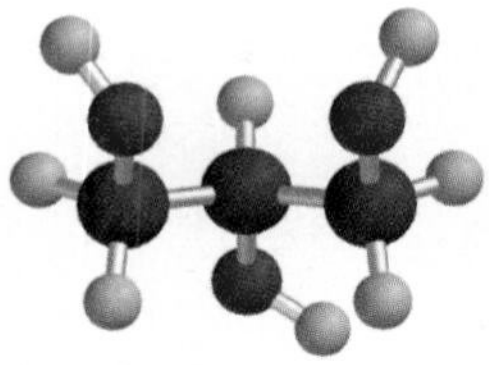

ball-and-stick model

Figure 11.7
Representations of glycerol, an alcohol.

Of interest to us here is that each −OH group of the glycerol molecule can form an ester with a fatty acid molecule. The result is a triglyceride.

3 fatty acid molecules + 1 glycerol molecule ⟶ 1 triglyceride molecule + 3 water molecules   **[11.1]**

Similar chemical reactions that form polyesters were shown earlier in Section 9.6.

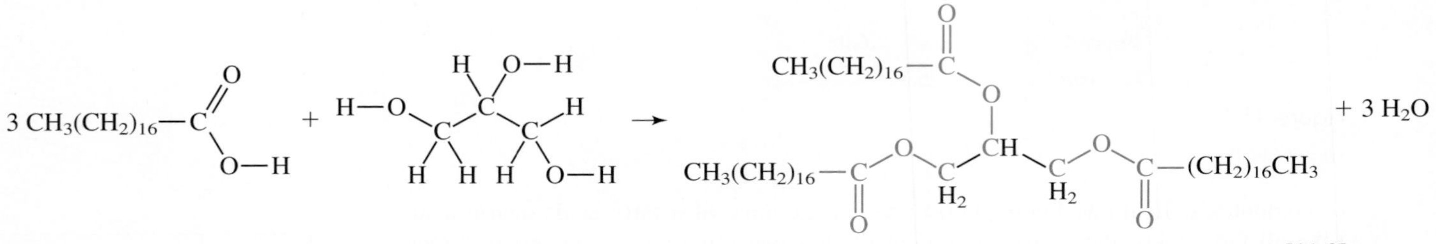

For example, three stearic acid molecules can combine with a glycerol molecule to form glyceryl tristearate, a triglyceride. The three ester functional groups in glyceryl tristearate are highlighted in red in equation 11.2.

[11.2]

The process shown in equation 11.2 is the basis for forming most animal fats and vegetable oils. In most cases, enzymes catalyze this process. Almost all of the fatty acids in our bodies are transported and stored in the form of triglycerides.

Your Turn 11.5   Triglyceride Formation

Like stearic acid, palmitic acid is a component of animal fats.

a. Construct a line–angle drawing for palmitic acid, $CH_3(CH_2)_{14}COOH$.
b. Name the functional group responsible for the acidic properties of both fatty acids.

Answers

a.

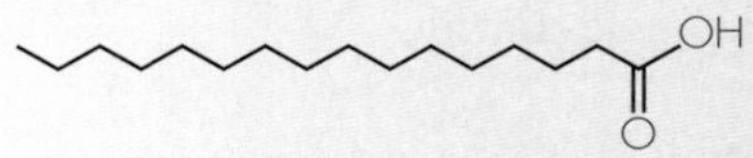

b. carboxylic acid group, −COOH
See Figures Alive! for more representations.

Finally, we need to more carefully distinguish the terms *fat* and *oil*. As we mentioned earlier, fats are triglycerides that are solids at room temperature, whereas oils are triglycerides that are liquids at room temperature. Why the difference? The properties of a particular fat or oil depend on the nature of the fatty acids incorporated into the triglyceride. Of key importance is whether the fatty acid molecule contains one or more C=C double bonds.

A fatty acid is **saturated** if the hydrocarbon chain contains only single bonds between the carbon atoms. In a saturated hydrocarbon chain, the C atoms contain the maximum number of H atoms that can be accommodated and therefore is saturated in hydrogen. This is the case with stearic acid. In contrast, fatty acids are **unsaturated** if they contain one or more C=C double bonds.

Unsaturated fatty acids are either monounsaturated or polyunsaturated. For example, oleic acid, with only one double bond between carbon atoms per molecule, is classified as **monounsaturated.** In contrast, linoleic acid (two C=C double bonds per molecule), and linolenic acid (three C=C double bonds per molecule) are both examples of polyunsaturated fatty acids. A **polyunsaturated** fatty acid contains more than one double bond between carbon atoms. In Figure 11.8, each of the unsaturated fatty acids contains 18 carbon atoms, but differs in the number and placement of the C=C double bonds. Your Turn 11.6 gives you a chance to work with different unsaturated fatty acids.

$$CH_3(CH_2)_7CH=CH(CH_2)_7COOH$$

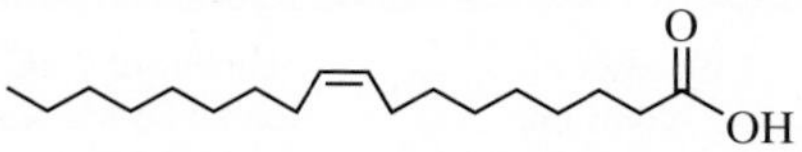

oleic acid, a **monounsaturated** fatty acid

$$CH_3(CH_2)_4CH=CHCH_2CH=CH(CH_2)_7COOH$$

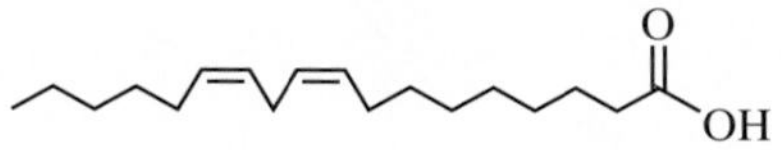

linoleic acid, a **polyunsaturated** fatty acid

$$CH_3CH_2CH=CHCH_2CH=CHCH_2CH=CH(CH_2)_7COOH$$

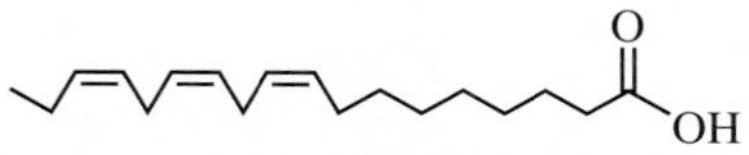

linolenic acid, a **polyunsaturated** fatty acid

Figure 11.8

 Examples of unsaturated fatty acids. See Figures Alive!

Your Turn 11.6   Unsaturated Fatty Acids and a Triglyceride

a. What structural feature identifies oleic, linoleic, and linolenic acids as unsaturated fatty acids?

b. Lauric acid, $CH_3(CH_2)_{10}COOH$, is a component of palm oil. Draw the line–angle representation for lauric acid and classify it as saturated or unsaturated.

Answers

a. Oleic, linoleic, and linolenic acid all have at least one C=C double bond.

b. It is a saturated fatty acid.

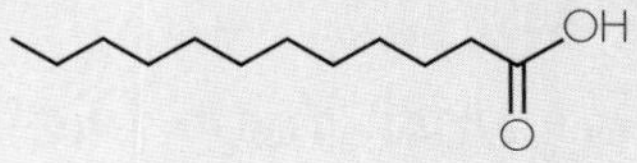

The three fatty acids that form a triglyceride molecule can be identical, two can be the same, or all three can be different. Moreover, these fatty acids can be saturated or unsaturated. They also can be sequenced differently in the molecule. All of these factors contribute to the variety of fats and oils that we find in animals and plants. Solid or semisolid animal fats, such as lard and beef tallow, tend to be high in saturated fats. In contrast, olive, safflower, and other plant oils consist mostly of unsaturated fats.

Table 11.2 indicates some trends within a given family of fatty acids. For example, in saturated fatty acids, the melting points increase as the number of carbon atoms per molecule (and the molecular mass) increases. On the other hand, in a series of fatty acids with a similar number of carbon atoms, increasing the number of C=C double bonds decreases the melting point. Thus, when the melting points of the 18-carbon fatty acids are compared, saturated stearic acid (no C=C double bonds) is found to melt at 70 °C, oleic acid (one C=C double bond per molecule) melts at 16 °C, and linoleic acid (two C=C double bonds per molecule) melts at −5 °C. These trends carry over to the triglycerides containing the fatty acids and explain why fats rich in saturated fatty acids are solids at room and body temperature, whereas ones with a high degree of unsaturation are liquids.

Stearic acid is a solid at body temperature, whereas oleic and linoleic acids are liquids.

Normal body temperature is 37 °C; room temperature is approximately 20 °C.

Table 11.2	Comparing Fatty Acids		
Name	Number of C Atoms per Molecule	Number of C=C Double Bonds per Molecule	Melting Point, °C
Saturated Fatty Acids			
capric acid	10	0	32
lauric acid	12	0	44
myristic acid	14	0	54
palmitic acid	16	0	63
stearic acid	18	0	70
Unsaturated Fatty Acids			
oleic acid	18	1	16
linoleic acid	18	2	−5
linolenic acid	18	3	−11

Your Turn 11.7   Hydrocarbons, Triglycerides, and Biodiesel

a. How does a molecule of octane compare with one of a fat or oil? List two differences.
b. How does a biodiesel molecule compare with one of a fat or oil?
   Hint: See Chapter 4.

Answer

a. A molecule of octane has fewer carbon atoms than a fat or oil. Octane contains neither an ester functional group nor any C=C double bonds. Fats and oils may.

As you might guess, fats and oils not only differ in their physical properties, but they also differ in how they affect your health. We turn to this topic in the next section.

11.4 | Fats, Oils, and Your Diet

People tend to be preoccupied with dietary fat, as fats pack more Calories than any other nutrient. But fats are far more than just a fuel. Fats enhance our enjoyment of food, improve "mouth feel," and intensify certain flavors. Almost every dessert tastes better with a bit of whipped cream! Fats also are essential for life. They provide insulation that retains body heat and that helps to cushion internal organs. Moreover, triglycerides and other lipids, including cholesterol, are the primary components of cell membranes and nerve sheaths and our brains are rich in lipids.

Fortunately, our bodies can synthesize almost all fatty acids from the foods we eat. The exceptions are linoleic and linolenic acids. These two fatty acids must be present in our diet; our bodies cannot produce them. Generally this does not pose a problem because many foods, including plant oils, fish, and leafy vegetables, contain linoleic and linolenic acid.

Figure 11.9 reveals some surprising differences in the composition of fats and oils we consume. For example, flaxseed oil is particularly rich in alpha-linolenic acid (α-linolenic acid, or ALA), a polyunsaturated fatty acid that is being studied for its health benefits. Palm kernel and coconut oils contain much more saturated fat than corn and canola oil. Ironically, the coconut oil used in some nondairy creamers contains about 87% saturated fat, far more than the percentage found in the cream it replaces. In fact, coconut oil contains more saturated fat than pure butterfat. Concern over the high degree of saturation in coconut and palm oil accounts for the statement sometimes printed on food labels: "Contains no tropical oils."

The solid form of coconut oil is called coconut butter. It melts to form an oil around room temperature.

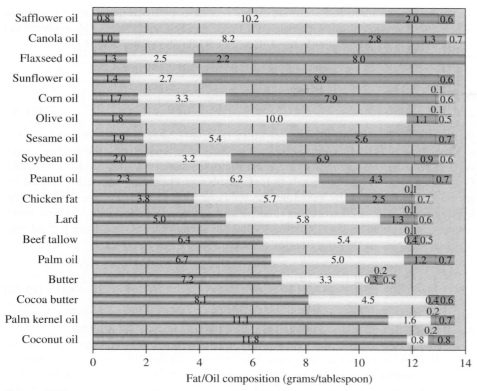

Figure 11.9

Saturated and unsaturated oils and fats. See Figures Alive!

Source: From Nutrition Action Health Letter by Center for Science in the Public Interest, December 2005, Vol. 32, No. 10, p. 8. Copyright © 2005 by Center for Science in the Public Interest. Reproduced with permission of Center for Science in the Public Interest via Copyright Clearance Center.

Consider This 11.8   Cooking Oil Chemistry

a. Consider this label from a popular brand of cooking oil. Is the major component likely to be safflower oil, canola oil, or soybean oil? Explain.

b. This brand of cooking oil has one unusual ingredient, vitamin E. Do you think this is a part of the oil itself or an added component?

Hint: Look ahead to Section 11.8.

Nutrition Facts
Serving Size 1 Tbsp (15 mL)
Servings Per Container about 63

Amount Per Serving	
Calories 120	Cal. from fat 120

	% Daily Value*
Total Fat 14g	**21%**
Saturated Fat 1g	**6%**
Trans Fat 0g	
Polyunsaturated 11g	
Monounsaturated 2g	
Cholesterol 0g	**0%**
Sodium 0g	**0%**
Total Carbohydrate 0g	
Protein 0g	

Vitamin E 20%

Not a significant source of dietary fiber, sugars, vitamin A, vitamin C, calcium, and iron

*Percent Daily Values are based on a 2,000 Calorie diet.

However, the higher degree of unsaturation in oils comes with a drawback. You may have noticed the slight rancid odor that oils acquire over time. The reason for this odor is because C=C double bonds are more susceptible to reaction with the oxygen in the air than are C−C single bonds. The "off-flavor" that you may detect in an oil most likely is a result of such reactions with oxygen. As a result, oils are sometimes treated to increase their saturation. In turn, this improves the shelf life of the food containing the oil.

One way to more fully saturate an oil or a fat is by **hydrogenation,** a process in which hydrogen gas, in the presence of a metal catalyst, adds to a C=C double bond and converts it to a C–C single bond. Equation 11.3a shows the details.

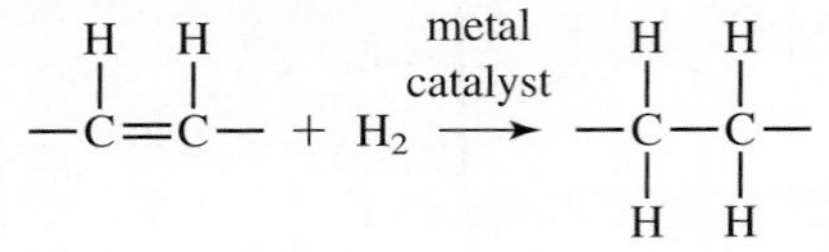

$$\overset{\overset{\displaystyle H}{|}\quad\overset{\displaystyle H}{|}}{-C=C-} \; + \; H_2 \;\; \xrightarrow{\substack{\text{metal}\\\text{catalyst}}} \;\; \underset{\underset{\displaystyle H}{|}\quad\underset{\displaystyle H}{|}}{\overset{\overset{\displaystyle H}{|}\quad\overset{\displaystyle H}{|}}{-C-C-}} \qquad\qquad \textbf{[11.3a]}$$

When oils are hydrogenated, some or all of their C=C double bonds are converted to C–C single bonds, increasing the degree of saturation and raising the melting point. As a result, the oil becomes more margarine-like, that is, semisolid and spreadable. Converting all C=C double bonds to C–C bonds would create an undesirable hard-to-spread solid. By carefully selecting the temperature and pressure, the extent of the hydrogenation can be controlled in order to yield products of the desired melting point, softness, and spreadability. Equation 11.3b shows this process with linoleic acid, one of the fatty acids in the triglycerides of peanut oil.

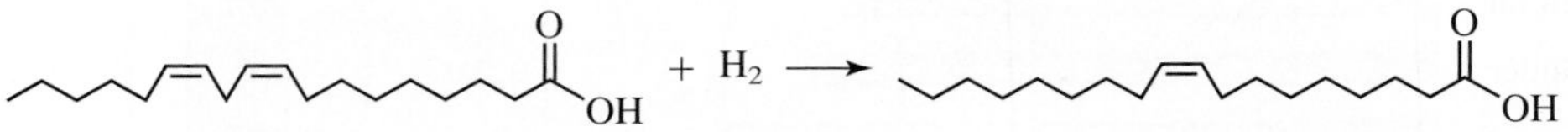

[11.3b]

Note that only one of the double bonds in linoleic acid was hydrogenated. The resulting customized fats and oils are used in margarines, cookies, and candy bars.

Although shelf life and spreadability are important considerations, they are not the only ones. It turns out that some fats and oils are healthier for your heart than others. To understand why, we need to look more closely at the geometry of the hydrogen atoms attached to the C=C double bonds of triglycerides. In most natural unsaturated fatty acids, the hydrogen atoms attached to the carbon atoms are on the *same* side of the C=C double bond. We call this bonding arrangement *cis*.

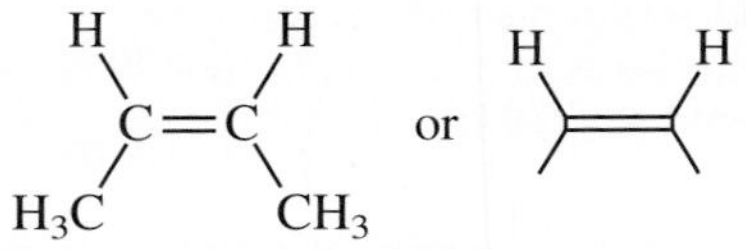

cis-2-butene

Alternatively, the hydrogen atoms can be diagonally across from each other on the C=C double bond. We call this bonding arrangement *trans*.

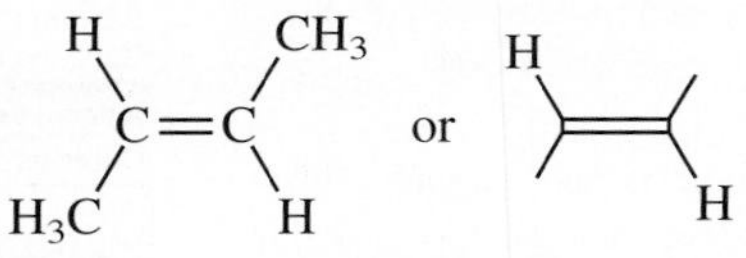

trans-2-butene

For example, oleic acid and elaidic acid are monounsaturated fatty acids that both have the same chemical formula. However, their properties, uses, and health effects are different. Oleic acid, a *cis* fatty acid, is a major component of the triglycerides in olive oil. In contrast, elaidic acid, a *trans* fatty acid, is found in some soft margarines made via hydrogenation. Compare the structures shown in Figure 11.10.

In a *cis* isomer, the H atoms are on the *same* side of the double bond:

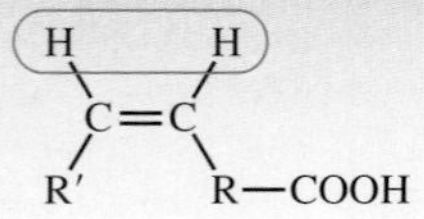

In a *trans* isomer, the H atoms are on the *opposite* side of the double bond:

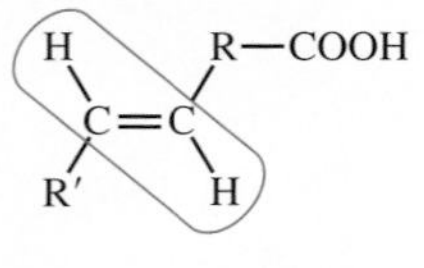

oleic acid, a *cis* fatty acid

elaidic acid, a *trans* fatty acid

Figure 11.10

Line–angle drawings of a *cis* and a *trans* fatty acid. Both have the same chemical formula, $CH_3(CH_2)_7CH=CH(CH_2)_7COOH$. See Figures Alive!

***Trans* fats** are triglycerides that are composed of one or more *trans* fatty acids. Scientific studies show that *trans* fats raise the level of triglycerides and "bad" cholesterol in the blood. This finding came as somewhat of a surprise because partially hydrogenated fats still contain some C=C double bonds, and unsaturation is definitely a plus in a healthy diet. However, *trans* fats are similar in properties to saturated fats. With their long "straight" hydrocarbon chains, saturated fat molecules tend to pack well together, one reason why they are solids at room temperature. With their *cis* geometries, the molecules of naturally occurring unsaturated edible oils have "bends" that do not pack as well, one reason they are liquids at room temperature. Natural oils all have these bends.

LDL (low–density lipoprotein) cholesterol is referred to as "bad" because of its tendency to build up on artery walls, causing heart attacks and strokes.

Revisit equation 11.3b to see that hydrogenation is not an all-or-nothing proposition. When partial hydrogenation takes place, some C=C bonds in the oil or fat remain. Although we would expect these to be *cis* because C=C bonds naturally occur this way in fats and oils, the process of hydrogenation converts some of these *cis* C=C bonds to the *trans* configuration. We can rewrite equation 11.3b to better show the *cis* and *trans* configurations.

[11.3c]

The fats containing these *trans* fatty acids more closely resemble the shape of saturated fats and therefore behave in a similar manner in the body.

What types of fats and oils are in your margarine? Check out the next activity.

Consider This 11.9   Margarines and Fat Content

This table lists the fat content for butter and three margarines. You will need to find other products to answer part **c**.

	Butter	Land O' Lakes (stick)	I Can't Believe It's Not Butter (tub)	Benecol Spread (tub)
Serving size	1 tbsp = 14 g	1 tbsp = 14 g	1 tbsp = 14 g	1 tbsp = 14 g
total fat (g)	11 g	11 g	9 g	8 g
saturated	7 g	2 g	2 g	1 g
trans	0 g	2.5 g	0 g	0 g
polyunsaturated	1 g	3.5 g	3.5 g	2 g
monounsaturated	3 g	2.5 g	2 g	4.5 g

a. Which margarine has the highest percent of saturated fat? How does it compare with butter?
b. In butter, what percent of the total fat is polyunsaturated?
c. Conduct a minisurvey. List the fat content for three different butters or margarines.

In March 2003, Denmark became the first country to strictly regulate foods containing *trans* fats. Canada followed suit in 2004. Starting in January 2006, the U.S. FDA required that food labels include values for *trans* fat. Although most medical professionals now recommend that consumers avoid products with *trans* fats, this may not be easy because of the way foods are labeled. In the United States, a label may show "zero grams *trans* fat" as long as this food contains less than 0.5 grams *trans* fat per serving. Thus, with multiple servings of what is not truly 0 grams, the amount of *trans* fat can add up.

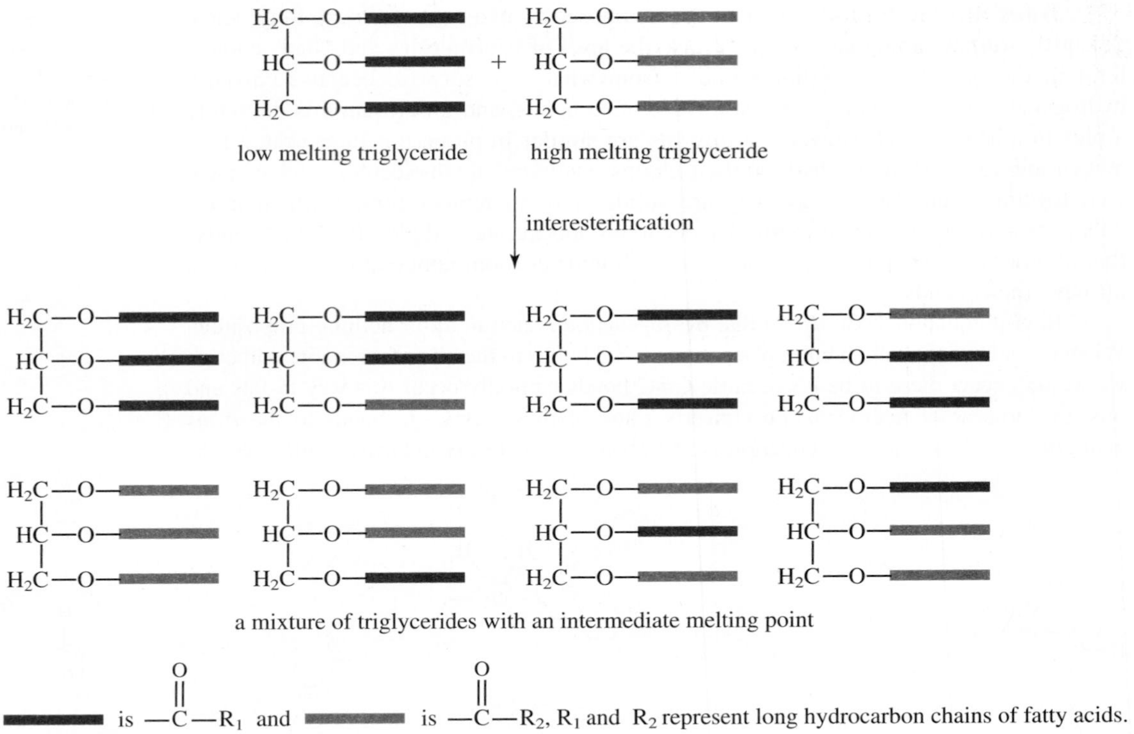

$$H_2C-O- \blacksquare \blacksquare \blacksquare$$
$$HC-O- \blacksquare \blacksquare \blacksquare \quad + \quad H_2C-O- \rule{}{} $$
$$H_2C-O- \blacksquare \blacksquare \blacksquare \qquad HC-O- \rule{}{} $$
$$\qquad\qquad\qquad\qquad H_2C-O- \rule{}{}$$

low melting triglyceride   high melting triglyceride

interesterification

$$H_2C-O-\blacksquare \quad H_2C-O-\blacksquare \quad H_2C-O-\blacksquare \quad H_2C-O-\rule{}{}$$
$$HC-O-\blacksquare \quad HC-O-\blacksquare \quad HC-O-\rule{}{} \quad HC-O-\rule{}{}$$
$$H_2C-O-\blacksquare \quad H_2C-O-\rule{}{} \quad H_2C-O-\blacksquare \quad H_2C-O-\blacksquare$$

$$H_2C-O-\rule{}{} \quad H_2C-O-\rule{}{} \quad H_2C-O-\rule{}{} \quad H_2C-O-\blacksquare$$
$$HC-O-\rule{}{} \quad HC-O-\rule{}{} \quad HC-O-\blacksquare \quad HC-O-\rule{}{}$$
$$H_2C-O-\rule{}{} \quad H_2C-O-\blacksquare \quad H_2C-O-\rule{}{} \quad H_2C-O-\rule{}{}$$

a mixture of triglycerides with an intermediate melting point

$$\blacksquare \text{ is } -\overset{O}{\overset{\|}{C}}-R_1 \text{ and } \rule{}{} \text{ is } -\overset{O}{\overset{\|}{C}}-R_2, R_1 \text{ and } R_2 \text{ represent long hydrocarbon chains of fatty acids.}$$

Figure 11.11

Interesterification: Scrambling of the fatty acids in lipids to produce a mixture of triglycerides.

Source: Adapted from Real–World Cases in Green Chemistry, Volume 2, Cann, M. and Umile, T., American Chemical Society, 2008.

Manufacturers are responding by looking for substitutes for *trans* fats. Using tropical oils such as palm or coconut oil would not be acceptable because of their high percentage of saturated fats. Some manufacturers are adding other oils to their products that are polyunsaturated, such as sunflower oil or flaxseed oil.

Food chemists also have been busy discovering alternatives to hydrogenation that produce semisolids but do not produce *trans* fats. **Interesterification** is any process in which the fatty acids on two or more triglycerides are scrambled to produce a mixture of different triglycerides (Figure 11.11). If you perform this process with a low-melting triglyceride (an oil) and a high-melting triglyceride (a fat), the result is a mixture of triglycerides with an intermediate melting point, a semisolid fat.

One way of carrying out an interesterification reaction uses a strong base as a catalyst. The use of this base raises concerns for worker safety, results in significant loss of the oils, requires large amounts of water, and produces wastes that are high in biological oxygen demand, BOD.

Fortunately, enzymes also can catalyze this reaction. However, using enzymes came with a high price tag until Novozymes and the Archer Daniels Midland Company teamed up to refine the reaction. For their efforts, they shared a Presidential Green Chemistry Challenge Award in 2005. Not only is their method more cost-effective, but also it has environmental benefits. These include a large reduction in both water usage and in the BOD of the aqueous waste streams, less decomposition of oils during the process, and the elimination of the base catalyst.

Catalysts were introduced in Chapter 1 in the context of catalytic converters.

Your Turn 11.10   Bring Home the Green

Revisit the key ideas of green chemistry listed on the inside front cover of this book. Which of the key ideas are met by the use of enzymes for interesterification developed by Novozymes and Archer Daniels Midland?

With this, we end our discussion of fats and oils. The next section tells the sweet tale of sugars and their not-as-sweet relatives, starches.

11.5 | Carbohydrates: Sweet and Starchy

Sugars are the sweet-tasting members of the carbohydrate family. Examples that you may recognize include glucose and fructose, both naturally occurring in fruits, vegetables, and honey. In addition, glucose and fructose are components of high fructose corn syrup (Figure 11.12).

Starch, a polymer of glucose introduced in Chapter 4, is another carbohydrate. It is found in nearly all types of grains, potatoes, and rice. Although pleasing to our taste buds, starch lacks a sweet taste and takes a bit longer to digest than sugars. Whether sweet or starchy, carbohydrates have the job of providing energy to the cells in our bodies.

Carbohydrates also are used commercially to produce ethanol, an energy source for vehicles. As discussed in Chapter 4, the starch found in corn kernels currently is fermented to produce millions of gallons of ethanol each year. But corn starch is not unique. The sugar or starch of almost any plant can be fermented to produce ethanol, including that found in alcoholic beverages. Grapes contain the sugars of choice for many wines; in contrast, barley and wheat contains the starch used to brew many beers.

Carbohydrates are compounds that contain carbon, hydrogen, and oxygen, with H and O atoms found in the same 2:1 ratio as in H_2O. This composition gives rise to the name *carbohydrate,* which implies "carbon plus water." However, the H and O atoms in carbohydrates are not in the form of H_2O molecules. Rather, these atoms are part of a larger molecule, typically a ring (or a long chain of rings, in the case of starch and cellulose). Verify this for yourself by examining these structural formulas.

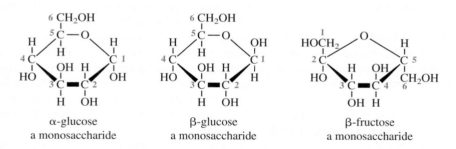

| α-glucose | β-glucose | β-fructose |
| a monosaccharide | a monosaccharide | a monosaccharide |

Fructose and glucose both have the same chemical formula, $C_6H_{12}O_6$, but different structures. These isomers are relatively easy to tell apart: glucose has a 6-membered ring and fructose a 5-membered ring. In contrast, the alpha (α) and beta (β) isomers of glucose are hard to distinguish without a model. To visualize the 3D structure of glucose, imagine that the ring is perpendicular to the plane of the paper, with the ring edge facing you. The −H atoms and −OH groups fall either above or below the plane of the ring. In α-glucose, the −OH group on carbon 1 is on the opposite side of the ring from the −CH₂OH group attached to carbon 5. In β-glucose, the −OH group on carbon 1 is on the same side.

Fructose is an example of a **monosaccharide,** that is, a single sugar. So is glucose. However, sucrose (ordinary table sugar) is a **disaccharide,** a "double sugar" formed by joining two monosaccharide units. In forming a sucrose molecule, an α-glucose and a β-fructose unit are connected by a C−O−C linkage created when an −H atom and an −OH group are split off to form a water molecule. Does this sound familiar? It is a condensation reaction analogous to those in Chapter 9 that formed polyesters. Figure 11.13 shows the chemical reaction that forms the sucrose molecule, a disaccharide, and releases a water molecule.

Figure 11.12

High fructose corn syrup is a mixture of fructose, glucose, and water. In pure form, sugars are white crystalline solids.

The ending −ose is typical in the names of sugars.

The C atom that bears an −OH group to the right of the O atom in the ring is number 1. The numbering of C atoms continues clockwise around the ring.

Condensation reactions were described in Sections 9.6 and 10.3.

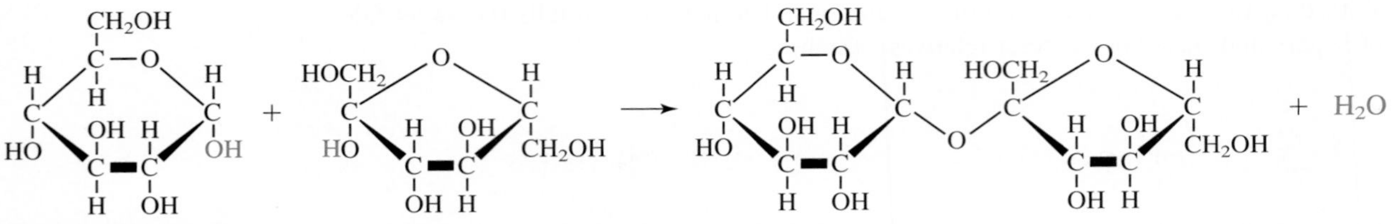

$$\alpha\text{-glucose} + \beta\text{-fructose} \longrightarrow \text{sucrose} + H_2O$$

Figure 11.13

Formation of sucrose, a disaccharide.

Your Turn 11.11   The Sweet Story

This table compares different sugars. See Table 11.3 for numerical sweetness values. The unit of Calorie (Cal) is equivalent to 1 kilocalorie (kcal) or 1000 calories (cal).

Sugar	Also Known As	Sweetness	Calories/gram	Chemical Formula
glucose	"blood sugar" "grape sugar" "corn sugar"	least sweet	3.87 Cal/g	$C_6H_{12}O_6$
fructose	"fruit sugar"	sweetest	3.87 Cal/g	$C_6H_{12}O_6$
sucrose	"table sugar" "granulated sugar"	intermediate	4.01 Cal/g	$C_{12}H_{22}O_{11}$

a. Propose a reason why these three sugars differ in their degree of sweetness.
b. Explain why these sugars are almost identical in their Calories per gram.

As you can see from the previous activity, the sugars we consume are remarkably similar in their chemical composition, in their Calories, and even in their sweet taste. Although sweetness varies, the difference between glucose and fructose is only about a factor of 2. So does it matter which sugars you eat? Actually there is a better question to ask. How *much* sugar are you eating? The quick answer may be "too much."

Monosaccharides also can link to form much bigger molecules. **Polysaccharides** are condensation polymers made up of thousands of monosaccharide units. As the name implies, these macromolecules consist of "many sugar units." Analogous to the formation of sucrose (Figure 11.13), the formation of a polysaccharide releases a water molecule each time a monosaccharide is incorporated into the polymer chain. Familiar examples of polysaccharides include starch and cellulose.

Our bodies can digest starch by breaking it down into glucose; in contrast, we cannot digest cellulose. Consequently, we depend on starchy foods such as potatoes or pasta rather than devouring toothpicks. The difference in digestibility stems from a subtle difference in how the glucose monomers are connected. In Figure 11.14, compare the alpha (α) linkage between the glucose units in starch with the beta (β) linkage between glucose units in cellulose. The enzymes of many mammals—including humans—are unable to catalyze the breaking of beta linkages in cellulose. Consequently, we can't dine on grass or trees.

In contrast, cows, goats, and sheep manage to break down cellulose with a little help. Their digestive tracts contain bacteria that decompose cellulose into glucose. The animals' own metabolic systems then take over. Termites also contain cellulose-hungry bacteria, which is why these insects can damage wooden structures.

When we have excess glucose in our bodies, it is polymerized to glycogen with the help of insulin and stored in our muscles and liver. When our glucose levels slip below normal, the glycogen is converted back into glucose. Glycogen has a molecular structure similar to that of starch except that its chains of glucose units are longer and more branched. Glycogen is vitally important because it stores energy for use in our bodies. It accumulates in muscles and especially in the liver, where it is available as a quick source of internal energy.

Starch is a polymer of α–glucose, hence the α linkage. Cellulose has a β linkage and is a polymer of β–glucose.

Like starch and cellulose, glycogen is a polysaccharide.

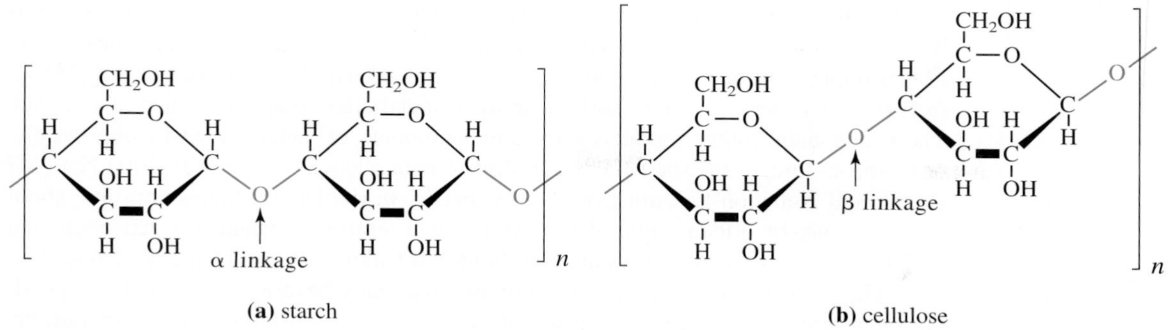

Figure 11.14

The bonding between glucose units in (a) starch and (b) cellulose.

As you may know, a healthful diet derives more of its carbohydrates from polysaccharides than from simple (and sweet) sugars. In the next section, we delve into topics related to sweetness.

11.6 | How Sweet It Is: Sugars and Sugar Substitutes

Got a sweet tooth? We seem to be born with a preference for sweets, and for most us, this lasts throughout our lives. Sweeteners come as syrups, small crystals in packages, and as cubes or tablets that you can drop into a cup of coffee. Some of these sweeteners are natural; others are synthetic ("artificial"). Some are very sweet; others less so. Some have been available since antiquity; others are relatively new on the market. Like all of the foods we eat, each one can affect both your health and the health of the planet.

How sweet is sweet? Table 11.3 indicates the relative sweetness of some common natural sweeteners, all compared with sucrose, which is assigned a value of 100. From this table, one would have to use less fructose to equal the sweetness of a teaspoon of sucrose (table sugar). In contrast, lactose (milk sugar) would require more than 6 teaspoons.

Does it matter which sugar you consume? Yes and no. As we pointed out earlier, for most people the issue is not which sugar. Rather, it is too much of all of them combined. Again, a healthful diet derives more of its carbohydrates from polysaccharides than from simple sugars. If you overindulge in sugar, you increase your risk both for becoming obese and for the diseases that accompany obesity, such as diabetes and high blood pressure.

Let's begin by getting a handle on how much sugar you consume. The next activity allows you to explore one possible source of sugar intake.

Consider This 11.12   Your Favorite Cola or UnCola

Soda has been referred to as liquid candy. Is this a fair characterization? Make an argument pro or con. In either case, cite the grams of sugar involved.

One reason that you consume sugars is because foods naturally contain them. All the sugars listed in Table 11.3 occur naturally. For example, fructose occurs in

Table 11.3	Approximate Relative Sweetness Values

NATURAL SWEETENERS					
lactose	maltose	glucose	honey	sucrose	fructose
16	32.5	74.3	97	100	173

Source: International Food Information Council.

Honey is primarily composed of fructose and glucose. Both cane sugar and beet sugar are primarily sucrose.

many fruits and lactose occurs in milk. Another reason that you consume sugar is because you add it during cooking or at the table or because food companies add it. For example, you may add sugar to your coffee or sprinkle it on your cereal. Manufacturers of processed foods add sugar to peanut butter, spaghetti sauce, and bread. These and many other products have small amounts of sugar added to improve the taste, the texture, or the shelf-life. According to data released in the 2001–2004 National Health and Nutrition Examination Survey, people in the United States consume about 22 teaspoons of added sugar daily. At about 4 grams of sugar per teaspoon and 4 Calories per gram, this translates to about 350 Calories daily from added sugar!

High-fructose corn syrup is used to sweeten many beverages and foods. Depending on where you live, high-fructose corn syrup goes by different names. In Europe, it is called isoglucose, and in Canada it goes by glucose–fructose. In this textbook we refer to it as HFCS.

Corn syrup primarily contains glucose. But if you treat corn syrup with enzymes, you can convert the glucose to fructose, which is sweeter. Several different "blends" of HFCS exist, depending on the end use. For example, a typical blend used in soft drinks is about 55% fructose, with the remainder being glucose.

Why is HFCS added to foods? Actually, many reasons exist. In 2009, Audrae Erickson, President of the Corn Refiners Association, pointed out that:

> High fructose corn syrup is used in the food supply because of its many functional benefits. For example, it retains moisture in bran cereals, helps keep breakfast and energy bars moist, maintains consistent flavors in beverages and keeps ingredients evenly dispersed in condiments. High fructose corn syrup enhances spice and fruit flavors in yogurts and marinades. In addition to its excellent browning characteristics for breads and baked goods, it is a highly fermentable nutritive sweetener and prolongs product freshness.

Opponents of HFCS have suggested that this corn sweetener is metabolized differently from sucrose. However, this does not appear to be true. The American Medical Association (AMA) has concluded that HFCS "does *not* appear to contribute more to obesity than other caloric sweeteners." Metabolically, HFCS is similar to sucrose.

So wherein lies the argument? Again, it lies in the amount of sugar—any type of added sugar—that we consume daily. The AMA recommendation has been that people limit the amount of added sugars to 32 grams or less, based on a 2000-Calorie diet. This translates to 8 teaspoons of sugar or about 128 Calories daily. In August 2009, the American Heart Association released a journal article that fine-tuned these values by age and gender:

> Most women should consume no more than 100 Calories (about 25 grams) of added sugars per day. Most men should consume no more than 150 Calories (about 37.5 grams) each day. That's about six teaspoons of added sugar a day for women and nine for men.

In contrast, the Corn Refiners Association quotes a recommendation of no more than 25% added sugar Calories a day, based on a 2002 report from the Institute of Medicine at the U.S. National Academies. This would translate to a maximum of 500 Calories of added sugar.

Bottom line? For personal health, we suggest moderation. No absolute number is likely to ever be set. Clearly, though, lower is better in terms of weight gain and diabetes.

In terms of the health of the planet, the issues are more complex. More so than any other major crop, corn requires the use of fertilizer, herbicides, and pesticides, all of which require the burning of fossil fuels to produce. The runoff from cornfields has the potential to pollute rivers and streams, including those far downstream.

For example, the fertilizer runoff is largely responsible for a huge dead zone in the Gulf of Mexico at the mouth of the Mississippi River (Figure 11.15). When the nitrogen- and phosphorus-rich waters reach the ocean, they promote algae blooms. In turn, the algae deplete the oxygen in the waters, killing aquatic life. So although HFCS may appear to be a bargain, its price does not include the high environmental costs related to growing corn.

We end this section by turning to artificial (synthetic) sweeteners, also called sugar substitutes. As you can see from Table 11.4, these are far sweeter than natural sugars.

A blend of fructose (55%) and glucose (45%) has a sweetness comparable to that of sucrose, table sugar.

In the United States, HFCS is less expensive than sucrose. Reasons include government subsidies for growing corn and tariffs on imported sugar.

Figure 11.15

Brown, nutrient–rich water from the Mississippi River meets the Gulf of Mexico, creating a "dead zone." The zone is approximately 6000–7000 square miles, varying in size seasonally.

Source: Nancy Rabalais, Louisiana Universities Marine Consortium.

The Calories per gram of aspartame is about the same as sucrose, but since it is about 200 times sweeter than sucrose, 1/200th of a teaspoon of aspartame is used as the equivalent of a teaspoon of sucrose. Saccharin, aspartame, sucralose, neotame, and acesulfame potassium are the five artificial sweeteners approved in the United States. Other countries have a slightly different list.

So are artificial sweeteners the way to go? These compounds certainly do offer the advantage of fewer Calories. For example, the sugar in a 12-ounce can of a soda pop accounts for about 140 Calories. In terms of a 2000-Calorie diet, this translates to about 7%. By contrast, the same beverage sweetened with a synthetic sweetener would have 0 Calories. Although people have been concerned about the health effects of using artificial sweeteners, studies indicate that the sweeteners currently on the market are safe for most people. However, a small percentage of the population must avoid aspartame, which we will describe in the next section.

Consider This 11.13   Chemicals!

A well–known U.S. medical clinic posted this statement online: "Artificial sweeteners are chemicals or natural compounds that offer the sweetness of sugar without as many Calories."

a. What is the problem with the categories "chemicals or natural compounds"?
b. How might you rewrite this language?

Table 11.4	Approximate Relative Sweetness Values			
SYNTHETIC SWEETENERS				
acesulfame potassium	aspartame	neotame	saccharin	sucralose
200	200	7,000–13,000	300	600

Source: International Food Information Council.

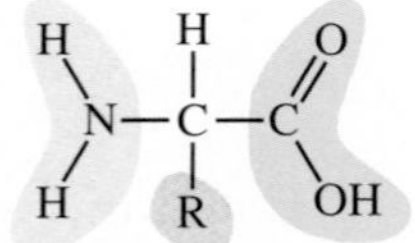

Figure 11.16

Generic structure for an amino acid, showing the amine group (yellow) and the carboxylic acid group (green). R stands for one of about 20 possible side chains.

−C₆H₅ designates the phenyl group, first introduced in Section 9.5.

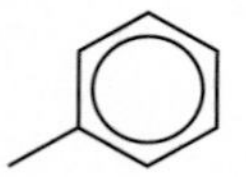

11.7 | Proteins: First Among Equals

The word *protein* derives from *protos,* Greek for "first." The name is misleading. Life depends on the interaction of thousands of chemicals, and to assign primary importance to any single compound or class of compounds is simplistic. Nevertheless, proteins are an essential part of every living cell. They are major components in hair, skin, and muscle. They also transport oxygen, nutrients, and minerals through the bloodstream. Many of the hormones that act as chemical messengers are proteins, as are most of the enzymes that catalyze the chemistry of life.

A **protein** is a polyamide or polypeptide, that is, a polymer built from amino acid monomers. The great majority of proteins are made from various combinations of the 20 different naturally occurring amino acids. Molecules of amino acids share a common structure. Four chemical species are attached to a carbon atom: a carboxylic acid group, an amine group, a hydrogen atom, and a side chain designated R, all shown in Figure 11.16.

Variations in the R side chain differentiate individual amino acids, as shown in Figure 11.17. For example, in the simplest amino acid (glycine), R is a hydrogen atom. In alanine, R is a −CH₃ group; in aspartic acid (found in asparagus), it is −CH₂COOH; and in phenylalanine, −CH₂(C₆H₅). Two of the 20 naturally occurring amino acids have R groups that bear a second −COOH functional group, three have R groups containing amine groups, and two others contain sulfur atoms.

Two amino acids can combine by a condensation reaction between the amine group on one amino acid and a carboxylic acid group on the other. For example, glycine can react with alanine as shown in equation 11.4a.

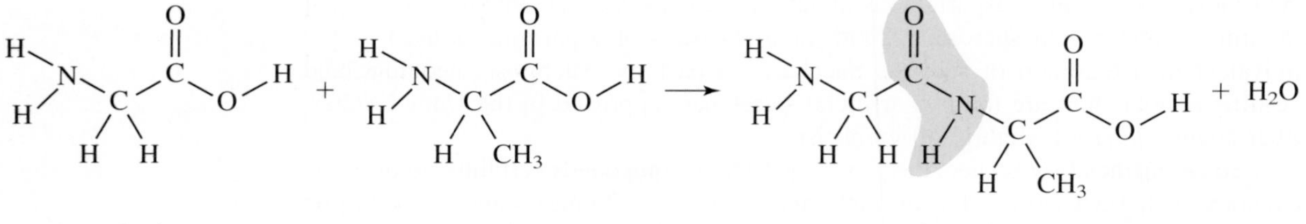

glycine + alanine → dipeptide + H₂O

$$\text{glycine} \qquad \text{alanine} \qquad \text{dipeptide} \qquad \text{water}$$

[11.4a]

The peptide bond that forms when two amino acids react was defined in Section 9.7 and will be further explored in the context of protein synthesis in Chapter 12.

Note that the acidic −COOH group of the glycine molecule reacts with the −NH₂ group of the alanine molecule. In the process, the two amino acids link through the C−N peptide bond shown in the blue shaded area. In addition, an H₂O molecule is produced. Once incorporated into the peptide chain, the amino acids are called **amino acid residues.**

Equation 11.4a labels the product as a **dipeptide,** a compound formed from two amino acids. Glycine and alanine can form two different dipeptides. Equation 11.4b shows the other possibility.

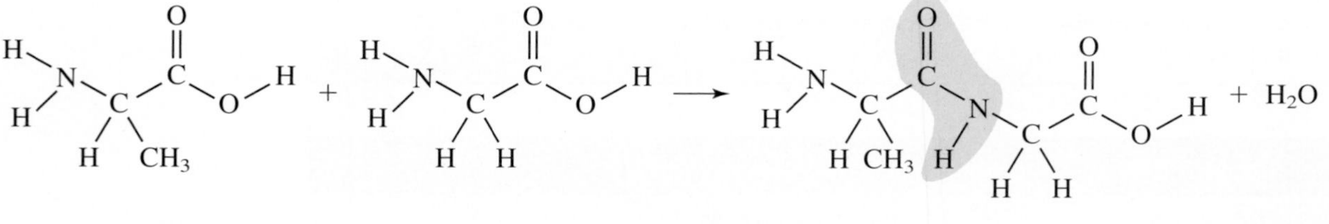

alanine + glycine → dipeptide + H₂O

$$\text{alanine} \qquad \text{glycine} \qquad \text{dipeptide} \qquad \text{water}$$

[11.4b]

This time in the condensation reaction, alanine provided the −COOH group and glycine the −NH₂ group.

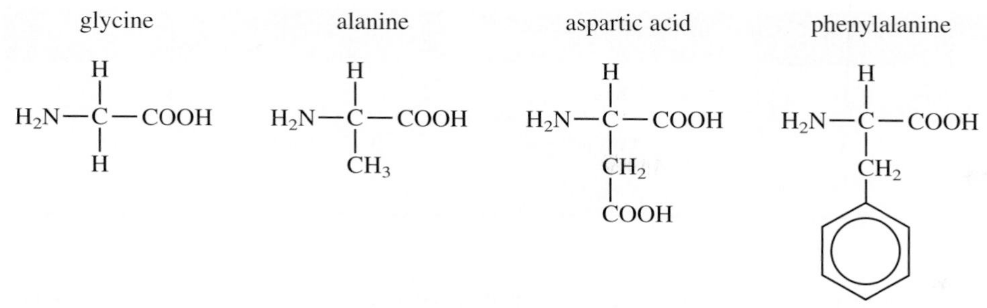

glycine　　　　　alanine　　　　aspartic acid　　　phenylalanine

$$H_2N-\overset{\overset{\displaystyle H}{|}}{\underset{\underset{\displaystyle H}{|}}{C}}-COOH$$

$$H_2N-\overset{\overset{\displaystyle H}{|}}{\underset{\underset{\displaystyle CH_3}{|}}{C}}-COOH$$

$$H_2N-\overset{\overset{\displaystyle H}{|}}{\underset{\underset{\underset{\displaystyle COOH}{|}}{CH_2}}{C}}-COOH$$

$$H_2N-\overset{\overset{\displaystyle H}{|}}{\underset{\underset{\displaystyle CH_2}{|}}{C}}-COOH$$

Figure 11.17
Examples of amino acids with different side chains.

Look closely to see that the two dipeptides are different. In the first dipeptide, the unreacted amine group is on the glycine residue and the unreacted acid group is on the alanine residue; in the second dipeptide, the $-NH_2$ is on the alanine residue and the $-COOH$ is on the glycine residue.

The point of all this is that the order of amino acid residues in a peptide makes a difference. The particular protein formed depends not only on which amino acids are present, but also on their sequence in the protein chain. Assembling the correct amino acid sequence to make a particular protein is like putting letters in a word; if they are in a different order, a completely new meaning results. Thus, a tripeptide consisting of three different amino acids is like a three-letter word containing the letters *a, e,* and *t.* There are six possible combinations of these letters. Three of them—*ate, eat,* and *tea*—form recognizable English words; the other three—*aet, eta,* and *tae*—do not. Similarly, some sequences of amino acids may be biological nonsense.

Still restricting ourselves to three-letter words and only the letters *a, e,* and *t,* but allowing the duplication of letters, we can make perfectly good words such as *tee* and *tat,* and lots of meaningless combinations such as *aaa* and *tte.* There are, in fact, a total of 27 possibilities, including the 6 identified earlier. Just as words can use letters more than once, most proteins contain specific amino acids more than once.

Putting the amino acids of a protein into their proper order is like assembling a train correctly by placing each car in the right sequence.

See Section 12.4 for more information about the structure and synthesis of proteins.

Your Turn 11.14　　Making Tripeptides

The equations in this section show that glycine (Gly) and alanine (Ala) can combine to form two dipeptides: GlyAla and AlaGly. If these two amino acids can be used more than once, two other dipeptides are possible: GlyGly and AlaAla. Thus, four different dipeptides can be made from two different amino acids. Eight different tripeptides can be made from supplies of two different amino acids, assuming that each amino acid can be used once, twice, three times, or not at all. Use the symbols Gly and Ala to write down representations of the amino acid sequence in all eight of these tripeptides.

Hint: Start with GlyGlyGly.

Normally, the body does not store a reserve supply of protein, so foods containing protein must be eaten regularly. As the principal source of nitrogen for the body, proteins are constantly being broken down and reconstructed. A healthy adult on a balanced diet is in nitrogen balance, excreting as much nitrogen (primarily as urea in the urine) as she or he ingests. Growing children, pregnant women, and persons recovering from long-term debilitating illness or burns have a positive nitrogen balance. This means that they consume more nitrogen than they excrete because they are using the element to synthesize additional protein. A negative nitrogen balance exists when more protein is being decomposed than is being made. This occurs in starvation, when the energy needs of the body are unmet from the diet, and muscle is metabolized to maintain physiological functions. In effect, the body feeds on itself.

Table 11.5	The Essential Amino Acids	
histidine	lysine	threonine
isoleucine	methionine	tryptophan
leucine	phenylalanine	valine

Another cause of a negative nitrogen balance may be a diet that does not include enough of the **essential amino acids,** those required for protein synthesis but that must be obtained from the diet because the human body cannot synthesize them. Of the 20 natural amino acids that make up our proteins, we can synthesize 11 in our bodies from simpler molecules. We must obtain the other 9 from the foods we eat. If your diet is missing any of the nine essential amino acids identified in Table 11.5, the result can be severe malnutrition.

Good nutrition thus requires protein in sufficient quantity and suitable quality. Beef, fish, and poultry contain all the essential amino acids in approximately the same proportions found in the human body. Therefore, all of these are "complete" proteins. However, most people of the world depend on grains and other vegetable crops rather than on meat or fish. If such a diet is not sufficiently diversified, some essential amino acids may be lacking. For example, Mexican and Latin American diets tend to be rich in corn and corn products, a protein source that is *incomplete* because corn is low in tryptophan, an essential amino acid. A person may eat enough corn to meet the total protein requirement, but still be malnourished because of insufficient tryptophan.

Fortunately for millions of vegetarians, a reliance on vegetable protein does not doom them to malnutrition. The trick is to apply a principle nutritionists call **protein complementarity,** combining foods that complement essential amino acid content so that the total diet provides a complete supply of amino acids for protein synthesis. Although some may worry that vegetarians need to strictly adhere to this principle, most are likely to do it automatically. Say, for example, you eat a peanut butter sandwich. Bread is deficient in lysine and isoleucine, but peanut butter supplies these amino acids. On the other hand, peanut butter is low in methionine, but it is provided by the bread. The traditional diets in many countries also tend to meet protein requirements. For example, in Latin America, beans are used to complement corn tortillas; soy foods are eaten with rice in parts of Southeast Asia and Japan. People in the Middle East combine bulgur wheat with chickpeas or eat hummus, a paste made from sesame seeds and chickpeas, with pita bread. In India, lentils and yogurt are eaten with unleavened bread. Thus it is likely that if you follow a balanced vegetarian diet, you will ingest sufficient quantities of essential amino acids, assuming that you are eating an adequate number of Calories.

We end this section by revisiting sweetness, the topic of the previous section. It may surprise you to learn that aspartame, a sugar substitute, is a dipeptide! Aspartame is composed primarily of the amino acids aspartic acid and phenyl alanine (Figure 11.18). It is one of the most highly studied food additives and for the vast majority of

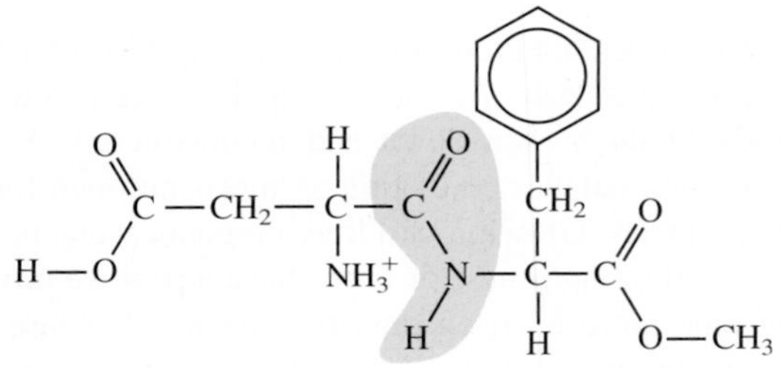

Figure 11.18

The structural formula of aspartame.

consumers, aspartame is a safe alternative to sugar. One group of people, however, definitely should not use aspartame. The warning on packets of artificial sweeteners and products containing aspartame is explicit: "Phenylketonurics: Contains Phenylalanine."

This is a case where one person's treat is another person's poison. Phenylalanine is an essential amino acid converted in the body to tyrosine, a different amino acid. Individuals with phenylketonuria, a genetically transmitted disease, lack the enzyme that catalyzes this transformation. Consequently, the conversion of dietary phenylalanine to tyrosine is blocked and the phenylalanine concentration rises. To compensate for the elevated phenylalanine, the body converts it to phenylpyruvic acid, excreting large quantities of this acid in the urine. Phenylpyruvic acid is termed a *keto* acid because of its molecular structure; hence, the disease is known as phenyl*keto*nuria or PKU. People with the disease are called phenylketonurics.

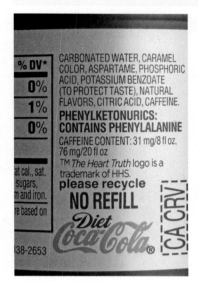

The ketone functional group was shown in Table 10.3.

Excess phenylpyruvic acid causes severe mental retardation. Therefore, the urine of newborn babies is tested for this compound using special test paper placed in the diaper. Infants diagnosed with PKU must be put on a diet severely limited in phenylalanine. This means avoiding excess phenylalanine from milk, meats, and other sources rich in protein. Commercial food products are available for such diets, their composition adjusted to the age of the user. Because phenylalanine is an essential amino acid, a minimum amount of it must still be available, even in phenylketonurics. Supplemental tyrosine may also be needed to compensate for the absence of the normal conversion of phenylalanine to tyrosine. A phenylalanine-restricted diet is recommended for phenylketonurics at least through adolescence. Adult phenylketonurics also must limit their phenylalanine intake and hence curtail their use of aspartame.

This last discussion has demonstrated that even small quantities of a substance can make a difference in your diet. The next section looks at other substances that are found in your diet in small quantity.

11.8 | Vitamins and Minerals: The Other Essentials

Yes, essential! Vitamins and minerals are **micronutrients,** substances that are needed only in miniscule amounts but still are essential to life. Nearly everyone in the United States knows that vitamins and minerals are important, but a thriving multimillion-dollar supplement industry reminds any who forget. Unfortunately, many processed foods that are high in sugars and fats lack essential micronutrients.

Only relatively recently have we come to understand the role of vitamins and minerals in our diet. Over the ages, humans learned that they became ill if certain foods were lacking. Systematic studies began early in the 20th century with the discovery of "Vitamine B_1" (thiamine). The particular designation, B_1, was the label on the test tube in which the sample was collected. The general term *vitamin* was chosen because the compound, which is vital for life, contains the amine group. The final "e" disappeared with the discovery that not all vitamins are amines.

Vitamins are organic compounds with a wide range of physiological functions. Although only small amounts are needed in the diet, vitamins are essential for good health, proper metabolic functioning, and preventing disease. In general, vitamins are not sources of energy for the body although some help break down macronutrients. They can be classified on the basis of being water- or fat-soluble. For example, examine the structural formula of vitamin A shown in Figure 11.19 to see that it contains almost exclusively C and H atoms. As a result, vitamin A is a nonpolar compound, lipid-soluble, and similar to the hydrocarbons derived from petroleum. Water-soluble vitamins often contain several −OH groups that can hydrogen bond with water molecules. Vitamin C is a case in point, shown in the same figure.

Hydrogen bonds were discussed in Section 5.2. The relationship between molecular structure and solubility was explored in Section 5.5.

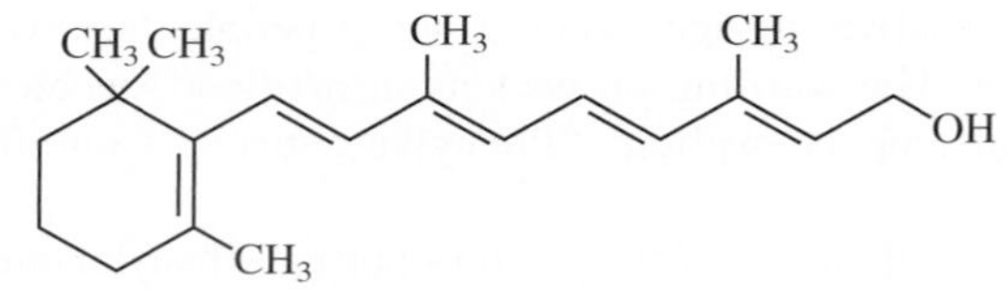

vitamin A, a lipid-soluble vitamin 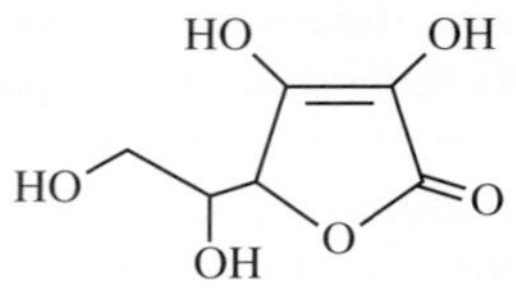   vitamin C, a water-soluble vitamin

Figure 11.19

An example of a lipid–soluble and a water–soluble vitamin.

Consider This 11.15   Classifying Vitamins

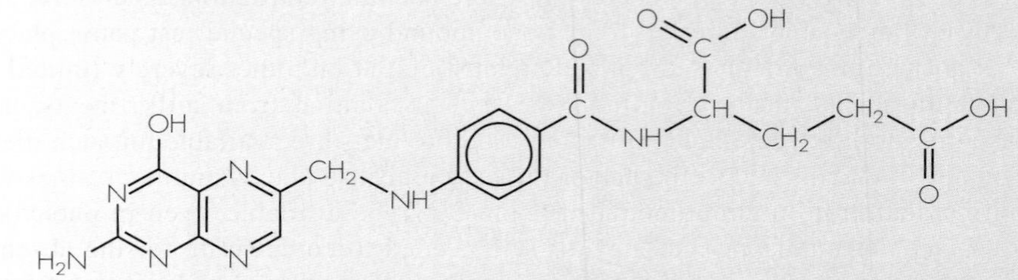

Folic acid helps prevent certain types of anemia and aids in nucleic acid synthesis. This vitamin is particularly important for pregnant women. Do you expect that it would be soluble in fat tissue (lipids) or in the bloodstream and cell tissue (water)? Explain your reasoning.

Recall from Section 5.9 that "like dissolves like."

The solubility of vitamins has significant implications for health. Because of their fat-solubility, vitamins A, D, E, and K are stored in cells rich in lipids, where they are available on biological demand. If swallowed in excess, fat-soluble vitamins can build up to a toxic level. For example, high doses of vitamin A can result in both troublesome symptoms such as fatigue and headache and in more serious ones such as blurred vision and liver damage. Although the toxic level of vitamin D is not known, similarly illness can result if too much vitamin D is ingested, including heart and kidney damage. High levels of these vitamins are not reached via diet; rather, they are a result of excessive use of vitamin supplements.

In contrast, water-soluble vitamins are excreted in the urine rather than stored in the body. As a result, you need to eat foods containing these vitamins frequently. Unfortunately, even water-soluble vitamins can accumulate at toxic levels when taken in large doses, although such cases are rare. For most people, a balanced diet provides the necessary vitamins and minerals, making vitamin supplements unnecessary. The one exception seems to be vitamin D, which is synthesized in the skin by using the energy of sunlight, rather than ingested. Recent research on vitamin D has led more physicians to check vitamin D blood levels as part of an annual physical exam and to use the results to determine whether taking a supplement is necessary.

Many of the water-soluble vitamins serve as **coenzymes,** molecules that work in conjunction with enzymes to enhance their activity. Members of the vitamin B family are particularly adept in acting as coenzymes. Niacin plays an essential role in energy transfer during glucose and fat metabolism. The synthesis of niacin in the body requires the essential amino acid tryptophan. Thus, a diet deficient in tryptophan may lead to niacin deficiency. Such a deficiency causes pellagra, a serious condition that is characterized by "the 4Ds" of diarrhea, dermatitis, dementia, and death. This disease is still common today in parts of the world, including several African nations.

Some vitamins were discovered when observers correlated diseases with the lack of specific foods. For example, vitamin C (ascorbic acid) must be supplied in the diet, typically via citrus fruits and green vegetables. An insufficient supply of the vitamin leads to scurvy, a disease in which collagen, an important structural protein, is broken down. The link between citrus fruits and scurvy was discovered more than 200 years ago when it was found that feeding British sailors limes or lime juice on long sea voyages prevented the disease. Thanks to Nobel laureate Linus Pauling who in 1970 authored *Vitamin C and the Common Cold*, vitamin C continues to be in the public eye.

This practice also led to British sailors being called "limeys."

Consider This 11.16   Megadoses of Vitamin C

Decades ago, Linus Pauling claimed that large doses of vitamin C were therapeutic in preventing the common cold.

a. What range of vitamin C daily constitutes a megadose?
b. Find evidence to either support or refute the claim of preventing the common cold. Cite your sources.
c. Interview three people of different age groups, including a nurse or physician if you are able. Ask if they take vitamin C and if so why.

We would be remiss not to mention vitamin E, which actually consists of several closely related fat-soluble vitamins rather than a single compound. Vitamin E is only synthesized by plants and in varying amounts. Vegetable oils and nuts are good sources of it. Nonetheless, it is so widely distributed in foods that it is difficult to create a diet deficient in vitamin E. Since the 1990s, this vitamin has been in the news as part of the antioxidant system that protects the body from chemically active and damaging free radicals. Although at one time taking vitamin E supplements was recommended, this no longer is the case. Skin preparations are another matter, though. Many products contain vitamin E and claim that it prevents or helps heal skin damage. Investigate for yourself in the next activity.

Consider This 11.17   Vitamin E and Your Skin

Check the advertisements and you will see that many hand lotions and beauty creams contain vitamin E.

a. Identify three skin products that contain vitamin E.
b. How is vitamin E thought to work in helping protect your skin?
c. Although it might seem logical that vitamin E would be good for the skin, it is difficult to find the evidence. Investigate this topic to see for yourself. Check the resources of the Internet to assist you.

Minerals are ions or ionic compounds that, like vitamins, have a wide range of physiological functions. You may be familiar with minerals such as sodium and calcium, but actually the list is much longer. Depending on how much of them you need, minerals are classified as either macro, micro, or trace.

- **Macrominerals** Ca, P, Cl, K, S, Na, and Mg
  These elements are necessary for life but not nearly as abundant in our bodies as O, C, H, and N. You need to ingest macrominerals daily, typically in the range of 1 to 2 g.
- **Microminerals** Fe, Cu, and Zn
  The body requires lesser amounts of these. You may recognize iron as a component of hemoglobin, a protein in the blood that carries oxygen.
- **Trace minerals** I, F, Se, V, Cr, Mn, Co, Ni, Mo, B, Si, and Sn
  These usually are measured in microgram quantities. Although the total amount of trace elements in the body is tiny, their small quantity belies the importance they have in good health.

Macrominerals are still micronutrients.

The periodic table in Figure 11.20 displays the essential dietary minerals. The metals exist in the body as cations, for example, Ca^{2+} (calcium ion), Mg^{2+} (magnesium ion), K^+ (potassium ion), and Na^+ (sodium ion). The nonmetals typically are present as anions. For example, chlorine is found as Cl^- (chloride ion) and phosphorus appears in PO_4^{3-} (phosphate ion).

Revisit Section 5.6 for more about ions.

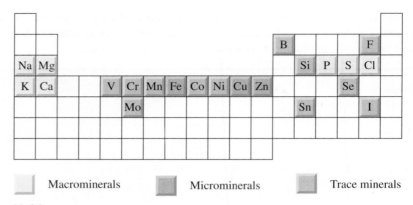

Figure 11.20

Periodic table indicating dietary minerals necessary for human life.

The physiological functions of minerals are widely diverse. Calcium is the most abundant mineral in the body. Along with phosphorus and smaller amounts of fluorine, it is a major constituent of bones and teeth. Blood clotting, muscle contraction, and transmission of nerve impulses all require the calcium ion, Ca^{2+}.

Sodium is also essential for life but not in the excessive amounts supplied by the diets of most people today. The salt we eat does not necessarily come from the salt-shaker. Rather, you perhaps unknowingly add salt to your diet from sauces, snack foods, fast foods, and even canned soup! Labels now are required to list the "sodium" content, meaning the number of milligrams of Na^+ per serving. For example, different brands of tomato soup may have between 700 and 1260 mg of Na^+ per serving. Compare this with the recommended daily value of no more than 2400 mg (2.4 grams) of Na^+ per day. The major concern with excess dietary sodium is its correlation with high blood pressure for some individuals. They may be advised by their doctors to limit their sodium intake.

> ## Your Turn 11.18   Sodium in Your Diet
>
> Compare sodium content for foods in the same category, such as different brands of pretzels, bread, frozen pizza, salad dressing, or even tomato soup. Have your findings surprised you or influenced your future choices? Recall that 1 g = 1000 mg.

Oranges, bananas, tomatoes, and potatoes all help supply the recommended daily requirement of 2 grams of potassium (in the form of K^+), another essential mineral. You may have heard both K^+ and Na^+ referred to as the "electrolytes" of sports drinks. Sodium and potassium ions are close chemical cousins, as they are both in Group 1A of the periodic table. They have similar chemical properties and physiological functions. Within cells, the concentration of K^+ is considerably greater than that of Na^+. The reverse situation holds true in the lymph and blood serum outside the cells in which the concentration of K^+ is low and that of Na^+ is high. The relative concentrations of K^+ and Na^+ are especially important for the rhythmic beating of the heart. Individuals who take diuretics to control high blood pressure may also take potassium supplements to replace potassium excreted in the urine. However, such supplements should be taken only under a physician's directions because they also can dramatically alter the potassium–sodium balance in the body and lead to cardiac complications.

In most instances, microminerals and trace elements have very specific biological functions and are incorporated in relatively few biomolecules. Iodine is an example. Most of the body's iodine is found in the thyroid gland incorporated into thyroxine, a hormone that regulates metabolism. Excess thyroxine production is associated with hyperthyroidism (Graves' disease) in which basal metabolism is accelerated to an

The Latin word for salt is *sal*. Salt was so highly valued in Roman times that soldiers were paid in *sal*, thereby forming the root for the modern word *salary*.

Electrolytes were described earlier in Section 5.6.

Seafood is one rich source of iodine. Another is iodized salt, sodium chloride (NaCl) to which 0.02% of potassium iodide (KI) has been added.

unhealthy level, rather like a racing engine. In contrast, a thyroxine deficiency, sometimes caused by a lack of dietary iodine, slows metabolism and results in tiredness and listlessness. The tendency of the thyroid gland to concentrate iodine makes possible the use of radioactive I-131 in treating thyroid disorders and in imaging the thyroid gland for diagnostic purposes. The next activity gives you the opportunity to combine what you have learned about radioactive I-131 and iodine as a trace mineral.

The explosion at Chornobyl released I–131 into the surrounding countryside. See Section 7.5 for more about the uptake of I–131 by children and the resulting thyroid cancer.

Consider This 11.19   Radioactive Iodine

Some individuals have an overactive thyroid gland (hyperthyroidism).

a. I–131 is used to treat hyperthyroidism. Explain how ingestion of this radioisotope can lead to a reduction in the function of the thyroid gland.
b. I–131 treatment has both risks and benefits for a patient. List two of each.
c. Patients treated with I–131 temporarily carry a source of radioactivity in their bodies. After 10 half–lives, a radioisotope can be said to be "gone." How much time is this for a patient treated with I–131? *Hint:* See Table 7.4.

11.9 | Energy from Food

The energy needed to keep our bodies warm and to run our complex chemical, mechanical, and electrical systems comes from the food we eat: fats, carbohydrates, and proteins. As noted in several earlier chapters, this energy initially arrives on Earth in the form of sunlight and then is absorbed by green plants. In the process of photosynthesis, CO_2 and H_2O are combined to form $C_6H_{12}O_6$. Hence the Sun's energy is stored in chemical bonds of the monosaccharide we know as glucose.

$$\text{energy (from sunshine)} + 6\,CO_2 + 6\,H_2O \xrightarrow{\text{chlorophyll}} C_6H_{12}O_6 + 6\,O_2 \quad \textbf{[11.5]}$$

During respiration, the outcome from photosynthesis is reversed. Glucose is converted into simpler substances (ultimately in most cases to CO_2 and H_2O), and the energy is released.

$$C_6H_{12}O_6 + 6\,O_2 \longrightarrow 6\,CO_2 + 6\,H_2O + \text{energy (from respiration)} \quad \textbf{[11.6]}$$

The energy balance between equations 11.5 and 11.6 can be schematically represented (Figure 11.21).

If you need a refresher on energy changes at the molecular level, see Section 4.6.

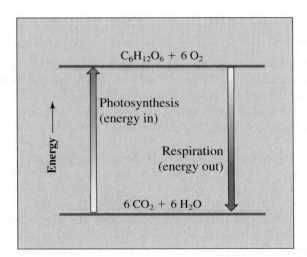

Figure 11.21

Glucose energy balance (photosynthesis and respiration).

Table 11.6	Average Energy Content of Macronutrients
fats	9 Cal/g
carbohydrates	4 Cal/g
proteins	4 Cal/g

1 dietary calorie = 1 Cal
= 1 kcal
= 1,000 calories

In addition to having a supply of sufficient energy, our bodies must have some way of regulating the rate at which the energy is released. Without such control, your body temperature would wildly fluctuate. The automobile provides an analogy. Dropping a lighted match into the fuel tank would burn all the gasoline at once and possibly the car as well. Under normal operating conditions, just enough fuel is delivered to the ignition system to supply the automobile with the energy it needs without raising the temperature of the car and its occupants beyond reason. By releasing a little energy at a time, the efficiency of the process is enhanced. So it is with the body. The conversion of foods ultimately into carbon dioxide and water occurs over many small steps, each one involving enzymes, enzyme regulators, and hormones. As a result, energy is released gradually, as needed, and body temperature is maintained within normal limits. The energy in Calories associated with the metabolism of a gram of fats, carbohydrates, and proteins is given in Table 11.6.

On a Calorie-per-gram basis, fats provide about 2.5 times as much energy as do proteins and carbohydrates. This observation makes it easy to understand the popularity of low-fat diets for losing weight. Although proteins, like carbohydrates, yield about 4 Cal/g if metabolized, proteins are not used in the body primarily as an energy source. Rather, proteins are used for building skin, muscles, tendons, ligaments, blood, and enzymes.

More information about lauric acid is revealed by writing its condensed structural formula of $CH_3(CH_2)_{10}COOH$.

The reason for the difference in energy content between fats and carbohydrates is evident from their chemical composition. Compare the chemical formula of a fatty acid, lauric acid, $C_{12}H_{24}O_2$, with that of sucrose (table sugar), $C_{12}H_{22}O_{11}$. Both compounds have the same number of carbon atoms per molecule and very nearly the same number of hydrogen atoms. When molecules such as these "burn" as fuel in your body, the C and H atoms that they contain combine with oxygen to form CO_2 and H_2O, respectively. But more oxygen is required to burn a gram of lauric acid, $C_{12}H_{24}O_2$, than a gram of sucrose, $C_{12}H_{22}O_{11}$. Examine these two reactions.

$$C_{12}H_{24}O_2 + 17\,O_2 \longrightarrow 12\,CO_2 + 12\,H_2O + 8.8\ \text{Cal/g} \qquad \textbf{[11.7]}$$
lauric acid

$$C_{12}H_{22}O_{11} + 12\,O_2 \longrightarrow 12\,CO_2 + 11\,H_2O + 3.8\ \text{Cal/g} \qquad \textbf{[11.8]}$$
sucrose

Oxygenated fuels were discussed in Section 4.7.

In the language of chemistry, the sugar is already more "oxygenated" or more "oxidized" than the fatty acid. Weaker C–H bonds (416 kJ/mol) have already been replaced by stronger O–H bonds (467 kJ/mol) in the sucrose. The result is that even though fewer O=O double bonds (498 kJ/mol) must be broken for sucrose to combine with O_2, less energy overall is released than is the case for the combustion of lauric acid.

Given how many tasty foods contain fat, it is easy to get an unhealthy percentage of our daily Calories from fats. The problem is illustrated by considering Skeptical Chemist 11.20. In accordance with the *Dietary Guidelines for Americans* released by the U.S. Department of Agriculture (USDA) and the U.S. Department of Health and Human Services (HHS) in 2010, 20–35% of Calories should come from fats, for adults. Furthermore, the guidelines recommend that less than 10% of Calories come from saturated fatty acids and that *trans* fat consumption be kept as low as possible.

Table 11.7	Estimated Calorie Requirements (United States)		
	ACTIVITY LEVEL		
Age (yr)	Sedentary*	Moderately Active†	Active‡
Females			
14–18	1800	2000	2400
19–30	2000	2000–2200	2400
31–50	1800	2000	2200
51+	1600	1800	2000–2200
Males			
14–18	2200	2400–2800	2800–3200
19–30	2400	2600–2800	3000
31–50	2200	2400–2600	2800–3000
51+	2000	2200–2400	2400–2800

*Sedentary means a lifestyle that includes only the light physical activity associated with typical day–to–day life.

†Moderately active means a lifestyle that includes physical activity equivalent to walking about 1–3 miles per day at 3–4 miles per hour, in addition to the light physical activity associated with typical day–to–day life.

‡Active means a lifestyle that includes physical activity equivalent to walking more than 3 miles per day at 3–4 miles per hour, in addition to the light physical activity associated with typical day–to–day life.

Source: Dietary Guidelines for Americans, USDA, 2005.

Skeptical Chemist 11.20   Low–Fat Cheese

A popular brand of low–fat shredded cheddar cheese advertises that it provides 1.5 g of fat per serving. Of this 1.5 g of fat, 1.0 g is saturated fat. In addition, a serving of this cheese is 28 grams (or 1/4 cup) and has 50 Calories, with 15 of these coming from fat. Is this a "low–fat" cheese? Support your answer with some numbers. Remember that the dietary recommendation is that 20–35% of Calories should come from fat.

So how many Calories does a person need? The answer is "It depends." The number of Calories your diet should supply each day is a function of your level of activity, the state of your health, your gender, age, body size, and a few other factors. Table 11.7 summarizes the daily food energy intakes that have been recommended for people in the United States. The estimated Calorie requirements are presented by gender and age groups at three different activity levels. Growing children (not included in the table) need a larger energy intake, both to fuel their high level of activity and to provide raw material for building muscle and bone. Children are particularly susceptible to under-nourishment and malnutrition. Indeed, mortality rates among infants and young children are disproportionately high in famine-stricken countries.

Your Turn 11.21   Calories by Gender and Age

Consider the information in Table 11.7 and the Dietary Guidelines for Americans, 2010, which can be found on the Internet.

a. Do males and females of the same age require the same number of Calories for the same level of activity? Explain.

b. As an active male or female grows older, how does the estimated Calorie requirement change?

Table 11.8	Energy Expenditure for Common Physical Activities*		
Moderate Physical Activity	Cal/hr	Vigorous Physical Activity	Cal/hr
hiking	370	jogging (5 mph)	590
light gardening/yard work	330	heavy yard work (chopping wood)	440
dancing	330	swimming (freestyle laps)	510
golf (walking, carrying clubs)	330	aerobics	480
bicycling (<10 mph)	290	bicycling (>10 mph)	590
walking (3.5 mph)	280	slower jogging (4.5 mph)	460
weight lifting (light workout)	220	weightlifting (vigorous workout)	440
stretching	180	basketball (vigorous)	440

* Values include both resting metabolic rate and activity expenditure for a 70–kg (154–pound) person. Calories burned per hour are higher for persons heavier than 70 kg and lower for persons who weigh less.

Each heartbeat uses about one joule (1 J), or 4.18 cal, of energy.

Your basal metabolic rate is approximately 1 Cal/kg body mass per hour.

$$\frac{1300\ \text{Cal}}{2200\ \text{Cal}} \times 100 = 59\%$$

Where does all this food energy go? The first call on the Calories you consume is to keep your heart beating, your lungs pumping air, your brain active, all major organs working, and your body temperature at about 37 °C. These requirements define the **basal metabolic rate (BMR),** the minimum amount of energy required daily to support basic body functions. This corresponds to approximately 1 Calorie per kilogram (2.2 pounds) of body mass per hour, although it varies with size and age.

To put this on a personal basis, consider a 20-year-old female weighing 55 kg (121 pounds). If her body has a minimum requirement of 1 Cal/(kg·h), her daily basal metabolic rate will be 1 Cal/(kg·h) × 55 kg × 24 h/day, or about 1300 Cal/day. According to Table 11.7, the recommended daily energy intake for a woman of this age and weight is a maximum of 2200 Cal if she is moderately active. This means that 59% of the energy derived from this food goes just to keep her body systems going.

Where do the rest of her Calories go? The law of conservation of energy decrees that the energy must go somewhere. If she "burns off" the extra Calories through exercise, none will be stored as added fat and glycogen. But, if the excess energy is not expended, it will accumulate in chemical form. Putting it more bluntly, "those who indulge, bulge."

How hard and how long we have to work (or play) to burn dietary Calories is reported in Table 11.8. In Table 11.9, exercise is related in readily recognizable units such as hamburgers, potato chips, and beer. Of course by combining the information in this section with the information in earlier parts of this chapter about the types of nutrients in food, it should be clear that a healthful diet cannot be achieved simply by consuming the correct number of Calories. A 2000-Calorie diet of only potato chips and beer would leave a person malnourished. Proper nutrition is not simply a matter of how much, but also of what kind of food a person consumes.

Your Turn 11.22   Basketball and Calories

A 70–kg person consumes a meal consisting of two hamburgers, 3 oz of potato chips, 8 oz of ice cream, and a 12–oz beer. Calculate the number of Calories in the meal and the number of minutes the person would have to vigorously play basketball in order to "work off" the meal.

Answer
about 1500 Calories, about 200 min

Table 11.9	How Much Must I Exercise if I Eat This Cookie?*		
Food	Calories	Walking at 3.5 mph Time (min)	Jogging at 5 mph Time (min)
apple	125	27	13
beer (regular) 8 ounces	100	21	10
chocolate chip cookie	50	11	5
hamburger	350	75	35
ice cream, 4 ounces	175	38	18
pizza, cheese, 1 slice	180	39	18
potato chips, 1 ounce	108	23	11

*Values include both resting metabolic rate and activity expenditure for a 70–kg (154–pound) person.

11.10 | Dietary Advice: Quality Versus Quantity

Which foods should you eat less of . . . and which ones more? One day the experts say one thing; the next day they seem to say the opposite. With so much information available, you may be confused or feel overwhelmed.

Indeed, dietary advice is changing. If you are a young adult, you may have parents or grandparents who remember "The Basic Four" and "The Food Pyramid." Take a trip back in time with Figure 11.22, courtesy of the U.S. Department of Agriculture. Both emphasize the concept of a daily serving.

In 2005, the U.S. Department of Agriculture introduced a new pyramid, "Steps to a Healthier You" (Figure 11.23a). It turned the 1991 food pyramid sideways, added stairs, and named it MyPyramid. In 2011, MyPlate was launched as a

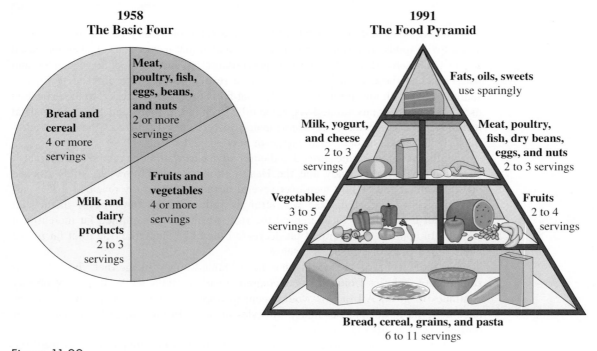

Figure 11.22

Dietary advice of the past, the USDA Basic Four and the Food Pyramid.

Source: United States Department of Agriculture.

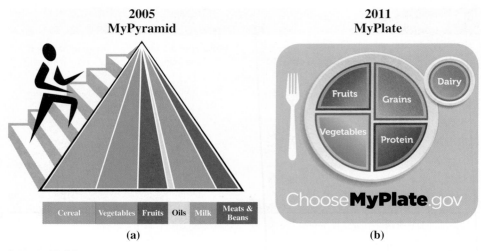

Figure 11.23

More recent dietary advice, **(a)** MyPyramid ("Steps to a Healthier You") and **(b)** MyPlate.

Source: United States Department of Agriculture.

more straightforward way to help people remember what to put on their plates (Figure 11.23b). The message was simple: at least half of your meal should be fruits and vegetables. The research of nutritional scientists supports this assertion.

Consider This 11.23   A Plate or a Pyramid?

People sounded off on the Internet when MyPlate was introduced. One criticism was that fats and oils were no longer as visible as they were in MyPyramid. Another was that dairy products are not a necessity for adults. Finally, critics noticed that "protein" is not a type of food; further-more, it overlaps with grains because these also provide protein. What do you think? Do your own research and then argue the merits or weaknesses of MyPlate against those of MyPyramid.

History can help us understand the recent surge of dietary advice. In the 1960s, studies with foods containing saturated fats revealed that participants showed increased serum cholesterol levels. In addition, polyunsaturated fats—found in vegetables and fish—reduced these cholesterol levels. As a result, people were advised to replace saturated fats with unsaturated ones. The "sat fat is bad" movement led to the expanded use of more highly unsaturated vegetable oils. Back in the 1960s and 1970s, the partial hydrogenation of vegetable oils unfortunately also produced *trans* fats that posed addi-tional health risks, as described earlier in Section 11.4.

Other research studies provided dietary advice as well. For example, the Harvard-based Nurses' Health Study and the Health Professionals Follow-Up Study tracked 90,000 women and 50,000 men over several decades. This study revealed that a par-ticipant's risk of heart disease was strongly influenced by the type of dietary fat consumed. Eating *trans* fat increased the risk substantially; saturated fat increased it slightly. In contrast, unsaturated fat decreased the risk. Therefore, the total fat intake alone is not the cause of heart disease.

Although the rise in obesity has been blamed on fat in the diet, the U.S. con-sumption of Calories from fat has decreased since the 1980s while the rate of obesity continues to grow. All of this would seem to imply that fat is not the culprit it was once believed to be. The sedentary lifestyles of many in the United States and larger portion sizes are also factors to consider.

Are "carbs" the culprit? Diet books about carbohydrate intake have spanned the spectrum from banning all carbs to taking a "good carb versus bad carb" approach. The latter claims that "bad" carbohydrates cause a quick rise in blood sugar, followed by a spike in blood insulin level. Insulin is a hormone secreted by the pancreas that allows the cells in your body to absorb and store sugar that is in the blood. The sugar that is not immediately burned for energy is converted to fat and stored in your cells. Conversely, glucagon is another hormone secreted by the pancreas that, essentially, has the opposite effect of insulin: It promotes the use of stored glucose in cells. The release of glucagon decreases after a "glucose spike," such as results from eating "bad carbs," but it is known to increase after consumption of proteins. Therefore, some "low-carb" diets promote eating more protein as a way to use up stored Calories. The long-term health effects of this approach are yet to be seen. Clearly, both nutrition and dieting involve a complex bit of chemistry!

11.11 | From Field to Fork

In previous sections, we have asserted that what you eat affects your health. In this section, we address how what you eat also more widely affects the planet, discussing connections among food production, energy use, and global climate change. We launch our discussion with two closely related topics: eating locally and monitoring the "food miles" for grocery items.

In regard to the first, people desire to eat local for many reasons. Picking a tomato from the vine or visiting a local farmer's market truly can be a pleasure. Table 11.10 lists five other reasons people choose to eat local. Does eating local really improve the health of the planet? In the next activity, you have the opportunity to examine the validity of the claims in Table 11.10.

"Food miles" approximate the distance that a food travels from the location it was grown to the location where it was consumed, that is, farm to plate. They are one measure of food sustainability because they reflect energy use.

Skeptical Chemist 11.24   Eat Local

Critically examine each statement in Table 11.10.

a. For a statement of your choice, provide a supporting example. For a second statement, provide a counterexample.
b. Since this list is not complete, suggest two other entries to add to the list.
c. Suggest an item on this list that should be removed or revised. Explain.

In regard to the second topic, people question food miles, that is, how far food travels to reach their table. Depending on the food, it could travel a few yards from your garden or several thousand miles from another country. Most of our foods must be transported. Would it help if all food were produced locally? Not necessarily. For example, it may be less energy-efficient to grow tomatoes locally in a greenhouse than

---

Table 11.10	Reasons to "Eat Local"

1. **Eating local means more for the local economy.** A dollar spent locally generates twice as much income for the local economy. When businesses are not owned locally, money leaves the community with every transaction.

2. **Locally grown produce is fresher and tastes better.** Produce at your local farmer's market often has been picked within 24 hours of your purchase. This freshness not only affects the taste of your food but also the nutritional value. Have you ever tried a tomato that was picked within 24 hours?

3. **Locally grown fruits and vegetables have longer to ripen.** Because the produce is handled less, locally grown fruit does not have to stand up to the rigors of shipping. You will get peaches so ripe that they fall apart as you eat them, and melons that were allowed to ripen on the vine until the last possible minute.

4. **Buying local food keeps us in touch with the seasons.** By eating with the seasons, our foods are at their peak taste and less expensive.

5. **Supporting local providers supports responsible land development.** When you buy locally, you give those with local open space—farms and pastures—an economic reason to resist further development.

Source: Adapted from "10 Reasons to Eat Local Food," Jennifer Maizer, EatLocalChallenge.com.

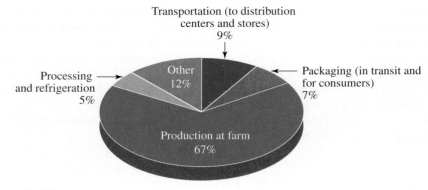

Figure 11.24

Carbon footprint for food before it reaches a grocery chain in Great Britain.

Source: How Bad Are Bananas? The Carbon Footprint of Everything, *Greystone Books, Mike Berners-Lee, 2011.*

to import them from a warmer climate. Transportation as well as other energy costs must be balanced against the food production costs.

If your primary reason for eating locally is to reduce fossil fuel consumption, you may be interested in a 2008 study from Carnegie Mellon University. The researchers report that "transportation as a whole represents only 11% of life-cycle greenhouse gas emissions, and final delivery from producer to retail contributes only 4%." So, if the majority of emissions and energy cost with food are not transportation related, where do they originate?

To answer this question, examine Figure 11.24, which shows carbon footprint data for food reaching a grocery chain in Great Britain. From Chapter 3, recall that carbon footprints estimate carbon dioxide emissions in a given time frame. Determining a "carbon footprint" for a particular food requires a set of assumptions. As a result, you will see different values for the same food because the researchers have based their calculations on different assumptions.

For food, the majority of the carbon footprint (67%) comes from the production on the farm, as shown in Figure 11.24. For example, operating farm machinery produces carbon dioxide, and using fertilizer stimulates microbes in soils to produce nitrous oxide. Farm animals also produce methane. In addition to the production of food, the figure points to other areas in which food contributes to the carbon footprint include:

- Transportation (9%)
  Relatively low unless air freight
- Packaging (7%)
  Primarily from disposal of the packaging
- Processing and refrigeration (5%)

Many small factors, including the leakage of refrigerant gases (all greenhouse gases), contribute as well. Although not included in Figure 11.24, food waste also increases the carbon footprint, which in some countries is up to 25% of all purchased food.

In reaching your table, clearly some foods have higher carbon footprints than others. Looking at the graph in Figure 11.25, you probably notice that steak and cheese are the highest of the items included. Why might this be the case? Revisit Figure 11.1 to see that the production of beef, unless grass-fed, requires grain production. In turn, both of these are associated with greenhouse gas emissions. You also may have noticed the low values for tomatoes and carrots. However, if these items had been transported instead of grown in your backyard, these values would increase. Similarly, had the tomatoes been grown in a greenhouse, the carbon footprint value would be higher.

Before we bring this section to a close, we return to the theme mentioned at the start of this chapter: eating vegetarian. According to the Carnegie Mellon food miles study mentioned earlier, a single meat-based meal with a vegetarian option

Most carbon footprints use a time frame of 1 year.

Nitrous oxide (N_2O), part of the nitrogen cycle (see Figure 6.18), comes from pathways connected to manure and fertilizers.

Cows produce methane in their digestive tracts in the range of 200 pounds per animal per year.

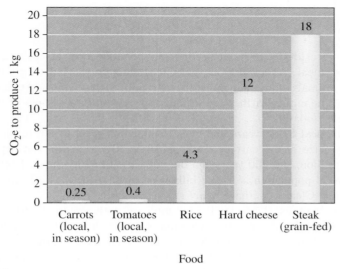

Figure 11.25

Carbon dioxide emissions (CO_2e) for food production.

Source: How Bad Are Bananas? The Carbon Footprint of Everything, *Greystone Books, Mike Berners-Lee, 2011.*

The term *carbon dioxide equivalent,* CO_2e, includes all greenhouse gases, not just CO_2. For example, in its ability to warm the atmosphere, 1 kg of methane is equivalent to 21 kg of carbon dioxide.

one day a week saved the equivalent of driving about 1200 fewer miles annually. In contrast, an all-local diet *every day of the week* saved the equivalent of driving 1000 fewer miles annually. In the next activity, you can connect these numbers to carbon dioxide emissions.

Your Turn 11.25   Local Produce and CO_2 Emissions

In an activity in an earlier chapter (Skeptical Chemist 3.18), we noted that a clean–burning automobile engine emits about 4.4 pounds of carbon (~2000 grams) in the form of CO_2 for every gallon of gasoline burned.

a. How many pounds of CO_2 is this?
b. If you saved the equivalent of 1000 fewer miles each year by eating locally, approximately how many pounds of CO_2 is this? List any assumptions you make.

Given what we know about food miles and eating locally, what actions make the most sense to lower the carbon footprint of the foods we eat? As we stated at the beginning of this section, carbon footprints are based on assumptions. As a result, the footprint of any particular item can differ, depending on the assumptions that were made. When deciding which foods to eat, you need to know which assumptions pertain to your particular situation. Even so, we can offer these more general suggestions that are likely to help you lower your food carbon footprint:

- Eat what you buy, don't waste it
- Reduce meat and dairy consumption
- Go seasonal, minimizing use of greenhouses and air freight when possible
- Avoid foods with excessive packaging
- Recycle packaging to the greatest extent possible
- Help stores reduce waste by taking items closest to expiration, handling food with care, and buying reduced-price items
- Buy misshapen or blemished fruit and vegetables
- Heat food efficiently

In this section, we have examined ways to decrease the carbon footprint of our food. However, we still are faced with the problem of feeding an ever-growing population. We address this issue in the final section of the chapter.

11.12 | Feeding a Hungry World

Our ancient ancestors were hunter-gatherers, spending most of each day searching for their next meal. About 10,000 years ago, humans learned to grow crops and domesticate animals, thus launching the agricultural revolution. At that time, the population of the entire Earth was estimated to be 4 million people or roughly that of Los Angeles today.

Over the next 8,000 years, the global population grew to 170 million people or about half the size of the current U.S. population. By 1000 CE, the population had risen to 310 million, and 200 years ago the population finally topped 1 billion people. Today, the world population is over 7 billion and within the next 40 years will likely rise to 9 billion. Clearly, we have many mouths to feed.

Thomas Malthus (1766–1834) and more recently entomologist Paul Ehrlich (b. 1932) predicted that the human population of the Earth would outstrip food production. During the first 100 years after Malthus published his essay, the population of the Earth grew by 60% to 1.6 billion. During the next 100 years (the 20th century), the population exploded with an additional 4.4 billion people. The Food and Agriculture Organization (FAO) of the United Nations estimated that we have managed to increase the world food supply to meet the needs of over 80% of the people. Even so, the remainder is undernourished.

Given that the population continues to grow, so must food production. Two methods largely have been responsible for food increases of the past: planting crops on more land and increasing crop yields. Can this increase to our food supply continue? Neither method has much room for growth. Almost all of the world's biologically productive land is now in use. Arable land is only likely to be increased by 5% as of 2050, according to FAO estimates. Furthermore, in many areas cropland is actually shrinking due to factors such as desertification, soil nutrient depletion, erosion, and urban development.

The 1940s saw the beginning of the Green Revolution. In the decades that followed, agricultural productivity per acre of corn, rice, and wheat more than doubled. Many factors were responsible, including the use of fertilizers and pesticides, irrigation, mechanization, double cropping, and most importantly, the advent of high yielding crop varieties. Billions of people across the world benefited.

In spite of its successes, the Green Revolution also resulted in economic, environmental, and societal costs. For example, producing crops requires water and energy, as we discussed in two previous sections. Other environmental costs of the Green Revolution come from the use of supplemental nitrogen fertilizers such as ammonia, urea, or nitrates, all of which are forms of "reactive nitrogen." Refresh your knowledge of the chemistry of nitrogen in the next activity.

In 1798, Thomas Malthus wrote his *Essay on Population*. In 1978, Paul Ehrlich wrote the book *The Population Bomb*.

Feeding people requires more than having enough food. Access to quality food depends on its price and having the income to buy it. Utilization of food depends on having a safe physical environment, including safe drinking water.

Revisit Section 5.3 to see that in many parts of the world, agriculture accounts for 70% of water use.

Recall from Chapter 6 that nitrogen gas (N_2) is chemically unreactive. In contrast, ammonia is a reactive form of nitrogen. See Section 6.9.

Your Turn 11.26 — Revisiting Nitrogen Chemistry

Agriculture, as we know it today, depends on the nitrogen cycle. For your convenience, we have reprinted this cycle from Chapter 6 in Figure 11.26.

a. Ammonia (NH_3) is applied to soil in the form of anhydrous ammonia, that is, ammonia without water. Ammonia is very soluble in water. Explain why. *Hint:* Revisit Chapter 5.
b. When ammonia is mixed with water, the resulting solution is basic. Explain why, including the ammonium ion (NH_4^+) as part of your answer. *Hint:* Revisit Chapter 6.
c. According to Figure 11.26, which chemical species of nitrogen is used (assimilated) by plants?
d. Microbes in the soil interconvert the chemical species of nitrogen. Before the ammonium ion can be assimilated by plants, another chemical species is formed. What is it?

Clearly fertilizers enhance the yield of crops, especially when used on nutrient poor or depleted soils. However, from Figure 11.26 you can see that soil bacteria convert nitrogen compounds into other reactive nitrogen species that move through the air, water, and soil. Since compounds containing the nitrate ion or the ammonium ion are

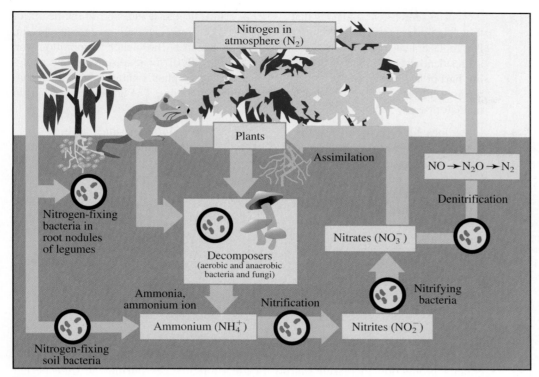

Figure 11.26

The nitrogen cycle (simplified), a set of chemical pathways whereby nitrogen moves through the biosphere.

very water-soluble, an excess of these ions ends up in waterways and promotes unwanted plant growth. For example, algal blooms in the Gulf of Mexico are caused by the runoff of fertilizers from farms in the watershed of the Mississippi River in states from as far away as Montana, Minnesota, and Pennsylvania (revisit Figure 11.15). These blooms affect the livelihood of all those who use the common waters of the Mississippi, including the fishing industry in the Gulf. Although unintended consequences can be minimized by using less fertilizer and timing its application more carefully, we have not yet been successful in avoiding such harm.

> Revisit Table 5.9 for more about the solubility of nitrates.

The use of synthetic pesticides, though integral in raising crop yields, results in another environmental cost of the Green Revolution. Like nitrogen fertilizers, pesticides impact our health and the health of the planet. The use of insecticides saves millions of pounds of crops from being devoured by pests in the field, but at the same time these chemicals can kill beneficial insects along with the intended target. Many persistent pesticides also end up in the environment as a chemical cocktail, the consequences of which we are still deciphering. More environmentally friendly pesticides that target only specific organisms or elicit a plant's own defenses have been developed.

Methyl bromide is an extremely effective pesticide used in sterilizing soils and as a fumigant. It kills a wide variety of insects and is particularly useful in preparing soil for crops such as strawberries and tomatoes. However, given its toxicity and its ability to deplete stratospheric ozone, the use of methyl bromide was phased out in 2005 under the Montreal Protocol, except for some specialized uses.

> As of 2012, allowable specialized uses ("critical exceptions") of methyl bromide include its use with certain crops for which no good alternative exists, including strawberries and tomatoes.

Your Turn 11.27   Methyl Bromide and the Ozone Hole

Draw the structural formula for methyl bromide. Why would you expect it to deplete the ozone layer? *Hint:* Revisit Your Turn 2.24.

The search for pesticides that are less harmful to our health and to the health of the planet presents a challenge to green chemists. Harpin, a naturally occurring protein, is a replacement for some uses of methyl bromide. EDEN Bioscience Corporation won a Presidential Green Chemistry Challenge Award in 2001 for its discovery that applying harpin to the stems and leaves of plants triggered a plant's natural defense mechanisms to diseases caused by bacteria, fungi, and nematodes. The advantages of harpin include that it:

- does not directly kill, so the pest is unlikely to acquire resistance to it.
- is produced from the fermentation of a genetically engineered laboratory strain of *Escherichia coli* that is benign.
- is produced from renewable materials and gives waste products that are biodegradable.
- is classified with the lowest hazard potential by the U.S. EPA.
- can be applied to fields using smaller concentrations than many other pesticides.
- is rapidly decomposed by sunlight and microorganisms.

Although harpin has many advantages, it is not a perfect solution. Some plants respond to it better than others. Furthermore, harpin needs to be reapplied at several week intervals. Because it is relatively new, over time some unintended consequences may be discovered.

Before we end our discussion of food production, let's briefly revisit the topic of biofuels from Chapter 4. The data presented in Consider This 4.20 showed that ethanol production increased sharply in the United States during the time period 2000–2010. Furthermore, this ethanol was produced almost exclusively from feed corn. In recent years (2007–2011), according to the USDA, corn production has been 12 to 13 billion bushels. Assuming 56 pounds of shelled corn per bushel, this translates to about 700 billion pounds or 350 million tons of corn annually. From the following activity you can see the urgency of developing processes that produce ethanol from nonedible biomass (cellulose).

> Genetic engineering is the topic of the next chapter.

> An EPA Fact Sheet states: "With no expected adverse effects to human health or the environment, use of the harpin protein has the potential to substantially reduce use of more toxic pesticides, especially fungicides and certain soil fumigants, such as methyl bromide."

Your Turn 11.28   Food or Fuel?

a. Using the data just provided together with the values in Consider This 4.20, what percentage of our corn crop has been used in recent years to produce ethanol? Assume that 100 gallons of ethanol can be produced from a ton (2000 lb) of corn.

b. The 2007 United States Energy Independence and Security Act set a mandate of producing 36 billion gallons of biofuels by 2022. If this goal were met by producing ethanol solely from corn, how many million tons of corn would be required?

Answers

a. Assuming an annual ethanol production of 13 billion gallons (data from Consider This 4.20), here is the math:

13,000,000,000 gallons ethanol $\times$ 2000 lb corn/100 gallons ethanol $\times$ 1 ton corn/2000 lb corn

= 130 million tons of corn.

This is about 37% of an annual production of 350 million tons of corn.

b. Using the same ratio of ethanol to corn calculated in part a, producing 36 billion gallons of ethanol would require 360 million tons of corn, essentially all of the current U.S. harvest of feed corn.

We end this section by returning to the question raised earlier of whether eating less meat translates to more available food. Indeed, eating less meat does have benefits in terms of energy use, land use, and water use. Eating the saturated fats of beef in moderation (together with eating more fruits, vegetables, and whole grains) also is part of a recommended diet. But those who study the issues are skeptical. Mark Rosegrant of the International Food Policy Research Institute was interviewed in a 2010 issue of *Science* devoted to food security: "When all the pluses and minuses are added up, Rosegrant is confident that cutting meat consumption could ultimately help improve global food security. But 'it's a small contribution,'. . . he says."

Even so, the small contributions of many people add up to larger benefits. What actions should each of us take? This final activity offers personal advice in simple terms.

Consider This 11.29   In Defense of Food

In his book, *In Defense of Food*, Michael Pollan offers this simple advice: "Eat food. Not too much. Mostly plants."

   a. List two ways in which this advice could connect to your own health.
   b. List two ways in which this advice could connect to the health of the planet.
   c. Are there drawbacks to what he proposes? If so, describe them. Support your proposal with data such as Calories and nutrients provided.

Where do we go from here? Some hope that a second green revolution will be fostered by genetically engineered crops, but in many areas of the world people oppose transgenic foods. In the next and final chapter of this book, we tackle the chemistry of genes and genetic engineering.

Conclusion

Even though our individual tastes vary, our biological needs are much the same. We need carbohydrates and fats as our energy sources; fats for cell membranes, synthesis, and lubrication; proteins to build muscle and create the enzymes that catalyze the intricate chemistry of life; and vitamins and minerals to help make that chemistry happen.

What and how much we eat affect not only our own health but also the health of the planet. In this chapter, we saw some of the human health and environmental consequences of our food choices. Some foods, including most meats, disproportionately use water, grain, fuel, and land to produce. Some crops, including corn, can stress not only the land of the farmer but also the ecosystems many miles downstream.

Meeting the dietary needs of all on our planet is one of the greatest challenges of our time. A little knowledge of chemistry allows us both to raise and answer good questions. But chemical knowledge alone cannot lead us to a more peaceful, more prosperous, and healthier world. Individual and community choices, which in turn are determined by wisdom from economic, social, religious, and political communities, also will help lead the way forward.

Chapter Summary

Having studied this chapter, you should be able to:
- Describe ways in which food production connects to land use, water use, and energy use and connects to issues of climate change (11.1, 11.11, 11.12)
- Question the assumptions behind any estimate, such as the estimate of land required to produce different types of food (11.1)
- Differentiate between malnutrition and undernourishment (11.2)
- Describe what makes a food "processed" (11.2)

- Describe the distribution of water, fats, carbohydrates, and proteins in the human body and in some typical foods (11.2)
- Identify sources of fats (saturated and unsaturated) and cholesterol and state their significance in the diet (11.3, 11.4)
- Show how fatty acids and glycerol can combine to form a triglyceride (11.3)
- Know why oils are hydrogenated and the connection between hydrogenation and *trans* fats (11.4)

- Describe the green chemistry key ideas associated with interesterification reactions (11.4)
- Explain how sugars, starch, and cellulose differ (11.5)
- Draw the general structural formula for an amino acid and explain how amino acids combine to form proteins (11.6)
- Discuss the importance of essential amino acids and their dietary significance (11.6)
- Explain the principle of protein complementarity (11.6)
- Describe the symptoms and cause of phenylketonuria (11.7)
- Discuss the effects of vitamins and minerals on human health (11.8)

- Explain why carbohydrates, fats, and proteins differ as energy sources (11.9)
- Identify and use basal metabolic rate, BMR (11.9)
- Know appropriate resources for obtaining up-to-date dietary advice (11.10)
- Discuss the pros and cons of using food miles as a guide to what you eat. Do the same for eating locally. (11.11)
- Describe ways to decrease the carbon footprint of the food you eat, stating the assumptions behind these ways (11.11)
- Describe the potential contribution of eating less meat to your health and the health of the planet as well as food security (11.12)

Questions

Emphasizing Essentials

1. One theme in this chapter is that what you eat affects not only your health but also the health of the planet. Provide two examples that illustrate this theme.

2. Select a profession of your choice, possibly one you intend to pursue. Name two ways in which a person in this profession could have a positive influence on healthy food choices.

3. Suggest at least two connections between food production and water quality. Do the same for water use.

4. Being a vegetarian is not an "all or nothing" proposition. Rather, it can make sense to eat meat, just less of it. Give two reasons that support this position.

5. In general, it requires more water and land to produce beef, chicken, and pork than it does to produce grains such as corn and soybeans. Give two reasons why.

6. Although producing meat generally requires more land and water than producing grains, this is not always the case. Explain why.

7. Eating properly involves more than filling your stomach. Explain the difference between malnutrition and undernourishment.

8. What is a processed food? Give five examples of processed foods, including ones that you eat.

9. Macronutrients provide a source of energy and raw materials for your body.

   a. Name the three different types of macronutrients.

   b. How do macronutrients differ in energy content? *Hint:* See Table 11.6.

10. Although water is not considered a macronutrient, it clearly is essential to maintaining health. Name three roles that water plays in our bodies. *Hint:* Refer back to Chapter 5.

11. Consider this pie chart.

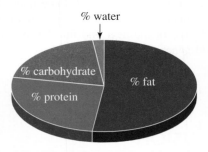

Based on the relative percentages of protein, carbohydrate, water, and fat, is this pie chart more likely to represent steak, peanut butter, or a chocolate chip cookie? Explain your choice.

12. Of the foods listed in Table 11.1,

   a. identify the best sources of carbohydrates and arrange them in decreasing order.

   b. identify the best sources of protein and arrange them in decreasing order.

   c. identify two foods that should be avoided if you are controlling your intake of fat.

13. At a local restaurant, an 18-ounce steak is the manager's special. Use Table 11.1 to calculate the ounces of protein, fat, and water in a portion of this size.

14. Although fats and fatty acids are related, they differ in terms of the size of their molecules, their functional groups, and their role in your diet. Elaborate on each of these differences.

15. List the similarities and differences between edible fats and oils, both in terms of their observable properties (pure and in foods) and in terms of their molecular structure.

16. Both unsaturated fats and saturated fats are triglycerides. Explain how they differ in terms of their chemical structures and their role in your diet.

17. In Figure 11.9, identify the fat or oil that contains the highest number of grams per tablespoon of:

   a. polyunsaturated fat.   c. total unsaturated fat.

   b. monounsaturated fat.   d. saturated fat.

18. How does a *trans* fat differ from other fats in terms of its chemical structure? In terms of its health benefits?

19. Name foods in which you would be likely to find these carbohydrates.

   a. lactose   c. sucrose

   b. fructose   d. starch

20. Explain each term and give an example.

   a. monosaccharide   c. polysaccharide

   b. disaccharide

21. Starch and cellulose are both polysaccharides. How are these two compounds similar in terms of their chemical structures? How are they different in terms of our ability to digest them?

22. Fructose, $C_6H_{12}O_6$, is an example of a carbohydrate.

   a. Rewrite the chemical formula of fructose to show that a *carbohydrate* can be thought of as "carbon plus water."

   b. Draw a structural formula for any isomer of fructose.

   c. Do you expect different isomers of fructose to have the same sweetness? Explain.

23. Fructose and glucose both have the chemical formula of $C_6H_{12}O_6$. How do their structural formulas differ?

24. Chemical names, especially for organic compounds, can give information about the structure of the molecules that these compounds contain. What does the term *amino acid* suggest about its molecular structure?

25. Proteins are polymers, sometimes referred to as polyamides. Similarly, nylons also are polymers and polyamides. What is the amide functional group? Compare and contrast proteins and nylon in terms of

   a. the functional groups present on the monomer(s).

   b. the variety of different proteins as compared to that of different nylons.

26. Analogous to equation 11.4a, show how glycine and phenylalanine react to form a dipeptide.

27. Some amino acids are called "essential amino acids." Explain why.

28. Why are people with phenylketonuria able to drink beverages sweetened with sucralose but should avoid those sweetened with aspartame?

29. Explain the nutritional significance of the elements shaded on this periodic table.

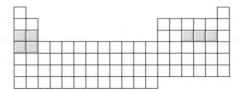

30. In recent years, which two methods primarily have been used to increase food production?

31. Fertilizers contain nitrogen in a "reactive" form. Explain the meaning of the term *reactive nitrogen*. Which chemical forms of nitrogen are present in fertilizers? Give an example of a form of nitrogen that is nonreactive.

Concentrating on Concepts

32. Sausage pizza contains both macronutrients and micronutrients. Identify two examples of each. How well does eating a meal of sausage pizza meet the dietary guidelines suggested by MyPlate?

33. Explain to a friend why it is impossible to go on a highly advertised "all organic, chemical-free" diet.

34. Indicate whether each statement is true, true only in some circumstances, or false. Explain your reasoning.

   a. Plant oils are lower in saturated fat than animal fats.

   b. Given time and exposure to the air, fats and oils become rancid.

   c. Fats are not necessary in our diet because our bodies can manufacture them from other substances we eat.

35. The label of a popular brand of soft margarine lists "partially hydrogenated soybean oil" as an ingredient. Explain the term *partially hydrogenated*. Why must the label report partially hydrogenated soybean oil rather than simply soybean oil?

36. A well-known medical clinic used the phrase "double trouble" to refer to *trans* fatty acids. Explain the logic behind this.

37. Explain why the process of interesterification is a useful alternative to hydrogenation.

38. Although interesterification is a useful alternative to hydrogenation, the process had several drawbacks until a green chemistry solution was developed.

   a. What were the drawbacks?

   b. What solution was developed?

   c. Which of the green chemistry key ideas did this solution address? *Hint:* See inside cover for a list.

39. Some people prefer to use nondairy creamer rather than cream or milk. Some but not all nondairy creamers use coconut oil derivatives to replace the butterfat in cream. Is a person trying to reduce dietary saturated fats wise to use nondairy creamers such as these? Explain.

40. Here is the condensed structural formula for lactic acid: $CH_3CH(OH)COOH$.

   a. Draw a structural formula for lactic acid that shows all the bonds and atoms.

   b. If considered as a fatty acid, would lactic acid be saturated or unsaturated?

   c. Is lactic acid a fatty acid? Explain.

41. A mother wanting to serve her family healthy nutritious foods made these two comments about milk. Evaluate the accuracy of each.

    a. "Milk contains a lot of sugar. Because of this, I don't serve it all that often."

    b. "Different types of milk—whole, 2%, and skim—contain different amounts of sugar. You need to check the labels carefully to be sure what you are getting."

42. Low-Calorie and zero-Calorie substitutes have been developed for fat ("fake fats" such as Olean) and sugar (sucralose and aspartame). Why aren't comparable zero-Calorie substitutes for protein being developed? Even so, some protein substitutes exist. Which groups of people might choose them?

43. Your friend wants to cut food costs and has learned that peanut butter is a good protein source. What additional information should your friend consider before eating peanut butter as a major dietary protein source? *Hint:* See Table 11.1.

44. Here is the composition of a fast-food meal. Do calculations to determine whether the meal meets the guideline that 8–10% of total Calories should come from saturated fats.

	Cheeseburger	French Fries	Shake
Calories	330	540	360
Calories from fat	130	230	80
total fat (g)	14	26	9
saturated fat (g)	6	4.5	6
cholesterol (mg)	45	0	40
sodium (mg)	830	350	250
carbohydrates (g)	38	68	60
sugars (g)	7	0	54
proteins (g)	15	8	11

45. American diets depend heavily on bread and other wheat products. A slice of whole wheat bread (36 g) contains approximately 1.5 g of fat (with 0 g saturated fat), 17 g of carbohydrate (with about 1 g of sugar), and 3 g of protein.

    a. Calculate the total Calorie content in a slice of this bread.

    b. Calculate the percent of Calories from fat.

    c. Do you consider bread a highly nutritious food? Explain your reasoning.

46. Describe three ways in which agriculture is connected to the use of fossil fuels.

47. Ethanol is an example of a biofuel.

    a. From which macronutrient does it originate: fats, carbohydrates, or proteins?

    b. Name two foods now used to produce ethanol for vehicles.

    c. By what process is the ethanol produced from these foods?

    d. Describe one of the current controversies in producing ethanol.

48. Biodiesel is another example of a biofuel. Answer the same questions for biodiesel that were asked in Question 47 about ethanol.

Exploring Extensions

49. Revisit the definition of sustainability provided in Chapter 0. Pick any one of the challenges of food production, discussing how this challenge connects to feeding the world sustainably now and in the future.

50. This chapter (together with Chapter 4) provided data for ethanol production through 2012. Use the resources of the Internet to update this information, particularly in regard to ethanol feedstocks, the energy required to produce ethanol, and how well producing ethanol meets the Triple Bottom Line (TBL). *Hint:* Revisit Chapter 0 for how the TBL is used to assess economic, environmental, and societal benefits.

51. Estimate your average yearly intake in grams of sugar from soft drinks, listing the assumptions you made in arriving at this estimate. By what amount (in grams) would this estimate increase if you included the sugar you added to beverages such as coffee and tea?

52. Here is information about the sugar content of different foods.

Food Product	Sugar	Calories	Serving Size
Altoids, peppermint	2 g	10	3 pieces (2 g)
Ginger snaps	9 g	120	4 cookies (28 g)
Critic's Choice Tomato Ketchup	3 g	15	1 tbsp (13 g)
Del Monte Pineapple Cup	13 g	50	Individual cup (113 g)
Dr Pepper soft drink	40 g	150	1.5 cups
French Vanilla Coffee Mate	5 g	40	1 tbsp (15 mL)
Hostess Twinkies	14 g	150	1.5 ounces
LifeSavers, Wint O Green	15 g	60	4 mints (16 g)
Tropicana HomeStyle Orange Juice	22 g	110	8 ounces (1 cup)
Snickers bar	29 g	200	2.1 ounces
Sunkist orange soda	52 g	190	1.5 cups
Wheatables crackers	4 g	130	13 crackers (29 g)

a. Examine this list. Which item has the highest ratio of grams of sugar to the number of Calories (g sugar/Cal) in one serving?

b. The sugar content of some of these foods may surprise you. If so, which ones?

c. Do you predict that the type(s) of sugar found in Dr Pepper would be the same as those found in Sunkist orange soda? In the orange juice or in the pineapple cup? Explain.

d. The complete label for Wint O Green Lifesavers shows 16 g of total carbohydrates per serving, 15 g of which is sugars. What might account for the other 1 g of carbohydrates?

53. A yellow packet of Splenda sugar substitute contains the compound sucralose. Use the resources of the Internet to answer these questions.

a. How many Calories does a packet of Splenda contain?

b. Splenda's slogan is "Made from Sugar, So It Tastes Like Sugar." Does it appear to you to be a helpful statement or misleading advertising? Explain your point of view.

54. Use the lock-and-key model discussed in Section 10.5 to offer a possible explanation as to why individuals who suffer from lactose intolerance can digest sugars such as sucrose and maltose, but not lactose. Use the resources of the Internet to find the structure of lactose.

55. Consider this structural formula for one of the forms of vitamin K.

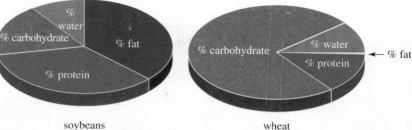

a. Do you expect it to be water-soluble or fat-soluble? Explain.

b. What role does vitamin K play in your body?

c. People rarely, if ever, experience vitamin K deficiencies. Propose a reason why.

56. Compare these two pie charts for the percentage of macronutrients in soybeans and wheat.

soybeans   wheat

a. Explain why the World Health Organization has helped develop soy rather than wheat-based food products for distribution in parts of the world where protein deficiency is a problem.

b. Suggest cultural reasons why soy might be preferable to wheat in some areas of the world.

57. Nature holds some surprises! An avocado is a tropical fruit; in fact, it is a fruit with a high fat content. However, this fat differs from the type found in coconut or palm oil. What is the primary type of fat found in avocados? How does this fat compare to tropical oils (coconut and palm) in terms of its effects on your health?

58. Let's say that an organization wanted to recognize the "Unnatural Food or Beverage of the Year." List the criteria by which you would judge nominations. From your own experiences with food and beverages, suggest two possible candidates. Explain the reasoning behind your choices.

59. Let's say your food is transported from another region by a truck powered with a diesel engine. Name three emissions in the exhaust that may accompany this form of transportation (depending on the pollution control devices installed) and one that always does.

60. Some view climate change and food security as "the twin grand challenges" that we face today. Name two ways in which these challenges connect to each other.

12 Genetic Engineering and the Molecules of Life

"No branch of science has created more acute or more subtle and interesting ethical dilemmas than genetics. . . . it is genetics that makes us recall, not simply our responsibilities to the world and to one another, but our responsibilities for how people will be in the future. For the first time we can begin to determine not simply who will live and who will die, but what all those in the future will be like."

Justine Burley and John Harris, Eds. *Companion to Genethics,* 2002.

A DNA sculpture becomes an intersection of art, science, and play. Lawrence Hall of Science, Berkeley, CA.

Have you thought of a future in which your food was tastier and more nutritious? Or have you considered a future in which growing crops was easier and yields were higher? Imagine a world in which our fields produce better biofuels, our farms create our drugs and vaccines, and our bacteria clean our wastewater.

Geneticists may have the power to create this utopia. Advocates of genetic engineering argue that by using our knowledge of genetics, we can solve world hunger, produce less expensive drugs, and have a cleaner environment. But is tampering with genes worth the risks? Opponents point to superbugs, super-resistant weeds, and a sharp decrease in the biodiversity of the planet. Our actions may take us far from utopia.

In part, the debate over genetic engineering stems from the complexities of the science involved. If a single cell is complex, whole organisms are *really* complex, and ecosystems are complex beyond description. If we make a microscopic genetic change in one seed, we may solve a problem, perhaps even a global problem. But that small change may create additional unforeseen changes in entire ecosystems. The bottom line is that it is difficult to predict the consequences of our actions, especially in the genetic arena.

But the debate also stems from social and ethical concerns. We humans have a responsibility to act wisely, both for current and future generations. A reasonable premise on which to decide whether to act or not to act is to "do no harm." But our needs are great and our societal problems are pressing. Therefore we must also consider whether our *inaction* might result in more harm than good. What are your thoughts about genetic engineering and, more specifically, about genetically modified or "GM" food? The next activity allows you to explore and record your point of view.

Consider This 12.1   Your Opinion of GM Foods

One way or another, you probably have heard of GM (genetically modified) food. Even if you have very little knowledge, you still may be able to answer these questions.

a. Given a choice between a GM food and one that was not, do you have a preference as to which one you would eat? Explain.

b. What circumstances, if any, would cause you to rethink your point of view? List at least two. Save your answers so that you can revisit them at the end of the chapter.

This chapter is about the chemistry of life. Can we and should we control this chemistry? If so, to what extent and with which safeguards in place? Once again, we can offer you good questions, but not always simple or immediately satisfying answers.

12.1 | Stronger and Better Corn Plants?

Ours is a wet planet. Oceans, rivers, lakes, and ice cover over 70% of our planet's surface. This leaves less than a third of the surface for the forests, grasslands, deserts, mountains, and fields that we know as land. Recent satellite data tell us that about 40% of this land is farmed. Why have we converted forests and grasslands to farm fields? In large part, we do this to feed a hungry planet.

For example, we grow crops such as wheat, corn, soybeans, potatoes, and rice. In this section, we'll focus on corn. Many of us consume it in large amounts both directly and indirectly—directly via products such as high-fructose corn syrup, corn meal, or cornstarch; indirectly by eating corn-fed animals. In addition, corn continues to be an important commodity for nonedible products such as bio-based ethanol and plastics. In an attempt to find better and easier-to-grow corn, scientists have genetically modified it. The same is true for soybeans, tomatoes, potatoes, cotton, and papayas, as

See Chapter 5 for a thorough discussion of our wet planet.

In 1700, less than 10% of the land was used for agriculture.

Corn was first cultivated in the Americas, perhaps as many as 7000 years ago.

495

(a)

(b)

Figure 12.1

(a) A cornfield, not quite as uniform as it may appear. (b) A European corn borer busily at work.

all of these exist in genetically modified forms for one reason or another. Here we consider the desire behind the genetic modification of corn.

To get started, examine Figure 12.1a. A cornfield is never simply a field of corn plants, although it may appear so. Rather, cornfields are small unbalanced ecosystems. From the perspective of the corn plant, the cornfield is home, a place with nutrients in the soil, the sunshine above, and lots of water. From the perspective of the weeds, the cornfield is a clear stretch of fertile land ready to be taken over. The weeds grow quickly, take up the nutrients, and some may block the sunlight. From the perspective of the insects, a cornfield is a nice home, an incubator for the young, and a very tasty meal (Figure 12.1b). Many insects have evolved to take advantage of the cornfields we plant.

If the corn is to grow and thrive, farmers must expend time, effort, money, and fuel to actively nurture the plants and protect them against insects and weeds. In the process, they may inadvertently damage ecosystems, both locally and further down the watershed. For example, consider what happens when farmers spray insecticides and herbicides to control insects and weeds. Using pesticides not only is expensive, but also, without enough care in the choice or application, these chemicals may damage the plants and the surrounding ecosystem. The combination of expense and trouble for the farmer coupled with environmental risk seems difficult to justify, but growing corn is extremely profitable. It is sold for use as food, animal fodder, or biofuel. With such a wide range of applications, we are unlikely to see an end to corn farms. Clearly, everybody would benefit if growing corn were easier and less harmful to the environment.

What do you remember about corn from previous chapters? This next activity may help jog your memory.

> Recall the green chemistry key idea: It is better to design materials that degrade into innocuous products at the end of their useful life. Many pesticides fail to meet this criterion.

Your Turn 12.2   Corn Chemistry

a. As mentioned in Chapter 4, starch is a carbohydrate found in corn kernels. Cellulose also forms part of the leaves of corn plants. Explain the relationship among these terms: starch, glucose, carbohydrate, cellulose.

b. As mentioned in Chapter 11, corn oil is a triglyceride, one with a high degree of unsaturation. Explain the relationship among these terms: fat, oil, unsaturated, saturated, triglyceride.

What if you could offer farmers a bag of seed to grow corn plants that are resistant to insects and weeds? Well, it turns out that you can. Two very common genetic modifications in corn can provide the farmer with a crop that is resistant to both insects, such as the European corn borer or Western corn rootworm, and an herbicide, such as Roundup. The corn plant produces its own insecticide, allowing the farmer to spray less pesticide. And the corn plant is resistant to one general herbicide, meaning the farmer can spray that herbicide rather than others that deposit more toxins in the watershed.

How can we get the corn plant to resist the herbicide or produce its own insecticide? We do this by "teaching" it to make some new chemicals. Inside each cell of the corn plant is the complete set of instructions, a guidebook if you like, on how to grow and reproduce. The guidebook passes from one generation to the next, often completely unchanged. This guidebook, termed the **genome,** is the primary route for inheriting the biological information required to build and maintain an organism.

The genome is divided into short sections of instructions to produce specific reactions, chemicals, or events in the cell. These specific pieces are the basic units of heredity, **genes,** short pieces of the genome that code for the production of proteins. A change within a gene changes an inheritable trait. For a corn plant, a change in the gene for color may switch the corn kernels from light yellow to white. But small changes within a gene are not enough to make the plant produce peas instead of corn or even to produce a new chemical, such as an insecticide. We need a more dramatic change.

What we really need to do is to insert a whole new set of instructions (that is, a gene) in the genome of the corn plant. Rather than create these instructions ourselves, we search for another organism that already has the instructions we want. For the European corn borer (Figure 12.1b) and Western corn rootworm, our search brings us to a protein that is toxic to these insects but is considered safe for humans. The protein occurs naturally and can even be used in organic agriculture. A group of small organisms, a soil bacterium called *Bacillus thuringiensis,* already has the instructions to make this protein. By taking a gene out of the bacterium and inserting it into the corn plant, we create corn plants that can produce an insecticidal protein.

The most common strain of corn, B73, contains over 32,000 genes in its genome, more genes than are in human DNA. Researchers spent four years cataloging the massive amount of information so that we may understand the genes behind beneficial traits, such as higher yields and disease or drought resistance.

Often called *Bt*, these bacteria produce *Bt* toxins, a wide variety of proteins that are toxic to different insects.

Your Turn 12.3   Proteins and Carbohydrates

a. We just used the term *insecticidal protein*. What is a protein? Describe the features of a protein molecule. *Hint:* You can review proteins in Sections 9.7 and 11.7.
b. What is a carbohydrate? Corn primarily is composed of carbohydrates. Describe carbohydrates at a molecular level.

The corn plant, the bacterium, and the cornfield are more complex than you might think. What exactly are we modifying when we genetically modify something? We turn to this topic in the next section.

12.2 | A Chemical That Codes Life

With each passing second, the corn plant is host to millions of chemical reactions. Some of these reactions decompose compounds, others synthesize them. Some reactions transfer chemical signals, others process them. Some reactions release energy, others utilize it. One very special chemical lies at the heart of this dazzling chemical complexity.

We require a lot from this very special chemical. As cells grow and multiply, this chemical must replicate itself without error. It must remain largely unharmed and unchanged by its environment. This one chemical must organize and securely store a lot of information. This information is context-sensitive, as some reactions are always going; others start and stop depending on specific signals. In short, we need a highly advanced database in chemical form.

The chemical we have just described is **deoxyribonucleic acid, or DNA,** the biological polymer that carries genetic information in all species. DNA is the template of life, containing all of the biochemical information to make a full corn plant. DNA can replicate easily, transfer information, and respond to feedback within the cell.

Like the corn plant, you have a special template of life written on a tightly coiled thread of DNA. Unraveled, the DNA in *each* of your cells is about 2 meters (roughly 2 yards) long. If all of the DNA in all 100 trillion of your cells were placed end to end, the resulting ribbon would stretch from here to the Sun and back, more than 600 times! But as you will soon discover, this astronomical figure is far from the most astounding feature of this amazing molecule.

Any strand of DNA—long or short—consists of three fundamental chemical units: nitrogen-containing bases, deoxyribose sugars, and phosphate groups. All are illustrated in Figure 12.2.

DNA contains not one nitrogen-containing base, but four. Each one differs slightly from the others. The larger bases, adenine (A) and guanine (G), have a six-membered ring and a five-membered ring of atoms fused together. The smaller bases, cytosine (C) and thymine (T), have only a six-membered ring. Notice that all of these compounds have nitrogen atoms embedded in their rings, leading to the name "nitrogen-containing bases." These bases also contain oxygen atoms that can participate in hydrogen bonding, as we will see in Your Turn 12.4.

The estimates for the number of cells in your body range from 50 to 100 trillion. The bacterial cells outnumber the human cells by an estimated 10 times.

Revisit Section 6.2 to review our first nitrogen–containing base, ammonia.

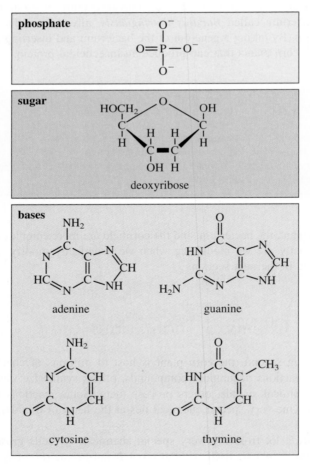

Figure 12.2

The components of deoxyribonucleic acid, DNA.

 Figures Alive!

Your Turn 12.4   Small But Important Differences

The size or number of rings is not the only difference between the nitrogen–containing bases. Let's examine each of the four bases more closely.

a. Draw Lewis structures for each of the four bases. Be sure to show the lone pairs of electrons on the nitrogen and oxygen atoms.
b. Identify the H atoms that could form hydrogen bonds.
c. Now identify the other (non–hydrogen) atoms that could participate in hydrogen bonding. *Hint:* Revisit Section 5.2 for information on hydrogen bonds.

Answers

For the base thymine (see Figure 12.2):

a. The Lewis structure shows lone pairs of electrons on two N atoms and on two O atoms.
b. Both of the H atoms attached to the N atoms could form hydrogen bonds.
c. Both O and N atoms could participate in hydrogen bonding. Look ahead to Figure 12.7.

DNA molecules also are built from sugar molecules. Unlike the nitrogen-containing bases in DNA, only one sugar is present, deoxyribose. Deoxyribose is a monosaccharide, a "single sugar," with chemical formula of $C_5H_{10}O_4$ (see Figure 12.2). The next activity gives you the opportunity to learn more about this sugar.

Monosaccharides were introduced in Section 11.5.

Consider This 12.5   Chemical Cousins: Ribose and Deoxyribose

Ribose is a close molecular cousin to deoxyribose. It is the monosaccharide found in ribonucleic acid (RNA). Compare the structural formula of deoxyribose (see Figure 12.2) with that of ribose:

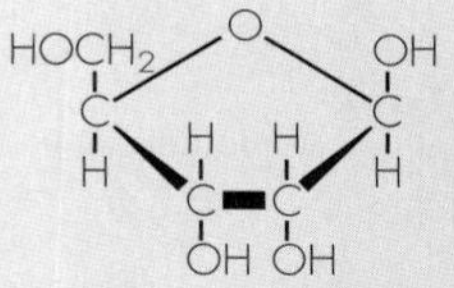

a. Give the chemical formula for each sugar.
b. How do the structural formulas of these two sugars differ?
c. Carbohydrates are compounds that typically have the chemical formula $C_nH_{2n}O_n$, as noted in Section 11.5. Do both ribose and deoxyribose fit this pattern?
d. In these two sugar molecules, which atoms have lone pairs of electrons that can form hydrogen bonds? *Hint:* See Section 5.2 for a review of hydrogen bonding.

In addition to a nitrogen-containing base and a sugar, DNA molecules also contain the phosphate group, in essence, a phosphate ion that has become attached. However, depending on the pH, phosphate may be in the form of HPO_4^{2-} or $H_2PO_4^-$. If three of the oxygen atoms in the phosphate are paired with H^+, the chemical form is H_3PO_4, or phosphoric acid. These hydrogen ions make nucleic acids acidic.

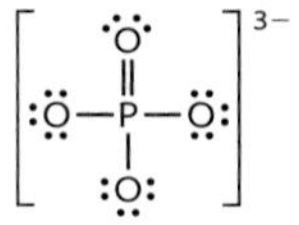

All three of the fundamental chemical units, the nitrogen-containing base, the sugar, and the phosphate group, have a valuable role to play in the structure of DNA. Joined together, these three pieces make up one monomer that in turn polymerizes to form DNA. Each monomer is called a **nucleotide,** that is, a covalently bonded combination of a base, a deoxyribose molecule, and a phosphate group. For example, Figure 12.3 shows the nucleotide named adenine phosphate. You can see that the sugar is bonded both to the phosphate group and to the base (adenine). Similar nucleotides can be formed using the other three nitrogen-containing bases of DNA: guanine, cytosine, and thymine.

Note in Figure 12.3 that one −OH on the deoxyribose ring remains available to react. It does so with the phosphate group of another nucleotide. A condensation reaction

The phosphate ion was introduced in Chapter 5. Here is one of its resonance structures.

Recall from Chapter 9 that polymers are big molecules made up from small monomers.

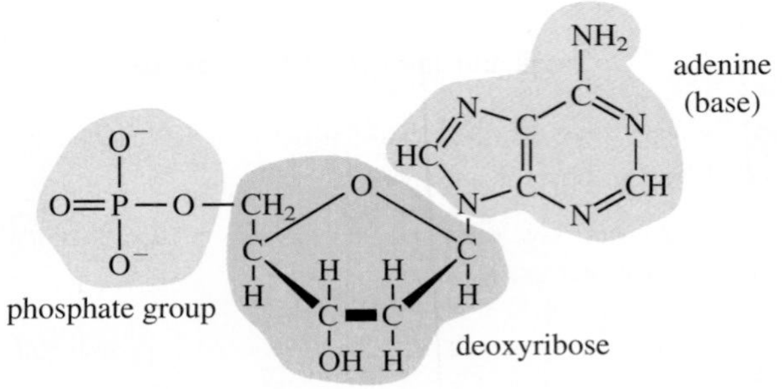

Figure 12.3

A nucleotide monomer built from a phosphate group, deoxyribose (a sugar), and adenine (a base).

occurs, thereby connecting the two nucleotides. If this happens repeatedly between nucleotides, the result is a long chain with an alternating sugar–phosphate backbone, better known as DNA. A typical DNA molecule consists of thousands of nucleotides. Consequently, a single strand of DNA may have a molecular mass in the millions.

The joining of nucleotides (monomers) to form the DNA polymer is an example of a condensation polymerization. The polymer increases in length as more and more nucleotides are joined, each time splitting out a water molecule. Figure 12.4 shows four nucleotides that have been linked in this manner to form a segment of DNA. The schematic drawing in the inset of Figure 12.4 shows the polymeric nature of DNA in which the monomers are the nucleotides.

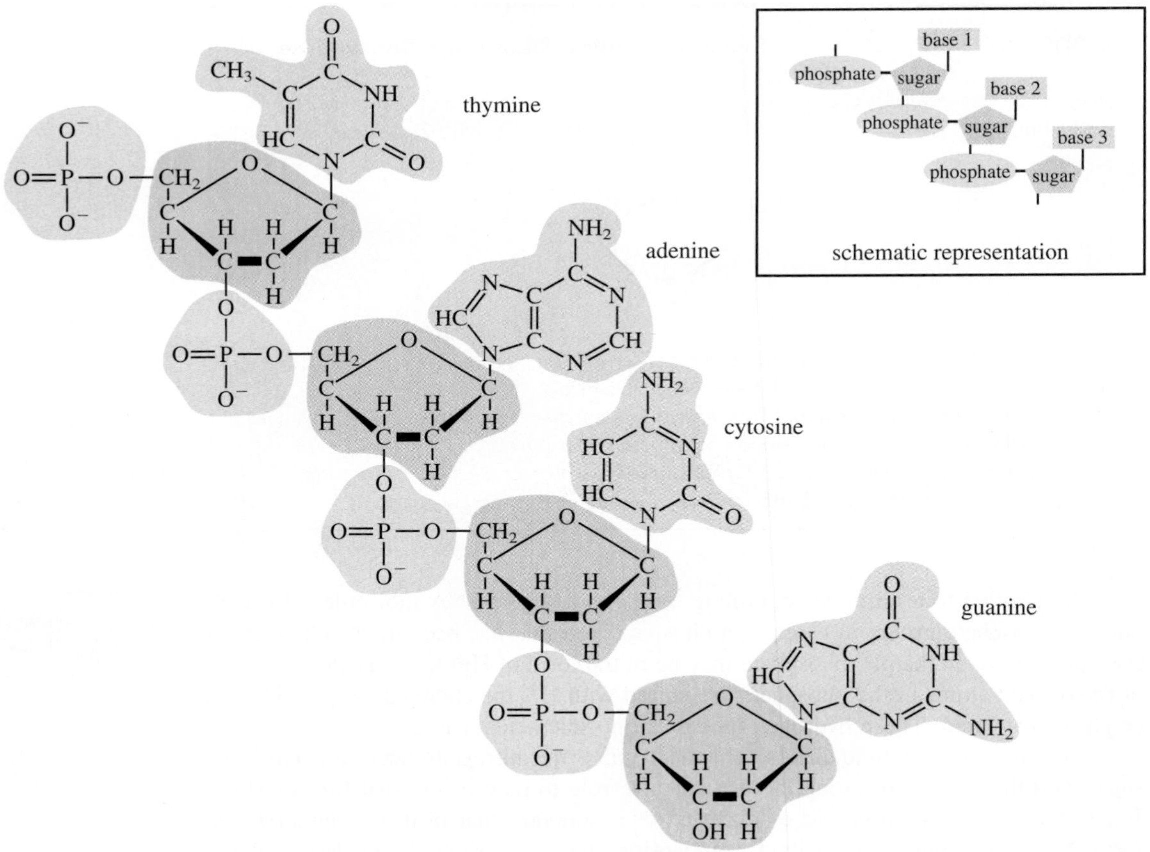

See Sections 9.6 and 9.7 for other examples of condensation polymerization.

Figure 12.4

A segment of DNA represented chemically and schematically (insert). The phosphate group connects one deoxyribose to an adjacent one. Each of the four bases, thymine (T), adenine (A), cytosine (C), or guanine (G), is attached to a deoxyribose sugar.

 Figures Alive!

Your Turn 12.6   Another Nucleotide

Analogous to Figure 12.3, draw the structural formula for the nucleotide containing cytosine.

12.3 | The Double Helix of DNA

DNA is a gorgeous molecule. If you look at the opening photos of this chapter, you find a sculptor's rendition of DNA with two silvery strands curving in a gentle spiral, both elegant and simple. Hidden within the structural simplicity is a powerful chemical code for information. The structure, both how the nucleotides are covalently bonded and how the strands pack together, contributes to the function of DNA. Understanding how DNA performs its many functions required solving the puzzle of the DNA structure.

To see the shape and submicroscopic details of DNA, scientists turned to the technique of X-ray diffraction. This technique has revolutionized our understanding of molecular structures and chemistry by helping us visualize chemical shapes. **X-ray diffraction** is an analytical technique in which a crystal is hit by a beam of X-rays to generate a pattern that reveals the positions of the atoms in the crystal. The X-ray photons interact with the electrons of the atoms in the crystal and are diffracted, or scattered. The crucial point is that the X-rays are only scattered at certain angles that are related to the distance between atoms, and that information can be used to determine the structures of a wide variety of crystalline materials. The X-ray diffraction pattern of a DNA fiber was obtained in late 1952 by the British crystallographer Rosalind Franklin (Figure 12.5).

James Watson and Francis Crick (see Figure 12.5) combined Franklin's X-ray diffraction data with earlier chemical and biological analyses to create a model of the structure of DNA. The pattern in Franklin's diffraction photograph was consistent with a repeating helical arrangement of atoms, similar to a loosely coiled spring. Moreover, the X-ray photographs contained evidence of a repeated pattern separated by 0.34 nm within a DNA molecule. The Watson–Crick model explained this repetition by twisting the strands of DNA into a **double helix,** a spiral consisting of two strands that coil

Return to Section 2.4 to find X-rays on the electromagnetic spectrum.

(a)   (b)   (c)   (d)

Figure 12.5

James Watson (a), Francis Crick (b), and Maurice Wilkins (c) shared the 1962 Nobel Prize in Physiology or Medicine for their contributions to the structural understanding of DNA. Though crystallography data from Rosalind Franklin (d) was vital, she died in 1958 and was not eligible for the Nobel Prize in 1962.

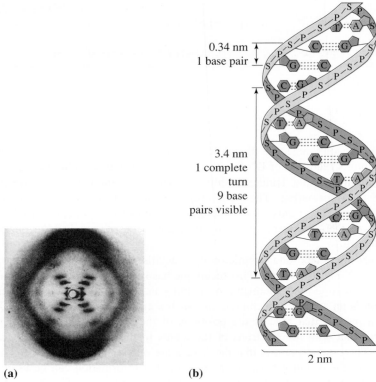

0.34 nm
1 base pair

3.4 nm
1 complete
turn
9 base
pairs visible

2 nm

(a)   **(b)**

Figure 12.6

(a) Rosalind Franklin's X–ray diffraction photo of a hydrated DNA fiber. The cross in the center is indicative of a helical structure, and the darkened arcs at the top and bottom are due to the stack of base pairs. **(b)** A model of DNA with P = phosphate group; S = the sugar, deoxyribose; and the bases A = adenine; T = thymine; C = cytosine; G = guanine. The sugar and phosphate groups alternate on the backbone, and the four bases attach to this backbone.

around a central axis as shown in Figure 12.6. The base pairs are parallel to each other, perpendicular to the axis of the DNA molecule, and separated by 0.34 nm, the same distance calculated from the diffraction pattern. In addition, Franklin's results also suggested a second repetition pattern separated by 3.4 nm. Watson and Crick took this to be the length of a complete helical turn consisting of 10 base pairs.

The letters in our English words have directionality. For example, the words *ward* and *draw* have the same letters in the same order, but the meaning is different because the direction is different. The same is true of the DNA polymer, with the bases being analogous to letters. For example, the base string TAC does not have the same meaning as CAT. The structure of the DNA backbone defines the directionality. Look carefully at the alternating phosphate and deoxyribose groups in the DNA backbone (see Figure 12.4) to see how the deoxyribose ring connects directly to the phosphate below it, and the one above it links through another carbon. The different types of chemical bonds make one direction different from the other. When the two strands of the DNA double helix come together, one strand must run in the opposite direction from the other.

Early chemical analyses showed that the nitrogen-containing bases in DNA come in pairs. No matter the species, the percent of A almost exactly equals the percent of T (Table 12.1). Similarly, the percent of G is essentially identical to the percent of C. The structural model of DNA validated these rules. Adenine and thymine bases fit almost perfectly together, like pieces in a jigsaw puzzle. A closer look shows these two bases linked by two hydrogen bonds (Figure 12.7). Similarly, cytosine and guanine are linked by three hydrogen bonds. This base pairing is the molecular basis underlying both the structure and much of the function of DNA. To repeat: A pairs with T, and G pairs with C.

Palindromes are the exception and can be read in either direction. For example, the word RACECAR reads the same in either direction.

The base pairing rules are termed *Chargaff's rules* after the discoverer, Austrian chemist Erwin Chargaff.

Table 12.1	The Percent Base Compositions of DNA for Various Species				
Scientific Name	Common Name	Adenine	Thymine	Guanine	Cytosine
Homo sapiens	human	31.0	31.5	19.1	18.4
Drosophila melanogaster	fruit fly	27.3	27.6	22.5	22.5
Zea mays	corn	25.6	25.3	24.5	24.6
Neurospora crassa	mold	23.0	23.3	27.1	26.6
Escherichia coli	bacterium	24.6	24.3	25.5	25.6
Bacillus subtilis	bacterium	28.4	29.0	21.0	21.6

Source: From I. Edward Alcamo, DNA Technology: The Awesome Skill, 2E © 2000 McGraw-Hill Education.

Your Turn 12.7   Complementary Base Sequences

Adenine and thymine are said to be complementary bases. So are cytosine and guanine. In both cases, the bases form hydrogen bonds when they pair. Using one–letter codes, write out the base sequences that are complementary to each of these codes.

a. ATACCTGC   b. GATCCTA

Answer
a. TATGGACG

The structure of DNA and the puzzle-piece pairing of its nucleotides inspired another vital discovery. One side of the DNA strand contains all the information required to generate its partner strand! Thus a single strand of DNA can guide the generation of its complement. **Replication** is the process of cell reproduction in which the cell must copy and transmit its genetic information to its progeny. The process is well understood and is diagrammed in Figure 12.8.

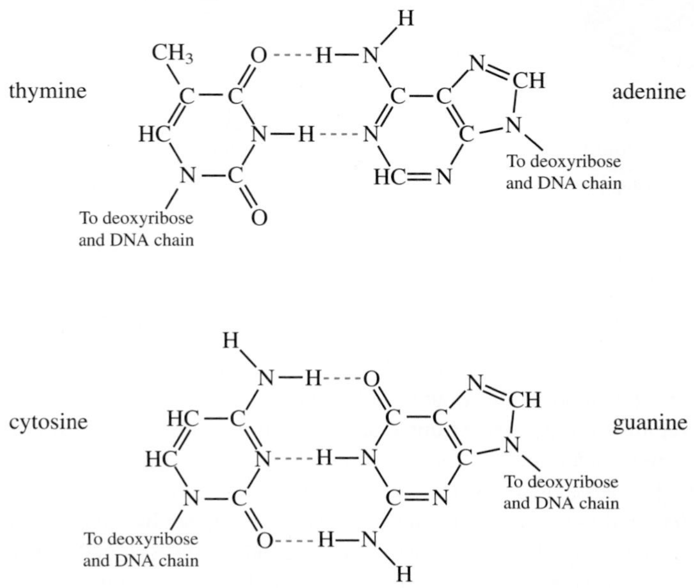

Figure 12.7

Base pairing of adenine with thymine and cytosine with guanine in DNA. Chemical bonds are solid black lines, and the hydrogen bonds are dashed red lines.

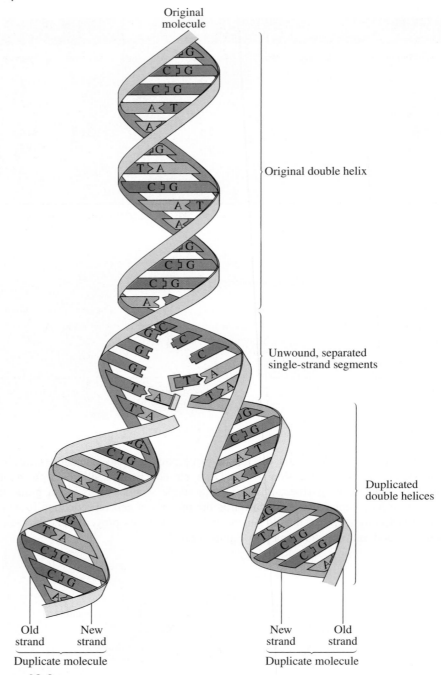

Figure 12.8

 Diagram of DNA replication. The original DNA double helix (*top portion of figure*) partially unwinds, and the two complementary portions separate (*middle*). Each of the strands serves as a template for the synthesis of a complementary strand (*bottom*). The result is two complete and identical DNA molecules. See Figures Alive!

Before a cell divides, the double helix rapidly, but only partially, unwinds. This results in a region of separated strands of DNA, as pictured in the middle portion of Figure 12.8. Free nucleotides in the cell are selectively hydrogen-bonded to these two single strands that serve as templates for a new DNA molecule: A to T, T to A, C to G, and G to C. Held in these positions, the nucleotides bond together by the action of an enzyme, a biological catalyst. By this mechanism, each strand of the original DNA generates a complementary copy of itself. The original strand and its newly synthesized complement coil to form a new molecule identical to the first. Similarly, the other separated strand of the original molecule twines around its new partner, forming another duplicate molecule. Thus, where there was originally one double helix, now there are two identical copies.

Return to Section 10.4 to review enzymes.

Consider This 12.8   A Gorgeous Molecule

Revisit the photograph that opens the chapter. It shows a sculpture of DNA that people can climb on. As a piece of art, it represents some parts of the DNA molecule better than others.

a. List three disadvantages of this DNA representation. What chemical details are omitted? What information is lost?
b. Now list three advantages. What information is highlighted? What is gained?
c. Find another artistic rendition of DNA, possibly on your campus or on the Internet, and repeat parts a and b. Cite your sources.

Consider This 12.9   DNA Sequence Repair

Remember from Section 12.2, DNA must be copied and copied perfectly. After replication, enzymes scan over strands of DNA to identify and correct errors in base pairing.

ATGCCATGAA
TACGGTATTT

a. Find the error in base pairing for this set of DNA strands and circle it.
b. Do you expect the mismatched strands to be more or less stable than a correct pair? Explain your reasoning.

See Figures Alive!

In most organisms, the newly copied DNA does not remain extended as a double helix but becomes coiled even further. This not only saves space, but also it further organizes and protects the genetic information. The coiling is carefully regulated so that small portions of DNA can be accessed when specific stored information is needed. This complete set of genetic information is packaged into **chromosomes,** rod-shaped, compact coils of DNA and specialized proteins packed in the nucleus of cells.

Your Turn 12.10   Is Your DNA Doin' the Twist?

The distance between base pairs in the double helix structure of DNA is 0.34 nm.

a. Calculate the length in centimeters (cm) of human chromosome 11 when extended in a double helix. *Hint:* Chromosome 11 consists of 135,000,000 base pairs.
b. Chromosomes can be visualized best immediately before cell division. In this compact state, the longest axis of chromosome 11 is approximately 4 μm. By what factor has the DNA been further condensed? *Hint:* 1 μm is 1×10^{-6} m.
c. Suggest a reason why this level of compaction is necessary. *Hint:* A typical human cell is only 10 μm in diameter.

Answer

a. $$\frac{0.34 \text{ nm}}{1 \text{ base pair}} \times \frac{1 \text{ m}}{1 \times 10^9 \text{ nm}} \times \frac{1 \times 10^2 \text{ cm}}{1 \text{ m}} \times \frac{1.35 \times 10^8 \text{ base pairs}}{\text{chromosome 11}} = \frac{4.6 \text{ cm}}{\text{chromosome 11}}$$

Every time a cell splits to reproduce, the complete set of chromosomes must be uncoiled and replicated perfectly so that each new cell contains an identical set. Some cell types, such as those in the skin and in a cancerous tumor, divide more rapidly than others. These cells are more susceptible to collecting and passing on DNA damaged by ionizing radiation, free radicals, or chemical agents.

Return to Chapter 7 to review ionizing radiation and Chapter 2 to review free radicals.

12.4 | Cracking the Chemical Code

Remember all of the complex chemistry happening in your cells every minute—the molecule of DNA organizes a lot of information. The billions of base pairs repeated in every corn cell provide the blueprint for producing one corn plant. The base pairs are ordered into specific sequences and grouped, sometimes into genes, to code for the production of proteins. Other information is present in the DNA, but our understanding of how it is used is in its infancy.

Although the information is carried in DNA, it is expressed in other, smaller, molecules. The best understood are proteins. Proteins are found throughout our bodies, in skin, muscle, hair, blood, and the thousands of enzymes that regulate the chemistry of life. By directing the synthesis of proteins, DNA can dictate many of the characteristics of the organism.

Section 11.7 defined proteins in the context of the foods we eat. Section 9.7 described proteins as polymers (polypeptides or polyamides).

Proteins are large molecules formed by the linking of amino acids. Recall that the 20 amino acids that commonly occur in proteins can be represented by this general structural formula that we reproduce from Chapter 11.

Refer back to Figure 11.16 in Chapter 11 for more about the general structure of an amino acid.

The amine or amino group is $-NH_2$, the acid group is $-COOH$, and R represents a side chain that is different for each of the 20 amino acids. In a condensation reaction, the $-COOH$ group of one amino acid reacts with the $-NH_2$ group of another. In this process a peptide bond is formed and a molecule of H_2O is formed. When many amino acids are connected, the result is a protein, that is, a polymer built from amino acid monomers. We also can describe a protein as a long chain of amino acid residues. **Amino acid residue** is the term used for an amino acid that has been incorporated into the peptide chain.

The discovery of the molecular code for genetic information arguably is history's most amazing example of cryptography, the science of writing in secret code.

The information in a sequence of DNA nucleotides translates via a code into a sequence of specific amino acids in a protein. The code cannot be a simple one-to-one correlation between bases and amino acids. There are only four bases in DNA. If each base corresponded to an individual amino acid, DNA could encode for only four amino acids. But 20 amino acids appear in our proteins. Therefore, the DNA code must consist of at least 20 distinct code "words," each word representing a different amino acid. And the words must be selected from a pool of only four letters—A, T, C, and G—or, more accurately, the bases corresponding to those letters.

Some simple statistics can help us determine the minimum length of these code words. To find out how many words of a given length can be made from an alphabet of known size, raise the number of letters available to a power *n,* corresponding to the number of letters per word.

$$\text{words} = (\text{letters})^n$$

For example, using 4 letters to make two-letter words generates 4^2 or 16 different words. Thus, DNA bases taken in pairs (akin to 2 letters per word) could only code for 16 amino acids, insufficient to provide a unique representation for each of the 20 amino acids. So we repeat the calculation and assume that the code is based on 3 sequential bases or, if you prefer, three-letter words. Now the number of different triplet-base combinations is 4^3, or $4 \times 4 \times 4 = 64$. This system provides more than enough capacity to do the job.

Your Turn 12.11   Quadruplet–Base Code

Suppose that the DNA code used four sequential base pairs instead of a triplet–base code. How many different four–base sequences would result?

Answer
$4 \times 4 \times 4 \times 4 = 4^4 = 256$ different four–base sequences

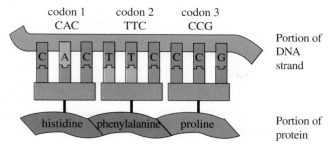

Figure 12.9

A nine–base nucleic acid sequence showing three codons.

The three letter groupings of nucleotides are the basis of the information transfer from DNA to proteins. Each grouping, or **codon,** is a sequence of three adjacent nucleotides that either guides the insertion of a specific amino acid or signals the start or end of protein synthesis. If you were to use the letters A, T, C, and G in a game of Scrabble, you could generate 64 different three-letter combinations. A few, CAT, TAG, and ACT, for example, make sense. Most are like AGC, TCT, and GGG and are meaningless—at least in English. Nature does far better than that; 61 of the 64 possible triplet codons specify amino acids. Thus, the codon sequence CAC in a DNA molecule signals that a molecule of the amino acid histidine should be incorporated into the protein, TTC codes for phenylalanine, and CCG stands for proline. The three-base sequences that do not correspond to amino acids are signals to stop the synthesis of the protein chain. An example of a nine-base nucleic acid segment and how it codes for three amino acids is shown in Figure 12.9.

Our calculations showed that three-letter groupings are the minimum necessary to cover the 20 amino acids, but did not show us how all 64 codons are used. The code has redundancy. Many amino acids have more than one codon. For example, leucine, serine, and arginine have six codons each. Also, three different codons tell protein synthesis to "stop." On the other hand, two amino acids (tryptophan and methionine) and the signal to start protein synthesis are represented by only a single codon.

Your Turn 12.12   Duplicate Codons

Suggest some advantages of a genetic code in which several codons represent the same amino acid.

The genetic code is identical in all living things. With only a handful of exceptions, the instructions to make people, bacteria, and trees are written in the same molecular language of those 64 codons. In the genetic code, we have a Rosetta Stone to translate any genetic sequence from any organism. The significance of this statement may not be immediately apparent. Looking back to our original example of genetically modified corn, this Rosetta Stone means that the gene sequence for the *Bt* toxin makes the same bug-destroying protein in the original bacteria *and* in the corn plant.

The markings on the Rosetta Stone were in several languages and helped to decipher Egyptian hieroglyphs.

12.5 | Proteins: Form to Function

Proteins are polymers. Admittedly they don't much resemble the clear polymer PET that may hold your favorite soft drink. Similarly, they don't seem to have much in common with the tough polypropylene that is used to make carpets. But nonetheless, proteins are big molecules built from little ones.

More specifically, proteins are polyamides. Like nylon, they are built by the chemical reaction of carboxylic acids and amines. Unlike nylon, though, a protein is built from 20 different amino acid monomers. Comparing proteins to nylon may leave you with the image of proteins as long strands, rather than complex three-dimensional molecules. This image is far too simple. Proteins exist in a complicated environment—the cell. Just like necklaces in a messy jewelry box, proteins refuse to stay extended and neat. Unlike jewelry, each protein collapses into a unique, and often very specific, three-dimensional form. The final shape may look a mess, but that exact shape is necessary for the chemistry the protein performs in the organism. In Chapter 9, we discussed proteins as polymers. In Chapter 11, we discussed them as nutrients. In this chapter, we discuss the function of proteins and their three-dimensional shapes.

Your Turn 12.13   How is Hamburger Like Nylon?

Take a moment to refresh your knowledge about two polyamides: the nylon from a sports jersey and the protein found in hamburger.

 a. What functional group do nylon and meat proteins have in common?
 b. Nylon is usually synthesized from two types of monomers; in contrast, proteins are synthesized from one type of monomer. What functional group(s) do the monomers for each contain?
 c. Are nylons and proteins addition polymers or condensation polymers?

Answer
 b. Typically, nylon is synthesized by the reaction of a monomer containing two carboxylic acids with a monomer containing two amine groups. For example, refer back to equation 9.7. In contrast, proteins are synthesized from a monomer (an amino acid) that contains one carboxylic acid and one amine group.

We begin our discussion of protein shapes with the **primary structure** of a protein, that is, the unique sequence of the amino acids that make up each protein (Figure 12.10). Primary structure is the first and most basic identifier of a protein, the list of amino acids read over the length of the polymer. Knowing that a short protein contains 3 valines (val), 2 glutamic acids (glu), and 1 histidine (his) may tell you the size and a few other details, but is not sufficient to specify a protein and explore its shape and function. The order and sequence of the amino acids matters. For example, val-glu-val-his-glu-val is a different protein from val-val-val-his-glu-glu. These short peptides behave differently as well!

Recall that each amino acid has a side chain group. This side chain interacts with other side chains or the molecules around and inside of the protein. Side chains can attract and "lock" together, and in so doing, they hold a protein in a particular overall shape. The order and identity of the amino acids defines how and where those side chain links can form. Each amino acid plays a role; changing just one can change the shape and, as a result, the function of a protein.

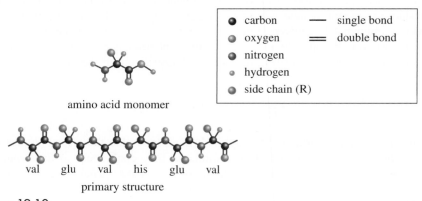

amino acid monomer

●	carbon	—	single bond
●	oxygen	═	double bond
●	nitrogen		
●	hydrogen		
●	side chain (R)		

val   glu   val   his   glu   val
primary structure

Figure 12.10

Representation of the primary structure of a protein.

Luckily, you do not need to memorize all 20 amino acids. We will group the side chains into two categories: polar (either charged or neutral) or nonpolar. Like oil and water, nonpolar and polar side chains tend to separate. In the typical environment for a protein (water), the polar side chains can stay in the water; nonpolar side chains instead group inside of the protein, avoiding unfavorable interactions with water in favor of attractive dispersion forces between the side chains.

Polar side chains can lead to more types of interactions: ionic or hydrogen bonds. Side chains that contain acidic or basic groups (such as carboxylic acids or amines) often become charged ions and attract their opposites to form ionic bonds. Noncharged yet polar side chains often contain hydroxyl groups or amides. Many of these side chains can form hydrogen bonds.

One very special amino acid contains a thiol group (–SH) in its side chain. In proteins, thiol groups perform an important and highly specialized function; namely, a thiol group can react with a second thiol group to form disulfide (S–S) bonds between the sulfur atoms. These strong bonds covalently link two different regions of a protein together. All of these tendencies—the nonpolar side chains grouping together, the polar groups making ionic or hydrogen bonds, and the thiol groups making disulfide bonds—serve to give each sequence of amino acids a unique signature.

We continue our discussion by examining the **secondary structure** of a protein, that is, the folding pattern within a segment of the protein chain. Many, but not all, protein chains form regular, repeating structures from the particular bond angles and attractions between neighboring amino acids. The two most common are the α-helix, a spiraling strand, and the β-pleated sheet, extended strands stretching alongside each other with a slight zigzag.

Both forms of secondary structure depend on the tendency of the protein backbone to form intramolecular hydrogen bonds. Figure 12.11 shows the hydrogen bonds between the backbone O and the N–H of the amide group as dotted lines. The number and regular spacing of these hydrogen bonds can pull together and align a protein strand, stabilizing the secondary structure. The choice of secondary structure, or even the complete lack of it, can be loosely predicted from the primary structure. Some side chains tend to pack well into β-pleated sheets, others tend toward the α-helix, and others even predispose the chain to disorder.

Proteins are large, three-dimensional molecules, but both primary and secondary structures are relatively flat. We need a more "global" description of their shape, the **tertiary structure,** or the overall molecular shape of the protein defined by the interactions between amino acids far apart in sequence, but close in space. If you imagine

Revisit Section 5.1 for more about polar and nonpolar molecules.

Section 9.4 discussed attractive dispersion forces between nonpolar groups in the context of plastics.

The importance of hydrogen bond formation in proteins was first mentioned in Section 5.2

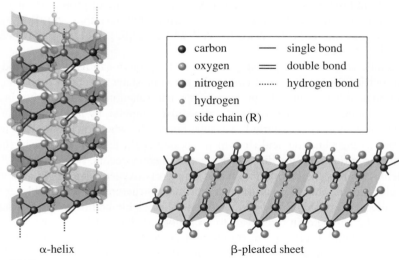

carbon — single bond
oxygen ═ double bond
nitrogen ⋯⋯ hydrogen bond
hydrogen
side chain (R)

α-helix   β-pleated sheet

Figure 12.11

Representations of the secondary structures of a protein. The two major types of secondary structures are the alpha (α)–helix and the beta (β)–pleated sheet.

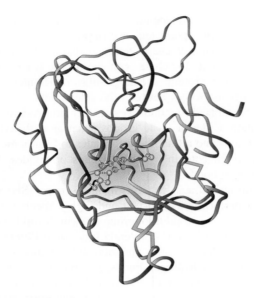

Figure 12.12

Tertiary structure of the enzyme chymotrypsin showing its active site. The "ribbon" portion represents the amino acid chain; the central colored portion is the active site at which the enzymatic chemistry takes place.

a protein as a jumbled charm bracelet, the secondary structure might be the kinks in the chain itself, but the tertiary structure forms from the contact between the Eiffel Tower charm near the clasp and the Statue of Liberty charm near the middle. The overall fold results in a net increase in stability, maintained through hydrogen bonds, ionic bonds, disulfide bonds, and interactions or avoidance of interactions between the side chains and water.

From only 20 amino acids, proteins make a wide variety of shapes and serve a large array of functions. Their three-dimensional shapes are well-suited to the functions. Enzymes catalyze chemical reactions. The shape of enzymes must create an **active site,** the catalytic region, often a crevice, in an enzyme that binds only specific reactants and accelerates the desired reaction (Figure 12.12). Enzymes are the most commonly discussed type of protein, but a number of other examples exist. Some proteins bind DNA, to protect it or send a signal. Again, form suits function. When these proteins fold, they display positively charged side chains to attract and bind the negatively charged DNA. Another type of protein funnels material through the membrane of the cell, forming channels that shuttle a specific chemical across the outer layers of the cell while keeping the cell impermeable to undesirable chemicals.

A subtle change in the primary structure of a protein can have a profound effect on its properties. Notice the word *can* in the previous statement. Sometimes, a change in an amino acid leaves both the protein's shape and function unchanged. For instance, a nonpolar leucine can be switched to a valine, also nonpolar, by just removing a $-CH_3$ group. The protein may be a little less stable, but on the whole the same. But, instead, change the wrong glutamic acid (in which the side chain is often negatively charged) to a nonpolar valine, and the disease sickle-cell anemia occurs.

Hemoglobin is the blood protein that transports oxygen. The single alteration of a particular glutamic acid to valine in the primary structure of hemoglobin creates a variant called hemoglobin S and the condition called sickle-cell disease. This substitution causes the hemoglobin to convert to an abnormal shape at low oxygen concentration, forcing red blood cells to distort into rigid sickle or crescent shapes (Figure 12.13). Because these cells lose their normal flexibility, they cannot pass through the tiny openings of the capillaries in the spleen and other organs. Some of the sickle cells are destroyed and anemia results. Others clog organs so badly that the blood supply to these organs is reduced.

Sickle–cell disease affects a sizable population, over 70,000 individuals in the United States alone, and lowers life expectancy to an average of 40 years.

Capillaries are the smallest vessels in the circulatory system of the blood at only about one red blood cell wide.

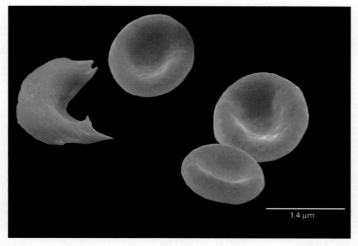

1.4 μm

Figure 12.13

An image from a scanning electron microscope showing both normal red blood cells and those that are distorted into a sickle or crescent shape.

Consider This 12.14   Function Follows Form

In sickle–cell anemia, a glutamic acid residue in the sequence of hemoglobin is replaced with a valine residue.

valine   glutamic acid

a. Describe the structural difference between these two amino acids: valine and glutamic acid.
b. Predict the solubility for each of these amino acids in water.
c. Explain how these differences could give rise to the deformed cells typified by sickle–cell anemia.

12.6 | The Process of Genetic Engineering

We started this chapter with thoughts of utopia; specifically, we dreamt of a perfect corn seed that could resist both herbicides and pests. We noted that this dream may be attainable with genetic engineering. We posed the question "What are we modifying when we genetically modify something?"

By now, we hope you know the answer. We modify the DNA in the cell. If we change the genes, we change the proteins that are synthesized by these genes. Ultimately, we change the chemistry of the cell. As the cell grows and develops, we generate a plant with new characteristics bestowed by different DNA.

Throughout history, humans have manipulated genes. This may surprise you, as you might think that our ability to modify genes has come about only recently. But consider, for example, how we have cultivated plants. We tended to grow ones that carried specific traits, such as a better taste or appearance. The others we rejected. To produce these strains with new and unique traits, we crossbred different strains.

Figure 12.14

Corn's early ancestor, teosinte, below modern ears of corn.

The process took many years, but eventually we "domesticated" plants and created the crops that feed us today. Our crops are so far removed from their wild forbearers that we hardly would recognize them.

Corn is an excellent example. As we noted earlier, corn was native to the Americas. The people native to the region manipulated the genes of the teosinte plant, one that bore seeds on the end of its stalks rather than on the body of the plant, a growth pattern seen in today's corncob (Figure 12.14). Domesticating the teosinte plant led to a food that was both more nutritious and more abundant.

Domesticating a plant is a process of genetic modification. Even without understanding the chemistry, we selected plants with certain sequences of DNA and rejected ones with other sequences. Over time—slowly over time—we encouraged changes in the DNA, allowing one sample of DNA to carry on, spread, and survive. Traits that conferred fitness that we could not see, taste, smell, or feel were often lost. Fast-growing yet scrawny plants were discarded. So were deep, persistent roots that were impossible to till. Similarly, disease resistance not immediately required was lost. Modern-day crops, like those found in the cornfield at the beginning of the chapter, are now unable to survive without humans to tend to them.

Nature carries out genetic modification as well. For example, all fields contain bacteria, and plants are susceptible to the different strains of bacteria to greater or lesser degrees. Let's suppose that a new, highly virulent bacterium appears in the field. Perhaps this bacterium arose through a mutation, a small random change in its genome. Over time, most of the wild grain plants in the field fall to the new pathogenic bacterium strain. But one particular plant contains the cell chemistry to resist the new onslaught. Suddenly, a gene that may not have mattered before is the key to survival. That plant is able to resist the bacterium while others cannot. The plant spreads and the gene survives.

The stress on the plant may take other forms as well, such as a three-year drought or a more aggressive weed. But the process is the same. Nature generally selects for plants that are more self-sufficient; humans tend to select for plants that look and taste better. In either case, the result is changes in the genome of the plant. The process of selective breeding, either in the wild or in human agriculture, is a long, slow, and somewhat random route toward modifying the gene pool. Neither natural nor artificial selection is genetic engineering. **Genetic engineering,** as we know it, is the direct manipulation of the DNA in an organism.

The easiest organisms to manipulate are small single-celled bacteria. These bacteria contain **plasmids,** or rings of DNA, in addition to their chromosomes. Scientists

While the terms are often interchanged, we use *genetic engineering* to describe the technical process and *genetic modification* to specifically discuss food products.

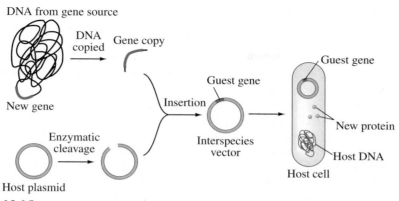

DNA from gene source

DNA copied   Gene copy

New gene

Enzymatic cleavage

Host plasmid

Insertion

Guest gene

Interspecies vector

Guest gene

New protein

Host DNA

Host cell

Figure 12.15

A representation of the process of genetic engineering.

can easily remove, change, and replace the plasmids to create new chemistry in the bacteria. They use special enzymes to cut open the plasmid at specific sites. Scientists then copy the DNA containing a promising gene from another organism, and the DNA from this organism is inserted into the plasmid ring from the bacterium. The result is a new interspecies DNA plasmid, or **vector,** a modified plasmid used to carry DNA back into the bacterial host (Figure 12.15). Once inside the cell, the chemistry of the bacterium takes over. The bacterium grows rapidly and produces new cells. Soon, the scientist has millions of copies of the "guest" gene and its protein product.

Inserting foreign DNA becomes a bit trickier as one climbs the evolutionary ladder from bacteria to plants. Higher organisms are better at protecting themselves against foreign DNA. For example, plants have thick cell walls. For another, many organisms have chemical mechanisms designed to detect and destroy foreign DNA. Even so, scientists have found ways to get around such defenses. One is to hijack a special soil bacterium that has the ability to infect plants. This bacterium creates a bridge into the plant cell and, in the process, transfers its own DNA into the genome of the plant. The bacterial genes induce points of large abnormal growth (Figure 12.16). You may have seen these growths (tumors) on a wide variety of plants and trees, including apple trees, rose bushes, and some vegetable plants.

Scientists are able to disable the bacterial gene and use the bacterium to insert a different gene of interest. If the gene of interest is the specific sequence from the soil bacterium, *Bacillus thuringiensis* (or *Bt*), that produces a *Bt* toxin, then the plant acquires the instructions to make the toxin itself. Earlier in the chapter, we described

Agrobacterium tumefaciens is commonly used to transform plants, particularly in the commercial seed industry.

Figure 12.16

A crown gall tumor (*Agrobacterium radiobacter*) on a chrysanthemum plant.

how this process of genetic transfer worked to create corn plants that were resistant to insects. Not only is there *Bt* corn, but also *Bt* cotton, *Bt* potatoes, and *Bt* rice, all producing toxins against crop-destroying pests!

The *Bt* toxin is but one example of genetically engineered possibilities. Not all examples of genetically engineered crops are **transgenic,** or an organism resulting from the transfer of genes across species. Genetic engineering is used to achieve the same aims as selective breeding, but with far more speed and control. Imagine you have a rice crop that grows well, tastes great, and cooks with a perfect level of stickiness, but it is being destroyed by a local plant virus. At the same time, a wild relative of your crop grows just beside it, resistant to the virus. Instead of securing the resistance trait by selective breeding, find and copy just the resistance gene from the wild plant, then splice it into your weak but otherwise perfect crop. Technically, the genetic engineering process is identical, but the result is a plant with only rice genes.

Transgenic rice plants have been developed for use in sub-Saharan Africa where the yellow mottle virus destroys much of the rice crop each year (Figure 12.17). At first, the gene that offered resistance to the rice plants was taken from a surprising source: the virus itself! The result was a transgenic plant with a small amount of viral code. The gene source is perhaps a concern, particularly to those that worry that consuming the viral proteins may result in allergic reactions. A preferable gene source is in development. Scientists are finding new potential genes by exploring the reason for viral resistance found in some rice varieties.

Perhaps you have a trait in mind, but have no source for the gene. In such a case, both traditional selective breeding and whole-gene transfer won't work. Neither of these can function if a trait does not already exist. Although in theory you could wait for a trait to evolve through natural, random mutations, most likely you would run low on patience. To speed up the process of evolution, scientists use either chemicals or ionizing radiation to produce random mutations in a batch of seeds. Upon planting, some seeds do not grow at all, others grow but with no apparent changes, and still others show unique traits. Once a useful trait appears, scientists can use either selective breeding to refine a new crop with the positive trait or genetic engineering to isolate the gene responsible for the trait and transfer it into a different plant.

Your Turn 12.15   Ionizing Radiation

Ionizing radiation is a term commonly used by both scientists and health professionals. We first introduced it in Chapter 7 and would like you to review it here.

   a. What is an ion? Give two examples. *Hint:* See Section 5.6.
   b. Some species have unpaired electrons. Give two examples. *Hint:* See Sections 1.11 and 2.8.
   c. How does radiation produce ions with unpaired electrons? *Hint:* See Section 7.6, "Nuclear Radiation and You."
   d. How do these ions (free radicals) lead to random mutations in DNA?

Figure 12.17

Virus–resistant transgenic rice.

Early in this chapter, we pointed out that as humans, we have a responsibility to act wisely, both for current and future generations. We also mentioned that our needs are great and our societal problems are pressing, asking whether our *inaction* might result in more harm than good. The sheer power of genetic engineering can frighten us. You may be automatically concerned at even the idea of transgenic organisms. The next section describes the benefits of genetic engineering to the chemical industry, both current and projected. In the section after, we delve into potential risks.

12.7 | Making Chemical Synthesis Green from Genetic Engineering

Pest and herbicide resistance are not the only reasons for genetic modification. Scientists also have modified the genes of corn, soybeans, and wheat with the aims of making them more resistant to disease; more tolerant of stresses such as salt, heat, or drought; and more nutritious. Although farmers have benefitted, many others have as well. Scientists have designed plants to absorb toxic metals from contaminated soil. Some are developing crops such as soybeans that produce high yields of biofuel per acre. Others are engineering bacteria to detect and remediate radioactive contamination. Of interest to us in this section is that genetic engineering can incorporate the key ideas of green chemistry into large-scale chemical production.

 A synthetic route to a desired chemical may require toxic chemicals, large amounts of solvents, and high temperatures. Although such processes yield many useful chemicals, they also produce a staggering amount of waste—up to 100 times the weight of the compound! One way to reduce the ecological footprint is to use enzymes, the biological catalysts described earlier. These "biological machines" perform reactions just as you would conventionally within flasks or beakers, but faster and safer with fewer toxic reagents, at lower temperatures, and with less waste. Another plus is that enzymes can be used over and over again. Minimal waste, reusable reagents, and low toxicity are green chemistry standards.

Via genetic engineering, scientists use enzymes to create new drugs or more efficiently build existing drugs. The gene coding for the drug is introduced into a host organism that, in turn, synthesizes the desired product. This application of genetic engineering is not only one of the most rapidly growing uses of the technology but also its oldest.

Consider the production of human insulin. Insulin is quite a small protein built from 51 amino acids, but its chemical synthesis is far from trivial. An insufficient supply of insulin to regulate blood sugar levels results in diabetes. Untreated, the disease may lead to kidney failure, cardiovascular problems, blindness, and even death. Luckily, those with diabetes can control the disease through proper diet, exercise, and insulin injections—a genetically engineered product.

Before 1982, all insulin used was isolated from the pancreatic glands of cows and pigs. But the insulin gathered from animals is not identical to that of humans. The insulin of cows ("bovine insulin") differs from the human hormone in 3 out of 51 amino acids; the insulin of pigs ("porcine insulin") and human insulin differ in only one amino acid. The slight differences are nonetheless significant. Some patients developed antibodies against the foreign insulin protein and rejected it.

In short, humans need human insulin. Although chemists were able to synthesize the insulin protein in the laboratory, the process is far too complex and costly for large-scale production. Luckily, in 1982, the common bacterium, *E. coli,* was coaxed into making human insulin. The gene for human insulin was placed in a plasmid which in turn was placed in the bacterium. The result was what we can depend on today—a steady and less expensive supply of human insulin.

Growing bacteria with natural or artificial genes is now a step in manufacturing small-molecule drugs. The process is particularly easy when the gene, or something similar, already exists. Sometimes, however, special tricks are required, as was the case in the synthesis of the drug Atorvastatin (Figure 12.18). Enzymes for specific reaction steps could not be found, so they had to be evolved. Scientists mimic natural selection

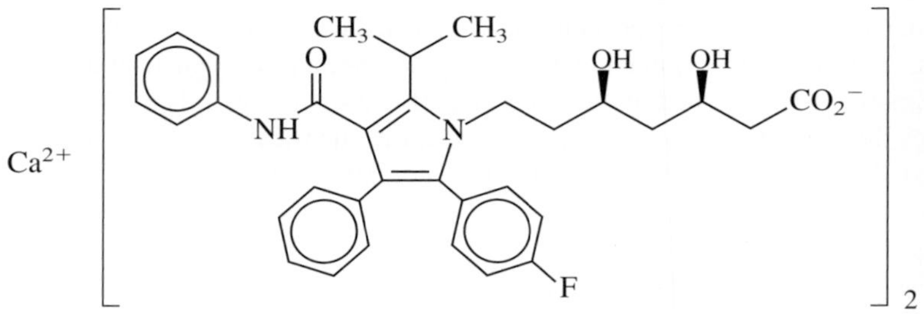

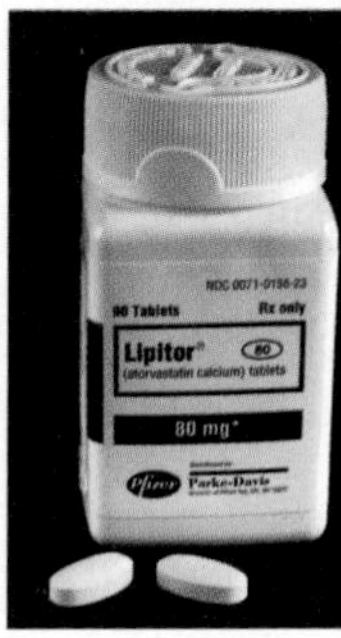

Figure 12.18

Atorvastatin, the active ingredient in Lipitor, requires enzyme–generated building blocks. The cholesterol–lowering drug produced by Pfizer had annual sales exceeding $10 billion before going off patent.

"Directed evolution" can also be performed without using bacteria by selecting, mutating, and multiplying DNA with enzymes.

Return to Chapter 9 for a review of plastic production, uses, and consequences.

Scientists and engineers at Metabolix earned a Presidential Green Chemistry Challenge Award in 2005 for their innovative and sustainable bioplastic technology.

by creating an environment where the bacteria must evolve a new trait in order to survive; the process is termed "directed evolution." Typically, the scientists start with a random variety of DNA sequences transferred into a population of bacteria. Over multiple generations grown under certain conditions, such as providing only certain chemicals as food, a new enzyme emerges.

Engineered organisms can even produce plastics. Most synthetic polymers are synthesized in large chemical plants using a process that consumes large amounts of chemical reagents and energy. Furthermore, these chemical reagents often are derived from petroleum. Scientists at Metabolix engineered organisms to improve the problems. These organisms produce monomers from renewable materials such as corn, sugarcane, and vegetable oil, and then catalyze the polymerization reaction. One example of a resulting polymer is polyhydroxybutyrate (PHB). This bioplastic is used to produce items such as plastic utensils and coatings for cups, much like polypropylene (PP). However, unlike PP, PHB is biodegradable. The process uses materials of low toxicity, is extremely efficient, and lowers greenhouse gas emissions.

Consider This 12.16   Algae for New Biofuels

Genetically engineered plants and organisms are becoming increasingly important in the search for sustainable alternative fuels. Using the Internet, explore algae as a source of fuel and of other products (Figure 12.19).

a. Name two biofuels that can be produced from algae.
b. List three advantages of algae over corn as a source of biofuel. *Hint:* Revisit Sections 4.9 and 4.10.
c. What else can algae produce? Describe two products and their uses.
d. Genetically engineered algae may lead to the better production of biofuels. Name two problems that genetic engineering may solve.

To finish our discussion, we ask you to revisit one of the lines from the opening paragraph of this chapter: "*. . . our farms create our drugs and vaccines . . .*" This is not a utopian dream, as our transgenic plants now can produce both. For example, vaccines against infectious diseases of the intestinal tract have been produced in potatoes and bananas. Anticancer antibodies have been expressed and introduced into wheat. Peptide drugs against HIV/AIDS have been produced from tobacco fields. Also, most vaccines require refrigeration or other special handling together with trained professionals to administer them. In some countries, health professionals cannot afford even the needles to inoculate people, leading to possible infections from reused needles. Vaccines produced within edible products may be difficult to correctly dose but would be easy to administer and transfer. Rather than yielding crops for food, these fields yield the hope of low-cost, readily available vaccines. Thus, these fields of transgenic plants can go hand-in-hand with good public health policy.

Figure 12.19

Developing strains of algae for new biofuels.

The technology is still developing, but the bonuses are already both apparent and immense. Compared with traditional methods, a genetically engineered enzyme, microorganism, or crop can yield highly pure products while reducing waste and by-products. The genetically engineered routes increase the yield with fewer steps and often eliminate labor, energy, and resource-intensive purification processes. They avoid the use of toxic and corrosive chemicals, which is better for the environment and increases overall worker safety.

This all being said, we end this section in a manner similar to the way in which we ended the previous one. We need to act wisely, both for current and future generations. The promise of developing technology and society's desperate needs can lead to rash choices. The risks of genetically engineered cures may be large, perhaps unacceptably so. In the next section, we delve into the potential risks.

12.8 | The New Frankenstein

In Mary Shelley's work of science fiction, Dr. Frankenstein created a man from the best "parts" of other men. However, he then lost control of his creation. Today, are we the new Dr. Frankensteins? In this era of genetic engineering, many have asked this very question.

Over recent years, people have rallied against genetically modified (GM) foods (Figure 12.20). These protests have occurred worldwide, including in Germany, Australia, Spain, the United Kingdom, and the United States. Have you run across the term *Frankenfood*? Consider This 12.17 offers you a chance to explore the meaning of this term as you learn more about the opposition to GM food.

Figure 12.20

Greenpeace activists dumping papayas during a protest in Bangkok.

Consider This 12.17   Frankenfood

a. Explain the term *Frankenfood*.
b. Search the Internet to find a context in which people oppose GM food. Give the country, the type of food, and the reasons for opposition.
c. Summarize three arguments given by those who oppose GM food.

As this activity most likely revealed, opposition takes many forms. We explore some of the arguments here.

GM plants will spread into the wild. Consider, for example, the new transgenic corn described at the opening of this chapter. This GM corn may spread by the accidental release of seeds or pollen and breed with the corn's distant, weedy relatives. If the wild-domesticated hybrid carries the new gene, this could lead to a new population of resistant superweeds. Although many countries prohibit the cultivation of GM crops in the vicinity of weedy relatives, the regulations do not prevent all illegal plantings or accidental growth. For example, GM corn has been found in cornfields in Mexico, an area with both a diverse population of specialized domestic corn and wild relatives.

Response: Chances remain slim, although not impossible, that a gene will transfer and survive in the wild. A natural barrier exists because GM or GM-wild hybrid plants compete poorly with wild plants. While a hybrid would likely contain the advantageous resistance gene, it also would receive other genes, including some that are weaknesses (e.g., a shallow root system, inability to compete for limited water). In experimental trials, hybrids have not been strong enough to survive in the wild. Alternatively, some GM plants are engineered to be sterile and prevent gene spread by breeding.

GM crops threaten the natural balance. In laboratory experiments, pollen from GM plants has harmed caterpillars and other insects distinct from the intended target pest. Damage to the general insect population may affect an entire food chain by poisoning or contaminating the food supply for birds. Too general of a pesticide may also risk insect populations important for pollination or soil rejuvenation. Although the laboratory experiments used more pollen than an actual farm field would contain, the exposure time in a field with GM crops will be significantly longer, even over generations. The long-term threats are still unknown.

Response: Ideally, a GM crop reduces general pesticide use. If the new genetically engineered trait is chosen well, only a target pest will be harmed and the risk to other insects can be minimized. A healthy variety of insects flourish by selectively killing only a few. In addition, advanced genetic engineering may control where and when the plant expresses an artificial gene. If the pesticide is produced only in the leaves of the plant, the risk to insects interacting with the pollen decreases. Finally, as we question risks to the natural balance, we must also consider the shifting baseline of how we understand the environment surrounding us.

Genetically modified crops will force pests to evolve. In the ecosystem surrounding a GM crop, the targeted weeds, bugs, or bacteria must move, die, or evolve. If the species evolves, the GM crop may have no resistance to it. Historically, we solved the problem of the evolution of a pest by finding a natural trait within the existing crop varieties and then using selective breeding to create a new, stronger hybrid. As we come to depend on a narrower set of crop varieties, we no longer have the genetic variety to utilize.

Response: Although new resistance traits easily evolve in insects in laboratories, only a few resistant insects have been reported in fields. Regulators in both the United States and the European Union require the cultivation of traditional crops without engineered toxins or resistance traits alongside GM varieties. The mix is intended to prevent resistance from evolving in pests as resistance to the crop will not be a survival requirement. As the engineered crops become more widespread, scientists may need to further test how much of the nonengineered crop is enough to minimize the risk of newly resistant pests.

These arguments and responses focus on the local environmental consequences of growing GM food crops. We also should consider the broader arguments that relate to people. For example, some people may develop allergies to GM food either due to a known allergen in an unexpected source or to a new combination of materials. As another example, consider the expense of GM seeds to small-scale farmers. The farmers must buy new seeds for each year. Traditional measures such as seed storing and breeding are impossible as GM crops are often sterile if not simply patent protected.

Other broader arguments relate to animals and commercial ventures. For example, consider the spread of GM crops engineered for nonhuman consumption, including corn solely tested and approved for use as animal feed, soybeans engineered to produce excess oil for fuel, and tobacco containing an anti-inflammatory protein destined for pharmaceutical use. We may need even more stringent controls on these as they are not generally safe to consume as food. Last, consider the rise of GM livestock. The application of GM technology to organisms that live longer than just a few months add even further complications to our methods of control.

Consider the proposition that *none* of these risks are worth taking. At the beginning of this chapter, we held up the image of a genetically engineered utopia. This has alternatively been discussed as a second "Green Revolution." Genetic engineering has been developing and spreading for decades. However, even in a time of rising food prices and continued starvation, genetic engineering has not provided the much-hoped-for second "Green Revolution." Perhaps it cannot or will not. Some argue that genetic engineering has provided nothing that traditional breeding methods could not. They claim that the research dollars are wasted and the environment unduly risked. Others would point out the already promising successes, but claim that current policies block true progress.

Recent examples of GM livestock include salmon designed to grow larger faster and a variety of pigs that release less phosphorus into the environment.

Return to Section 11.12 for a thorough discussion of the agriculture developments leading to the first "Green Revolution."

Consider This 12.18   Your Opinion of GM Foods (revisited)

As promised, we return to the question posed at the opening of this chapter.

a. Given a choice between a GM food and one that was not, do you have a preference as to which one you would eat? Explain.
b. Whichever preference you expressed, now make an argument for the other side.

Concern or cynicism about the rapid application of a new science is justifiable. Any decision that attempts to fix a problem in the short term without regard for the future is fraught with danger. For any problem, to ignore or severely hamper a promising technology, particularly out of fear or minimal information, may also disregard the future. As with many controversies, it is easy to identify the extreme positions. However, it is much harder to find the middle ground. We hope this discussion has both given you some answers and, more important, posed new questions.

Conclusion

This final chapter of the book, like almost all that preceded it, ends with a dilemma: How can we balance the great benefits of modern chemical sciences and technology and the risks that seem inevitably to accompany them? Both those for or against genetic engineering can easily invoke the precautionary principle. Genetic engineering is, at its heart, a tool in the fight against many potentially irreversible global problems. Still, the unintended consequences if we lose control of this tool are perhaps more complicated and wide-ranging than the science of genetic engineering itself.

Throughout this text, the authors have occasionally looked, with myopic professorial vision, into the cloudy crystal ball of the future. It is in the nature of science that we cannot confidently predict what new discoveries will be made by tomorrow's scientists. Nor can we know the applications of those discoveries, good or bad. Such uncertainty is one of the delights of our discipline. A chemist must learn to live with ambiguity, indeed, to thrive on it, in the search to better understand the nature of atoms and their intricate combinations, in all their various guises.

But all citizens of this planet must at least develop a tolerance for ambiguity and a willingness to take reasonable risks, especially considering that life itself is a biological, intellectual, and emotional risk. Of course, we all seek to maximize benefits, but we must recognize that individual gain must sometimes be sacrificed to benefit society. We live in multiple contexts—the context of our families and friends, our towns and cities, our states, our countries, our special planet. We have responsibilities to all. *You,* the readers of this book, will help create the context of the future. We wish you well.

Chapter Summary

Having studied this chapter, you should be able to:

- Discuss the complications of corn farming as an example of inspiration for genetic engineering (12.1)
- Understand that cells function by a complex series of chemical reactions (12.2)
- Discuss deoxyribonucleic acid (DNA) as a storage device of information to run chemical reactions in cells (12.2)
- Describe the chemical composition of DNA, a polymer of nitrogen-containing bases, deoxyribose, and phosphate groups (12.2)
- Interpret evidence for the double-helical structure of DNA and its base pairing (12.3)
- Understand the structural basis of DNA replication (12.3)
- Explain how the genetic code is written in groupings of three DNA bases called codons (12.4)
- Understand how the codons relate to amino acids across organisms (12.4)
- Discuss the primary, secondary, and tertiary structure of proteins (12.5)

- Recognize the general properties of amino acid side chains (12.5)
- Relate the properties of amino acids to the interactions formed in protein structure (12.5)
- Discuss, with examples, how small changes in protein sequence may result in disease (12.5)
- Understand the essential steps in carrying out recombinant DNA techniques (12.6)
- Describe what is meant by transgenic organisms and give examples (12.6)
- Give brief examples of natural selection, selective breeding, and genetic engineering (12.6)
- Discuss, with examples, how genetic engineering has changed the chemical industry (12.7)
- Analyze controversial issues associated with transgenic organisms and GM food (12.8)
- Debate issues associated with the prudent and ethical applications of genetic engineering (12.8)

Questions

Emphasizing Essentials

1. The theme of this chapter is that DNA guides the chemistry of every living organism on the planet. Name three traits you possess that were determined by your DNA.

2. Suggest three industries that have changed with the rise of genetic engineering.

3. The first section in this chapter is called "Stronger and Better Corn Plants?"

   a. Name three ways in which a corn plant could be stronger or better.

   b. Why is there a question mark in the title of the section? In your explanation, make use of the word *genome*.

4. What is the difference between a genome and a gene?

5. Consider the structural formulas in Figure 12.2.

   a. What functional group(s) are found in the adenine molecule?

   b. What functional group(s) are found in the deoxyribose molecule?

   c. From what you learned in Section 11.5, why is deoxyribose a sugar and adenine is not?

6. a. What three units must be present in a nucleotide?

   b. What type of bonding holds these three units together?

7. DNA contains the four bases: adenine, cytosine, guanine, and thymine. Name two similarities among the four bases. Highlight one feature unique to each.

8. Circle and name the functional groups in this nucleotide. Also label the sugar, the base, and the phosphate group.

9. Compare the DNA segment in Figure 12.4 with the nucleotide shown in question 8. Name the two parts of the nucleotide that react to form a polymer similar to DNA.

10. What does each letter in DNA stand for? Examine Figure 12.4. Which aspects of the DNA molecule does the name DNA highlight? Which aspects of the DNA molecule are not part of the name?

11. Here is the structural formula for the base thymine, as attached to the DNA chain.

To deoxyribose and DNA chain

    a. Label the H atoms that can hydrogen bond with a water molecule.

    b. Use electronegativity differences to explain why only these H atoms can form hydrogen bonds.

12. Explain why the base sequence ATG is different from the base sequence GTA.

13. Given a short sequence of DNA: TATCTAG

    a. Write and align a DNA code that complements the sequence given.

    b. Draw connecting lines between the sequences to represent the number of hydrogen bonds between each base pair.

14. What is a codon and what is its role in the genetic code?

15. Only 61 of the possible 64 codons code for an amino acid. What is the function of the other three codons?

16. In relation to DNA, what is a gene?

17. Amino acids are the monomers used to build proteins.

    a. Draw the *general* structural formula for an amino acid.

    b. Name the functional groups in the structural formula you just drew.

18. Amino acids can be classified as nonpolar or polar. The polar amino acids can be further grouped as acidic, basic, or neutral.

    a. Draw an example of a possible amino acid for each type of polar amino acid.

    b. Describe each category in more detail. What functional groups would you expect in the side chains?

19. Give two examples of amino acids that have side chains that are categorized as nonpolar. Explain what characteristics make them nonpolar.

20. Describe what is meant by the primary, secondary, and tertiary structure of a protein.

21. Explain how an error in the primary structure of a protein in hemoglobin causes sickle-cell anemia.

22. List two advantages and two disadvantages of GM crops over traditional crops.

23. Explain one similarity and one difference between selective breeding and genetic engineering of plants.

Concentrating on Concepts

24. This chapter opens stating "Geneticists may have the power to create a utopia." Explain.

25. Figure 12.4 represents a segment of DNA.

    a. What part of each nucleotide becomes the backbone of the polymer?

    b. What part hangs off the backbone?

    c. How is the backbone represented in sculpture at the beginning of the chapter and Figure 12.6?

26. Compare the two representations of a segment of DNA in Figure 12.4. For each, discuss a strength and a weakness.

27. Use Figure 12.7 to help explain why stable base pairing does *not* occur between adenine and cytosine. Name another base pair for which this is also true. Explain why.

28. Use Figure 12.7 to explain why adenine–thymine base pairs are less stable than cytosine–guanine base pairs.

29. Ionizing radiation can damage DNA. One or more strands of DNA may be disrupted when damaging radiation breaks covalent bonds within the backbone or a nucleotide. A cell can more easily repair damage to a single strand in a DNA double helix than to a double-strand break. Explain.

30. UV-C light is germicidal. Two thymine residues will absorb UV-C light and react together to form a new covalent bond, or cross link.

    a. List a potential consequence of a cross link forming between two thymine molecules on a single strand of DNA.

    b. List a potential consequence of a cross link forming between two thymine molecules from two complementary strands.

31. Many compounds damage DNA and very effectively kill bacterial cells. Why are these compounds not typically used as antibacterial medicines?

32. Errors sometimes occur in the base sequence of a strand of DNA. But not all of these errors result in the incorporation of an incorrect amino acid in a protein for which the DNA codes. Explain why a single base change may not change the amino acid.

33. Several diseases are caused by a single amino acid change in a specific enzyme. For example, familial amyotrophic lateral sclerosis (FALS), an inheritable form of Lou Gehrig's disease, can be caused by the alteration of a single amino acid in the enzyme superoxide dismutase.

    a. For any protein, how many base pairs are responsible for specifying an amino acid in the gene that codes for the protein? What is the minimum number of base pairs that would have to be changed to switch one amino acid for another?

    b. One hereditary mutant superoxide dismutase replaces a glycine with alanine. Using a reputable online resource or your library, find a "codon table" that specifies the codons for each amino acid, then list the codon(s) that code for glycine and for alanine. Identify the minimum number of base pairs changed.

34. Almost all organisms use the same four bases and the same codons. Explain why this consistent code is necessary for genetic engineering.

35. A clone is an identical copy of a cell or organism, often created by transferring the nucleus from an adult cell into an egg cell lacking a nucleus.

    a. Explain why the nucleus from an adult cell can be used to create an identical organism.

    b. Explain why the egg cell must lack a nucleus.

    c. Explain two ways in which this process differs from genetic engineering.

36. The medicines human insulin and human growth hormone both result from the genetic engineering of bacteria. List two possible reasons this has not received the same amount of public concern as the use of genetic engineering in plants.

37. Create a graph showing the relative amounts of GM or transgenic crops grown by six different countries. Include the source of your data with your graph.

38. Consider the idea of mixing genes as an improvement on nature.

    a. Describe what is meant by the term *transgenic organisms*.

    b. Why is the alteration of the genetic makeup of plants by genetic engineering preferred to traditional selective breeding methods?

Exploring Extensions

39. The genetic engineering of corn is the focus for this chapter's opening section. In light of the projected environmental and population changes discussed in other chapters, name three traits not mentioned in this chapter that you would propose to add to corn or other common crops. Discuss the advantages and disadvantages of each of your traits.

40. Consider the structural formula of deoxyribose shown in Figure 12.2. Draw an isomer of deoxyribose, one that would still form a nucleotide with a base and with phosphate. Compare your isomer side-by-side with the structural formula of deoxyribose.

41. Of the major players in the discovery of the structure of DNA, Rosalind Franklin was not included in the 1962 Nobel Prize given for solving the structure of DNA. What was her background and experience that enabled her to make significant contributions? Suggest why she did not receive adequate credit and recognition for her work. Summarize your findings, citing your sources.

42. a. What are X-rays? *Hint:* Revisit Chapters 2 and 7.

    b. How is X-ray diffraction used to determine a crystal structure?

    c. The first X-ray diffraction patterns were of simple salts, such as sodium chloride. The X-ray diffraction studies of nucleic acids and proteins did not come until much later. Suggest two reasons why.

43. The genetic traits leading to sickle-cell disease are more common in people of African, African-American, or Mediterranean heritage. Using the Internet, explain a proposed reason that the sickle-cell trait has persisted rather than being discarded through evolution.

44. Proteins may search through a number of possible shapes and interactions before finding the right final fold. Explore the research program called folding@home, a distributed computer simulation based at Stanford University that can utilize your home computer or game console. How does the computer simulation repeat the natural process? Finally, explore one of the results from the program and write a single-paragraph report.

45. List two advantages and two disadvantages of issuing patents for genetically modified plants and seeds.

46. To clone or to breed? Grieving owners may find the opportunity to clone (genetically replicate) a beloved dog too tantalizing to resist. Even so, many professional dog breeders and their organizations advise against cloning. Phil Buckley, a spokesperson for the Kennel Club in England, argues, "Canine cloning runs contrary to the Kennel Club's objective to promote in every way the general improvement of dogs." Explain why cloning cannot improve dog breeds.

47. Transgenic plants have not been widely accepted in all countries.

    a. For the European Union, find two examples of transgenic plants that have been banned. Compare these to two that have been allowed. Discuss the differences between those allowed and those rejected.

    b. Create a timeline of five events key for the rapid increase or subsequent leveling (or both) of the adoption of transgenic crops in the United States. Briefly discuss each of your choices.

48. Consider the government controls on the planting of GM food crops described in the text. Suggest two additional regulations that you would like to see on the growth of GM crops that generate medicines. Describe a specific reason that you feel that these additional precautions are necessary.

49. One reason why science fiction is successful is that it starts with a known scientific principle and extends, elaborates, and sometimes embroiders it. *Jurassic Park* began with the known scientific principle of copying and manipulating DNA and was expanded to the production of prehistoric creatures. Now it is your turn. Choose any scientific principle from this text. Then write a one- or two-page outline for a story based on that principle. Be sure to identify the chemical concepts and any pseudoscience that you employ.

50. Gene therapy involves the use of recombinant DNA techniques. Use the Internet to gather information on this medical tool. Write a one- to two-page report on gene therapy, including specific examples of diseases that are being treated and how the patients are faring.

51. Find a transgenic organism not discussed in the text. Describe the motivation for engineering this organism, its gene source, and a general description for the genetic modification.

52. You are the head of a government facing another year of a long drought and a serious risk of famine. Another nation has offered you a supply of genetically modified corn to feed your people. List two advantages and two disadvantages of accepting the aid. Decide whether you would accept it.

Appendix 1

Measure for Measure

Metric Prefixes, Conversion Factors, and Constants

Metric Prefixes

Prefix	Symbol	Value	Scientific Notation
pico	p	$1/10^{12}$ or 0.000000000001	10^{-12}
nano	n	$1/10^{9}$ or 0.000000001	10^{-9}
micro	μ	$1/10^{6}$ or 0.000001	10^{-6}
milli	m	1/1000 or 0.001	10^{-3}
centi	c	1/100 or 0.01	10^{-2}
deci	d	1/10 or 0.1	10^{-1}
deka/deca	da	10	10^{1}
hecto	h	100	10^{2}
kilo	k	1000	10^{3}
mega	M	1,000,000	10^{6}
giga	G	1,000,000,000	10^{9}
tera	T	1,000,000,000,000	10^{12}

Conversion Factors

Length

1 centimeter (cm) = 0.394 inches (in.)

1 meter (m) = 39.4 inches (in.) = 3.28 feet (ft)
        = 1.08 yards (yd)

1 kilometer (km) = 0.621 miles (mi)

1 inch (in.) = 2.54 centimeters (cm) = 0.0833 feet (ft)

1 foot (ft) = 30.5 centimeters (cm) = 0.305 meters (m)
        = 12 inches (in.)

1 yard (yd) = 91.44 centimeters (cm) = 0.9144 meters (m)
        = 3 feet (ft) = 36 inches (36 in.)

1 mile (mi) = 1.61 kilometers (km)

Volume

1 cubic centimeter (cm^3) = 1 milliliter (mL)

1 liter (L) = 1000 milliliters (mL)
        = 1000 cubic centimeters (cm^3)
        = 1.057 quarts (qt)

1 quart (qt) = 0.946 liter (L)

1 gallon (gal) = 4 quarts (qt) = 3.78 liters (L)

Mass

1 gram (g) = 0.0352 ounces (oz) = 0.00220 pounds (lb)

1 kilogram (kg) = 1000 grams (g) = 2.20 pounds (lb)

1 pound (lb) = 454 grams (g) = 0.454 kilograms (kg)

1 tonne or metric ton (t) = 1000 kilograms (kg)
        = 2200 pounds (lb)
        = 1 long ton (t) = 1.10 tons (T)

1 ton (T) = 909 kilograms (kg)
        = 2000 pounds (lb)
        = 1 short ton (T)
        = 0.909 tonnes (t)

Time

1 year (yr or y) = 365.24 days (d)

1 day (d) = 24 hours (hr or h)

1 hour (hr or h) = 60 minutes (min)

1 minute (min) = 60 seconds (s)

Energy

1 joule (J) = 0.239 calories (cal)

1 calorie (cal) = 4.184 joules (J)

1 exajoule (EJ) = 10^{18} joules (J)

1 kilocalorie (kcal) = 1 dietary Calorie (Cal)
        = 4184 joules (J)
        = 4.184 kilojoules (kJ)

1 kilowatt-hour (kWh) = 3,600,000 joules (J)
        = 3.60×10^{6} J

Constants

Speed of light (c) = 3.00×10^{8} meters per second (m/s)

Planck's constant (h) = 6.63×10^{-34} joule-seconds (J · s)

Avogadro's number = 6.02×10^{23} objects per mole
        (objects/mol)

Unified atomic mass unit (u) = 1 Dalton (Da)
        = 1.66×10^{-24} grams (g)

Scientific (or exponential) notation provides a compact and convenient way of writing very large and very small numbers. The idea is to use positive and negative powers of 10. Positive exponents are used to represent large numbers. The exponent, which is written as a superscript, indicates how many times 10 is multiplied by itself. For example,

$$10^1 = 10$$
$$10^2 = 10 \times 10 = 100$$
$$10^3 = 10 \times 10 \times 10 = 1000$$

Note that the positive exponent is equal to the number of zeros between the 1 and the decimal point. Thus, 10^6 corresponds to 1 followed by six zeros, or 1,000,000. This same rule applies to 10^0, which equals 1. One billion, 1,000,000,000, can be written as 10^9.

When 10 is raised to a negative exponent, the number being represented is always less than 1. This is because a negative exponent implies a reciprocal, that is, 1 over 10 raised to the corresponding positive exponent. For example,

$$10^{-1} = 1/10^1 = 1/10 = 0.1$$
$$10^{-2} = 1/10^2 = 1/100 = 0.01$$
$$10^{-3} = 1/10^3 = 1/1000 = 0.001$$

It follows that the larger the negative exponent, the smaller the number. The negative exponent is always one more than the number of zeros between the decimal point and the 1. Thus, 1×10^{-4} is equal to 0.0001. Conversely, 0.000001 in scientific notation is 1×10^{-6}.

Of course, most of the quantities and constants used in chemistry are not simple whole-number powers of 10. For example, Avogadro's number is 6.02×10^{23}, or 6.02 multiplied by a number equal to 1 followed by 23 zeros. Written out, this corresponds to $6.02 \times 100,000,000,000,000,000,000,000$, or 602,000,000,000,000,000,000,000. Switching to very small numbers, a wavelength at which carbon dioxide absorbs infrared radiation is 4.257×10^{-6} m. This number is the same as 4.257×0.000001, or 0.000004257 m.

Your Turn	Scientific Notation

Express these numbers in scientific notation.

a. 10,000	b. 430
c. 9876.54	d. 0.000001
e. 0.007	f. 0.05339

Answers

a. 1×10^4	b. 4.3×10^2
c. 9.87654×10^3	d. 1×10^{-6}
e. 7×10^{-3}	f. 5.339×10^{-2}

Your Turn	Decimal Notation

Express these numbers in conventional decimal notation.

a. 1×10^6	b. 3.123×10^6
c. 25×10^5	d. 1×10^{-5}
e. 6.023×10^{-7}	f. 1.723×10^{-16}

Answers

a. 1,000,000	b. 3,123,000
c. 2,500,000	d. 0.00001
e. 0.0000006023	f. 0.0000000000000001723

Appendix 3

Clearing the Logjam

You may have encountered logarithms in mathematics courses but wondered if you would ever use them. In fact, logarithms (or "logs" for short) are extremely useful in many areas of science. The essential idea is that they make it much easier to deal with very large *ranges* of numbers, for example, moving by powers of 10 from 0.0001 to 1,000,000.

It is likely that you have met logarithmic scales without necessarily knowing it. The Richter scale for expressing magnitudes of earthquakes is one example. On this scale, an earthquake of magnitude 6 is 10 times more powerful than one of magnitude 5. An earthquake of magnitude 8 would be 100 times more powerful than one of magnitude 6. Another example is the decibel (dB) scale. Each increase of 10 units represents a 10-fold increase in sound level. Therefore, a normal conversation between two people 1 m apart (60 dB) is 10 times louder than quiet music (50 dB) at the same distance. Loud music (70 dB) and extremely loud music (80 dB) are 10 times and 100 times louder than a normal conversation.

A simple exercise using a pocket calculator can be a good way to learn about logs. You will need a calculator that "does" logs and preferably has a "scientific notation" option. Start by finding the logarithm of 10. Simply enter 10 and press the "log" button. The answer should be 1. Next, find the log of 100 and then the log of 1000. Write down the answers. What pattern do you see? (The pattern may be more obvious if you recall that 100 can be written as 10^2 and 1000 is the same as 10^3.) Predict the log of 10,000 and then check it out. Then try the log of 0.1, or 10^{-1}, and the log of 0.01 (10^{-2}). Predict the log of 0.0001 and check it out.

So far so good, but we have been considering only whole-number powers of 10. It would be helpful to be able to obtain the logarithm of any number. Once again, your handy little calculator comes to the rescue. Try calculating the logs of 20 and 200, then 50 (5×10^1) and 500 (5×10^2). Predict the log of 5×10^3, or 5000. Now for something slightly trickier: the log of 0.05. Finally, try the log of 2473 and the log of 0.000404. In each of the three cases, does the answer seem to be in the right ballpark? Remember that your calculator will happily provide you with many more digits than have any meaning, so you will need to do some reasonable rounding.

In Chapter 6, the concept of pH is introduced as a quantitative way to describe the acidity of a substance. A pH value is simply a special case of a logarithmic relationship. It is defined as the negative of the logarithm of the H^+ concentration, expressed in units of molarity (M). Square brackets are used to indicate molar concentrations. The mathematical relationship is given by the equation pH $= -\log [H^+]$. The negative sign indicates an inverse relationship; as the H^+ concentration diminishes, the pH increases. Let us apply the equation by using it to calculate the pH of a beverage with a hydrogen ion concentration of 0.000546 M. We first set up the mathematical equation and substitute the hydrogen ion concentration into it.

$$\text{pH} = -\log [H^+] = -\log (5.46 \times 10^{-4}\,\text{M})$$

Next, we take the negative logarithm of the H^+ concentration by entering it into a calculator and pressing the log button, then the "plus/minus" button to change the sign. This gives 3.26 as the pH of the beverage. (It may display 3.262807357 if you have not preset the number of digits, but common sense prompts you to round the displayed value.) Apply the same procedure to calculate the pH of milk with a hydrogen ion concentration of 2.20×10^{-7} M.

If we can convert hydrogen ion concentration into pH, how do we go in the reverse direction, that is, how to convert pH into a hydrogen ion concentration? Your calculator can do this for you if it has a button labeled "10^x." (Alternatively, it may use two buttons: first "Inv" and then "log.") To demonstrate the procedure, suppose you wish to find the hydrogen ion concentration of human blood with a pH of 7.40. Proceed as follows: Enter 7.40, use the "plus/minus" button to change the sign to negative, and then hit 10^x (or follow whatever steps are appropriate for your calculator). The display should give the hydrogen ion concentration as 3.98×10^{-8} M. Now apply the same procedure to calculate the H^+ concentration of an acid rain sample with a pH of 3.6.

Your Turn   pH

Find the pH concentration in each sample.

a. tap water, $[H^+] = 1.0 \times 10^{-6}$ M

b. milk of magnesia, $[H^+] = 3.2 \times 10^{-11}$ M

c. lemon juice, $[H^+] = 5.0 \times 10^{-3}$ M

d. saliva, $[H^+] = 2.0 \times 10^{-7}$ M

Answers

a. 6.0	b. 10.5
c. 2.3	d. 6.7

Your Turn H^+ Concentration

Find the H^+ concentration in each sample.

a. tomato juice, pH = 4.5

b. acid fog, pH = 3.3

c. vinegar, pH = 2.5

d. blood, pH = 7.6

Answers

a. 3.2×10^{-5} M	b. 5.0×10^{-4} M
c. 3.2×10^{-3} M	d. 2.5×10^{-8} M

Chapter 0

0.3 c. Search the Internet for "aluminum can recycling" to find some amazing statistics. Sites that you might wish to explore include Earth 911 and the Aluminum Association.

0.5 a. In 2012, the population of the United States was about 315 million.

c. Doing the math, 2.5 billion hectares divided by 12 billion hectares is about 0.21, or 21% of the biologically productive land available. For purposes of reference, the United States has about 4.5% of the world's population.

Chapter 1

1.7 b. Yes. Judging by Table 1.2, $PM_{2.5}$ must have more serious health consequences than PM_{10} because the concentrations are set at lower limits.

1.8 a. $\dfrac{44 \ \mu g \ SO_2}{0.625 \ m^3} = \dfrac{70 \ \mu g \ SO_2}{1 \ m^3}$

She would not exceed the 1-hr limit of $210 \ \mu g/m^3$.

b. At the same inhalation rate, she would not surpass the 1-hr or the 3-hr rates of $210 \ \mu g/m^3$ or $1300 \ \mu g/m^3$.

1.9 Examples of preventing air pollution include (1) not burning leaves (produces smoke and particulate matter), but rather letting them compost or otherwise decompose, (2) burning low-sulfur coal rather than high-sulfur coal, using a scrubber to remove SO_2 if burning high-sulfur coal, or conserving so as to burn less coal of any type, (3) choosing methods of transportation, such as bicycling or walking, that do not release air pollutants.

1.11 a. Hydrogen (H_2) and helium (He) are elements.

b. Other substances found in the air include nitrogen, N_2 (element), oxygen, O_2 (element), argon, Ar (element), carbon dioxide, CO_2 (compound), and water vapor, H_2O (compound).

c. Hydrogen (0.54 ppm, or 0.000054%), helium (5 ppm, or 0.0005%), and methane (17 ppm, or 0.0017%).

1.13 b. SO_2 is sulfur dioxide; SO_3 is sulfur trioxide.

1.14 a. The *eth-* in ethanol indicates 2 C atoms in the chemical formula.

c. The *prop-* in propanol indicates 3 C atoms in the chemical formula.

1.15 b.

Balanced equation: $\quad N_2 + 2 O_2 \longrightarrow 2 NO_2$

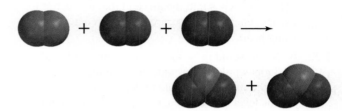

1.17 Equation 1.7 contains 16 C, 36 H, and 34 O on each side.

1.19 Your list should include: O_2, N_2, CO_2, CO, H_2O, NO, soot (particulate matter), and VOCs. The exhaust also contains tiny amounts of Ar and even tinier amounts of He, but we usually omit these gases as they are inert and at low concentration.

1.20 b. $CuS + O_2 \longrightarrow Cu + SO_2$

1.21 a. Other gasoline-powered machines or vehicles include some lawn mowers, leaf blowers, forklifts, chain saws, snow blowers, and electrical generators.

b. One example is lawn and garden equipment, such as mowers and blowers. The U.S. EPA set emissions reductions for 2012. The regulations will reduce both fuel evaporation and exhaust gas pollutants. For the latter, emissions control technology will be used, just as currently done for larger engines.

1.27 a. A concentration of 1193 μg of particulate matter per cubic meter of air exceeds the National Ambient Air Quality Standards for both PM_{10} and for $PM_{2.5}$.

b. Breathing fine particles at this level is hazardous for everybody. The primary danger is to the cardiovascular system, as the particles, when inhaled, pass into the bloodstream and cause or further aggravate heart disease.

1.28 Indoor activities that generate pollutants include burning incense, cigarette or cigar smoking, frying foods (especially when something burns), operating a faulty furnace or space heater, painting or varnishing (except low-VOC paints), using some cleaning products such as ammonia or spray oven cleaner, using aerosol hair sprays and some hair-coloring products, using some furniture polishes, using spray insecticides, and many others.

1.30 The green chemistry key ideas met by the new coalescents include that it is better to prevent waste than to treat or clean up waste after it is formed (i.e., not to put VOCs into the air), to use renewable materials (i.e., produced from vegetable oils), and to use materials that degrade into innocuous products at the end of their useful life. Those met by the new undercoat include that it is better to prevent waste than to treat or clean up waste after it is formed (i.e., not to put VOCs into the air) and that it is better to use less energy (i.e., to cure the undercoat without using heat).

1.32 b. No, it wouldn't be more valid. The additional digits would not provide any real information, as the meter is not able to determine values with this level of precision. Compare this to dividing $20 evenly among seven people. Even if your calculator displayed the result of $2.857142857, each person would not receive this amount because we have no coins in the United States smaller than pennies.

Chapter 2

2.2 b. The maximum is 12,000 ozone molecules per billion molecules and atoms of all gases that make up the stratosphere (see paragraph that precedes this activity).

c. The EPA limit is 0.075 ppm for an 8-hr average, equivalent to 75 ppb, or 75 ozone molecules per billion molecules and atoms of all gases that make up the troposphere (see Table 1.2).

2.4 c. 17 protons, 17 electrons

d. 24 protons, 24 electrons

2.5 c. Group 5A; 5 outer electrons

d. Group 8A; 8 outer electrons

2.6 b. Beryllium (Be), magnesium (Mg), calcium (Ca), strontium (Sr), barium (Ba), and radium (Ra) all have two outer electrons and are members of Group 2A.

2.7 c. 53 protons, 78 neutrons

2.8 b. 2 Br atoms (:B̈r·) × 7 outer electrons per atom = 14 outer electrons

Here is the Lewis structure for Br_2.

$$:\ddot{Br}:\ddot{Br}: \text{ or } :\ddot{Br}-\ddot{Br}:$$

2.9 b. 1 C atom (·Ċ·) × 4 outer electrons per atom = 4 outer electrons

2 Cl atoms (:C̈l·) × 7 outer electrons per atom = 14 outer electrons

2 F atoms (:F̈·) × 7 outer electrons per atom = 14 outer electrons

Total = 32 outer electrons

Here is the Lewis structure for CCl_2F_2.

$$:\ddot{Cl}:\ddot{C}:\ddot{F}: \text{ or } :\ddot{Cl}-\underset{\underset{:\ddot{F}:}{|}}{\overset{\overset{:\ddot{Cl}:}{|}}{C}}-\ddot{F}:$$

2.10 b. 1 S atom (·S̈·) × 6 outer electrons per atom = 6 outer electrons

2 O atoms (·Ö·) × 6 outer electrons per atom = 12 outer electrons

Total = 18 outer electrons

Here are two resonance forms for the Lewis structure of SO_2.

$$\ddot{O}{=}\overset{\cdot\cdot}{S}{\diagdown}\ddot{O}: \longleftrightarrow :\ddot{O}{\diagup}\overset{\cdot\cdot}{S}{=}\ddot{O}$$

2.12 b. Radio waves have an average wavelength of about 10^1 m. In contrast, the average wavelength for an X-ray is about 10^{-9} m, thus making a radio wave approximately 10^{10} times longer.

2.14 a. UV-C < UV-B < UV-A

b. No, the order is not the same. Rather, it is reversed because wavelength and energy are inversely proportional.

2.16 a. O_3 forms from O and O_2.

$$O + O_2 \longrightarrow O_3$$

b. The source of the O atoms is the breakdown of the oxygen molecule (naturally occurring in the atmosphere) in the presence of UV light.

$$O_2 \longrightarrow 2\,O$$

c. O_3 molecules in the stratosphere break down by several mechanisms, both part of the Chapman cycle. One is that they decompose into O_2 and O.

$$O_3 \longrightarrow O_2 + O$$

The other is that they combine with atomic oxygen to form 2 molecules of O_2.

$$O_3 + O \longrightarrow 2\,O_2$$

2.23 a. 1 H atom (H·) × 1 outer electron per atom = 1 outer electron

1 O atom (·Ö·) × 6 outer electrons per atom = 6 outer electrons

Total = 7 outer electrons

Here is the Lewis structure for the ·OH radical.

$$·\ddot{O}:H \text{ or } ·\ddot{O}-H$$

2.23 b. 1 N atom (·$\ddot{\text{N}}$·) × 5 outer electrons per atom
= 5 outer electrons

1 O atom (·$\ddot{\ddot{\text{O}}}$·) × 6 outer electrons per atom
= 6 outer electrons

Total = 11 outer electrons

Here is the Lewis structure for the ·NO radical. Note the unpaired electron on the N atom.

$$\dot{\text{N}}=\ddot{\text{O}}$$

c. 2 N atoms (·$\ddot{\text{N}}$·) × 5 outer electrons per atom
= 10 outer electrons

1 O atom (·$\ddot{\ddot{\text{O}}}$·) × 6 outer electrons per atom
= 6 outer electrons

Total = 16 outer electrons

Here is one possible Lewis structure for N_2O.

$$:\text{N}\equiv\text{N}-\ddot{\ddot{\text{O}}}:$$

2.24 a. The chemical equations with bromine, analogous to equations 2.10 and 2.15 are

$$2\,\text{Br}\cdot + 2\,\text{O}_3 \longrightarrow 2\,\text{BrO}\cdot + 2\,\text{O}_2$$
$$\text{Br}\cdot + \text{O}_3 \longrightarrow \text{BrO}\cdot + \text{O}_2$$

2.28 a. Sulfur dioxide (SO_2) mainly causes respiratory ailments in humans. The SO_2 can react with water vapor in the lungs to form an acid.

2.29 a. Halon-1301 and HFC-23 have chemical formulas of $CBrF_3$ and CHF_3, respectively. Halon-1301 would be expected to deplete ozone because it contains bromine. Since HFC-23 contains neither bromine nor chlorine, it does not deplete ozone.

c. Figure 2.21 shows that HFC-23 has a high global warming potential. For this reason, it is unlikely to be used in future years.

Chapter 3

3.2 b. infrared, visible, ultraviolet

3.3 a. 25% of energy from the Sun is reflected from the atmosphere, 6% is reflected from the surface, 9% is emitted from the surface, and 60% is emitted from the atmosphere. These percents add up to 100%.

b. 23% of the incoming radiation is directly absorbed in the atmosphere, and an additional 37% is absorbed in the atmosphere after the Earth radiates longer wavelength heat energy. These values add up to 60%, the total energy emitted from the atmosphere.

c. The colors differentiate the wavelengths of light emitted from the Sun and Earth. Yellow represents a mixture of all incoming wavelengths, blue represents the shorter wavelength (higher energy) UV radiation, and red represents the longer wavelength (lower energy) IR radiation.

3.5 a. The atmospheric CO_2 concentration in 1962 was about 318 ppm; in 2012 it was about 393 ppm. The percent increase is

$$\frac{393\ \text{ppm} - 318\ \text{ppm}}{318\ \text{ppm}} \times 100 = 23.6\%$$

b. Within a given year, the atmospheric CO_2 concentration varies by 6–7 ppm.

3.8 b. Total outer electrons: $4 + 2(7) + 2(7) = 32$. Eight go around the central C atom to form four single bonds, one to each Cl atom and one to each F atom. The other 24 outer electrons are nonbonding pairs on the Cl or F atoms. The CCl_2F_2 molecule is tetrahedral, the same shape as CH_4 and CCl_4.

Lewis structure: Molecular shape:

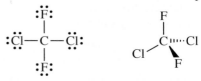

c. Total outer electrons: $2(1) + 6 = 8$. These eight all go around the central S atom to form two single bonds, one to each H atom, and two nonbonded pairs. The H_2S molecule is bent, like H_2O.

Lewis structure: Molecular shape:

$$\text{H}-\ddot{\text{S}}-\text{H}$$ $$\text{H}\underset{<\,109°}{\overset{\text{S}}{\diagup\diagdown}}\text{H}$$

3.9 SO_2, total outer electrons: $6 + 2(6) = 18$. Eight go around the central S atom to form one single bond to an O atom, one double bond to an O atom, and one nonbonded pair. The other 10 outer electrons are nonbonding pairs on the O atoms. The SO_2 molecule is bent, just as the O_3 molecule is bent. Only one resonance form is shown.

Lewis structure: Molecular shape:

$$\ddot{\ddot{\text{O}}}=\ddot{\text{S}}-\ddot{\ddot{\text{O}}}:$$ $$\ddot{\ddot{\text{O}}}\underset{120°}{\overset{\text{S}}{\diagdown\diagup}}\ddot{\ddot{\text{O}}}:$$

3.11 a. The processes that add carbon to the atmosphere include emissions from oceans, respiration, burning fossil fuels, and deforestation.

b. Photosynthesis, absorption in oceans, and reforestation are processes that remove carbon from the atmosphere.

c. The two largest reservoirs of carbon are fossil fuels and carbonate minerals.

d. The parts of the carbon cycle most influenced by human activities are burning fossil fuels and deforestation. The extra anthropogenic atmospheric CO_2 also increases the rate of CO_2 absorption into the oceans.

3.12 a. The atomic number of N is 7 and the atomic mass is 14.01.

b. A neutral N-14 atom has 7 protons, 7 neutrons, and 7 electrons.

c. A neutral N-15 atom has 7 protons, 8 neutrons, and 7 electrons. Only the number of neutrons differs.

d. N-14 is the most abundant natural isotope, given that the atomic mass is 14.01.

3.14 b. 5×10^{12} N atoms $\times \dfrac{2.34 \times 10^{-23} \text{ g N}}{1 \text{ N atom}}$

$= 1.17 \times 10^{-10}$ g N

c. 6×10^{15} N atoms $\times \dfrac{2.34 \times 10^{-23} \text{ g N}}{1 \text{ N atom}}$

$= 1.40 \times 10^{-7}$ g N

3.15 b. 1 mol N_2O = 44.0 g N_2O

c. 1 mol CCl_3F = 137.4 g CCl_3F

3.16 c. The mass ratio compares the molar mass of N to the molar mass of N_2O.

$$\frac{1.0 \text{ mol } N_2O}{44.0 \text{ g } N_2O} \times \frac{2 \text{ mol N}}{1 \text{ mol } N_2O} \times \frac{14.0 \text{ g N}}{1 \text{ mol N}} = \frac{0.636 \text{ g N}}{1 \text{ g } N_2O}$$

To find the mass percent of N in N_2O, multiply the mass ratio by 100.

$$\frac{0.636 \text{ g N}}{1.00 \text{ g } N_2O} \times 100 = 63.6\% \text{ N in } N_2O$$

3.17 b. The mass ratio of S to SO_2 is known from Your Turn 3.16.

$$142 \times 10^6 \text{ t } SO_2 \times \frac{32.1 \times 10^6 \text{ t S}}{64.1 \times 10^6 \text{ t } SO_2} = 7.11 \times 10^7 \text{ t S}$$

3.19 For CO_2: $\dfrac{396 \text{ ppm} - 270 \text{ ppm}}{270 \text{ ppm}} \times 100 = 47\%$

For CH_4: $\dfrac{1.816 \text{ ppm} - 0.70 \text{ ppm}}{0.70 \text{ ppm}} \times 100 = 159\%$

For N_2O: $\dfrac{0.324 \text{ ppm} - 0.275 \text{ ppm}}{0.275 \text{ ppm}} \times 100 = 18\%$

Order: $CH_4 > CO_2 > N_2O$

3.23 Infrared, visible, and ultraviolet radiation are the main types of solar radiation striking the Earth. Visible light accounts for the largest percentage.

3.25 b. Increases in greenhouse gas concentration and changes in the Earth's albedo are additional forcings required to accurately recreate the temperature data for the 20th century.

3.30 $(5 \times 10^6 \text{ metric tons}/6 \times 10^9 \text{ metric tons}) \times 100\%$
$= 0.08\%$.

3.31 a. 19 tons $CO_2 \times \dfrac{2000 \text{ lb } CO_2}{1 \text{ ton } CO_2} \times \dfrac{1 \text{ tree}}{25 \text{ lb } CO_2}$

$= 1520$ trees

If 50 lb per tree is used, the answer is 760 trees.

b. Using 50 lb CO_2 per tree:

12×10^9 trees $\times \dfrac{50 \text{ lb } CO_2}{1 \text{ tree}} \times \dfrac{1 \text{ ton } CO_2}{2000 \text{ lb } CO_2}$

$= 3.0 \times 10^8$ tons CO_2 absorbed

$$\frac{3.0 \times 10^8 \text{ tons } CO_2 \text{ absorbed}}{6.0 \times 10^9 \text{ tons } CO_2 \text{ emitted}} \times 100\% = 5.0\%$$

Chapter 4

4.3 During the composting process, one of the compounds produced is water. The process also gives off heat that may convert the water from a liquid to a gas. On a cool day, the water vapor may come in contact with the chilly air and condense to form "steam." *Note:* The "steam" that you can see is actually condensed water vapor, such as in fog or a cloud. Water vapor itself is invisible.

4.4 b. When coal combusts, 12 g of carbon produces 44 g of carbon dioxide. Plant A burns 4.4×10^8 g of coal per day, creating 1.6×10^9 g of CO_2. Plant B burns 3.6×10^8 g of coal per day, creating 1.3×10^9 g of CO_2. Therefore, Plant B emits 3.0×10^8 fewer grams of CO_2 each day than Plant A.

4.9 a. Coal contains small amounts of sulfur that combine with oxygen during combustion to produce SO_2. Volcanoes are a natural source of SO_2 in the atmosphere.

b. Although coal does contain small amounts of nitrogen that combine with oxygen during combustion, the major portion of NO is formed from the reaction of N_2 and O_2 from the air in the high temperatures produced in the combustion process. Other sources of NO include engine exhaust, lightning, and grain silos.

4.11 a. 1500 kJ $\times \dfrac{1 \text{ g } CH_4}{50.1 \text{ kJ}} \times \dfrac{1 \text{ mol } CH_4}{16 \text{ g } CH_4} \times$

$\dfrac{1 \text{ mol } CO_2}{1 \text{ mol } CH_4} \times \dfrac{44 \text{ g } CO_2}{1 \text{ mol } CO_2} = 82 \text{ g } CO_2$

b. For bituminous coal from Maryland, which releases 30.7 kJ/g, 150 g of CO_2 is released when 1500 kJ of heat is produced.

4.17 From Section 2.3, here are the resonance forms for ozone:

$$\ddot{O}=\ddot{O}-\ddot{O}: \longleftrightarrow :\ddot{O}-\ddot{O}=\ddot{O}$$

And here is the Lewis structure for oxygen:

$$\ddot{O}::\ddot{O} \text{ or } \ddot{O}=\ddot{O}$$

The bond energy for O_3 is *intermediate* between the O−O single bond (146 kJ/mol) and the O=O double bond (498 kJ/mol) values, that is, it is less than the bond energy for the O=O double bond in O_2 (498 kJ/mol). Energy is inversely proportional to wavelength. Therefore, the *higher* bond energy of O_2 requires radiation of *shorter* wavelength to break its bonds.

4.18 a. One possible pair of products is C_8H_{18} and C_8H_{16}. Their structural formulas are:

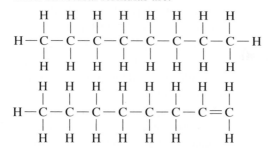

c. The generic chemical formula is C_nH_{2n}, where n is an integer.

4.22 a. Structural formulas for methanol and ethanol

$$H - \overset{\displaystyle H}{\underset{\displaystyle H}{\overset{|}{\underset{|}{C}}}} - O - H \qquad H - \overset{\displaystyle H}{\underset{\displaystyle H}{\overset{|}{\underset{|}{C}}}} - \overset{\displaystyle H}{\underset{\displaystyle H}{\overset{|}{\underset{|}{C}}}} - O - H$$

methanol   ethanol

4.24 a. $C_2H_5OH + 3\,O_2 \longrightarrow 2\,CO_2 + 3\,H_2O$ (Note that this chemical equation is shown in Figure 4.16.)

b. $2\,C_{19}H_{38}O_2 + 55\,O_2 \longrightarrow 38\,CO_2 + 38\,H_2O$ (*Hint:* Balance the C and H atoms first.)

Chapter 5

5.3 b. The O–H bond is more polar. The electron pair is more strongly attracted to the O atom.

c. The O–S bond is more polar. The electron pair is more strongly attracted to the O atom.

d. The Cl–C bond is more polar. The electron pair is more strongly attracted to the Cl atom.

5.5 a. The dashed lines represent hydrogen bonds, that is, a weak attraction between a H atom bonded to an electronegative atom (F, N, or O) and a neighboring electronegative atom on another molecule.

b. Any of the H atoms on the water molecules could be labeled δ^+. Similarly, any of the O atoms could be labeled δ^-. The molecules are oriented so that the opposite charges are in close proximity.

c. Hydrogen bonds are intermolecular forces because they occur *between* two molecules.

5.12 a. 1.6×10^{-2} ppm; 16 ppb

b. No, the mercury concentration is eight times higher than the standard of 2 ppb.

5.13 a. 8.0×10^{-8} M

b. A 500 mL sample of 1.5 M NaCl contains 0.75 mol of solute. A 500 mL sample of 0.15 M NaCl contains 0.075 mol of solute.

c. The solution made from 0.60 mol NaCl is more concentrated. Converting to molarity, it has a concentration of 3.0 M compared with 2.0 M for the other solution.

d. No, the resulting solution is not 2.0 M. When 40.0 g of $CuSO_4$ is dissolved in a 1.0 L of water, the solution contains only 0.25 mol of solute.

5.14 a. Li and K form cations; S and N form anions.

b. Mg^{2+}, Lewis structures: $\cdot Mg \cdot$ (atom) and Mg^{2+} (ion)

O^{2-}, Lewis structures: $\cdot \overset{\cdot\cdot}{\underset{\cdot\cdot}{O}} \cdot$ (atom) and $\left[:\overset{\cdot\cdot}{\underset{\cdot\cdot}{O}}: \right]^{2-}$ (ion)

Al^{3+}, Lewis structures: $\cdot \overset{\cdot}{Al} \cdot$ (atom) and Al^{3+} (ion)

5.15 a. CaS, calcium sulfide

b. KF, potassium fluoride

c. From Figure 5.19, Mn can form two ions: Mn^{2+} and Mn^{4+}. O forms the oxide ion, O^{2-}. The possible chemical formulas are MnO, manganese(II) oxide and MnO_2, manganese(IV) oxide.

d. $AlCl_3$, aluminum chloride

5.16 c. $Al(C_2H_3O_2)_3$ **d.** K_2CO_3

5.17 c. Sodium hydrogen carbonate or sodium bicarbonate

d. Calcium carbonate   **e.** Magnesium phosphate

5.18 a. NaClO   **b.** $MgCO_3$ **c.** NH_4NO_3

5.20 b. Soluble. All sodium salts are soluble.

c. Insoluble. Most sulfides are insoluble (except those with Group 1A or NH_4^+ cations).

d. Insoluble. Most hydroxides are insoluble (except those with Group 1A or NH_4^+ cations).

5.21 All of the oxygen atoms should be labeled δ^-. Only the hydrogen atoms attached to the oxygen atoms should be labeled as δ^+. The hydrogen atoms bonded to carbon atoms do not carry a partial positive charge, as the C–H bond is nonpolar. The carbon atom bonded to the oxygen atom is slightly positive.

5.22 C–C bonds are nonpolar. C–H bonds are also nonpolar, as the electronegativity difference between C and H is small.

5.26 a. The sample with a concentration of 20 ppb lead ion (20 μg/L) is higher than that of 0.003 mg/L lead (3 μg/L or 3 ppb).

b. A concentration of 20 ppb Pb^{2+} is greater than the 15 ppb standard, and 3 ppb Pb^{2+} is less than the 15 ppb standard.

5.28 a. Sulfate ion is SO_4^{2-}, hydroxide ion is OH^-, calcium ion is Ca^{2+}, and aluminum ion is Al^{3+}.

b. Calcium sulfate, $CaSO_4$; calcium hydroxide, $Ca(OH)_2$, aluminum sulfate, $Al_2(SO_4)_3$; aluminum hydroxide, $Al(OH)_3$

c. Sodium hypochlorite NaClO, calcium hypochlorite $Ca(ClO)_2$

5.29 a. Possibilities include $CHCl_3$, $CHBr_3$, $CHBrCl_2$, and $CHBr_2Cl$. The Lewis structures for these are analogous to the one shown here for $CHClF_2$.

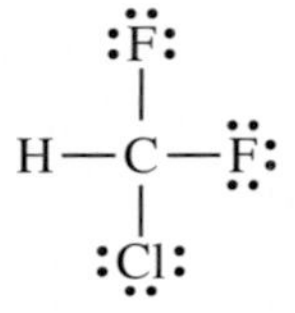

b. THMs do not contain fluorine atoms.

5.35 Here are three other green chemistry key ideas that apply: (1) It is better to prevent waste than to treat or clean up waste after it is formed, (2) It is better to minimize the amount of materials used in the production of a product, and (4) It is better to use less energy.

Chapter 6

6.1 a. Possibilities include hydrochloric acid, sulfuric acid, acetic acid, nitric acid, phosphoric acid, lactic acid, and citric acid.

b. Possibilities include having used any of these acids in chemistry experiments, having heard about lactic acid buildup in muscles, and having seen phosphoric acid or citric acid listed as an ingredient in soft drinks.

6.2 a. $HI(aq) \longrightarrow H^+(aq) + I^-(aq)$

b. $HNO_3(aq) \longrightarrow H^+(aq) + NO_3^-(aq)$

6.4 a. $KOH(s) \xrightarrow{H_2O} K^+(aq) + OH^-(aq)$

b. $LiOH(s) \xrightarrow{H_2O} Li^+(aq) + OH^-(aq)$

c. $Ca(OH)_2(s) \xrightarrow{H_2O} Ca^{2+}(aq) + 2\,OH^-(aq)$

6.5 a. $HNO_3(aq) + KOH(aq) \longrightarrow KNO_3(aq) + H_2O(l)$

$H^+(aq) + NO_3^-(aq) + K^+(aq) + OH^-(aq) \longrightarrow$
$K^+(aq) + NO_3^-(aq) + H_2O(l)$

$H^+(aq) + OH^-(aq) \longrightarrow H_2O(l)$

b.

$HCl(aq) + NH_4OH(aq) \longrightarrow NH_4Cl(aq) + H_2O(l)$

$H^+(aq) + Cl^-(aq) + NH_4^+(aq) + OH^-(aq) \longrightarrow$
$NH_4^+(aq) + Cl^-(aq) + H_2O(l)$

$H^+(aq) + OH^-(aq) \longrightarrow H_2O(l)$

6.6 b. The solution is basic because $[OH^-] > [H^+]$.

$[H^+][OH^-] = 1 \times 10^{-14}$

Solving, $[H^+] = 1 \times 10^{-8}$ M.

c. The solution is basic because $[OH^-] > [H^+]$.

$[H^+][OH^-] = 1 \times 10^{-14}$

Solving, $[OH^-] = 1 \times 10^{-4}$ M.

6.7 a. When potassium hydroxide dissociates, one hydroxide ion is released for each potassium ion. The basic solution contains much more OH^- than H^+. $OH^-(aq) = K^+(aq) > H^+(aq)$

b. When nitric acid dissociates, one hydrogen ion is released for each nitrate ion. The acidic solution contains much more H^+ than OH^-.
$H^+(aq) = NO_3^-(aq) > OH^-(aq)$

c. When sulfuric acid dissociates, two hydrogen ions are released for each sulfate ion. The acidic solution contains much more H^+ than OH^-.
$H^+(aq) > SO_4^{2-}(aq) > OH^-(aq)$

6.9 a. Although the pH values differ only by 1, the lake water sample is 10 times more acidic and (for an equal volume) would have 10 times more H^+ than the rain sample.

b. Although the pH values differ only by 3, the tap water sample is 1000 times more acidic and (for an equal volume) would have 1000 times more H^+ than the ocean water sample.

6.13 $H_2SO_3(aq) \longrightarrow H^+(aq) + HSO_3^-(aq)$
$HSO_3^-(aq) \longrightarrow H^+(aq) + SO_3^{2-}(aq)$
$H_2SO_3(aq) \longrightarrow 2\,H^+(aq) + SO_3^{2-}(aq)$

6.14 c. 1.68×10^4 tons S $\times \dfrac{64 \text{ tons } SO_2}{32 \text{ tons S}}$
$= 3.36 \times 10^4$ tons SO_2

d. The SO_3 can react with water to form sulfuric acid: $SO_3(g) + H_2O(l) \longrightarrow H_2SO_4(aq)$

6.15 It requires 946 kJ of energy to break a mole of triple bonds between nitrogen atoms. This is one of the highest bond energies in Table 4.4.

6.16 Nitrogen monoxide (NO) is a gas that forms in automobile combustion engines. As you saw in Chapter 1, once released in the exhaust, it reacts in the atmosphere to produce NO_2.

$$N_2 + O_2 \xrightarrow{\text{high temperature}} 2\,NO$$
$$2\,NO + O_2 \longrightarrow 2\,NO_2$$

NO also reacts with ozone to form nitrogen dioxide (NO_2).

$$NO(g) + O_3(g) \longrightarrow NO_2(g) + O_2(g)$$

Nitrogen dioxide (NO_2) is a toxic brown gas. One indication of its reactivity is the damage it does to your lungs if you breathe it. If NO_2 were inert, it would not be such a health hazard. Ammonia (NH_3) is a gas that you may have encountered in the context of "household ammonia," an aqueous solution of ammonia. One indication of the reactivity of NH_3 is that it is a good cleaning agent. In addition, ammonia is a base that reacts quickly with acids.

6.17 SO_2 decreased more than NO_x, both in the actual amount and in the % reduction. The most likely reason for the decrease is the cap and trade component of the EPA's Acid Rain Program.

6.18 a. Iron (Fe) is a metal.

b. Aluminum (Al) is a metal.

c. Fluorine (F) is a nonmetal.

d. Calcium (Ca) is a metal.

e. Zinc (Zn) is a metal.

f. Oxygen (O) is a nonmetal.

6.19 $4\,Fe(s) + 2\,O_2(g) + \cancel{8\,H^+(aq)} \longrightarrow$
$$\cancel{4\,Fe^{2+}(aq)} + \cancel{4\,H_2O(l)}$$

$\cancel{4\,Fe^{2+}(aq)} + O_2(g) + \cancel{4\,H_2O(l)} \longrightarrow$
$$2\,Fe_2O_3(s) + \cancel{8\,H^+(aq)}$$

$$\overline{4\,Fe(s) + 3\,O_2(g) \longrightarrow 2\,Fe_2O_3(s)}$$

6.20 **a.** Fe is the metal form of iron.

c. Fe^{2+} and Fe^{3+} have lost two and three valence electrons, respectively.

6.21 **a.** $MgCO_3(s) + 2\,H^+(aq) \longrightarrow$
$$Mg^{2+}(aq) + CO_2(g) + H_2O(l)$$

b. Sodium bicarbonate is soluble in water. Section 5.8 does not contain this information explicitly, but any experience using baking soda (i.e., sodium bicarbonate) in cooking will show that it is indeed soluble in water.

6.22 $CaCO_3(s) + H_2SO_4(aq) \longrightarrow$
$$CaSO_4(s) + CO_2(g) + H_2O(l)$$

6.25 $S(s) + O_2(g) \longrightarrow SO_2(g)$
$2\,SO_2(g) + O_2(g) \longrightarrow 2\,SO_3(g)$
$SO_3(g) + H_2O(l) \longrightarrow H_2SO_4(aq)$

6.26 **a.** $H_2SO_4(aq) + NH_4OH(aq) \longrightarrow$
$$NH_4HSO_4(aq) + H_2O(l)$$

b. $H_2SO_4(aq) + 2\,NH_4OH(aq) \longrightarrow$
$$(NH_4)_2SO_4(aq) + 2\,H_2O(l)$$

6.28 **b.** The hydrogen carbonate ion is acting as a base because it is reacting with an acid, that is, a hydrogen ion.

Chapter 7

7.5 U-234 has 92 protons and 142 neutrons compared to 92 protons and 146 neutrons for U-238.

7.6 **b.** ${}^{1}_{0}n + {}^{235}_{92}U \longrightarrow {}^{137}_{52}Te + {}^{97}_{40}Zr + 2\,{}^{1}_{0}n$

7.7 For anthracite coal:

$$9.0 \times 10^{10}\,kJ \times \frac{1.0\,g\ anthracite\ coal}{30.5\,kJ} \times \frac{1\,kg}{1000\,g}$$
$$= 3.0 \times 10^6\,kg\ anthracite\ coal$$

The equivalent masses for the other grades are calculated in the same way: bituminous coal, 2.9×10^6 kg; subbituminous coal, 3.8×10^6 kg; lignite (brown coal), 5.6×10^6 kg; peat, 6.9×10^6 kg.

7.8 ${}^{241}_{95}Am \longrightarrow {}^{237}_{93}Np + {}^{4}_{2}He$
${}^{9}_{4}Be + {}^{4}_{2}He \longrightarrow {}^{12}_{6}C + {}^{1}_{0}n + {}^{0}_{0}\gamma$

7.9 In an emergency such as an earthquake, the fuel rods should be inserted in preparation for shutdown in order to slow the nuclear fission reaction in the reactor core.

7.10 The cloud is tiny droplets of condensed water vapor. People sometimes call this "steam," but technically this is not correct. Steam (water vapor) is invisible until it condenses. The cloud does not contain any nuclear fission products.

7.12 **c.** "Radiation" refers to UV radiation, a region of the electromagnetic spectrum.

d. "Radiation" refers to the nuclear radiation (alpha particles) emitted by uranium nuclei.

7.13 **b.** ${}^{239}_{94}Pu \longrightarrow {}^{235}_{92}U + {}^{4}_{2}He$

7.14 **a.** :Ï·   :Ï:Ï: [:Ï:]⁻
atom   molecule   ion

b. The iodine atom is the most reactive here because it has one unpaired electron, that is, it is a free radical.

7.15 **a.** -249 kJ per mol H_2 and -125 kJ per gram H_2, both energy released.

b. From Figure 4.16, methane releases -50.1 kJ per gram when burned. Using the value calculated in part **a** as the basis for comparison, H_2 releases two and a half times more!

7.18 **a.** ${}^{222}_{86}Rn \longrightarrow {}^{218}_{84}Po + {}^{4}_{2}He$

c. Polonium-218 and the other decay products of radon are all solids. These may lodge in the lungs, continually emitting radiation as one product decays into the next. Nuclear radiation is weakly carcinogenic, so although exposure may cause cancer, it does not always cause cancer.

7.21 $\dfrac{3.5 \times 10^{14}\ \text{C-14 atoms}}{3.0 \times 10^{26}\ \text{all C atoms}} \times 100$
$$= 1.17 \times 10^{-10}\ \%\ \text{of carbon-14}$$

7.23 **a.** The other isotope is U-238. A trace amount of U-234 is present as well.

b. U-238 is not fissionable under the conditions present in a nuclear reactor.

c. These other radioisotopes are fission products. U-235 splits in many different ways, so many radioisotopes are formed.

7.25 After 10 half-lives, 0.0975% of the original sample remains.

# of half-lives	% decayed	% remaining
0	0	100
1	50	50
2	75	25
3	87.5	12.5
4	93.75	6.25
5	96.88	3.12
6	98.44	1.56
7	99.22	0.78
8	99.61	0.39
9	99.805	0.195
10	99.9025	0.0975

7.26 After 36.9 years (3 half-lives), 12.5% of the original tritium will remain.

7.27 **a.** Radium is a product in the natural decay series of uranium-238, the isotope of uranium of highest natural abundance. Therefore if uranium is present in the rocks and soils, radium will be present as well.

b. Five half-lives (5×3.8 days $= 19$ days) are required for the level of radioactivity to drop from 16 pCi to 0.5 pCi.

c. Radon will continue to enter your basement because the uranium in the soils and rocks underneath your home continuously produces it. See part **a**.

7.28 $^{1}_{0}n + ^{235}_{92}U \longrightarrow ^{143}_{54}Xe + ^{90}_{38}Sr + 3\,^{1}_{0}n$

Chapter 8

8.2 Equations **c** and **e** are reduction half-reactions because electrons are gained, appearing on the reactant side of the equations. Equations **b** and **d** are oxidation half-reactions because electrons are lost, appearing on the product side.

8.3 **a.** Each equation is balanced from the standpoint of number and type of atoms.

b. Each equation is balanced from the standpoint of charge, but the total charge does not have to be zero on each side, just the same.

c. Electrons do not appear in the overall cell reaction, but are shown in half-reactions.

8.4 **a.** $Zn \longrightarrow Zn^{2+} + 2\,e^{-}$

b. $Cu^{2+} + 2\,e^{-} \longrightarrow Cu$

c. To be rechargeable, the products need to remain near the reactants rather than dispersing. In the case of this cell, the ions formed are mobile and disperse throughout the solution rather than staying near the electrodes.

8.6 **b.** Metallic lead, Pb(s) loses two electrons to form aqueous lead ion, $Pb^{2+}(aq)$. Metallic lead is oxidized.

c. The battery discharge is the forward reaction of equation 8.12. As in part **b**, metallic lead, Pb(s), is oxidized to form lead ion, $Pb^{2+}(aq)$.

8.7 **a.** Metals are elements that are good conductors of electricity and heat. They have a shiny appearance. In contrast, nonmetals are poor conductors of electricity and heat and are not shiny. See Section 1.6. Metals have low electronegativity values in comparison to nonmetals. This explains why metals tend to lose electrons to form cations (while nonmetals tend to gain electrons to form anions). See Chapter 5 for more information about electronegativity.

c. $CdS(s) + O_2(g) \longrightarrow Cd(s) + SO_2(g)$

In CdS(s), the cadmium ion (Cd^{2+}) gains 2 electrons to form Cd(s) and is reduced.

d. Sulfur dioxide released from smelting containing ores contributes to air pollution. The EPA monitors the level of SO_2 as part of ambient air quality standards due to the serious nature of this air pollutant as a respiratory irritant.

8.15 **b.** The reactions are endothermic. More energy is required to break bonds than is released in bond formation.

c. Although there is general agreement (+182 kJ vs. +165 kJ), remember that Table 4.4 gives *average* bond energies, not specific energies associated with the bonds in these compounds (with the exception of CO_2).

8.18 **a.** Doping with phosphorus forms an *n*-type semiconductor. Phosphorus is in Group VA and has one more electron per atom than a silicon atom does.

b. Doping with boron forms a *p*-type semiconductor. Boron is in Group IIIA and has one fewer electron per atom than a silicon atom.

8.19 **b.** Uses include providing electricity to power lighting, heating, and other electrical needs in a building or in a process used by the business. For example, PVs have been used to generate enough electricity to power the electrical needs of a small microbrewery.

c. Uses include supplying electricity to part or all of a home. At present, some homes that have a PV system are even able to sell electricity back to electric power companies. A PV system also can be used for electrical back-up in locations in which storms occur that disrupt the power.

8.22 **a.** A solar collector with a heat exchange fluid system would replace the burner/boiler systems.

b. Advantages of distributed generation for collecting solar energy include (1) a distributed generation system does not require a condenser and does not generate thermal pollution, and (2) it is suitable for locations not reached by power lines. Advantages of a centralized location for conventional energy generation include (1) the efficiency of scale—a concentrated energy source servicing many users, and (2) the user is not required to install the energy generation equipment.

Chapter 9

9.3 **a.**

b.

9.4 Items typically made of HDPE include pearly shampoo bottles, brightly colored detergent bottles, opaque or translucent milk jugs, and squeeze glue bottles. HDPE containers are often used for soaps and nonoily food items. In contrast, you are more likely to find LDPE as a plastic packing material or plastic baggie. Yes, HDPE and LDPE differ in flexibility. LDPE is usually softer and more flexible. They also differ in that HDPE is usually opaque or translucent, whereas some forms of LDPE are transparent.

9.10 a.

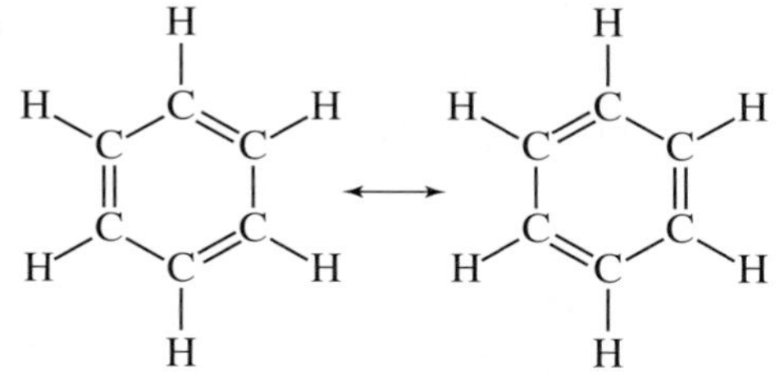

benzene

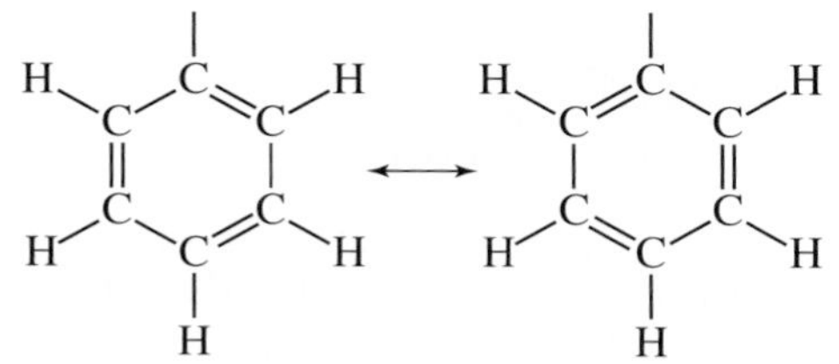

phenyl group

9.12

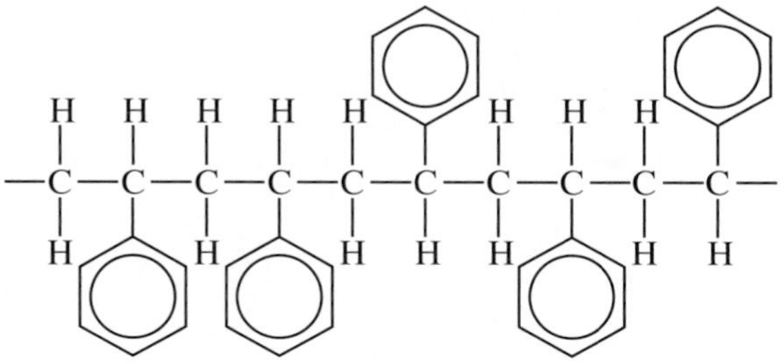

The head-to-tail arrangement is favored because this spaces the benzene rings as far apart as possible, minimizing repulsions between them. In the head-to-head, tail-to-tail arrangement, the rings would fall on carbons that are right next to each other.

9.15

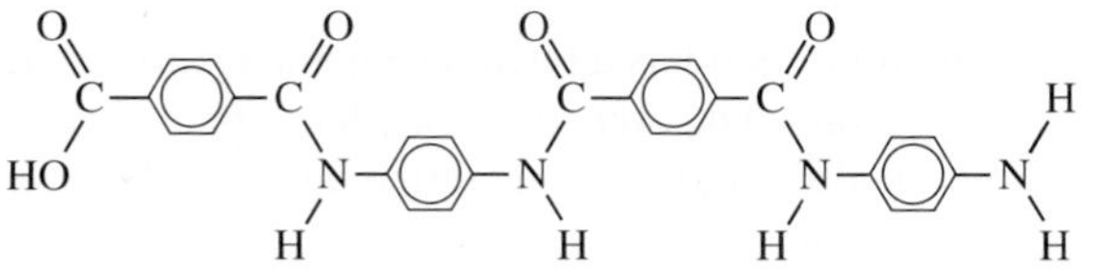

9.20 a. Propylene is $H_2C=CHCH_3$ or C_3H_6.

$$2500\ C_3H_6 + 11250\ O_2 \longrightarrow 7500\ CO_2 + 7500\ H_2O$$

9.23 Recyclable items that you might purchase include many plastic containers and jugs, beverages in aluminum cans, and newspapers. Examples of recycled-content items include paper products (some paper napkins, towels, toilet paper) and plastic items (some outdoor picnic tables, park benches, lumber, and even railroad ties). Yes, in theory, anything that contains postconsumer waste can be recycled again. In practice, however, this depends on local recycling services.

9.26 a.

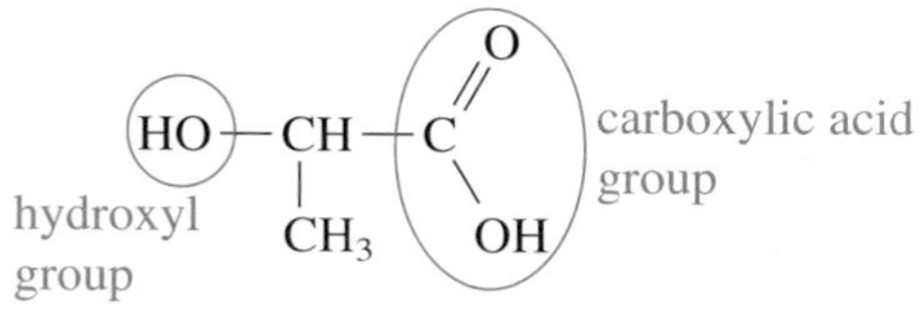

c. Here is a way to represent the polymer (with its repeating unit).

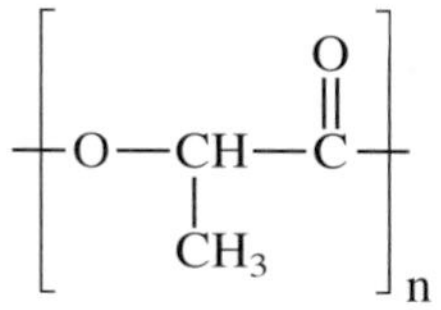

9.28 a. Advantages of glass bottles include that they are reusable, attractive, and relatively inexpensive. Disadvantages include that they are heavy and breakable. Advantages of plastic bottles include that they are light-weight, recyclable, inexpensive, and nonbreakable. Disadvantages include that they are petroleum based (a nonrenewable resource) and eventually make their way to the landfill.

b. Beer is occasionally sold in plastic bottles when glass would be unsafe (for example at sporting events), but consumer acceptance has been low. PET, the clear plastic bottle of choice, is slightly permeable to oxygen, which may chemically react with beer and change its taste.

9.30 a. Esters are a functional group, that is, a characteristic arrangement of atoms that impart certain properties to the molecule. The ester functional group was introduced in Chapter 4 and also shown in Table 9.2. Here is the structural formula for an ester.

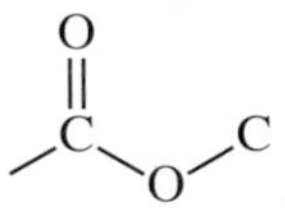

b.

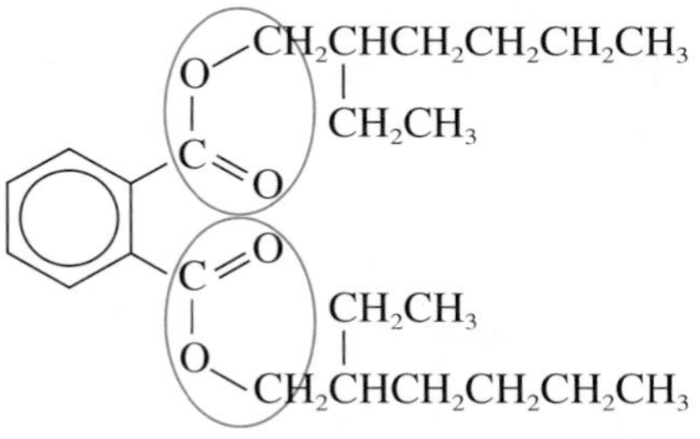

DEHP

c.

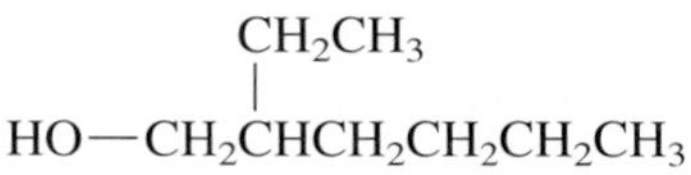

Chapter 10

10.4 a. Each carbon atom in Figure 10.2 is surrounded by 8 electrons (4 bonds), so the octet rule is followed.

b. Carbon monoxide, CO. Carbon only has three bonds in this molecule.

10.5 c.

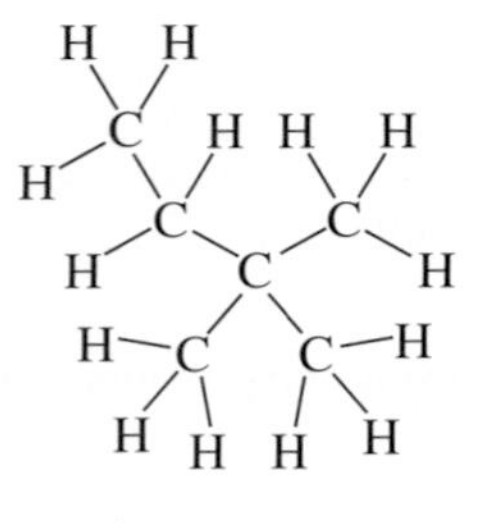

d.

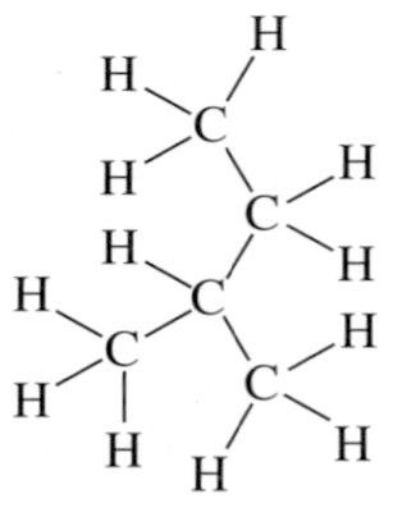

10.6 c.

d.

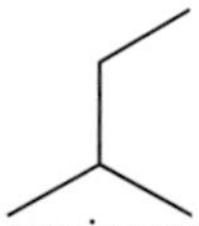

10.7 a. Yes, *n*-butane and *iso*butane are isomers. They have the same formula, C_4H_{10}, but different structures.

b. No, *n*-hexane (C_6H_{14}) and cyclohexane (C_6H_{12}) are not isomers. They have different formulas as well as different structures.

c.

Structural Formula	Condensed Structural Formula and Line-Angle Drawing
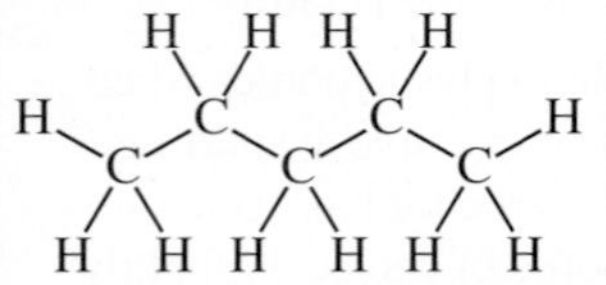	$CH_3CH_2CH_2CH_2CH_3$ 
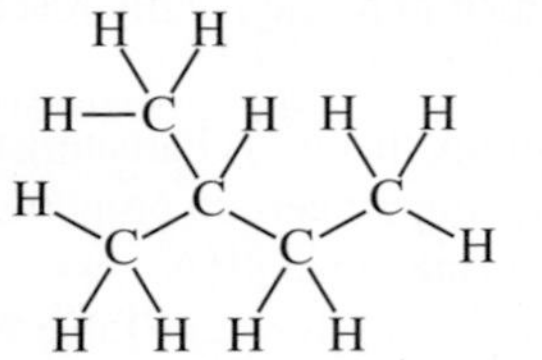	$CH_3CH(CH_3)CH_2CH_3$ 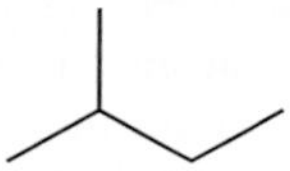
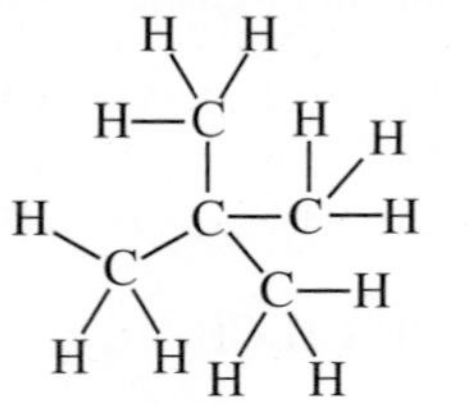	$C(CH_3)_4$ 

10.8 c.

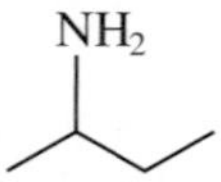

amine

d.

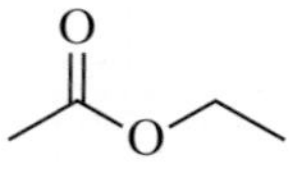

ester

e.

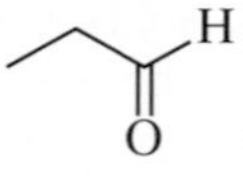

aldehyde

10.9 a.

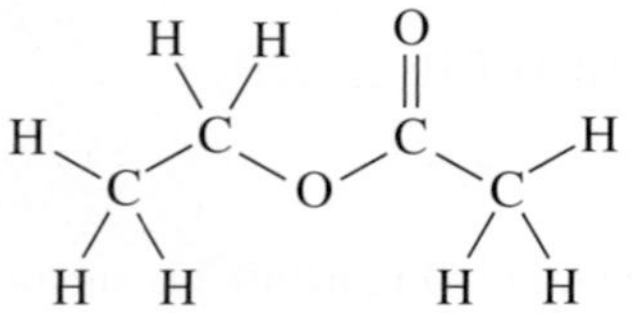

b.

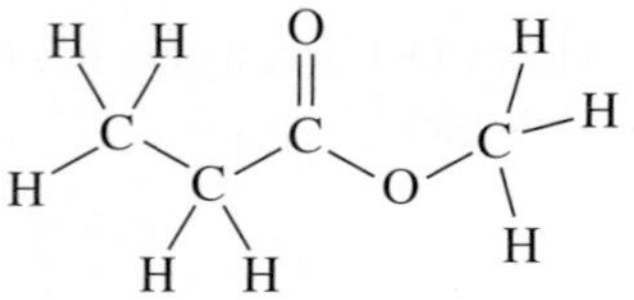

10.10 All three molecules have a benzene ring with attached functional groups that can form hydrogen bonds with water. Both aspirin and ibuprofen have a carboxylic acid group attached.

10.16 b.

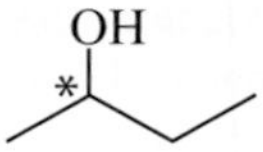

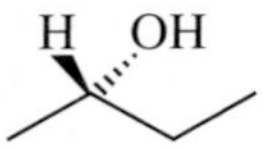

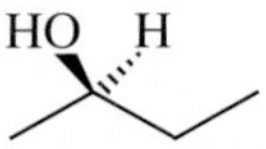

c.

*CHClFCH₃

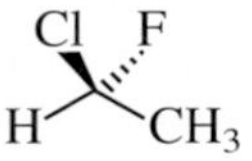

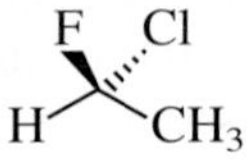

d.

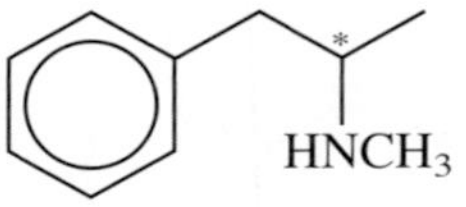

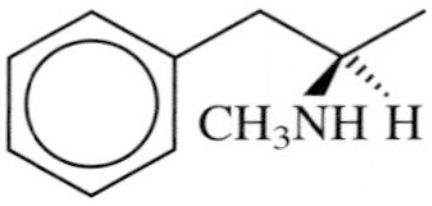

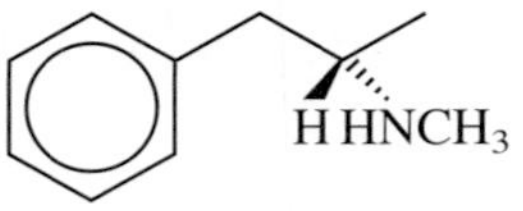

10.17 a. The chiral carbons are indicated with an asterisk in these structures. *Note:* Enantiomers are drawn here for part c—the chiral carbon is the same for both enantiomers.

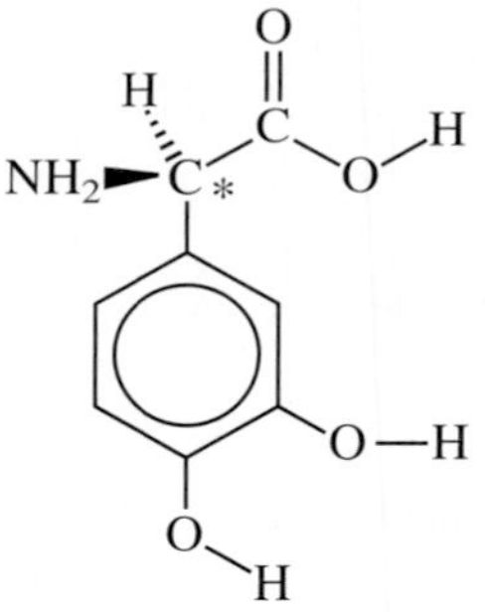

(+)-dopa 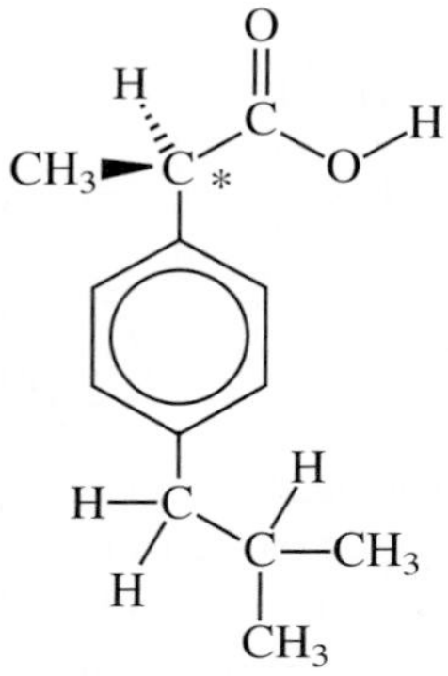　　　　　　(−)-ibuprofen

b. Ibuprofen has a phenyl ring and a carboxylic acid group. The dopa molecule has a phenyl ring, two hydroxyl groups, an amine, and a carboxylic acid group.

c. Drawings are given in part **a.**

10.19 a.

estradiol	progesterone
−OH group on the D ring	C=O group off the D ring
−CH₃ group on CD ring intersection	C=O and C=C on the A ring
	−CH₃ groups on CD and AB ring intersections

estradiol	testosterone
−OH group on the D ring	−OH group on the D ring
−CH₃ group on CD ring intersection	−CH₃ groups on CD and AB ring intersections
	C=O and C=C on the A ring

cholic acid	cholesterol
−OH groups on the A, B, and C rings	−OH group on the A ring
carboxylic acid group on D ring side chain	double bond in A ring
−CH₃ groups on CD and AB ring intersections	−CH₃ groups on CD and AB ring intersections

corticosterone	cortisone
C=O and C=C on the A ring	C=O and C=C on the A ring
−OH group on C ring	C=O group on C ring, and also on D ring side chain
−OH group on D ring side chain	−OH groups on D ring and D ring side chain
−CH₃ groups on CD and AB ring intersections	−CH₃ groups on CD and AB ring intersections

prednisone	cortisone
C=O and 2 C=C bonds on the A ring	C=O and C=C on the A ring
−OH group on C ring	C=O group on C ring, and also on D ring side chain
−OH group on D ring side chain	−OH groups on D ring and D ring side chain
−CH₃ groups on CD and AB ring intersections	−CH₃ groups on CD and AB ring intersections

b.

estradiol	$C_{18}H_{24}O_2$	testosterone	$C_{19}H_{28}O_2$
progesterone	$C_{21}H_{30}O_2$	cholic acid	$C_{24}H_{40}O_5$
prednisone	$C_{21}H_{26}O_5$	corticosterone	$C_{21}H_{30}O_4$
cortisone	$C_{21}H_{28}O_5$	cholesterol	$C_{27}H_{46}O$

10.26 Hydrochloric acid, HCl(*aq*), is used to form the salt of oxycodone. This is the structure for the salt. The N atom no longer has a lone pair of electrons, which is what characterizes the freebase form.

Chapter 11

11.7 b. Biodiesel is the methyl ester of a fatty acid. Fats and oils are triglycerides, that is, triple esters of glycerol.

11.10 The process of interesterification allows food producers to use fats and oils for food without *trans* fats. This follows green chemistry key idea #3: It is better to use and generate substances that are not toxic.

11.11 a. Sweetness is related to the molecular structure (and shape). Since the sugars have different structures, they will interact with the receptors on your tongue in a different manner, resulting in a different degree of sweetness.

    b. Although these sugars differ in their chemical structures, their chemical composition is essentially the same. Fructose and glucose have the same chemical formula, and sucrose is nearly the same. With the same chemical formula, the same amount of heat is liberated when these sugars are metabolized (or burned).

11.14 GlyGlyGly, GlyGlyAla, GlyAlaAla, GlyAlaGly, AlaAlaAla, AlaAlaGly, AlaGlyGly, AlaGlyAla

11.18 Processed food tends to be "heavy" in salt, that is, have a sodium content per serving that is relatively high compared with the daily requirement. For some people, this tastes quite normal. But for others, this is noticeably salty. For example, a can of soup can be 800 mg or more of sodium per serving. The low salt choices have less sodium but still include some salt.

11.21 a. No. Males require more calories than females.

    b. As males and females grow through their teens and into their 20s, their estimated calorie requirement increases. After age 30 and beyond, the calorie requirement declines.

11.25 a. $2000 \text{ g C} \times \dfrac{1 \text{ mol CO}_2}{12 \text{ g C}} \times \dfrac{44 \text{ g CO}_2}{1 \text{ mol CO}_2} \times \dfrac{1 \text{ lb CO}_2}{454 \text{ g CO}_2}$

= about 16 pounds of CO_2 emitted per gallon of gas.

11.25 b. Let's assume that your car gets 30 miles to the gallon. 1000 miles would then translate to 33 gallons of gas burned.

33 gallons $\times$ 16 pounds CO_2 per gallon
= 530 pounds of CO_2

11.26 a. From Chapter 5, "like dissolves like." In this case, both ammonia and water are polar molecules. Substances that are polar dissolve well in each other.

b. From Chapter 6, here is the chemical equation 6.5a that shows that ammonia gas dissolves in water.

$$NH_3(g) \xrightarrow{H_2O} NH_3(aq)$$

Small amounts of the hydroxide ion are released when ammonia dissolves in water, as shown in equation 6.5b, reproduced here.

$$NH_3(aq) + H_2O(l) \xrightarrow{\text{only to a small extent}} NH_4^+(aq) + OH^-(aq)$$

c. From Figure 11.26, the nitrate ion is assimilated by plants.

d. From Figure 11.26, the ammonium ion (NH_4^+) is first converted to the nitrite ion (NO_2^-) by microbes and then to the nitrate ion (NO_3^-), a form that plants can utilize. Here is a representation from Chapter 6.

$$NH_4^+ \xrightarrow{\text{bacteria in the soil}} NO_2^- \xrightarrow{\text{bacteria in the soil}} NO_3^-$$

11.27 Here is the structural formula for methyl bromide:

$$H-\underset{\underset{H}{|}}{\overset{\overset{H}{|}}{C}}-Br$$

Methyl bromide contains a C—Br bond. This bond will split in the presence of UV light in the stratosphere to release bromine atoms that in turn react with ozone molecules, thus destroying them.

Chapter 12

12.2 a. Carbohydrate is a general term for all three of the other terms. Glucose is a monosaccharide or simple carbohydrate. Both cellulose and starch are polysaccharides or complex carbohydrates. Both are, in fact, structurally different polymers using the same monomer of glucose.

b. Triglycerides are a class of molecules that include both fats and oils. Fats are solid at room temperature as they contain more saturated fatty acids; oils are liquid at room temperature as they contain more unsaturated fatty acids.

12.3 a. A protein is a large molecule (a polymer) built from amino acids (smaller molecules, monomers). Protein molecules are characterized by features such as their composition, their distinctive shape, and their biological function.

b. A carbohydrate is a molecule composed of only C, H, and O in the ratio of CH_2O. Many carbohydrates, such as starch and cellulose, are large molecules (polymers) built from smaller molecules (sugar monomers).

12.6

deoxyribose

12.7 b. CTAGGAT

12.10 b. The chromosome must be condensed over 1000-fold to go from the extended double helix length of 4.6 cm (4.6×10^{-2} m) to approximately 4 μm (4×10^{-6} m).

c. This level of compaction is necessary to fit in an organized manner within the cell.

12.12 If several codons represent the same amino acid, then changes in single base pairs are less likely to result in a change to the amino acid sequence the gene encodes. The redundancy in the genetic code makes it more robust.

12.13 a. Nylon and proteins (such as those in meat) both contain the amide functional group.

c. Both nylons and proteins are condensation polymers. When they form, a small molecule (all proteins, but only some nylons) is released.

12.15 a. An ion is an atom or group of atoms with a positive or negative charge. Examples include the hydroxide ion (OH^-) and the sodium ion (Na^+).

b. ·OH and H· are examples of species with an unpaired electron.

c. When radiation of high enough energy collides with a molecule, it knocks out an electron, producing an ion with an unpaired electron.

d. In some cases, the ions produced by ionizing radiation are highly reactive because they have unpaired electrons. For example, this occurs when the water molecule is ionized (see Chapter 7). Random mutations occur in DNA because these reactive species damage the strand of DNA at random locations.

Answers to Selected End-of-Chapter Questions Indicated in Color in the Text

Chapter 0

9. These representations are similar in that they both contain the same elements: the economy, the society, and the environment. Both also depict these elements as overlapping. They differ in how these three elements overlap. As drawn for this question, the environment encompasses both the economy and society. Some would argue that this is essential, as without the environment, the other two cannot exist. Others, however, represent the environment, the economy, and the society as equally important (with the same area), as is the case with Figure 0.1.

13. When you are riding the bus, your footprints are reduced in the sense that your feet don't hit the pavement. In addition, your ecological footprint is lower, because you are using public transportation rather than your own vehicle. Of course, if you normally would walk rather than take the bus, you are "reducing your footprints" only in the first sense.

22. For example, as a teacher you could work with students and administrators in your school to conserve energy (power down computers when not in use) or produce less waste (compost coffee grounds and food scraps). As a gardener, you might want to consult with those who practice sustainable gardening in your local community. For example, one way to prevent fertilizers from getting into lakes and rivers is to reduce the runoff from lawns and gardens by catching rain in rain barrels. This water can then be released when the soils dry out, reducing the need to use municipal water systems.

Chapter 1

1. a. $\dfrac{0.5\ \text{L}}{1\ \text{breath}} \times \dfrac{15\ \text{breaths}}{1\ \text{min}} \times \dfrac{60\ \text{min}}{1\ \text{hr}} \times 8\ \text{hr}$

$= 3600\ \text{L}$

b. Possibilities include burning less (wood, vegetation, cooking fuels, gasoline, incense), using products that pollute less (low-emission paints), and using motor-less appliances and tools (hand-operated lawnmower, egg beater, broom, rake).

3. a. $Rn < CO < CO_2 < Ar < O_2 < N_2$

b. CO and CO_2

5. Like the other noble gases, radon is colorless, tasteless, odorless, and relatively unreactive. However, radon is radioactive and the others are not.

6. a. 0.9 parts per hundred

$\times\ \dfrac{1{,}000{,}000\ \text{parts per million}}{100\ \text{parts per hundred}}$

$= 9000\ \text{parts per million}$

(Move the decimal 4 places to the right.)

7. a. Compound (2 molecules of one compound made up of two different elements)

b. Mixture (2 atoms of one element plus 2 atoms of another)

c. Mixture (three different substances, two elements and one compound)

d. Element (4 atoms of the same element)

10. a. 85,000 g   **b.** 210,000,000 gallons

11. a. $2.2 \times 10^{-4}\ \text{g/m}^3$

b. No, because CO is odorless.

13. a. Group 1A and Group 7A

b. 1A: lithium, sodium, potassium, rubidium, cesium, francium
7A: fluorine, chlorine, bromine, iodine, astatine

16. a. The chemical formula CH_4 indicates two types of atoms (C and H). A molecule of methane consists of 1 carbon atom and 4 hydrogen atoms. Similarly, SO_2 indicates two types of atoms (S and O). A molecule of sulfur dioxide consists of 1 sulfur atom and 2 oxygen atoms. The chemical formula O_3 indicates only one type of atom. A molecule of ozone consists of 3 oxygen atoms.

b. CH_4 (methane), SO_2 (sulfur dioxide), O_3 (ozone)

18. a. $N_2(g) + O_2(g) \longrightarrow 2\ NO(g)$
(occurs at high temperature)

b. $O_3(g) \longrightarrow O_2(g) + O(g)$
(occurs in the presence of UV light)

c. $2\ S(s) + 3\ O_2(g) \longrightarrow 2\ SO_3(g)$

24. a. platinum (Pt), palladium (Pd), rhodium (Rh)

b. All three metals are in Group 8B on the periodic table. Platinum is directly under palladium, and rhodium is just to the left of palladium.

c. These metals are solids at the temperature of the exhaust gases, so they must have relatively high melting points. Also, they do not undergo permanent chemical change when catalyzing the reaction of CO to CO_2 in the exhaust stream.

26. The Hilo photograph shows a wall, presumably built by humans (requiring fuel to be burned in the process of moving the stones). If the stones are cemented, the cement also emits gases as it dries. The cut lawn implies that a lawn mower was used, probably a power one, given the size of the lawn. The vegetation may have herbicides or pesticides applied, all of which can be carried by the air. The airport photograph is easier. The jet engines and the vehicles on the tarmac both leave air prints as they burn fuel. Any spilled fuel may evaporate into the air. The haze is most likely the result of emissions from vehicles and industry.

31. a. Normally, the exhaust gases are released to the atmosphere through the tailpipe and don't find their way back into the interior of the car. The tailpipe does not have a connection to the interior. However, if the gases are released into an enclosed space like a snow bank, they may seep back into the car as there is no easy escape path into the wider environment.

   b. CO is an odorless, colorless, and tasteless gas.

34. CO is termed the "silent killer" because your senses cannot detect this colorless, tasteless, and odorless gas. The same term cannot be applied to pollutants such as O_3 or SO_2 because each has a distinctive odor that can be detected at concentrations below the level of toxicity.

37. Ozone up high is "good" because it protects us by absorbing incoming ultraviolet radiation from the Sun. Ozone nearby is "bad" because it can be dangerous to breathe and damages vegetation and materials such as rubber.

38. a. The elderly, the young, and people with respiratory diseases such as asthma and emphysema are most affected by ozone.

   b. 3 days

   c. Ozone is highly reactive, thus does not persist long in the atmosphere. Since no ozone is produced at night when the Sun isn't shining, its concentration falls.

   d. Answers will vary. Possibilities include overcast skies, rain, or high winds. It could be a day when fewer people are driving or that industries are shut down.

   e. Ozone levels in Atlanta, Georgia, are lower in December because there is less daylight in the winter months.

40. a. 15 ppm is 0.0015% and 2% is 20,000 ppm. 15 ppm is roughly 1300 times smaller than 20,000.

47. CO is a hazard when present at the part per million level, and instruments can easily detect CO at this concentration. In contrast, radon levels are much lower, on the order of parts per 10^{20}. Most radon detection kits sample the air over a period of time in order to get a high enough reading.

Chapter 2

3. a. Yes, this is over the detection minimum of 10 ppb.

$$\frac{0.118 \text{ parts } O_3}{1{,}000{,}000 \text{ parts air}} = \frac{118 \text{ parts } O_3}{1{,}000{,}000{,}000 \text{ parts air}} \text{ or } 118 \text{ ppb}$$

   b. Yes, this is well over the detection minimum of 10 ppb.

$$\frac{25 \text{ parts } O_3}{1{,}000{,}000 \text{ parts air}} = \frac{25{,}000 \text{ parts } O_3}{1{,}000{,}000{,}000 \text{ parts air}} \text{ or } 25{,}000 \text{ ppb}$$

8. a. A neutral atom of oxygen has 8 protons and 8 electrons.

   b. A neutral atom of nitrogen has 7 protons and 7 electrons.

10. a. helium, He   **c.** copper, Cu

   b. potassium, K

11. c. 92 protons, 146 neutrons, and 92 electrons

   f. 88 protons, 138 neutrons, and 88 electrons

12. c. $^{222}_{86}\text{Rn}$

13. a. $\cdot\text{Ca}\cdot$ **c.** $:\ddot{\text{Cl}}\cdot$

   b. $\cdot\ddot{\text{N}}\cdot$ **d.** $\text{He}:$

14. b. There are $2(1) + 2(6) = 14$ outer electrons. The Lewis structure is

$$\text{H}:\ddot{\underset{\cdot\cdot}{\text{O}}}:\ddot{\underset{\cdot\cdot}{\text{O}}}:\text{H} \quad \text{or} \quad \text{H}-\ddot{\underset{\cdot\cdot}{\text{O}}}-\ddot{\underset{\cdot\cdot}{\text{O}}}-\text{H}$$

   c. There are $2(1) + 6 = 8$ outer electrons. The Lewis structure is

$$\text{H}:\ddot{\underset{\cdot\cdot}{\text{S}}}:\text{H} \quad \text{or} \quad \text{H}-\ddot{\underset{\cdot\cdot}{\text{S}}}-\text{H}$$

16. a. Wave 1 has a longer wavelength than wave 2.

   b. Wave 1 has lower frequency than wave 2.

   c. Both waves travel at the same speed.

19. In order of increasing energy per photon: radiowaves < infrared < visible < gamma rays

21. a. In order of increasing wavelength: UV-C < UV-B < UV-A

   b. In order of increasing energy: UV-A < UV-B < UV-C

   c. In order of increasing potential for biological damage: UV-A < UV-B < UV-C

25. a. methane, CH_4

$$\text{H}-\underset{\underset{\displaystyle \text{H}}{|}}{\overset{\overset{\displaystyle \text{H}}{|}}{\text{C}}}-\text{H}$$

ethane, C_2H_6

$$\text{H}-\underset{\underset{\displaystyle \text{H}}{|}}{\overset{\overset{\displaystyle \text{H}}{|}}{\text{C}}}-\underset{\underset{\displaystyle \text{H}}{|}}{\overset{\overset{\displaystyle \text{H}}{|}}{\text{C}}}-\text{H}$$

b. Three different CFCs are based on methane. They are: $CClF_3$, CCl_3F, and CCl_2F_2.

26. a. $Cl\cdot$ has 7 outer electrons. Its Lewis structure is $:\!\overset{..}{\underset{..}{Cl}}\!\cdot$

$\cdot NO_2$ has $5 + 2(6) = 17$ outer electrons. Its Lewis structure is

$$\overset{..}{\underset{..}{O}}::\!N\!:\!\overset{..}{\underset{..}{O}}: \quad \text{or} \quad \overset{..}{\underset{..}{O}}\!=\!\dot{N}\!-\!\overset{..}{\underset{..}{O}}:$$

$ClO\cdot$ has $7 + 6 = 13$ outer electrons. Its Lewis structure is

$$:\!\overset{..}{\underset{..}{Cl}}\!:\!\overset{..}{\underset{..}{O}}\!\cdot \quad \text{or} \quad :\!\overset{..}{\underset{..}{Cl}}\!-\!\overset{..}{\underset{..}{O}}\!\cdot$$

$\cdot OH$ has $6 + 1 = 7$ outer electrons. Its Lewis structure is

$$\cdot\overset{..}{\underset{..}{O}}\!:\!H \quad \text{or} \quad \cdot\overset{..}{\underset{..}{O}}\!-\!H$$

b. They all contain an unpaired electron.

29. The message is that ground-level ozone is a harmful air pollutant. Ozone in the stratosphere, on the other hand, is beneficial because it can absorb harmful UV-B before it reaches the surface of the Earth.

31. a. The most energetic fraction is the UV-C light.

b. Up in the stratosphere where the air is very thin, UV-C splits oxygen molecules, O_2, into two oxygen atoms, O. These in turn react with other oxygen molecules to produce ozone, O_3. See the reactions of the Chapman cycle. Without the UV-C light (which does not reach the surface of our planet), the ozone layer would not form.

41. Although UV-C radiation causes damage to both animals and plants, it is completely absorbed by the O_2 in our atmosphere before it can reach the surface of the Earth.

44. $Cl\cdot$ acts as a catalyst in the series of reactions in which stratospheric O_3 molecules react to produce O_2 molecules. As it is not consumed in the reaction, $Cl\cdot$ can continue to catalyze the breakdown of O_3.

52. O_2, O_3, and N_2 all have an even number of valence electrons. In contrast, N_3 would have 15 valence electrons. Molecules with odd numbers of electrons cannot follow the octet rule and are more reactive.

53. a. $90 + 12 = 102$. The compound contains one carbon atom, no hydrogen atoms, and two fluorine atoms. The chemical formula for CFC-12 is CCl_2F_2.

b. CCl_4 contains 1 carbon atom, 0 hydrogen atoms, and 0 fluorine atoms. Therefore, the code number for CCl_4 is 100 or $90 + 10$. The name is CFC-10.

c. Yes, the "90" method will work for HCFCs. $90 + 22 = 112$, so HCFC-22 would be composed of 1 carbon atom, 1 hydrogen atom, and 2 fluorine atoms, and its chemical formula would be $CHClF_2$.

d. No, this method will not work for halons as there is no guideline for handling bromine.

Chapter 3

4. a. $6\,CO_2 + 6\,H_2O \longrightarrow C_6H_{12}O_6 + 6\,O_2$

b. The number of atoms of each element on either side is the same. $C = 6$, $O = 18$, $H = 12$.

c. No, the number of molecules is not the same. There are 12 on the left, but only 7 on the right. The glucose molecule on the product side contains 24 atoms!

6. a. The rest of the Sun's energy is absorbed or reflected by the atmosphere.

7. a. As of 2013, the atmospheric concentration of CO_2 was about 400 ppm; however, 20,000 years ago, the concentration was only about 190 ppm. Looking back to 120,000 years ago, the concentration was about 270 ppm, still ~40% below current levels.

b. The mean atmospheric temperature at present is somewhat above the 1950–1980 mean atmospheric temperature. The mean atmospheric temperature 20,000 years ago was lower by about 15 °F. However, 120,000 years ago the mean atmospheric temperature was higher than the present temperature by only about 6 °F.

c. Although there appears to be a *correlation* between mean atmospheric temperature and CO_2 concentration, this graph does not prove *causation* of either factor by the other.

11. a. $H\!-\!\overset{..}{\underset{..}{S}}\!-\!H$ bent

b. $:\!\overset{..}{\underset{..}{Cl}}\!-\!\overset{..}{\underset{..}{O}}\!-\!\overset{..}{\underset{..}{Cl}}\!:$ bent

c. $:\!\overset{..}{N}\!=\!N\!=\!\overset{..}{\underset{..}{O}}:$ or $:\!N\!\equiv\!N\!-\!\overset{..}{\underset{..}{O}}:$ or $:\!\overset{..}{\underset{..}{N}}\!-\!N\!\equiv\!O:$ linear

13. a. $3(1) + 4 + 6 + 1 = 14$ outer electrons. This is the Lewis structure.

$$\begin{array}{c} H \\ | \\ H\!-\!C\!-\!\overset{..}{\underset{..}{O}}\!-\!H \\ | \\ H \end{array}$$

b. The geometry around the C atom is tetrahedral, and there are no lone pairs. A H−C−H bond angle of about 109.5° is predicted.

c. There are four pairs of electrons around the O atom, two of which are bonding pairs and two are nonbonded pairs. Repulsion between the two nonbonded electron pairs and their repulsion of the bonding pairs is predicted to cause the H−O−C bond angle to be less than 109.5°.

15. All can contribute to the greenhouse effect. In each case, the atoms move as the bond stretches or bends, and therefore the charge distribution changes. Unlike the linear CO_2 molecule, the water molecule is bent and so its polarity changes with each of these modes of vibration.

16. a. Use $E = \dfrac{hc}{\lambda}$ to calculate the energies.

The value of h is in Appendix 1.

$$E = \frac{(6.63 \times 10^{-34}\,\text{J}\cdot\text{s}) \times (3.00 \times 10^{8}\,\text{m}\cdot\text{s}^{-1})}{4.26\,\mu\text{m} \times \dfrac{1\,\text{m}}{10^{6}\,\mu\text{m}}}$$
$$= 4.67 \times 10^{-20}\,\text{J}$$

$$E = \frac{(6.63 \times 10^{-34}\,\text{J}\cdot\text{s}) \times (3.00 \times 10^{8}\,\text{m}\cdot\text{s}^{-1})}{15.00\,\mu\text{m} \times \dfrac{1\,\text{m}}{10^{6}\,\mu\text{m}}}$$
$$= 1.33 \times 10^{-20}\,\text{J}$$

19. a. $C_6H_{12}O_6 \longrightarrow 3\,CO_2 + 3\,CH_4$

b. in one day:

$$1.0\,\text{mg glucose} \times \frac{1\,\text{g}}{1000\,\text{mg}} \times \frac{1\,\text{mol glucose}}{180\,\text{g glucose}} \times$$

$$\frac{3\,\text{mol }CO_2}{1\,\text{mol glucose}} \times \frac{44\,\text{g }CO_2}{1\,\text{mol }CO_2} = 7.3 \times 10^{-4}\,\text{g }CO_2$$

in one year: 7.3×10^{-4} g CO_2/day
$\times$ 365 days/year = 0.27 g CO_2/year

21. a. A neutral atom of Ag-107 has 47 protons, 60 neutrons, and 47 electrons.

b. A neutral atom of Ag-109 has 47 protons, 62 neutrons, and 47 electrons. Only the number of neutrons has changed.

24. a. 2(1.0) g/mol + 16.0 g/mol = 18.0 g/mol

b. 12.0 g/mol + 2(19.0) g/mol + 2(35.5) g/mol
= 121.0 g/mol

28. Properties include the estimated atmospheric lifetime of the substance and its ability to absorb infrared radiation.

33. Scientists have several ways of estimating the past temperatures of the Earth. For example, they can analyze the deuterium-to-hydrogen ratio in ice cores and recreate the temperatures in the distant past. They also can analyze drilled ocean cores for the number or type of microorganisms present. Another correlating piece of evidence is the changing alignment of the magnetic field in particles in the sediment over time.

39. a. $C_2H_5OH + 3\,O_2 \longrightarrow 3\,H_2O + 2\,CO_2$

b. 2 mol CO_2

c. 30 mol O_2

44. 73×10^6 metric tons $CH_4 \times \dfrac{12\,\text{metric tons C}}{16\,\text{metric tons }CH_4}$
$= 5.5 \times 10^7$ metric tons C

Chapter 4

2. a. CO_2, carbon dioxide

b. SO_2 is an air pollutant. Although sulfur is present in low concentration in coal, large amounts of coal are burned, and correspondingly large amounts of SO_2 are released.

c. The nitrogen present in air reacts with O_2 (also present in air) at high temperatures to form NO.

$$N_2 + O_2 \xrightarrow{\text{high temperature}} 2\,NO$$

d. Revisit Chapter 1 for the details. From the EPA website: "Particle exposure can lead to a variety of health effects. For example, numerous studies link particle levels to increased hospital admissions and emergency room visits and even to death from heart or lung diseases. Both long- and short-term particle exposures have been linked to health problems. Long-term exposures, such as those experienced by people living for many years in areas with high particle levels, have been associated with problems such as reduced lung function and the development of chronic bronchitis and even premature deaths."

9. A typical power plant burns 1.5 million tons of coal each year. The first calculation is for coal with 50 ppb mercury; the second is for 200 ppb mercury.

$$\frac{x\,\text{ton Hg}}{1.5 \times 10^6\,\text{ton coal}} = \frac{50\,\text{ton Hg}}{1 \times 10^9\,\text{ton coal}} \qquad x = 0.075\,\text{ton Hg}$$

$$\frac{x\,\text{ton Hg}}{1.5 \times 10^6\,\text{ton coal}} = \frac{200\,\text{ton Hg}}{1 \times 10^9\,\text{ton coal}} \qquad x = 0.30\,\text{ton Hg}$$

Assuming mercury concentrations in the range of 50–200 ppb, the plant releases between 0.075 and 0.30 ton Hg per year.

10. Hydrocarbons are alike in many ways. These include that they all consist only of the elements carbon and hydrogen. Furthermore, they all are flammable. When burned, they produce carbon dioxide, carbon monoxide, and/or soot plus water vapor. They all are insoluble in water. Hydrocarbons differ in many ways, including in the number of C and H atoms they contain. They also differ in their boiling or melting points. Some hydrocarbons are saturated; others are unsaturated.

13. a.

```
     H   H   H   H
     |   |   |   |
 H — C — C — C — C — H
     |   |   |   |
     H   H   H   H
```

b.

```
           H
           |
       H — C — H
       H   |   H
       |   |   |
 H  —  C — C — C  — H
       |   |   |
       H   H   H
```

14. Pentane should be a liquid because room temperature (20 °C) is below its boiling point (36 °C) but above its melting point (−130 °C). Triacontane should be solid at room temperature because room temperature is below its melting point (66 °C). Propane should be a gas because room temperature is above its boiling point (−42 °C).

16. a. $2 C_2H_6 + 7 O_2 \longrightarrow 4 CO_2 + 6 H_2O$

b.

$$2 H-\overset{\overset{\displaystyle H}{|}}{\underset{\underset{\displaystyle H}{|}}{C}}-\overset{\overset{\displaystyle H}{|}}{\underset{\underset{\displaystyle H}{|}}{C}}-H \ + \ 7 \ \ddot{\ddot{O}}=\ddot{\ddot{O}} \longrightarrow$$

$$4 \ \ddot{\ddot{O}}=C=\ddot{\ddot{O}} \ + \ 6 \ \overset{\ddot{\ddot{O}}}{H{\diagdown}} {\diagup}_H$$

c. $1.0 \ \text{mol} \ C_2H_6 \times \dfrac{30 \ \text{g} \ C_2H_6}{1 \ \text{mol} \ C_2H_6} \times \dfrac{52.0 \ \text{kJ}}{\text{mol} \ C_2H_6}$

$= 1560 \ \text{kJ/mol} \ C_2H_6$

21. a. Bonds broken in the reactants
1 mol N≡N triple bonds = 1(946 kJ) = 946 kJ
3 mol H−H single bonds = 3(436 kJ) = 1308 kJ
Total energy *absorbed* in breaking bonds = 2254 kJ

Bonds formed in the products
6 mol N−H single bonds = 6(391 kJ) = 2346 kJ
Total energy *released* in forming bonds = 2346 kJ

Net energy change is (+2254 kJ)
+ (−2346 kJ) = −92 kJ
The overall energy change is negative, characteristic of an exothermic reaction.

24. a. None of these are isomers. All have different chemical formulas.

b. No other isomers are possible for ethene.

c. One other isomer is possible, although it is not like anything that you have encountered in this textbook. Here is its condensed structural formula: CH_3-O-CH_3.

26. Section 1.11 described the catalytic converters in automobiles. Section 2.9 described the catalytic destruction of ozone by chlorine free radicals.

33. a. The source of biodiesel is a triglyceride (a fat or an oil). In contrast, the source of ethanol is usually cellulose, a starch, or a sugar.

b. Biodiesel is produced by a one-step reaction (transesterification). In contrast, ethanol is produced by fermentation, which requires several steps followed by distillation to separate the ethanol.

c. On complete combustion, both produce CO_2 and H_2O.

d. Ethanol mixes with water in any proportion (as any bartender knows). In contrast, biodiesel is insoluble in water. This difference is important because ethanol has to be blended with gasoline with care, so as not to introduce any water into the fuel mixture.

43. A royal flush is an ace, king, queen, jack, and ten of the same suit. It is a highly improbable hand in poker (1 in about 650,000 five-card hands). It exhibits a higher degree of order (low entropy) and is more highly valued than a simple high card hand (a higher degree of entropy). The hand with the least entropy wins!

46. a. To break the bond, the C−F bond requires 485 kJ/mol, the C−Cl bond requires 327 kJ/mol, and the C−Br single bond requires 285 kJ/mol. The C−Br bond is the weakest. Thus, when Halon-1211 absorbs UV radiation, bromine atoms are likely to form and react with ozone.

b.

$$\ddot{\underset{..}{\ddot{F}}}-\overset{\overset{\displaystyle H}{|}}{\underset{\underset{\displaystyle :\ddot{Cl}:}{|}}{C}}-\overset{\overset{\displaystyle :\ddot{F}:}{|}}{\underset{\underset{\displaystyle :\ddot{F}:}{|}}{C}}-\ddot{\underset{..}{\ddot{F}}}:$$

bond most
easily broken

In this molecule, the C−Cl bond has the lowest bond energy and thus is the most easily broken.

Chapter 5

5. a. N and C, 3.0 − 2.5 = 0.5

O and S, 3.5 − 2.5 = 1.0

N and H, 3.0 − 2.1 = 0.9

S and F, 4.0 − 2.5 = 1.5

b. N more strongly than C

O more strongly than S

N more strongly than H

F more strongly than S

6. a. The Lewis structure for ammonia is

$$H-\overset{\displaystyle \ddot{N}}{\underset{\underset{\displaystyle H}{|}}{}}-H$$

b. Each N−H bond is polar. The difference in electronegativity between N and H is 3.0 − 2.1 = 0.9.

c. The ammonia molecule is triangular pyramidal. This geometry, together with the polarity of the N−H bonds, causes the molecule to be polar.

8. a. Examples of nonmetals include C, H, O, S, Cl, and N. Nonmetals generally have higher electronegativity values than metals.

13. a. Partially soluble. Orange juice concentrate contains some solids (pulp) that do not dissolve in water.

b. Very soluble. Note that ammonia is a gas. If you ever have seen a lecture demonstration involving ammonia and water (e.g., "the ammonia fountain"), you know that ammonia dissolves almost instantly in water. Ammonia dissolves in water in any proportion.

d. Very soluble. When you add laundry detergent to your load of wash, it dissolves in the water (or at least it should dissolve—sometimes solid laundry detergent cakes together).

16. **a.** A chlorine atom gains one electron to form a chloride ion with a charge of 1−. The octet rule is satisfied.

$$:\ddot{\underset{..}{Cl}}\cdot \quad \text{and} \quad \left[:\ddot{\underset{..}{Cl}}:\right]^{-}$$

d. A barium atom loses two electrons to form a barium ion, with a charge of 2+. The octet rule is satisfied.

$$\cdot Ba\cdot \quad \text{and} \quad \left[Ba\right]^{2+}$$

17. **a.** NaBr sodium bromide

d. Al_2O_3 aluminum oxide

18. **a.** $Ca(HCO_3)_2$

b. $CaCO_3$

19. **a.** potassium acetate

e. calcium hypochlorite

24. **a.** The solution will conduct electricity and the bulb will light. Based on Table 5.9, $CaCl_2$ is a soluble salt and therefore releases ions (Ca^{2+} and Cl^- when it dissolves). These ions carry the current.

b. The solution will not conduct electricity. Although ethanol (C_2H_5OH) is soluble in water, it is a covalent compound and does not form ions.

27. The concentration of Mg^{2+} is 2.5 M, and the concentration of NO_3^- is 5.0 M.

28. **a.** To prepare 2 liters of 1.50 M KOH, weigh out 168 g of KOH and place it into a 2-L volumetric flask. Add distilled (or deionized) water to fill the flask to the mark. *Note:* If you don't have a 2-L volumetric flask, you will need to repeat the procedure twice with a 1-L flask with 84 g KOH in each.

b. To prepare 1 liter of 0.050 M NaBr, weigh out 5.2 g of NaBr and place it into a 1-L volumetric flask. Add water as in part **a.**

30. Chocolate requires 1700 L of water to produce a 100-gram bar. This includes the water necessary to grow and process the cacao and the sugar used to sweeten it. A pint of beer requires about 140 L of water, mainly for growing and producing the malted barley. These are average global values given on the Water Footprint Network (http://www.waterfootprint.org).

35. **a.** The electronegativities of the elements generally increase from left to right across a period (until Group 8A is reached) and from bottom to top within any group. Thus, the element in position 2 is predicted to have the highest electronegativity.

b. Ranking the other elements is not straightforward. Element 1 is expected to be more electronegative than element 3, based on their relative positions in the same group. Element 4 will likely be more electronegative than elements 1 and 3 and less electronegative than 2. However, because element 4 is not in the same period with any other element, this prediction cannot be made

with certainty. Here are the values found in references (they do not appear in Table 5.1): 0.8 for element 1, 2.4 for element 2, 0.7 for element 3, and 1.9 for element 4. These values confirm the relative ranking in order of decreasing electronegativity: 2, 4, 1, 3.

38. Like water, NH_3 is a polar molecule. It has polar N−H bonds and a triangular pyramidal geometry. Therefore, despite its low molar mass, considerable energy must be added to liquid NH_3 to overcome the intermolecular forces (hydrogen bonding) among NH_3 molecules.

39. **a.** A single covalent bond holds together the two H atoms in H_2.

b. Hydrogen bonding is a type of *inter*molecular force, a force of attraction between a H atom on one molecule and an electronegative atom on another molecule (or in some cases, between a H atom and an electronegative atom on a different part of the same molecule).

42. For a given contaminant, the MCLG (a goal) and the MCL (a legal limit) are usually the same. However, the levels may differ when it is not practical or possible to achieve the health goal as set by the MCLG. This sometimes is the case for carcinogens, for which the MCLG is set at zero (under the assumption that any exposure presents a cancer risk).

44. **a.** Nitrate ion (NO_3^-) and nitrite ion (NO_2^-)

b. In the body, oxygen is needed to metabolize ("burn") glucose to produce energy.

c. The nitrate ion is not volatile. It is a solute that does not evaporate or decompose with heat.

Chapter 6

3. **a.** As of 2013, the approximate atmospheric concentration of CO_2 was 400 ppm.

b. The concentration of carbon dioxide in the atmosphere is increasing because humans are burning fossil fuels and cutting down forests, which absorb CO_2.

c. Here is the Lewis structure. $\ddot{\underset{..}{O}}{=}C{=}\ddot{\underset{..}{O}}$

d. No, you would not. Carbon dioxide is a nonpolar compound, and seawater is a polar solution of primarily water and sodium chloride. "Like dissolves like." Even so, carbon dioxide is slightly soluble in seawater and dissolves to form H_2CO_3.

4. Anthropogenic emissions, such as those of carbon dioxide, nitrogen oxides, and sulfur dioxide, are generated by human activities.

6. **a.** Possibilities include nitric acid (HNO_3), hydrochloric acid (HCl), sulfuric acid (H_2SO_4), sulfurous acid (H_2SO_3), phosphoric acid (H_3PO_4), carbonic acid (H_2CO_3), and hydrobromic acid (HBr).

b. In general, acids taste sour, turn litmus paper red (and have characteristic color changes with other indicators), are corrosive to metals such as iron and aluminum, and release carbon dioxide ("fizz") when mixed with a carbonate. These properties may not be observed if the acid is not sufficiently concentrated.

7. a. $HBr(aq) \longrightarrow H^+(aq) + Br^-(aq)$

b. $H_2SO_3(aq) \longrightarrow H^+(aq) + HSO_3^-(aq)$

8. a. Possibilities include sodium hydroxide (NaOH), potassium hydroxide (KOH), ammonium hydroxide (NH_4OH), magnesium hydroxide ($Mg(OH)_2$), and calcium hydroxide ($Ca(OH)_2$).

b. In general, bases taste bitter, turn litmus paper blue (and have characteristic color changes with other indicators), have a slippery feel in water, and are caustic to your skin.

9. a. $KOH(s) \longrightarrow K^+(aq) + OH^-(aq)$

12. a. $KOH(aq) + HNO_3(aq) \longrightarrow KNO_3(aq) + H_2O(l)$

13. a. The solution of pH = 6 has 100 times more $[H^+]$ than the solution of pH = 8.

d. The solution with $[OH^-] = 1 \times 10^{-2}$ M has $[H^+] = 1 \times 10^{-12}$ M. The solution with $[OH^-] = 1 \times 10^{-3}$ M has $[H^+] = 1 \times 10^{-11}$ M. Thus, in the second solution ($[OH^-] = 1 \times 10^{-3}$ M), the $[H^+]$ is higher by a factor of 10.

17. $S(s) + O_2(g) \longrightarrow SO_2(g)$

21. Sulfur dioxide reacts with calcium carbonate as follows:

$$CaCO_3(s) + SO_2(g) + H_2O(l) \longrightarrow$$
$$Ca^{2+}(aq) + HCO_3^-(aq) + HSO_3^-(aq)$$

The molar masses of SO_2 and $CaCO_3$ are needed to solve the problem. Note that it is not necessary to change tons to grams. The ratio of the number of grams per mole is the same as the ratio of the number of kilograms per kilomole or the ratio of the number of tons per ton-mole.

$$1.00 \text{ ton } SO_2 \times \frac{1 \text{ ton-mole } SO_2}{64.1 \text{ tons } SO_2} \times \frac{1 \text{ ton-mole } CaCO_3}{1 \text{ ton-mole } SO_2}$$
$$\times \frac{100 \text{ tons } CaCO_3}{1 \text{ ton-mole } CaCO_3} = 1.56 \text{ tons } CaCO_3$$

26. a. If we compare cola (pH = 2.7) with the average for acid rain (pH = 4.0), we find that the beverage is about 10 times more acidic. For rainwater (pH = 5.5), the beverage is about 1000 times more acidic.

29. c. The chemical formula $HC_2H_3O_2$ has the advantage of being written in the same format we have used for other acids, that is, with the acidic H atom written first. The advantage of using CH_3COOH is that it gives a better indication of how the atoms in the molecule are bonded.

31. a. $[H_2O] > [Na^+] = [OH^-] > [H^+]$

32. a. Combustion engines, such as those associated with jet aircraft, directly emit CO, CO_2, and NO. If small amounts of sulfur are present in the fuel, SO_2 and SO_3 are emitted as well.

33. Fuel combustion contributes greatly to the emissions of SO_2, with the major source being the burning of coal. Although fuel combustion contributes less to the emissions of NO_x, the percentage still is substantial. In contrast, transportation makes a small contribution to the emissions of SO_2 and a much larger one to the emissions of NO_x. Nitrogen monoxide is produced from N_2 and O_2 in the air whenever there is a high temperature. Thus, both automobile engines and power plants are big contributors of NO_x.

39. a. The slightly higher pH values in the lab indicate that the acidity decreased slightly between collection and measurement.

b. One possibility is that the field samples contained naturally occurring acids that were not stable over time. They decomposed, thus making the solution less acidic. Another possibility is that some of the acids present in the sample reacted with other molecules in the sample or with the sample container itself between the time the sample was collected and analyzed.

Chapter 7

1. One carbon atom can differ from another in the number of neutrons (such as C-12 and C-13) and in the number of electrons (carbon ions do exist, but we do not discuss them in this text). All carbon atoms differ from all uranium atoms in the number of protons, neutrons, and electrons. Carbon atoms also differ from uranium atoms in their chemical properties.

3. a. 94 protons

b. Np (neptunium), Pu (plutonium)

4. a. C-14 has 6 protons and 8 neutrons.

10. Neutrons are needed to initiate the process of nuclear fission of U-235.

$$_{0}^{1}n + _{92}^{235}U \longrightarrow [_{92}^{236}U] \longrightarrow _{56}^{141}Ba + _{36}^{92}Kr + 3\,_{0}^{1}n$$

The fission products include two or three neutrons that can initiate more fission reactions. In this manner, a self-sustaining chain reaction can be established in which the products of one reaction can initiate another.

12. **A** is the control rod assembly, **B** is the cooling water out of the core, **C** is the control rods, **D** is the cooling water into the core, and **E** is the fuel rods.

15. a. $_{0}^{1}n + _{5}^{10}B \longrightarrow [_{5}^{11}B] \longrightarrow _{2}^{4}He + _{3}^{7}Li$

b. Boron can be used in control rods because it is a good neutron absorber.

17. **a.** $^{239}_{94}\text{Pu} \longrightarrow {}^{235}_{92}\text{U} + {}^{4}_{2}\text{He}$

$^{131}_{53}\text{I} \longrightarrow {}^{131}_{54}\text{Xe} + {}^{0}_{-1}\text{e} + {}^{0}_{0}\gamma$

b. In a particulate form such as a powder or a dust, plutonium can be inhaled. If plutonium particles become lodged in the lungs, the ionizing radiation they emit (alpha particles) can damage lung cells. The decay products also are radioactive and can damage tissue.

c. Iodine accumulates in the thyroid gland.

d. After about 10 half-lives, samples have decayed to very low levels. The half-life of Pu-239 is about 24,000 years, so the timescale for a decrease to background level is on the order of hundreds of thousands of years. The half-life of I-131 is 8.5 days, so 10 half-lives is 85 days or about 3 months. A sample of I-131 decays to low levels on a timescale of months.

21. For this type of question, it is helpful to construct a chart.

# of half-lives	% remaining	% decayed
0	100	0
1	50	50
2	25	75
3	12.5	87.5
4	6.25	93.75
5	3.12	96.88
6	1.56	98.44

26. The natural abundances of U-238 and U-235 are 99.3% and 0.7%, respectively. U-235 can be induced to undergo nuclear fission and thus is suitable as a fuel for nuclear power plants and nuclear weapons. Because U-235 has such a low natural abundance, it is more difficult to procure in large quantities. Also, it is *extremely* difficult to separate U-235 from U-238. Had U-235 been readily available, far more countries would have had access to nuclear weapons.

34. See question 21. After 7 half-lives, 99% of a sample has decayed which is a reasonable approximation of being "gone." However, actually the radioactivity is *not* gone, as 0.78% of the radioactive sample still remains. Thus, if you start with a large amount of a radioactive substance (for example, 2000 pounds), after 7 half-lives you still have about 10 pounds left!

49. **a.** The sum of the masses of the reactants is 5.02838 g, and the sum for the products is 5.00878 g. The difference is 0.0196 g.

b. To use Einstein's equation, $E = mc^2$, you need to pay close attention to the units. The speed of light is 3.00×10^8 meters/second. In order to have joules (J) as the unit of energy, the mass must be in kilograms (kg), so you need to convert g to kg. In addition, you need the conversion factor that $1 \text{ J} \times 1 \text{ kg-meter}^2/\text{second}^2$. Whew! Here is the calculation.

$$E = 0.0196 \text{ g} \times \frac{1 \text{ kg}}{10^3 \text{g}} \times \left[\frac{3.00 \times 10^8 \text{ m}}{\text{s}}\right]^2 \times \frac{1 \text{ J}}{\text{kg-m}^2/\text{s}^2}$$

$$E = 1.76 \times 10^{12} \text{ J}$$

Chapter 8

1. **a.** Oxidation is a process in which an atom, ion, or molecule *loses* one or more electrons. Reduction is a process in which an atom, ion, or molecule *gains* one or more electrons.

b. Electrons are transferred from the species losing electrons to the species gaining electrons.

3. $Zn(s)$ is oxidized to Zn^{2+} in zinc oxide. $O_2(g)$ is reduced to O^{2-} in zinc oxide.

4. A galvanic cell is a type of electrochemical cell that converts the energy released in a chemical reaction into electrical energy. An example of a galvanic cell, an alkaline cell, is shown in Figure 8.5. A battery is a series of galvanic cells connected together. An example is the lead–acid storage battery made of several galvanic cells. *Note:* The term *battery* commonly is used interchangeably with *cell* (galvanic cell). For example, sometimes the D cell (a type of galvanic cell) is referred to as a D cell battery.

6. **a.** The anode is $Zn(s)$. The oxidation half-reaction is

$$Zn(s) \longrightarrow Zn^{2+}(aq) + 2 \text{ e}^-$$

b. The cathode is $Ag(s)$. The reduction half-reaction is

$$2 \text{ Ag}^+(aq) + 2 \text{ e}^- \longrightarrow 2 \text{ Ag}(s)$$

11. **a.** The electrolyte completes the electrical circuit. It provides a medium for transport of ions, thus allowing charge to be transferred.

b. $KOH(aq)$ (in a paste-like form)

c. concentrated sulfuric acid

13. It represents the reduction half-reaction. The conversion of O_2 to H_2O requires a supply of electrons.

17. Oxidation half-reaction:
$$CH_4(g) + 8 \text{ OH}^-(aq) \longrightarrow CO_2(g) + 6 \text{ H}_2O(l) + 8 \text{ e}^-$$

Reduction half-reaction:
$$2 \text{ O}_2(g) + 4 \text{ H}_2O(l) + 8 \text{ e}^- \longrightarrow 8 \text{ OH}^-(aq)$$

Overall reaction:
$$CH_4(g) + 2 \text{ O}_2(g) \longrightarrow CO_2(g) + 2 \text{ H}_2O(l)$$

23. Each Si atom is surrounded by 8 electrons, but the atom in the center (the one that is doping the semiconductor) is surrounded by 9 electrons. Silicon is in Group 4A and has 4 outer electrons. Thus central atom in the figure must have 5 outer electrons. This is consistent with an element in Group 5A, such as arsenic, so this is an *n*-type silicon semiconductor.

25. In every electrochemical process described in this chapter, energy is produced through electron transfer. Chemical reactions (such as those that take place in galvanic cells, batteries, and fuel cells) produce electrons that can do work because the anode and cathode are physically separated in space. The transfer of electrons also may be initiated when light strikes a photovoltaic cell.

29. The primary difference is that these produce electricity using different chemical reactions. In addition, a lead–acid storage battery converts chemical energy into electrical energy by means of a reversible reaction. No reactants or products leave the "storage" battery, and the reactants can be reformed during the recharging cycle. A fuel cell also converts chemical energy into electrical energy, but the reaction is not reversible. A fuel cell continues to operate only if fuel and oxidant are continuously added, which is why it is classed as a "flow" battery.

40. **a.** Conversion of fuel:

$$C_8H_{18}(l) + 4\,O_2(g) \longrightarrow 9\,H_2(g) + 8\,CO(g)$$

Fuel cell reaction:

$$CO(g) + H_2O(g) \xrightarrow{\text{catalyst}} CO_2(g) + H_2(g)$$

b. This type of fuel cell is convenient because it runs on a liquid fuel, gasoline, rather than using gaseous hydrogen. Currently, most nations have an infrastructure for gasoline refueling. However, the liquid fuel is still petroleum-based and therefore nonrenewable. It also burns to produce CO_2, a greenhouse gas. Therefore, although such fuel cells may find specialty applications in the near future, their long-term prospects are not promising.

Chapter 9

1. Cotton, silk, rubber, wool, and DNA are examples of natural polymers. Synthetic polymers include Kevlar, polyvinyl chloride (PVC), Dacron, polyethylene, polypropylene, and polyethylene terephthalate.

3. The *n* on the left side of the equation gives the number of monomers that react to form the polymer. This *n* is a coefficient. In contrast, the *n* on the right side is a subscript and represents the number of repeating units in the polymer.

6. The bottle on the left most likely is made of low-density polyethylene; the one on the right, high-density polyethylene. The molecular structures of LDPE and HDPE help explain at a molecular level the difference in properties. LDPE is a more highly branched polymer, lessening molecular attractions between the chains and causing the plastic to be softer and more easily deformed. HDPE molecules, with fewer branches, can more closely approach each other, increasing the molecular attractions.

9. Each ethylene monomer has a molar mass of 28 grams. To determine the number of monomers in the polymer, divide 40,000 (the molar mass of the polymer) by 28 (the molar mass of the monomer). The result is 1428 monomers. To determine the number of carbon atoms present in the polymer, note that each monomer contains two carbon atoms ($H_2C=CH_2$). Accordingly, the polymer contains 2×1428 carbon atoms, or 2856 carbon atoms. In round numbers, there are roughly 3000 carbon atoms.

11. This is the tail-to-tail, head-to-head arrangement of PVC formed from three monomer units.

20. **a.** Pentanoic acid.

b.

c. CH_3CH_2CH_2

22. **a.** A blowing agent is a gas (or a substance capable of producing a gas) used to manufacture a foamed plastic. For example, a blowing agent is used to produce Styrofoam from PVC.

b. Carbon dioxide can replace the CFCs or the HCFCs that once were used as blowing agents. Although CO_2 is a greenhouse gas, it still is preferable because CFCs and HCFCs both deplete the ozone layer as well as being potent greenhouse gases.

28. Factors other than the chemical composition of the monomer(s) influence the properties of the polymer. These include length of the chain (the number of monomer units), the three-dimensional arrangement of the chains, the degree of branching in the chain, and orientation of monomer units within the chain.

30. For addition polymerization, the monomer must have a C=C double bond. Although some monomers have benzene rings as part of their structures (styrene, for example), the double bond involved in addition polymerization must not be in the ring. An example is the formation of PP from propylene. For condensation polymerization, each monomer must have two functional groups that can react and eliminate a small molecule such as water. For example, an alcohol and a carboxylic acid can react to eliminate water. An example is the formation of PET from ethylene glycol and terephthalic acid.

31. In vinyl chloride, each carbon atom has 3 bonds (2 single bonds and 1 double bond) around each carbon. These 3 bonds form an equilateral triangle (trigonal) and the Cl−C−H bond angle is about 120°. In the polymer, each carbon atom is connected to other atoms by 4 single bonds. The double bond is no longer present, and the 4 bonds point to the corners of a tetrahedron with a bond angle of about 109°.

32. a. Here is the Lewis structure for the monomer.

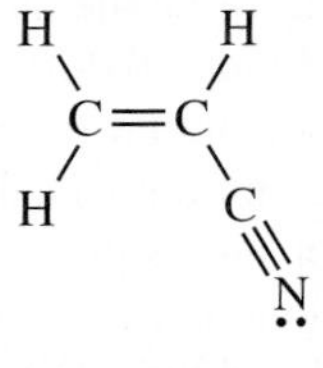

    b. When Acrilan fibers burn, one of the combustion products is the poisonous gas hydrogen cyanide, HCN.

38. a. PLA stands for polylactic acid, a polymer.

    b. The monomer of PLA is lactic acid. In the United States, lactic acid is produced from corn.

    c. Reasons include that (1) corn is a renewable resource, (2) PLA is compostable, and (3) PLA is not a petroleum-based polymer.

    d. (1) Although corn is a renewable resource, corn is a crop with its share of controversies. These include the degradation of the land on which it is grown and the runoff of fertilizers and pesticides into nearby waterways. (2) Although PLA is compostable, this is true only in industrial composters that most communities do not have. It degrades slowly if at all in a landfill. (3) Although no oil is used in its production, fuels such as petroleum are nonetheless used in the growing of corn and its transportation.

44. The Big Six polymers are generally large (in fact huge) molecules with low water solubility. Furthermore, many are hydrocarbons (HDPE, LDPE, PS, PP) and therefore would not be expected to dissolve in polar solvents, such as water. The generalization explained in Chapter 5 is that "like dissolves like." However, some polymers, including HDPE and LDPE, soften in hydrocarbons or chlorinated hydrocarbons because these nonpolar solvents interact with the nonpolar polymeric chains.

Chapter 10

1. a. An antipyretic drug is intended to reduce fever.

    b. An analgesic drug is intended to reduce pain.

    c. An anti-inflammatory drug is intended to reduce inflammation, that is, swelling and pain caused by irritation, injury, or infection.

2. Organic chemists study the chemistry of carbon compounds.

3. The condensed formulas are $CH_3CH_2CH_2CH_2CH_3$ [or $CH_3(CH_2)_3CH_3$], $CH_3CH_2CH(CH_3)CH_3$, and $CH_3C(CH_3)_2CH_3$. Here are the line-angle drawings.

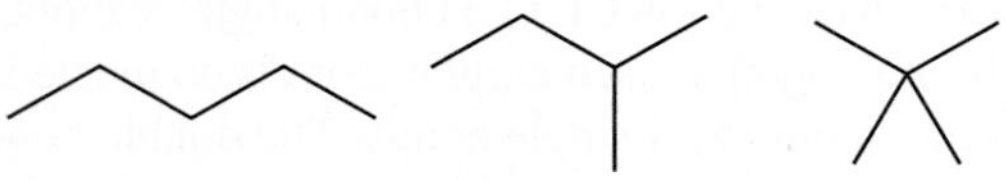

5. For the chemical formula C_4H_9OH, four isomers that contain an –OH group exist. Here are the structural formulas, with the H atoms omitted for clarity.

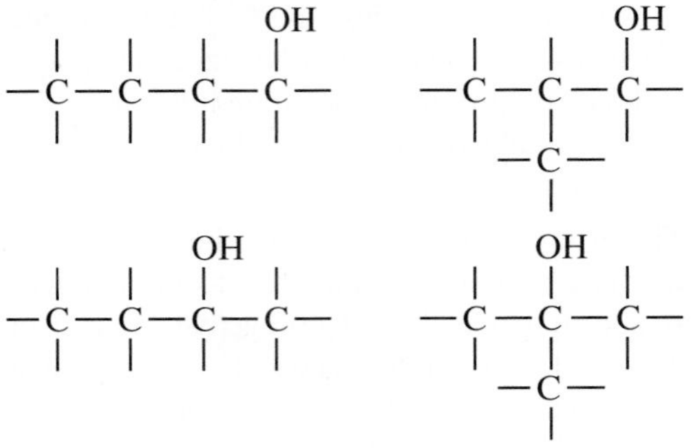

6. a.

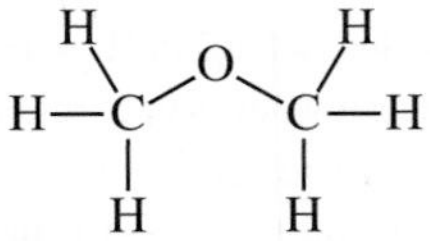

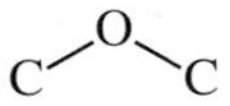

    functional group and is an ether.

    b.

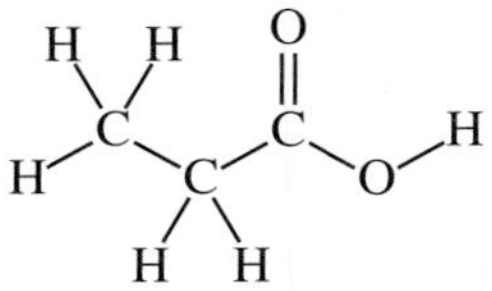

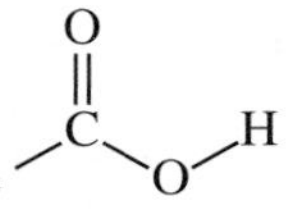

    functional group and is a carboxylic acid.

    c.

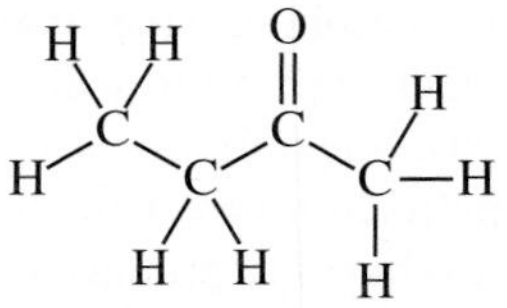

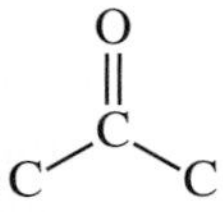

    functional group and is a ketone.

    d.

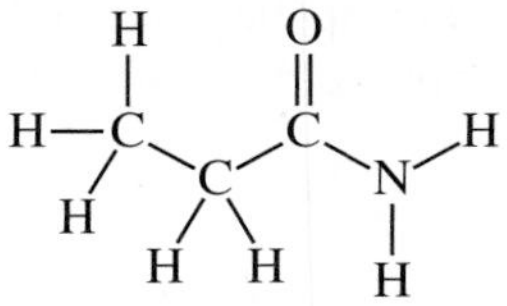

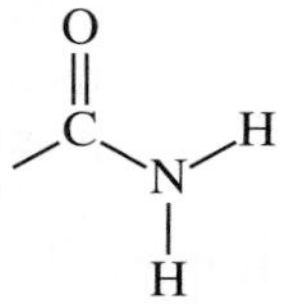

    functional group and is an amide.

    e.

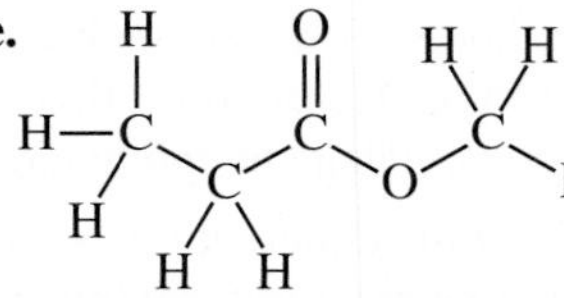

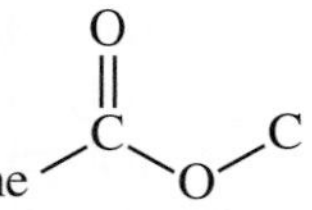

    functional group and is an ester.

7. With an alcohol, an aldehyde, or a carboxylic acid, a compound with 1 C atom is possible. The other functional groups require more than 1 C atom.

    a. Alcohol. The simplest compound is methanol, CH_3OH.

    b. Aldehyde. The simplest example is methanal (commonly called formaldehyde), CH_2O.

    d. Ester. The simplest example has two carbons: $HCOOCH_3$. It is called methyl methanoate, or methyl formate (but these names may be beyond the scope of your study).

8. a. The compound is an alcohol (ethanol). An isomer with a different functional group is an ether.

b. The compound is an aldehyde (propanal). An isomer with a different functional group is a ketone.

c. The compound is an ester (propyl formate). An isomer with a different functional group is a carboxylic acid.

10. a. Here is the structural formula for acetaminophen.

b. The chemical formula is $C_8H_9NO_2$.

11. a. There are two amide groups.

14. a. *n*-propanol, $CH_3CH_2CH_2OH$

b. *iso*propanol, $(CH_3)_2CHOH$

c. *t*-butanol, $(CH_3)_3COH$

16. a. $H-C\equiv N:$

17. No, aspirin would not be more active if it were to interact with prostaglandins directly. Its effectiveness would require a direct correspondence between the number of molecules of aspirin and prostaglandin. When aspirin blocks a COX enzyme, it prevents the synthesis of many prostaglandin molecules, since one enzyme is responsible for increasing the rate of synthesis of the prostaglandins.

18. If you started with 2 active functional groups, you would have 4 different products after 2 synthetic steps. If the reagent used in the first step had 2 reactive groups itself, you would produce 8 different products after the 2 synthetic steps (assuming the second step had a reagent with only 1 reactive group).

21. A pharmacophore is the three-dimensional arrangement of atoms, or groups of atoms, responsible for the biological activity of a drug molecule.

22. Sulfanilamide has the same basic shape and contains similar functional groups in the same regions as *para*-aminobenzoic acid, so it replaces the nutrient in some biologically important process. Without the key nutrient, the bacteria die.

23. a. This compound cannot exist in chiral forms. The central carbon atom is bonded to two equivalent $-CH_3$ groups.

b. This compound can exist in chiral forms. The four groups attached to the central carbon atom are all different.

c. This compound can exist in chiral forms. The four groups attached to the central carbon atom are all different.

d. This compound cannot exist in chiral forms. The central carbon atom is bonded to two equivalent $-CH_3$ groups.

25. A freebase is a nitrogen-containing molecule in which the nitrogen is in possession of its lone pair of electrons. Treating methamphetamine hydrochloride with a base (e.g., hydroxide ions, OH^-) strips off one of the hydrogen atoms attached to the nitrogen atom, freeing up its lone pair.

27.

29. a. Four single bonds, one triple bond

b. Six single bonds, one double bond

31. Only three isomers are shown here, because some structures are duplicates. Numbers 1 and 5 are different paper-and-pencil representations of the *same* isomer. Numbers 2, 3, and 4 are all different paper-and-pencil representations of the *same* isomer. Number 6 is an isomer *different* from numbers 1 and 5, and from numbers 2–4.

32.

35. a. Aspirin produces a physiological response in the body.

b. Morphine produces a physiological response in the body.

c. Antibiotics kill or inhibit the growth of bacteria that cause infections.

e. Amphetamine produces a physiological response in the body.

37. The drug (−)-dopa is effective because the molecule fits in the receptor site, but the nonsuperimposable mirror image form, (+)-dopa, does not. This is the structure of (−)-dopa, with the chiral carbon atom marked in red. Note that there are four different groups attached to the starred carbon atom.

39. There is a very specific fit between a chiral molecule and its asymmetrical binding site. It must be that the (−)-methorphan has a much better fit and is able to act as a narcotic, but (+)-methorphan does not fit as well, and is therefore not as potent a drug. Because

(+)-methorphan has less activity, it can be added to over-the-counter medicines with some safety, assuming that consumers follow the label directions on the over-the-counter drugs containing this compound.

45. a. There are 6(4) + 6(1) or 30 electrons available. Here is a possible linear isomer for benzene.

Structural formula

b. This is the condensed structural formula:

$CH_2{=}C{=}CH{-}CH{=}C{=}CH_2$

c. First check to see if all of the structures correctly represent C_6H_6 and that each carbon has four bonds. If these conditions are met, the structures with double bonds should differ only in the placement of the C–C bond. However, structures including carbon–carbon triple bonds can also be drawn; these would be distinctly different.

Chapter 11

4. Several answers are possible. As examples, (1) an all-or-nothing diet, such as eating no meat, leaves no middle ground. If you are not careful in your food choices, the absence of meat can lead to an unbalanced diet depriving you of the types of protein that you need to stay healthy; (2) this diet doesn't leave you the option of choosing certain meats, such as those with minimal impacts on the land that are locally raised or that those that are killed in hunting season to reduce overpopulation of a particular animal, such as deer; and (3) a less strict diet may be more successfully followed over a lifetime, thus substantially reducing your consumption of certain meats.

6. Some farmers graze animals on land that otherwise would not be suitable for crop production. Additionally, in some parts of the country, people raise birds, such as chickens, in their backyards for eggs and meat. These birds may feed on insects rather than grain. They also may feed on an amazing assortment of foods left over from the kitchen (search on the Internet for a list). Pigs are omnivores and will eat just about anything. These animals also are able to forage and will eat food scraps if available.

11. The pie chart indicates more carbohydrate is present than would be found in steak, and more protein than would be found in chocolate chip cookies. Of the choices given, the pie chart is likely to be a representation of peanut butter. (See Table 11.1 for confirmation.)

14. Fatty acids are smaller molecules than fat molecules, roughly one-third smaller (depending on the particular fat and fatty acid). The reason for the size difference is that fats are triglycerides synthesized from three fatty acids and the 3-carbon "triple" alcohol glycerol. Fatty acids contain the carboxylic acid functional group; in contrast, fats contain the ester functional group. In terms of the role in your diet, you consume fats from many of the foods you eat, both animal and plant based. In contrast, your foods do not contain fatty acids because these are pretty unappealing to eat alone or in combination with other foods.

15. **Similarities:** In terms of observable properties, oils and fats both feel greasy, are insoluble in water, and taste good in foods. Both can go rancid, although this happens more quickly with oils than fats. On a molecular level, fats and oils are both triglycerides, that is, triple esters. These molecules are characterized by the presence of long, nonpolar hydrocarbon chains.

Differences: In terms of observable properties, fats are solid and oils are liquid at room temperature. On a molecular level, oils tend to be more unsaturated than fats and, as a result, their molecules have more bends than fats.

21. Both starch and cellulose are polymers in which the monomer is glucose. But the glucose units are hooked together in a different manner. Our bodies possess an enzyme that can digest starch. In contrast, we are unable to digest cellulose. In essence, we can derive nutritional value from a potato but not from a piece of paper.

24. The "amino" in *amino acid* indicates that there is an amine functional group present. The "acid" indicates there is an acidic functional group, in this case, a carboxylic acid.

31. *Reactive nitrogen* refers to the chemical species of nitrogen that cycle relatively quickly through the biosphere and interconvert via several pathways. Reactive nitrogen includes forms found in fertilizers (the nitrate ion and the ammonium ion) that plants can utilize in their growth. Atmospheric nitrogen gas (N_2) is an unreactive form of nitrogen. See Section 6.9 for more about the nitrogen cycle.

36. *Trans* fats both increase the "bad" cholesterol and decrease the "good cholesterol." In essence, this is a double whammy.

40. **a.** Here is the structural formula for lactic acid.

$$H-\overset{\overset{\displaystyle H}{|}}{\underset{\underset{\displaystyle H}{|}}{C}}-\overset{\overset{\displaystyle OH}{|}}{\underset{\underset{\displaystyle H}{|}}{C}}-\overset{\overset{\displaystyle O}{\|}}{C}\!-\!OH$$

b. As a fatty acid, lactic acid would be saturated because the hydrocarbon chain contains only single bonds between the carbon atoms.

c. No, lactic acid is not a fatty acid. Although it has the carboxylic acid group characteristic of a fatty acid, it lacks the long hydrocarbon chain (12–24 carbon atoms). Lactic acid also has a hydroxyl group ($-OH$) that is not found in fatty acids.

41. **a.** Milk does contain the disaccharide lactose, which contributes about 40% of the calories to whole cow's milk. However, milk also contains valuable nutrients including proteins, calcium, and vitamin D.

b. You certainly should read food labels carefully. In this case mom is wrong in that the whole milk, 2%, and skim all contain the same amount of carbohydrates (sugar). Mom has confused sugar with fat content. Whole cow's milk contains about 3.3% fat, "2% milk" contains 2% fat, and skim milk contains 0% fat.

Chapter 12

1. Traits that are determined by an individual's DNA include hair and eye color, fingerprints, and the shape of earlobes (attached or hanging). Several other answers are possible for this question. Some traits, such as body type, will result from diet and environment as well as genes.

4. A genome is made up of all the genetic information in a cell, while a gene is a small subsection of the genome that codes for a single protein.

6. **a.** A nucleotide links a nitrogen-containing base, a sugar, and a phosphate group.

b. Covalent bonds hold the units together.

8.

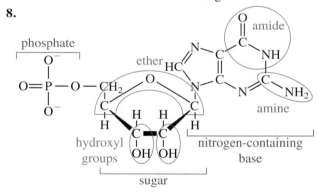

10. DNA stands for **d**eoxyribo**n**ucleic **a**cid. The name highlights the **d**eoxyribose sugar, the **a**cidic nature of the phosphate groups, and the fact that DNA is a chain of **n**ucleotides. The name does not highlight the amines important in the bases. Nor does the name suggest the polymer nature of DNA, in contrast to **poly**amides or **poly**esters.

13. **a.** The complementary base sequence is ATAGATC.

b. Your answer should have two lines between each A and T and three lines between each C and G in the sequence.

$$\begin{array}{c}\text{T A T C T A G}\\ \| \ \| \ \| \ \| \ \| \ \| \ \| \| \| \\ \text{A T A G A T C}\end{array}$$

14. Each codon consists of a three-nucleotide sequence that is specific for an amino acid or the start/stop of protein synthesis. All of the codons together make up the code for translating a sequence of DNA into the amino acid sequence of a protein.

17. **a.** Below is the general formula for an amino acid, where R represents a side chain that is different in each of the 20 amino acids.

b. The functional groups are $-COOH$, the carboxylic acid group, and $-NH_2$, the amine group.

21. Only a minor change in the amino acid composition of human hemoglobin leads to sickle-cell anemia. In the hemoglobin S chain, a nonpolar valine replaces a specific charged glutamic acid in the sequence. This seemingly innocuous change in the protein's primary structure dramatically affects the shape of the protein. The tertiary structure must change to accommodate the change in side chain; the nonpolar valine cannot positively interact with water or other polar groups in the same ways as glutamic acid. The change in protein shape leads to sickled red blood cells (under certain conditions) and a number of health problems.

23. Both selective breeding and genetic engineering are techniques to create a plant with certain desired traits. Selective breeding results in a plant with a mixture of traits from both parents, while genetic engineering transfers only specific traits to the final plant. Also, selective breeding requires the parents to be similar enough to breed, while genetic engineering can take traits from a wide array of organisms.

25. **a.** The phosphates and sugars combine to form the backbone of the DNA molecule. In Figure 12.4, these can be found along the left.

b. The nitrogen bases hang off the backbone, never connecting to each other. In the figure, these are found along the right.

c. In Figure 12.6 the backbone is represented with ribbons that use "s" and "p" to represent the alternating sugar and phosphate groups. The nitrogen bases are shown as colored hexagons hanging off these two ribbons. The sculpture at the beginning of the chapter represents the backbones with the silver coils without distinguishing sugars from phosphate. The bases between the coils are represented with colored plastic pieces for each type of base.

27. Figure 12.7 gives clear evidence of the importance of "fit" for the bases as they interact through hydrogen bonding. Adenine and thymine match up with each other to form two hydrogen bonds. The first bond pairs an O atom from thymine with an N–H on adenine; the second pairs an N–H on thymine with an N atom on adenine. Cytosine and guanine match up with each other to form three hydrogen bonds. Here, the pairings are different. Adenine and cytosine would not match efficiently because the bases are not in the right positions to permit the hydrogen bonds to form. This is also true of thymine and guanine.

29. The two DNA strands are complimentary, meaning that the sequence on one strand can be reconstructed from the other. If a single strand breaks, the other strand can be used by repair enzymes to correctly replace any lost nucleotides and reassemble the backbone. If both strands break, the information on how to repair the break is lost and the correct sequence of DNA will be permanently altered.

31. The DNA-damaging agents that kill bacteria can also damage the DNA in other species, including humans. The risks involved with such drugs outweigh any potential benefits.

35. **a.** The nucleus contains all of the genetic information necessary to create the organism. A skin cell has all of the same genetic information as a nerve cell, even though much of the material is not in use.

b. The egg cell must have its own nuclear material removed. Otherwise, the genes from the egg's source may be expressed instead of those genes in the transferred nucleus.

c. This method of cloning differs from genetic engineering as (1) the host's genetic material is removed in cloning but is only altered in genetic engineering, and (2) cloning transfers all genes while genetic engineering transfers only a few.

38. **a.** Transgenic organisms are plants and animals whose genome contains genes from one or more other species.

b. Traditional selective breeding methods blend the genes of both parents and require many generations to create a crop with the desired trait. Because they are not able to target a single trait, the results are less predictable.

42. **a.** In the electromagnetic spectrum, X-rays have high energies and short wavelengths. They are similar to gamma rays.

b. A beam of X-rays is directed at an unknown substance. The nuclei in the substance scatter the X-rays. A detector measures the intensity and pattern of scattered X-rays. If the atoms in the substance are arranged in a regular pattern, the diffracted X-rays can be used to calculate the distance between atoms.

c. One reason is that salts, such as sodium chloride, easily form crystals. In contrast, nucleic acids and proteins are much larger and do not easily form crystals. Another reason is that when nucleic acids and proteins do crystallize, their X-ray diffraction patterns are far more complex and difficult to interpret.

46. With well-chosen parents, a dog with more strengths and fewer problems can result from breeding, while cloning can only produce the same dog. Except in cases of inbreeding, breeding will create a dog with unique mixtures of traits from each parent and therefore creates opportunities for an improved overall breed. In contrast, cloning produces an identical dog containing identical genetic traits.

Glossary

The numbers at the end of each entry indicate the section in the text where the term first appears.

A

acid a compound that releases hydrogen ions, H^+, in aqueous solution 6.1

acid deposition a more inclusive term than acid rain that includes wet forms such as rain, snow, fog, and cloud-like suspensions of microscopic water droplets as well as the "dry" forms of acids 6.6

acid rain rain with a pH below 5 6.6

acid-neutralizing capacity the capacity of a lake or other body of water to resist a decrease in pH 6.13

activation energy the energy necessary to initiate a chemical reaction 4.8

active site the catalytic region, often a crevice, in an enzyme that binds only specific reactants and accelerates the desired reaction 12.5

addition polymerization a type of polymerization in which the monomers add to the growing chain in such a way that the polymer contains all the atoms of the monomer. No other products are formed. 9.3

aerosols liquid or solid particles that remain suspended in the air rather than settling out 1.11

albedo a measure of the reflectivity of a surface; the ratio of electromagnetic radiation reflected from a surface relative to the amount of radiation incident on it 3.9

alcohol a hydrocarbon substituted with one or more –OH groups (hydroxyl groups) bonded to its carbon atoms 4.9

alkanes hydrocarbons with only single bonds between carbon atoms 4.4

alpha particle (α) a type of nuclear radiation. An alpha particle is a positively charged particle emitted from the nucleus. It consists of two protons and two neutrons (the nucleus of a He atom) and has a 2+ charge since no electrons accompany the helium nucleus. 7.4

ambient air the air surrounding us, usually meaning the outside air 1.3

amino acid residues amino acids which have been incorporated into the peptide chain 11.7 and 12.4

amino acid monomer from which our body builds proteins. Each amino acid molecule contains two functional groups: an amine group ($-NH_2$) and a carboxylic acid group ($-COOH$). 9.7

amorphous regions in a polymer, a region in which the long polymer molecules are in a random, disordered arrangement and packed more loosely 9.5

anaerobic bacteria bacteria that can function without the use of molecular oxygen 3.8

anion a negatively charged ion 5.6

anode the electrode at which oxidation takes place 8.1

anthropogenic caused or produced by human activities, such as industry, transportation, mining, and agriculture 3.1

aqueous solution a solution in which water is the solvent 5.5

atom the smallest unit of an element that can exist as a stable, independent entity 1.7

atomic mass the mass (in grams) of the same number of atoms that are found in exactly 12 g of carbon-12 3.6

atomic number the number of protons in the nucleus of an atom 2.2

Avogadro's number the number of atoms in exactly 12 grams of carbon-12 3.6

B

background radiation the level of radiation, on average, that is present at a particular location. It can arise from both natural and human-made sources. 7.6

basal metabolic rate (BMR) the minimum amount of energy required per day to support basic body functions 11.9

base a compound that releases hydroxide ions, OH^-, in aqueous solution 6.2

becquerel (Bq) the international unit of radioactivity equivalent to one disintegration (alpha, beta, or gamma) per second 7.6

beta particle (β) a type of nuclear radiation. A beta particle is a high-speed electron emitted from the nucleus. 7.4

biofuel a generic term for a renewable fuel derived from a biological source, such as trees, grasses, animal waste, or agricultural crops 4.9

biological oxygen demand (BOD) a measure of the amount of dissolved O_2 that microorganisms use up as they decompose the organic wastes found in water. A low BOD is one indicator of good water quality. 5.11

biomagnification the increase in concentration of certain persistent chemicals in successively higher levels of a food chain 5.9

biomimetic materials materials that try to replicate specific properties of biological materials for use in human applications 9.7

blowing agent either a gas or a substance capable of producing a gas used to manufacture a foamed plastic 9.5

bond energy the amount of energy that must be absorbed to break a specific chemical bond 4.6

breeder reactor a nuclear reactor that can produce more fissionable fuel (usually Pu-239) than it consumes (usually U-235) 7.9

C

calorie (cal) the amount of heat necessary to raise the temperature of one gram of water by one degree Celsius 4.2

calorimeter a device used to experimentally measure the quantity of heat energy released in a combustion reaction 4.5

carbohydrate a compound that contains carbon, hydrogen, and oxygen, with H and O atoms found in the same 2:1 ratio as in H_2O 11.5

carbon capture and storage (CCS) the process of separating CO_2 from other combustion products and storing (sequestering) it in a variety of geologic locations 3.11

carbon footprint an estimate of the amount of CO_2 and other greenhouse gas emissions in a given time frame, usually a year 3.9

carbon neutral a situation in which the CO_2 added to the atmosphere is balanced by the CO_2 removed by photosynthesis, sequestration, a carbon offset, or some other process 4.11

carcinogenic capable of causing cancer 1.13

catalyst a chemical substance that participates in a chemical reaction and influences its rate without undergoing permanent change 1.11

catalytic cracking a process in which catalysts are used to crack larger hydrocarbon molecules into smaller ones at relatively low temperatures 4.7

catalytic reforming a process in which the atoms within a molecule are rearranged, usually starting with linear molecules and producing ones with more branches 4.7

cathode the electrode at which reduction takes place. The cathode receives the electrons produced at the anode. 8.1

cation a positively charged ion 5.6

cellulose a naturally-occurring compound composed of C, H, and O that provides structural rigidity in plants, shrubs, and trees. Cellulose is a natural polymer of glucose. 4.9 and 9.2

cellulosic ethanol ethanol produced from any plant containing cellulose, typically cornstalks, switchgrass, wood chips, and other materials that are nonedible by humans 4.9

chain reaction a term that generally refers to any reaction in which one of the products becomes a reactant and thus makes it possible for the reaction to become self-sustaining 7.2

Chapman cycle the first set of natural steady-state reactions proposed for stratospheric ozone 2.6

chemical equation a representation of a chemical reaction using chemical formulas 1.9

chemical formula a symbolic way to represent the elementary composition of a substance 1.7

chemical reaction a process whereby substances described as reactants are transformed into different substances called products 1.9

chemical symbol a one- or two-letter abbreviation for an element. Also sometimes called an atomic symbol. 1.6

chiral (optical) isomers compounds with the same chemical formula but different three-dimensional molecular structures and different interaction with plane polarized light 10.6

chlorofluorocarbons (CFCs) compounds composed of the elements chlorine, fluorine, and carbon (but do not contain the element hydrogen) 2.9

chromosomes rod-shaped, compact coils of DNA and specialized proteins packed in the nucleus of cells 12.3

climate a term that describes regional temperatures, humidity, winds, rain, and snowfall over decades, not days. Contrast with *weather.* 3.10

climate adaptation the ability of a system to adjust to climate change (including climate variability and extremes), to moderate potential damage, to take advantage of opportunities, or to cope with the consequences 3.11

climate mitigation any action taken to permanently eliminate or reduce the long-term risk and hazards of climate change to human life, property, or the environment 3.11

coalescents chemicals added to soften the latex particles in paint so that these particles spread to form a continuous film of uniform thickness 1.13

codon a sequence of three adjacent nucleotides that either guides the insertion of a specific amino acid or signals the start or end of protein synthesis 12.4

coenzymes molecules that work in conjunction with enzymes to enhance the enzyme's activity 11.8

combinatorial chemistry systematic creation of large numbers of molecules in "libraries" that can be rapidly screened in the lab for biological activity and the potential for becoming new drugs 10.5

combustion the chemical process of burning; the rapid reaction of fuel with oxygen to release energy in the form of heat and light 1.9 and 4.1

compostable under the conditions of either a home composter or an industrial composter, able to undergo biological decomposition to form a material (compost) that contains no materials toxic to plant growth 9.10

compound a pure substance made up of two or more different elements in a fixed, characteristic chemical combination. Compounds contain two or more different types of atoms. 1.6

concentration the ratio of the amount of solute to the amount of solution 5.5

condensation polymerization a type of polymerization in which a small molecule such as water is split out (eliminated) when the monomers join to form a polymer 9.6

condensed structural formula a structural formula in which some bonds are not shown; rather, the structural formula is understood to contain an appropriate number of bonds 4.4

conductivity meter an apparatus that produces a signal to indicate that electricity is being conducted 5.6

control rods in a nuclear reactor, rods that are composed primarily of an excellent neutron absorber, such as cadmium or boron, that can be positioned to absorb fewer or more neutrons 7.3

copolymer a polymer formed by the combination of two or more different monomers 9.6

covalent bond a bond formed when electrons are shared between two atoms 2.3

cradle-to-cradle a term coined in the 1970s that refers to a regenerative approach to the use of things in which the end of the life cycle of one item dovetails with the beginning of the life cycle of another, so that everything is reused rather than disposed of as waste 0.4, 7.0, and 9.9

cradle-to-grave an approach to analyzing the life cycle of an item, starting with the raw materials from which it came and ending with its ultimate disposal someplace, presumably on Earth 0.4

critical mass the amount of fissionable fuel required to sustain a chain reaction 7.2

crystalline regions in a polymer, a region in which the long polymer molecules are arranged neatly and tightly in a regular pattern 9.5

curie (Ci) a measure of the radioactivity of a sample, approximately equivalent to the activity of one gram of radium 7.6

current (electrical) the rate of electron flow through a circuit 8.2

D

denitrification the process of converting nitrates to nitrogen gas 6.9

density the mass per unit volume 5.2

deoxyribonucleic acid (DNA) the biological polymer that carries genetic information in all species 12.2

depleted uranium uranium composed almost entirely of U-238 (~99.8%) because much of the U-235 that it once naturally contained has been removed; nicknamed DU 7.7

desalination any process that removes sodium chloride and other minerals from salty water 5.12

diatomic molecule a molecule consisting of two atoms 1.7

dietary supplements vitamins, minerals, amino acids, enzymes, herbs, and other botanicals 10.9

dipeptide a compound formed from two amino acids 11.7

disaccharide a "double sugar" formed by joining two monosaccharide units, such as sucrose (table sugar) 11.5

dispersion forces attractions between molecules that result from a distortion of the electron cloud that causes an uneven distribution of the negative charge 9.4

distillation a separation process in which a liquid solution is heated to its boiling point and the vapors are condensed and collected 4.4 and 5.12

distributed generation generating electricity on-site where it is used (i.e., with a fuel cell), thus avoiding the losses of energy that occur over long electric transmission lines 8.5

doping the process of intentionally adding small amounts of other elements to pure silicon to modify its semiconductor properties 8.7

double bond a covalent bond consisting of two pairs of shared electrons 2.3

double helix a spiral consisting of two strands that coil around a central axis 12.3

E

ecological footprint a means of estimating the amount of biologically productive space (land and water) necessary to support a particular standard of living or lifestyle 0.5

effective stratospheric chlorine a measurement reflecting both chlorine and bromine-containing gases in the stratosphere 2.11

electricity the flow of electrons from one region to another that is driven by a difference in potential energy 8.1

electrodes the electrical conductors (anode and cathode) in an electrochemical cell that serve as sites for chemical reactions 8.1

electrolysis the process of passing a direct current of electricity of sufficient voltage to cause a chemical reaction to occur. For example, the electrolysis of water decomposes it into H_2 and O_2. 8.6

electrolyte a solute that conducts electricity in an aqueous solution 5.6

electrolytic cell a type of electrochemical cell in which electrical energy is converted to chemical energy 8.6

electromagnetic spectrum continuum of waves that ranges from short, high-energy X-rays and gamma rays to long, low-energy radio waves 2.4

electron a subatomic particle with a mass much smaller than that of a proton or neutron and with a negative electric charge equal in magnitude to that of a proton, but opposite in sign 2.2

electronegativity a measure of the attraction of an atom for an electron in a chemical bond 5.1

element one of the 100 or so pure substances in our world from which compounds are formed. Elements contain only one type of atom. 1.6

endocrine disrupter a compound that affects the human hormone system, including hormones for reproduction and sexual development 9.11

endothermic a term applied to any chemical or physical change that absorbs energy 4.5

enhanced greenhouse effect the process in which atmospheric gases trap and return *more than* 80% of the heat energy radiated by the Earth 3.1

enriched uranium uranium, typically to fuel nuclear reactors or nuclear weapons, that has a higher percentage of U-235 than its natural abundance of about 0.7% 7.7

entropy a measure of how much energy gets dispersed in a given process 4.2

enzymes proteins that act as biochemical catalysts, influencing the rates of chemical reactions 10.4

essential amino acids those amino acids required for protein synthesis but that must be obtained from the diet because the body cannot synthesize them 11.7

exothermic a term to describe any chemical or physical change accompanied by the release of heat 4.5

exposure the amount of a substance encountered 1.3

F

fats triglycerides that are solids at room temperature 4.10 and 11.3

first law of thermodynamics also called the law of conservation of energy; states that energy is neither created nor destroyed 4.1

fossil fuel combustible substances derived from the remnants of prehistoric organisms. The most common examples are coal, petroleum, and natural gas. 3.2

free radical a highly reactive chemical species with one or more unpaired electrons 2.8

freebase nitrogen-containing molecule in which the nitrogen is in possession of its lone pair of electrons 10.3

frequency the number of waves passing a fixed point in 1 second 2.4

fuel cell an electrochemical cell that produces electricity by converting the chemical energy of a fuel directly into electricity without burning the fuel 8.5

functional group a distinctive arrangement of a group of atoms that imparts characteristic properties to the molecules that contain this group 4.9, 9.6, and 10.3

G

galvanic cell a type of electrochemical cell that converts the energy released in a spontaneous chemical reaction into electrical energy 8.1

gamma ray (γ) a type of nuclear radiation. A gamma ray is emitted from a radioactive nucleus and has no charge or mass. It is a short-wavelength, high-energy photon. 7.4

gaseous diffusion a process in which gases with different molecular weights are forced through a series of permeable membranes 7.7

generic drug a drug that is the chemical equivalent of a pioneer drug but that cannot be marketed until the patent protection on the pioneer drug has run out after 20 years 10.8

genes short pieces of the genome that code for the production of proteins 12.1

genetic engineering the direct manipulation of DNA in an organism 12.6

genome the primary route for inheriting biological information required to build and maintain an organism 12.1

global atmospheric lifetime characterizes the time required for a gas added to the atmosphere to be removed. It is also referred to as the "turnover time." 3.8

global climate change sometimes used interchangeably with global warming, this term refers to changes in the weather over time 3.1–3.12

global warming a popular term used to describe the increase in average global temperatures that results from an enhanced greenhouse effect 3.1

global warming potential (GWP) a number that represents the relative contribution of a molecule of an atmospheric gas to global warming 3.8

green chemistry the design of chemical products and processes that reduce or eliminate the use and generation of hazardous substances 0.6, 1.5

greenhouse effect the natural process by which atmospheric gases trap a major portion (about 80%) of the infrared radiation radiated by the Earth 3.1

greenhouse gases gases capable of absorbing and emitting infrared radiation, thereby warming the atmosphere. Examples include water vapor, carbon dioxide, methane, nitrous oxide, ozone, and chlorofluorocarbons. 3.1

groundwater fresh water found in underground reservoirs also known as aquifers 5.3

group a column on the periodic table that organizes elements according to the important properties they have in common. Groups are numbered left to right. 1.6

H

half-life ($t_{1/2}$) the time required for the level of radioactivity to fall to one half of its initial value 7.8

half-reaction a type of chemical equation that shows the electrons either lost or gained by the reactants 8.1

halogen one of the reactive nonmetals in Group 7A, such as fluorine (F), chlorine (Cl), bromine (Br), or iodine (I) 1.6

halons inert, nontoxic compounds that contain chlorine or fluorine (or both, but no hydrogen). In addition, they contain bromine. 2.9

heat the kinetic energy that flows from a hotter object to a colder one 4.5

heat of combustion the quantity of heat energy given off when a specified amount of a substance burns in oxygen 4.5

high-level radioactive waste (HLW) nuclear waste that has high levels of radioactivity and, because of the long half-lives of the radioisotopes involved, requires essentially permanent isolation from the biosphere 7.9

hormones chemical messengers produced by the body's endocrine glands 10.4

hybrid electric vehicle (HEV) a vehicle propelled by a combination of a conventional gasoline engine and an electric motor run by batteries 8.4

hydrocarbon a compound made up only of the elements hydrogen and carbon 1.8 and 4.4

hydrochlorofluorocarbons (HCFCs) compounds of hydrogen, chlorine, fluorine, and carbon (and no other elements) used as replacements for CFCs 2.12

hydrofluorocarbons (HFCs) compounds of hydrogen, fluorine, and carbon (and no other elements) used as replacements for CFCs and HCFCs 2.13

hydrogen bond an electrostatic attraction between a H atom bonded to a highly electronegative atom (O, N, or F) and a neighboring O, N, or F atom, either in another molecule or in a different part of the same molecule 5.2

hydrogenation a process in which hydrogen gas, in the presence of a metallic catalyst, adds to a C=C double bond and converts it to a single bond 11.4

hygroscopic describes a substance that readily absorbs water from the atmosphere and retains it 6.12

I

infrared (IR) a region of the electromagnetic spectrum that lies adjacent to red light, but at longer wavelength 2.4

interesterification any process in which the fatty acids on two or more triglycerides are scrambled to produce a mixture of different triglycerides 11.4

intergenerational justice the obligation of each generation, in turn, to act in ways that are fair and just to those that will follow 4.0

intermolecular force a force that occurs between molecules 5.2 and 9.4

ion an atom or group of atoms that has acquired a net electric charge as a result of gaining or losing one or more electrons 5.6

ionic bond a chemical bond formed when oppositely charged ions attract 5.6

ionic compound a compound composed of ions that are present in fixed proportions and arranged in a regular, geometric structure 5.6

ionizing radiation a term that refers collectively to X-rays and nuclear radiation that can remove electrons from the atoms and molecules they hit. Cosmic rays from space are also ionizing radiation. 7.6

isomers molecules with the same chemical formula, but with different structures and properties 4.7 and 10.2

isotopes two or more forms of the same element (same number of protons) whose atoms differ in number of neutrons and hence in mass 2.2

J

joule (J) a unit of energy equal to 0.239 cal 4.2

K

kinetic energy the energy of motion 4.1

L

law of conservation of matter and mass a law stating that in a chemical reaction, matter and mass are conserved 1.9

lead compound drug (or a modified version of that drug) that shows high promise for becoming an approved drug 10.5

Lewis structure a representation of an atom or molecule that shows its outer electrons 2.3

line-angle drawing simplified version of a structural formula that is most useful for representing larger molecules 10.2

lipids a class of compounds that includes not only all triglycerides, but also related compounds such as cholesterol and other steroids 11.3

low-level radioactive waste (LLW) nuclear waste that contains smaller quantities of radioactive materials than HLW and specifically excludes spent nuclear fuel 7.9

M

macrominerals elements that are necessary for life (Ca, P, Cl, K, S, Na, and Mg) but not nearly as abundant in the body as O, C, H, and N 11.8

macronutrient the fats, carbohydrates, and proteins that provide essentially all of the energy and most of the raw material for body repair and synthesis 11.2

malnutrition caused by a diet lacking in proper nutrients, even though the energy content of the food may be adequate 11.2

mass number the sum of the number of protons and neutrons in the nucleus of an atom 2.2

maximum contaminant level (MCL) the legal limit for the concentration of a contaminant expressed in parts per million or parts per billion 5.10

maximum contaminant level goal (MCLG) the maximum level of a contaminant in drinking water at which no known or anticipated adverse effect on human health would occur 5.10

megacity an urban area with over 10 million people, such as Tokyo, New York City, Mexico City, or Mumbai 1.5

metabolism the complex set of chemical processes that are essential in maintaining life 11.2

metal an element that is shiny and conducts electricity and heat well, such as copper, iron, or magnesium 1.6

metalloid an element that lies between metals and nonmetals on the periodic table and does not fall cleanly into either category. Sometimes called a semimetal. 1.6

microgram (μg) a millionth of a gram (g) or 10^{-6} g 1.3

micrometer (μm) a millionth (10^{-6}) of a meter (m), sometimes referred to simply as a micron 1.2

microminerals nutrients that the body requires lesser amounts of, such as Fe, Cu, and Zn 11.8

micronutrients substances such as vitamins and minerals that are needed only in miniscule amounts, but remain essential for the body to produce enzymes, hormones, and other substances needed for proper growth and development 11.8

minerals ions or ionic compounds that, like vitamins, have a wide range of physiological functions 11.8

mixture a physical combination of two or more pure substances present in variable amounts 1.1

moderator in a nuclear reactor, slows the neutrons, thus making them more effective in producing fission 7.3

molar mass the mass of Avogadro's number, or one mole, of whatever particles are specified 3.7

molarity (M) a unit of concentration represented by the number of moles of solute present in one liter of solution 5.5

mole (mol) an Avogadro's number of objects 3.7

molecule two or more atoms held together by chemical bonds in a certain spatial arrangement 1.7

monomer a small molecule used to synthesize a larger polymer (from *mono* meaning "one" and meros meaning "unit") 9.2

monosaccharide a single sugar, such as fructose or glucose 11.5

monounsaturated fatty acid a fatty acid containing only one double bond between carbon atoms in the hydrocarbon chain 11.3

municipal solid waste (MSW) garbage, that is, everything you discard or throw into your trash, including food scraps, grass clippings, and old appliances. MSW does not include all sources, such as waste from industry, agriculture, mining, or construction sites. 9.9

N

nanometer (nm) one billionth of a meter (m) 2.4

nanotechnology a subdiscipline that relates to the creation of materials at the atomic and molecular (nanometer) scale which is between 1 and 100 nm [1 nanometer (nm) = 1×10^{-9} m] 1.7

neutral solution a solution that is neither acidic nor basic, that is, it has equal concentrations of H^+ and OH^- 6.3

neutralization reaction a chemical reaction in which the hydrogen ions from an acid combine with the hydroxide ions from a base to form water molecules 6.3

neutron a subatomic electrically neutral particle having almost exactly the same mass as a proton 2.2

nitrification the process of converting ammonia in the soil to the nitrate ion 6.9

nitrogen cycle a set of chemical pathways whereby nitrogen moves through the biosphere 6.9

nitrogen-fixing bacteria bacteria that remove nitrogen from the air and convert it to ammonia 6.9

noble gas one of the inert elements in Group 8A that undergoes few, if any, chemical reactions 1.6

nonelectrolyte a solute that is nonconducting in an acqueous solution 5.6

nonmetal an element that does not conduct heat or electricity well, such as sulfur, chlorine, and oxygen. Nonmetals have no one characteristic appearance. 1.6

nonpolar covalent bond a covalent bond in which the electrons are shared equally or nearly equally between atoms 5.1

_n_-type semiconductor a semiconductor in which there are freely moving negative charges (electrons) 8.7

nonrenewable resources those resources that have a limited supply or are consumed more quickly than they are produced 0.1

nuclear fission the splitting of a large nucleus into smaller ones with the release of energy 7.2

nuclear fuel cycle a way of conceptualizing all the different processes that can happen when uranium ore is mined, processed, used to fuel a reactor, and then dealt with as waste 7.7

nucleotide covalently bonded combination of a base, a deoxyribose molecule, and a phosphate group 12.2

nucleus the minuscule and very dense center of an atom composed of protons and neutrons 2.2

O

ocean acidification the lowering of the ocean pH due to increased atmospheric carbon dioxide 6.5

octet rule a generalization that electrons are arranged around atoms so that these atoms have a share in eight electrons. Hydrogen is an exception. 2.3 and 4.4

oils triglycerides that are liquids at room temperature 4.10 and 11.3

organic chemistry the branch of chemistry devoted to the study of carbon compounds 10.2

organic compound a compound that always contains carbon, almost always contains hydrogen, and may contain other elements such as oxygen and nitrogen 1.11

osmosis the passage of water through a semipermeable membrane from a solution that is less concentrated to a solution that is more concentrated 5.12

outer (valence) electrons the electrons that are found in the highest energy level and help to account for many of the observed trends in chemical properties 2.2

oxidation a process in which a chemical species loses electrons 8.1

oxygenated gasoline a blend of petroleum-derived hydrocarbons with added oxygen-containing compounds such as MTBE, ethanol, or methanol 4.7

ozone layer a designated region in the stratosphere of maximum ozone concentration 2.1

P

parts per billion (ppb) one part out of one billion, or 1000 times less concentrated than 1 part per million 1.3 and 5.5

parts per million (ppm) a concentration of one part out of a million. One ppm is a unit of concentration 10,000 times smaller than 1% (one part per hundred). 1.2 and 5.5

peptide bond the covalent bond that forms when the –COOH group of one amino acid reacts with the –NH$_2$ group of another, thus joining the two amino acids 9.7

percent (%) parts per hundred. For example, 15% is 15 parts out of 100. 1.1 and 5.5

periodic table an orderly arrangement of all the elements based on similarities in their properties 1.6

pH a number, usually between 0 and 14, that indicates the acidity (or basicity) of a solution 6.4

pharmacophore the three-dimensional arrangement of atoms or groups of atoms responsible for the biological activity of a drug molecule 10.5

photon a way of conceptualizing light as a particle that has energy but no mass 2.5

photosynthesis the process by which green plants (including algae) and some bacteria capture the energy of sunlight to produce glucose and oxygen from carbon dioxide and water 2.5 and 4.1

photovoltaic cell (PV) a device that converts light energy directly to electrical energy; sometimes called a solar cell 8.7

plasticizer a compound added in small amounts to a polymer to make the polymer softer and more pliable 9.5

plasmids rings of DNA 12.6

plug-in hybrid electric vehicle (PHEV) a vehicle that uses rechargeable batteries for short daily commutes to run an electric motor and switches to a combustion engine to travel longer distances 8.4

PM$_{10}$ (particulate matter) particles with an average diameter of 10 μm or less, a length on the order of 0.0004 inches 1.2

PM$_{2.5}$ (particulate matter) a subset of PM$_{10}$ and includes particles with an average diameter of less than 2.5 μm; sometimes called "fine particles" 1.2

polar covalent bond a covalent bond in which the electrons are not equally shared, but rather are closer to the more electronegative atom 5.1

polar stratospheric clouds (PSCs) thin clouds composed of tiny ice crystals formed from the small amount of water vapor present in the stratosphere 2.10

polyamide a condensation polymer that contains the amide functional group 9.7

polyatomic ion two or more atoms covalently bound together that have an overall positive or negative charge 5.7

polymer a large molecule built from smaller ones (monomers) that consists of a long chain or chains of atoms covalently bonded together 9.2

polysaccharide a condensation polymer made up of thousands of monosaccharide units. Examples include starch and cellulose. 11.5

polyunsaturated fatty acid a fatty acid containing more than one double bond between carbon atoms in the hydrocarbon chain 11.3

postconsumer content material used by a consumer that would otherwise have been discarded as waste 9.9

potable water water safe for drinking and cooking 5.3

potential energy stored energy or the energy of position 4.1

precautionary principle stresses the wisdom of acting, even in the absence of full scientific data, before the adverse effects on human health or the environment become significant or irrevocable 2.0, 4.11, and 9.11

preconsumer content waste left over from the manufacturing process itself, such as scraps and clippings 9.9

primary coolant in a nuclear reactor, a liquid that comes in direct contact with the fuel bundles and control rods and carries away heat. *See also secondary coolant.* 7.3

primary structure the unique sequence of the amino acids that make up each protein 12.5

processed foods foods that have been altered from their natural state by techniques such as canning, cooking, freezing, or adding chemicals such as thickeners or preservatives 11.2

protein a polyamide or polypeptide, that is, a polymer built from amino acid monomers 11.7

protein complementarity combining foods that complement essential amino acid content so that the total diet provides a complete supply of amino acids for protein synthesis 11.7

proton a subatomic positively charged particle with approximately the same mass as a neutron 2.2

p-type semiconductor a semiconductor in which there are freely moving positive charges, or holes 8.7

Q

quantized an energy distribution that is not continuous, but rather consists of many individual steps 2.5

R

racemic mixture mixture consisting of equal amounts of each optical isomer of a compound 10.6

rad a unit, short for "radiation absorbed dose"; a measure of the energy deposited in tissue defined as the absorption of 0.01 joule of radiant energy per kilogram of tissue 7.6

radiant energy the entire collection of different wavelengths in the electromagnetic spectrum, each with its own energy 2.4

radiation sickness the illness characterized by early symptoms of anemia, nausea, malaise, and susceptibility to infection that are the result of a large dose of radiation 7.6

radiative forcings factors (both natural and anthropogenic) that influence the balance of Earth's incoming and outgoing radiation 3.9

radioactive decay series a characteristic pathway of radioactive decay that begins with a radioisotope and progresses through a series of steps to eventually produce a stable isotope 7.4

radioactivity the spontaneous emission of radiation by certain elements 7.4

reactive nitrogen the compounds of nitrogen that cycle through the biosphere and interconvert with each other relatively quickly 6.9

recycled-content products products made from material that otherwise would have been in the waste stream 9.9

reduction a process in which a chemical species gains electrons 8.1

reformulated gasoline (RFG) an oxygenated gasoline that also contains a lower percentage of certain more volatile hydrocarbons found in nonoxygenated conventional gasoline 4.7

rem a unit, short for "roentgen equivalent man"; a measure of the dose of radiation that takes into account the damage caused to human tissue. It is calculated by multiplying Q by the number of rads. 7.6

renewable resources those resources that are replenished more quickly over time than they are being consumed 0.1

replication the process of cell reproduction in which the cell must copy and transmit its genetic information to its progeny 12.3

residual chlorine the name given to chlorine-containing chemicals that remain in the water after the chlorination step. These include hypochlorous acid (HClO), the hypochlorite ion (ClO^-), and dissolved elemental chlorine (Cl_2). 5.11

resonance forms Lewis structures that represent hypothetical extremes of electron arrangements in a molecule 2.3

respiration the process of metabolizing the foods we eat to produce carbon dioxide and water and to release the energy that powers other chemical reactions in our bodies 1.1

reverse osmosis a process that uses pressure to force the movement of water through a semipermeable membrane from a solution that is more concentrated to a solution that is less concentrated 5.12

risk assessment the process of evaluating scientific data and making predictions in an organized manner about the probabilities of an outcome 1.3

S

saturated fatty acid a hydrocarbon containing only single bonds between the carbon atoms 11.3

scientific notation a system for writing numbers as the product of a number and 10 raised to the appropriate power 1.3

second law of thermodynamics a law that can be stated in many ways, including that the entropy of the universe is constantly increasing 4.2

secondary coolant in a nuclear reactor, the water in the steam generators that does not come in contact with the reactor. *See also primary coolant.* 7.3

secondary pollutant a pollutant produced from chemical reactions involving one or more other pollutants 1.12

secondary structure the folding pattern within a segment of the protein chain 12.5

semiconductor a material that does not normally conduct electricity well, but can do so under certain conditions, such as exposure to sunlight 8.7

shifting baseline the idea that what people expect as "normal" on our planet has changed over time, especially with regard to ecosystems 0.0, 1.5, and 9.11

sievert (Sv) a unit that measures the dose of radiation, taking into account the damage that occurs to human tissue when this dose is absorbed. 1 sievert = 100 rem. 7.6

significant figure a digit that is included (or excluded) to correctly represent the accuracy with which an experimental quantity is known 1.14

single covalent bond a bond formed when two electrons (one pair) are shared between two atoms 2.3

solute the solid, liquid, or gas that dissolves in a solvent 5.5

solution a homogeneous (of uniform composition) mixture of a solvent and one or more solutes 5.5

solvent a substance, often a liquid, capable of dissolving one or more pure substances 5.5

specific heat the quantity of heat energy that must be absorbed to increase the temperature of one gram of a substance by one degree Celsius 5.2

spent nuclear fuel (SNF) the radioactive material remaining in fuel rods after they have been used to generate power in a nuclear reactor 7.9

starch a carbohydrate found in many grains, including corn and wheat. Starch is a natural polymer of glucose. 4.9 and 9.2

steady state a condition in which a dynamic system is in balance so that there is no net change in concentration of the major species involved 2.6

steroid a class of naturally occurring or synthetic fat-soluble organic compounds that share a common carbon skeleton arranged in four rings 10.7

strong acid an acid that dissociates completely in water 6.1

strong base a base that dissociates completely in water 6.2

structural formula a representation of how the atoms in a molecule are connected. It is a Lewis structure from which the nonbonding electrons have been removed. 2.3

structure-activity relationship (SAR) study a study in which systematic changes are made to a drug molecule followed by an assessment of the resulting changes in activity 10.5

substituent an atom or functional group substituted for a hydrogen atom in a molecule 10.3

substrate a substance whose reaction is catalyzed by an enzyme 10.5

surface water fresh water found in lakes, rivers, and streams 5.3

surfactant a molecule that has both polar and nonpolar regions that allows it to help solubilize different classes of molecules 5.9

sustainable packaging the design and use of packaging materials to reduce their environmental impact and improve the sustainability of all practices 9.8

sustainability "meeting the needs of the present without compromising the ability of future generations to meet their own needs." (from *Our Common Future,* a 1987 report of the United Nations) 0.2, 1.5

T

temperature a measure of the average kinetic energy of the atoms and/or molecules present in a substance 4.5

tertiary structure the overall molecular shape of the protein defined by the interactions between amino acids far apart in sequence, but close in space 12.5

tetrahedron a four-cornered geometric shape with four equal triangular sides; sometimes called a triangular pyramid 3.3

thermal cracking a process that breaks large hydrocarbon molecules into smaller ones by heating them to a high temperature 4.7

thermoplastic polymer a plastic that can be melted and reshaped over and over again 9.5

toxicity the intrinsic health hazard of a substance 1.3

trace mineral an element present in the body, usually at microgram levels, such as I, F, Se, V, Cr, Mn, Co, Ni, Mo, B, Si, and Sn 11.8

tragedy of the commons the situation in which a resource is common to all and used by many, but has no one in particular responsible for it. As a result, the resource may be destroyed by overuse to the detriment of all that use it. 1.12

trans **fat** a triglyceride that is composed of one or more *trans* fatty acids 11.4

transgenic an organism resulting from the transfer of genes across species 12.6

triglycerides a class of compounds that includes both fats and oils. Triglycerides contain three ester functional groups and are formed from a chemical reaction with three fatty acids and the alcohol glycerol 4.10 and 11.3

trihalomethanes (THMs) compounds such as $CHCl_3$ (chloroform), $CHBr_3$ (bromoform), $CHBrCl_2$ (bromodichloromethane), and $CHBr_2Cl$ (dibromochloromethane) that form from the reaction of chlorine or bromine with organic matter in drinking water 5.11

triple bond a covalent linkage made up of three pairs of shared electrons 2.3

Triple Bottom Line a three-way measure of the success of a business based on its benefits to the economy, to society, and to the environment 0.3

troposphere the lower region of the atmosphere in which we live that lies directly above the surface of the Earth 1.5

U

ultraviolet (UV) region the region that lies adjacent to the violet end of the visible region of the electromagnetic spectrum, but at shorter wavelengths 2.4

undernourishment a condition in which a person's daily caloric intake is insufficient to meet metabolic needs 11.2

unsaturated fatty acid a fatty acid in which the hydrocarbon chain contains one or more double bonds between carbon atoms 11.3

V

vector a modified plasmid used to carry DNA back into the bacterial host 12.6

vitamin an organic compound with a wide range of physiological functions and essential for good health, proper metabolic functioning, and disease prevention 11.8

vitrification a process in which the spent fuel elements or other mixed waste are encased in ceramic or glass 7.9

volatile a term describing a substance that readily passes into the vapor phase, that is, it evaporates easily 1.11

volatile organic compounds (VOCs) carbon-containing compounds that pass easily into the vapor phase 1.11

voltage the difference in electrochemical potential between two electrodes 8.1

volumetric flask a type of glassware that contains a precise amount of solution when filled to the mark on its neck 5.5

W

water footprint an estimate of the volume of fresh water used to produce a particular good or to provide a service 5.3

wavelength the distance between successive peaks 2.4

weak acid an acid that dissociates only to a small extent in aqueous solution 6.1

weak base a base that dissociates only to a small extent in aqueous solution 6.2

weather includes the daily high and low temperatures, the drizzles and downpours, the blizzards and heat waves, and the fall breezes and hot summer winds, all of which have relatively short durations. Contrast with *climate.* 3.10

X

X-ray diffraction an analytical technique in which a crystal is hit by a beam of X-rays to generate a pattern that reveals the positions of the atoms in the crystal 12.3

Credits

Photos

Photo Research by Jerry Marshall

FRONT MATTER

Bonfire: © Péter Gudella/Shutterstock.com; Coral Reef: © Manamana/Shutterstock.com; Lightning: © Tomonari Tsuji/Amana Images/Getty Images.

CHAPTER 0

Opener: Image by Reto Stockli, NASA, Goddard Space Flight Center. Enhancements by Robert Simmon; Page 3, p. 4, p. 5(top): Cathy Middlecamp; p. 5(middle): Cover logo and mechanicals reproduced with permission from Chem. Eng. News, June 25, 2012. Copyright 2012 American Chemical Society. Cover photo © Shutterstock; p. 6: Cathy Middlecamp; p. 8: Cover logo and mechanicals reproduced with permission from Chem. Eng. News, March 19, 2012. Copyright 2012 American Chemical Society. Cover photo © Zuma Press Newscom; p. 9: © 2002, William McDonough and Michael Braungart. Published by North Point Press; p. 13(top): U.S. EPA; p. 13(bottom): Image by Reto Stockli, NASA, Goddard Space Flight Center. Enhancements by Robert Simmon; p. 14: © Fahd Shadeed/AFP/Getty Images.

CHAPTER 1

Opener, Page 17, p. 18, 1.3, 1.4: Cathy Middlecamp; 1.5: © Jill Braaten; 1.6: Courtesy Missouri Botanical Garden Plant Finder; 1.7: Cathy Middlecamp; 1.10b: © Tom Smart/Deseret News; p. 29: NASA; 1.13: Image originally created by IBM Corporation; 1.14: © McGraw-Hill Education. Bob Coyle, photographer; 1.15: Cathy Middlecamp; 1.17b: © Courtesy, Corning Incorporated; p. 46: Courtesy of the U.S. EPA's AirNow Program; 1.19: © Environment Canada, Meteorological Service of Canada. Reproduced with the permission of the Minister of Public Works and Government Services Canada, 2013; p. 49: Cathy Middlecamp; p. 50(Cigar): © Sascha Burkhard/Shutterstock.com; 1.20a: © Image Source/Corbis RF; 1.20b: © Digital Vision Vol. DV384/Getty Images RF; 1.21: © YOLO Colorhouse®; 1.22: © McGraw-Hill Education. Ken Karp, photographer; 1.23: © David M. Grossman/Science Source; 1.24: © Sheila Terry/Science Source; p. 58: Cathy Middlecamp; p. 59(both): Cathy Middlecamp; p. 61: Courtesy of the U.S. EPA's AirNow Program; p. 62(both): National Science Foundation.

CHAPTER 2

Opener: NASA/Goddard Space Flight Center; 2.1: © Galen Rowell/Corbis; Page 68: Earth Sciences and Image Analysis Laboratory/Johnson Space Center/NASA; 2.3: © McGraw-Hill Education. Stephen Frisch, photographer; 2.6: © Philip McAulay/Shutterstock.com; p. 82: NASA p. 84: © Image Source/Alamy RF; 2.13: © McGraw-Hill Education. Stephen Frisch, photographer; p. 91: Courtesy Carlye Calvin; 2.16: © Ross J. Salawitch, University of Maryland; p. 94. p. 96: UNEP; 2.19: © McGraw-Hill Education. Mark A. Dierker, photographer; 2.20: © Courtesy Pyrocool Technologies, Inc.; p. 101: © Stockbyte/Getty Images RF.

CHAPTER 3

Opener © Fuse/Getty Images RF; 3.1: NASA; 3.4a: © Lonnie G. Thompson, Ohio State University; 3.4b: © Vin Morgan/AFP/Getty Images; 3.4c: © W. Berner, 1978, PhD Thesis University of Bern, Switzerland. (D. Lüthi, M. Le Floch, B. Bereiter, T. Blunier, J.-M. Barnola, U. Siegenthaler, D. Raynaud, J. Jouzel, H. Fischer, K. Kawamura, and T.F. Stocker, *High-resolution carbon dioxide concentration record 640,000–800,000 years before present,* Nature, 453, 379–382, 2008.); 3.8: NASA/GISS; 3.10: © Mark Hall/Taxi/Getty Images; 3.22: Courtesy Conrad Stanitski; 3.23a–b: Ocean Drilling Program; 3.24: Courtesy of the Oak Ridge National Laboratory, managed by the U.S. Department of Energy by UT-Battelle, LLC; Page 136: © Photodisc/Getty Images RF; 3.28 : NASA GSFC Scientific Visualization Studio; p. 141 (Coral): © Helmut Corneli/imagebroker.net/SuperStock; p. 141 (Butterfly): www.wisconsinbutterflies.org; 3.29: Cathy Middlecamp.

CHAPTER 4

Opener: © Péter Gudella/Shutterstock.com; 4.1a–d: Cathy Middlecamp; 4.5: © Charles D. Winters/Science Source; 4.7(left): © Martin Shields/Science Source; 4.7(right): © Mark A. Schneider/Science Source; 4.8: © AP Photo/Wade Payne; Page 166: © Jim Maynard; 4.10: © Corbis RF; 4.13: © Martin Bond/Science Source; p. 172: © Digital Vision, Vol. DV418/Getty Images RF; 4.19: © Justin Sullivan/Getty Images; p. 183: © Sustainability Institute; 4.21: © Khuong Huang/iStockphoto.com; 4.22: © David R. Frazier Photolibrary, Inc./Alamy; 4.23 Warren Gretz/NREL/U.S. Dept. of Energy; 4.24a: © & Courtesy of David & Associates, Hastings, NE; 4.24b: © Ashley Cooper pics/Alamy; 4.25a–b: © Cathy Middlecamp; 4.26: © Photodisc/Getty Images RF; 4.27a: © AP/Wide World Photos; p. 192: © Bon Appetit/Alamy; 4.29a: © Romeo Gacad/AFP/Getty Images; 4.29b: © Universal Images Group via Getty Images.

CHAPTER 5

Opener: © Rich Armstrong; 5.6a: Cathy Middlecamp; 5.6b: Reclaimed water booster pump station piping at City of Surprise, AZ. Courtesy of Malcolm Pirnie, the Water Division of ARCADIS; 5.7: Cathy Middlecamp; 5.10: © Jaimie Duplass/Shutterstock.com; 5.11a: © Noah Seelam/AFP/Getty Images; 5.11b: Andrea Booher/FEMA; 5.12a © AP Photo/Denis Couch; 5.12b © Bill Bachman/Alamy; 5.14a–c: EROS Data Center, U.S.G.S.; 5.14d: NASA image created by Jesse Allen; 5.15 © Universal Images Group/Getty Images; 5.16: © Laurence Gough/iStockphoto.com; 5.17a–c: © Tom Pantages; 5.25: © Charles D. Winters/Science Source; Page 230: © Alfred Eisenstaedt/Time

& Life Pictures/Getty Images; 5.29: © airviewonline.com.au; 5.30b: © & Courtesy of SolAqua; 5.32: Courtesy of Katadyn; 5.33: © Vestergaard Frandsen; 5.34: USDA/National Resources Conservation Service; 5.35: Artwork © Robert Schiller. Photograph by Sally Mitchell.

CHAPTER 6

Opener: © Manamana/Shutterstock.com; 6.1: © PhotoDisc Vol. 77/ Getty Images RF; 6.2: © McGraw-Hill Education. Photo by Eric Misko, Elite Images Photography; 6.3: © McGraw-Hill Education. C.P. Hammond, photographer; 6.7: © Owen Sherwood; 6.8: © Charles D. Winters/Science Source; 6.9a, ,6.10a–c: Cathy Middlecamp; 6.13: © E.R. Degginger/Alamy; 6.15: © Dan Chenier; 6.17: © M. Kaleb/ Custom Medical Stock Photo; 6.20: Cathy Middlecamp; 6.22a: © NYC Parks Photo Archive/Fundamental Photographs NYC; 6.22b: © Kristen Brochmann/Fundamental Photographs NYC; 6.23: © A. J. Copley/Visuals Unlimited; 6.24(top): © iPhotos/Shutterstock. com; 6.24(bottom): © Anton Hazewinkel/Flickr/Getty Images; 6.25b: Courtesy of Pittsburgh Post Gazette Archives; Page 278: Cathy Middlecamp; p. 283(Jet): © Stock Portfolio/Stock Connection/ Picture Quest RF; p. 283(Hail): Cathy Middlecamp.

CHAPTER 7

Opener: Cathy Middlecamp; Page 288: © McGraw-Hill Education. Photo by Eric Misko. Elite Images Photography; 7.2 © Georgia Power Company; p. 290: © Rob Crandall/The Image Works; 7.4: © Bettmann/Corbis; 7.6: U.S. Dept. of Energy; 7.8: © McGraw-Hill Education. C.P. Hammond, photographer; 7.9, 7.10: © AP/Wide World Photos; p. 299: © Corbis RF; 7.11: © Hulton-Deutsch Collection/Corbis; 7.14: © AP/Wide World Photos; 7.15: © Chuck Nacke/Time Life Pictures/Getty Images; 7.16 © AP Photo/Kyodo News; 7.17: © Southern Illinois University/Science Source; p. 310: © Burke Triolo Productions/ Getty Images RF; 7.20: © & Courtesy of URENCO Ltd.; 7.22: © AP/Wide World Photos; 7.24: U.S. Dept. of Energy; 7.25: U.S. Nuclear Regulatory Commission; 7.27: © Science Source; 7.28b: U.S. Dept. of Energy; p. 324: © AP Photo/Wade Payne; 7.30: Cathy Middlecamp; 7.31a: © esolla/iStockphoto.com.

CHAPTER 8

Opener: © Tomonari Tsuji/Amana Images/Getty Images; 8.2: © McGraw-Hill Education. Jill Braaten, photographer; 8.4: © McGraw-Hill Education. Photo by Eric Misko, Elite Images Photography; Page 341: © Steven Good/Shutterstock.com; 8.7: © McGraw-Hill Education. Stephen Frisch, photographer; 8.8: © mazoncini/iStockphoto.com; 8.9a–b: © Jill Braaten; 8.13: © National Hydrogen Association (www.HydrogenAssociation.org); 8.18: © Michael Barnes, University of California; 8.20: Warren Gretz/ NREL/U.S. Dept. of Energy; 8.21b: NREL/U.S. Dept. of Energy; 8.21c: © Daniel Karmann/DPA/Corbis; 8.26, 8.27: NREL/U.S. Dept. of Energy; 8.28a: © Langrock/Solar Millennium/SIPA/Newscom; 8.28b: © Boris Roessler/Deutsche Presse-Agentur/Newscom; 8.29: © AP Photo/Tim Wright; p. 371: © Arctic Images/Corbis.

CHAPTER 9

Opener: © Tom Bean/Stone/Getty Images; Page 373: © Dynamic Graphics/JupiterImages RF; p. 374: © Everday Objects OS06/ Getty Images RF; 9.2(both): 9.3a: Cathy Middlecamp; 9.5a–d: © McGraw-Hill Education. Jill Braaten, photographer; 9.6a: © Bill Aron/PhotoEdit, Inc.; p. 382: © Santoosh Kumar/ Shutterstock.com; p. 384: © Image Club RF; 9.9b: © McGraw-Hill Education. Jill Braaten, photographer; p. 387: © joingate/ Shutterstock.com; 9.10: © McGraw-Hill Education. Jill Braaten,

photographer; 9.12, 9.13: Courtesy DuPont; p. 391: © Ingram Publishing/Fotosearch RF; 9.14: © The Garbage Project, University of Arizona; 9.18: © Thinkstock/SuperStock RF; 9.19a: © Gayna Hoffman/Stock Boston. 9.19b: Cathy Middlecamp; 9.20a: © GIPhotoStock X/Alamy; 9.20b: © Roger Ressmeyer/ Corbis; 9.20c: © Tim Gainey/Alamy; 9.21a: © Todd Franklin/ Neato Cool Creative, LLC; 9.21b: © jvphoto/Alamy; p. 402: © McGraw-Hill Education. Mark A. Dierker, photographer.

CHAPTER 10

Opener(top): © Eduardo Rivero/Shutterstock.com; Opener(bottom): © Steve Gorton/Dorling Kindersley/Getty Images; 10.1: © Terry Wild Studio; 10.7(all): © McGraw-Hill Education. Jill Braaten, photographer; 10.10: Courtesy of the Alexander Fleming Laboratory Museum, St. Mary's Hospital, Paddington, London; 10.11: Library of Congress; 10.15: Photo courtesy John M. Rimoldi, University of Mississippi; 10.25(left): © Bill Aron/PhotoEdit, Inc.; 10.25(right): © McGraw-Hill Education. Jill Braaten, photographer; 10.26(both): © Michael P. Gadomski/Science Source; 10.27(left): © Gerald & Buff Corsi/Visuals Unlimited; 10.27(right): © James Leynse/Corbis; 10.29: © Chris Knapton/Science Source; 10.31: © Norma Jean Gargasz/Alamy.

CHAPTER 11

Opener: © Jonelle Weaver/Brand X Pictures/Getty Images RF; Page 451: Cathy Middlecamp; p. 452(right): United Nations World Water Day; p. 452(left): © Royalty Free/Corbis RF; 11.12: © McGraw-Hill Education. Mark A. Dierker, photographer; 11.15: © Nancy Rabalais, Louisiana Universities Marine Consortium; p. 473: © Jill Braaten; p. 475: © SunnyS/Shutterstock.com; p. 483(middle): Mike McCann; p. 483(Tomatoes): © Steve Bower/ Shutterstock.com. p. 487: © PhotoAlto/PunchStock RF.

CHAPTER 12

Opener(top): © Michael Halberstadt/Siliconvalleystock.com; Opener(bottom): © Eric Huang; 12.1a: © Brand X Pictures/ PunchStock RF; 12.1b: © Scott Camazine/Science Source; 12.5a–b: © Bettmann/Corbis; 12.5c: History of Medicine/National Library of Medicine; 12.5d: Courtesy of National Library of Medicine; 12.6a: King's College London Archives; 12.13: © Dr. Stanley Flegler/ Visuals Unlimited; 12.14: © & Courtesy of Hugh Iltis/The Doebley Lab; 12.16: © Nigel Cattlin/Science Source; 12.17: © Dung Vo Trung/ Corbis; 12.18: © McGraw-Hill Education. Jill Braaten, photographer; 12.19: © Hank Morgan/Science Source; 12.20: © AFP/Greenpeace/ Getty Images; Page 517(right): © Bettmann/Corbis.

Text and Illustrations

CHAPTER 1

Table 1.2–4, 8: Environmental Protection Agency; 1.9: Arizona Department of Environmental Quality; 1.12: Raymond Chang, *General Chemistry: The Essential Concepts, Third Edition.* Copyright © 2003, The McGraw-Hill Companies, New York, NY. Reprinted by permission; 1.19: www.airnow.gov; EOC #46: www.airnow.gov; p. 62: www.airnow.gov.

CHAPTER 2

Opener: http://ozonewatch.gsfc.nasa.gov/Scripts/big_image. php?date=2012-10-08&hem=S; 2.1: Environmental Protection Agency; 2.2: "Global Ozone Research and Monitoring Project Report", No. 44, 1998. Reprinted with permission of World Meteorological Organization; 2.5: Environmental Protection

Agency; 2.7_3: http://www.epa/gov/sunwise/uviscale.html; 2.8: Muhammad Iqbal, *An Introduction to Solar Radiation*, Academic Press, Copyright © 1983. Reprinted with permission from Elsevier; 2.11: National Cancer Institute, SEER Fast Stats, 2012; 2.12: http://ozonewatch.gsfc.nasa.gov/meteorology/ytd_data.txt, http://ozonewatch.gsfc.nasa.gov/meteorology/annual_data.html; 2.14: United Nations Environment Programme; 2.15: World Meteorological Organization, United Nations Environment Programme; 2.17: United Nations Environment Programme; 2.19: "Scientific Assessment of Ozone Depletion: 2002," World Meteorological Organization, United Nations Environmental Programme; 2.11_1: http://ozone.unep.org/new_site/en/index.php; 2.21: D.W. Fahey, "Twenty Questions and Answers about the Ozone Layer—2006 Update", a supplement to Scientific Assessment of Ozone Depletion: 2006, the World Meteorological Organization Global Ozone Research and Monitoring Project—Report No. 50, released 2007, and reproduced here with the kind permission of the United Nations Environment Programme; EOC #104: Reprinted with permission. www.ScienceCartoonsPlus.com.

CHAPTER 3

3.7: http://www.ncdc.noaa.gov/cmb-faq/anomalies.php; 3.8: http://data.giss.nasa.gov/gistemp/maps/; 3.20: Purves, Orians, Heller and Sadava, *Life, The Science of Biology, Fifth Edition*, 1998, p. 1186. Reprinted with permission of Sinauer Associates, Inc.; 3.21: IPCC Fourth Assessment Report, Working Group III , 2007; 3.25–27, 3.6: Adapted from "Climate Change 2007: The Physical Science Basis. Contribution of Working Group I to the Fourth Assessment Report of the Intergovernmental Panel on Climate; 3.28: Earth Observatory, NASA; 3.31: "Clearing the Air, The Facts About Capping and Trading Emissions," 2002, p. 3; p. 151: The Wall Street Journal—Permission, Cartoon Features Syndicate.

CHAPTER 4

Table 4.4: Darrell D. Ebbing, G*eneral Chemistry, Fourth Edition*, 1993. Houghton Mifflin Co. Data originally from James E. Huheey, *Inorganic Chemistry: Principles of Structure and Reactivity, Third Edition*, 1983, Addison Wesley Longman; 4.6: Annual Energy Review, 2008. DOE/EIA-0384, June 2009; 4.9: Statistical Review of World Energy, 2012, p. 36, http://www.bp.com/sectionbodycopy.do?categoryId=7500&contentId=7068481. Reprinted by permission of BP; 4.12: U.S. Energy Information Administration, 2009; 4.22: http://www.ethanolproducer.com/plantmap/http://www.ethanolrfa.org/bio-refinery-locations/; 4.27: www.biodiesel.org; 4.28: Renewable Energy Policy Network for the 21st Century (2010) Renewables 2010: Global Status Report, Paris, REN21 Secretariat; 4.6: Nuffield Council on Bioethics, Biofuels: Ethical Issues, 2011, p. 84.

CHAPTER 5

Figure 5.2–3: Water Footprint Network, 2012. Reprinted by permission; 5.26: William Cunningham and Mary Ann Cunningham, *Environmental Science: A Global Concern, Tenth Edition*, 2008. Reprinted with permission of The McGraw-Hill Companies, New York, NY. Reprinted by permission; 5.27: Environmental Waikato, 2000; 5.9: United States Geological Survey.

CHAPTER 6

Figure 6.9b: National Atmospheric Deposition Program, 2006. NADP Program Office, Illinois State Water Survey, http://nadp.sws.uiuc.edu/sites/sitemap.asp?state=il; 6.11–12a–b: Reprinted by permission of the National Atmospheric Deposition Program

(NRSP-3). 2007. NADP Program Office, Illinois State Water Survey, 2204 Griffith Dr., Champaign, IL 61820; 6.14, 16: Environmental Protection Agency; 6.19: *BioScience* by American Institute of Biological Sciences, April 2003, Vol. 53, No. 4, p. 342. Copyright © 2003 by University of California Press-Journals. Reproduced with permission of University of California Press-Journals via Copyright Clearance Center; 6.21a–b: Environmental Protection Agency; 6.2: Adapted from "Emission Trends and Effects in the Eastern U.S., United States General Accounting Office, Report to Congressional Requesters," March 2000; 46: S. J. Smith, J. van Aardenne, Z. Klimont, R. J. Andres, A. Volke, and S. Delgado Arias. *Atmospheric Chemistry and Physics*, Copyright © 2011, Copernicus Publications, 1101–1116.

CHAPTER 7

Figure 7.2: Energy Information Administration; 7.2: http://www.nei.org/publicpolicy/stateactivities/statenuclearfacts/; 7.3: International Atomic Energy Agency, http://www.iaea.org/pris/ as of 08/05/13. Reprinted by permission; 7.18: National Council on Radiation Protection and Measurements; 7.19: Michael G. Stabin, et al. *Health Physics: The Radiation Safety Journal.* Vol. 100, Issue 2, Jan 1, 2011. Reprinted by permission of Wolters Kluwer Health; 7.2: Environmental Protection Agency, American Nuclear Society; 7.26: *Disposition of High-Level Wastes and Spent Nuclear Fuel*, Copyright © 2000. National Academy Press; 7.28a: Department of Energy; 7.31b: http://www.sciencebase.com/satiricalcartoonist. html cartooncreator.nl. Reprinted by permission; 7.34: www.cartoonstock.com.

CHAPTER 8

Figure 8.1: Tom Thaves. Reprinted with permission; 8.2: Environmental Protection Agency; 8.10: American Honda Motor Company; 8.19: Billy Roberts, National Renewable Energy Laboratory for the U.S. Department of Energy, 2008; 8.27: International Energy Agency.

CHAPTER 9

Figure 9.15–16a–b: Environmental Protection Agency, EPA-530-F-11-005, November, 2011; 9.4: American Chemistry Council, 2010; 9.17: Reprinted by permission of the National Association for PET Container Resources.

CHAPTER 11

Figure 11.1: Vaclav Smil, *Feeding the World: A Challenge for the Twenty-First Century.* Copyright © 2000, Massachusetts Institute of Technology, by permission of The MIT Press; 11.2: Agriculture, Food and Agriculture Organization of the United Nations, 2012. http://www.fao.org/docrep/014/am859e/am859e01.pdf. Reproduced with permission; 11.9: *Nutrition Action Health Letter*, Center for Science in the Public Interest, December 2005, Vol. 32, No. 10, p. 8. Copyright © 2005 by Center for Science in the Public Interest. Reproduced with permission of Center for Science in the Public Interest via Copyright Clearance Center; 11.11: Michael Cann, adapted from *Real-World Cases in Green Chemistry, Volume 2*, Copyright © 2008. American Chemical Society; 11.24–25: Mike Berners-Lee, *How Bad Are Bananas? The Carbon Footprint of Everything*, 2011. Copyright © 2011. Greystone Books. Reprinted by permission.

CHAPTER 12

Table 12.1: I. Edward Alcamo, *DNA Technology: The Awesome Skill, Second Edition*. Copyright © 2001, 1996. Academic Press. Reprinted with permission.

Index